Lagrangian Intersection Floer Theory

AMS/IP

Studies in
Advanced
Mathematics

Volume 46.1

Lagrangian Intersection Floer Theory

Anomaly and Obstruction, Part I

Kenji Fukaya
Yong-Geun Oh
Hiroshi Ohta
Kaoru Ono

American Mathematical Society · International Press

Shing-tung Yau, General Editor

2010 *Mathematics Subject Classification.* Primary 53D12, 53D40;
Secondary 14J32, 81T30, 37J10, 18D50, 55P62.

For additional information and updates on this book, visit
www.ams.org/bookpages/amsip-46

Library of Congress Cataloging-in-Publication Data

Lagrangian intersection floer theory : anomaly and obstruction / Kenji Fukaya ... [et al.].
    p. cm. — (AMS/IP studies in advanced mathematics ; v. 46)
    Includes bibliographical references and index.
    ISBN 978-0-8218-4831-9 (set : alk. paper) – ISBN 978-0-8218-4836-4 (pt. 1 : alk. paper) –
ISBN 978-0-8218-4837-1 (pt. 2 : alk. paper)
    1. Floer homology.   2. Lagrangian points.   3. Symplectic geometry.   I. Fukaya, Kenji, 1959–

QA665.L34   2009
516.3′6—dc22

                                                                                2009025925

AMS softcover ISBN 978-0-8218-5249-1

Contents

Volume I

Volume II

Preface

With the advent of the method of pseudo-holomorphic curves developed by Gromov in the 80's and the subsequent Floer's invention of elliptic Morse theory resulted in Floer cohomology, the landscape of symplectic geometry has changed drastically. Many previously intractable problems in symplectic geometry were solved by the techniques of pseudo-holomorphic curves, and the concept of symplectic topology gradually began to take shape. This progress was accompanied by parallel developments in physics most notably in closed string theory.

In 1993, partially motivated by Donaldson's pants product construction in Floer cohomology, the first named author introduced the structure of an A_∞-category in symplectic geometry whose objects are Lagrangian submanifolds and whose morphisms are the Floer cohomologies (or complexes). Based on this algebraic framework, Kontsevich proposed the celebrated homological mirror symmetry between the derived category of coherent sheaves and the Fukaya category of Lagrangian submanifolds in his 1994 ICM talk in Zürich. Enhanced by the later development in open string theory of D-branes, this homological mirror symmetry has been a source of many new insights and progresses in both algebraic geometry and symplectic geometry as well as in physics. However the rigorous formulation of homological mirror symmetry has not been made, largely due to lack of understanding the Floer theory of Lagrangian submanifolds itself.

In this book, we explain how the obstruction to and anomaly in the construction of Floer cohomology arise, provide a precise formulation of the obstructions and then carry out detailed algebraic and analytic study of deformation theory of Floer cohomology. It turns out that even a description of such an obstruction (in a mathematically precise way) requires new homological algebra of filtered A_∞-algebras. In addition, verification of existence of such an algebraic structure in the geometric context of Lagrangian submanifolds requires non-trivial analytic study of the corresponding moduli space of pseudo-holomorphic discs. We also provide various immediate applications of the so constructed Floer cohomology to problems in symplectic topology. Many of these improve the previously known results obtained via Floer theory and some firsthand applications to homological mirror symmetry are new. We expect more nontrivial applications of the theory will soon follow as its true potential is unveiled and then realized.

While we have been preparing this book, there have been several important developments in symplectic geometry and in related fields. The relationship between topological strings, D-branes and pseudo-holomorphic curves and symplectic Floer theory is now more clearly understood. The usage of higher algebraic structures in Floer theory, which we have been promoting while writing this book, has now become a popular and essential area of research. Furthermore advances of the techniques handling various moduli spaces of solutions to nonlinear PDE's, intertwined with the formalism of higher algebraic structures, has now made the geometric picture more transparent. This will help facilitate the further progression of the geometric theory. In this book we take full advantage of these developments and provide the Floer theory of Lagrangian submanifolds in the most general form available at this time. We hope that this book will be a stepping stone for future advancements in symplectic geometry and homological mirror symmetry.

Our collaboration which has culminated in completion of this book started during the 1996 (8 July–12 July) conference held in Ascona, Switzerland. We hardly imagined then that our project would continue to span more than 10 years. We have greatly enjoyed this collaboration and hope to continue it into the coming decades. In fact our second journey into newly landscaped field of symplectic topology and mirror symmetry has already begun, and we hope to garner more fruits of collaboration: The scene in front looks very different and much more exciting than the one we left behind 13 years ago!

June 9 2009. Kenji Fukaya, Yong-Geun Oh, Hiroshi Ohta, Kaoru Ono.

CHAPTER 1

Introduction

1.1. What is the Floer (co)homology

Floer homology is a semi-infinite ($\infty/2$) dimensional homology theory on an infinite (∞) dimensional space in general. It has been defined in various contexts and proven to be an extremely deep and useful tool to study many problems arising in the various areas including symplectic geometry, gauge theory and the low dimensional topology.

Floer's main motivation to introduce Floer homology in symplectic geometry [**Flo88IV**] was to prove Arnold's conjecture [**Arn65**] for the fixed points of *Hamiltonian diffeomorphisms* (or exact symplectic diffeomorphisms). One version of Arnold's conjecture is that any Hamiltonian diffeomorphism $\phi : (M, \omega) \to (M, \omega)$ on a compact M satisfies

$$(1.1) \qquad \# \operatorname{Fix} \phi \geq \sum_k \operatorname{rank} H_k(M)$$

provided all of its fixed points are nondegenerate. A Hamiltonian diffeomorphism (or exact symplectic diffeomorphism) is a symplectic diffeomorphism obtained as the time one map of a (time-dependent) Hamiltonian flow.

By considering the diagonal $\Delta \subset (M \times M, \omega \oplus -\omega)$, which is a Lagrangian submanifold in the product, one can instead ask its intersection theoretic version, which is indeed the original approach taken by Floer in [**Flo88IV**].

Let $L_1, L_0 \subset (M, \omega)$ be two compact Lagrangian submanifolds. The ideal statement one might expect for Floer homology is as follows:

(1.2.1)   We can assign a (graded) abelian group (or $\mathbb{Z}_2$ vector space), denoted by $HF(L_1, L_0)$, to each pair (L_1, L_0) of Lagrangian submanifolds. We call $HF(L_1, L_0)$ the Floer homology.

(1.2.2)   Floer homology is invariant under the Hamiltonian diffeomorphisms. Namely if ϕ_i, $i = 0, 1$ are two Hamiltonian diffeomorphisms, then

$$HF_*(L_1, L_0) \simeq HF_*(\phi_1 L_1, \phi_0 L_0).$$

(1.2.3)   If $L_0 = L_1 = L$, then the Floer homology group coincides with the standard homology group of Lagrangian submanifold L. Namely $HF_*(L, L) \simeq H_*(L; \mathbb{Z}_2)$.

(1.2.4)   When L_0 is transversal to L_1, Floer homology $HF_*(L_1, L_0)$ is a homology group of the chain complex that is given by

$$(1.3) \qquad CF_*(L_1, L_0) = \sum_{p \in L_1 \cap L_0} \mathbb{Z}_2[p]$$

as a group.

Actually Floer defined $HF(L_1, L_0)$ as the homology of the chain complex (1.3) where the matrix element $\langle \partial p, q \rangle$ of the boundary operator ∂ is defined by counting the number of pseudo-holomorphic (cornered) discs with each half of its boundary lying on L_0 and L_1 respectively, and with its asymptotic limits given by $p, q \in L_1 \cap L_0$ (see Section 2.3 for more details). The main task to be carried out is to justify this definition and to prove the boundary property $\partial \partial = 0$ of the operator ∂.

In [**Flo88IV**], Floer carried out this analysis, defined the Floer homology group $HF(L_1, L_0)$, and proved the properties (1.2.1)-(1.2.4) above for the case where

$$L_0 = \phi(L), \quad L_1 = L$$

for L satisfying $\pi_2(M, L) = 0$ and $\phi : M \to M$ a Hamiltonian diffeomorphism.

After Floer, the second named author generalized the construction of Floer homology to the arbitrary pairs (L_1, L_0) of *monotone Lagrangian submanifolds* with minimal Maslov number > 2 in [**Oh93,95I**] (See Subsection 2.4.5 and Theorem 2.4.42 for its definition). He also proved (1.2.2),(1.2,4) but observed that (1.2.3) does not hold in general.

Both authors used $\mathbb{Z}_2$-coefficients.

At first sight, these conditions look rather restrictive and technical especially when compared to the development of the other version of Floer homology, Floer homology for Hamiltonian diffeomorphisms, and of Arnold's conjecture (1.1).

Namely, for the case of diffeomorphisms, the following result has been already proved for arbitrary compact symplectic manifold M: For any Hamiltonian diffeomorphism $\phi : M \to M$, one can associate a graded abelian group, Floer homology $HF(M; \phi)$ with suitable coefficients, such that

$$HF(M; \phi) \cong H(M)$$
$$\sum_k \operatorname{rank} HF_k(M; \phi) \leq \# \operatorname{Fix}(\phi).$$

Here $\operatorname{Fix}(\phi)$ is the fixed point set of ϕ.

In [**Flo89I**], Floer gave the definition of $HF(M; \phi)$ for Hamiltonian diffeomorphisms and proved that $HF(M; \phi) \cong H(M; \mathbb{Z})$, when (M, ω) is monotone. As a consequence, he proved Arnold's conjecture for the monotone case. (For this matter, we should mention the earlier result by Conley-Zehnder [**CoZe83**] for the case of symplectic tori and by Floer himself for the case where $\pi_2(M) = 0$ as a consequence of [**Flo88IV**]). This was generalized by Hofer-Salamon [**HoSa95**] and the fourth named author [**Ono95**] to semi-positive symplectic manifolds. Construction of the Floer homology and proof of Arnold's conjecture for the general case have been carried out in [**FuOn99II, LiuTi98, Rua99**] over $\mathbb{Q}$, and by the first and fourth named authors in [**FuOn01**] over $\mathbb{Z}$. (The detail of [**FuOn01**] is still to be written.) Since $HF(M; \phi)$ is isomorphic to the homology group $H(M)$ of M, the group itself does not give rise to a new invariant of the symplectic manifold (M, ω). However defining Floer homology itself has application to Arnold's conjecture in various settings.

On the other hand, we can not expect the theory of Lagrangian intersection Floer homology would completely resemble that of Hamiltonian diffeomorphisms. Namely we can not expect all of the properties (1.2.1)-(1.2.4) hold in general.

Firstly, Lagrangian intersection Floer homology concerns pairs (L_1, L_0) of Lagrangian submanifolds, but cannot be defined for completely arbitrary pairs.

Secondly, unlike the case of diffeomorphisms, the relevant moduli spaces are neither (stably almost) complex spaces nor deformable to them and so do not carry canonical orientations in general. For the case of cotangent bundles, orientation problem in the Lagrangian intersection Floer homology was previously studied by the second named author in [**Oh97II**] where he improved Floer's result [**Flo88IV**] to define the Floer homology over $\mathbb{Z}$ coefficients. In general, providing an orientation on the moduli space of pseudo-holomorphic discs (or bordered Riemann surfaces) attached to a Lagrangian submanifold is not always possible, and is a rather nontrivial family index problem of the Cauchy-Riemann operator over the bordered Riemann surface. This leads to the condition on the spin structure on the Lagrangian submanifold (see Definition 1.6 below).

Thirdly, even when $HF(L_1, L_0)$ is defined, the (symplectic) geometric meaning of the invariants $HF(L_1, L_0)$ becomes less clear. For example, let us consider a pair (L_1, L_0) of compact Lagrangian submanifolds of $\mathbb{C}^n$ ($\mathbb{C}^n$ is noncompact but is tame in the sense of Gromov [**Grom85**] which still allows one to do the Floer theory for compact Lagrangian submanifolds in the same way). Then obviously there exists a Hamiltonian isotopy ϕ_t of compact support such that $\phi_1(L_1) \cap L_0 = \emptyset$. This fact and (1.2.2), (1.2.4) would mean that if one could define Floer homology of the pair (L_1, L_0) of Lagrangian submanifolds invariant under the Hamiltonian isotopy, then it should become necessarily trivial. Hence it appears at the first sight that the Floer theory would give nothing interesting for the important case of Lagrangian submanifolds of $\mathbb{C}^n$. However there are various results on Lagrangian submanifolds of $\mathbb{C}^n$ which one can prove using the Floer theory, just knowing that it is defined. For example, using the Floer theory, one can prove Gromov's theorem of nonexistence of exact Lagrangian submanifold [**Grom85**] and some topological obstruction to the Maslov class of compact Lagrangian embedding in $\mathbb{C}^n$ as illustrated in [**Oh96I,96II**]. This line of ideas has been further developed by others, most notably by Biran and Cieliebak [**BiCi01,02**].

Therefore it is an important task to understand when the Floer homology can be defined and when not. As pointed out in [**Oh93**], if we define the operator ∂ just by counting the number of pseudo-holomorphic discs as Floer did in [**Flo88IV**], then ∂ will not satisfy the boundary property, i.e., $\partial\partial \neq 0$ in general. This fact was applied to a variant of Floer homology in [**Ono96**]. In physical terms, $\partial\partial \neq 0$ might be regarded as the breaking of BRST symmetry by soliton effects (i.e., by the presence of pseudo-holomorphic discs). The word "anomaly" in the sub-title of the present book indicates this (BRST) symmetry breaking. This means that the mathematical framework for the Floer homology of Lagrangian submanifolds will be more involved (and interesting) than that of Hamiltonian diffeomorphisms.

The main result that we establish in this book is an obstruction theory to defining the Floer homology of Lagrangian intersections. We also describe how the homology of L is related to the Floer homology $HF(L, L)$ and provide various applications of Floer homology to the study of geometry of Lagrangian submanifolds. The result of this book is also fundamental to make precise formulation of the celebrated homological mirror symmetry conjecture proposed by Kontsevich [**Kon95I**]: This is based on the framework of Floer cohomology, or more precisely of the A_∞ category that the first named author introduced in [**Fuk93**]. The most important steps towards a rigorous construction of the A_∞ category on a general symplectic manifold are given in this book.

Recently there are many works both by physicists and by mathematicians on the calculation of the number of (pseudo)holomorphic discs attached to a given Lagrangian submanifold. (See for example, [**KatLi01, LiSo01, AAMV05**].) As in the closed case of Gromov-Witten invariants, they mainly use the fixed point localization under the torus action in their computations. As is widely known by now, the number itself of holomorphic discs is not well defined in that the number depends on the various choices involved, such as perturbations to make the moduli space transversal. Therefore, it is a highly nontrivial problem to extract an object, out of the numbers calculated by localization and others, that is mathematically well defined. In this book, we have solved this problem by constructing an algebraic structure, the *filtered A_∞ algebra*, whose structure constants are the numbers of pseudo-holomorphic discs and satisfy various relations. We prove that the homotopy equivalence class of this filtered A_∞ algebra associated to a given Lagrangian submanifold is independent of various choices involved. It is not yet very clear to the authors precisely how the numbers obtained by the localization and others are related to the structure studied in this book in general, although it is quite apparent that they must be related.

The algebraic basis of the present work is the theory of A_∞ algebras, which we will explain more in the next section. The notion of A_∞ algebra was introduced by Stasheff [**Sta63**] in the homotopy theory using the idea of Sugawara [**Sug57**] in 1960's. Witten [**Wit86**] (the end of 1980's) and Zwiebach [**Zwi91,97**] (the beginning of 1990's) observed that A_∞ structure is a natural frame work for the open string theory. Just after that, inspired by Donaldson's lecture, the first named author independently introduced the A_∞ structure to the Floer theory. In those days the relationship between these works was well understood by neither the researchers in mathematics nor in physics.

We are quite happy to see that the developments in both sides in the last decade have completely changed this landscape which made the relationship between the (topological) open string with D-brane and the Floer cohomology much clearer. Now appearance of the A_∞ structures in both fields is not an alien but a natural phenomenon. In this midst the relationship of this A_∞ structure to that of homotopy theory has also become clearer.

In the beginning of 1990's when the idea of using the A_∞ structure or homological algebra of that kind in the Floer theory was first incepted, it was so alien that it was not well-received among the symplectic geometers. Only recently the study of various algebraic structures in Floer theory became natural and unavoidable among the researchers. On the other hand, Floer cohomology, especially the one arising in symplectic geometry, is still rarely understood in detail by theoretical physicists working on the string theory. (After the work of Vafa [**Vaf99**], Douglas [**Dou02**] etc., it becomes more familiar of some physicists.) We sincerely hope that publication of this book will improve the situation even more.

We would also like to mention that the basic technology developed in the second half of 1990's ([**FuOn99II, LiTi98, Rua99, Sie96**]) for the purpose of handling the moduli spaces defined by nonlinear elliptic partial differential equations has made it possible to work out the mathematical details needed for the systematic construction of various algebraic structures coming out of the moduli space. Especially the method of using Kuranishi structure and multi-sections (or something equivalent to them) is crucial for such constructions. The machinery of Kuranishi structure and multi-sections was developed by the first and the fourth named authors in 1996 for the purpose of handling many transversality problems needed in the construction of appropriate (virtual) fundamental *cycles* in various contexts. In this book, we employ them in an even more nontrivial way of defining (virtual) fundamental *chains*.

This book is a research monograph. All the results are new unless otherwise mentioned.

1.2. General theory of Lagrangian Floer cohomology

From now on we use the cohomological notation for the Floer theory. Therefore we will exclusively use cohomology, not homology, unless otherwise stated.

To obtain the whole picture of Floer cohomology of Lagrangian submanifolds, it turns out necessary to use the language of filtered A_∞ algebras and filtered A_∞ modules. We will describe them systematically in Chapters 3-5. Here we give only the definitions that are necessary in stating Theorem A below.

Firstly we introduce our coefficient ring $\Lambda_{0,nov}$.

$$\Lambda_{0,nov} = \left\{ \sum_{i=0}^{\infty} a_i T^{\lambda_i} e^{n_i} \;\middle|\; a_i \in \mathbb{Q}, \; \lambda_i \in \mathbb{R}_{\geq 0}, \; n_i \in \mathbb{Z} \text{ and } \lim_{i \to \infty} \lambda_i = \infty \right\}.$$

Here T and e are formal generators of $\deg e = 2$ and $\deg T = 0$. We call $\Lambda_{0,nov}$ the *universal Novikov ring*. We may assume that $\lambda_0 = 0$.

Consider a graded vector space C (over $\mathbb{Q}$) and its shifted one $C[1]$ defined by $C[1]^k = C^{k+1}$. We consider a series of operations

$$\mathfrak{m}_{k,i} : \underbrace{C[1] \otimes \cdots \otimes C[1]}_{k} \to C[1]$$

of degree $1 - \mu_i$. Here μ_i are even numbers and $\mu_0 = 0$. For each $k = 0, 1, 2, \cdots$, we put

$$\mathfrak{m}_k = \sum_{i=0}^{\infty} T^{\lambda_i} e^{\mu_i/2} \mathfrak{m}_{k,i}.$$

Here λ_i are nonnegative real numbers such that $\lambda_0 = 0$, $\lambda_i > 0$ for $i > 0$, $\lim_{i \to \infty} \lambda_i = \infty$. We assume $\mathfrak{m}_{0,0} = 0$. The operations $\mathfrak{m}_k$ define homomorphisms

$$\mathfrak{m}_k : \underbrace{(C[1] \hat{\otimes} \Lambda_{0,nov}) \otimes \cdots \otimes (C[1] \hat{\otimes} \Lambda_{0,nov})}_{k} \to (C[1] \hat{\otimes} \Lambda_{0,nov}).$$

Here and hereafter $\hat{\otimes}$ stands for the completion of algebraic tensor product with respect to appropriate filtration. (See Sections 3.1 and 3.2.)

We say that the operations $\mathfrak{m}_k$ define the structure of *filtered A_∞ algebra* on $C[1] \hat{\otimes} \Lambda_{0,nov}$ if they satisfy the quadratic relations

$$(1.4) \qquad \sum_{k_1 + k_2 = k+1} \sum_{j=1}^{k_1} (-1)^* \mathfrak{m}_{k_1}(x_1, \cdots, \mathfrak{m}_{k_2}(x_j, \cdots, x_{j+k_2-1}), \cdots, x_k) = 0$$

for each $k = 0, 1, 2, \cdots$, where $* = \deg x_1 + \cdots + \deg x_{j-1} + j - 1$. We call (1.4) the A_∞ *relation* or A_∞ *formula*. (See Definition 3.2.20 and Remark 3.2.21.)

REMARK 1.5. The ring $\Lambda_{0,nov}$ is a version of the one introduced by Novikov [**Nov81**] in his Morse theory of closed one forms, which is closely related to Floer cohomology. Therefore we call it the (universal) Novikov ring in this book. (A similar ring have been appeared in some different contexts before Novikov.) It was Floer [**Flo89I**] who first observed that Novikov ring is the correct coefficient ring to be used for the Floer cohomology. The fourth named author [**Ono95**] and Hofer-Salamon [**HoSa95**] independently used Novikov ring in their proofs of Arnold's conjecture (1.1) for semi-positive symplectic manifolds.

To study the general Floer theory over the rational coefficients, we need to assume that Lagrangian submanifolds L_i, $i = 0, 1$ are relatively spin.

DEFINITION 1.6. We call a submanifold $L \subset M$ *relatively spin* if it is orientable and there exists a class $st \in H^2(M; \mathbb{Z}_2)$ that restricts to the second Stiefel-Whitney class $w_2(L)$ of L.

We call a pair of submanifolds (L_1, L_0) of M *relatively spin* if they are orientable and there exists a class $st \in H^2(M; \mathbb{Z}_2)$ that restricts to the second Stiefel-Whitney classes $w_2(L_i)$ of both of L_i, $i = 0, 1$.

We put $H^*(L; \Lambda_{0,nov}) = H^*(L; \mathbb{Q}) \otimes_{\mathbb{Q}} \Lambda_{0,nov}$.

THEOREM A. *To each relatively spin Lagrangian submanifold L we can associate a structure of filtered A_∞ algebra $\mathfrak{m}_k$ on $H^*(L; \Lambda_{0,nov})$, which is well-defined up to isomorphism.*

If $\psi : (M, L) \to (M', L')$ is a symplectic diffeomorphism, then we can associate to it an isomorphism $\psi_* := (\psi^{-1})^* : H^*(L; \Lambda_{0,nov}) \to H^*(L'; \Lambda_{0,nov})$ of filtered A_∞ algebras whose homotopy class depends only of isotopy class of symplectic diffeomorphism $\psi : (M, L) \to (M', L')$.

The Poincaré dual $PD([L]) \in H^0(L; \Lambda_{0,nov})$ of the fundamental class $[L]$ is the unit of our filtered A_∞ algebra. The homomorphism ψ_* is unital.

Here, an isomorphism of a filtered A_∞ algebra is by definition a filtered A_∞ homomorphism that has an inverse. The notion of filtered A_∞ homomorphism is defined in Definition 3.2.29. A homotopy between them is defined in Definition 4.2.35. See Definition 3.2.20 and 3.3.11 for the definition of a unit and the unitality of filtered A_∞ homomorphisms. The proof of Theorem A is completed in Section 5.4 (Corollary 5.4.6) *based on the results of Chapters 7 and 8.*

Much of the rigorous construction in this whole book is based on the results in Chapters 7 and 8, which deal with the problems of transversality and of orientation respectively. Therefore we will not repeat this kind of the phrase in italic from now on.

The filtered A_∞ algebra in Theorem A will be homotopy equivalent to the de Rham complex when we forget the contribution of nontrivial pseudoholomorphic discs. (Theorem X.)

We remark that the filtered A_∞ structure appearing in Theorem A is defined for an *arbitrary* relatively spin Lagrangian submanifold L. It induces a coderivation $\hat{d}$ on the free (formal) coalgebra

$$BH(L; \Lambda_{0,nov})[1] = \bigoplus_k \underbrace{H(L; \Lambda_{0,nov})[1] \otimes \cdots \otimes H(L; \Lambda_{0,nov})[1]}_{k}$$

(see Section 3.2 formula (3.2.1)) and the A_∞ relation (1.4) is equivalent to $\hat{d}\hat{d} = 0$. Thus we obtain a differential graded coalgebra $(BH(L; \Lambda_{0,nov})[1], \hat{d})$. This is an A_∞ analog to the classical bar resolution of differential graded algebra (see [**Mac63**] Chapter 3 Section 3.5). We call it the *bar complex*.

The bar complex of A_∞ algebra is studied in [**GeJo90**], for example. Compared to the notation of [**GeJo90**], our notation $BH(L; \Lambda_{0,nov})[1]$ corresponds to $BH(L; \Lambda_{0,nov})$ in [**GeJo90**].

The dual of a bar complex is a differential graded algebra in general. A similar differential graded algebra was defined by Chekanov [**Chek02**] for a Legendrian knots in $\mathbb{R}^3$. (The idea of using this kind of bar complex in Floer theory is independently discovered by Chekanov and by the present authors in 1990's. See also [**EGH00**].) The second half of Theorem A implies that cohomology of the bar complex $(BH(L; \Lambda_{0,nov})[1], \hat{d})$ is an invariant of L. However cohomology of $(BH(L; \Lambda_{0,nov})[1], \hat{d})$ is isomorphic to $\Lambda_{0,nov}$, since it is an A_∞ analogue of the bar complex of a differential graded algebra *with unit*. (See for example in [**Mac63**] p 306.)

Some reduced and/or symmetrized versions of the bar complex (for example the reduced or the cyclic and reduced ones) have nontrivial cohomology. (See [**Fuk05II**] for its relation to the loop space.) Theorem A also implies that the cohomology of them is an invariant of the relatively spin Lagrangian submanifold.

However rather than studying these reduced versions, we study another cohomology also induced naturally from the A_∞ algebra, whose definition we will explain below. We call this cohomology the *Floer cohomology*. There are several reasons for doing this. Firstly cohomology of (versions of) the bar complex is usually of infinite dimension when it is nontrivial. This makes it harder to apply: For example its rank is not a good invariant. Secondly, Floer cohomology is more directly related to various geometric properties of the Lagrangian submanifold, such as the classical cohomology of Lagrangian or the number of intersection points between them. Thirdly, it is Floer cohomology (and not the cohomology of bar complex), that corresponds to sheaf cohomology (or Ext group) under the homological mirror symmetry correspondence. (See Conjecture R.)

To obtain Floer cohomology of L out of Theorem A, we proceed in the following way. Let $(C, \mathfrak{m}_k)$ be a filtered A_∞ algebra. Note that we assume $\mathfrak{m}_{0,0} = 0$ but do not assume $\mathfrak{m}_{0,i} : \mathbb{Q} \to C[1]$ is zero for $i > 0$. This is related to the phenomenon that $\delta\delta \neq 0$ in general Floer theory: Namely (1.4) for $k = 2$ implies

$$\mathfrak{m}_1 \circ \mathfrak{m}_1(x) = (-1)^{\deg x + 1} \mathfrak{m}_2(x, \mathfrak{m}_0(1)) + \mathfrak{m}_2(\mathfrak{m}_0(1), x).$$

There are three different levels on how one can arrive at a coboundary operator $\delta : C \to C$, i.e, the map satisfying $\delta\delta = 0$:
  (1) The case where we have $\mathfrak{m}_0(1) = 0$
  (2) The case where $\mathfrak{m}_0(1)$ is a multiple of the fundamental class $PD[L]$
  (3) The cases where we can deform $\mathfrak{m}$ to $\mathfrak{m}^{(b_1, b_0)}$ for which the corresponding $\mathfrak{m}_0^{(b_1, b_0)}$ satisfies (1) or (2).
For the first case, it is obvious that the operator $\delta : C \to C$ defined by $\delta = \mathfrak{m}_1$ satisfies $\delta\delta = 0$ and so defines a coboundary map. For the second case, one can check that the two terms of the right hand side of the above equation cancel each other and again $\delta = \mathfrak{m}_1$ satisfies $\delta\delta = 0$. (See Addendum [**Oh93**], [**ChOh03**] and Subsection 3.6.3 for this cancellation argument.) In the case (3), we call the A_∞

algebra $(C, \mathfrak{m})$ *unobstructed* (respectively *weakly unobstructed*) if it can be deformed to the case (1) (respectively to (2)).

Now we explain how we deform δ for the unobstructed case. In this case we consider the deformed operator δ_{b_1,b_2} given by

$$(1.7) \qquad \delta_{b_1,b_0}(x) = \sum_{k=0}^{\infty} \sum_{\ell=0}^{\infty} \mathfrak{m}_{k+\ell+1}(\underbrace{b_1, \cdots, b_1}_{k}, x, \underbrace{b_0, \cdots, b_0}_{\ell}).$$

Then it can be shown (see Section 3.8) that $\delta_{b_1,b_0} \circ \delta_{b_1,b_0} = 0$ if

$$(1.8) \qquad \sum_{k=0}^{\infty} \mathfrak{m}_k(\underbrace{b_j, \cdots, b_j}_{k}) = 0, \quad \text{for } j = 0, 1.$$

We call b a *bounding cochain* if b satisfies (1.8).

One can also deform the A_∞ algebra $(C, \mathfrak{m})$ by a cohomology class coming from the ambient symplectic manifold (See Section 3.8). We call this deformation *a bulk deformation*. By amplifying the above deformation argument to the case of bulk deformations, we obtain the following Theorem B. Here

$$\Lambda_{0,nov}^+ = \left\{ \sum_{i=0}^{\infty} a_i T^{\lambda_i} e^{n_i} \in \Lambda_{0,nov} \;\middle|\; \lambda_i > 0 \right\}.$$

See (Conv.4) at the end of Chapter 1.

THEOREM B. *To each relatively spin Lagrangian submanifold $L \subset M$, we can associate a set $\mathcal{M}_{\text{weak,def}}(L)$, and the maps*

$$\pi_{\text{amb}} : \mathcal{M}_{\text{weak,def}}(L) \to H^2(M; \Lambda_{0,nov}^+), \quad \mathfrak{PO} : \mathcal{M}_{\text{weak,def}}(L) \to \Lambda_{0,nov}^+,$$

with the following properties: Hereafter we put

$$(1.9) \qquad \begin{aligned} &\mathcal{M}_{\text{weak,def}}(L) \times_{(\pi_{\text{amb}}, \mathfrak{PO})} \mathcal{M}_{\text{weak,def}}(L) \\ &= \{(\mathbf{b}_1, \mathbf{b}_0) \mid \pi_{\text{amb}}(\mathbf{b}_1) = \pi_{\text{amb}}(\mathbf{b}_0),\ \mathfrak{PO}(\mathbf{b}_1) = \mathfrak{PO}(\mathbf{b}_0)\}. \end{aligned}$$

(B.1)   *There is a Floer cohomology $HF((L, \mathbf{b}_1), (L, \mathbf{b}_0); \Lambda_{0,nov})$ parameterized by $(\mathbf{b}_1, \mathbf{b}_0) \in \mathcal{M}_{\text{weak,def}}(L) \times_{(\pi_{\text{amb}}, \mathfrak{PO})} \mathcal{M}_{\text{weak,def}}(L)$.*

(B.2)   *There exists a product structure*

$$\begin{aligned} \mathfrak{m}_2 : HF((L, \mathbf{b}_2), (L, \mathbf{b}_1); \Lambda_{0,nov}) &\otimes HF((L, \mathbf{b}_1), (L, \mathbf{b}_0); \Lambda_{0,nov}) \\ &\to HF((L, \mathbf{b}_2), (L, \mathbf{b}_0); \Lambda_{0,nov}) \end{aligned}$$

if $(\mathbf{b}_1, \mathbf{b}_0), (\mathbf{b}_2, \mathbf{b}_1) \in \mathcal{M}_{\text{weak,def}}(L) \times_{(\pi_{\text{amb}}, \mathfrak{PO})} \mathcal{M}_{\text{weak,def}}(L)$. $\mathfrak{m}_2$ is associative. In particular, $HF((L, \mathbf{b}), (L, \mathbf{b}); \Lambda_{0,nov})$ has a ring structure for $\mathbf{b} \in \mathcal{M}_{\text{weak,def}}(L)$.

(B.3)   *If $\psi : (M, L) \to (M', L')$ is a symplectic diffeomorphism, then it induces a bijection $\psi_* : \mathcal{M}_{\text{weak,def}}(L) \to \mathcal{M}_{\text{weak,def}}(L')$ such that*

$$\pi_{\text{amb}} \circ \psi_* = \psi_* \circ \pi_{\text{amb}}, \quad \mathfrak{PO} \circ \psi_* = \mathfrak{PO}.$$

The map ψ_* depends only on the isotopy class of symplectic diffeomorphism ψ. Here $\psi_* = (\psi^{-1})^*$ on the right hand side.

(B.4)   *In the situation of (B.3), we have an isomorphism*

$$\psi_* : HF((L, \mathbf{b}_1), (L, \mathbf{b}_0); \Lambda_{0,nov}) \cong HF((L', \psi_*(\mathbf{b}_1)), (L', \psi_*(\mathbf{b}_0)); \Lambda_{0,nov}).$$

And ψ_* commutes with $\mathbf{m}_2$.

(B.5) *The isomorphism ψ_* in (B.4) depends only on the isotopy class of symplectic diffeomorphism $\psi : (M, L) \to (M', L')$. Moreover $(\psi \circ \psi')_* = \psi_* \circ \psi'_*$.*

See (4.3.27) for Π_{amb} and Lemma 4.3.28 for $\mathfrak{PO}$. Construction of the Floer cohomology and the proof of (B.2) of Theorem B are completed in Subsection 3.8.10. Statement (B.1), especially the statement that Floer cohomology depends only of the pair $(\mathbf{b}_1, \mathbf{b}_0)$, follows from Proposition 4.3.29 which is a consequence of Corollary 5.2.40 in Subsection 5.2.4. The proofs of (B.3)-(B.5) are completed in Subsection 4.6.5. Theorem B follows from Theorem A (and its 'def' version) by a purely algebraic argument. (In this book we give a proof of Theorem B before the proof of Theorem A is completed, however.)

We also consider the following subsets of $\mathcal{M}_{\mathrm{weak,def}}(L)$: $\mathcal{M}_{\mathrm{weak}}(L) = \mathrm{Zero}(\mathfrak{PO})$, $\mathcal{M}_{\mathrm{def}}(L) = \mathrm{Zero}(\pi_{\mathrm{amb}})$, $\mathcal{M}(L) = \mathrm{Zero}(\pi_{\mathrm{amb}}) \cap \mathrm{Zero}(\mathfrak{PO})$.

Then $\mathcal{M}(L)$ will be identified with the set of gauge equivalence classes of the bounding cochains b, i.e., solutions of (1.8). (See Section 4.3 Definition 4.3.1 for the definition of gauge equivalence.) Each of these sets will be regarded as a quotient of the zero set of a formal power series as we will describe in Theorem M. The Floer cohomology, denoted by $HF((L, b_1), (L, b_0); \Lambda_{0,nov})$, for $b_1, b_0 \in \mathcal{M}(L)$, is the cohomology group of the boundary operator δ_{b_1,b_0} defined by (1.7). The version $HF((L, \mathbf{b}_1), (L, \mathbf{b}_0); \Lambda_{0,nov})$ for

$$(\mathbf{b}_1, \mathbf{b}_0) \in \mathcal{M}_{\mathrm{weak,def}}(L) \times_{(\pi_{\mathrm{amb}}, \mathfrak{PO})} \mathcal{M}_{\mathrm{weak,def}}(L)$$

is its generalization. More precisely speaking, for the generalization of the definition of Floer cohomology from $\mathcal{M}(L)$ to $\mathcal{M}_{\mathrm{weak}}(L)$, we need to study the *unit* of our filtered A_∞ algebra (See Sections 3.3, 7.3 and Subsection 3.7.3.), and for the generalization from $\mathcal{M}(L)$ to $\mathcal{M}_{\mathrm{def}}(L)$, we need to study bulk deformations of the filtered A_∞ algebra in Theorem A. (See Section 3.8.)

Theorem B implies that Floer cohomology is defined if $\mathcal{M}_{\mathrm{weak,def}}(L) \neq \emptyset$. We would like to note that the set $\mathcal{M}_{\mathrm{weak,def}}(L)$ could be empty, however. A sufficient condition for the non-emptiness of $\mathcal{M}_{\mathrm{weak,def}}(L)$ can be described in terms of the cohomology group of L.

THEOREM C. *There exists a series of* **positive** *integers $m_k < \dim L/2$ and classes*

$$[o_k^{2m_k}(L; \mathrm{weak, def})] \in \frac{H^{2m_k}(L; \mathbb{Q})}{\mathrm{Im}\ (i^* : H^{2m_k}(M; \mathbb{Q}) \to H^{2m_k}(L; \mathbb{Q}))}$$

$k = 1, 2, \cdots$, *such that, if the obstruction classes $[o_k^{2m_k}(L; \mathrm{weak, def})]$ are all zero, then $\mathcal{M}_{\mathrm{weak,def}}(L)$ is nonempty. The number $2 - 2m_k$ is a sum of the Maslov indices of a finite collection of the homotopy classes in $\pi_2(M, L)$ realized by pseudoholomorphic discs (with respect to a given almost complex structure on M).*

Theorem C is a consequence of Theorems 3.8.41, 3.8.50 and 3.8.96, which is proved in Subsections 3.8.5 and 3.8.9. The proof of Theorem C is completed in Subsection 3.8.10.

REMARK 1.10. The classes $[o_k^{2m_k}(L; \mathrm{weak, def})]$ are *not* invariants of L itself because they will depend on various choices in general, let alone the given almost complex structure. A more functorial (or invariant) way of describing the set $\mathcal{M}_{\mathrm{weak}}(L)$ is Theorem M.

We next describe how we need to modify (1.2.3) in the general situation. Hereafter we denote the Poincaré duality by PD.

THEOREM D. *For each*

$$(\mathbf{b}_1, \mathbf{b}_0) \in \mathcal{M}_{\text{weak,def}}(L) \times_{(\pi_{\text{amb}}, \mathfrak{PD})} \mathcal{M}_{\text{weak,def}}(L),$$

there exists a spectral sequence with the following properties:

(D.1) $E_2^{p,q} = \bigoplus_k H^k(L; \mathbb{Q}) \otimes (T^{q\lambda}\Lambda_{0,nov}/T^{(q+1)\lambda}\Lambda_{0,nov})^{(p-k)}$. *Here* $\lambda > 0$.

(D.2)   *There exists a filtration* $\mathfrak{F}^* HF((L, \mathbf{b}_1), (L, \mathbf{b}_0); \Lambda_{0,nov})$ *on the Floer cohomology* $HF((L, \mathbf{b}_1), (L, \mathbf{b}_0); \Lambda_{0,nov})$ *such that*

$$E_\infty^{p,q} \cong \frac{\mathfrak{F}^q HF^p((L, \mathbf{b}_1), (L, \mathbf{b}_0); \Lambda_{0,nov})}{\mathfrak{F}^{q+1} HF^p((L, \mathbf{b}_1), (L, \mathbf{b}_0); \Lambda_{0,nov})}.$$

(D.3)   *Consider the subgroup* $K_r \subset E_r = \bigoplus_{p,q} E_r^{p,q}$ *defined by*

$$K_2^{p,q} = \bigoplus_k PD(\text{Ker}(H_{n-k}(L; \mathbb{Q}) \to H_{n-k}(M; \mathbb{Q})))$$

$$\otimes (T^{q\lambda}\Lambda_{0,nov}/T^{(q+1)\lambda}\Lambda_{0,nov})^{(p-k)},$$

$$K_{r+1} = \frac{K_r \cap \text{Ker } \delta_r}{K_r \cap \text{Im } \delta_r} \subset E_{r+1}.$$

Then we have $\text{Im } \delta_r \subseteq K_r$ *for every* r, *under the additional assumption that* $\mathbf{b}_0 = \mathbf{b}_1$.

In particular, the spectral sequence collapses at the E_2 *level, if the inclusion-induced homomorphism* $i_* : H_*(L; \mathbb{Q}) \to H_*(M; \mathbb{Q})$ *is injective.*

(D.4)   *The spectral sequence is compatible with the ring structure in* (B.2). *In other words we have the following. Each of* E_r *has a ring structure* $\mathfrak{m}_2$ *which satisfies:*

$$\delta_r(\mathfrak{m}_2(x,y)) = -\mathfrak{m}_2(\delta_r(x), y) + (-1)^{\deg x}\mathfrak{m}_2(x, \delta_r(y)).$$

The filtration $\mathfrak{F}$ *is compatible with the ring structure in* (B.2). *The isomorphisms in* (D.1) *and* (D.2) *are ring isomorphisms.*

The proof of Theorem D is completed in Subsection 6.4.5.

For various applications in practice, it is important to know when Floer cohomology does not vanish, which will then give rise to an existence theorem of a suitable form of pseudo-holomorphic curves. For this purpose, one may often use either the point class $PD[pt] \in H^n(L; \mathbb{Q})$ or the fundamental class $PD[L] \in H^0(L; \mathbb{Q})$, that we know are not zero at least in the classical cohomology:

THEOREM E. *In the situation of Theorem* D *we assume* $\mathbf{b}_0 = \mathbf{b}_1$. *Then, there exists a cohomology class* $PD[L]' \in H^n(L; \Lambda_{0,nov})$ *with* $PD[L]' \equiv PD[L]$ *mod* $\Lambda_{0,nov}^+$ *which has the following properties.*

(E.1)   *For each* $r \in \mathbb{Z}_{\geq 0}$ *we have* $\delta_r(PD[L]') = 0$ *and* $PD[pt] \notin \text{Im}(\delta_r)$, *where* δ_r *is the differential of the spectral sequence in Theorem* D.

(E.2)   *If the Maslov index of all the pseudo-holomorphic discs bounding* L *are non-positive, then* $\delta_r(PD[pt]) = 0$ *and* $PD[L]' \notin \text{Im}(\delta_r)$.

Theorem E is Theorem 6.1.9 which is proved in Chapter 6 Subsection 6.4.3. Theorem E holds over Λ_{nov} coefficient. (Λ_{nov} is defined in (Conv.3) at the end of Chapter 1.)

REMARK 1.11. The properties of $PD[L]'$ in Theorem E is closely related to the fact that the filtered A_∞ algebra in Theorem A has a unit $PD[L]$. (See Section 3.2 Condition 3.2.18 and Definition 3.2.20, for the definition of unit.) The statement on $PD[pt]$ is related to the fact that the map $H_0(L;\mathbb{Q}) \to H_0(M;\mathbb{Q})$ is injective, and also to the operator $\mathfrak{p}$ discussed in Section 3.8.

We next discuss Floer cohomology of a pair of Lagrangian submanifolds. Let (L_1, L_0) be a relatively spin pair of Lagrangian submanifolds. We assume that they have clean intersection. Namely we assume that the dimension of $T_x L_1 \cap T_x L_0$ is a locally constant function of $x \in L_1 \cap L_0$. (This is the Bott-Morse theory ([**Bot59**]) version of the Floer theory.) Let $\bigcup_h R_h = L_1 \cap L_0$ be the decomposition to the connected components. In Subsection 3.7.5 and Section 8.8, we will define a local system $\Theta^-_{R_h}$ on R_h defined by a homomorphism $\pi_1(R_h) \to \{\pm 1\} = \mathrm{Aut}(\mathbb{Z}) \subset \mathrm{Aut}(\mathbb{Q})$. We then put

$$C(L_1, L_0; \Lambda_{0,nov}) = \bigoplus_h H(R_h; \Theta^-_{R_h})[\mu_L(R_h)] \otimes \Lambda_{0,nov}.$$

Here $\mu_L(R_h)$ is the Bott-Morse version of Maslov index which is defined in Proposition 3.7.59, (3.7.60.1). (Note $\mu_L([h, w]) = \mu_L(R_h)$, where the left hand side is defined in Proposition 3.7.59.) Actually we need to fix an extra data, (denoted by w there) to define the Bott-Morse version of the Maslov index. $[\cdot]$ denotes the degree shift. (Namely $C[k]^d = C^{k+d}$.) See Section 8.8 for the reason why this degree shift occurs.

THEOREM F. $C(L_1, L_0; \Lambda_{0,nov})$ *has the structure of a unital filtered A_∞ bimodule over the pair* $((H(L_1; \Lambda_{0,nov}), \mathfrak{m}_*), (H(L_0; \Lambda_{0,nov}), \mathfrak{m}_*))$. *This is well-defined up to a unital filtered A_∞ bimodule isomorphism.*

The definition of filtered A_∞ bimodules is given in Section 3.7. An isomorphism of A_∞ bimodules is a filtered A_∞ bimodule homomorphism that has an inverse. The filtered A_∞ bimodule homomorphism is defined in Subsection 3.7.2. The proof of Theorem F is completed in Section 5.4 (Corollary 5.4.21).

Using Theorem F, we can define Floer cohomology of a pair of Lagrangian submanifolds and obtain the following Theorem G.

THEOREM G. *Let* (L_1, L_0) *be a relatively spin pair of Lagrangian submanifolds of M and* $(\mathbf{b}_1, \mathbf{b}_0) \in \mathcal{M}_{\mathrm{weak,def}}(L_1) \times_{(\pi_{\mathrm{amb}}, \mathfrak{PO})} \mathcal{M}_{\mathrm{weak,def}}(L_0)$, *(see (1.9) for the definition of right hand side). Then, we can associate a Floer cohomology* $HF((L_1, \mathbf{b}_1), (L_0, \mathbf{b}_0); \Lambda_{0,nov})$ *with properties* (G.1) - (G.4). *Let*

$$HF((L_1, \mathbf{b}_1), (L_0, \mathbf{b}_0); \Lambda_{0,nov}) \otimes_{\Lambda_{0,nov}} \Lambda_{nov} = HF((L_1, \mathbf{b}_1), (L_0, \mathbf{b}_0); \Lambda_{nov}).$$

(G.1)   *If $L_0 = L_1 = L$, then $HF((L_1, \mathbf{b}_1), (L_0, \mathbf{b}_0); \Lambda_{0,nov})$ coincides with the one in Theorem B.*

(G.2)   *If L_1 and L_0 have clean intersection, then we have*

$$\mathrm{rank}_{\Lambda_{nov}} HF((L_1, \mathbf{b}_1), (L_0, \mathbf{b}_0); \Lambda_{nov}) \leq \sum_{h,k} \mathrm{rank}_{\mathbb{Q}} H^k(R_h; \Theta^-_{R_h}),$$

where each R_h is a connected component of $L_0 \cap L_1$ and $\Theta^-_{R_h}$ is a local system on it associated with certain representation $\pi_1(R_h) \to \mathrm{Aut}(\mathbb{R}) = \{\pm 1\}$.

(G.3)   *If $\psi : M \to M'$ is a symplectic diffeomorphism with $\psi(L_i) = L_i'$, $(i = 0, 1)$, then we have a canonical isomorphism*

$$\psi_* : HF((L_1, \mathbf{b}_1), (L_0, \mathbf{b}_0); \Lambda_{0,nov}) \cong HF((L_1', \psi_* \mathbf{b}_1), (L_0', \psi_* \mathbf{b}_0); \Lambda_{0,nov})$$

where $\psi_* : \mathcal{M}_{\mathrm{weak,def}}(L_i) \to \mathcal{M}_{\mathrm{weak,def}}(L_i')$ is as in Theorem B. The isomorphism ψ_* depends only on the isotopy class of symplectic diffeomorphism ψ with $\psi(L_i) = L_i'$. We also have $(\psi \circ \psi')_* = \psi_* \circ \psi_*'$.

(G.4)   *If $\psi_i^s : M \to M$ $(i = 0, 1,\ s \in [0, 1])$ are Hamiltonian isotopies with $\psi_i^0 = identity$, $\psi_i^1(L_i) = L_i'$, then it induces an isomorphism*

$$(\psi_1^s, \psi_0^s)_* : HF((L_1, \mathbf{b}_1), (L_0, \mathbf{b}_0); \Lambda_{nov})$$
$$\cong HF((L_1', \psi_{1*}^1 \mathbf{b}_1), (L_0', \psi_{0*}^1 \mathbf{b}_0); \Lambda_{nov}).$$

The isomorphism $(\psi_1^s, \psi_0^s)_*$ depends only on the isotopy class of the Hamiltonian isotopies $\psi_i^s : M \to M$ $(i = 0, 1,\ s \in [0, 1])$ with $\psi_i^0 = identity$, $\psi_i^1(L_i) = L_i'$. The isomorphism $(\psi_1^s, \psi_0^s)_*$ is functorial with respect to composition of the Hamiltonian isotopies.

(G.5) $HF((L_1, \mathbf{b}_1), (L_0, \mathbf{b}_0); \Lambda_{0,nov})$ *is a bimodule over the ring pair*

$$\left(HF((L_1, \mathbf{b}_1), (L_1, \mathbf{b}_1); \Lambda_{0,nov}), HF((L_0, \mathbf{b}_0), (L_0, \mathbf{b}_0); \Lambda_{0,nov}) \right).$$

The isomorphisms (G.3), (G.4) are bimodule isomorphisms.

REMARK 1.12. (G.3) above asserts that the Floer cohomology remains to be isomorphic when we move L_1, L_0 by the same symplectic diffeomorphism. (G.4) above asserts that Floer cohomology does not change even when we move L_1, L_0 independently by *different Hamiltonian* isotopies. The latter invariance property holds only over the Λ_{nov} coefficient but not over the $\Lambda_{0,nov}$ coefficient. This point will be further explored in Theorem J.

Construction of the Floer cohomology and the proofs of (G.1), (G.5) of Theorem G are completed in Subsection 3.8.10. (G.3) is a consequence of Theorems 4.1.4 and 5.3.64, which are proved in Subsections 5.3.1 and 5.3.6, respectively. (G.4) is a consequence of Theorems 4.1.5 and 5.3.65, which are proved in Subsections 5.3.2-5.3.6. The proofs of (G.3), (G.4) are completed in Subsection 5.3.7. (G.2) is proved in Subsection 5.4.6. It also follows from Theorem 6.1.4 which is proved in Chapter 6. For the case of non-clean intersection, we need some more arguments to prove Theorem G. It is given in Subsection 6.5.4 (Proposition 6.5.38, Definition 6.5.39).

Theorem G is also a consequence of the functoriality of the filtered A_∞ bimodule given in Theorem F. (See Theorems 5.3.1 and 5.3.14.) (But, in this book, we give the proof of Theorem G before we complete the proof of Theorem F.)

We remark that Theorem F implies that we can construct various kinds of bar complex for an *arbitrary* relatively spin pair (L_1, L_0) whose cohomology is independent of the choices. We do not need to assume $\mathcal{M}(L_1) \neq \emptyset, \mathcal{M}(L_0) \neq \emptyset$ to obtain such a bar complex. (See Definition 3.7.5.) We use elements of $\mathcal{M}(L_j)$ to cut down the bar complex to a more reasonable and applicable size.

We also have a spectral sequence for a pair of Lagrangian submanifolds (L_1, L_0) of clean intersection (see Theorem 6.1.4).

We can amplify this to a product structure involving three or more Lagrangian submanifolds. Namely we obtain a filtered A_∞ category. Existence of such a category was observed by the first named author around 1993 inspired by Donaldson's lecture at University of Warwick 1992. The details of its construction are provided in [**Fuk02II**], where the contents of present book are assumed.

1.3. Applications to symplectic geometry

In this section, we describe applications of the Floer cohomology to symplectic topology of Lagrangian submanifolds. We first state the following consequence of Theorems B,C,D and G combined.

THEOREM H. *Let L be a relatively spin Lagrangian submanifold and assume that the natural map $H_*(L; \mathbb{Q}) \to H_*(M; \mathbb{Q})$ is injective. Then, for any Hamiltonian diffeomorphism $\phi : M \to M$ such that $L \pitchfork \phi(L)$, we have*

$$\#(L \cap \phi(L)) \geq \sum_k \operatorname{rank} H_k(L; \mathbb{Q}).$$

The proof of Theorem H is given in Subsection 6.5.1. We remark that the diagonal $\Delta \subset M \times M$ satisfies the assumption in Theorem H and so the version of Arnold's conjecture established in [**FuOn99II, LiuTi98, Rua99**] for Hamiltonian diffeomorphisms (over $\mathbb{Q}$-coefficients) follows from Theorem H. The following is a more precise version of Theorem H.

THEOREM I. *Let L be relatively spin and assume that $\mathcal{M}_{\mathrm{weak,def}}(L)$ is nonempty. Denote $A = \sum_* \operatorname{rank} H_*(L; \mathbb{Q})$, $B = \sum_* \operatorname{rank} \operatorname{Ker}(H_*(L; \mathbb{Q}) \to H_*(M; \mathbb{Q}))$. Then we have*

$$\#(L \cap \phi(L)) \geq A - 2B$$

for any Hamiltonian diffeomorphism $\phi : M \to M$ such that $L \pitchfork \phi(L)$.

The proof of Theorem I is completed in Subsection 6.5.2.

As we mentioned before, the Floer cohomology over $\Lambda_{0,nov}$ is not independent of the Hamiltonian isotopies of the pair of Lagrangian submanifolds L_1, L_0, while Floer cohomology over Λ_{nov} is so. We study this phenomenon more closely and relate the 'torsion part' of the Floer cohomology to the Hofer distance between Hamiltonian diffeomorphisms. (See [**HoZe94**] for the definition of Hofer distance.) We first remark that Floer cohomology $HF((L_1, \mathbf{b}_1), (L_0, \mathbf{b}_0); \Lambda_{0,nov})$ has the decomposition

$$(1.13) \qquad HF((L_1, \mathbf{b}_1), (L_0, \mathbf{b}_0); \Lambda_{0,nov}) \cong (\Lambda_{0,nov})^a \oplus \bigoplus_{i=1}^b \frac{\Lambda_{0,nov}}{T^{\lambda_i} \Lambda_{0,nov}}$$

in general (Theorem 6.1.20). We call $a \in \mathbb{Z}_{\geq 0}$ the *Betti number* and $\lambda_i \in (0, \infty)$ *torsion exponents* of the Floer cohomology. (The integer b is finite if L_1 has clean intersection with L_0 but may be infinite in general. (Example 6.5.40).)

THEOREM J. *Let (L_1, L_0) be a relatively spin pair of Lagrangian submanifolds of M and $(\mathbf{b}_1, \mathbf{b}_0) \in \mathcal{M}_{\mathrm{weak,def}}(L_1) \times_{(\pi_{\mathrm{amb}}, \mathfrak{PD})} \mathcal{M}_{\mathrm{weak,def}}(L_0)$. Let $\phi : M \to M$ be a Hamiltonian diffeomorphism and μ its Hofer norm $\mu = \|\phi\|$. Assume that $\phi(L_1)$ is transversal to L_0 and denote*

$$b(\mu) = \#\{i \mid \lambda_i \geq \mu\}$$

where λ_i are the torsion exponents in (1.13). *Then we have*

$$\#(\phi(L_1) \cap L_0) \geq a + 2b(\mu).$$

The proof of Theorem J is completed in Subsection 6.5.3. Theorem J is closely related to Chekanov's work [**Chek96,98**] and we use Chekanov's idea in the proof of Theorem J. Actually a slight improvement of Theorem J (Theorem 6.5.47 in Subsection 6.5.5) implies Chekanov's theorem. In Subsection 6.5.3 we prove a stronger result than Theorem J. Namely we prove that the torsion exponents λ_i are Lipschitz function with Lipschitz constant 1 with respect to Hofer's distance, when we move L_i in the Hamilton isotopy class (Theorem 6.1.25).

Next application concerns the Maslov class $\mu_L \in H^1(L; \mathbb{Z})$ of a Lagrangian embedding $L \subset \mathbb{C}^n$. The general folklore conjecture says that this Maslov class is non-trivial for any compact Lagrangian embedding in $\mathbb{C}^n$. There have been several partial results towards this conjecture (see [**Vit90, Pol91I, Oh96I**]). Here we add another:

THEOREM K. *Let L be a compact spin Lagrangian submanifold of $\mathbb{C}^n$ that satisfies $H^2(L; \mathbb{Q}) = 0$. Then its Maslov class $\mu_L \in H^1(L; \mathbb{Z})$ is nonzero.*

Theorem K follows from Corollary 6.1.16 which is proved in Subsection 6.4.4. Theorem K can be generalized to the case of more general (M, L). See Theorem L and Corollary 6.1.16.

There is another application (Theorem 6.4.35) using the compatibility of the spectral sequence with the multiplicative structure (Theorem D (D.4)).

THEOREM L. *Let $L \subset (M, \omega)$ be a relatively spin Lagrangian submanifold such that the Maslov index homomorphism $I_\mu : \pi_2(M, L) \to \mathbb{Z}$ is trivial. We assume $H^2(L; \mathbb{Q}) = 0$. Then for any Hamiltonian diffeomorphism $\phi : M \to M$, we have $L \cap \phi(L) \neq \emptyset$. Moreover if L is transversal to $\phi(L)$, there exists $p \in L \cap \phi(L)$ whose Maslov index is 0.*

Theorem L is proved in Subsection 6.4.3. A special class of pairs (M, L) for which the Maslov index homomorphism $I_\mu : \pi_2(M, L) \to \mathbb{Z}$ is trivial consists of those for which (M, ω, J) is a Calabi-Yau manifold and $L \subset M$ is a Lagrangian submanifold whose Maslov class is trivial: In this case, the Maslov index $\mu_L(\beta)$ depends only on $\partial\beta \in \pi_1(L)$ and so induces a well-defined cohomology class in $H^1(L, \mathbb{Z})$, which is called the *Maslov class* of L. (See [**Mor81, Daz81, HaLa82**] for more explanations.) Theorem L is then used by Thomas and Yau [**ThYa02**] in their proof of a uniqueness theorem of special Lagrangian homology 3-sphere (i.e., L with $H^1(L, \mathbb{Z}) = 0$) in its Hamiltonian isotopy class in Calabi-Yau 3-folds.

As we mentioned already, Floer cohomology $HF((L, b), (L, b); \Lambda_{0,nov})$ is not necessarily isomorphic to the cohomology of L. The difference is determined by the differentials δ_r of the spectral sequence in Theorem D. The differentials are in turn determined by the fundamental chains of appropriate moduli spaces of pseudo-holomorphic discs. Therefore it is in general very hard to analyze this spectral sequence in the actual computation of $HF((L, b), (L, b); \Lambda_{0,nov})$, because it requires a careful study of the counting problem of pseudo-holomorphic discs. This counting problem is even more delicate and non-trivial than the counting problem of pseudo-holomorphic spheres in the usual Gromov-Witten theory. On the other hand, Theorem A implies that there are various product structures on the ordinary cohomology and Floer cohomology of a Lagrangian submanifold which may be exploited in calculations. However computing these products in examples is also a non-trivial problem in general. Here is a list of some calculations.

(1.14.0)   If $\pi_2(M, L) = \pi_1(L) = 0$, then Theorem X implies that the filtered A_∞ algebra in Theorem A is nothing but the real homotopy type of L.

(1.14.1)   There are some calculations carried out by C.-H. Cho and the second named author for the case of Lagrangian torus orbits of toric Fano manifolds [**Cho04I, ChOh03**]. Their works are partially motivated by the works of Hori and Vafa [**HoVa00, Hor01**]. In particular, a variant of the function $\mathfrak{PO} : \mathcal{M}_{\text{weak,def}}(L) \to \Lambda_{0,nov}^+$ in Theorem B is calculated in [**ChOh03**], which corresponds to the Landau-Ginzburg superpotential in physics [**HoVa00**]. Roughly speaking, they proved that the torus orbits that have non-trivial Floer cohomology correspond to the critical points of this superpotential via the mirror map. Cho and the second named author call those orbits *balanced torus fibers* in [**ChOh03**].

It is also proved in [**ChOh03**] that for the balanced torus fibers whose Floer cohomology $HF(L, L)$ is isomorphic to the classical cohomology group $H^*(T^n; \Lambda_{nov})$. In [**Cho04II**], Cho proved that the natural ring structure on $HF(L, L)$ arising from the A_∞ structure becomes isomorphic to the Clifford algebra associated to the quadratic form of the Hessian of the Landau-Ginzburg superpotential after the Landau-Ginzburg mirror map is applied. This was earlier predicted by Hori [**Hor01**] and Kapustin-Li [**KapLi04**]. In particular, this computation provides an example in which the Floer cohomology is isomorphic to the classical one but its ring structure is deformed from the classical cup product. Recall that the cohomology ring of the torus is isomorphic to the exterior algebra generated by the degree one cohomology thereof.

(1.14.2)   The result of [**ChOh03**] is used and generalized in [**FOOO08I**] and [**FOOO08II**], where the present authors apply many of the results of this book to study Floer cohomology of Lagrangian submanifolds which are T^n orbits in a compact toric manifold (which is not necessary Fano).

(1.14.3)   When $L \subseteq \mathbb{C}^{n+1}$ is a Lagrangian submanifold homotopy equivalent to $S^1 \times S^n$, the spectral sequence is studied in detail in the paper [**FOOO09I**].

(1.14.4)   Some calculation is carried out in [**FOOO09II**] for the case of L obtained by the Lagrangian surgery from flat Lagrangian sub-tori in T^{2n}. (See also [**Fuk02III**].) Theta functions appear in the calculation. We obtain various other examples in [**FOOO09II**].

(1.14.5)   Homological mirror symmetry conjecture, if proved, will become a powerful tool for the computation of Floer cohomology and the filtered A_∞ algebras of Lagrangian submanifolds. For example, P. Seidel's proof of homological mirror symmetry of quartic surface [**Sei03II**] should give rise to some consequences on the calculation of these structures.

(1.14.6)   There are numerous results on the counting problem of holomorphic discs attached to a given Lagrangian submanifold in the physics literature, especially when the ambient symplectic manifold is a noncompact Calabi-Yau manifold in relation to the local mirror principle (see [**AAMV05, DiFl05, LLLZ04**] and the references therein.) It is, however, not yet clear how one can use these studies in actual calculation of the structures we have constructed in this book.

1.4. Relation to mirror symmetry

So far we have explained various applications of the Floer theory to the problems in symplectic topology. Another direction of applications are towards the proof of the celebrated homological mirror symmetry conjecture proposed by Kontsevich [**Kon93,95I**] around 1994, in which the A_∞ category introduced by the first named author [**Fuk93**] plays a key role in its formulation. (Vafa [**Vaf99**] made an interpretation of this proposal into the physics language around 2000.) There remain many more things to be carried out towards this goal. We would like to explain the relationship of our work with the homological mirror symmetry briefly here (See also [**Fuk02I,02III,03I,03II**] for other explanations).

In this respect, we recall that the set

$$\mathcal{M}(L) = (\text{Zero}(\pi_{\text{amb}}) \cap \text{Zero}(\mathfrak{PD}))/\sim$$

which was introduced in the paragraph right after Theorem B is consisting of the gauge equivalence classes of bounding cochains. (Here and hereafter in this section, L is assumed to be a relatively spin Lagrangian submanifold of M.) Because this set plays a central role in the application to homological mirror symmetry, we first state a theorem in which the set is described as a *formal scheme*. Let C_0, C_1 be two finitely generated free $\Lambda_{0,nov}$ modules. We choose bases $\{\mathbf{v}_1, \cdots, \mathbf{v}_m\}$ of C_0 and $\{\mathbf{w}_1, \cdots, \mathbf{w}_\ell\}$ of C_1 respectively. A *formal map* $\mathfrak{P} : C_0 \to C_1$ is defined to be a linear combination $\mathfrak{P} = \sum_j \mathfrak{P}_j \mathbf{w}_j$ where each $\mathfrak{P}_j$ a formal power series

$$(1.15) \qquad \mathfrak{P}_j \left(\sum_{i=1}^m s_i \mathbf{v}_i \right) = \sum_{k_1=0}^\infty \cdots \sum_{k_m=0}^\infty a_{k_1\cdots,k_m}^j s_1^{k_1} \cdots s_m^{k_m}$$

with the coefficients $a_{k_1\cdots,k_m}^j \in \Lambda_{0,nov}$. We note that although the formula (1.15) will not make sense in general if we substitute elements of $\Lambda_{0,nov}$ in s_j, it does if we substitute elements from $\Lambda_{0,nov}^+$ in s_j. This is because the right hand side of (1.15) will converge in the $\Lambda_{0,nov}^+$-adic topology for the latter case. Therefore we may put

$$(\mathfrak{P}^{-1}(0))(\Lambda_{0,nov}^+) := \left\{ \sum s_j \mathbf{v}_j \in \Lambda_{0,nov}^+ C_0 \ \middle| \ \mathfrak{P}\left(\sum_{i=1}^m s_i \mathbf{v}_i \right) = 0 \right\}$$

and regard this set as the set of $\Lambda_{0,nov}^+$-valued points (or rigid points) of an affine formal scheme $\text{Spf}(R(\mathfrak{P}; \Lambda_{0,nov}))$ associated to the (commutative non-Noetherian) complete valuational ring

$$R(\mathfrak{P}; \Lambda_{0,nov}) = \frac{\Lambda_{0,nov}[[s_1, \cdots, s_m]]}{(\mathfrak{P}_1, \cdots, \mathfrak{P}_\ell)}.$$

Here $(\mathfrak{P}_1, \cdots, \mathfrak{P}_\ell)$ is the ideal generated by the elements $\mathfrak{P}_1, \cdots, \mathfrak{P}_\ell$ of the formal power series ring $\Lambda_{0,nov}[[s_1, \cdots, s_m]]$. Namely we have the identification

$$(\mathfrak{P}^{-1}(0))(\Lambda_{0,nov}^+) = Hom(R(\mathfrak{P}; \Lambda_{0,nov}), \Lambda_{0,nov})$$

where the right hand side is the set of continuous $\Lambda_{0,nov}$ algebra homomorphisms. (See Proposition 5.4.15 in Subsection 5.4.1.)

For each element $\mathfrak{b} \in H^2(M; \Lambda_{0,nov}^+)$, we consider the inverse image $\pi_{\text{amb}}^{-1}(\mathfrak{b})$ of the map $\pi_{\text{amb}} : \mathcal{M}_{\text{weak,def}}(L) \to H^2(M; \Lambda_{0,nov}^+)$ and define the sets $\mathcal{M}_{\text{weak}}^{\mathfrak{b}}(L)$ and $\mathcal{M}^{\mathfrak{b}}(L)$ by

$$\mathcal{M}_{\text{weak}}^{\mathfrak{b}}(L) = \pi_{\text{amb}}^{-1}(\mathfrak{b}), \quad \mathcal{M}^{\mathfrak{b}}(L) = \pi_{\text{amb}}^{-1}(\mathfrak{b}) \cap \text{Zero}(\mathfrak{PO}).$$

THEOREM M. *There exist a map*

$$\mathfrak{P}_{L,\text{weak}}^{\mathfrak{b}} : H^1(L; \Lambda_{0,nov}^+) \to H^2(L; \Lambda_{0,nov}^+)$$

and an equivalence relation $\sim$ on $((\mathfrak{P}_{L,\text{weak}}^{\mathfrak{b}})^{-1}(0))(\Lambda_{0,nov}^+)$ so that we have

$$\mathcal{M}_{\text{weak}}^{\mathfrak{b}}(L) = ((\mathfrak{P}_{L,\text{weak}}^{\mathfrak{b}})^{-1}(0)(\Lambda_{0,nov}^+))/\sim .$$

The continuous isomorphism class of $R(\mathfrak{P}_{L,\text{weak}}^{\mathfrak{b}}; \Lambda_{0,nov})$ as the $\Lambda_{0,nov}$ algebra depends only on the pair (M, L) up to a symplectic diffeomorphism. A similar statement holds for $\mathcal{M}^{\mathfrak{b}}(L)$ if we consider $\mathfrak{P}_L^{\mathfrak{b}} : H^1(L; \Lambda_{0,nov}^+) \to H^2(L; \Lambda_{0,nov}^+)$ instead.

Theorem M is a consequence of Theorem 5.4.12 and Proposition 5.4.15 and is proved in Subsection 5.4.6.

Now we consider a relatively spin pair (L_0, L_1) of Lagrangian submanifolds. For a given $\mathfrak{b} \in H^2(M; \Lambda_{0,nov}^+)$ and $b_i \in \mathcal{M}_{\text{weak}}^{\mathfrak{b}}(L_i)$, we denote by

$$\varphi_{b_i} : R(\mathfrak{P}_{L_i}^{\mathfrak{b}}; \Lambda_{0,nov}) \longrightarrow \Lambda_{0,nov}$$

a homomorphism corresponding to a representative of b_i via the identification given in Theorem M. For the case of the pair (L_1, L_0) that is relatively spin, we obtain the following:

THEOREM N. *There exists a complex $(\mathfrak{D}(L_1, L_0; \Lambda_{0,nov}), \mathfrak{d})$ where the $\Lambda_{0,nov}$ module $\mathfrak{D}(L_1, L_0; \Lambda_{0,nov})$ is a finitely generated complete bimodule over the ring pair $(R(\mathfrak{P}_{L_1}^{\mathfrak{b}}; \Lambda_{0,nov}), R(\mathfrak{P}_{L_0}^{\mathfrak{b}}; \Lambda_{0,nov}))$ and the coboundary map*

$$\mathfrak{d} : \mathfrak{D}(L_1, L_0; \Lambda_{0,nov}) \longrightarrow \mathfrak{D}(L_1, L_0; \Lambda_{0,nov})$$

is continuous with respect to the topology on $\mathfrak{D}(L_1, L_0; \Lambda_{0,nov})$ induced by the filtration.

The complex is independent of the various choices made up to isomorphism and has the following properties:

(N.1) *Consider $b_i \in \mathcal{M}^{\mathfrak{b}}(L_i)$ $(i = 0, 1)$ a pair of bounding cochains and let $\varphi_{b_i} : R(\mathfrak{P}_{L_i}^{\mathfrak{b}}; \Lambda_{0,nov}) \longrightarrow \Lambda_{0,nov}$ be their representatives, respectively. Then cohomology of the complex of the $\Lambda_{0,nov}$ bimodule*

$$(\Lambda_{0,nov\varphi_{b_1}} \otimes_{R(\mathfrak{P}_{L_1}^{\mathfrak{b}}; \Lambda_{0,nov})} \mathfrak{D}(L_1, L_0; \Lambda_{0,nov}) {}_{R(\mathfrak{P}_{L_0}^{\mathfrak{b}}; \Lambda_{0,nov})} \otimes_{\varphi_{b_0}} \Lambda_{0,nov}, 1 \otimes \mathfrak{d} \otimes 1)$$

is isomorphic to the Floer cohomology $HF((L_1, \mathbf{b}_1), (L_0, \mathbf{b}_0); \Lambda_{0,nov})$ as a $\Lambda_{0,nov}$ bimodule. (Here $\mathbf{b}_i = (\mathfrak{b}, b_i), (i = 0, 1)$.)

(N.2) *If $\phi_i : (M, L_i) \longrightarrow (M, L_i')$ $(i = 0, 1)$ are Hamiltonian isotopies, we have a chain homotopy equivalence*

$$(\phi_1, \phi_0)_* : (\mathfrak{D}(L_1, L_0; \Lambda_{0,nov}), \mathfrak{d}) \otimes_{\Lambda_{0,nov}} \Lambda_{nov}$$
$$\longrightarrow (\mathfrak{D}(L_1', L_0'; \Lambda_{0,nov}), \mathfrak{d}) \otimes_{\Lambda_{0,nov}} \Lambda_{nov}$$

over the ring isomorphisms $\phi_{i*} : R(\mathfrak{P}^{\flat}_{L_i}; \Lambda_{0,nov}) \to R(\mathfrak{P}^{\flat}_{L'_i}; \Lambda_{0,nov})$. *Under the isomorphism given in* (N.2), $(\phi_1, \phi_0)_*$ *induces the isomorphism of Floer cohomology provided in* (G.5).

Statement (N.1) above can be reinterpreted as follows: By the general theory of formal schemes, the complex $(\mathfrak{D}(L'_1, L'_0; \Lambda_{0,nov}), \mathfrak{d})$ defines an object of the derived category of coherent sheaves on the affine formal scheme

$$\operatorname{Spf}(R(\mathfrak{P}^{\flat}_{L_1}; \Lambda_{0,nov})) \times \operatorname{Spf}(R(\mathfrak{P}^{\flat}_{L_0}; \Lambda_{0,nov})).$$

Then the fiber at the (rigid) point $(\mathbf{b}_1, \mathbf{b}_0)$ is the Floer cohomology. Theorem N is proved in Subsection 5.4.6.

REMARK 1.16. In Theorem N we considered $\mathcal{M}^{\flat}(L)$. We can use $\mathcal{M}^{\flat}_{\text{weak}}(L)$ as well to obtain similar conclusions. Namely using the morphism

$$\mathfrak{PO}^{\flat}_L : \mathcal{M}^{\flat}_{\text{weak}}(L) \to \Lambda^{+}_{0,nov}$$

(which is a continuous ring homomorphism $\Lambda^{+}_{0,nov} \to R(\mathfrak{P}^{\flat}_{L,\text{weak}}; \Lambda_{0,nov})$), we can define the fiber product

$$R(\mathfrak{P}^{\flat}_{L_1,\text{weak}}; \Lambda_{0,nov}) \hat{\otimes}_{\Lambda^{+}_{0,nov}} R(\mathfrak{P}^{\flat}_{L_0,\text{weak}}; \Lambda_{0,nov}).$$

Then $\mathfrak{D}(L_1, L_0; \Lambda_{0,nov})$ can be extended to a chain complex of modules over

$$R(\mathfrak{P}^{\flat}_{L_1,\text{weak}}; \Lambda_{0,nov}) \hat{\otimes}_{\Lambda^{+}_{0,nov}} R(\mathfrak{P}^{\flat}_{L_0,\text{weak}}; \Lambda_{0,nov}).$$

Its fibers at rigid points define a family of Floer cohomology parameterized by

$$\mathcal{M}^{\flat}_{\text{weak}}(L_1) \times_{\Lambda^{+}_{0,nov}} \mathcal{M}^{\flat}_{\text{weak}}(L_0),$$

where the fiber product is taken with respect to $\mathfrak{PO}^{\flat}_{L_i}$.

The rest of this section discusses the relationship of the result obtained in this book with the mirror symmetry. This discussion will not be used for the rest of the book except for the purpose of making similar remarks in the book from time to time.

For the application to mirror symmetry, the most relevant class of Lagrangian submanifolds is the one consisting of those $L \subset M$ where M is a Calabi-Yau manifold and L has vanishing Maslov class. Therefore we will restrict ourselves to this class of Lagrangian submanifolds for the discussion below. (However the results of this book apply to the Fano case as well which also plays an important role in mirror symmetry.)

We first remark that we do not need to use the formal parameter e, which encodes the Maslov index of the discs, in $\Lambda_{0,nov}$ for such Lagrangian submanifolds. (See Subsection 5.4.6.) Therefore we consider the smaller rings $\Lambda_0, \Lambda, \Lambda_+$ instead of $\Lambda_{0,nov}, \Lambda_{nov}, \Lambda^{+}_{0,nov}$, respectively. (See (Conv.5) at the end of Chapter 1.) We note that the ring Λ is a field in this case. Then we can define the structure of a filtered A_∞ algebra on $H(L; \Lambda_0)$. And we can define a formal scheme as before for this smaller ring in the same way as for $\Lambda^{+}_{0,nov}$. To make this change explicit, we denote the corresponding formal scheme by $\mathcal{M}(L; \Lambda_+)$ to highlight the dependence on Λ_+. The following version of Theorems G and M is useful to describe the relationship of the Floer cohomology studied in this book with mirror symmetry.

COROLLARY O. *Let (M, ω) satisfy $c_1(M) = 0$. Let L be a relatively spin Lagrangian submanifold of M with vanishing Maslov class and $\mathfrak{b} \in H^2(M; \Lambda_+)$. Then there exists a map $\mathfrak{P}_L^{\mathfrak{b}} : H^1(L; \Lambda_+) \to H^2(L; \Lambda_+)$ such that the set*

$$\mathcal{M}^{\mathfrak{b}}(L; \Lambda_+) = (\mathfrak{P}_L^{\mathfrak{b}})^{-1}(0)(\Lambda_+) = \{b \in H^1(L; \Lambda_+) \mid \mathfrak{P}_L^{\mathfrak{b}}(b) = 0\}$$

has the following properties: Let (L_0, L_1) be a relatively spin pair of such Lagrangian submanifolds of M.

(O.1) *For each $b_i \in \mathcal{M}^{\mathfrak{b}}(L_i; \Lambda_+)$, we put $\mathbf{b}_i = (\mathfrak{b}, b_i)$. Then we have a Floer cohomology*

$$HF(((L_1, \mathbf{b}_1), (L_0, \mathbf{b}_0); \Lambda_0).$$

(O.2) *For the case $(L_1, \mathbf{b}_1) = (L_0, \mathbf{b}_0) = (L, \mathbf{b})$, the Floer cohomology group $HF((L, \mathbf{b}), ((L, \mathbf{b}); \Lambda_0)$ has a ring structure.*
(O.3) *The Floer cohomology $HF((L_1, \mathbf{b}_1), (L_0, \mathbf{b}_0); \Lambda_0)$ has a structure of a left $HF(((L_1, \mathbf{b}_1), (L_1, \mathbf{b}_1); \Lambda_0)$ and right $HF(((L_0, \mathbf{b}_0), (L_0, \mathbf{b}_0); \Lambda_0)$ filtered bimodule.*
(O.4) *If $m[\omega] \in H^2(M, L; \mathbb{Z})$ for some integer m, then we can reduce the coefficient ring Λ_0 to the ring $\mathbb{Q}[[T^{1/m}]] \subset \Lambda_0$ of formal Puiseux series in the above statements.*

REMARK 1.17. (1) Contrary to the case of Theorem M, for the case of vanishing Maslov class, we do not need to divide the zero set of $\mathfrak{P}_L^{\mathfrak{b}}$ by an equivalence relation to obtain $\mathcal{M}^{\mathfrak{b}}(L; \Lambda_+)$. See Subsection 5.4.6 Lemma 5.4.71.

(2) In fact we can extend the statements in this corollary to those in the context of the filtered A_∞ *category* by considering arbitrary finite chains $(L_0, L_1, \cdots, L_k)$ of Lagrangian submanifolds. In this book, we restrict ourselves to those statements up to the definitions of objects (one Lagrangian) and morphisms (two Lagrangians) referring to [**Fuk02II**] for the discussion in this general context of A_∞ category.

Corollary O is a minor modification of Theorems G and M. Only the point mentioned in Remark 1.17 (1) and the statement (O.4) do not immediately come from Theorems G, M. We will discuss these points and complete the proof of Corollary O in Subsection 5.4.6.

Now we rewrite Corollary O with the language of formal scheme. Consider the situation of Corollary O. We put

$$m = \dim H^1(L; \mathbb{Q}), \qquad \ell = \dim H^2(L; \mathbb{Q})$$

and fix a basis of $H^1(L, \mathbb{Q})$. Denote by $s_1, \cdots, s_m$ the associated coordinates on $H^1(L, \mathbb{Q})$ and

$$R(\mathfrak{P}_L^{\mathfrak{b}}; \Lambda_0) = \frac{\Lambda_0[[s_1, \cdots, s_m]]}{((\mathfrak{P}_L^{\mathfrak{b}})_1, \cdots, (\mathfrak{P}_L^{\mathfrak{b}})_\ell)}.$$

Here $\mathfrak{P}_L^{\mathfrak{b}} = ((\mathfrak{P}_L^{\mathfrak{b}})_1, \cdots, (\mathfrak{P}_L^{\mathfrak{b}})_\ell)$ is regarded as a formal power series of $s_1, \cdots, s_m$.

COROLLARY P. *Let L, M be as in Corollary O. The ring $R(\mathfrak{P}_L^{\mathfrak{b}}; \Lambda_0)$ is an invariant of L. Moreover, to each relatively spin pair (L_0, L_1), we can associate a cochain complex $(\mathfrak{D}(L_1, L_0; \Lambda_0), \mathfrak{d})$ of finitely generated continuous complete bimodules over the ring pair $(R(\mathfrak{P}_{L_1}^{\mathfrak{b}}; \Lambda_0), R(\mathfrak{P}_{L_0}^{\mathfrak{b}}; \Lambda_0))$ such that if $b_i \in \mathcal{M}^{\mathfrak{b}}(L_i; \Lambda_+)$ and $\varphi_{b_i} : R(\mathfrak{P}_{L_i}^{\mathfrak{b}}; \Lambda_0) \to \Lambda_0$ is its representative, then cohomology of the complex*

$$(\Lambda_0 \; {}_{\varphi_{b_1}}\!\otimes_{R(\mathfrak{P}_{L_1}^{\mathfrak{b}}; \Lambda_0)} \mathfrak{D}(L_1, L_0; \Lambda_0) \; {}_{R(\mathfrak{P}_{L_0}^{\mathfrak{b}}; \Lambda_0)}\!\otimes_{\varphi_{b_0}} \Lambda_0, 1 \otimes \mathfrak{d} \otimes 1)$$

is isomorphic to Floer cohomology $HF((L_1, \mathbf{b}_1), (L_0, \mathbf{b}_0); \Lambda_0)$, where $\mathbf{b}_i = (\mathfrak{b}, b_i)$. Up to chain homotopy equivalence, the bimodule $(\mathfrak{D}(L_1, L_0; \Lambda_0), \mathfrak{d})$ is independent of various choices made in its construction. (O.4) still applies.

Corollary P is a minor modification of Theorem N and is proved in Subsection 5.4.6.

Now we describe the conjectural mirror picture of the structures in Corollaries O and P. To describe this mirror in the algebraic (rather than transcendental) context, we need some restrictions on M and L, in addition to M being Calabi-Yau and L having the vanishing Maslov class.

CONDITION 1.18. *We assume that L is rational. Namely $(m\omega) \cap \beta \in \mathbb{Z}$ for all $\beta \in H_2(M, L; \mathbb{Z})$ for a nonnegative integer m.*

We remark that it automatically implies $m[\omega] \in H^2(M, L; \mathbb{Z})$. We consider the ring of the Peiseux series $\mathbb{Q}[[T^{1/m}]] \subset \Lambda_0$. (See [**Fuk03I**] more about this assumption.)

CONJECTURE Q. *Let (M, ω) be a Calabi-Yau manifold such that for some integer m, $m[\omega] \in H^2(M; \mathbb{Z})$. Consider an element $\mathfrak{b} \in H^2(M; \mathbb{Q}[[T^{1/m}]]) \subset H^2(M; \Lambda_0)$ and suppose the formal power series $\mathfrak{b}$ has its radius of convergence strictly positive at $T = 0$. Then we can associate a holomorphic family*

$$\text{(1.19)} \qquad \pi : \mathfrak{X}_{(M, \omega, \mathfrak{b})} \longrightarrow D^2(\epsilon)$$

over a disc $D^2(\epsilon) \subset \mathbb{C}$ for some sufficiently small $\epsilon > 0$, so that its fiber $\pi^{-1}(q)$ at each $q \neq 0$ is a Calabi-Yau manifold. The fiber $\pi^{-1}(0)$ at $q = 0$ is singular in a way that the family defines a maximally degenerating family as $q \to 0$.

See [**LTY05**] for the definition of a maximally degenerating family. We give a brief explanation how Conjecture Q follows from the various facts that are widely believed (but not proved) among the researchers on mirror symmetry. (The description below, except the way how $\mathfrak{b}$ enters, is not new. See [**Fuk03II**], for example.)

Let $\mathfrak{b} = \sum_{k=1}^{\infty} \mathfrak{b}_k T^{k/m}$, where $\mathfrak{b}_k \in H^2(M; \mathbb{Q})$. We choose closed 2 forms representing the classes $\mathfrak{b}_k$ and denote them by the same symbols. After these choices made, assume that the series has positive radius of convergence. For $\tau \in \mathfrak{h} = \{\tau \in \mathbb{C} \mid \text{Im}\, \tau > 0\}$, we put $q = e^{2\pi\sqrt{-1}\tau/m}$. Heuristically, one may regard $q = T^{1/m}$. However T is a formal parameter while $q \in D^1(\epsilon)$ is a genuine complex number. For each such τ, we define a complex valued closed two form by

$$\text{(1.20)} \qquad \omega_\tau(\mathfrak{b}) = \frac{2\pi}{\sqrt{-1}}\left(\tau\omega + \sum \mathfrak{b}_k q^k\right).$$

By the convergence assumption on $\mathfrak{b}$, it follows from this expression that $\omega_\tau(\mathfrak{b})$ varies holomorphically over $\tau \in \mathfrak{h}$. It is also easy to see that $\text{Re}(\omega_\tau(\mathfrak{b}))$ is nondegenerate and so defines a symplectic form on M, as long as $\text{Im}(\tau)$ is sufficiently large. We regard the family (1.20) as a holomorphic family of complexified symplectic structures on M. The imaginary part of $\omega_\tau(\mathfrak{b})$ is called a *B-field*. We remark that $m[\omega] \in H^2(M; \mathbb{Z})$ implies

$$\text{(1.21)} \qquad \tau - \tau' \in m\mathbb{Z} \Longrightarrow \omega_\tau(\mathfrak{b}) - \omega_{\tau'}(\mathfrak{b}) \in 2\pi\sqrt{-1}H^2(M; \mathbb{Z}).$$

Here comes a fact that is widely believed to be true:

To each $(M, \omega_\tau(\mathfrak{b}))$ that is a Calabi-Yau manifold with a B field, we can associate its mirror $X_{\omega_\tau(\mathfrak{b})}$ that is also a Calabi-Yau manifold. Moreover if the difference between two complexified symplectic structures is in $2\pi\sqrt{-1}H^2(M;\mathbb{Z})$, then they correspond to the same mirror manifold.

Therefore it is expected from (1.21) that we have defined the family parameterized by q alluded in (1.19).

We remark that for $\beta \in H_2(M;\mathbb{Z})$ we have the identity

$$(1.22) \qquad \exp(-\omega_\tau(\mathfrak{b})[\beta]) = q^{m(\omega[\beta])} \exp\left(2\pi\sqrt{-1}\sum(\mathfrak{b}_k[\beta])q^k\right).$$

We can see from (1.20) and (1.22) that or the cohomology class $\mathfrak{b}$ deforms the symplectic form ω as $q \to 0$ in the way

$$\frac{\sqrt{-1}}{2\pi}\frac{\omega_\tau(\mathfrak{b})}{\tau} \to \omega \quad \text{as} \quad \operatorname{Im}\tau \to \infty.$$

This is the reason why we use 'def' in the notation $\mathcal{M}_{\mathrm{def}}(L)$.

Now we want to formulate a conjecture which describes the conjectural mirror object of the pair (L, b), where L is a spin Lagrangian submanifold that satisfies Condition 1.18 and $\mu_L = 0$, and $b \in \mathcal{M}^\mathfrak{b}(L; \Lambda_+)$. (We can include a flat complex bundle on L with a slight modification of our construction. We omit its discussion here. One may look at [**Fuk02II**] for the detailed explanation on such a modification.)

We consider a formal completion $\hat{\mathfrak{X}}_{(M,\omega,\mathfrak{b})}$ of $\mathfrak{X}_{(M,\omega,\mathfrak{b})}$ at $\pi^{-1}(0)$. (See [**GrDi60**] I Section 10 for its meaning.) Let $\hat{\mathfrak{F}}_i$ be an object of the derived category of coherent sheaves on $\hat{\mathfrak{X}}_{(M,\omega,\mathfrak{b})}$ for $i = 1, 2$. The right derived functor $\mathrm{RHom}(\hat{\mathfrak{F}}_1, \hat{\mathfrak{F}}_2)$ of Hom is defined as a $\mathbb{C}[[q]]$ module. (Since we take formal completion, q is now a formal parameter.)

REMARK 1.23. (1) There does not seem to exist a canonical choice for the singular fiber $\pi^{-1}(0)$. So we need to consider $\mathrm{RHom}(\hat{\mathfrak{F}}_1, \hat{\mathfrak{F}}_2) \otimes_{\mathbb{C}[[q]]} \mathbb{C}[[q]][q^{-1}]$ in reality. (See [**Fuk03I**] Section 4 for a more precise formulation.) In the point of view in [**Ray74**], forgetting the information of the fiber at 0 means that we regard $\hat{\mathfrak{F}}_i$ as an object of derived category of associated rigid analytic space when we take RHom. This point may be related to Remark 1.12.

(2) In order for the formal scheme $\hat{\mathfrak{X}}_{(M,\omega,\mathfrak{b})}$ to exist, we may not even need to assume, in Conjecture Q, that $\mathfrak{b}$ converges.

CONJECTURE R. *To each pair (L, b) with L a spin Lagrangian submanifold satisfying Condition 1.18 and $\mu_L = 0$, and $b \in \mathcal{M}^\mathfrak{b}(L; \Lambda_+)$, we can associate to $\hat{\mathfrak{F}}(L, b)$, an object of the derived category of coherent sheaves on $\hat{\mathfrak{X}}_{(M,\omega,\mathfrak{b})}$ so that the following holds:*

(R.1) *The formal neighborhood of b in $\mathcal{M}^\mathfrak{b}(L; \Lambda_+)$ is isomorphic to a formal neighborhood of $\hat{\mathfrak{F}}(L, b)$ in its moduli space.*

(R.2) *We have a canonical isomorphism*

$$HF((L_1, \mathbf{b}_1), (L_0, \mathbf{b}_0); \mathbb{C}[[q]][q^{-1}])$$
$$\cong \mathrm{RHom}(\hat{\mathfrak{F}}(L_1, b_1), \hat{\mathfrak{F}}(L_0, b_0)) \otimes_{\mathbb{C}[[q]]} \mathbb{C}[[q]][q^{-1}].$$

Here $\mathbf{b}_i = (\mathfrak{b}, b_i)$. (*It follows from* (O.4) *that the Floer cohomology of the left hand side is defined over the ring* $\mathbb{C}[[q]][q^{-1}]$.)
(R.3)   *The ring and bimodule structures in* (O.2), (O.3) *are isomorphic to those in the right hand side of* (R.2) *respectively.*

One can generalize Conjecture R to the context of the filtered A_∞ category by considering arbitrary finite chains of Lagrangian submanifolds as described in [**Fuk02II**].

REMARK 1.24. We remark that the moduli space of objects in the derived category is a notion that is not well established yet in algebraic geometry. In many important cases, the mirror object is a coherent sheaf on $\widehat{\mathfrak{X}}_{(M,\omega,\mathfrak{b})}$, not just an object of its derived category. In these cases, the moduli space mentioned in (R.1) is well established in algebraic geometry.

For the general case, one may use the notion of filtered A_∞ algebras studied in this book to give a rigorous meaning to (R.1): We first observe that both co-homology groups appearing in (R.2) are $\delta_{\mathbf{b}_1,\mathbf{b}_0}$ cohomology of some filtered A_∞ bimodule. For the case of Floer cohomology, this follows from the results of this book. More specifically from Theorem A and Definition 3.6.9. For the case of RHom, this follows from Theorem W and the standard construction of RHom in homological algebra. We can amplify (R.3) to a conjecture that they are isomorphic as a filtered A_∞ bimodule. We next recall that a formal neighborhood of the mod-uli space is controlled by the (filtered) A_∞ structure. Namely (1.8) is the equation that determines the formal neighborhood of the moduli space. (See [**Fuk03II**] for more explanation.) In this sense, the amplified version of (R.3) contains (R.1) as a special case.

We note that (R.1) above would mean that the formal map $\mathfrak{P}_L^\mathfrak{b}$ given in Corol-lary O coincides with the Kuranishi map of the moduli space of holomorphic vector bundles (or coherent sheaves) of its mirror. After the substitution of $T^{1/m} = q$, the map $\mathfrak{P}_L^\mathfrak{b}$ is regarded as a map from $H^1(L; q\mathbb{C}[[q]])$ to $H^2(L; q\mathbb{C}[[q]])$ (see [**Fuk03I**]), and has the form

$$(1.25) \qquad \mathfrak{P}_L^\mathfrak{b}(b) = \sum_{k=0}^{\infty} \mathfrak{m}_k(\underbrace{b, \cdots, b}_{k}).$$

(Strictly speaking, (1.25) is the formula in the chain level. To define $\mathfrak{P}_L^\mathfrak{b}$ on the cohomology $H^1(L; \mathbb{C}[[q]])$, we need to use Theorem W below and the filtered A_∞ homomorphism defined in Subsection 5.4.3.)

The right hand side of (1.25) may be regarded as a generating function of the numbers of pseudo-holomorphic discs attached to L, which is an open string analogue of the Gromov-Witten potential. (The Gromov-Witten potential is the generating function of (genus zero) Gromov-Witten invariants defined by counting pseudo-holomorphic spheres). (In case $\dim L = 3$, the map $\mathfrak{P}_L^\mathfrak{b}$ is the differential of a super potential which is a more direct analog to the Gromov-Witten potential. See Subsection 3.6.4.) Therefore (R.1) is a conjecture on the relationship between the number of pseudo-holomorphic discs attached to L and the deformation theory of vector bundles on its mirror. In this sense, Conjecture R can be regarded as the open string version of the famous conjecture

quantum cup product = Yukawa coupling

which was discovered by Candelas et al. [**COGP91**] and partially proved by Givental [**Giv96**]. (See also [**LLY97**].) The open string analogue of this kind was first discovered by Kontsevich [**Kon95I**] for the case of elliptic curve. The case of elliptic curve was further explored by Polishchuk-Zaslow [**PoZa98**] and was partially generalized to higher dimensions by first named author [**Fuk02III**]. Recently a few more cases have been studied including the cases (1.14.1) and (1.14.5) mentioned at the end of Section 1.3.

Next we outline a scheme of the proof of Conjecture R by using Corollary P combined with some rigid analytic geometry.

REMARK 1.26. The idea of using rigid analytic geometry to prove homological mirror symmetry is due to Kontsevich and Soibelman [**KoSo01**]. There is an approach closely related to but different from this: This is the approach using *asymptotic analysis* proposed by the first named author [**Fuk05I**]. We mention that Gross and Siebert [**GrSi03I,03II**] use the log scheme in their attempt to construct mirror manifold, which is also of a similar flavor.

In the rest of this section we only consider the case $\mathfrak{b} = 0$ for the simplicity of exposition.

Motivated by the picture of Strominger-Yau-Zaslow [**SYZ96**], we start with a $2n$-dimensional symplectic manifold M that has a singular fibration over a manifold B whose general fiber is a Lagrangian torus T^n with its Maslov class being zero. We assume that ω is integral, i.e., $[\omega] \in H^2(M;\mathbb{Z})$. We denote by B_{sm} the subset of B consisting of the points $y \in B$ at which its fiber F_y is smooth. Under the assumptions given on the fibration, we can construct a $GL(n;\mathbb{Z})\tilde{\times}\mathbb{Z}^n$ (flat affine) structure on B_{sm}. (See [**Dui80, KoSo01, GrSi03I**].) We also assume that the codimension of $B \setminus B_{\mathrm{sm}}$ is bigger than or equal to 2. Define $B^{\mathbb{Q}}$ to be the set of points whose affine coordinates are rational. When $\pi_1(M) = 1$, a point y being in $B^{\mathbb{Q}}$ is equivalent to the condition that F_y is a rational Lagrangian submanifold.

REMARK 1.27. Let $y \in B^{\mathbb{Q}}$. If F_y is singular, the definition of Floer cohomology of F_y is not given in this book. In many important cases, the singular fiber F_y turns out to be an immersed Lagrangian submanifold. Therefore it would be desirable to extend our story to such cases. (See [**Aka05, AkJo08**].)

CONJECTURE S. *Suppose $y \in B^{\mathbb{Q}}$ and let $\mathfrak{P}_{F_y}$ be the formal power map introduced in (1.25). Then we have $\mathfrak{P}_{F_y} \equiv 0$, i.e., $\mathcal{M}(F_y;\Lambda_+) = H^2(F_y,\Lambda_+)$.*

We next consider the pair (L, b) as in Conjecture R. We obtain

$$(1.28) \qquad (\Lambda_0 \;_{\varphi_b}\hat{\otimes}_{R(\mathfrak{P}_L;\Lambda_0)} \mathfrak{D}(L, F_y;\Lambda_0), 1 \otimes \mathfrak{d})$$

from Corollary P. This defines an object of the derived category of coherent sheaves on

$$\mathrm{Spf}(R(\mathfrak{P}_{F_y};\Lambda_0)) = \mathrm{Spf}(\Lambda_0[[s_1, \cdots, s_n]]).$$

We recall that the set of rigid points of the formal scheme $\mathrm{Spf}(R(\mathfrak{P}_{F_y};\Lambda_0))$ is Λ_+^n where $s_1, \cdots, s_n$ are its coordinates. In fact, the natural coordinates are not s_i but their exponentials $e^{s_i} = x_i$. (See Subsection 3.6.4 for some discussion on this point.) The set $\exp(H^2(F_y,\Lambda_+))$ is an infinitesimally small (open) neighborhood of $(1, \cdots, 1) \in (\Lambda_0 \setminus \{0\})^n$.

CONJECTURE T. *The object given in* (1.28) *descends to an object on the open set* $\exp(H^2(F_y, \Lambda_+))$ *and can be extended to an object on the annular region*

$$A_{1-\epsilon,1+\epsilon}(x_1, \cdots, x_n) = \{(x_1, \cdots, x_n) \in (\Lambda_0 \setminus \{0\})^n \mid 1 - \epsilon < \|x_i\| < 1 + \epsilon\}$$

for some sufficiently small $\epsilon > 0$. *Here the norm* $\|\cdot\|$ *is the non-Archimedean norm defined by*

$$\left\| \sum a_i T^{\lambda_i} \right\| = e^{-\lambda_1}$$

where λ_1 *is the leading exponent, i.e., satisfies* $a_1 \neq 0$ *and* $\lambda_i > \lambda_1$ *for* $i > 1$.

To specify the base point $y \in B$ in our discussion of the infinitesimal neighborhood and its coordinates, we write x_i^y in place of x_i. Namely we define $x_i^y = \exp(s_i)$ where s_i are the chosen coordinates of $\mathrm{Spf}(R(\mathfrak{P}_{F_y}; \Lambda_0))$. Let $y' = (y_1', \cdots, y_n')$ be a point in the neighborhood of $y = (y_1, \cdots, y_n)$ expressed in the given affine coordinates of B. By comparing symplectic areas of the discs attached to each of the Lagrangian submanifolds F_y and $F_{y'}$, we observe that it is natural to define the relation between the coordinates $x_i^{y'}$ and x_i^y by

(1.29) $$x_i^{y'} = T^{y_i' - y_i} x_i^y.$$

CONJECTURE U. *There is a coordinate change map* $\Phi_{yy'}$ *(of the rigid analytic space) from*

(1.30) $$A_{1-\epsilon,1+\epsilon}(x_1^y, \cdots, x_n^y) \cap A_{1-\epsilon,1+\epsilon}(x_1^{y'}, \cdots, x_n^{y'}) \subset A_{1-\epsilon,1+\epsilon}(x_1^y, \cdots, x_n^y)$$

to

(1.31) $$A_{1-\epsilon,1+\epsilon}(x_1^y, \cdots, x_n^y) \cap A_{1-\epsilon,1+\epsilon}(x_1^{y'}, \cdots, x_n^{y'}) \subset A_{1-\epsilon,1+\epsilon}(x_1^{y'}, \cdots, x_n^{y'}).$$

The map $\Phi_{yy'}$ *is induced by an appropriate filtered* A_∞ *homomorphism* $H(F_{y'}; \Lambda_0) \to H(F_y; \Lambda_0)$. *We can glue* $\{A_{1-\epsilon,1+\epsilon}(x_1^{y'}, \cdots, x_n^{y'})\}$ *by transition maps* $\Phi_{yy'}$ *from* (1.30) *to* (1.31) *and obtain a rigid analytic space* $\hat{\mathfrak{X}}$.

Moreover we can glue the objects obtained in Conjecture T *by* $\Phi_{yy'}^L$ *to obtain an object* $\hat{\mathfrak{F}}(L, b)$ *of derived category of coherent sheaves on* $\hat{\mathfrak{X}}$. *The transition maps* $\Phi_{yy'}^L$ *are induced by appropriate filtered* A_∞ *bimodule homomorphisms.*

Conjecture U, if proved, will give a way of constructing the mirror object $\hat{\mathfrak{F}}(L, \mathbf{b})$ provided in Conjecture R. Then functoriality of the construction would imply that there is a filtered A_∞ homomorphism from the left hand side of (R.2) to the right hand side of (R.2). More arguments are needed to show that it is an isomorphism.

To carry out the scheme described above, there still remain other difficulties. One outstanding problem is the study of the singular fibers and various structures associated to them. We expect the results of [**FOOO09II**] will be useful for this purpose.

We point out that the scheme described above uses a family version of Floer cohomology. The idea of using the family version of Floer cohomology to prove homological mirror symmetry dates back to the summer of 1997 in the discussion between the first named author and M. Kontsevich at IHES. It was partially realized for the case of abelian varieties in [**Fuk02III**]. In this particular case, all the operations $\mathfrak{m}_k$ appearing in [**Fuk02III**] indeed converge since they are reduced to multi-theta functions, and so translation of the story in the language of the formal scheme or the rigid analytic space was not needed in [**Fuk02III**]. See also [**Fuk02I**].

The approach of using the family version of Floer cohomology to the homological mirror symmetry conjecture that we have described above seems to be the most promising approach at this stage, which we hope to carry through in a near future.

Before closing out this section, we would like to indicate a few possible generalizations of our story. Our construction of the Floer cohomology and of the A_∞ structure in this book uses the moduli space of pseudo-holomorphic maps from the disc D^2. We may also consider pseudo-holomorphic maps from bordered Riemann surface of higher genus, and consider more general flat bundles than flat line bundles on L. If we perform these constructions for the zero section of the cotangent bundle of a 3-manifold, the corresponding open string theory is expected to coincide with the Chern-Simons perturbation theory, [**AxSi91I,91II, Bar91, GMM89, Kon94**]. This fact was pointed out by Witten in [**Wit95**]. (See also [**Fuk96I,97III, FuOh97**].) Its mirror would be a version of the quantum Kodaira-Spencer theory of Bershadsky-Ceccoti-Ooguri-Vafa [**BCOV94**], or more precisely its analog of the moduli space of coherent sheaves. In [**BCOV94**], the quantum Kodaira-Spencer theory of the moduli space of complex structure on a manifold was described. Unfortunately, formulating a conjecture of this coincidence in a mathematically precise form such as in Conjecture R is still beyond our reach.

One might, however, be able to say something rigorous for the case of genus one. Namely in the symplectic side, the genus one part would correspond to an invariant defined by Hutchings and Lee, [**HuLe99**], after including quantum contributions. This invariant is related to the number of pseudo-holomorphic annuli and the Reidemeister torsion. (See also [**Fuk97I, Lee01**].) In the complex side, the genus one part would correspond to the analytic torsion of $\overline{\partial}$ operator with $Hom(\hat{\mathfrak{F}}(L,b), \hat{\mathfrak{F}}(L,b))$ as its coefficients. The relationship of the analytic torsion of $\overline{\partial}$ operator to the Quillen metric on the moduli space of coherent sheaves and others has been discussed by various people, for example, by Bismut [**Bis98**]. The first step towards the study of the higher genus analog to Conjecture R would be to prove the coincidence of these invariants defined for the genus-one case.

1.5. Chapter-wise outline of the main results

Lagrangian intersection Floer theory as a whole turns out to be a highly complex and non-trivial theory partly because many basic constructions are required to be carried out in the chain level. This chain level constructions are intricately intertwined with by now the well-known construction of (virtual) fundamental chains of the various moduli spaces of pseudo-holomorphic maps, via the Kuranishi structure [**FuOn99II**] or the equivalent kind. This partly explains why the theory requires many disciplines of modern mathematics like infinite dimensional topology, non-linear elliptic partial differential equation, deformation theory and higher algebraic structures in addition to symplectic geometry. On top of this, the theory has been further enhanced by the physics of open string theory with D-branes. We have attempted to set the rigorous foundation of this complex theory in all aspects having applications both to symplectic topology and to homological mirror symmetry in mind.

This explains why the volume of the book is unusually bulky as a research monograph. Since we expect that not only mathematicians from related fields but also physicists working on the string theory may be reading at least some part of the book depending on their interest, we would like to give a brief outline of the

contents of the book chapter-wise and assist them to decide where to look for what
they are interested in.

Now chapter-wise summary of the contents of the book is in order. Along the
way, we will also provide brief outlines of the proofs of the main theorems already
stated before. We remark that many of the chapters have their own introduc-
tions (Sections 3.1, 4.1, 6.1, and the beginning of Chapter 7) where more detailed
summary of the chapters are given.

Chapter 2 is mostly devoted to a review of the Floer's original version of
Floer cohomology [**Flo88IV**] and explains how this definition meets obstruction
as soon as we leave the world of Lagrangian submanifolds L that Floer looked at in
[**Flo88IV**], i.e., of those without quantum effects or of L satisfying $\pi_2(M, L) = \{e\}$.
In Sections 2.1-2.2, we give the definitions of various kinds of Maslov indices and
of the stable map moduli space of pseudo-holomorphic discs on which the whole
constructions in the book are based on. In Section 2.3, we explain the basic idea
of Floer's construction of Lagrangian intersection Floer cohomology that is due to
Floer himself [**Flo88IV**]. Then in Section 2.4, we first review the Floer cohomology of monotone Lagrangian submanifolds that the second named author studied
in [**Oh93,95I**] and then explain where the direct generalization of these works fail
in general and indicate how one might be able to overcome the failure.

Proofs of our basic results, Theorems A and F, begin in Chapter 3. Chapters
3-5 are occupied by the basic constructions leading to the definition of our *deformed
Floer cohomology* and then to the proofs of Theorems A and F. For this purpose, we
use the (virtual) fundamental chains of the moduli spaces of pseudo-holomorphic
discs of various kinds. Two essential points needed for the construction are postponed until Chapters 7 and 8: one is the transversality problem in Chapter 7 and
the other is the orientation problem in Chapter 8.

The way how Chapters 3-5 are written is always, first develop necessary homological (homotopical) algebra of *filtered A_∞ algebras* and *filtered A_∞ modules* in
the purely algebraic context, and then apply the algebraic machinery to our geometric context of Lagrangian submanifolds. In this way, the parts of homological
(homotopical) algebra can be read separately from the geometric theory of Floer
cohomology, which may be beneficial to some algebraically minded readers. For
the geometric constructions in Chapters 3,4 and most part of Chapter 5, we need
to work in the (co)chain level. Our filtered A_∞ structure of a given Lagrangian
submanifold $L \subset (M, \omega)$ is constructed on a cochain complex of L whose cohomology group is isomorphic to that of L. As in the usual cohomology theory, there
are several different choices of the cochain complex that realizes the cohomology
group of L. We have experimented several different choices while (and before) we
were writing this book. Eventually, in this version of the book, we mostly use
the version of singular chain complex. More precisely speaking, we construct a
filtered A_∞ structure on a countably generated sub-complex of the smooth singular
chain complex of L. We regard it as a cochain complex by identifying k chain as a
$\dim L - k$ cochain. (This can be regarded as a kind of Poincaré duality.)

Chapter 3 gives the definition of filtered A_∞ algebras and their deformation
theory. Notions of obstruction cycles and of bounding cochains are introduced
first in the algebraic context. Then we associate a filtered A_∞ algebra to each
Lagrangian submanifold L over a countably generated complex on L in Section 3.5.
The algebraic arguments explaining how to proceed from the filtered A_∞ algebra
to the definitions of (deformed) Floer cohomology and of the moduli space $\mathcal{M}(L)$

that parameterizes the Floer cohomologies are given in Section 3.6. Our deformed Floer cohomology on a *single* Lagrangian submanifold L should be regarded as a version of Bott-Morse type Floer cohomology. Then to each pair of Lagrangian submanifolds we associate a filtered A_∞ bimodule which is given in Section 3.7. The filtered A_∞ structure *on the cohomology group* itself used in the statements of Theorems A and F is constructed only at the end of Chapter 5.

There are two other important issues discussed in Chapter 3. One is the issue of the *unit* of filtered A_∞ algebra. Due to the transversality problem, which is solved in Chapter 7, we need to introduce the notion of *homotopy unit*. Its definition is given in Section 3.3. The relationship of the unit with the moduli space $\mathcal{M}_{\mathrm{weak}}(L)$ of *weak bounding cochains* is explained in Subsection 3.6.3.

The other issue discussed in Section 3.8 is the deformation of the filtered A_∞ algebra by the cohomology classes from the ambient symplectic manifold. We use various operators denoted by $\mathfrak{p}$, $\mathfrak{q}$ and $\mathfrak{r}$ for this purpose. To define these operators, we use the moduli space of pseudo-holomorphic discs that have marked points both in the interior and on the boundary of the disc. This is the first step towards involving the *open-closed string* moduli spaces in the Floer theory. We expect that more extensive penetration of the ideas from the open closed string theory into the Floer theory and symplectic geometry will occur. (See [**FOOO08II**].) Such an idea is already used in this book in the proof of Theorems H and I. The relationship of the operator $\mathfrak{q}$ with the moduli space $\mathcal{M}_{\mathrm{def}}(L)$ is discussed in Section 3.8, and the operator $\mathfrak{p}$ is used in Chapter 6 to study spectral sequence and prove (D.3).

The filtered A_∞ algebra on the countably generated sub-complex of a singular cochain complex constructed in Chapter 3 depends on the various choices we make in the construction. In Chapters 4 and 5, we discuss in what sense it is independent of the choices made, and prove that the filtered A_∞ algebra is unique up to the homotopy equivalence of filtered A_∞ algebras. However before stating this homotopy equivalence, we need to give the definitions of various basic concepts in the homological algebra of A_∞ structures. In Chapter 4, we give the definition of homotopy equivalence between (filtered) A_∞ algebras and prove its basic properties. We provide a detailed exposition of homological (homotopical) algebra of (filtered) A_∞ algebras in this chapter. There are some literature in which this notion of homotopy equivalence between A_∞ algebras is defined (see, for example, [**Smi00, MSS02**]). However we make our exposition self-contained as much as possible. There are various reason for doing this.

One reason is that several different versions of the definition of homotopy equivalence are used in the literature which we feel is too confusing to directly borrow for our purpose. We give our definition of homotopy between two A_∞ homomorphisms in Definition 4.2.35. Our idea is to use the notion that is an algebraic counterpart to the operation of taking the product of a space with the interval $[0,1]$ in geometry, and to mimic this operation in defining the homotopy of A_∞ homomorphisms. Depending on the way how we algebraically realize the multiplication by the interval $[0,1]$, we obtain several different versions of the definition of homotopy. We, however, prove that the different choices are all equivalent in a precise sense. (This is a consequence of Theorem 4.2.34.)

The other reason for making our exposition self-contained is that we also need to generalize the homological algebra of A_∞ algebra in two different directions. The first one is to define the filtered version of A_∞ structures and the other is to consider the case where the coefficient ring is not $\mathbb{Q}$, but $\mathbb{Z}$ or $\mathbb{Z}_2$. Our exposition is designed so that this generalization can be easily carried out.

Now we describe two basic results, among others, in the homological algebra of filtered A_∞ structures. Let $\mathfrak{f} : (C_1, \mathfrak{m}_*) \to (C_2, \mathfrak{m}_*)$ be a filtered A_∞ homomorphism between two filtered A_∞ algebras over the ring $\Lambda_{0,nov}(R)$. We assume that C_i and $\mathfrak{f}$ are *gapped* in the sense of Definitions 3.2.26 and 3.2.29. We reduce the coefficient ring $\Lambda_{0,nov}(R)$ to R to obtain an A_∞ homomorphism $\overline{\mathfrak{f}} : (\overline{C}_1, \overline{\mathfrak{m}}_*) \to (\overline{C}_2, \overline{\mathfrak{m}}_*)$ over R. For the (unfiltered) A_∞ algebra $(\overline{C}, \overline{\mathfrak{m}}_*)$, we always assume $\overline{\mathfrak{m}}_0 = 0$ and so $\overline{\mathfrak{m}}_1$ satisfies $\overline{\mathfrak{m}}_1 \circ \overline{\mathfrak{m}}_1 = 0$. Namely, for the unfiltered case, we always assume that we are given a genuine cochain complex $(\overline{C}, \overline{\mathfrak{m}}_1)$. For our geometric application, this will be nothing but a version of singular chain complex of L.

We now state the first main theorem in the homological algebra of filtered A_∞ algebras, which is an algebraic counterpart of Whitehead's theorem in topology.

THEOREM V. *If $\overline{\mathfrak{f}}$ induces a chain homotopy equivalence $(\overline{C}_1, \overline{\mathfrak{m}}_1) \to (\overline{C}_2, \overline{\mathfrak{m}}_1)$, then $\mathfrak{f} : (C_1, \mathfrak{m}_*) \to (C_2, \mathfrak{m}_*)$ has a homotopy inverse (of gapped filtered A_∞ algebra).*

Theorem V is useful for the purpose of proving that various filtered A_∞ homomorphisms we define throughout the book are homotopy equivalences. We would like to point out that Theorem V does *not* hold in the category of differential graded algebras in general. Thanks to Theorem V, we do not need to 'invert the quasi isomorphism' which is an essential ingredient in the standard homological (homotopical) algebra of differential graded algebras. Because of this reason, the homotopy theory of A_∞ algebras is much closer to that of spaces than the homotopy theory of differential graded algebras.

Theorem V is Theorem 4.2.45 whose proof is given in Section 4.5. Then in Section 4.6 we use this algebraic machinery and prove that the filtered A_∞ algebra constructed for a Lagrangian submanifold L in Chapter 3 is independent of various choices up to this homotopy equivalence.

Another matter for which we need to use homological algebra of A_∞ algebras concerns the notion of *gauge equivalence* of solutions of (1.8). We define $\mathcal{M}(L)$ to be the set of gauge equivalence classes of solutions of (1.8). We define the gauge equivalence between two solutions to be a version of homotopy that is again an algebraic counterpart of taking the product with $[0,1]$. In this way, we can associate the set $\mathcal{M}(C)$ to each filtered A_∞ algebra $(C, \mathfrak{m}_*)$ in a functorial way (Theorem 4.3.13). Then we prove that $\mathcal{M}(C)$ is an invariant of the homotopy type of the filtered A_∞ algebra $(C, \mathfrak{m}_*)$ (Corollary 4.3.14).

Chapter 5 is devoted to the filtered A_∞ bimodule version of Chapter 4. In Section 5.1, we first discuss the relationships between various Novikov rings, $\Lambda_{0,nov}$ and others, and how they behave when we move Lagrangian submanifolds. In Section 5.2, we discuss the homological algebra of filtered A_∞ bimodules, and especially define the notion of homotopy between them. We then prove in Section 5.3 that the filtered A_∞ bimodule associated to a relative spin pair (L_0, L_1) of Lagrangian submanifolds is independent of various choices involved up to the chain homotopy equivalence.

In Section 5.4, we transfer various A_∞ structures constructed in the cochain level to those defined on the cohomology. In this regard, the following is the second main theorem in the homological algebra of filtered A_∞ structures.

THEOREM W. *Let R be a field. For any gapped filtered A_∞ algebra $(C, \mathfrak{m}_*)$ there exists a gapped filtered A_∞ structure on $H(\overline{C}, \overline{\mathfrak{m}}_1) \otimes_R \Lambda_{0,nov}(R)$ that is homotopy equivalent to $(C, \mathfrak{m}_*)$.*

Theorem W is the filtered A_∞ algebra version of a classical result in homological algebra which dates back to [**Kad82**]. Our proof is based on the Feynman diagram technique of summing over trees which is similar to the one given by [**KoSo01**] and to the argument in Section A.6 of the year-2000-version [**FOOO00**] of this book.

The purpose of Chapter 6 is to construct a spectral sequence appearing in Theorem D and to explain its various applications to symplectic geometry and topology. The universal Novikov ring $\Lambda_{0,nov}$ has a filtration defined by $F^\lambda \Lambda_{0,nov} = T^\lambda \Lambda_{0,nov}$. (See (Conv.6.)) However the filtration is given by real numbers λ, not by integers. It turns out that constructing a spectral sequence and proving its convergence out of such a filtered complex is a nontrivial problem. In Chapter 6, this problem is solved and Theorem E is proved. For this purpose, we also use the operator $\mathfrak{p}$ and the existence of unit in the filtered A_∞ algebra attached to the given Lagrangian submanifold L.

In Chapter 7, we discuss the problem of transversality. This is one of the two main ingredients in the construction of the virtual fundamental chains of various moduli spaces of pseudo-holomorphic discs used in this book. (The other is the problem of orientation which is discussed in Chapter 8.) For this purpose, we systematically use the notion of the Kuranishi structure and its multi-sections introduced in [**FuOn99II**].

The Kuranishi structure and perturbations by multi-sections provide an *optimal* framework to study the transversality problem in the *general* moduli problem, where the concerned objects have finite automorphism groups. This established machinery still seems to be overlooked by many researchers in the related areas, although more than 10 years have passed since its first appearance in January 1996. Because of this, in Appendix Section A1 we provide a rather detailed account on the Kuranishi structure and on the construction of virtual fundamental chains via the Kuranishi structure. We would also like to give rather detailed account of the contents of Chapter 7 here.

In Section 7.1, we give a construction of the Kuranishi structures on the moduli spaces of various type of pseudo-holomorphic discs used in the book. In our circumstances of defining the A_∞ algebra and the Floer cohomology, we need to use virtual fundamental *chains* in place of virtual fundamental *cycle*. This means that the structure constants of various algebraic structures we construct *depend* on the choice of various perturbations, and so only their homotopy types could possibly become an invariant independent of such perturbations. Because we need to consider a whole family of moduli spaces attached to a Lagrangian submanifold L or its pair (L_0, L_1), we need to choose perturbations of various moduli spaces so that they satisfy certain compatibility conditions, if one hopes the final outcome to be an invariant of L or (L_0, L_1) itself. (This point is of sharp contrast to the case of usual Gromov-Witten invariants, where we can safely take perturbations individually for each moduli space, because the corresponding invariant is defined in the homology level.) We define the fiber product of Kuranishi structures in Section A1 and use this to formulate the compatibility of Kuranishi structures defined on the different strata of the compactified moduli spaces in Subsection 7.1.1. In Section 7.2, we carefully state the compatibility conditions of multi-sections (perturbations) using this compatibility of Kuranishi structures. We emphasize that without precisely stating the compatibility condition of perturbations, any statement asserting the well-definedness of various algebraic structures defined by using the compactified moduli space would not make sense and not be well-founded.

In Subsections 7.1.2-7.1.3, we discuss the analytic part of construction of Kuranishi structures of the disc moduli spaces of our concern. Many arguments there are combinations of various techniques that have already appeared in the literature. For example, the gluing technique in the Bott-Morse situation appeared in [**Fuk96II**], the study of pseudo-holomorphic discs together with moduli parameters in [**FuOh97**], and gluing construction of Kuranishi structures in [**FuOn99II**] respectively.

Our construction of Kuranishi structures of the disc moduli spaces used for the definition of the filtered A_∞ structures associated to Lagrangian submanifolds is completed in Subsection 7.1.4.

In Subsection 7.1.5, we study the moduli space that we use to define a filtered A_∞ homomorphism between the filtered A_∞ algebras attached to Lagrangian submanifolds. To give a construction of Kuranishi structures that satisfy the above mentioned compatibility conditions, we need to study certain cell decomposition of a disc D^n, which in turn is used to define the notion of the A_∞ map (Theorem 7.1.51.)

Note that the Stasheff cell or rather Stasheff's cell decomposition of a disc D^n is used to define the notion of the A_∞ space ([**St63**]) and is related to both the moduli space of marked bordered Riemann surface of genus zero and to the moduli space of metric ribbon trees. (See [**FuOh97**].) Stasheff told us that the cell decomposition of the disc which leads a definition of A_∞ maps was known to him. (See also [**MSS02, BoVo73**].) However, it seems that our geometric description of this cell decomposition is new.

We emphasize that novelty of our exposition on the transversality in this book does not lie in the analytic part, which has been in principle understood since 1996, but rather lies in its topological part that we present in Section 7.2. In Section 7.2, for the purpose of constructing the filtered A_∞ structure and others, we make suitable inductive strata-wise perturbations of the Kuranishi map of the given pseudo-holomorphic equation on each stratum of the compactified moduli space, and make a choice of *countably* generated sub-complex of the singular cochain complex.

REMARK 1.32. In this book, we use singular chain complex for the construction of the A_∞ structure associated to Lagrangian submanifolds. This is the outcome of some deliberation of ours. We point out that there are also two other possible choices. We briefly mention the other choices and explain why we have made the current choice in this book.

One such choice is to be using the de Rham complex. This choice works as explained in [**Fuk05II**] and worked out in [**Fuk07I, FOOO08II**], (where the contents of present book is assumed). It has some of its own advantage. For example, it makes easier to keep more symmetry like the cyclic symmetry in the construction of A_∞ structures. However with the de Rham complex, we are unable to work over the $\mathbb{Z}_2$ coefficient. Usage of the $\mathbb{Z}_2$ coefficient is essential for several applications to symplectic geometry, especially to the study of the Arnold-Givental conjecture. We will discuss the partial generalization of our story to $\mathbb{Z}$ or $\mathbb{Z}_2$ coefficient and apply it to prove Arnold-Givental conjecture in some cases in [**FOOO09I**]. There we use the algebraic (as well as other) frame works of this book. So we did not use the de Rham complex in this book, except in Section 7.5 and Theorem X.

The other choice is to use the Morse complex. In fact this is the approach that the first named author initiated in 1993. (See [**Fuk93**] and (3.3), Figure 8 in [**Fuk97III**].) The second named author also used this approach to construct a spectral sequence similar to the one in Theorem D and pointed out that this approach could be amplified to a construction of A_∞-category in [**Oh96I, 96II**]. We used a similar argument in pp 287 - 291 of the year-2000-version of this book for the proof of weak finiteness (Definition 6.3.27), exploiting the obvious fact that the Morse complex of a compact manifold is always finitely generated. During the preparation of the current revision, we have discovered a (purely algebraic and simpler) proof of weak finiteness of our countably generated complex, and preferred to include this simpler proof and to drop the old proof from this current version.

We believe that the approach of using the Morse complex would work to some extent. However we would like to point out that there is some trouble that occurs in this approach. Recall that the product structure on the (filtered) A_∞ algebra associated to L is a deformation of the cup product on the cohomology $H^*(L)$. As studied by the first named author [**Fuk93,97III**] and Betz-Cohen [**BeCo94**], one needs to simultaneously use several different Morse functions on a manifold to study the product of Morse homology in the chain level. The product in Morse homology is defined by considering the moduli space of maps from the "Y-graph" to the given manifold. To define the structure constants, we want this moduli space to be transversal. Note that this moduli space will be never transversal, *if one consider the same Morse function on the three edges* of the Y-graph. This transversality problem is a fundamental issue in algebraic topology and seems to be extremely hard to resolve unless one uses several Morse functions simultaneously. See [**FOOO08III**].

One implication of the above discussion is that one can only construct a (kind of) filtered A_∞ *category* in which morphisms (= Floer cohomology) can be composed only generically. This leads to the notion of topological A_∞ category. As a consequence, it is difficult to define a unit which is nothing but the identity morphism. The problem of the unit is discussed in the context of topological A_∞ category by the first named author in [**Fuk97II**]. However the exposition in [**Fuk97II**] was quite unsatisfactory. Only after we succeeded in constructing the (filtered) A_∞ *algebra* for each L as in the way taken in this book (or by using de Rham cohomology), we have been able to properly understand the unit of (filtered) A_∞ category. (See [**Fuk02II**].)

The unit plays a very important role in applications to symplectic geometry, because the unit can be used to prove non-triviality of Floer cohomology in some favorable circumstances. (See Theorem E, for example.) The unit also plays an important role in the application to mirror symmetry. For example, the proof of Yoneda's lemma for the A_∞ category is based on the existence of a unit. (See [**Fuk02II**].) Therefore having a proper definition of the unit in this story is an important ingredient for the A_∞ category of Lagrangian submanifolds. Because it does not seem to be easy to give a proper definition of the unit in the context of the approach using Morse functions, we do not use Morse homology either in this book.

The problem of transversality already occurs even if we do not take contributions from (pseudo-)holomorphic discs into account. The problem in classical algebraic topology is then, that of defining an A_∞ structure on the singular chain complex that realizes the intersection product *in the chain level*, for example. The main trouble for the singular chain complex is that a chain is never transversal to itself and so pairing between the same chain is not well-defined unless the chain is the fundamental chain of the underlying manifold. Among the algebraic topologists, this trouble is well known as well as the difficulty of the problem of realizing the intersection product in the chain level (unless one use the de Rham complex). We have solved this transversality problem by carefully perturbing the usual intersection pairing of chains over $\mathbb{Z}$. However, then, associativity of the resulting product inevitably breaks down. We compensate the failure of associativity by systematically introducing the higher product operations $\overline{\mathfrak{m}}_k$ through which we obtain an A_∞ algebra on a countably generated (co)chain complex. Once we have done this, we then continue to incorporate contributions of pseudo-holomorphic discs in a certain compatible way, and define our filtered A_∞ algebra associated to the given Lagrangian submanifold L.

In Section 7.3, we provide the construction of the homotopy unit.

In Section 7.5, we prove the following theorem, which is close to the equivalence statement of various approaches, that was mentioned in Remark 1.32, to the construction of the filtered A_∞ algebra appearing in Theorem A.

We recall that the de Rham complex is a differential graded algebra which can be regarded as an A_∞ algebra. (See Remark 3.2.4 (2) for the precise meaning of this statement.)

THEOREM X. *Let $(H^*(L; \Lambda_{0,nov}), \mathfrak{m}_*)$ be the filtered A_∞ algebra given in Theorem A and $(H^*(L; \mathbb{Q}), \overline{\mathfrak{m}}_*)$ the reduction of the coefficient ring to $\mathbb{Q}$. Then the A_∞ algebra $(H^*(L; \mathbb{Q}), \overline{\mathfrak{m}}_*) \otimes_{\mathbb{Q}} \mathbb{R}$ is homotopy equivalent to the de Rham complex of L as an A_∞ algebra.*

This theorem implies that if we take the coefficient $\mathbb{R}$, then the filtered A_∞ algebra in Theorem A is a deformation of the real homotopy type of L.

One might say that it is intuitively clear that all three approaches, singular, de-Rham, and Morse, will boil down to the same theory. However giving a rigorous proof of such an equivalence is not an easy problem. Theorem X gives a part of the proof of the equivalence between the de Rham cohomology version and the singular cohomology version. It is very likely that further refining of these arguments leads to a complete proof of this equivalence using the de Rham version constructed in [**Fuk07I**].

As for the equivalence between the Morse homology (or Morse homotopy) version and de Rham cohomology version in the classical topology, a relevant statement is that the Morse A_∞ category of a given compact manifold, which was constructed in [**FuOh97**], is homotopy equivalent to the rational homotopy type of the manifold. We have no doubt that this is true as we mentioned in [**FuOh97**]. Unfortunately such a statement is not proved in detail in the literature yet. It appears that the discussion of Kontsevich and Soibelman in page 239 around Theorem 2 [**KoSo01**] is related to such a statement. Detail of the proof of that statement, however, is missing in [**KoSo01**]. (However their idea of the proof proposed there is convincing and very likely to be correct.)

REMARK 1.33. We conjecture that $(H^*(L; \mathbb{Q}), \{\overline{\mathfrak{m}}_k\}_{k=0}^{\infty})$ is homotopy equivalent to the $\mathbb{Q}$-de Rham complex (see [**Sul78**]). This does not follows from Theorem X. In fact, there is an example of a pair of differential graded algebras over $\mathbb{Q}$ which are homotopy equivalent to each other over $\mathbb{R}$ but are not homotopy equivalent to each other over $\mathbb{Q}$. (See [**BrSz89**].)

In Section 7.4 we present the details of the construction outlined in Section 3.8. Namely we deform our filtered A_{∞} algebra attached to the Lagrangian submanifold using the moduli space of pseudo-holomorphic discs with both interior and boundary marked points.

There are two main issues we discuss in this section. One is about compactification of the moduli space of pseudo-holomorphic discs with interior marked points but without boundary marked points. One essential new phenomenon we discovered is the fact that the standard stable map compactification does *not* give a correct compactification in this case. Because of this phenomenon, the term containing Gromov-Witten invariant appears in the formula (3.8.10.3) which spells out the main property of the operator $\mathfrak{p}$.

Another issue dealt with in Section 7.4 is to provide an algebraic framework for the description of the bulk deformation of $(H(L; \Lambda_{0,nov}), \mathfrak{m}_*)$. The general strategy in the deformation theory (whose origin goes back to Gerstenhaber) states that deformations of an algebraic system are controlled by an appropriate Lie algebra. For the case of filtered A_{∞} algebra C, we have the Hochschild chain complex $CH(C, C) = \prod_k Hom(B_k C[1], C[1])$ which is a differential graded Lie algebra. We regard this complex as an L_{∞} algebra which we denote by $\mathrm{DerB}(C[1])$. (See Definition 7.4.26). (See Section A3 for the definition of L_{∞} algebra.) Its unital version is denoted by $\mathrm{DerB}^{\mathrm{unit}}(C[1])$. On the other hand, the cohomology group $H(M; \Lambda_{0,nov})[1]$ (with degree shifted) of our ambient symplectic manifold is regarded as an L_{∞} algebra with all the operations trivial. The main properties of our operator $\mathfrak{q}$ can be stated in the language of L_{∞} algebra as follows:

THEOREM Y. *There exists a strict and filtered L_{∞} homomorphism*

$$\mathfrak{q}^o : H(M; \Lambda_{0,nov})[1] \to \mathrm{DerB}^{\mathrm{unit}}(H(L; \Lambda_{0,nov})[1])$$

such that after the reduction of the coefficient ring to $\mathbb{Q}$, the map $\mathfrak{q}^o$ reduces to a linear map $H(M; \mathbb{Q}) \to Hom(\mathbb{Q}, H(L; \mathbb{Q})) \cong H(L; \mathbb{Q})$ induced by the inclusion into the cohomology group $H(L; \mathbb{Q})$.

If $\psi : (M, L) \to (M', L')$ is a symplectic diffeomorphism we have the following diagram which commutes up to an L_{∞} homotopy:

$$
\begin{array}{ccc}
H(M, \Lambda_{0,nov})[1] & \xrightarrow{\;\mathfrak{q}^o\;} & \mathrm{DerB}^{\mathrm{unit}}(H(L; \Lambda_{0,nov})[1]) \\
\Big\downarrow{\psi_*} & & \Big\downarrow{\psi_*} \\
H(M', \Lambda_{0,nov})[1] & \xrightarrow{\;\mathfrak{q}^o\;} & \mathrm{DerB}^{\mathrm{unit}}(H(L'; \Lambda_{0,nov})[1])
\end{array}
$$

Theorem Y is the combination of Theorems 7.4.118 and 7.4.120 which are proved in Subsections 7.4.5 and 7.4.6.

We can use the notion of L_{∞} modules to state a similar result for the map $\mathfrak{r}$: This is the operator appearing in the deformation of Floer cohomology of the pair by the cohomology class of ambient symplectic manifold. See Theorems 7.4.154, 7.4.156, 7.4.162 in Sections 7.4.7-9. The operator $\mathfrak{p}$ has an interpretation in terms of the cyclic bar complex of $H(L; \Lambda_{0,nov})$ and an L_∞ module structure over $\text{DerB}^{\text{unit}}(H(L; \Lambda_{0,nov})[1])$ on it. See Theorems 7.4.192 and 7.4.195 in Subsection 7.4.11.

The results in Section 7.4 are closely related to the loop space formulation of Lagrangian Floer theory [**Fuk05II**] and to the generalization of our story to the higher genus cases.

Chapter 8 is devoted to the other technical heart of matter in our constructions, the problem of orientation. In Section 8.1, we study the moduli space of pseudo-holomorphic discs *without marked points*. This problem is naturally related to the index theory for the family of elliptic operators. In our case of holomorphic discs (or the case of bordered Riemann surfaces in general), we need an index theory for the family of elliptic operators with boundary conditions. We show how the second Stiefel-Whitney class comes into this index theory, and prove that the moduli space of pseudo-holomorphic discs without marked points is orientable if the Lagrangian submanifold is relatively spin. More precisely, we prove the following Theorem Z. We denote by $\mathcal{M}(L; \beta)$ the stable map compactification of the moduli space of pseudo-holomorphic discs $w : (D^2, \partial D^2) \to (M, L)$ in homology class $\beta \in H_2(M, L)$.

THEOREM Z. *The moduli space $\mathcal{M}(L; \beta)$ is orientable, if $L \subset (M, \omega)$ is a relatively spin Lagrangian submanifold. Furthermore the choice of relative spin structure on L canonically determines an orientation on $\mathcal{M}(L; \beta)$ for all $\beta \in H_2(M, L)$ in a coherent way.*

We refer to Chapter 8 Definition 8.1.2 for the definition of relative spin structure. We would like to remark that Theorem Z is proved independently by de Silva [**Sil97**].

To illustrate that the index bundle of the Cauchy-Riemann operator *with boundary conditions* is not orientable in general, we give an explicit example for which the index bundle (of the Cauchy-Riemann operator on the disc with totally real boundary condition) is not orientable.

Other sections of Chapter 8 are devoted to defining coherent orientations on various moduli spaces of pseudo-holomorphic discs with respect to the fiber product. This problem turns out to be an essential point in our construction of the A_∞-algebra.

The problem of giving the coherent orientations is closely tied to that of finding a good sign convention for the A_∞ formulae, and also very much related to the supersymmetry. According to Getzler-Jones [**GeJo90**], there are basically two different kinds of the sign convention for the A_∞ formulae. We now briefly recall the differences between them here: Consider the (singular) chain complex $C(L)$ of L. Let $x_i \in C$ and let the degree be $d_i = \text{codim}\, x_i$.

In the first convention, we shift its degree by one and regard it as an element of degree $d_i + 1$ in the shifted complex. In this convention, the sign change we get is $(-1)^{(d_1+1)(d_2+1)}$ when one commutes two elements in the product.

In the second convention, each element will have two different degrees, one the usual degree in the graded complex and the other the super-degree. In this convention, an element $x_i \in C(L)$ has the usual degree d_i coming from the grading and has super degree 1. The sign change we get is $(-1)^{d_1 d_2 + 1}$ when one commutes two elements in the product .

For this matter, Getzler-Jones used the notation $\widetilde{\mathfrak{m}}$ for the operator with the first sign convention and $\mathfrak{m}$ for the second sign convention. They are related by the map b in pp 259-260 [**GeJo90**]. Our convention in this book seems to coincide with the *first sign convention*. (Note that the second sign convention was used in [**Fuk02III**].)

From the geometric point of view, these two sign conventions correspond to two different ways of equipping with orientation on the moduli space of pseudo-holomorphic discs with marked points on the boundary.

Thus, Sections 8.2-8.10 are devoted to a detailed description of the orientations of the various moduli spaces, and to the verification of the A_∞ formulae *with sign* using the first sign convention. We include a thorough account on this orientation problem because it is a complicated and confusing matter. Without the thorough analysis, there would be no way to see the correct formulae with sign throughout the book.

1.6. Acknowledgments

We owe M. Kontsevich the idea of constructing a series of obstruction classes and deforming Floer's boundary map when the obstruction classes are trivial, in the study of Floer theory of general Lagrangian submanifolds. We have also learned many things from his papers which are used in several places of this book in an essential way. We like to thank U. Frauenfelder for pointing out one essential error in relation to the proof of the Arnold-Givental conjecture in the year-2000 version of this book. We also thank C.-H. Cho for several valuable discussions, especially the ones related to the isomorphism between quantum cohomology and Floer cohomology of the diagonal and also for a comment that led us to writing Subsections 7.4.2-11. We also thank K. Hori, J. Stasheff, N. Minami, M. Furuta, T. Gocho, A. Kono and F. Kato, for providing various useful information on potential function & Landau-Ginzburg model, A_∞ algebra, rational homotopy theory, renormalization theory, relation of noncommutative symplectic geometry to A_∞ algebra, homology of loop space, and rigid analytic geometry, respectively, during the preparation or revision of this book.

We started the project of writing this book in 1998 and a preliminary version was completed in December of the year 2000. Since then, we have put it on the home page (http://www.math.kyoto-u.ac.jp/~fukaya/) of the first named author. Since the appearance of the year-2000 version of the current book, our revision process of completing this final version has taken much more time than we originally expected. In the mean time, many results out of this book have been further explained in various articles of the authors. (See [**ChOh03, Fuk03II,05II, Oht01**].) The contents of the book have been much modified and improved from those in the year-2000 version. Therefore some explanations on the relationship between the year-2000 version and the present final version should be in order.

First, we would like to point out that there are several errors in the year-2000 version. The most conspicuous one is the extra condition of spherical positivity of (M, ω) needed for the authors to prove the Arnold-Givental conjecture at the time of writing this book. Except this added condition, all errors in the proofs of the theorems stated in the introduction of the year-2000 version are corrected in this book or in several other previous papers [**FOOO09I,09II**]. We emphasize that all the theorems stated in the introduction of the year-2000 version hold true as stated there, with the exception of 'Theorem H' of the year-2000 version, for which we need an additional assumption. (See [**FOOO09I**].) For the readers of the year-2000 version or of the year-2006 version who are interested in finding out the differences between the year-2000 version and this final version, we prepared the document [**FOOO09III**] that describes the difference. Actually two chapters which were included in the previous year-2007 version of this book are excluded from this final version due to the publisher's page restriction on this AMS/IP series: One chapter studies Lagrangian Floer cohomology over $\mathbb{Z}$ or $\mathbb{Z}_2$ coefficient under the additional assumption 'spherically positivity' of Lagrangian submanifolds. The other one studies the relationship between Lagrangian Floer cohomology and Lagrangian surgery. These two chapters will be published elsewhere as separate papers [**FOOO09I,09II**]. We would like to point out, though, the two chapters in the year-2007 version of this book are already in the final form. One drawback of this departure of the two chapters from this book is that not many examples of calculation of Lagrangian Floer cohomology are included in this book. We refer readers to [**FOOO08I,08II,09I,09II**] for more examples of such calculations.

The first named author (K.F.) would like to thank IHES, where he had fruitful discussion with M. Kontsevich related to this project during his visit of IHES in 1997. The first, the third and the fourth named authors (K.F., H.O., K.O.) would also like to thank Y.-G. Oh and KIAS for their hospitality during their visits of KIAS in 1999 and 2000. They are also grateful to ETH, University of Warwick, Johns Hopkins University and Max Planck Institute für Mathematik, Bonn for the hospitality during their visits. In these visits, they are benefited much from these institutions where they provide excellent working environment so that they could focus their attention on this project. The second named author (Y.O.) thanks K. Fukaya and RIMS for its financial support and hospitality during his stay in RIMS in the fall of 1999. The fourth named author would like to thank IHES for its hospitality during his stay in the summer of 1998.

The authors would like to thank Professor S.T. Yau for suggesting to publish this book as a volume in the series, AMS/IP Studies of Mathematics. They would also like to thank Mrs. Tanaka for drawing excellent figures in this book.

1.7. Conventions

(**Conv.1**)   The Hamiltonian vector field X_H is defined by $dH = \omega(X_H, \cdot)$.

(**Conv.2**)   An almost complex structure is called tame to ω if the bilinear from $\omega(\cdot, J\cdot)$ is positive and compatible to ω if the bilinear form defines a Riemannian metric (which is also bounded at infinity if M is non-compact).

(**Conv.3**)   Let $\mathbf{x} \in BC[1]$ be an element of bar complex. We define a coassociative coproduct $\Delta : BC[1] \to BC[1] \otimes BC[1]$ by

$$(1.34) \qquad \Delta(x_1 \otimes \cdots \otimes x_n) = \sum_{k=0}^{n} (x_1 \otimes \cdots \otimes x_k) \otimes (x_{k+1} \otimes \cdots \otimes x_n).$$

We consider its $n-1$ iteration,

$$\Delta^{n-1} : BC[1] \to \underbrace{BC[1] \otimes \cdots \otimes BC[1]}_{n \text{ times}}.$$

We write

$$(1.35) \qquad \Delta^{n-1}(\mathbf{x}) = \sum_c \mathbf{x}_c^{n:1} \otimes \cdots \mathbf{x}_c^{n:n},$$

where c runs on some index set depending n and $\mathbf{x}$.

In the case $n = 2$ we also write

$$(1.36) \qquad \Delta(\mathbf{x}) = \sum_c \mathbf{x}_c' \otimes \mathbf{x}_c''.$$

(Conv.4) Let R be a commutative ring with unit. We use the following version of Novikov ring:

$$\Lambda_{0,nov}(R) = \left\{ \sum_{i=0}^{\infty} a_i T^{\lambda_i} e^{n_i} \,\middle|\, a_i \in R,\ \lambda_i \in \mathbb{R}_{\geq 0},\ n_i \in \mathbb{Z},\ \lim_{i \to \infty} \lambda_i = \infty \right\}.$$

Here T and e are formal generators of $\deg e = 2$ and $\deg T = 0$. We all it the *universal Novikov ring*. We define:

$$\Lambda_{nov}(R) = \left\{ \sum_{i=0}^{\infty} a_i T^{\lambda_i} e^{n_i} \,\middle|\, a_i \in R,\ \lambda_i \in \mathbb{R},\ n_i \in \mathbb{Z},\ \lim_{i \to \infty} \lambda_i = \infty \right\}.$$

This is a localization of $\Lambda_{0,nov}(R)$ and is a field of fraction of in case R is a field. We denote by $\Lambda_{0,nov}^+(R)$ an ideal of $\Lambda_{0,nov}(R)$ given by it

$$\Lambda_{0,nov}^+(R) = \left\{ \sum_{i=0}^{\infty} a_i T^{\lambda_i} e^{n_i} \in \Lambda_{0,nov}(R) \,\middle|\, \lambda_i > 0 \right\}.$$

We remark that

$$(1.37) \qquad \frac{\Lambda_{0,nov}(R)}{\Lambda_{0,nov}^+(R)} \cong R[e, e^{-1}].$$

We denote by $\Lambda_{0,nov}^{(d)}(R)$ and $\Lambda_{nov}^{(d)}(R)$ the degree d parts of them, respectively. In case $R = \mathbb{Q}$ we omit R and write $\Lambda_{0,nov}$ etc.

(Conv.5) We also consider the ring.

$$\Lambda_0(R) = \left\{ \sum_{i=0}^{\infty} a_i T^{\lambda_i} \,\middle|\, a_i \in R,\ \lambda_i \in \mathbb{R}_{\geq 0}, \text{and} \lim_{i \to \infty} \lambda_i = \infty \right\}$$

and

$$\Lambda_+(R) = \Lambda_0(R) \cap \Lambda_{0,nov}^+$$

and the localization $\Lambda(R) = \Lambda_0(R)[T^{-1}]$. We denote $\Lambda_0(\mathbb{Q})$ etc. by Λ_0 etc..

(Conv.6) We define a filtration on $\Lambda_{0,nov}(R)$ by

$$(1.38) \qquad F^\lambda \Lambda_{0,nov}(R) = T^\lambda \Lambda_{0,nov}(R).$$

($\lambda \geq 0$.) It induces a filtrations $F^\lambda \Lambda_{nov}(R)$ of $\Lambda_{nov}(R)$, where $\lambda \in \mathbb{R}$. It also induces a filtration on $\Lambda_{0,nov}^+(R)$. Those filtrations induce metrics on $\Lambda_{0,nov}(R)$, $\Lambda_{nov}(R)$, $\Lambda_{0,nov}^+(R)$. These rings are complete with respect to this metric.

We define filtrations on $\Lambda_0(R)$, $\Lambda_+(R)$, $\Lambda(R)$ in a similar way.

CHAPTER 2

Review: Floer cohomology

2.1. Bordered stable maps and the Maslov index

Floer's original construction of Floer cohomology does not meet any *obstruction* when there occurs no bubbling phenomenon. When bubbling occurs, one needs to study how bubbling interacts with the classical Smale-Morse-Witten-Floer boundary map. By now, this analysis has been thoroughly carried out for the Floer cohomology of Hamiltonian diffeomorphisms using the virtual fundamental cycle techniques in [**FuOn99II, LiTi98, Rua99**]. The outcome is that there occurs no *anomaly* in the construction of Floer cohomology in that case.

However for the Lagrangian intersection Floer cohomology, anomaly occurs even under the simplest possible bubbling contribution: the case of non-exact *monotone* Lagrangian submanifolds. In this chapter, we review construction of Floer cohomology for a *monotone* Lagrangian pair (L_0, L_1) and explain how the anomaly occurs and can be resolved in some favorable situations just making a generic choice of almost complex structures. We refer to [**Oh93,96I,96II**] for more details of this construction for the monotone case. However we need to make clearer usages of the Novikov ring and the geometric set-up needed for our construction of Lagrangian intersection Floer cohomology beyond the monotone case. These points were not addressed in [**Oh93,96I,96II**] or in other previous literature. (Except them, the contents of this chapter is not new.) To carry out a self-contained explanation of these points, we provide a review on the Maslov index and the Novikov ring of Lagrangian submanifolds.

2.1.1. The Maslov index: the relative first Chern number. We consider the standard symplectic vector space $(\mathbb{R}^{2n}, \omega_0)$ with the canonical coordinates $(x_1, \cdots, x_n, y_1, \cdots, y_n)$ with $\omega_0 = \sum_{i=1}^{n} dx_i \wedge dy_i$. The Lagrangian Grassmanian $\Lambda(n)$ in $(\mathbb{R}^{2n}, \omega_0)$ is defined to be

$$\Lambda(n) = \{V \mid V \text{ is a Lagrangian subspace of } (\mathbb{R}^{2n}, \omega_0)\}.$$

When we equip $\mathbb{R}^{2n}$ with the standard complex multiplication and identify it with $\mathbb{C}^n$ by the map $(x_i, y_i) \mapsto z_i = x_i + \sqrt{-1}y_i$ any Lagrangian subspace $V \subset \mathbb{C}^n$ can be written as $V = A \cdot \mathbb{R}^n$ for a complex matrix $A \in U(n)$. Obviously $A \cdot \mathbb{R}^n = \mathbb{R}^n$ if and only if the matrix A is a real matrix. These show that $\Lambda(n)$ is a homogeneous space $\Lambda(n) \cong U(n)/O(n)$. It is shown in [**Arn67**] that $H^1(\Lambda(n), \mathbb{Z}) \cong \mathbb{Z}$ and $\Lambda(n)$ carries the well-known characteristic class $\mu \in H^1(\Lambda(n), \mathbb{Z})$, the *Maslov class* [**Arn67**]. This assigns an integer to each given loop $\gamma : S^1 \to \Lambda(n)$ given by

$$\mu(\gamma) = \deg(\det{}^2 \circ \gamma).$$

Furthermore two loops γ_1, γ_2 are homotopic if and only if $\mu(\gamma_1) = \mu(\gamma_2)$.

In fact, there is a purely symplectic description of the Maslov class which we describe now. Let (S, Ω) be a symplectic vector space and let $\Lambda(S, \Omega)$ be the set of Lagrangian subspaces. Let V_0 be a given Lagrangian subspace and consider the stratification of $\Lambda(S, \Omega)$

$$\Lambda(S, \Omega) \supset \Lambda_1(S, \Omega; V_0) \supset \cdots \supset \Lambda_n(S, \Omega; V_0) = \{V_0\}$$

where $\Lambda_k(S, \Omega; V_0)$ is the subset of $\Lambda(S, \Omega)$ defined by

$$\Lambda_k(S, \Omega; V_0) = \{V \in \Lambda(S, \Omega) \mid \dim(V \cap V_0) \geq k\} \qquad \text{for } k = 0, \cdots, n.$$

It is proven in [**Arn67**] that $\Lambda_k(S, \Omega; V_0)$ is compact and $\Lambda_1(S, \Omega; V_0)$ is *co-oriented* and so defines a cycle whose Poincaré dual is precisely the Maslov class $\mu \in H^1(\Lambda(S, \Omega), \mathbb{Z})$.

More precisely, Arnold proved the following Proposition 2.1.3. This proposition will be used in our construction of Novikov covering space in the next section.

LEMMA 2.1.1. *There exists a neighborhood U of $V_0 \in \Lambda(S, \Omega)$, the set*

$$U \setminus \Lambda_1(S, \Omega; V_0)$$

has exactly $n + 1$ connected components each of which contains V_0 in its closure.

PROOF. We identify $S = T^*V_0$ as a symplectic vector space. Then any $V \in U$ is uniquely identified to a graph $\mathrm{Graph}(df_V)$ for a function $f_V : V_0 \to \mathbb{R}$ such that $f_V(0) = 0$. f_V is a quadratic form. If $V \notin \Lambda_1(S, \Omega; V_0)$ then f_V is nondegenerate. We put

$$(2.1.2) \qquad U_k(V_0) = \{\mathrm{Graph}(df_V) \mid \mathrm{Index}\, f_V = k\} \setminus \Lambda_1(S, \Omega; V_0).$$

It is easy to see that $U_k(V_0)$ is connected (and is nonempty if $k = 0, \cdots, n$). The lemma follows. $\qquad \square$

PROPOSITION 2.1.3. *Let (S, Ω) be a symplectic vector space and $V_0 \in (S, \Omega)$ be a given Lagrangian subspace of (S, Ω). Let $V_1 \in \Lambda(S, \Omega) \setminus \Lambda_1(S, \Omega; V_0)$ i.e., be a Lagrangian subspace with $V_0 \cap V_1 = \{0\}$. Consider smooth paths $\alpha : [0, 1] \to \Lambda(S, \Omega)$ satisfying*

(2.1.4.1) $\alpha(0) = V_0$, $\alpha(1) = V_1$.
(2.1.4.2) $\alpha(t) \in \Lambda(S, \Omega) \setminus \Lambda_1(S, \Omega; V_0)$ *for all* $0 < t \leq 1$.
(2.1.4.3) $\alpha(t) \in U_0(V_0)$ *for small t, where $U_0(V_0)$ is as in* (2.1.2).

Then any two such paths α_1, α_2 are homotopic to each other via a homotopy $s \in [0, 1] \mapsto \alpha_s$ such that each α_s also satisfies the condition (2.1.4).

See [**Arn67**] or [**GuiSt77**] for the proof of Proposition 2.1.3.

In relation to the study of the relative version of the Riemann-Roch formula, it is useful to generalize the Maslov index to a loop of (maximally) *totally real subspace*. A real subspace $V \subset \mathbb{C}^n$ is called totally real if $V \cap \sqrt{-1}V = \{0\}$ and $\dim_{\mathbb{R}} V = n$. We denote the set of totally real subspaces by $\mathcal{R}(n)$.

Any totally real subspace V in $\mathbb{C}^n$ can be written as $V = A \cdot \mathbb{R}^n$ for some $A \in GL(n, \mathbb{C})$ and $A_1 \cdot \mathbb{R}^n = A_2 \cdot \mathbb{R}^n$ if and only if $A_2^{-1} A_1 \in GL(n, \mathbb{R})$. Therefore the set $\mathcal{R}(n)$ of totally real subspaces is a homogeneous space $\mathcal{R}(n) = GL(n, \mathbb{C})/GL(n, \mathbb{R})$. The following lemma from [**Oh95II**] is a useful fact for the study of index problem.

LEMMA 2.1.5. *Consider the subset*

$$\widetilde{\mathcal{R}}(n) = \{D \in GL(n, \mathbb{C}) \mid D\overline{D} = I_n\}$$

where I_n is the identity matrix. Then the map

$$B : \mathcal{R}(n) \cong GL(n, \mathbb{C})/GL(n, \mathbb{R}) \to \widetilde{\mathcal{R}}(n); \quad A \cdot \mathbb{R}^n \mapsto A^{-1}\overline{A}$$

is a diffeomorphism with respect to the obvious smooth structures on $\mathcal{R}(n)$ and $\widetilde{\mathcal{R}}(n)$.

Next we specialize Lemma 2.1.5 to the subset of Lagrangian subspaces. Noting that when A is a unitary matrix we have $\overline{A}^{-1} = A^t$, A^t the transpose of A. Therefore we have the following corollary of Lemma 2.1.5.

COROLLARY 2.1.6. *Denote by $\widetilde{\Lambda}(n) \subset \widetilde{\mathcal{R}}(n)$ the image of B restricted to $\Lambda(n) \subset \mathcal{R}(n)$, i.e.,*

(2.1.7) $$\widetilde{\Lambda}(n) := \{D \in U(n) \mid D = D^t\}$$

the set of symmetric unitary matrices. Then B restricts to a diffeomorphism on $\Lambda(n)$.

The following generalizes the above Maslov index to loops of totally real subspaces.

DEFINITION 2.1.8. (Generalized Maslov index) Let $\gamma : S^1 \to \mathcal{R}(n)$ be a loop. The *generalized Maslov index* $\mu(\gamma)$ is defined to be the winding number of

$$\det \circ B \circ \gamma : S^1 \to \mathbb{C} \setminus \{0\}.$$

Now we adopt the terminology of *bundle pairs* used by de Silva [**Sil97**] and Katz-Liu [**KatLi01**]. We will treat two cases separately, one the *complex* case and the other the *symplectic* case.

Let Σ be an oriented compact surface with boundary $\partial\Sigma$. We denote by g the genus of Σ and h be the number of connected components of $\partial\Sigma$.

We start with the case of complex vector bundles $\mathcal{V} \to \Sigma$. Note that if $\partial\Sigma \neq \emptyset$, then any complex vector bundle $\mathcal{V} \to \Sigma$ is topologically trivial.

DEFINITION 2.1.9. A *complex bundle pair* $(\mathcal{V}, \lambda)$ is a complex vector bundle $\mathcal{V} \to \Sigma$ with a (maximally) totally real bundle $\lambda \to \partial\Sigma$ and with an isomorphism

(2.1.10) $$\mathcal{V}|_{\partial\Sigma} \cong \lambda \otimes \mathbb{C}.$$

We fix a trivialization $\Phi : \mathcal{V} \to \Sigma \times \mathbb{C}^n$ and let $\partial_1\Sigma, \cdots, \partial_h\Sigma$ be the connected components of $\partial\Sigma$ with boundary orientation induced from Σ. Then due to the given isomorphism $\mathcal{V}|_{\partial\Sigma} \cong \lambda \otimes \mathbb{C}$, $\Phi(\lambda \otimes \mathbb{R}|_{\partial_i\Sigma})$ gives rise to a loop $\gamma^i_{\Phi,\lambda} : S^1 \to \mathcal{R}(n)$. Setting $\mu(\Phi, \partial_i\Sigma) = \mu(\gamma^i_{\Phi,\lambda})$, we have

PROPOSITION 2.1.11. *Let $(\mathcal{V}, \lambda)$ be a complex vector bundle pair over $(\Sigma, \partial\Sigma)$. Then the sum $\sum_{i=1}^h \mu(\Phi, \partial_i\Sigma)$ is independent of the choice of trivialization $\Phi : \mathcal{V} \to \Sigma \times \mathbb{C}^n$ depending only on the pair $(\mathcal{V}, \lambda)$.*

We refer to, for example, [**KatLi01**] for the details of the proof of this proposition or see the proof below for an analogous proof for the case of symplectic bundle pairs. Proposition 2.1.11 says that the following definition is well-defined.

DEFINITION 2.1.12. The Maslov index of the complex bundle pair $(\mathcal{V}, \lambda)$ is defined by

$$\mu(\mathcal{V}, \lambda) = \sum_{i=1}^{h} \mu(\Phi, \partial_i \Sigma)$$

where $\Phi : \mathcal{V} \to \Sigma \times \mathbb{C}^n$ is a (and so any) trivialization.

Next we consider the case of symplectic vector bundles $\mathcal{V} \to \Sigma$: each fiber $\mathcal{V}_x$ carries a symplectic inner product ω_x depending smoothly on $x \in \Sigma$.

We first note that the symplectic Lie group

$$Sp(2n) = \{A \in GL(2n, \mathbb{R}) \mid A^* \omega_0 = \omega_0\}$$

has the maximal compact subgroup consisting of the matrices

$$\widehat{U}(n) := \left\{ \begin{pmatrix} X & Y \\ -Y & X \end{pmatrix} \in GL(2n, \mathbb{R}) \;\middle|\; X + \sqrt{-1}\,Y \in U(n) \right\}.$$

In particular, we have the polar decomposition of $A = UP$ of $A \in Sp(2n)$ into $U \in \widehat{U}(n)$. We denote by $U = \widehat{A}$ and call it the *angular part* of A.

It follows from this observation that if $\partial \Sigma \neq \emptyset$ any symplectic vector bundle on Σ is *symplectically* trivial as in the case of complex vector bundle.

DEFINITION 2.1.13. A *symplectic bundle pair* is a pair $(\mathcal{V}, \lambda)$ where $\mathcal{V} \to \Sigma$ is a symplectic vector bundle and $\lambda \to \partial \Sigma$ is a Lagrangian subbundle of $\mathcal{V}|_{\partial \Sigma}$.

We fix a trivialization $\Psi : \mathcal{V} \to \Sigma \times (\mathbb{R}^{2n}, \omega_0)$. Similarly as in the complex case, the restriction $\Psi(\lambda|_{\partial_i \Sigma})$ gives rise to a loop $\gamma^i_{\Psi, \lambda} : S^1 \to \Lambda(n)$. We denote $\mu(\Psi, \partial_i \Sigma) = \mu(\gamma^i_{\Psi, \lambda})$. Then we have the following:

PROPOSITION 2.1.14. *Let $(\mathcal{V}, \lambda)$ be a symplectic bundle pair over $(\Sigma, \partial \Sigma)$. Then the sum $\sum_{i=1}^{h} \mu(\Psi, \partial_i \Sigma)$ is independent of the choice of symplectic trivialization $\Psi : \Sigma \to \Sigma \times \mathbb{C}^n$.*

PROOF. Let $\Psi_1, \Psi_2 : \mathcal{V} \to (\mathbb{R}^{2n}, \omega_0)$ be two trivializations. The map

$$\Psi_2 \circ \Psi_1^{-1} : (\mathbb{R}^{2n}, \omega_0) \to (\mathbb{R}^{2n}, \omega_0)$$

is given by the assignment $(x, v) \to (x, g(x)v)$ for a map $g : \Sigma \to Sp(2n, \mathbb{R})$. We write the natural action of $Sp(2n, \mathbb{R})$ on $\Lambda(n)$ by $g \cdot V$. Then we have the identity

$$g(x) \gamma^i_{\Psi_1, \lambda}(x) = \gamma^i_{\Psi_2, \lambda}(x) \quad \text{for } x \in \partial_i \Sigma.$$

This identity gives rise to

$$\mu(\Psi_2, \partial_i \Sigma) = \mu(\Psi_1, \partial_i \Sigma) + 2\,\mathrm{ind}(g|_{\partial_i \Sigma}).$$

Here $\mathrm{ind}(g|_{\partial_i \Sigma})$ is defined to be the degree of the loop

$$\det(\widehat{g}|_{\partial_i \Sigma}) : S^1 \to U(1)$$

where $\widehat{g}|_{\partial_i \Sigma}$ is the angular part of $g|_{\partial_i \Sigma}$. Since $\widehat{g}|_{\partial \Sigma} = \coprod_{i=1}^{h} \widehat{g}|_{\partial_i \Sigma}$ and g extends to Σ and so does $\widehat{g}$, we have $\sum_{i=1}^{h} \deg(\widehat{g}|_{\partial_i \Sigma}) = 0$ by the cobordism invariance of the degree map. This finishes the proof. $\square$

This proposition allows us to define the Maslov index $\mu(\mathcal{V}, \lambda)$ for the symplectic bundle pair $(\mathcal{V}, \lambda)$.

DEFINITION 2.1.15. The Maslov index of the symplectic bundle pair $(\mathcal{V}, \lambda)$ is defined by

$$\mu(\mathcal{V}, \lambda) = \sum_{i=1}^{h} \mu(\Psi, \partial_i \Sigma)$$

where $\Psi : \mathcal{V} \to \Sigma \times \mathbb{C}^n$ is a (and so any) trivialization.

Now when we are given a smooth map $f : (\Sigma, \partial \Sigma) \to (M, L)$ with $L \subset (M, \omega)$ being Lagrangian, we can associate a symplectic bundle pair $(f^*TM, f|_{\partial \Sigma}^* TL)$. We define the Maslov index, denoted by $\mu_L(f)$, of a smooth map $f : (\Sigma, \partial \Sigma) \to (M, L)$ by

$$\mu_L(f) = \mu(f^*TM, f|_{\partial \Sigma}^* TL).$$

We will just denote $\mu(f) = \mu_L(f)$ when there is no danger of confusion. It is easy to check that $\mu_L(f)$ is invariant under the homotopy of f.

2.1.2. The moduli space of bordered stable maps. We first recall that a *marked semi-stable curve* $(S, \vec{z})$ is a pair of (complex) one dimensional variety S and $\vec{z} = (z_1, \cdots, z_k), z_i \in S$ and $z_i \neq z_j$ for $i \neq j$ where S has at worst ordinary double points as singular points and all z_i's are away from double points. A marked semi-stable curve $(S, \vec{z})$ is stable if and only if the automorphism group of $(S, \vec{z})$ is finite (See [**KoMa94**] for example). We first review several basic facts on bordered Riemann surfaces (cf. [**Sep84,91, SeSi89**]).

DEFINITION 2.1.16. A *real marked semi-stable curve* is a system

$$(S, \tau, \vec{z}, \vec{z}^{\pm}) = (S, \tau, (z_1, \ldots, z_k), (\{z_1^+, z_1^-\}, \ldots, \{z_\ell^+, z_\ell^-\}))$$

where S is a semi-stable curve (without boundary) and $\tau : S \to S$ is an anti-holomorphic involution such that

$$\tau(z_i) = z_i \quad \text{for} \quad i = 1, \ldots, k$$
$$\tau(z_i^+) = z_i^- \quad \text{for} \quad i = 1, \ldots, \ell$$

and that $z_1, \ldots, z_k, z_1^+, \ldots, z_\ell^+, z_1^-, \cdots, z_\ell^-$ are all distinct and are nonsingular.

Note that $(S, \tau, \vec{z}, \vec{z}^{\pm})$ is unchanged when we interchange z_i^+ and z_i^- since the pairs $\{z_i^+, z_i^-\}$ are assumed to be *unordered*.

We define the genus of a real marked semi-stable curve $(S, \tau, \vec{z}, \vec{z}^{\pm})$ to be the genus of S. We denote by $\mathcal{M}_{g,k,\ell}^{\mathbb{R}}$ the set of all isomorphism classes of real marked stable curve of genus g and with (k, ℓ) marked points. For each $(S, \tau, \vec{z}, \vec{z}^{\pm}) \in \mathcal{M}_{g,k,\ell}^{\mathbb{R}}$, we consider the set of fixed points of τ,

$$S^\tau = \{z \in S \mid \tau z = z\}.$$

We note that if S^τ is non empty, it is a union of finitely many circles glued at finitely many points.

DEFINITION 2.1.17. A *marked semi-stable bordered Riemann surface of genus* $g = 0$ *and with* (k, ℓ) *marked points* is a real marked semi-stable curve of genus 0 and with (k, ℓ) marked points together with an orientation *ori* of S^τ, assuming that S^τ is non empty.

We call a marked bordered semi-stable Riemann surface $(S, \tau, \vec{z}, \vec{z}^{\pm}, ori)$, *stable* if the corresponding semi-stable curve $(S, \vec{z}, \vec{z}^{\pm})$ is stable.

In case $g \geq 1$ (which will not be needed in this paper though), we need two additional assumptions on *ori* which we will be included in the description below.

For each marked semi-stable bordered Riemann surface $(S, \tau, \vec{z}, \vec{z}^{\pm}, ori)$, we select a closed subset $\Sigma \subset S$ with $\partial \Sigma = S^{\tau}$ in the following way: Let $S_i \subset S$ be an irreducible component with $S_i \cap S^{\tau} \neq \emptyset$. The set $S_i \backslash S^{\tau}$ will have two connected components. We select one of the components, denoted by Σ_i, so that the induced orientation on $\partial \Sigma_i = S^{\tau} \cap S_i$ coincides with the given orientation, *ori*. In case when $S^{\tau} \cap S_i$ is connected (which is always the case when $g = 0$), the existence of Σ_i will be automatic. Otherwise, we *impose* the existence of Σ_i as a part of the definition of bordered Riemann surface.

We take Σ_0, a union of components of $S \backslash \bigcup_{i: S_i \cap S^{\tau} \neq \emptyset} \overline{\Sigma_i}$, so that the set $\Sigma_0 \cup \bigcup_{i: S_i \cap S^{\tau} \neq \emptyset} \Sigma_i$ is connected, $\Sigma_0 \cap \tau(\Sigma_0) = \emptyset$ and that the set

$$\left(\Sigma_0 \cup \bigcup_{i: S_i \cap S^{\tau} \neq \emptyset} \Sigma_i \right) \cup \left(\tau(\Sigma_0) \cup \bigcup_{i: S_i \cap S^{\tau} \neq \emptyset} \tau(\Sigma_i) \right)$$

is dense in S. In case $g = 0$, such Σ_0 always exists. Otherwise, Σ_0 may or may not exist and so we *impose* that Σ_0 exists as a part of the definition of semi-stable curves with boundary. If Σ_0 exists, then Σ_0 is always unique. We then put

$$\Sigma = \overline{\Sigma_0 \cup \bigcup_{i: S_i \cap S^{\tau} \neq \emptyset} \Sigma_i}.$$

See Figure 2.1.1.

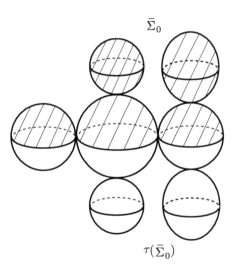

$$\overline{\Sigma}_0$$

$$\tau(\overline{\Sigma}_0)$$

Figure 2.1.1

Once we have selected Σ, we can and will choose the marked points z_i^+, z_i^- so that $z_i^+ \in \Sigma$.

From now on, we will denote the marked semi-stable bordered Riemann surface $(S, \tau, \vec{z}, \vec{z}^{\pm}, ori)$ by $(\Sigma, \vec{z}, \vec{z}^+)$.

We note that $(\Sigma, \vec{z}, \vec{z}^+)$ determines $(S, \tau, \vec{z}, \vec{z}^{\pm}, ori)$ in an obvious way.

DEFINITION 2.1.18. We denote by $\mathcal{M}_{g,k,\ell}$ the set of all isomorphism classes of marked stable bordered Riemann surface of genus g and with (k, ℓ) marked points.

We can provide a topology on $\mathcal{M}_{g,k,\ell}$ using the topology on the set $\mathcal{M}_{g,k+2\ell}$ of stable curves. (See [**FuOn99II**] Section 10 for details).

To give some intuition on the above topology defined on $\mathcal{M}_{g,k,\ell}$, let us consider the topology of the case $g = 0$, $k = 2$, $\ell = 1$. In this case, the topology on $\mathcal{M}_{0,2,1}$ is induced from the $\mathcal{M}_{0,4}$. We would like to describe the limit of a sequence $(\Sigma_j, \vec{z}_j, \{z_j^+\}) \in \mathcal{M}_{0,2,1}$ such that the sequence does not have a smooth limit and the interior marked points approach to the boundary. When this happens, the two marked points z_j^+ and z_j^- collide as $j \to \infty$ by definition of the double. Therefore the corresponding sequence of doubles $(S_j, \tau_j, \vec{z}_j, \{z_j^+, z_j^-\})$ as elements in $\mathcal{M}_{0,4}$ converges to a stable map that is the union of two irreducible components

$$(S_\infty^1, \tau_\infty^1, \vec{z}_\infty^2, \emptyset) \cup (S_\infty^2, \tau_\infty^2, \vec{z}_\infty^2, \{z_\infty^+, z_\infty^-\}).$$

Here $\#(\vec{z}_\infty^1) = 3$ and $\#(\vec{z}_\infty^2) = 1$ and S_∞^1 and S_∞^2 are glued at one element from $\vec{z}_\infty^1$ and the unique element in $\vec{z}_\infty^2 = \{z_\infty^2\}$. Therefore we conclude that the limit of $(\Sigma_j, \vec{z}_j, \{z_j^+\})$ is the half

$$(\Sigma_\infty^1, \vec{z}_\infty^1, \emptyset) \cup (\Sigma_\infty^2, \{z_\infty^2\}, \{z_\infty^+\})$$

where Σ_∞^1 and Σ_∞^2 are glued similarly. See Figures 2.1.2 and 2.1.3.

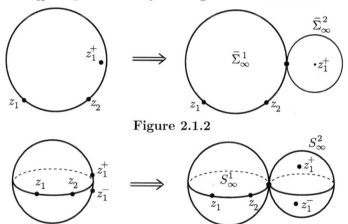

Figure 2.1.2

Figure 2.1.3

We also remark that in our compactification sphere bubble at the boundary is regarded as the (trivial) disc bubble plus sphere bubble at the interior of this bubbled disc. (See Figure 2.1.4.)

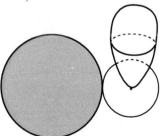

Figure 2.1.4

From now on, we will consider only the case of $g = 0$ with one boundary component, and so denote $\mathcal{M}_{k,\ell}$ in place of $\mathcal{M}_{0,k,\ell}$. In other words, Σ does not have holes or the boundary of the domain Σ is a connected union of a finite number of circles.

We also write $\mathcal{M}_k$ for $\mathcal{M}_{k,0}$. Namely $\mathcal{M}_k$ is the moduli space of genus zero bordered Riemann surface with k boundary marked points (and no interior marked point). Some discussion on $\mathcal{M}_k$ was given in [**FuOh97**]. Our discussion here basically follows it, although we need a slight modification.

LEMMA 2.1.19. $\mathcal{M}_{k,\ell}$ has exactly $(k-1)!$ connected components.

PROOF. Let $(\Sigma, \vec{z}, \vec{z}^+) = (S, \tau, \vec{z}, \vec{z}^{\pm}, ori) \in \mathcal{M}_{k,\ell}$. The orientation of $S^{\mathbb{R}} = S^{\tau}$ determines a cyclic order of $\{z_1, \ldots, z_k\}$. There are $(k-1)!$ ways to cyclically order a set of order k. It is not difficult to see that this choice of cyclic order determines a connected component of $\mathcal{M}_{k,\ell}$. □

Now, we study orientation of the moduli space $\mathcal{M}_{k,\ell}$. Let us denote by $\mathcal{M}_{k,\ell}^{\mathrm{reg}}$ the set of all elements $(S, \tau, \vec{z}, \vec{z}^{\pm}, ori)$ of $\mathcal{M}_{k,\ell}$ such that S is nonsingular. We remark that there exists an obvious fibration $\mathcal{M}_{k,\ell}^{\mathrm{reg}} \to \mathcal{M}_k^{\mathrm{reg}}$ whose fiber is a complex variety and so that it suffices to define an orientation of $\mathcal{M}_k$.

We denote the upper half plane by $\mathbb{H}$.

DEFINITION 2.1.20. Let $k \geq 3$. We consider the pair $(D^2, (z_1, \ldots, z_k))$ where $(z_1, \ldots, z_k)$, $z_i \in \partial D^2$ respects the cyclic order of $\partial D^2 = S^1$ with respect to the usual counter clockwise orientation on $\partial D^2 = S^1$. There is a component of $\mathcal{M}_k$ that contains this element. We call this the *main component* and denote it by $\mathcal{M}_k^{\mathrm{main}}$. We put $\mathcal{M}_k^{\mathrm{main,reg}} = \mathcal{M}_k^{\mathrm{main}} \cap \mathcal{M}_k^{\mathrm{reg}}$.

When $k \geq 3$, the main component $\mathcal{M}_k^{\mathrm{main,reg}}$ is diffeomorphic to $\mathbb{R}^{k-3}$. For readers' convenience, we recall the proof of this well-known fact. We define a map $\mathcal{M}_m^{b,\mathrm{main,reg}} \to \mathcal{M}_{k-1}^{\mathrm{main,reg}}$ by forgetting the last marked point z_k,

$$(D^2, (z_1, \ldots, z_k)) \to (D^2, (z_1, \ldots, z_{k-1})).$$

Identifying D^2 with the upper half plane $\mathbb{H} \cup \infty$, we have the identification

$$(\partial D^2, (z_1, \ldots, z_k)) \cong (\mathbb{R} \cup \infty, (x_1, \cdots, x_k)),$$

where $x_1 < \cdots < x_k$. Then it is easy to see that the above forgetful map defines a fiber bundle whose fiber is diffeomorphic to $\mathbb{R}$. Note that $\mathcal{M}_3^{\mathrm{main,reg}}$ consists of a single point. Therefore, we conclude $\mathcal{M}_k^{\mathrm{main,reg}} \cong \mathbb{R}^{k-3}$ by induction. (In Subsection 7.1.3 we will prove that $\mathcal{M}_{k,\ell}^{\mathrm{main}}$ is a smooth manifold (Theorem 7.1.44) for reader's convenience.) Using this diffeomorphism, we now define an orientation of $\mathcal{M}_k^{\mathrm{main,reg}}$: A fiber of $\mathcal{M}_k^{\mathrm{main,reg}} \to \mathcal{M}_{k-1}^{\mathrm{main,reg}}$ at $(D^2, (z_1, \ldots z_{k-1})) \in \mathcal{M}_{k-1}^{\mathrm{main,reg}}$ for $k \geq 4$ can be identified with an open subset of $S^1 \cong \mathbb{R} \cup \{\infty\}$ which is the interval between x_{k-1} and x_1. Hence each fiber is naturally oriented, which together with the orientation of $\mathcal{M}_{k-1}^{\mathrm{main}}$ induces that of $\mathcal{M}_k^{\mathrm{main}}$. Thus by induction, we obtain an orientation of the main component.

Now, let us look at other components of $\mathcal{M}_k$. Each permutation $\sigma : \{1, \ldots, k\} \to \{1, \ldots, k\}$ induces a homeomorphism $\sigma_* : \mathcal{M}_k \to \mathcal{M}_k$ defined by

$$\sigma_* : (S, \tau, (z_1, \ldots, z_k)) \mapsto (S, \tau, (z_{\sigma(1)}, \ldots, z_{\sigma(k)})).$$

Denote by $\sigma_0 : \{1, \ldots, k\} \to \{1, \ldots, k\}$ the shift $\sigma_0(i) = i + 1 \mod k$. This $(\sigma_0)_* : \mathcal{M}_k^{\mathrm{reg}} \to \mathcal{M}_k^{\mathrm{reg}}$ preserves each component of $\mathcal{M}_k^{\mathrm{reg}}$ and in particular the main component.

LEMMA 2.1.21. $(\sigma_0)_* : \mathcal{M}_k^{\mathrm{main,reg}} \to \mathcal{M}_k^{\mathrm{main,reg}}$ is orientation preserving if and only if k is odd.

PROOF. Let $\widehat{\mathcal{M}}_k^{\mathrm{main,reg}}$ be the set of all $(z_1, \ldots, z_k) \in (\mathbb{R}P^1)^k$ such that $[\mathbb{C}P^1, \mathbb{R}P^1, (z_1, \ldots, z_k)] \in \mathcal{M}_m^{\mathrm{main,reg}}$. Note that $\widehat{\mathcal{M}}_k^{\mathrm{main,reg}}/PSL(2, \mathbb{R}) \cong \mathcal{M}_k^{\mathrm{main,reg}}$. The map $(\sigma_0)_* : \mathcal{M}_k^{\mathrm{main,reg}} \to \mathcal{M}_k^{\mathrm{main,reg}}$ lifts to $\widehat{\mathcal{M}}_m^{b,\mathrm{main,reg}}$ as a $PSL(2, \mathbb{R})$-invariant map, which is nothing but the shift map on $(\mathbb{R}P^1)^k$. This shift map σ_0 has the parity $k - 1 \pmod{2}$. This finishes proof of Lemma 2.1.21. $\square$

PROPOSITION 2.1.22. There exists a unique orientation on $\mathcal{M}_k^{\mathrm{reg}}$ such that:

(2.1.23.1) It coincides with the orientation of $\mathcal{M}_k^{\mathrm{main,reg}}$ described as above.
(2.1.23.2) $\sigma_* : (S, \tau, (z_1, \ldots, z_k)) \mapsto (S, \tau, (z_{\sigma(1)}, \ldots, z_{\sigma(k)}))$ is orientation preserving if and only if σ is even.

PROOF. We note that $\sigma_*(\mathcal{M}_k^{\mathrm{main,reg}}) \cap \mathcal{M}_k^{\mathrm{main,reg}} \neq \emptyset$ if and only if $\sigma = \sigma_0^i$ for some i, and that σ_0 is even is and only if k is odd. Proposition 2.1.22 then follows from Lemma 2.1.21 by transferring the orientation on $\mathcal{M}_k^{\mathrm{main,reg}}$ to other components through appropriate σ_*. It is obvious that the corresponding orientation satisfies (2.1.23.1) and (2.1.23.2). $\square$

In Chapter 8, we will use Proposition 2.1.22 to provide an orientation of the moduli space of stable maps from genus 0 bordered Riemann surface, which we now define below. We like to mention that M.C. Liu has proved orientability of the moduli space $\mathcal{M}_{g,k,\ell}$ for the higher genus case Theorem 3.9 [**Liu02**].

Let (M, ω, J) be a symplectic manifold (M, ω) together with a compatible almost complex structure J and let $L \subset (M, \omega)$ be a Lagrangian submanifold.

DEFINITION 2.1.24. A genus 0 stable map from a bordered Riemann surface with (k, ℓ) marked points is a pair $((\Sigma, \vec{z}, \vec{z}^+), w)$ such that $(\Sigma, \vec{z}, \vec{z}^+)$ is a bordered genus 0 semi-stable curve with (k, ℓ) marked points, and $w : (\Sigma, \partial\Sigma) \to (M, L)$ is a pseudo-holomorphic map such that the set of all $\varphi : \Sigma \to \Sigma$ satisfying the following properties is finite:

(2.1.25.1) φ is biholomorphic.
(2.1.25.2) $\varphi(z_i) = z_i, \quad \varphi(z_i^+) = z_i^+.$
(2.1.25.3) $w \circ \varphi = \omega.$

Each genus 0 stable map from open curve $((\Sigma, \vec{z}, \vec{z}^+), w)$ determines a homology class $w_*([\Sigma]) \in H_2(M, L; \mathbb{Z})$ in an obvious way.

We say that $((\Sigma, \vec{z}, \vec{z}^+), w)$ is isomorphic to $((\Sigma', \vec{z}', \vec{z}'^+), w')$ if there exists a biholomorphic map $\varphi : \Sigma \to \Sigma'$ such that

(2.1.26.1) $w' = w \circ \varphi^{-1}$
(2.1.26.2) $\varphi(z_i) = z_i', \quad \varphi(z_i^+) = z_i'^+.$

DEFINITION 2.1.27.
(2.1.28.1) Let $\beta \in H_2(M, L; \mathbb{Z})$ and denote by $\mathcal{M}_{k,\ell}(\beta)$ the set of all isomorphism classes of genus 0 stable maps from bordered Riemann surface with (k, ℓ) marked

points, $((\Sigma, \vec{z}, \vec{z}^+), w)$ such that $w_*([\Sigma]) = \beta$. We put

$$\mathcal{M}_{k,\ell}^{\mathrm{sing}}(\beta) = \mathcal{M}_{k,\ell}(\beta) \setminus \mathcal{M}_{k,\ell}^{\mathrm{reg}}(\beta).$$

(2.1.28.2)   We denote

$$\mathcal{M}_{k,\ell}^{\mathrm{main}}(\beta) = \{((\Sigma, \vec{z}, \vec{z}^+), w) \mid (\Sigma, \vec{z}, \vec{z}^+) \in \mathcal{M}_{k,\ell}^{\mathrm{main}}, [w] = \beta\}.$$

We define a topology of the moduli space $\mathcal{M}_{k,\ell}(\beta)$ in a way similar to Section 10 [**FuOn99II**]. (See Subsection 7.1.4.) However there is a case which needs special attention: This is the case when $k = 0$ and $\beta \in H_2(M, L)$ is mapped to the zero element in $H_1(L)$ under the boundary map $H_2(M, L) \to H_1(L)$. In this case the standard stable map moduli space turns out *not* to be compact and requires a compactification including some map that has continuous family of automorphisms. We refer to Section 3.8 in Chapter 3 and Subsection 7.4.1 in Chapter 7 for the relevant discussions on this phenomenon.

Knowing this, we state the following basic result. (See Section A1, for the definition of Kuranishi structure.)

THEOREM 2.1.29. *We assume $k \neq 0$. Then, the moduli space $\mathcal{M}_{k,\ell}^{\mathrm{main}}(\beta)$ of stable maps is compact and Hausdorff, and has a Kuranishi structure. Moreover the family of Kuranishi structures over different choices of $(k, \ell; \beta)$ are compatible to one another.*

Theorem 2.1.29 is Propositions 7.1.1 and 7.1.2 (in case $\ell = 0$) and is proved in Subsection 7.1.5 (including the case $\ell \neq 0$).

We next state the following Theorem 2.1.30 whose proof will be given in Chapter 8. Let $L \subset M$ be a relatively spin Lagrangian submanifold: in other words, we assume that there exists a class $st \in H^2(M; \mathbb{Z}_2)$ which restricts to the second Stiefel-Whitney class of L. We will prove in Section 8.1 in Chapter 8 that $\mathcal{M}_{k,\ell}(\beta)$ is orientable under this condition.

In fact we will prove the following stronger theorem there. We refer to Section 8.1 for the definition of *relative spin structure* of the embedding $L \subset M$.

THEOREM 2.1.30. *Let L be relatively spin. Then a choice of relative spin structure of $L \subset M$ canonically induces an orientation of $\mathcal{M}_{k,\ell}^{\mathrm{main}}(\beta)$.*

We next consider the evaluation maps.

DEFINITION 2.1.31. We define $ev : \mathcal{M}_{k,\ell}^{\mathrm{main}}(\beta) \to L^k \times M^\ell$ by

$$ev((\Sigma, \vec{z}, \vec{z}^+), w) = (w(z_1), \ldots, w(z_k), w(z_1^+), \ldots, w(z_\ell^+)).$$

We would like to regard $\mathcal{M}_{k,\ell}^{\mathrm{main}}(\beta)$ as a smooth singular chain on $L^k \times M^\ell$. However in general the space $\mathcal{M}_{k,\ell}^{\mathrm{main}}(\beta)$ is not a smooth manifold (with boundary or corner), and is not of correct dimension. In this regard, the following is an essential transversality result that will be needed for the construction of our obstruction class. We will make the notion 'virtual fundamental chain' in this statement precise in the later chapters. (See Propositions 3.5.2, 7.2.35, Definition A1.28.)

THEOREM 2.1.32. *There is a family of multisections* $\mathfrak{s} = \{\mathfrak{s}(k, \ell; \beta)\}$ *of the obstruction bundle of the Kuranishi structure given in Theorem 2.1.29 for which the perturbed moduli space* $\mathcal{M}_{k,\ell}^{\mathrm{main}}(\beta)^{\mathfrak{s}(k,\ell;\beta)}$ *of the moduli space* $\mathcal{M}_{k,\ell}^{\mathrm{main}}(\beta)$ *have a (virtual) fundamental chain (of* $\mathbb{Q}$ *coefficient) of dimension* $n + \mu_L(\beta) + k + 2\ell - 3$ *where* $\mu_L(\beta)$ *is the Maslov index of* $\beta \in H_2(M, L)$. *Furthermore the perturbations are compatible to one another under the gluing map.*

Next we describe the boundary of the chain $\mathcal{M}_{k,\ell}^{\mathrm{main}}(\beta)^{\mathfrak{s}(k,\ell;\beta)}$.

THEOREM 2.1.33. *Let* $\mathfrak{s}$ *be as in Theorem 2.1.32. Then the boundary of the chain* $\mathcal{M}_{k,\ell}^{\mathrm{main}}(\beta)^{\mathfrak{s}(k,\ell;\beta)}$ *is the virtual fundamental chain of the space of all equivalent classes of elements* $((\Sigma, \vec{z}, \vec{z}^{+}), w) \in \mathcal{M}_{k,\ell}^{\mathrm{main}}(\beta)^{\mathfrak{s}(k,\ell;\beta)})$ *with* Σ *having exactly one singular point.*

The chain $(\mathcal{M}_{k,\ell}^{\mathrm{main}}(\beta)^{\mathfrak{s}(k,\ell;\beta)}, ev)$ will be used for identifying the obstruction cycles for the definition of Floer cohomology later in this book.

2.2. The Novikov covering and the action functional

Let (L_0, L_1) be a pair of connected compact Lagrangian submanifolds of (M, ω) which are transversal. We like to note that we do *not* assume our Lagrangian submanifolds are connected at the moment.

We consider the space of paths

$$\Omega = \Omega(L_0, L_1) = \{\ell : [0,1] \to M \mid \ell(0) \in L_0, \ell(1) \in L_1\}.$$

On this space, we are given the *action one-form* α defined by

$$(2.2.1) \qquad \alpha(\ell)(\xi) = \int_0^1 \omega(\dot{\ell}(t), \xi(t)) \, dt$$

for each $\xi \in T_\ell \Omega$. Using the Lagrangian property of (L_0, L_1), a straightforward calculation shows that this form is *closed*. (See Proposition 2.2.8.) The Floer homology theory is a semi-infinite version of Novikov Morse theory of closed one-forms.

Note that $\Omega(L_0, L_1)$ is not connected but has countably many connected components. When we work on a particular fixed connected component of $\Omega(L_0, L_1)$, we specify the particular component by choosing a *base path* which we denote by ℓ_0. We denote the corresponding component by $\Omega(L_0, L_1; \ell_0) \subset \Omega(L_0, L_1)$. The base path ℓ_0 automatically picks out a connected component from each of L_0 and L_1 as its initial and final points $x_0 = \ell_0(0) \in L_0$, $x_1 = \ell_0(1) \in L_1$. Then $\Omega(L_0, L_1; \ell_0)$ is a subspace of the space of paths between the corresponding connected components of L_0 and L_1 respectively. Because of this *we will always assume that* L_0, L_1 *are connected from now on*, unless otherwise said.

Next we describe some covering space which we call *the Novikov covering* of the component $\Omega(L_0, L_1; \ell_0)$ of $\Omega(L_0, L_1)$. We first start with describing the universal covering space of $\Omega(L_0, L_1; \ell_0)$. Consider the set of all pairs (ℓ, w) such that $\ell \in \Omega(L_0, L_1)$ and $w : [0,1]^2 \to M$ satisfies the boundary condition

$$(2.2.2) \qquad \begin{cases} w(0, \cdot) = \ell_0, & w(1, \cdot) = \ell \\ w(s, 0) \in L_0, & w(s, 1) \in L_1 \quad \text{for all } s \in [0,1]. \end{cases}$$

Considering w as a continuous path $s \mapsto w(s, \cdot)$ in $\Omega(L_0, L_1; \ell_0)$ from ℓ_0 and ℓ, the fiber at ℓ of the universal covering space of $\Omega(L_0, L_1; \ell_0)$ can be represented by the set of path homotopy classes of w relative to the its end $s = 0, 1$.

2.2.1. The Γ-equivalence. To carry out the idea of Novikov's Morse theory [**Nov81**], it is crucial to have some abelian covering of $\Omega(L_0, L_1; \ell_0)$. In this regard, the universal covering space is too large. We will now define a smaller covering space of $\Omega(L_0, L_1; \ell_0)$ by modding out the space of paths in $\Omega(L_0, L_1; \ell_0)$ by another equivalence relation that is weaker than the homotopy. This is the analog to the Novikov covering space of the contractible loop space introduced by Hofer-Salamon [**HoSa95**] and the 4-th named author [**Ono95**]. The deck transformation group of this covering space will be shown to be *abelian* by construction.

Note that when we are given two pairs (ℓ, w) and (ℓ, w') from $\Omega(L_0, L_1; \ell_0)$, the concatenation

$$\overline{w} \# w' : [0, 1] \times [0, 1] \to M$$

defines a loop $c : S^1 \to \Omega(L_0, L_1; \ell_0)$. One may regard this loop as a map $C : S^1 \times [0, 1] \to M$ satisfying the boundary condition $C(s, 0) \in L_0$, $C(s, 1) \in L_1$. Obviously the symplectic area of C, denoted by

$$(2.2.3) \qquad\qquad I_\omega(c) = \int_C \omega$$

depends only on the homotopy class of C satisfying (2.2.2) and so defines a homomorphism on $\pi_1(\Omega(L_0, L_1; \ell_0))$, which we also denote by

$$I_\omega : \pi_1(\Omega(L_0, L_1; \ell_0)) \to \mathbb{R}.$$

Next we note that for the map $C : S^1 \times [0, 1] \to M$ satisfying (2.2.2), it associates a symplectic bundle pair $(\mathcal{V}, \lambda)$ defined by

$$\mathcal{V}_C = C^* TM, \quad \lambda_C = c_0^* TL_0 \sqcup c_1^* TL_1$$

where $c_i : S^1 \to L_i$ is the map given by $c_i(s) = C(s, i)$ for $i = 0, 1$. This allows us to define another homomorphism

$$I_\mu : \pi_1(\Omega(L_0, L_1), \ell_0) \to \mathbb{Z}; \quad I_\mu(c) = \mu(\mathcal{V}_C, \lambda_C)$$

where $\mu(\mathcal{V}_C, \lambda_C)$ is the Maslov index of the bundle pair $(\mathcal{V}_C, \lambda_C)$.

Using the homomorphisms I_μ and I_ω, we define an equivalence relation $\sim$ on the set of all pairs (ℓ, w) satisfying (2.2.2). For given such pair w, w', we denote by $\overline{w} \# w'$ the concatenation of $\overline{w}$ and w' along ℓ, which defines a loop in $\Omega(L_0, L_1; \ell_0)$ based at ℓ_0. We introduce the notion of Γ-*equivalence* borrowing the terminology Seidel used in [**Sei97**] in the context of Floer homology of Hamiltonian diffeomorphisms.

DEFINITION 2.2.4. We say that (ℓ, w) is Γ-equivalent to (ℓ, w') and write $(\ell, w) \sim (\ell, w')$ if the following conditions are satisfied $I_\omega(\overline{w} \# w') = 0 = I_\mu(\overline{w} \# w')$. We denote the set of equivalence classes $[\ell, w]$ by $\widetilde{\Omega}(L_0, L_1; \ell_0)$ and call the *Novikov covering space*.

There is a canonical lifting of $\ell_0 \in \Omega(L_0, L_1; \ell_0)$ to $\widetilde{\Omega}(L_0, L_1; \ell_0)$: this is just $[\ell_0, \widetilde{\ell}_0] \in \widetilde{\Omega}(L_0, L_1; \ell_0)$ where $\widetilde{\ell}_0$ is the map $\widetilde{\ell}_0 : [0, 1]^2 \to M$ with $\widetilde{\ell}_0(s, t) = \ell_0(t)$. In this way, $\widetilde{\Omega}(L_0, L_1; \ell_0)$ also has a natural base point which we suppress from the notation.

We denote by $\Pi(L_0, L_1; \ell_0)$ the group of deck transformations of the covering space $\widetilde{\Omega}(L_0, L_1; \ell_0) \to \Omega(L_0, L_1; \ell_0)$. It is easy to see that the isomorphism class of $\Pi(L_0, L_1; \ell_0)$ depends only on the connected component containing ℓ_0.

The two homomorphisms I_ω and I_μ push down to homomorphisms

$$E : \Pi(L_0, L_1; \ell_0) \to \mathbb{R}, \qquad \mu : \Pi(L_0, L_1; \ell_0) \to \mathbb{Z}$$

defined by

$$E(g) = I_\omega[C], \quad \mu(g) = I_\mu[C]$$

for any map $C : S^1 \times [0, 1] \to M$ representing the class $g \in \Pi(L_0, L_1; \ell_0)$.

COROLLARY 2.2.5. *The group $\Pi(L_0, L_1; \ell_0)$ is an abelian group.*

PROOF. By definition of $\Pi(L_0, L_1; \ell_0)$, the map $E \times \mu : \Pi(L_0, L_1; \ell_0) \to \mathbb{R} \times \mathbb{Z}$ is an injective group homomorphism. Therefore we conclude that $\Pi(L_0, L_1; \ell_0)$ is abelian since $\mathbb{R} \times \mathbb{Z}$ is abelian. □

We now define the Novikov ring $\Lambda(L_0, L_1; \ell_0)$ associated the abelian covering $\widetilde{\Omega}(L_0, L_1; \ell_0) \to \Omega(L_0, L_1; \ell_0)$ as a completion of the group ring $R[\Pi(L_0, L_1; \ell_0)]$. Here R is a commutative ring with unit.

DEFINITION 2.2.6. $\Lambda_k^R(L_0, L_1; \ell_0)$ denotes the set of all (infinite) sums

$$\sum_{\substack{g \in \Pi(L_0, L_1; \ell_0) \\ \mu(g) = k}} a_g[g]$$

such that $a_g \in R$ and that the following holds:

(2.2.7)   For each C, the set $\{g \in \Pi(L_0, L_1; \ell_0) \mid E(g) \leq C, \ a_g \neq 0\}$ is of finite order.

We put

$$\Lambda^R(L_0, L_1; \ell_0) = \bigoplus_k \Lambda_k^R(L_0, L_1; \ell_0).$$

We mainly use $R = \mathbb{Q}$. In case $R = \mathbb{Q}$ we write $\Lambda(L_0, L_1; \ell_0)$ in place of $\Lambda^{\mathbb{Q}}(L_0, L_1; \ell_0)$.

The ring structure on $\Lambda^R(L_0, L_1; \ell_0)$ is defined by the convolution product

$$\left(\sum_{g \in \Pi(L_0, L_1; \ell_0)} a_g[g] \right) \cdot \left(\sum_{g \in \Pi(L_0, L_1; \ell_0)} b_g[g] \right) = \sum_{g_1, g_2 \in \Pi(L_0, L_1; \ell_0)} a_{g_1} b_{g_2} [g_1 g_2].$$

It is easy to see that the term in the right hand side is indeed an element in $\Lambda^R(L_0, L_1; \ell_0)$, i.e., satisfies the finiteness condition (2.2.7) in its definition. Thus $\Lambda^R(L_0, L_1; \ell_0) = \oplus_k \Lambda_k^R(L_0, L_1; \ell_0)$ becomes a graded ring under this multiplication. We call this graded ring the *Novikov ring* associated to the pair (L_0, L_1) and the connected component containing ℓ_0.

2.2.2. The action functional and the Maslov-Morse index. Now for a given pair (ℓ, w), we define the *action functional*

$$\mathcal{A} : \widetilde{\Omega}(L_0, L_1; \ell_0) \to \mathbb{R}$$

by the formula

$$\mathcal{A}(\ell, w) = \int w^*\omega.$$

It follows from the definition of $\Pi(L_0, L_1; \ell_0)$ that the integral depends only on the Γ-equivalence class $[\ell, w]$ and so pushes down to a well-defined functional on the covering space $\widetilde{\Omega}(L_0, L_1; \ell_0)$. A straightforward calculation shows the following whose proof we omit.

PROPOSITION 2.2.8. *Let* $\pi : \widetilde{\Omega}(L_0, L_1; \ell_0) \to \Omega(L_0, L_1; \ell_0)$ *be the* Γ-*covering space and* α *be the action one-form on* $\Omega(L_0, L_1; \ell_0)$. *Then we have*

$$d\mathcal{A} = -\pi^*\alpha.$$

An immediate corollary of this proposition and the definition of α is the following characterization of the critical point set of $\mathcal{A}$.

COROLLARY 2.2.9. *The set* $Cr(L_0, L_1; \ell_0)$ *of critical points of* $\mathcal{A}$ *consists of the pairs of the type* $[\ell_p, w]$ *where* ℓ_p *is the constant path with* $p \in L_0 \cap L_1$ *and* w *is as in (2.2.2).* $Cr(L_0, L_1; \ell_0)$ *is invariant under the action of* $\Pi(L_0, L_1; \ell_0)$ *and so forms a principal bundle over a subset of* $L_0 \cap L_1$ *with its fiber isomorphic to* $\Pi(L_0, L_1; \ell_0)$.

We put

$$Cr(L_0, L_1) = \bigcup_{\ell_{0,i}} Cr(L_0, L_1; \ell_{0,i})$$

where $\ell_{0,i}$ runs over the set of base points of connected components of $\Omega(L_0.L_1)$.

Next, we assign an *absolute* Morse index to each critical point of $\mathcal{A}$. In general, assigning such an absolute index is not a trivial matter because the obvious Morse index of $\mathcal{A}$ at any critical point is infinite. For this purpose, we will use the Maslov index of certain bundle pair naturally associated to the critical point $[\ell_p, w] \in Cr(L_0, L_1; \ell_0)$.

We call this Morse index of $[\ell_p, w]$ the *Maslov-Morse index* (relative to the base path ℓ_0) of the critical point. The definition of $\mu([\ell_p, w])$ will somewhat resemble that of $\mathcal{A}$. However to define this, we also need to fix a section λ^0 of $\ell_0^*\Lambda(M)$ such that

$$\lambda^0(0) = T_{\ell_0(0)}L_0, \quad \lambda^0(1) = T_{\ell_0(1)}L_1.$$

Here $\Lambda(M)$ is the bundle of Lagrangian Grassmanians of TM

$$\Lambda(M) = \bigcup_{p \in M} \Lambda(T_pM)$$

where $\Lambda(T_pM)$ is the set of Lagrangian subspaces of the symplectic vector space (T_pM, ω_p). Let

$$\Lambda^{ori}(M) = \bigcup_{p \in M} \Lambda^{ori}(T_pM)$$

be the oriented Lagrangian Grassmanian bundle which is a double cover of $\Lambda(M)$. In case when L_0 and L_1 are oriented, we assume that λ^0 is a section of $\Lambda^{ori}(M)$ and respects the orientations at the end points.

Let $[\ell_p, w] \in Cr(L_0, L_1; \ell_0) \subset \widetilde{\Omega}(L_0, L_1; \ell_0)$ be an element whose projection corresponds to the intersection point $p \in L_0 \cap L_1$.

Using Proposition 2.1.3, we will associate a symplectic bundle pair $(\mathcal{V}_w, \lambda_w)$ over the square $[0,1]^2$, which will be defined uniquely upto the homotopy. We first choose $\mathcal{V}_w = w^*TM$. To define λ_w, let us choose a path $\alpha^p : [0,1] \to \Lambda(T_pM, \omega_p)$ satisfying

(2.2.10)
$$\begin{cases} \alpha^p(0) = T_pL_0, \ \alpha^p(1) = T_pL_1 \subset T_pM, \\ (\alpha^p)(t) \pitchfork T_pL_0, \\ \alpha^p(t) \in U_0(T_pL_0) \quad \text{for small } t, \end{cases}$$

where $U_0(T_pL_0)$ is as in (2.1.2). Proposition 2.1.3 implies that any two such choices of α^p are homotopic to each other.

Then we consider a continuous Lagrangian subbundle $\lambda_w \to \partial[0,1]^2$ of $\mathcal{V}|_{\partial[0,1]^2}$ by the following formula: the fiber at each point of $\partial[0,1]^2$ is given as

(2.2.11)
$$\begin{cases} \lambda_w(s,0) = T_{w(s,0)}L_0, \quad \lambda_w(1,t) = \alpha^p(t), \\ \lambda_w(s,1) = T_{w(s,1)}L_1, \quad \lambda_w(0,t) = \lambda^0(0,t). \end{cases}$$

It follows from Proposition 2.1.3 that the homotopy type of the bundle pair constructed as above does not depend on the choice of α^p either

DEFINITION 2.2.12. We define the *Maslov-Morse index* of $[\ell_p, w]$ (relative to λ^0) by
$$\mu([\ell_p, w]; \lambda^0) = \mu(\mathcal{V}_w, \lambda_w).$$

We will just denote $\mu([\ell_p, w])$ for $\mu([\ell_p, w]; \lambda^0)$ as we are not going to vary the reference section λ^0. We will make a comment in Remark 2.4.45 on the dependence on the choice of λ^0 of the grading of the Floer chain module.

2.3. Review of Floer cohomology I: without anomaly

In this section, we will study the set of *bounded gradient trajectories* $u : \mathbb{R} \to \Omega(L_0, L_1; \ell_0)$ of the action functional $\mathcal{A} : \Omega(L_0, L_1; \ell_0) \to \mathbb{R}$ for each given transversal pair (L_0, L_1). Due to noncompactness of the domain $\mathbb{R} \times [0,1]$, one needs to put a certain decay condition of the derivatives of u to study the compactness property and the deformation theory of solutions u. This will be achieved by imposing certain *boundedness* of the trajectories. The boundedness of the trajectories is measured by the symplectic area of u.

2.3.1. The L^2-gradient equation of $\mathcal{A}$. Recall the identity
$$d\mathcal{A} = -\pi^*\alpha.$$

If we identify the tangent space $T_{[\ell,w]}\widetilde{\Omega}(L_0, L_1; \ell_0)$ with $T_\ell\Omega(L_0, L_1)$ via the covering projection, we can write this identity as

(2.3.1)
$$d\mathcal{A}([\ell, w])(\xi) = \int_0^1 \omega(\xi(t), \dot\ell(t)) \, dt$$

on the Novikov-covering space $\widetilde{\Omega}(L_0, L_1; \ell_0)$. As in the finite dimensional Morse theory, we will study the gradient flow of $\mathcal{A}$ in terms of a given "Riemannian metric" on $\widetilde{\Omega}(L_0, L_1; \ell_0)$.

For each given pair (L_0, L_1) and a pair J_0, J_1 of compatible almost complex structures on (M, ω), we consider a path of compatible almost complex structures $\{J_t\}_{0 \leq t \leq 1}$ on (M, ω) joining them. We denote

$$\mathcal{J}_\omega = \mathcal{J}_\omega(M) = \text{the space of compatible almost complex structures.}$$
$$\mathcal{P}(\mathcal{J}_\omega) = C^\infty([0,1], \mathcal{J}_\omega)$$
$$= \text{the space of parameterized compatible almost complex structures.}$$

We denote by $\{J_t\}_t$ an element of $\mathcal{P}(\mathcal{J}_\omega)$. We put

$$(2.3.2) \qquad \mathcal{P}(\mathcal{J}_\omega; J_0, J_1) = \{\{J_t\}_t \in \mathcal{P}(\mathcal{J}_\omega) \mid J_0 = J_0, \ J_1 = J_1\}.$$

Then for each given $\{J_t\}_t$, we define an L^2 metric on Ω by the formula

$$\langle \xi_1, \xi_2 \rangle_{\{J_t\}_t} := \int_0^1 \omega(\xi_1(t), J_t \xi_2(t)) \, dt,$$

using the one parameter family of Riemannian metrics on M

$$g_t := \omega(\cdot, J_t \cdot).$$

It follows from (2.3.1) that the L^2-gradient equation of the action functional $\mathcal{A}$ becomes

$$(2.3.3) \qquad \begin{cases} \dfrac{du}{d\tau} + J_t \dfrac{du}{dt} = 0 \\ u(\tau, 0) \in L_0, \quad u(\tau, 1) \in L_1, \end{cases}$$

for a map $u : \mathbb{R} \times [0,1] \to M$ if one considers u as the path $\tau \to u(\tau)$ in $\Omega_0(L_0, L_1)$ where $u(\tau)$ is the path defined by $u(\tau)(t) = u(\tau, t)$.

In the point of view of analysis, controlling the geometric energy of u defined by

$$E(u; \{J_t\}_t) := \frac{1}{2} \int \left(\left| \frac{\partial u}{\partial \tau} \right|^2_{J_t} + \left| \frac{\partial u}{\partial t} \right|^2_{J_t} \right) dt \, d\tau$$

is essential for the deformation theory of solutions of (2.3.3). On the other hand, we have the following identity

$$(2.3.4) \qquad E(u; \{J_t\}_t) = \int u^* \omega$$

for maps u satisfying

$$\frac{\partial u}{\partial \tau} + J_t \frac{\partial u}{\partial t} = 0,$$

as long as $\{J_t\}_t$ is a family of compatible almost complex structures. In the physics language, they would say that (2.3.4) holds *on shell*. We note that the symplectic area $\int u^* \omega$ is invariant under the homotopy.

Now let L_0, L_1 be Lagrangian submanifolds of (M, ω) which are transverse. For each given $J \in \mathcal{J}_\omega$, we study the Cauchy-Riemann equation (2.3.3) and define the space of bounded solutions thereof by

$$(2.3.5) \quad \widetilde{\mathcal{M}}^{\mathrm{reg}}(L_1, L_0; \{J_t\}_t) = \left\{ u \ \middle| \ u \text{ satisfies (2.3.3) and} \int_{\mathbb{R} \times [0,1]} u^* \omega < \infty \right\}.$$

Here 'reg' in the notation stands for 'regular'. We put it since this moduli space consists of pseudo-holomorphic maps from $\mathbb{R} \times [0,1]$.

We will suppress $\{J_t\}_t$ from various notations sometimes. We also remark that we put L_1 *first instead of L_0* in the notation of the moduli space, which is purely of matter of our choice.

The following proposition provides an automatic exponential convergence result as $\tau \to \pm\infty$ for an element $u \in \widetilde{\mathcal{M}}^{\mathrm{reg}}(L_1, L_0)$, *provided L_0 is transverse to L_1.* We refer to [**Flo88IV**] for its proof.

PROPOSITION 2.3.6. *Let L_0, L_1 be compact Lagrangian submanifolds intersecting transversely. Then for any solution u of (2.3.3) with finite symplectic area, we have the limit*

$$\lim_{\tau \to \infty} u(-\tau, \cdot) = \ell_p, \quad \lim_{\tau \to \infty} u(\tau, \cdot) = \ell_q$$

where ℓ_p, ℓ_q are constant paths corresponding to some unique p, $q \in L_0 \cap L_1$ respectively.

This proposition provides a decomposition of $\widetilde{\mathcal{M}}^{\mathrm{reg}}(L_1, L_0)$ into

$$\widetilde{\mathcal{M}}^{\mathrm{reg}}(L_1, L_0) = \bigcup_{p, q \in L_0 \cap L_1} \widetilde{\mathcal{M}}^{\mathrm{reg}}(p, q)$$

where we define

$$\widetilde{\mathcal{M}}^{\mathrm{reg}}(p, q) = \left\{ u \in \mathcal{M}^{\mathrm{reg}}(L_1, L_0) \;\middle|\; \lim_{\tau \to \infty} u(-\tau, \cdot) = \ell_p, \lim_{\tau \to \infty} u(\tau, \cdot) = \ell_q \right\}$$

for each given pair p, $q \in L_0 \cap L_1$. This $\widetilde{\mathcal{M}}^{\mathrm{reg}}(p, q)$ plays a role of the space of *connecting orbits*, i.e, the trajectories connecting two critical points of a smooth function in the finite dimensional Morse theory.

Because the family $\{J_t\}_t$ does not depend on τ, there is a natural $\mathbb{R}$ action of τ translations on the domain of the map $u : \mathbb{R} \times [0, 1] \to M$ preserves $\widetilde{\mathcal{M}}^{\mathrm{reg}}(p, q)$ and so induces an action on it. We denote the quotient of this action by

$$\mathcal{M}^{\mathrm{reg}}(p, q) = \widetilde{\mathcal{M}}^{\mathrm{reg}}(p, q)/\mathbb{R},$$

for each given pair p, $q \in L_0 \cap L_1$. In fact, the space $\mathcal{M}^{\mathrm{reg}}(p, q)$ has a further decomposition according to the homotopy class of the elements. It is important to study this decomposition to properly encode the bubbling phenomena.

DEFINITION 2.3.7. Let p, $q \in L_0 \cap L_1$. We denote by $\pi_2(p, q) = \pi_2(p, q; L_0, L_1)$ the set of homotopy classes of smooth maps $u : [0, 1] \times [0, 1] \to M$ relative to the boundary

$$u(0, t) \equiv p, \quad u(1, t) = q; \quad u(s, 0) \in L_0, \quad u(s, 1) \in L_1.$$

We denote by $[u] \in \pi_2(p, q)$ its homotopy class and by B a general element in $\pi_2(p, q)$.

We also denote by $\pi_2(p)$ the set of homotopy classes of the pair (ℓ_p, w) i.e., of the map $w : [0, 1]^2 \to M$ relative to its end $w(0, \cdot) = \ell_0$, $w(1, \cdot) = \ell_p$, where $w(s, \cdot) \in \Omega(L_0, L_1)$ for all $s \in [0, 1]$.

For given $B \in \pi_2(p, q)$, we denote by $Map(p, q; B)$ the set of such w's in class B. Each element $B \in \pi_2(p, q)$ induces a map $(\cdot)\#B : \pi_2(p) \to \pi_2(q)$ given by the obvious gluing map $w \mapsto w\#u$ for a map $u \in Map(p, q; B)$. More specifically we define the map $w\#u : [0, 1]^2 \to M$ by the formula

$$(w\#u)(s, t) = \begin{cases} w(2s, t) & \text{for } 0 \le s \le \frac{1}{2} \\ u(2s - 1, t) & \text{for } \frac{1}{2} \le s \le 1 \end{cases}$$

once and for all. There is also the natural gluing map $\pi_2(p, q) \times \pi_2(q, r) \to \pi_2(p, r)$ induced by the concatenation $(u_1, u_2) \mapsto u_1\#u_2$. We also explicitly represent the map $u_1\#u_2 : [0, 1]^2 \to M$ in the same way as above.

By the Lagrangian property of L_0 and L_1, the following lemma is standard.

LEMMA 2.3.8. *Let $p, q \in L_0 \cap L_1$ be given. Then the symplectic area of $u \in Map(p, q; B)$ is constant. We denote by $\omega(B)$ the common area of the elements from $Map(p, q; B)$.*

There is also a well-defined notion of *relative index*, the Maslov-Viterbo index, $\mu(p, q; B)$ associated to the triple $(p, q; B)$. We refer to its definition to [**Vit87, Flo88I**]. The following explains the relation between the absolute index $\mu([\ell_p, w])$ and the relative index $\mu(p, q; B)$.

DEFINITION & PROPOSITION 2.3.9. (Maslov-Viterbo index) Let u be an element of $Map(p, q; B)$. The difference $\mu([\ell_p, w]) - \mu([\ell_q, w\#B])$ depends only on (p, q) and the homotopy class B without depending on the choice of w. In fact, we have $\mu([\ell_q, w\#B]) - \mu([\ell_p, w]) = \mu(p, q; B)$.

Definition & Proposition 2.3.9 follows from Proposition 3.7.59 (3.7.60.1) in Chapter 3. The Maslov-Viterbo index governs the dimension of the Floer moduli space in the transversal case.

DEFINITION 2.3.10. We denote by

$$\begin{aligned} \widetilde{\mathcal{M}}^{\text{reg}}(p, q; B) &= \widetilde{\mathcal{M}}^{\text{reg}}(p, q; B; \{J_t\}_t) \\ &= \widetilde{\mathcal{M}}^{\text{reg}}(L_1, L_0, p, q; B) = \widetilde{\mathcal{M}}^{\text{reg}}(L_1, L_0, p, q; B; \{J_t\}_t) \end{aligned}$$

the set finite energy solutions of the Cauchy-Riemann equation (2.3.3) with the asymptotic condition and the homotopy condition

$$u(-\infty, \cdot) \equiv \ell_p, \quad u(\infty, \cdot) \equiv \ell_q, \quad [u] = B.$$

Here we remark that although u is a priori defined on $\mathbb{R} \times [0, 1]$, it can be compactified into a continuous map $\overline{u} : [0, 1] \times [0, 1] \to M$ with the corresponding boundary condition due to the exponential decay property of solutions u of the Cauchy-Riemann equation when L_0 and L_1 intersects transversely: for example, we can define $\overline{u}$ to be the composition $\overline{u}(s, t) = u(h^{-1}(s), t)$ where $h : \mathbb{R} \times [0, 1] \to (0, 1) \times [0, 1]$ is the function defined by

$$h(\tau) = \frac{1}{2} \left(\frac{\tau}{\sqrt{1 + \tau^2}} + 1 \right).$$

It follows from the exponential decay property of u that $\overline{u}$ continuously extends to $[0, 1] \times [0, 1]$. We will call $\overline{u}$ the *compactified map* of u. By an abuse of notation, we also denote by $[u]$ the class $[\overline{u}] \in \pi_2(p, q)$ of the compactified map $\overline{u}$.

The following basic transversality result and the dimension result were proven by Floer [**Flo88I,88II**]. Also see [**FHS95, Oh93,97I**] for more details concerning some technical results on the general structure of Floer trajectories that are needed for completing Floer's transversality proof.

THEOREM 2.3.11. (Floer, [**Flo88I,88II**]) *Let* J_0, $J_1 \in \mathcal{J}_\omega$ *be any fixed pair of compatible almost complex structures. Then there exists a dense subset*

$$\mathcal{P}(\mathcal{J}_\omega)^{\mathrm{reg}}(L_0, L_1; J_0, J_1) \subset \mathcal{P}(\mathcal{J}_\omega; J_0, J_1)$$

such that, for each $\{J_t\}_t \in \mathcal{P}(\mathcal{J}_\omega)^{\mathrm{reg}}(L_0, L_1; J_0, J_1)$ *the moduli space*

$$\widetilde{\mathcal{M}}^{\mathrm{reg}}(L_1, L_0, p, q; B; \{J_t\}_t)$$

is transversal and a smooth manifold of dimension $\mu(p, q; B)$*, when non-empty, for any* p, $q \in L_0 \cap L_1$ *and* $B \in \pi_2(p, q)$.

2.3.2. Floer's definition: $\mathbb{Z}_2$-coefficients. In this section, we recall Floer's original definition [**Flo88IV**] of Floer cohomology for the pair (L_0, L_1) with $\mathbb{Z}_2$-coefficients. Definition of the integer coefficients require the nontrivial orientation question whose study will be postponed until the Chapter 8.

DEFINITION 2.3.12. Let L_0, L_1 be transverse. We denote

$$\mathrm{Int}(L_1, L_0; \ell_0) = \{p \in L_0 \cap L_1 \mid \ell_p \text{ lies in } \Omega(L_0, L_1; \ell_0)\}$$
$$CF_{\mathbb{Z}_2}(L_1, L_0; \ell_0) = \text{the } \mathbb{Z}_2 \text{ vector space whose basis is } \mathrm{Int}(L_0, L_1; \ell_0).$$

Suppose that $\{J_t\}_t \in \mathcal{P}(\mathcal{J}_\omega)$ satisfies the following conditions:

(2.3.12.1)   For any pair $(p, q) \subset \mathrm{Int}(L_1, L_0; \ell_0)$ satisfying $\mu(p, q; B) \leq 0$, we have $\mathcal{M}(p, q; B; \{J_t\}_t) = \emptyset$ unless $p = q$ and $B = 0$ in $\pi_2(p, q)$. When $p = q$ and $B = 0$, the only solutions are the stationary solution, i.e., $u(\tau, t) \equiv p = q$ for all $(\tau, t) \in \mathbb{R} \times [0, 1]$.

(2.3.12.2)   For any pair $(p, q) \subset \mathrm{Int}(L_1, L_0; \ell_0)$ and a homotopy class $B \in \pi_2(p, q)$ satisfying $\mu(p, q; B) = 1$, the moduli space $\widetilde{\mathcal{M}}(p, q; B; \{J_t\}_t)/\mathbb{R}$ is a smooth manifold (Fredholm-regular). Moreover the quotient space

$$\mathcal{M}(p, q; B; \{J_t\}_t) = \widetilde{\mathcal{M}}(p, q; B; \{J_t\}_t)/\mathbb{R}$$

is compact, and so a finite set. We denote

$$n(p, q; B) = \#\mathcal{M}(p, q; B; \{J_t\}_t) \quad \mathrm{mod}\ 2$$

the algebraic count of the elements of the space $\mathcal{M}(p, q; B; \{J_t\}_t)$. We set

$$n(p, q; B) = 0$$

unless $\mu(p, q; B) \neq 1$.

(2.3.12.3)   For any pair $(p, q) \subset \mathrm{Int}(L_1, L_0; \ell_0)$ and $B \in \pi_2(p, q)$ satisfying

$$\mu(p, q; B) = 2,$$

$\mathcal{M}(p, q; B; \{J_t\}_t)$ can be compactified into a smooth one-manifold with boundary consisting only of the collection of the broken trajectories $[u_1]\#_\infty[u_2]$ where $u_1 \in \widetilde{\mathcal{M}}(p, q; B_1; \{J_t\}_t)$ and $u_2 \in \widetilde{\mathcal{M}}(q, r; B_2; \{J_t\}_t)$ for all possible $q \in \mathrm{Int}(L_1, L_0; \ell_0)$ and $B_1 \in \pi_2(p, q)$, $B_2 \in \pi_2(q, r)$ satisfying

$$B_1 \# B_2 = B; \quad u_1 \in \mathcal{M}(p, q; B_1; \{J_t\}_t), \quad u_2 \in \mathcal{M}(q, r; B_2; \{J_t\}_t)$$

and $\mu(p, q; B_1) = \mu(q, r; B_2) = 1$. We call any such $\{J_t\}_t$ (L_0, L_1)-*regular* and call any such triple $(L_0, L_1; \{J_t\}_t)$ *Floer regular*.

The main hypotheses in this definition concern some transversality and compactness properties of the zero dimensional (for (2.3.12.2)) and the one dimensional (for (2.3.12.3)) components of $\mathcal{M}(L_1, L_0; \{J_t\}_t)$.

Floer [**Flo88II,88IV**] proved that the hypotheses hold for a family $\{J_t\}_t$ in a dense subset of $\mathcal{P}(\mathcal{J}_\omega)$ for the pair $L_0 = L$, $L_1 = \psi_1^H(L)$ of Lagrangian submanifolds satisfying $\pi_2(M, L) = \{e\}$ where ψ_1^H is the Hamiltonian diffeomorphism generated by the time dependent function $H : [0, 1] \times M \to \mathbb{R}$. In this case, assuming L is connected, Floer restricts to the canonical connected component of $\Omega(L_0, L_1)$ containing the path ℓ_{can} defined by

$$\ell_{can}(t) = \psi_t^H(p_0)$$

where $p_0 \in L$ is a fixed point. It is not difficult to check that in the case when $\pi_2(M, L) = 0$, the set $\pi_2(p, q)$ contains the unique element for each given pair $p, q \in L_0 \cap L_1$ and so we drop the dependence on B from the notations of various objects we defined above. In particular, the action functional $\mathcal{A}$ and the Maslov-Morse index μ are already well-defined on the path space $\Omega(L_0, L_1; \ell_{can})$ (modulo the universal shifts of a constant) and the Novikov ring is not needed in the formulation of the Floer cohomology. Therefore in this case, the definition closely resembles that of the finite dimensional Morse theory [**Mil63, Flo89II**].

The upshot of the above definition is that for a Floer regular triple $(L, \psi_1^H(L); \{J_t\}_t)$ the Floer coboundary map

$$\delta_0 : CF_{\mathbb{Z}_2}(\psi_1^H(L), L; \ell_{can}) \to CF_{\mathbb{Z}_2}(\psi_1^H(L), L; \ell_{can})$$

is defined by the matrix elements $n(p, q)$, i.e.,

$$\delta_0 p = \sum_{p \in L \cap \psi_1^H(L)} n(p, q) p$$

and satisfies $\delta_0 \delta_0 = 0$.

The Floer cohomology of the Floer regular triple $(\psi_1^H(L), L; \{J_t\}_t)$ is then defined by

(2.3.13) $$HF^*(\psi_1^H(L), L; \{J_t\}_t) := \text{Ker } \delta_0 / \text{Im } \delta_0.$$

Floer [**Flo88IV**] also proved that this cohomology remains to be isomorphic under the change of Hamiltonians H and of the family $\{J_t\}_t$ of almost complex structures. His original proof of this invariance in [**Flo88IV**] uses a bifurcation argument. This was then replaced in [**Oh93**] by a more natural cobordism argument using the Cauchy-Riemann equation with moving Lagrangian boundary condition $u(\tau, 0) \in \psi_{\chi(\tau)}^H(L)$, $u(\tau, 1) \in L$, where $\chi : \mathbb{R} \to [0, 1]$ is a smooth function such that $\chi(\tau) = 0$ for τ sufficiently small and $\chi(\tau) = 1$ for τ sufficiently large. This was in turn motivated by a similar construction of Floer's in [**Flo89I**] for the periodic orbit case.

Floer [**Flo89II**] then studied the case of the zero section $L = o_N$ on the cotangent bundle $\pi : T^*N \to N$ with the pair $(\{J_t\}_t, H)$ given by

$$H = (\epsilon f) \circ \pi, \quad J_t \equiv (\psi_t^H)_* J_g$$

where J_g is the canonical almost complex structure on T^*N associated to the Levi-Civita connection of a given Riemannian metric g on the base N and (f, g) is a Morse-Smale pair.

In this case $\psi_t^H(o_N)$ is the graph $\mathrm{Graph}(\epsilon t df)$ of the one form $\epsilon t df$.

For sufficiently small $\epsilon > 0$, Floer established one-one correspondence between the solution space $\mathcal{M}(p, q)$ of (4.3) and that of gradient trajectories satisfying

$$\dot{\chi} - \mathrm{grad}_g f(\chi) = 0$$

issued at p ending at q. Then using the Morse homology argument from [**Mil63, Wit82, Con78**], he proves that $HF^*(\mathrm{Graph}(\epsilon t df), o_N; \{J_t\}_t)$ is isomorphic to $H^*(N; \mathbb{Z}_2)$.

Floer then concludes that this consideration of the cotangent bundle, via the Darboux-Weinstein theorem, implies that $HF^*(\psi_1^H(L), L; \{J_t\}_t)$ is isomorphic to $H^*(L; \mathbb{Z}_2)$ for the case $\pi_2(M, L) = \{e\}$. However we would like to point out that this last step of proof for the general (M, L) satisfying $\pi_2(M, L) = \{e\}$ is not completely trivial in that it requires to prove that as $\psi = \psi_1^H$ converges to identity all the elements of $\mathcal{M}(\psi(L), L; \{J_t\}_t)$ become thin so that the images of them are contained in a Darboux-Weinstein neighborhood. For the Floer case $\pi_2(M, L) = \{e\}$, this is indeed not difficult to show by a little bit of convergence argument of the Floer trajectory space when combined with the uniform C^1-bound which will follow from the fact that *the assumption $\pi_2(M, L) = \{e\}$ prevents the bubbling phenomenon.* We refer to [**Oh96I**] for a detailed explanation on this point. We will come back to these points in the next section when we introduce the Bott-Morse version of Floer cohomology and mention its relation to $HF^*(\psi(L), L; \{J_t\}_t)$ for $\psi \neq id$.

2.3.3. Bott-Morse Floer cohomology.
When one considers the Hamiltonian isotopic pair (L_0, L_1) with

$$L_0 = L, \quad L_1 = \psi_1^H(L)$$

for a Hamiltonian $H : [0, 1] \times M \to \mathbb{R}$, one would hope to be able to use the invariance property of $HF(\psi_1^H(L), L; \{J_t\}_t)$ and compute the Floer cohomology $HF(\psi_1^H(L), L; \{J_t\}_t)$ by choosing a special type of the pair $(\{J_t\}_t, H)$ as Floer did for the zero section in the cotangent bundle. However when there exist non-constant bubbles around in the picture, one needs to analyze how the bubbles interact with the Floer boundary map. When ψ^H is far from the identity or more precisely when $\psi_1^H(L)$ is far from L, the bubblings are mixed up with the Floer trajectories and hard to de-couple from the latter. On the other hand, when ψ^H is C^1-close to the identity, the Floer boundary map undergoes the *thick-thin decomposition*: in this decomposition *thin trajectories*, or more precisely the trajectories whose image are contained in a given Darboux-Weinstein neighborhood of L, correspond to the Morse gradient trajectories when one writes

$$\psi_1^H = \mathrm{Graph}(\epsilon df), \quad H = \epsilon f \circ \pi$$

in the Darboux neighborhood. All other trajectories, called *thick trajectories*, are combinations of bubbles and the Morse gradient trajectories. In fact, many non-trivial results concerning symplectic topology of compact Lagrangian embeddings were previously obtained by studying this thick-thin decomposition in the Floer cohomology. See [**Chek98, Oh96I**] for such applications, and [**Fuk97III, Oh96I,**

96II] for the description of the limiting picture as $\epsilon \to 0$. A precise study of this adiabatic degeneration turns out to be highly non-trivial and technical.

One might even hope to study the degenerate case

$$(2.3.14) \qquad H = 0 \,(\text{or } \psi^H = id), \quad J_t \equiv J_0 \text{ time independent}$$

directly instead of taking the above adiabatic limit. Indeed the definition of Floer cohomology can be generalized to the pair (L_0, L_1) with *clean intersections*. In that case, our functional $\mathcal{A}$ is an infinite dimensional analogue of Bott-Morse functional [**Bot59**]. For example, one can directly consider the pair $L_0 = L_1 = L$. We refer to Subsection 3.7.5 for the details of this construction. Bott-Morse theory in Floer homology was first carried out by the first named author in the gauge theory setting [**Fuk96II**] in 1992. (Mrowka's work [**Mro89**] which appeared before [**Fuk96II**] is also closely related to it.) In the Floer theory setting for the Hamiltonian diffeomorphisms, the construction was proposed by Piunikhin [**Piu94**] and also by Ruan-Tian [**RuTi95**], and a somewhat different approach (using a similar moduli space to one which had been introduced in [**Fuk97III**]) was outlined by Piunikhin-Salamon-Schwarz [**PSS96**]. (According to line 11 page 171 in [**PSS96**] the analytic detail is not given in [**PSS96**].) Chapter 7 Sections 7.1 and 7.2 of this book provide materials to work out the analytic details needed to establish this Bott-Morse theory indicated in [**Piu94**] and [**RuTi95**]. Recently, Zhu and the second named author [**OhZhu07**] developed the scale-dependent gluing, which provides the analytic details for the approach adopted in [**PSS96**], although one could avoid rescaling target manifolds and could write down a proof following the more standard approach of Floer's gluing but in Bott-Morse setting. A related study in the Lagrangian intersections had been carried out before by Pozniak [**Poz99**] when there is no bubbling phenomenon around. (See Subsection 7.2.2 for more discussion.)

One advantage of directly working with the Bott-Morse setting (2.3.14) is that the bubbling phenomenon or the *quantum contributions* can be completely decoupled from the classical part of the cohomology. Here we use the singular cohomology instead of the Morse cohomology, while the latter will emerge if one takes the approach of adiabatic degeneration as $\epsilon \to 0$ for non-zero Morse function f. This enables one to reduce computation of Floer cohomology to a study of holomorphic discs in some favorable cases. This idea has been exploited by Cho and second named author for the computation of Floer cohomology of the Lagrangian torus fibers of Fano toric manifolds [**Cho04I, ChOh03**], which mathematically proves a mirror-symmetry prediction made by Hori [**Hor01**] in relation to the A-model on the toric manifolds and its Landau-Ginzburg B-model.

Our construction in Chapter 3 of the A_∞ algebra associated to a Lagrangian submanifold can be regarded as the Bott-Morse version of the Floer theory (with product structure), where all the objects of Lagrangian submanifolds simultaneously collapse to a single Lagrangian submanifold. In particular its $\mathfrak{m}_1$-cohomology, when defined, will be isomorphic to the Floer cohomology $HF^*(\psi_1^H(L), L)$. We refer to Chapter 5 Section 5.3 for the proof of this latter statement.

2.4. Review of Floer cohomology II: anomaly appearance

Let $L_i, i = 0, 1$ be two Lagrangian submanifolds of (M, ω), which are transverse to each other. In the beginning we will not impose any conditions on the Lagrangian submanifolds L_i, but introduce them as we go along when needed. In this section R denotes a commutative ring with unit.

2.4.1. The Floer cochain module. We recall that the critical point set of the action functional $\mathcal{A}$ is

$$Cr(L_0, L_1; \ell_0) = \{[\ell_p, w] \in \widetilde{\Omega}(L_0, L_1; \ell_0) \mid p \in L_0 \cap L_1\}.$$

The action of the group $\Pi(L_0, L_1; \ell_0)$ on $\widetilde{\Omega}(L_0, L_1; \ell_0)$ preserves the critical point set $Cr(L_0, L_1; \ell_0)$: for each $g \in \Pi(L_0, L_1; \ell_0)$ and $[\ell_p, w] \in Cr(L_0, L_1; \ell_0)$, we have

$$(2.4.1) \qquad\qquad g \cdot [\ell_p, w] = [\ell_p, g \# w].$$

This action induces a natural $R[\Pi(L_0, L_1; \ell_0)]$-module structure on the free R-module generated by $Cr(L_0, L_1; \ell_0)$. This free module is not finitely generated, but it is free and finitely generated as an $R[\Pi(L_0, L_1; \ell_0)]$-module and its rank is $\#(L_0 \cap L_1)$.

On the other hand, the Maslov-Morse index $\mu([\ell_p, w])$ provides a natural grading and the action functional $\mathcal{A}$ provides a filtration on $Cr(L_0, L_1; \ell_0)$. This makes the R-module becomes a graded filtered module.

In particular, the module has a natural non-Archimedean topology. As noted by Novikov [**Nov81**] and Floer [**Flo89I**], it is crucial to complete this module with respect to this topology. We now explain this completed module, which we call the *(Novikov) Floer cochain module*:

DEFINITION 2.4.2. For each $k \in \mathbb{Z}$, we consider the formal (infinite) sum

$$(2.4.3) \qquad\qquad \mathfrak{x} = \sum_{\mu([\ell_p, w]) = k} a_{[\ell_p, w]} [\ell_p, w], \quad a_{[\ell_p, w]} \in R.$$

(2.4.4.1)   We call those $[\ell_p, w]$ with $a_{[\ell_p, w]} \neq 0$ *generators* of the sum $\mathfrak{x}$ and write $[\ell_p, w] \in \mathfrak{x}$.

(2.4.4.2)   We define the *support* of $\mathfrak{x}$ by

$$\mathrm{supp}(\mathfrak{x}) := \{[\ell_p, w] \in Cr(L_0, L_1; \ell_0) \mid a_{[\ell_p, w]} \neq 0 \text{ in the sum } (2.4.3) \}.$$

(2.4.4.3)   We call the formal sum $\mathfrak{x}$ above a *(Novikov) Floer cochain* of degree k, if it satisfies the finiteness condition

$$\#\left(\mathrm{supp}(\mathfrak{x}) \cap \{[\ell_p, w] \mid \mathcal{A}([\ell_p, w] \leq \lambda\}\right) < \infty$$

for any $\lambda \in \mathbb{R}$. We define $CF_R^k(L_1, L_0; \ell_0)$ to be the set of Floer cochains of degree k.

(2.4.4.4)   We then define the $\mathbb{Z}$-graded free R module $CF_R^*(L_1, L_0; \ell_0)$ by

$$CF_R^*(L_1, L_0; \ell_0) = \bigoplus_k CF_R^k(L_1, L_0; \ell_0).$$

We now describe the graded module structure of $CF_R^*(L_1, L_0; \ell_0)$ over the graded ring, the Novikov ring

$$\Lambda^R(L_0, L_1; \ell_0) = \bigoplus_k \Lambda_k^R(L_0, L_1; \ell_0).$$

Let $\mathfrak{y} = \sum b_g[g] \in \Lambda^R(L_0, L_1; \ell_0)$ and $\mathfrak{x} = \sum a_{[\ell_p, w]}[\ell_p, w]$. We define

$$\mathfrak{y} \cdot \mathfrak{x} = \sum b_g a_{[\ell_p, w]}(g \cdot [\ell_p, w])$$

where $g \cdot [\ell_p, w]$ is defined as in (2.4.1). It is not difficult to see that the term in the right hand side defines a Novikov Floer cochain i.e., satisfies the finiteness condition (2.4.4.3) in Definition 2.4.2 and so lies in $CF_R^*(L_1, L_0; \ell_0)$. This action makes $CF_R^*(L_1, L_0; \ell_0)$ a graded $\Lambda^R(L_1, L_0; \ell_0)$-module.

Then we would like to define the Floer coboundary map

$$\delta_0 : CF_R^*(L_1, L_0; \ell_0) \to CF_R^{*+1}(L_1, L_0; \ell_0)$$

satisfying $\delta_0 \circ \delta_0 = 0$ as proposed in Definition 2.3.12. This map will be defined by assigning the matrix element $\langle \delta_0([\ell_p, w]), [\ell_q, w'] \rangle$ for each given pair $[\ell_p, w]$, $[\ell_q, w']$. As in the case of Floer homology of periodic orbits, one would like this matrix element to be defined using the Floer moduli space of connecting orbits from $[\ell_p, w]$ to $[\ell_q, w']$. While this will be partially the case, the story becomes much more complex (and interesting) for the Lagrangian intersection Floer theory, which is partially responsible for the volume of the present book.

2.4.2. The Floer moduli space. A solution $u : \mathbb{R} \times [0, 1] \to M$ of Equation (2.3.3) naturally defines a path in $\Omega(L_0, L_1; \ell_0)$ which can be lifted to an L^2-gradient trajectory of $\mathcal{A}$ to the covering space $\widetilde{\Omega}(L_0, L_1; \ell_0)$. Each choice $[\ell_p, w] \in \widetilde{\Omega}(L_0, L_1; \ell_0)$ of a lifting of the asymptotic path $u(-\infty, \cdot) = \ell_p$ lifts the moduli space $\widetilde{\mathcal{M}}^{\mathrm{reg}}(p, q; B; \{J_t\}_t)$ to the moduli space of gradient trajectories of $\mathcal{A}$ which we denote by

$$\widetilde{\mathcal{M}}^{\mathrm{reg}}([\ell_p, w], [\ell_q, w']; \{J_t\}_t)$$

where

(2.4.5) $$[\ell_q, w'] = [\ell_q, w \# B].$$

Here 'reg' in the notation stands for 'regular'.

We would like to point out that for given $[\ell_p, w]$, $[\ell_q, w']$ there could be many different choices of $B \in \pi_2(p, q)$ satisfying (2.4.5). The ambiguity can be precisely described in the following:

LEMMA & DEFINITION 2.4.6. *Let $B, B' \in \pi_2(p, q)$ and $[\ell_p, w]$ be given. Then $[\ell_q, w \# B] = [\ell_q, w \# B']$ in $\widetilde{\Omega}(L_0, L_1; \ell_0)$ if and only if $[\overline{B} \# B'] \in \pi_1(\Omega(L_0, L_1; \ell_0))$ satisfies*

(2.4.7) $$[\overline{B} \# B'] \in \mathrm{Ker}\, I_\omega \cap \mathrm{Ker}\, I_\mu.$$

We say that B and B' are Γ-*equivalent* in $\pi_2(p, q)$ and denote $B \sim B'$ if (2.4.7) holds. We also denote by $[B]$ the corresponding equivalence class of B in $\pi_2(p, q)$, by $G(p, q) = G(L_0, L_1; p, q)$ the set of such equivalence classes of $\sim$.

When we are given two critical points $[\ell_p, w]$, $[\ell_q, w']$ we define the moduli space $\widetilde{\mathcal{M}}^{\mathrm{reg}}([\ell_p, w], [\ell_q, w']; \{J_t\}_t)$ by the union

(2.4.8) $$\widetilde{\mathcal{M}}^{\mathrm{reg}}([\ell_p, w], [\ell_q, w']; \{J_t\}_t) := \bigcup_{B \in [\overline{w} \# w']} \widetilde{\mathcal{M}}^{\mathrm{reg}}(p, q; B; \{J_t\}_t)$$

where $[\overline{w} \# w'] \in G(p, q)$ is the equivalence class corresponding to the glued map $\overline{w} \# w' \in Map(p, q)$.

It is clear from Lemma 2.4.6 that for a given pair $[\ell_p, w]$, $[\ell_q, w']$ there are exactly $\#(\mathrm{Ker}\, I_\omega \cap \mathrm{Ker}\, I_\mu)$ different homotopy classes of $B \in \pi_2(p, q)$ satisfying $B \in [\overline{w}\#w']$. In general $\#(\mathrm{Ker}\, I_\omega \cap \mathrm{Ker}\, I_\mu)$ could be infinite and so it is not obvious whether the union (2.4.8) is a finite union. However (2.4.8) is actually a finite union by the following proposition and the identity

$$\omega(B) = \mathcal{A}([\ell_q, w']) - \mathcal{A}([\ell_p, w]) < \infty.$$

PROPOSITION 2.4.9. *Let $\{J_t\}_t \in \mathcal{P}(\mathcal{J}_\omega)$ be given and $C > 0$. Then there are only a finite number of B for which $\widetilde{\mathcal{M}}^{\mathrm{reg}}(p, q; B; \{J_t\}_t) \neq \emptyset$ and $\omega(B) \leq C$.*

PROOF. Suppose to the contrary that there is an infinite sequence B_j whose elements are all different in $\pi_2(p, q)$, which satisfies $\omega(B_j) \leq C$, and for which $\mathcal{M}(p, q; B_j; \{J_t\}_t) \neq \emptyset$. Let $u_j \in \mathcal{M}(p, q; B_j; \{J_t\}_t)$ be any element respectively for each j. Then we have the energy

$$E(u_j; \{J_t\}_t) = \omega(B_j) \leq C$$

for all j and

$$(2.4.10) \qquad \lim_{\tau \to -\infty} u(\tau, \cdot) = \ell_p, \qquad \lim_{\tau \to \infty} u(\tau, \cdot) = \ell_q.$$

Using the energy bound and the asymptotic condition, we apply Gromov-Floer compactness theorem to extract a subsequence, again denoted by u_j, such that u_j converges to a stable broken Floer trajectory from p to q. It is known that this convergence preserves the homotopy class in $\pi_2(p, q)$ and in particular there must exist some $N \in \mathbb{N}$ such that $B_j = [u_j] = [u_N] = B_N$ for all $j \geq N$. This contradicts to the assumption that B_j are mutually different in $\pi_2(p, q)$. This finishes the proof. $\qquad \square$

Therefore we can also define the moduli space $\widetilde{\mathcal{M}}^{\mathrm{reg}}([\ell_p, w], [\ell_q, w']; \{J_t\}_t)$ as the set of maps $u : \mathbb{R} \times [0, 1] \to M$ satisfying

$(2.4.11.1) \quad u(\mathbb{R} \times \{0\}) \subset L_0, \quad u(\mathbb{R} \times \{1\}) \subset L_1,$
$(2.4.11.2) \quad u$ satisfies

$$\begin{cases} \dfrac{\partial u}{\partial \tau} + J_t \dfrac{\partial u}{\partial t} = 0 \\ \lim_{\tau \to -\infty} u(\tau, t) = p, \quad \lim_{\tau \to +\infty} u(\tau, t) = q, \end{cases}$$

$(2.4.11.3) \quad w\#u \sim w'$, where $w\#u$ is the obvious concatenation of w and u along the constant path ℓ_p.

For each $\tau_0 \in \mathbb{R}$, $u(\tau, t) \mapsto u(\tau + \tau_0, t)$ defines an $\mathbb{R}$ action on the moduli space $\widetilde{\mathcal{M}}^{\mathrm{reg}}([\ell_p, w], [\ell_q, w']; \{J_t\}_t)$. We put

$$(2.4.12) \qquad \mathcal{M}^{\mathrm{reg}}([\ell_p, w], [\ell_q, w']; \{J_t\}_t) = \frac{\widetilde{\mathcal{M}}^{\mathrm{reg}}([\ell_p, w], [\ell_q, w']; \{J_t\}_t)}{\mathbb{R}}.$$

Unlike the case where $\pi_2(M, L) = \{e\}$, the space $\mathcal{M}^{\mathrm{reg}}([\ell_p, w], [\ell_q, w']; \{J_t\}_t)$ will not satisfy the properties stated in Definition 2.3.12 in general because of the presence of bubbling phenomena. There are two different aspects on what the bubbling phenomenon affects on the Floer cohomology theory:

(2.4.13.1)   One comes from the phenomenon of bubbling off multiple covers of *negative* holomorphic spheres or discs. This is the phenomenon which already exists in the Floer cohomology of periodic orbits or of the *closed strings*.

(2.4.13.2)   The other is the unique phenomenon of *anomaly appearance*

$$\delta_0 \circ \delta_0 \neq 0$$

for the original Floer coboundary map δ_0 in the case of open strings. This is closely related to the fact that bubbling off a *disc* is a phenomenon of *codimension one*, while bubbling off a *sphere* is that of codimension two in general.

As well-known by now, the problem (2.4.13.1) of bubblings of negative Chern number or of negative Maslov index can be treated by considering the Kuranishi structure and the perturbation theory of multi-valued sections. In Floer theory, we need to work in the *chain level* of this virtual moduli cycle machinery, unlike the case of Gromov-Witten invariants for which only the *homology level* theory is needed. In a broad sense, a large part of difficulties present in our geometric construction of various moduli objects in this book are due to (2.4.13).

On the other hand, even when we consider the case where the phenomenon (2.4.13.1) does not occur as in the semi-positive case, the anomaly appearance (2.4.13.2) cannot be ruled out. This is largely responsible for our introduction of A_∞ algebras associated to Lagrangian submanifolds and their deformation theory.

The following simple example already illustrates the "instanton effects" that cause an anomaly on the coboundary property of Floer coboundary map. A similar example was already looked at in [**Oh93**].

EXAMPLE 2.4.14.   Consider $(M, \omega) = (\mathbb{C}, \omega_0)$ and

$$L_0 = \mathbb{R} + \sqrt{-1} \cdot 0, \quad L_1 = S^1 = \partial D^2(1).$$

Both L_0 and M are not compact. However one can conformally compactify $\mathbb{C}$ to $\mathbb{P}^1 \cong S^2$ so that both $\mathbb{R}$ and S^1 become equators. L_0 and L_1 intersect at two points which we denote $p = (-1, 0)$, $q = (1, 0)$.

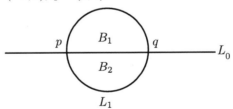

Figure 2.4.1

We now look at the moduli spaces $\mathcal{M}(p, q)$, $\mathcal{M}(q, p)$ and $\mathcal{M}(p, p)$ respectively. It is easy to see that $\pi_2(p, q) = \pi_2(L_0, L_1; p, q)$ is a principal homogeneous space of $\pi_2(\mathbb{C}, S^1) \cong \pi_1(S^1)$. Denote by $B_1 \in \pi_2(p, q)$ the homotopy class represented by the obvious upper semi-disc. Similarly we denote by $B_2 \in \pi_2(q, p)$ the class represented by the lower semi-disc. Then we denote by $B \in \pi_2(p, p)$ the homotopy class given by $B = B_1 \# B_2$. By a simple Maslov index calculation, we derive $\mu(p, q; B_1) = \mu(q, p; B_2) = 1$ and so $\mu(p, p; B) = 2$.

By a simple application of the Riemann mapping theorem with boundary, we prove that $\mathcal{M}(p, q; B_1)$ has the unique element which is represented by $u_1 : \mathbb{R} \times [0, 1] \to \mathbb{C}$ whose image is the obvious upper semi-disc. Similarly $\mathcal{M}(q, p; B_2)$ has the unique element whose image is the lower semi-disc. And by a simple linear analysis of Riemann-Hilbert problem, one can also prove that these maps are also regular in that its linearization map is surjective. By a dimensional consideration, we derive the formula

$$\delta_0([\ell_p, w]) = [q, w \# B_1], \quad \delta_0([\ell_q, w']) = [p, w' \# B_2]$$

for all bounding discs w of ℓ_p and w' of ℓ_q.

Now we analyze the moduli space $\mathcal{M}(p, p; B)$. Considering each element of $\mathcal{M}(p, p; B)$ as the unparameterized curve corresponding to an element of $\widetilde{\mathcal{M}}(p, p; B)$, we can prove by the Riemann mapping theorem that it consists of the holomorphic maps $u_\ell : \mathbb{R} \times [0, 1] \to \mathbb{C}$ for $-1 < \ell < 1$ that satisfy

$$u(\mathbb{R} \times \{0\}) \subset \mathbb{R} \times \{0\}, \quad u(\mathbb{R} \times \{1\}) \subset \partial D^2, \, [u_\ell] = B$$
$$u_\ell(-\infty, \cdot) = u_\ell(\infty, \cdot) = \ell_p, \quad u_\ell(0, 0) = (\ell, 0).$$

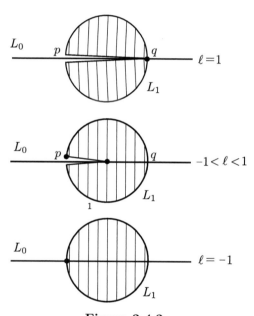

Figure 2.4.2

By the symmetry consideration, we derive that u_ℓ must also satisfy $u_\ell(0, 1) = (1, 0)$. One can show that the above family indeed comprise all the elements of $\mathcal{M}(p, p; B)$ and all of these maps are Fredholm regular. From this description, a natural compactification of $\mathcal{M}(p, p; B)$ is the one obtained by adding the broken trajectory $u_1 \# u_2$ which corresponds to the limit as $\ell \to 1$, and the other end in the limit as $\ell \to -1$. We note that the map u_ℓ satisfies

(2.4.15.1) $u_\ell(\mathbb{R} \times \{0\}) \subset \{(t, 0) \mid -1 < t \leq \ell\}$ and in particular as $\ell \to -1$ the $u_\ell|_{\mathbb{R} \times \{0\}}$ converges to the constant map $(-1, 0)$.

(2.4.15.2)   The image of $u_\ell|_{\mathbb{R} \times \{1\}}$ wraps around the boundary ∂D^2 exactly once.

One can also check that on any compact subset $K \subset \mathbb{R} \times [0, 1] \setminus \{(0, 1)\}$, we have $\|du_\ell\|_{\infty, K} \to 0$ as $\ell \to -1$, and $|du_\ell(0, 1)| \nearrow \infty$. From this analysis, we conclude that the real scenario behind the above picture as $\ell \to -1$ is appearance of the *stable trajectory* corresponding to the following singular curve

$$(u_\infty, \mathbb{R} \times [0,1], \{(0,1)\}) \cup (w, D^2, \{pt\})$$

where

(2.4.16.1) $(u_\infty, \mathbb{R} \times [0,1], (0,1))$ is the principal component $u_\infty : \mathbb{R} \times [0,1] \to \mathbb{C}$ is the constant map $p = (-1,0)$ with its domain given by

$$(\mathbb{R} \times [0,1], \{(0,1)\}) \cong (D^2 \setminus \{\pm 1\}, \{i\}),$$

(2.4.16.2) $w : (D^2, \partial D^2) \to (\mathbb{C}, L_1)$ is the obvious inclusion map with its domain being the disc D^2 with one marked point on the boundary ∂D^2.

We note that this configuration is an admissible stable trajectory: u_∞ is stable because its domain has 3 special points on the boundary, and w is stable because it is a non-constant map and so both maps have trivial automorphism groups. This analysis of $\mathcal{M}(p, p; B)$ together with (2.4.15) computes the matrix element

$$\langle (\delta_0 \circ \delta_0)([\ell_p, w]), [\ell_p, w \# B] \rangle = 1,$$

and

$$\langle (\delta_0 \circ \delta_0)([\ell_p, w]), [\ell_p, w \# B'] \rangle = 0$$

for any other $B' \in \pi_2(p, p)$ with $B' \neq B$. This clearly shows $\delta_0 \circ \delta_0 \neq 0$. This example illustrates that the boundary of $\mathcal{M}(p, p; B)$ with $\mu(B) = 2$ can have a boundary component which is not of the type of broken trajectories. And we note that *the Maslov index of the disc w above is two*. We will see later that this latter fact is not coincidental.

As indicated above, a compactification of the space $\mathcal{M}^{\mathrm{reg}}([\ell_p, w], [\ell_q, w']; \{J_t\}_t)$ requires to add an object consisting of the union of Floer trajectories and holomorphic spheres or discs. We will describe this compactification in Subsection 3.7.4. We write $\mathcal{M}([\ell_p, w], [\ell_q, w']; \{J_t\}_t)$ the compactified moduli space. We define a topology on it in a similar way as done in [Fl088II, FuOn99II] which makes our moduli space $\mathcal{M}([\ell_p, w], [\ell_q, w']; \{J_t\}_t)$ a compact Hausdorff space whose induced topology on $\mathcal{M}^{\mathrm{reg}}([\ell_p, w], [\ell_q, w']; \{J_t\}_t)$ is the strong C^∞ topology. We refer to Subsection 7.1.4 or [FuOn99II] for a detailed description of the topology.

At this stage, we would like to emphasize that this compactification is defined as a topological space for *any* choice of $\{J_t\}_t$ for a transversal pair L_0, L_1 of Lagrangian submanifolds. The topological space $\mathcal{M}([\ell_p, w], [\ell_q, w']; \{J_t\}_t)$ will not be a smooth manifold even for a generic choice of $\{J_t\}_t$ in case the pair (L_0, L_1), in general.

However there is a particular class of Lagrangian submanifolds, that of *monotone* Lagrangian submanifolds, for which the moduli space $\mathcal{M}([\ell_p, w], [\ell_q, w']; \{J_t\}_t)$ becomes a smooth manifold with corners of the expected dimension for a dense set of

$$\{J_t\}_t \in \mathcal{P}(\mathcal{J}_\omega)^{\mathrm{reg}}(L_0, L_1) \subset \mathcal{P}(\mathcal{J}_\omega)$$

at least for strata of dimension ≤ 2. We will discuss this case in Subsection 2.4.5.

2.4.3. The Novikov ring $\Lambda^R(L)$. As Example 2.4.14 illustrates, a proper description of a compactification of the Floer moduli space $\mathcal{M}^{\mathrm{reg}}([\ell_p, w], [\ell_q, w'])$ in general requires a study of pseudo-holomorphic spheres and discs with boundary lying either on L_0 or L_1. As usual by now, we will use a stable map type compactification of $\mathcal{M}^{\mathrm{reg}}([\ell_p, w], [\ell_q, w'])$. This requires a careful study of the moduli space of pseudo-holomorphic discs with Lagrangian boundary condition provided in Subsection 2.1.2.

To encode the effects of the pseudo-holomorphic discs on the coboundary map of Floer cochain complex, we also need to study the Novikov ring associated to Lagrangian submanifolds. The definition of this Novikov ring is now in order.

Let $L \subset M$ be a compact Lagrangian submanifold. We recall that there are natural group homomorphisms

$$I_\omega : \pi_2(M, L) \to \mathbb{R}, \quad I_\mu : \pi_2(M, L) \to \mathbb{Z} :$$

For each given $A \in \pi_2(M, L)$, the values of these are defined by the symplectic area $\omega(w)$ and the Maslov index $\mu_L(w)$ of a map $w : (D^2, \partial D^2) \to (M, L)$ representing A. These homomorphisms factor through the Hurewitz map $\pi_2(M, L) \to H_2(M, L)$ by definition.

DEFINITION 2.4.17. We define the equivalence relation $\beta \sim \beta'$ in $\pi_2(M, L)$ by setting

$$\omega(\beta) = \omega(\beta') \quad \text{and} \quad \mu_L(\beta) = \mu_L(\beta'),$$

and denote the set of equivalence classes by $\Pi(L) = \Pi(M; L)$.

We will abuse the notation β also for the elements of $\Pi(L)$. As in the case of $\Pi(L_0, L_1; \ell_0)$, it follows that $\Pi(L)$ is a free abelian group of its rank less than the rank of $H_2(M, L)$. Therefore we can define a completed ring of the group ring $R[\Pi(L)]$ in the same way as $\Lambda^R(L_0, L_1; \ell_0)$ for the pair (L_0, L_1). We denote this by $\Lambda^R(L)$ and call the *Novikov ring* of L. We remark that in later chapters, we use universal Novikov ring $\Lambda_{0,nov}$ rather than $\Lambda^R(L)$ or $\Lambda^R(L_0, L_1; \ell_0)$. The relation between them will be explained in Section 5.1.

We note that there exist natural group homomorphisms

(2.4.18) $\Pi(L_i) \to \Pi(L_0, L_1; \ell_0), \quad i = 0, 1.$

We will just describe this for $i = 0$ since the one for $i = 1$ is entirely similar. To define this homomorphism, it suffices to find an action of $\Pi(L_0)$ on $\widetilde{\Omega}(L_0, L_1; \ell_0)$ that is compatible with the covering $\widetilde{\Omega}(L_0, L_1; \ell_0) \to \Omega(L_0, L_1; \ell_0)$. Let $\beta \in \Pi(L_0)$ and $w_\beta : (D^2, \partial D^2) \to (M, L_0)$ be its representative. We define the map

$$g_\beta : \widetilde{\Omega}(L_0, L_1; \ell_0) \to \widetilde{\Omega}(L_0, L_1; \ell_0)$$

by the formula

$$g_\beta([\ell_p, w]) = \beta \cdot [\ell_p, w] := [\ell_p, w \# w_\beta]$$

where $w \# w_\beta$ is the gluing of w_β to the $w|_{[0,1] \times \{0\}}$: More precisely, we take any path joining $\ell_0(0)$ and $w_\beta(1)$ on L_0 and use this path to define a boundary connected sum $w \# w_\beta$. It is easy to see that the Γ-equivalence class of $(\ell, u \# w_\beta)$ is independent of the choice of the path and the representatives w_β and u. We note that the following diagrams commute

$$
\begin{array}{ccc}
\Pi(L_0,L_1) \xrightarrow{g \mapsto g \cdot [\ell_0, w]} \widetilde{\Omega}(L_0,L_1; \ell_0) & \quad & \Pi(L_0,L_1) \xrightarrow{g \mapsto g \cdot [\ell_0, w]} \widetilde{\Omega}(L_0,L_1; \ell_0) \\
\downarrow{\scriptstyle E} \qquad \qquad \downarrow{\scriptstyle \mathcal{A} - \mathcal{A}([\ell_0, w])} & & \downarrow{\scriptstyle \mu} \qquad \qquad \downarrow{\scriptstyle \mu - \mu([\ell_0, w])} \\
\mathbb{R} \qquad = \qquad \mathbb{R} & & \mathbb{Z} \qquad = \qquad \mathbb{Z}
\end{array}
$$

Diagram 2.4.1

respectively. This proves that this map is well-defined and respects the covering map $\widetilde{\Omega}(L_0, L_1; \ell_0) \to \Omega(L_0, L_1; \ell_0)$. Obviously g_β is a bijective map and satisfies $g_{\beta_1 \beta_2} = g_{\beta_1} \cdot g_{\beta_2}$ for all $\beta_1, \beta_2 \in \Pi(L_0)$. This finishes the construction of the homomorphism (2.4.18).

EXAMPLE 2.4.19. We first consider the Clifford torus $T^n \subset \mathbb{P}^n$

$$T^n = \{[z_0 : z_1 : \cdots : z_n] \in \mathbb{P}^n \mid |z_i| = 1\}.$$

This is an example of *monotone* Lagrangian submanifolds considered in [**Oh93**]. It is easy to check that $\pi_2(\mathbb{P}^n, T^n)$ splits

$$\pi_2(\mathbb{P}^n, T^n) \cong \pi_1(T^n) \oplus \pi_2(\mathbb{P}^n).$$

If we denote by β_i the class of the disc

$$D_i = \{[z_0 : z_1 : \cdots : z_n] \in \mathbb{P}^n \mid z_j \equiv e^{\sqrt{-1}\theta_i^0} \text{ fixed except for } j = i\},$$

then we have the relation

$$\beta_0 + \cdots + \beta_n = \alpha \quad \text{in } \pi_2(\mathbb{P}^n, T^n)$$

where α is the (positive) generator of $\pi_2(\mathbb{P}^n)$. Furthermore it follows that

(2.4.20.1) $$\mu(\beta_i) = 2 = \frac{c_1(\alpha)}{n+1},$$

(2.4.20.2) $$\omega(\beta_i) = \frac{\omega(\alpha)}{n+1} = 2\pi.$$

Therefore all β_i define the *same* element, which we denote by β, in $\Pi(\mathbb{P}^n; T^n)$ and $\alpha = (n+1)\beta$. Hence we have

$$\Pi(\mathbb{P}^n; T^n) \cong \mathbb{Z}.$$

Next we consider other standard tori given by

$$T_{(c_0, \cdots, c_n)} = \{[z_0 : \cdots : z_n] \in \mathbb{P}^n \mid |z_i| = c_i > 0\}$$

and denote by β_i and α the classes defined similarly as in the above case where $c_0 = \cdots = c_n$. Now (2.4.20.1) still holds but (2.4.20.2) is no longer the case. Depending on the rational dependence of the numbers

$$\{\omega(\beta_0), \cdots, \omega(\beta_n), \omega(\alpha) = 2\pi\}$$

the ranks of $\Pi(\mathbb{P}^n; T_{(c_0, \cdots, c_n)})$ are changing between 1 and $n + 1$.

Let J be a compatible (time-independent) almost complex structure on M. For each given $\beta \in \Pi(M; L)$, we define the moduli space of pseudo-holomorphic discs attached to L.

DEFINITION 2.4.21. We define

$$\widetilde{\mathcal{M}}(L; \beta; J) = \{w : D^2 \to M \mid w \text{ is } J \text{ holomorphic}, w(\partial D^2) \subset L, [w] = \beta\}.$$

We write $\widetilde{\mathcal{M}}(\beta)$ for $\widetilde{\mathcal{M}}(L; \beta; J)$ in case no confusion can occur. However we would like to emphasize that *the almost complex structure J may vary for a different choice of the Lagrangian submanifold L*.

We remark that the group $PSL(2;\mathbb{R}) = \mathrm{Aut}(D, j_D)$ acts on $\widetilde{\mathcal{M}}(L;\beta;J)$ by $\varphi \cdot w = w \circ \varphi^{-1}$. We put

$$\mathcal{M}(L;\beta;J) = \widetilde{\mathcal{M}}(L;\beta;J)/PSL(2;\mathbb{R}).$$

This moduli space will not be a smooth manifold even for a generic choice of J for a Lagrangian submanifold again due the phenomenon of multiple cover of spheres or discs of negative indices. In Subsection 2.1.2 (and more in Subsection 7.1.4), we have provided a description of the moduli space of stable maps (with marked points) which will be used to overcome the latter phenomenon similarly as in the moduli space of stable maps from a closed Riemann surface.

2.4.4. Monotone Lagrangian submanifolds. In this subsection, we will restrict to a special class of Lagrangian submanifolds studied by the second named author in [**Oh93,96I**] in his study of Floer homology and its application to the symplectic topology of such Lagrangian submanifolds.

We begin with the definition of monotone Lagrangian submanifolds used in [**Oh93**], which is in turn the analogue to monotone symplectic manifolds that Floer [**Flo89I**] used for the periodic orbit problem.

Let I_ω, $I_\mu : \pi_2(M, L) \to \mathbb{R}$, $\mathbb{Z}$ respectively which are the homomorphisms given in Subsection 2.4.3.

DEFINITION 2.4.22. A compact Lagrangian submanifold $L \subset (M, \omega)$ is called *monotone* if

$$I_\omega = \lambda I_\mu \quad \text{for some } \lambda \geq 0.$$

We define the *minimal Maslov number* $\Sigma(L)$ to be the positive generator of the image of I_μ.

Note that this case includes the so called *weakly exact* case i.e., the case of $I_\omega = 0$ in a trivial way. This case can be studied in the exactly same way as in the Floer's case $\pi_2(M, L) = \{0\}$, if one ignores the grading problem. Therefore we assume that $L \subset M$ is monotone with $\lambda > 0$ and $I_\mu \neq 0$ from now on. The $\mathbb{R}P^n \subset \mathbb{C}P^n$ or the Clifford torus considered in Example 2.4.19 are examples of monotone Lagrangian submanifolds.

As pointed out in [**Oh93**], it is easy to see that if M allows any monotone Lagrangian submanifold, (M, ω) itself must be a monotone symplectic manifold in the sense of Floer [**Flo89I**]: a symplectic manifold (M, ω) is called *monotone* if there exists $\lambda > 0$ such that

$$c_1(\alpha) = \lambda \int_\alpha \omega$$

for any homology class $\alpha \in H_2(M, \mathbb{Z})$ in the image of the Hurewitz homomorphism $\pi_2(M) \to H_2(M, \mathbb{Z})$.

The following proposition illustrates some special symplectic topology of this class of Lagrangian submanifolds against the general ones.

PROPOSITION 2.4.23. *Let $L \subset (M, \omega)$ be a monotone Lagrangian submanifold. Then $\Pi(L)$ is a free abelian group of rank 1 and its associated Novikov ring $\Lambda^R(L)$ becomes a field.*

The following theorem can be proven by a dimension counting argument based on the Sard-Smale theorem. We refer readers [**Oh93**] for the details of its proof.

For $J, J' \in \mathcal{J}_\omega$ we put

$$\mathcal{P}(\mathcal{J}_\omega; J, J') = \{\{J_t\}_t \in \mathcal{P}(\mathcal{J}_\omega) \mid J_0 = J, J_1 = J'\}.$$

THEOREM 2.4.24. (Oh) *We assume that L_0, L_1 are monotone with non-zero minimal Maslov number. Then there exists a subset $\mathcal{J}_\omega^0(L_0, L_1) \subset \mathcal{J}_\omega$ and a subset $\mathcal{P}^0(\mathcal{J}_\omega; J_0, J_1) \subset \mathcal{P}(\mathcal{J}_\omega; J_0, J_1)$ for J_0, $J_1 \in \mathcal{J}_\omega^0(L_0, L_1)$, such that for any $\{J_t\}_t \in \mathcal{P}^0(\mathcal{J}_\omega; J_0, J_1)$ the followings hold:*

(2.4.25.1)   *For all $[\ell_p, w], [\ell_q, w'] \in Cr(L_0, L_1)$ with $\mu([\ell_q, w']) = \mu([\ell_p, w])$, the moduli space $\mathcal{M}([\ell_p, w], [\ell_q, w']; \{J_t\}_t)$ is empty unless $[\ell_p, w] = [\ell_q, w']$.*
(2.4.25.2)   *For all $[\ell_p, w], [\ell_q, w'] \in Cr(L_0, L_1)$ with $\mu([\ell_q, w']) = \mu([\ell_p, w]) + 1$, the moduli space $\mathcal{M}([\ell_p, w], [\ell_q, w']; \{J_t\}_t)$ is a compact manifold and so is a finite set.*
(2.4.25.3)   *If $\mu([\ell_q, w']) < \mu([\ell_p, w])$, then $\mathcal{M}([\ell_p, w], [\ell_q, w']; \{J_t\}_t) = \emptyset$.*

This theorem implies that for a generic choice of $\{J_t\}_t$, the hypotheses (2.3.12.1) and (2.3.12.2) of Definition 2.3.12 hold. This allows us to be able to at least define the Floer coboundary map δ_0 for any monotone pair for such a generic choice of $\{J_t\}_t$. Let us make this statement more precise incorporating the effects of the deck transformation $\Pi(L_0, L_1; \ell_0)$ on the Novikov covering space $\widetilde{\Omega}(L_0, L_1; \ell_0)$ and on its Morse theory.

Another important issue is that of *coherent orientation* on our moduli space $\mathcal{M}([\ell_p, w], [\ell_q, w']; \{J_t\}_t)$. We will prove in Subsection 8.1.3 Theorem 8.1.14 of Chapter 8 that if the pair (L_0, L_1) is *relatively spin*, then there exists a canonical way to put a coherent orientation on the collections of the moduli spaces $\mathcal{M}([\ell_p, w], [\ell_q, w']; \{J_t\}_t)$. Therefore if the pair (L_0, L_1) is also relatively spin then *integer*

$$n([\ell_p, w], [\ell_q, w']) = \#(\mathcal{M}([\ell_p, w], [\ell_q, w']; \{J_t\}_t))$$

for $\mu[\ell_q, w'] = \mu([\ell_p, w]) + 1$ is well-defined. We use it as a matrix element to define the standard Floer coboundary map $\delta_0 : CF_R^k(L_1, L_0; \ell_0) \to CF_R^{k+1}(L_1, L_0; \ell_0)$ as follows.

$$(2.4.26) \qquad \delta_0([\ell_p, w]) = \sum_{\mu(\ell_q, w') = \mu(\ell_p, w) + 1} n([\ell_p, w], [\ell_q, w']) \cdot [\ell_q, w'].$$

Here $R = \mathbb{Z}$ in case (L_0, L_1) is a relatively spin pair and $R = \mathbb{Z}_2$ in general. Proposition 2.4.9 implies that the right hand side is in $CF_R^*(L_1, L_0; \ell_0)$.

Refining Floer's proof in [**Flo88IV**], the second named author [**Oh93**] proved that $\delta_0 \circ \delta_0 = 0$ in the case of monotone Lagrangian submanifolds *with the minimal Maslov number > 2* with some topological restriction on the pair (L_0, L_1). This latter topological restriction will not be needed once we use the Novikov Floer cochain modules $CF_R^*(L_1, L_0)$ as defined in this book. (See Theorem 2.4.42.) However the restriction on Maslov index turns out to be something that cannot be entirely removed even with the usage of Novikov rings as Example 2.4.14 illustrates. We will amplify this example by relating the matrix element $\langle (\delta_0 \circ \delta_0)([\ell_p, w]), [\ell_q, w'] \rangle$ with certain singular chains on L_0 or on L_1 or on both in the next subsection. This non-zero contribution arises from the presence of extra boundary components of the compactification $\mathcal{M}([\ell_p, w], [\ell_q, w']; \{J_t\}_t)$ when $\mu([\ell_q, w']) - \mu([\ell_p, w]) = 2$ other than the broken trajectories as illustrated by Example 2.4.14.

2.4.5. Appearance of the primary obstruction. We go back to the general pair (L_0, L_1) for the moment. We first describe the complement of the smooth moduli space $\mathcal{M}^{\mathrm{reg}}([\ell_p, w], [\ell_q, w'])$ in its compactification $\mathcal{M}([\ell_p, w], [\ell_q, w'])$. We consider

$$\mathcal{M}^{\mathrm{sing}}([\ell_p, w], [\ell_q, w']) := \mathcal{M}([\ell_p, w], [\ell_q, w']) \setminus \mathcal{M}^{\mathrm{reg}}([\ell_p, w], [\ell_q, w']).$$

For the study of boundary of $\mathcal{M}([\ell_p, w], [\ell_q, w'])$, we need to describe the stratum "codimension one", that is the top dimensional stratum of the singular locus $\mathcal{M}^{\mathrm{sing}}([\ell_p, w], [\ell_q, w'])$. We write it as $\partial \mathcal{M}([\ell_p, w], [\ell_q, w'])$. In a transversal case, this stratum will be given by either a broken trajectory with two components or a trajectory with a disc attached to its boundary.

We denote

$$(2.4.27) \qquad \overset{\circ}{\mathcal{M}}_{1,0}([\ell_p, w], [\ell_q, w'_0]) \cong \overset{\circ}{\mathcal{M}}_{0,1}([\ell_p, w], [\ell_q, w'_0])$$
$$= \widetilde{\mathcal{M}}^{\mathrm{reg}}([\ell_p, w], [\ell_q, w'_0]).$$

This is a special case of Definition 3.7.24, where $\overset{\circ}{\mathcal{M}}_{k_1, k_0}([\ell_p, w], [\ell_q, w'_0])$ is defined. We define a map $ev : \overset{\circ}{\mathcal{M}}_{1,0}([\ell_p, w], [\ell_q, w'_0]) \to L_1$, or $ev : \overset{\circ}{\mathcal{M}}_{0,1}([\ell_p, w], [\ell_q, w'_0]) \to L_0$, by

$$(2.4.28) \qquad ev(u) = u(0, 1), \quad \text{or} \quad ev(u) = u(0, 0),$$

respectively. (We remark that when we reagard u as an element of the moduli space $\overset{\circ}{\mathcal{M}}_{1,0}([\ell_p, w], [\ell_q, w'_0])$, the point $(0, 1) \in \mathbb{R} \times [0, 1]$ is regarded as a marked point. On the other hand when we reagard u as an element of the moduli space $\overset{\circ}{\mathcal{M}}_{0,1}([\ell_p, w], [\ell_q, w'_0])$, the point $(0, 0) \in \mathbb{R} \times [0, 1]$ is regarded as a marked point.)

DEFINITION 2.4.29. Let $[\ell_p, w], [\ell_q, w'] \in Cr(L_0, L_1)$ and $\beta_{(0)} \in \Pi(L_0)$ and $\beta_{(1)} \in \Pi(L_1)$. For each $i = 0, 1$, we put

$$\mathrm{Int}\,\mathcal{N}([\ell_p, w], [\ell_q, w'] : L_1, \beta_{(1)})$$
$$= \bigcup_{\beta_{(1)}, w''_1; w''_1 \# \beta_{(1)} = w'} \frac{\overset{\circ}{\mathcal{M}}_{1,0}([\ell_p, w], [\ell_q, w''_1])_{ev} \times_{ev_0} \mathcal{M}_1(L_1; \beta_{(1)}; J_1)}{\mathbb{R}},$$

$$\mathrm{Int}\,\mathcal{N}([\ell_p, w], [\ell_q, w'] : L_0, \beta_{(0)})$$
$$= \bigcup_{\beta_{(0)}, w''_0; w''_0 \# \beta_{(0)} = w'} \frac{\overset{\circ}{\mathcal{M}}_{0,1}([\ell_p, w], [\ell_q, w''_0])_{ev} \times_{ev_0} \mathcal{M}_1(L_0; \beta_{(0)}; J_0)}{\mathbb{R}}.$$

We define the moduli space $\mathcal{N}([\ell_p, w], [\ell_q, w'] : L_1, \beta_{(1)})$ as the closure of the moduli space $\mathrm{Int}\,\mathcal{N}([\ell_p, w], [\ell_q, w'] : L_1, \beta_{(1)})$ in $\mathcal{M}([\ell_p, w], [\ell_q, w'])$. The definition of $\mathcal{N}([\ell_p, w], [\ell_q, w'] : L_0, \beta_{(0)})$ is similar. (See Figure 2.4.3.)

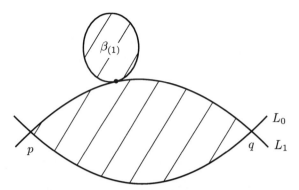

Figure 2.4.3: $\mathcal{N}([\ell_p, w], [\ell_q, w'] : L_1, \beta_{(1)})$

As we pointed out before, we would like to say that $\mathcal{N}([\ell_p, w], [\ell_q, w'] : L_i, \beta_{(i)})$ is of codimension one. This statement, in a naive sense, will not make sense even for a generic choice of $\{J_t\}_t$ in general. (It *does* make sense in general if we regard them as spaces with Kuranishi structures.) However this is really the case if one can choose such $\{J_t\}_t$ and if (L_0, L_1) is monotone. We restrict ourselves to monotone case here.

We recall that a pseudo-holomorphic map $u : \Sigma \to M$ (from a Riemann surface Σ which may or may not be bordered) is said to be *somewhere injective*, if there exists $p \in \Sigma$ and a neighborhood U of p such that

$(2.4.30.1)$ $\qquad\qquad\qquad u(p) \cap u(\Sigma \setminus U) = \emptyset,$

$(2.4.30.2)$ $\qquad\qquad\qquad u$ is an immersion at p.

We recall that the following facts hold for generic $J \in \mathcal{J}_\omega$ [**McD87**].

$(2.4.31.1)$ If $\partial\Sigma = \emptyset$ then any pseudo-holomorphic map $u : \Sigma \to M$ decomposes $u = \overline{u} \circ \pi$ where $\pi : \Sigma \to \overline{\Sigma}$ is a branched covering and $\overline{u} : \overline{\Sigma} \to M$ is somewhere injective.

$(2.4.31.2)$ If $u : \Sigma \to M$ is somewhere injective then the moduli space of pseudo-holomorphic maps is smooth and of correct dimension in a neighborhood of u.

(We do not use somewhere-injectivity except this section. So the reader can skip the rest of this section and proceed to the next chapter if he is not familiar with somewhere-injectivity.)

THEOREM 2.4.32. *Suppose that L_0, L_1 are monotone, $J_0, J_1 \in \mathcal{J}_\omega^0(L_0, L_1)$ and $\{J_t\}_t \in \mathcal{P}^0(\mathcal{J}_\omega; J_0, J_1)$ are as in Theorem 2.4.24. We assume that*

$(2.4.33)$ $\qquad\qquad\qquad \mu([\ell_q, w']) - \mu([\ell_p, w]) \le 2.$

Then $\mathcal{N}([\ell_p, w], [\ell_q, w'] : L_i, \beta_{(i)})$ for both $i = 0, 1$ are smooth manifolds of dimension $\mu([\ell_q, w']) - \mu([\ell_p, w]) - 2$.

PROOF. This will follow from a simple dimension counting of the fiber product in Definition 2.4.29. We consider only the case $i = 1$.

By definition, $\mathcal{N}([\ell_p, w], [\ell_q, w'] : L_1, \beta_{(1)})$ is the fiber product

$(2.4.34)$ $\qquad \dfrac{\overset{\circ}{\mathcal{M}}_{1,0}([\ell_p, w], [\ell_q, w_1''])_{ev} \times_{ev_0} \mathcal{M}_1(L_1; \beta_{(1)}; J_1)}{\mathbb{R}} = \dfrac{(ev \times ev_0)^{-1}(\Delta)}{\mathbb{R}}.$

Here $\Delta \subset L_1 \times L_1$ is the diagonal and $\overset{\circ}{\mathcal{M}}_{1,0}([\ell_p, w], [\ell_q, w_1''])$ is as in (2.4.27). We recall:

$$\text{vir} \dim \overset{\circ}{\mathcal{M}}_{1,0}([\ell_p, w], [\ell_q, w'']) = \mu([\ell_q, w'']) - \mu([\ell_p, w]),$$
$$\text{vir} \dim \mathcal{M}_1(L_1, J_1; \beta_{(1)}) = n + \mu(\beta_{(1)}) - 2$$

and

$$\mu(\beta_{(1)}) = \mu([\ell_q, w']) - \mu([\ell_q, w'']).$$

By monotonicity, we find that $\mu(\beta_{(1)}) > 0$ if $\mathcal{M}(L_1; \beta_{(1)}; J_1) \neq \emptyset$. (Note $\beta_{(1)} \neq 0$.) Hence, (2.4.33) implies

$$\mu([\ell_q, w'']) - \mu([\ell_p, w]) \leq 1.$$

We first consider the case when $\mu([\ell_q, w'']) - \mu([\ell_p, w]) = 1$. Then, by Theorem 2.4.24, the moduli space

$$\overset{\circ}{\mathcal{M}}_{1,0}([\ell_p, w], [\ell_q, w_1'']) \subseteq \mathcal{M}([\ell_p, w], [\ell_q, w'']) \times \mathbb{R}$$

is smooth and of dimension $\mu([\ell_q, w'']) - \mu([\ell_p, w]) = 1$.

It follows that every element of $\mathcal{M}(L_1; \beta_{(1)}; J_1)$ is somewhere injective. In fact if $v \in \mathcal{M}(L_1; \beta_{(1)}; J_1)$ is not somewhere injective, then [**KwOh00, Lazz00**] imply that there exists v_i $(i = 1, \cdots, a, a \geq 2)$ such that $\sum[v_i] = [v]$ and $\mathcal{M}(L_1; [v_i]; J_1)$ is nonempty. This is impossible since $\mu_{L_1}(v_i) > 0$.

Hence $\mathcal{M}_1(L_1; \beta_{(1)}; J_1)$ is smooth and of dimension $n - 1$. Then by an argument which is by now standard, we can use somewhere-injectivity to show that the evaluation map

$$ev \times ev_0 : \overset{\circ}{\mathcal{M}}_{1,0}([\ell_p, w], [\ell_q, w_1'']) \times \mathcal{M}_1(L_1; \beta_{(1)}; J_1) \to L_1 \times L_1$$

is transverse to Δ for generic $J_0, J_1, \{J_t\}_t$. Therefore, the moduli space (2.4.34) becomes a smooth manifold of dimension

(2.4.35)
$$\mu([\ell_q, w_1'']) - \mu([\ell_p, w]) + n + \mu(\beta_{(1)}) - 2 - n$$
$$= \mu([\ell_q, w_1'']) - \mu([\ell_p, w]) + \mu(\beta_{(1)}) - 2$$
$$= \mu([\ell_q, w_1']) - \mu([\ell_p, w]) - 2,$$

as required.

We next consider the case $\mu([\ell_q, w_1'']) - \mu([\ell_p, w]) \leq 0$. Let us assume that (2.4.34) is nonempty. Then, Theorem 2.4.24 implies that $[\ell_q, w_1''] = [\ell_p, w]$ and that $\overset{\circ}{\mathcal{M}}_{1,0}([\ell_p, w], [\ell_q, w''])$ must consist of a stationary element $u \equiv p$. Moreover if (u, v) is an element of (2.4.34) (where $u \in \overset{\circ}{\mathcal{M}}_{1,0}([\ell_p, w], [\ell_q, w''])$ and $v \in \mathcal{M}_1(L_1; \beta_{(1)}; J_1)$) then v must pass through p. Furthermore we have $\mu(\beta_{(1)}) \leq 2$.

If v is not somewhere injective, then the image of v is contained in a union of $v_i : (D^2, \partial D^2) \to (M, L_1)$ such that $\mu([v_i]) < \mu([v]) \leq 2$ ([**KwOh00, Lazz00**]). Hence $\mathcal{M}_1(L_1; [v_i]; J_1)$ is a compact and smooth manifold of dimension

$$\dim \mathcal{M}_1(L_1; [v_i]; J_1) \leq n - 1.$$

Therefore, by re-choosing J_1 if necessary, the image of the evaluation map $ev : \mathcal{M}_1(L_1; [v_i]; J_1) \to L_1$ can avoid the zero dimensional set $L_0 \cap L_1$.

Thus we may assume that v is always somewhere injective if (u, v) is an element of (2.4.34). It follows that $\mathcal{M}_1(L_1; \beta_{(1)}; J_1)$ is a smooth manifold and the fiber product (2.4.34) is transversal.

The proof of Theorem 2.4.32 is complete. $\qquad\qquad\square$

Therefore we derive

THEOREM 2.4.36. *Let L_0, L_1 and $\{J_t\}_t$ be as in Theorem 2.4.32. We assume* (2.4.33). *Then we have the identity*

$$\partial \mathcal{M}([\ell_p, w], [\ell_q, w'])$$

$$= \bigcup_{\mu([\ell_r, w''])=\mu([\ell_q, w'])-1} \mathcal{M}([\ell_p, w], [\ell_r, w'']) \times \mathcal{M}([\ell_r, w''], [\ell_q, w'])$$

$$+ \bigcup_{\beta_{(0)}} \mathcal{N}([\ell_p, w], [\ell_q, w'] : L_0, \beta_{(0)}) + \bigcup_{\beta_{(1)}} \mathcal{N}([\ell_p, w], [\ell_q, w'] : L_1, \beta_{(1)}).$$

PROOF. Let u_i be a divergent sequence of elements of $\mathcal{M}([\ell_p, w], [\ell_q, w'])$. By Gromov's compactness theorem, one of the followings must occur in the limit (after taking a subsequence if necessary):

(2.4.37.1) u_i splits into a sum of various connecting orbits.
(2.4.37.2)   Bubbling-off spheres occur at some points of $\mathbb{R} \times [0, 1]$.
(2.4.37.3)   Bubbling-off discs occur at some boundary points of $\mathbb{R} \times [0, 1]$, i.e., at some points in $\mathbb{R} \times \{0, 1\}$.

(2.4.37.1) corresponds to the first term of Theorem 2.4.36 and (2.4.37.3) corresponds to the second and third terms there. (2.4.37.2) is a phenomenon of codimension 2 and so does not occur in the boundary of codimension 1. The last dimension counting argument is allowed by Theorem 2.4.32. Hence the proof.   □

By the standard cobordism argument, Theorem 2.4.36 implies the identity

$$0 = \langle (\delta_0 \circ \delta_0)([\ell_p, w]), [\ell_q, w'] \rangle + \sum_{\beta_{(0)}} \# \mathcal{N}([\ell_p, w], [\ell_q, w'] : L_0, \beta_{(0)})$$

(2.4.38)

$$+ \sum_{\beta_{(1)}} \# \mathcal{N}([\ell_p, w], [\ell_q, w'] : L_1, \beta_{(1)})$$

where $\langle (\delta_0 \circ \delta_0)([\ell_p, w]), [\ell_q, w'] \rangle$ denotes the coefficient of $[\ell_q, w']$ in $(\delta_0 \circ \delta_0)([\ell_p, w])$. Here $\#$ is the order with sign. We do not explain sign (that is the orientation of the moduli space) here, since it will be discussed in detail in later chapters, especially in Chapter 8.

Now we would like to study the following two cases separately as in [**Oh93, 96I**]:

(2.4.39.1)   the case where L_0, L_1 have the minimal Maslov number > 2,
(2.4.39.2)   the case where one or both of L_0, L_1 have the minimal Maslov number 2.

We start with the case (2.4.39.1). Based on the observation that if $\beta_{(i)} \in \Pi(M; L_i)$ satisfies $\mu(\beta_{(i)}) > 2$, then $\mathcal{N}([\ell_p, w], [\ell_q, w'] : L_i, \beta_{(i)}) = \emptyset$ for a generic choice of $\{J_t\}_t$ when $\mu([\ell_q, w']) - \mu([\ell_p, w]) = 2$, the second named author proved [**Oh93**] that the extra terms in (2.4.38) become zero by a dimension counting argument. We recall this argument below in the more current language used in this book.

Let us consider only the case $i = 1$. In [**Oh93**] the following moduli space

$$\mathcal{M}^\partial(L_1; \beta_{(1)}) = (\widetilde{\mathcal{M}}(L_1; \beta_{(1)}) \times S^1)/PSL(2; \mathbb{R})$$

and the evaluation map

$$ev^\partial : \mathcal{M}^\partial(L_1; \beta_{(1)}) \to L_1; \quad ev^\partial([w, t]) = w(t)$$

are considered. Note that the dimension of $\mathcal{M}^\partial(L_1; \beta_{(1)})$ is $\mu(\beta_{(1)}) + n - 2$. We also remark that $\mathcal{M}^\partial(L_1; \beta_{(1)})$ in fact coincides with $\mathcal{M}_1(L_1; \beta_{(1)})$ and ev^∂ coincides with $ev_0 : \mathcal{M}_1(L_1; \beta_{(1)}) \to L_1$. Therefore if we assume the minimal Maslov numbers of L_0, L_1 are greater than 2 and so $\mu(\beta_{(1)}) > 2$, we have $\dim \mathcal{M}_1(L_1; \beta_{(1)}) > \dim L_1$ when $\mathcal{M}_1(L_1; \beta_{(1)})$ is transverse and has the correct dimension. In this case, the chain $ev_0 : \mathcal{M}_1(L_1; \beta_{(1)}) \to L_1$ is degenerate and so becomes zero *as a chain* of dimension $\dim \mathcal{M}_1(L_1; \beta_{(1)})$ on L_1, which turns out to be the reason behind the argument below.

We recall that $\langle(\delta_0 \circ \delta_0)([\ell_p, w]), [\ell_q, w']\rangle$ is nonzero only when $\mu([\ell_q, w']) - \mu([\ell_p, w]) = 2$. Therefore from the dimension formula (2.4.35)

$$\mu([\ell_q, w_1'']) - \mu([\ell_p, w]) + \mu(\beta_{(1)}) - 2$$

of the fiber product

(2.4.40)
$$\frac{\overset{\circ}{\mathcal{M}}_{1,0}([\ell_p, w], [\ell_q, w_1''])_{ev} \times_{ev_0} \mathcal{M}_1(L_1; \beta_{(1)})}{\mathbb{R}}$$

and from Theorem 2.4.24, we derive its dimension to be $\mu([\ell_q, w_1'']) - \mu([\ell_p, w]) + \mu(\beta_{(1)}) - 2 = 0$. Therefore we have

(2.4.41)
$$\mu([\ell_q, w_1'']) - \mu([\ell_p, w]) = 2 - \mu(\beta_{(1)}) < 0$$

due to the hypothesis (2.4.39.1).

(2.4.41), (2.4.25.3) implies:

$$\overset{\circ}{\mathcal{M}}_{1,0}([\ell_p, w], [\ell_q, w_1'']) = \emptyset$$

and so $\mathcal{N}([\ell_p, w], [\ell_q, w'] : L_1, \beta_{(1)})$ must be empty. This proves the following theorem which was proved by the second named author in [**Oh93**]. (The statement below is slightly improved. For example $R = \mathbb{Z}$ in case L_1, L_0 is a relatively spin pair.)

THEOREM 2.4.42. (Oh) *Let L_0, L_1 be monotone Lagrangian submanifolds. We assume that their minimal Maslov number are larger than 2. Then the coboundary operator*

$$\delta_0 : CF_R^*(L_1, L_0; \ell_0) \to CF_R^{*+1}(L_1, L_0; \ell_0)$$

defined by (2.4.26) satisfies

$$\delta_0 \circ \delta_0 = 0.$$

Here we put $R = \mathbb{Z}$ if L_0, L_1 is a relatively spin pair and $R = \mathbb{Z}_2$ in general.

Hence, in case (2.4.39.1), we define Floer cohomology

$$HF(L_1, L_0; \ell_0) = \text{Ker } \delta_0 / \text{Im } \delta_0.$$

We can prove that it is independent of Hamiltonian isotopy classes of L_0, L_1. We do not give its detail here since we prove more general results later in Chapter 5.

Now we study the case (2.4.39.2) where the minimal Maslov number of L_1 or of L_0 is 2. In this case (2.4.41) is replaced by

$$\mu([\ell_q, w_1'']) - \mu([\ell_p, w]) = 2 - \mu(\beta_{(1)}) \leq 0$$

and so we must have $\mu([\ell_q, w_1'']) - \mu([\ell_p, w]) = 0$ and $\mu(\beta_{(1)}) = 2$. By Theorem 2.4.24, $\mu([\ell_q, w_1'']) - \mu([\ell_p, w]) = 0$ implies that $p = q$ and v must pass through p, where (u, v) is an element of (2.4.40). Furthermore the chain $ev_0 : \mathcal{M}_1(L_1; \beta_{(1)}) \to L_1$ defines an n dimensional compact cycle and so a multiple of the fundamental class $[L_1]$. This cycle can indeed be non-zero as Example 2.4.14 illustrates and so the corresponding fiber product can really exist. The outcome is that $\delta_0 \circ \delta_0 \neq 0$ can really occur even for the monotone Lagrangian submanifolds for which most of the needed transversality properties can be obtained *just by perturbing the almost complex structures*.

In the case when $L_1 = \psi(L_0)$ for some Hamiltonian diffeomorphism ψ, the equality $\delta_0 \circ \delta_0 = 0$ holds under the milder assumption that the minimal Maslov number is not smaller than 2. See [**Oh93**] or Subsection 3.6.3 of this book.

One important idea introduced in the present book to define Floer cohomology of Lagrangian submanifold beyond the case of Theorem 2.4.42 is that we impose a *homological* condition on L_i that the chain $ev_0 : \mathcal{M}_1(L_i; \beta_{(i)}) \to L_i$, which becomes a cycle when $\beta_{(i)}$ is of the minimal possible symplectic area, is homologous to zero, and then use a chain bounding this cycle to modify the standard Floer coboundary map δ_0 to δ in order to achieve $\delta \circ \delta = 0$. It turns out that a coherent explanation on the this dependence on the parameters together with the transversality issues requires a bulk of algebraic machinery of new homological algebra and deformation theory of *filtered A_∞ algebra*.

REMARK 2.4.43. Using the terminology of filtered A_∞ bimodule introduced in Section 3.7, Theorem 2.4.36 can be written as:

$$
(2.4.44) \quad
\begin{aligned}
\langle (\mathfrak{n}_{0,0} \circ \mathfrak{n}_{0,0})([\ell_p, w]), [\ell_q, w'] \rangle = \; &\pm \, \langle \mathfrak{n}_{1,0}(\mathfrak{m}_0(1), [\ell_p, w]), [\ell_q, w'] \rangle \\
&\pm \, \langle \mathfrak{n}_{0,1}([\ell_p, w], \mathfrak{m}_0(1)), [\ell_q, w'] \rangle.
\end{aligned}
$$

Namely the second and the third terms of (2.4.38) is the right hand side of (2.4.44). On the other hand, the first term of (2.4.38) is the left hand side of (2.4.44). We remark that (2.4.44) follows from the equality

$$(\mathfrak{n}_{0,0} \circ \mathfrak{n}_{0,0})(x) \pm \mathfrak{n}_{1,0}(\mathfrak{m}_0(1), x) \pm \mathfrak{n}_{0,1}(x, \mathfrak{m}_0(1)) = 0,$$

which is a special case of the defining equation of the filtered A_∞ bimodule. Actually it is the $Hom(D, D) = Hom(B_0 C_1[1] \otimes D \otimes B_0 C_0[1], D)$ component of $\hat{d}^2 = 0$. See Definition 3.7.5 (1).

REMARK 2.4.45. We remark the role of the based path ℓ_0 in our construction. The point of view that our Lagrangian intersection theory should be about the *based* space of paths, rather than the space of paths will be important in defining the chain homomorphism under the Hamiltonian isotopy of Lagrangian submanifolds (See Section 5.3). The choice of section λ^0 of $\ell_0^* \Lambda(M)$ (see Subsection 2.2.2) is also needed to provide an *absolute* grading of the Floer complex and to define a *degree preserving* chain homomorphism between the Floer cohomology *over the Novikov rings* under the Hamiltonian isotopy. We refer to Section 5.1 for more explanations on this point.

CHAPTER 3

The A_∞ algebra associated to a Lagrangian submanifold

3.1. Outline of Chapter 3

As we explained in the previous chapter, Floer cohomology for Lagrangian intersection can not be defined, in general. This trouble comes from the existence of pseudo-holomorphic discs bubbling off at the boundary of a pseudo-holomorphic strip. When one considers the stable map compactification of moduli spaces of certain pseudo-holomorphic discs or strips to define the "coboundary operator" in the usual way, the bubbling-off discs appear in the *real codimension one* boundary components. On the other hand, it is known that Floer cohomology of the periodic Hamiltonian system can be defined for arbitrary closed symplectic manifolds ([**FuOn99II, LuTi98, Rua99**]). In this case, we use the moduli spaces of stable maps of genus zero without boundary to define the coboundary operator, where the bubbling-off spheres appear in the strata of *real codimension two* (i.e., complex codimension one). Therefore, after we settle transversality argument by using the Kuranishi structure introduced in [**FuOn99II**], we can prove that these bubbling off spheres do not contribute to the coboundary operator. Thus the theory can be formulated in the (co)homology level. In the Lagrangian intersection case, however, it is necessary to develop our theory in the *(co)chain level*, because of this existence of the real codimension one strata corresponding to bubbling off discs. For this purpose, we introduce and construct a certain homotopical algebra called a *filtered A_∞ algebra*. Roughly speaking, an A_∞ algebra is a graded module $\oplus C^\bullet$ with infinitely many operations $\mathfrak{m} = \{\mathfrak{m}_k\}_{k=0,1,2,\cdots}$;

$$\mathfrak{m}_k : \underbrace{C^* \otimes \cdots \otimes C^*}_{k \text{ times}} \longrightarrow C^*, \qquad (k = 0, 1, 2, \cdots)$$

which satisfy certain relations called the A_∞ formula, or the A_∞ relation. We call $\mathfrak{m}$ an A_∞ structure. See Definition 3.2.3 (unfiltered A_∞ algebra) and Definition 3.2.20 (filtered A_∞ algebra) for the precise definitions. We will provide the basic material of A_∞ algebras and filtered A_∞ algebras in Section 3.2. Historically, J. Stasheff introduced the notion of (unfiltered) A_∞ algebras in [**Sta63**] inspired by M. Sugawara's work [**Sug57**], to study the homotopy theory of loop spaces. (See [**Ada78, BoVo73**] for related works.) One geometric aspect of the A_∞ structure is that it describes the codimension one degeneration of trees (contractible 1-dimensional CW complex). Since all the configurations of bubbling off holomorphic discs (genus zero) can be described by trees, the A_∞ structure appears naturally in our story. An A_∞ algebra can be regarded as generalizations of D.G.A. (differential graded algebra) and has played an important role in the deformation theory (see [**GoMi88,90, GugSt86**] for example). We will investigate a deformation theory of Lagrangian submanifolds and their Floer cohomology in terms of our A_∞ algebra. This is the main theme of Chapters 4 and 5.

Before we state the main results of this chapter, we like to mention the issue of orientations. The moduli space of pseudo-holomorphic discs with the Lagrangian boundary condition is not always orientable, while it is well known that the moduli space of pseudo-holomorphic maps from a closed Riemann surface is always orientable and has a canonical orientation. Moreover, since we use the stable map compactification of pseudo-holomorphic maps and the Kuranishi structure, the fundamental chain of the moduli spaces are defined over $\mathbb{Q}$, not over $\mathbb{Z}$ in general. In particular, we can not work over $\mathbb{Z}/2\mathbb{Z}$-coefficients in general and hence can not avoid the orientation problem. These points will be studied in Chapter 8 in detail.

Here we introduce the notion of relative spinness which gives a condition for orientability of the moduli space of pseudo-holomorphic discs with Lagrangian boundary condition. The proof will be given in Section 8.1.

DEFINITION 3.1.1. (1) Let L be an oriented Lagrangian submanifold in a symplectic manifold M. We call L a *relatively spin* Lagrangian submanifold, if there exists $st \in H^2(M; \mathbb{Z}/2\mathbb{Z})$ such that $st|_L = w_2(TL) \in H^2(L; \mathbb{Z}/2\mathbb{Z})$.

(2) A pair of oriented Lagrangian submanifolds $(L^{(0)}, L^{(1)})$ in M is called a *relatively spin pair*, if there exists $st \in H^2(M; \mathbb{Z}/2\mathbb{Z})$ such that $st|_{L^{(0)}} = w_2(TL^{(0)})$ and $st|_{L^{(1)}} = w_2(TL^{(1)})$ simultaneously.

For example, if L is spin, it is obviously relatively spin. In particular, when $\dim_{\mathbb{R}} M \leq 6$, every orientable Lagrangian submanifolds is automatically relatively spin. To specify an orientation on the moduli space of pseudo-holomorphic discs with a Lagrangian boundary condition, we need some more data, which we call relative spin structure. See Definition 8.1.2 in Chapter 8.

Throughout this chapter, we assume that L is a relatively spin Lagrangian submanifold and $(L^{(0)}, L^{(1)})$ is a relatively spin pair, unless otherwise mentioned.

The first main result (Theorem 3.5.11) of this chapter is the construction of a filtered A_∞ algebra associated to a relatively spin Lagrangian submanifold L which encodes contributions of all pseudo-holomorphic discs attached to L. The obstruction to defining Floer cohomology can be seen in terms of this filtered A_∞ algebra. We use universal Novikov ring $\Lambda_{0,nov}(R)$. See (Conv.4) in Chapter 1. (In the algebraic part of the story we mostly work with $\Lambda_{0,nov}(R)$ for a commutative ring R with unit such as $R = \mathbb{Z}$ or $R = \mathbb{Z}/2$. Those algebraic materials are used in [**FOOO09I**].) The relationship between this ring and the standard Novikov ring in the literature (and in Chapter 2) will be explained in Section 5.1, Chapter 5. We denote by $\Lambda_{nov}^{(k)}$ and $\Lambda_{0,nov}^{(k)}$ the grading k parts of them, respectively. When we need to specify the ring R, we write $\Lambda_{nov}(R)$, $\Lambda_{0,nov}(R)$ etc. (We also write them as Λ_{nov}^R, $\Lambda_{0,nov}^R$ sometimes.)

The rings $\Lambda_{nov}, \Lambda_{0,nov}, \Lambda_{0,nov}^+$ have filtrations $F^\lambda \Lambda_{nov}$ etc. See (Conv.6), (1.37). Thus Λ_{nov} and $\Lambda_{0,nov}$ become filtered graded rings which are complete. We note that Λ_{nov} is a localization of $\Lambda_{0,nov}$.

We will construct a filtered A_∞ algebra over $\Lambda_{0,nov}(\mathbb{Q})$ associated to a relatively spin Lagrangian submanifold. We will also construct a deformed Floer cohomology with $\Lambda_{0,nov}(\mathbb{Q})$-coefficients, when it is possible. In this case the parameter λ_i geometrically stands for the symplectic area (or the energy) of a pseudo-holomorphic disc and $2n_i$ for its Maslov index. The ring $\Lambda_{nov}(\mathbb{Q})$ will be used when we study the invariance of Floer cohomology under the Hamiltonian isotopy.

We start with the geometric realization of an (unfiltered) A_∞ algebra in the classical picture. In this case, we can construct an A_∞ algebra over $\mathbb{Z}$ since we can use a system of single-valued sections but not of multi-values ones in the construction of associated fundamental chains. (See Section 3.4 for the details.) Let $S^k(L;\mathbb{Z})$ be the free $\mathbb{Z}$ module generated by all codimension k smooth singular simplices of L. We regard $S(L;\mathbb{Z}) = \bigoplus_k S^k(L;\mathbb{Z})$ as a *cochain* complex. Choose a countable set $\mathcal{X}_L$ of smooth singular simplices and denote by $\mathbb{Z}\mathcal{X}_L$ the free $\mathbb{Z}$ submodule of $S(L;\mathbb{Z})$ generated by $\mathcal{X}_L$. Then we prove the following theorem in Section 3.4 (Theorem 3.4.8).

We take an appropriate smooth simplicial decomposition of L and represent the fundamental class as a smooth singular chain $PD[L]$. (Here we write $PD[L]$ in place of $[L]$ since we regard a codimension k singular chain as a k cochain. This identification may be regarded as a Poincaré duality.)

THEOREM 3.1.2. *For any oriented manifold L, there exists $\mathcal{X}_L$ such that we can construct an A_∞ structure denoted by $\overline{\mathfrak{m}}^L$ over $\mathbb{Z}$ on $\mathbb{Z}\mathcal{X}_L$. It has a homotopy unit $PD[L]$. Moreover, the cohomology group of $(\mathbb{Z}\mathcal{X}_L, \overline{\mathfrak{m}}_1^L)$ is isomorphic to the cohomology group (over $\mathbb{Z}$-coefficient) of L.*

We will give the definition of a homotopy unit of an A_∞ algebra in Section 3.3 (Definition 3.3.2). Here we have to choose a suitable countable set $\mathcal{X}_L$ because we need and use the transversality argument and the Baire category theorem.

REMARK 3.1.3. In Section 4.6, we will prove that the weak homotopy equivalence class of the A_∞ algebra $(\mathbb{Z}\mathcal{X}_L, \overline{\mathfrak{m}}^L)$ constructed above is uniquely determined by L. Moreover, when we put $\mathbb{R}\mathcal{X}_L = \mathbb{Z}\mathcal{X}_L \otimes \mathbb{R}$ and extend $\overline{\mathfrak{m}}^L$ to $\mathbb{R}\mathcal{X}_L$, then $(\mathbb{R}\mathcal{X}_L, \overline{\mathfrak{m}}^L)$ is homotopy equivalent to the de Rham D.G.A. of L over $\mathbb{R}$. See Section 7.5 as for more discussions on the relationship between our results and the rational homotopy theory due to Quillen and Sullivan [**Qui69, Sull78**].

Next, we will construct a filtered A_∞ algebra over $\Lambda_{0,nov}(\mathbb{Q})$ associated to a Lagrangian submanifold L. Denote by $\mathcal{X}_1(L)$ a countable set of smooth singular simplices such that $\mathcal{X}_1(L) \supset \mathcal{X}_L$ where $\mathcal{X}_L$ is chosen as in Theorem 3.1.2 above. We sometimes write an element in $\mathcal{X}_1(L)$ as $P = (|P|, f)$. Here $|P|$ is an $n-k$ dimensional simplex and $f : |P| \to L$ is a smooth map. We denote by $C^k(L;\mathbb{Q})$ a submodule of $S^k(L;\mathbb{Q})$ generated by $\mathcal{X}_1(L)$. We define $C^\bullet(L;\Lambda_{0,nov})$ to be the completion of $C^\bullet(L;\mathbb{Q}) \otimes \Lambda_{0,nov}$;

$$C^\bullet(L;\Lambda_{0,nov}) := (C^\bullet(L;\mathbb{Q}) \otimes_{\mathbb{Q}} \Lambda_{0,nov})\widehat{}$$

with respect to the uniform structure induced by a filtration similar to (1.38). To an element $xT^\lambda e^n \in C(L;\Lambda_{0,nov})$ with $x \in C(L;\mathbb{Q})$, we assign a degree defined by $\deg(xT^\lambda e^n) := \deg x + 2n$, where $\deg x$ is the degree of x as cochain. We put $C[1]^k = C^{k+1}$ and denote by $\deg'$ the shifted degree, that is, $\deg'(xT^\lambda e^n) = \deg(xT^\lambda e^n) - 1$.

Let $\mathcal{M}_{k+1}^{\mathrm{main}}(\beta)$ be the main component of moduli space of bordered stable pseudo-holomorphic maps to (M, L) of genus zero with $k+1$ marked points on the boundary, whose homotopy class is $\beta \in \Pi(M; L) = \pi_2(M; L)/\sim$. (See Definition 2.4.17.) For $P_i \in \mathcal{X}_1(L)$, we consider a fiber product

$$(3.1.4) \qquad \mathcal{M}_{k+1}^{\mathrm{main}}(\beta) \, {}_{(ev_1,\cdots,ev_k)}\times_{f_1\times\cdots\times f_k} (P_1 \times \cdots \times P_k),$$

where ev_i $(i = 0, 1, \cdots, k)$ is the evaluation map at the i-th marked point. Here and hereafter we write P_i in place of $|P_i|$ in case no confusion can occur. We can show that (3.1.4) is a space with Kuranishi structure. We denote the set (3.1.4) by $\mathcal{M}_{k+1}^{\mathrm{main}}(\beta; \vec{P})$, where $\vec{P} = (P_1, \cdots, P_k)$. The following is our first main theorem in this chapter.

THEOREM 3.1.5. *Let L be a relatively spin Lagrangian submanifold. Then for any given $\mathcal{X}_L$ satisfying Theorem 3.1.2 there exist choices of $\mathcal{X}_1(L) \supset \mathcal{X}_L$ and of a system of multisections $\mathfrak{s}_{\beta,\vec{P}}$ of $\mathcal{M}_{k+1}^{\mathrm{main}}(\beta; \vec{P})$ with which we can construct a filtered A_∞ structure $\mathfrak{m} = \{\mathfrak{m}_k\}$ over $\Lambda_{0,nov}$ on $C^\bullet(L; \Lambda_{0,nov})$. Moreover, it has a homotopy unit and satisfies the $G(L)$-gapped condition.*

We will give the definition of the G-gapped condition in Section 3.2 (Definition 3.2.26), which is related to Gromov's compactness property of pseudo-holomorphic curves. Let $G \subset \mathbb{R}_{\geq 0} \times 2\mathbb{Z}$ be a submonoid of $\mathbb{R}_{\geq 0} \times 2\mathbb{Z}$. (Namely, $(0,0) \in G$, $\beta, \beta' \in G \Rightarrow \beta + \beta' \in G$). We assume the following:

CONDITION 3.1.6.
(3.1.7.1)   Let $\pi : \mathbb{R}_{\geq 0} \times 2\mathbb{Z} \to \mathbb{R}_{\geq 0}$ be the projection. Then $\pi(G) \subset \mathbb{R}_{\geq 0}$ is discrete.
(3.1.7.2) $G \cap (\{0\} \times 2\mathbb{Z}) = \{(0,0)\}$.
(3.1.7.3) $G \cap (\{\lambda\} \times 2\mathbb{Z})$ is a finite set for any λ.

In Theorem 3.1.5, we take $G(L)$ as follows: We define $G(L)_0$ by

$$G(L)_0 = \{(\omega[\beta], \mu_L(\beta)) \mid \beta \in \Pi(L), \ \mathcal{M}(L; \beta; J) \neq \emptyset\},$$

where $\omega[\beta]$ is the symplectic area and $\mu_L(\beta)$ is the Maslov index. See Definition 2.4.17 as for the notation $\Pi(L)$. Now we define

(3.1.8) $G(L) = $ the submonoid of $\mathbb{R}_{\geq 0} \times 2\mathbb{Z}$ generated by $G(L)_0$.

Then $G(L)$ satisfies Condition 3.1.6 by Gromov's compactness theorem. (Recall that the Maslov index for an oriented Lagrangian submanifold is always even.) We remark that $G(L)$ may depend on the compatible almost complex structure J, in general.

There are nontrivial issues of the transversality and of the sign that we have to solve in relation to the choice of $\mathcal{X}_1(L)$ and to the construction of the system of multisections $\mathfrak{s}_{\beta,\vec{P}}$ in the theorem above. Postponing the study of the transversality till Chapter 7 and the sign problems till Chapter 8, we will prove Theorem 3.1.5 in Section 3.5 (Theorem 3.5.11). Since we use the notions of Kuranishi structures and of multisections, various fundamental chains are defined over $\mathbb{Q}$, not $\mathbb{Z}$ in general. This is the reason why we take $R = \mathbb{Q}$ in this construction.

By reducing the coefficient ring $\Lambda_{0,nov}$ to $\mathbb{Q}$, we discard the contribution of pseudo-holomorphic discs as we mentioned before. Then we obtain the following result (3.5.12.3) Theorem 3.5.11. Its proof will be completed in Subsection 7.2.8 using the results of Subsection 7.2.9 and Section 8.9.)

THEOREM 3.1.9. *Let $(C(L; \mathbb{Q}), \overline{\mathfrak{m}})$ be the A_∞ algebra over $\mathbb{Q}$ with $\overline{\mathfrak{m}}_0 = 0$ as the reduction of $(C(L; \Lambda_{0,nov}), \mathfrak{m})$ in Theorem 3.1.5. Then the restriction of $\overline{\mathfrak{m}}$ to $\mathbb{Q}\mathcal{X}_L \subset C(L; \mathbb{Q})$ coincides with $\overline{\mathfrak{m}}^L$ which is constructed in Theorem 3.1.2.*

Thus our filtered A_∞ algebra $(C(L; \Lambda_{0,nov}), \mathfrak{m})$ can be interpreted as a quantum deformation of the rational (more precisely real) homotopy type of L. The word of 'quantum' here means to include all nonlinear contributions coming from pseudo-holomorphic discs (called *disc instantons* in physics literature).

Due to the presence of non-zero $\mathfrak{m}_0$ in a filtered A_∞ algebra $(C(L;\Lambda_{0,nov}),\mathfrak{m})$, the operator $\mathfrak{m}_1$ in Theorem 3.1.10 does *not* satisfy $\mathfrak{m}_1 \circ \mathfrak{m}_1 = 0$ in general. This is the obstruction to defining Floer cohomology of L. On the other hand, using any $b \in C[1]^0 = C^1$, we can deform $\mathfrak{m}$ to $\mathfrak{m}^b$ by

$$\mathfrak{m}_k^b(x_1,\cdots,x_k)$$
$$= \sum_{\ell_0,\cdots,\ell_k} \mathfrak{m}_{k+\sum \ell_i}(\underbrace{b,\cdots,b}_{\ell_0},x_1,\underbrace{b,\cdots,b}_{\ell_1},\cdots,\underbrace{b,\cdots,b}_{\ell_{k-1}},x_k,\underbrace{b,\cdots,b}_{\ell_k})$$
$$= \mathfrak{m}(e^b x_1 e^b x_2 \cdots x_{k-1} e^b x_k e^b)$$

for $k = 0,1,2\cdots$, so that $(C,\mathfrak{m}^b)$ is also a filtered A_∞ algebra. (See Definition 3.6.9). Here we use a notation

$$e^b := 1 + b + b \otimes b + b \otimes b \otimes b + \cdots.$$

In addition, if b satisfies an A_∞ version of *Maurer-Cartan equation*:

$$(3.1.10) \qquad \mathfrak{m}(e^b) := \mathfrak{m}_0(1) + \mathfrak{m}_1(b) + \mathfrak{m}_2(b,b) + \mathfrak{m}_3(b,b,b) + \cdots = 0,$$

we achieve $\mathfrak{m}_0^b = 0$ (Proposition 3.6.10). Then $\mathfrak{m}_1^b \circ \mathfrak{m}_1^b = 0$ and we can define the cohomology of $(C(L;\Lambda_{0,nov}),\mathfrak{m}_1^b)$. We call a solution b of the Maurer-Cartan equation (3.1.10) a *bounding cochain*. (We also assume that $b \equiv 0 \mod \Lambda_{0,nov}^+$ for the sake of convergence of the left hand side in (3.1.10).)

We denote the set of solutions by $\widehat{\mathcal{M}}\big((C(L;\Lambda_{0,nov}),\mathfrak{m})\big) = \widehat{\mathcal{M}}(L)$ and say that L is *unobstructed* if $\widehat{\mathcal{M}}(L) \neq \emptyset$. If L is unobstructed, we define Floer cohomology deformed by $b \in \widehat{\mathcal{M}}(L)$;

$$HF(L,b;\Lambda_{0,nov}) := H(C(L;\Lambda_{0,nov}),\mathfrak{m}_1^b).$$

The next problem is to obtain some condition for L to be unobstructed. For this purpose, we will construct a sequence of elements $\{[o_k(L)]\}_{k=1,2,\cdots}$ of $H(L;\mathbb{Q})$, which we call the *(Floer) obstruction classes*. Since $G(L)$ satisfies Condition 3.1.6, we may put

$$G(L) = \{(\lambda_i,\mu_i) = (\omega[\beta_i],\mu_L(\beta_i)) \mid i = 0,1,2,\cdots\}$$

such that $i < j \Rightarrow \lambda_i \leq \lambda_j$. (Note that $\lambda_0 = \mu_0 = 0$ and $0 < \lambda_1$.) If $\omega[\beta] = \omega[\beta']$ for some β,β', there is more than one way of enumerating $G(L)$. However the results we obtain are independent of the enumeration.

THEOREM 3.1.11. *Let $(C(L;\Lambda_{0,nov}),\mathfrak{m})$ be the filtered A_∞ algebra constructed in Theorem 3.1.5. Then we have the sequences of cochains $o_k(L)$ and $b_k(L)$ ($k = 1,2,\cdots$) with the following properties:*

(3.1.12.1) $[o_k(L)] \in H^{2-\mu_k}(L,\mathbb{Q})$ *and* $b_k(L) \in C^{1-\mu_k}(L;\mathbb{Q})$. *Here* $\mu_k = \mu_L(\beta_k)$ *is the Maslov index of β_k which is even.*
(3.1.12.2)   *The cocycle $o_k(L)$ is defined if $b_j(L)$ and $o_j(L)$ for j with $\lambda_j \lneqq \lambda_k$ are defined. $[o_k(L)]$ depends on $b_j(L)$ and $o_j(L)$ for j with $\lambda_j \lneqq \lambda_k$.*
(3.1.12.3) $b_k(L)$ *is defined to be a cochain satisfying* $-\mathfrak{m}_{1,0}(b_k) = o_k$ *if* $[o_k(L)] = 0$.

(3.1.12.4)   *L is unobstructed if and only if there exists an inductive choice of* $b_k(L)$ *such that* $[o_k(L)]$ *are all zero.*

The obstruction classes can be constructed purely algebraically in any abstract filtered A_∞ algebra satisfying the G-gapped condition. In fact, we carry out this construction in Subsection 3.6.2 (Theorem 3.6.18) in this general setting.

Moreover, we can define a refinement of the obstruction classes denoted by $[o_k(L; \text{weak})]$ where the preceding obstruction classes are assumed to vanish only for *non-positive* Maslov index. See Theorem 3.6.43. The refined obstruction classes $[o_k(L; \text{weak})]$ are related to a weaker condition to define the Floer cohomology as follows.

Recall that our A_∞ algebra $(C(L; \Lambda_{0,nov}), \mathfrak{m})$ has a homotopy unit. For an A_∞ algebra with homotopy unit, we introduce a weaker condition for defining Floer cohomology in Subsection 3.6.3. Let $(C, \mathfrak{m})$ be an A_∞ algebra over $\Lambda_{0,nov}$ with unit **e**. (See Definition 3.2.20 (3).) For $b \in C[1]^0$, we consider the equation

(3.1.13) $\mathfrak{m}(e^b) = ce\mathbf{e}$

for some $c \in \Lambda_{0,nov}^{+(0)}$ weaker than the Maurer-Cartan equation. (Here $\deg \mathbf{e} = 0$ and $\deg e = 2$. Thus $\deg(ce\mathbf{e}) - 1 = +1$.) We set

$$\widehat{\mathcal{M}}_{\text{weak}}(C) = \{b \in C[1]^0 \mid \mathfrak{m}(e^b) = ce\mathbf{e} \text{ for some } c \in \Lambda_{0,nov}^{+(0)}\}.$$

We say that an A_∞ algebra over $\Lambda_{0,nov}$ with unit **e** is *weakly unobstructed* if $\widehat{\mathcal{M}}_{\text{weak}}(C) \neq \emptyset$. For an A_∞ algebra $(C, \mathfrak{m})$ with homotopy unit, we have an associated A_∞ algebra $(C^+, \mathfrak{m}^+)$ with unit $\mathbf{e}^+$ (Definition 3.3.2). We say that an A_∞ algebra $(C, \mathfrak{m})$ with homotopy unit is *weakly unobstructed* if $\widehat{\mathcal{M}}_{\text{weak}}(C^+) \neq \emptyset$. For $b \in \widehat{\mathcal{M}}_{\text{weak}}(C^+)$, we define $\delta_{b,b}$ by

$$\delta_{b,b}(x) = \sum_{k_1, k_2 \geq 0} \mathfrak{m}^+_{k_1+k_2+1}(\underbrace{b, \cdots, b}_{k_1}, x, \underbrace{b, \cdots, b}_{k_2}),$$

which is nothing but $\mathfrak{m}_1^{+b}(x)$. Then it follows that $\delta_{b,b} \circ \delta_{b,b} = 0$ for $b \in \widehat{\mathcal{M}}_{\text{weak}}(C^+)$ (Lemma 3.6.33). Therefore if $(C(L; \Lambda_{0,nov}), \mathfrak{m})$ is weakly unobstructed, we can still define a Floer cohomology deformed by $b \in \widehat{\mathcal{M}}_{\text{weak}}(L) := \widehat{\mathcal{M}}_{\text{weak}}(C(L; \Lambda_{0,nov})^+)$ as

$$HF(L, b; \Lambda_{0,nov}) := H(C(L; \Lambda_{0,nov})^+, \mathfrak{m}_1^{+b}).$$

Theorem 3.6.43 shows that if all the refined obstruction classes $[o_k(L; \text{weak})]$ vanish then L is weakly unobstructed.

Now considering pseudo-holomorphic discs with *one interior marked point* in addition to the boundary marked points, we will show the following in Section 3.8. (See Theorem 3.8.11.)

THEOREM 3.1.14. *Let* $L \subset M$ *be a relatively spin Lagrangian submanifold of dimension* n. *Then*

(1) *If* $[GW_{0,1}(M)(L)] \neq 0$, *then* $\mathcal{M}(L) = \emptyset$.

(2) *If* $[GW_{0,1}(M)(L)] = 0$, *then the obstruction* $[o_k(L)]$ *lies in the kernel of the Gysin homomorphism* $i_! : H^{2-\mu_k}(L; \mathbb{Q}) \to H^{n+2-\mu_k}(M; \mathbb{Q})$.

Here

$$[GW_{0,1}(M)(L)] \in H(M; \mathbb{Q}) \otimes \Lambda_{0,nov}$$

is the Gromov-Witten invariant of genus zero with two marked points, one of that is attached to L. See Subsection 3.8.1 for the precise definition. See Corollaries 3.8.16 - 3.8.19 in Subsection 3.8.2 for some applications.

THEOREM 3.1.15. *There exists a sequence of obstruction classes*

$$[o_k(L; \mathrm{def})] \in \frac{H^{2-\mu_k}(L; \mathbb{Q})}{\mathrm{Im}\, i^* : H^{2-\mu_k}(M; \mathbb{Q}) \to H^{2-\mu_k}(L; \mathbb{Q})}$$

and $b_k \in C_2^{1-\mu_k}(L; \mathbb{Q})$, $\mathfrak{b}_k \in C^{2-\mu_k}(M; \mathbb{Q})$, $(\delta_M \mathfrak{b}_k = 0)$ *with the following properties.*

(3.1.16.1)   *The cocycle* $o_k(L; \mathrm{def})$ *is defined if* b_j *and* o_j *for* j *with* $\lambda_j \lneqq \lambda_k$ *are defined.* $[o_k(L; \mathrm{def})]$ *depends on* b_j *and* o_j *for* j *with* $\lambda_j \lneqq \lambda_k$.
(3.1.16.2) b_k, $\mathfrak{b}_k$ *are defined if* $[o_k(L; \mathrm{def})] = 0$.
(3.1.16.3) L *is unobstructed after bulk deformations if all of the obstruction classes* $[o_k(L; \mathrm{def})]$ *are defined and are zero.*

COROLLARY 3.1.17. *If* $i^* : H^{2k}(M; \mathbb{Q}) \to H^{2k}(L; \mathbb{Q})$ *is surjective for all* k, *then* L *is unobstructed after bulk deformations.*

If L is unobstructed after bulk deformation, we can also define Floer cohomology deformed by $(b, \mathfrak{b}) \in \widehat{\mathcal{M}}_{\mathrm{def}}(L)$, (Lemma 3.8.60). See Definition 3.8.40 for the set $\widehat{\mathcal{M}}_{\mathrm{def}}(L)$.

Involving the unit or the homotopy unit, we can similarly define $\widehat{\mathcal{M}}_{\mathrm{weak,def}}(L)$ and a sequence of obstruction cocycles $o_k(L; \mathrm{weak,def})$ which gives a generalization of Theorem 3.1.15. See Subsection 3.8.5.

So far, we have considered the case of single Lagrangian submanifolds. Next, we consider the case of pairs $(L^{(0)}, L^{(1)})$ of relatively spin Lagrangian submanifolds.

We first assume that $L^{(0)}$ is transversal to $L^{(1)}$, in Subsection 3.7.4. For such a pair $(L^{(0)}, L^{(1)})$ we define a graded filtered $\Lambda_{0,nov}$ module, $C(L^{(1)}, L^{(0)}; \Lambda_{0,nov})$ (see Definition 3.7.20). On the other hand, we have the filtered A_∞ algebra $(C(L^{(i)}, \Lambda_{0,nov}), \mathfrak{m}^{(i)})$ for each $L^{(i)}$ $(i = 0, 1)$. Then we will construct a *filtered A_∞ bimodule structure* on $C(L^{(1)}, L^{(0)}; \Lambda_{0,nov})$ (Theorem 3.7.21).

THEOREM 3.1.18. *Let* $(L^{(0)}, L^{(1)})$ *be a relatively spin pair of Lagrangian submanifolds which are transverse to each other.*
Then there exists a left $(C(L^{(1)}; \Lambda_{0,nov}), \mathfrak{m}^{(1)})$ *and right* $(C(L^{(0)}; \Lambda_{0,nov}), \mathfrak{m}^{(0)})$ *filtered A_∞ bimodule structure on* $C(L^{(1)}, L^{(0)}; \Lambda_{0,nov})$.
It is $G(L^{(1)}, L^{(0)})$-*gapped. Furthermore the pair of the homotopy units* $\{\mathbf{e}_1, \mathbf{e}_0\}$ *of* $(C(L^{(1)}; \Lambda_{0,nov}), \mathfrak{m}^{(1)})$ *and* $(C(L^{(0)}; \Lambda_{0,nov}), \mathfrak{m}^{(0)})$ *acts as a homotopy unit.*

The precise definitions of various notions appearing in the theorem will be given in Subsection 3.7.1. See also (3.7.43) for the definition of $G(L^{(1)}, L^{(0)})$. Moreover we can show the following (Theorem 3.7.45).

THEOREM 3.1.19. *Let* $(L^{(0)}, L^{(1)})$ *be a relatively spin pair of Lagrangian submanifolds which are transversal to each other. Then for each* $b_0 \in \widehat{\mathcal{M}}(L^{(0)})$, $b_1 \in \widehat{\mathcal{M}}(L^{(1)})$, *there exists a cohomology* $HF((L^{(1)}, b_1), (L^{(0)}, b_0); \Lambda_{0,nov})$ *which we call Floer cohomology of* $(L^{(0)}, L^{(1)})$ *deformed by* (b_0, b_1).

Let $\Omega(L^{(0)}, L^{(1)})$ be the space of all paths $\ell : [0, 1] \to M$ joining $L^{(0)}$ and $L^{(1)}$. We remark

$$\pi_0(\Omega(L^{(0)}, L^{(1)})) = i_*(\pi_1(L^{(0)})) \backslash \pi_1(M) / i_*(\pi_1(L^{(1)})),$$

if $L^{(0)}, L^{(1)}$ are connected.

Each point $p \in L^{(0)} \cap L^{(1)}$ determines a constant path $t \mapsto p$ and hence an element of $\pi_0(\Omega(L^{(0)}, L^{(1)}))$. It induces the following decomposition of Floer cohomology group (See Remark 3.7.46.)

$$\begin{aligned} &HF((L^{(1)}, b_1), (L^{(0)}, b_0); \Lambda_{0,nov}) \\ (3.1.20) \qquad &\cong \bigoplus_{[\ell_0] \in \pi_0(\Omega(L^{(0)}, L^{(1)}))} HF((L^{(1)}, b_1), (L^{(0)}, b_0); \ell_0; \Lambda_{0,nov}). \end{aligned}$$

We note that when $L^{(0)}$ and $L^{(1)}$ are weakly unobstructed, we can *not* define a Floer cohomology of $(L^{(0)}, L^{(1)})$ deformed by $b_i \in \widehat{\mathcal{M}}_{\text{weak}}(L^{(i)})$ in general, while we can define the Floer cohomology $HF(L^{(i)}, b_i; \Lambda_{0,nov})$ for each $i = 0, 1$. This fact is an important point for various applications. To describe a condition for the deformed Floer cohomology of the pair $(L^{(0)}, L^{(1)})$ to be defined, we introduce a function

$$\mathfrak{PO} : \widehat{\mathcal{M}}_{\text{weak}}(L) \to \Lambda_{0,nov}^{+(0)}$$

called a *potential function* by $\mathfrak{PO}(b) = c$ in the equation (3.1.13). Then we can show the following (Proposition 3.7.17).

THEOREM 3.1.21. *Let $(L^{(0)}, L^{(1)})$ be a relatively spin pair of Lagrangian submanifolds which are transversal to each other. Then, for each $b_0 \in \widehat{\mathcal{M}}_{\text{weak}}(L^{(0)})$, $b_1 \in \widehat{\mathcal{M}}_{\text{weak}}(L^{(1)})$ with $\mathfrak{PO}(b_0) = \mathfrak{PO}(b_1)$, we can define a Floer cohomology $HF((L^{(1)}, b_1), (L^{(0)}, b_0); \Lambda_{0,nov})$ deformed by b_0, b_1.*

A similar decomposition as (3.1.20) also exists.

We can define $\mathfrak{PO} : \widehat{\mathcal{M}}_{\text{weak,def}}(L) \to \Lambda_{0,nov}^{+(0)}$ in a similar way.

In Subsection 3.7.5, we will study the case that $L^{(0)}$ intersects $L^{(1)}$ cleanly. (Namely Bott-Morse version of Floer cohomology.) The connected components of the intersection $L^{(1)} \cap L^{(0)}$ are smooth manifolds but not necessary orientable. By a careful consideration of orientation sheaves, we can obtain the same conclusion as in the transversal case.

THEOREM 3.1.22. *Let $(L^{(0)}, L^{(1)})$ be a relatively spin pair. Assume that $L^{(0)}$ intersects $L^{(1)}$ cleanly. Then the conclusions in Theorem 3.1.18, 3.1.19 and 3.1.21 still hold.*

We note that the filtered A_∞ algebra $(C(L; \Lambda_{0,nov}), \mathfrak{m})$ itself can be regarded as a left $(C(L; \Lambda_{0,nov}), \mathfrak{m})$ and right $(C(L; \Lambda_{0,nov}), \mathfrak{m})$ filtered A_∞ bimodule (see Example 3.7.6). On the other hand, when $L^{(0)} = L^{(1)}(=: L)$ in Theorem 3.1.22, we have a left $(C(L; \Lambda_{0,nov}), \mathfrak{m})$ and right $(C(L; \Lambda_{0,nov}), \mathfrak{m})$ filtered A_∞ bimodule as well. Then we can show that the two A_∞ bimodules can be identified if $\{J_t\}_t$, a family of almost complex structures which is used to construct the A_∞ bimodule structure, is independent of t (Proposition 3.7.75). Thus when L is unobstructed or weakly unobstructed, we have

$$HF(L, b; \Lambda_{0,nov}) \cong HF((L, b), (L, b); \Lambda_{0,nov}).$$

Furthermore, if we consider the case that $L^{(1)} = \psi(L^{(0)})$ where ψ is a Hamiltonian diffeomorphism in Theorem 3.1.22, we have a deformed Floer cohomology $HF((\psi(L), \psi_*(b)), (L, b); \Lambda_{0,nov})$. (See Section 4.1 Theorem 4.1.3 for $\psi_*(b)$.) As we will see in examples given in Subsection 3.7.6, this is *not* independent of ψ in general. However, we will prove in Chapter 5 that

$$HF((\psi(L), \psi_*(b)), (L, b)); \Lambda_{nov}) := HF((\psi(L), \psi_*(b)), (L, b); \Lambda_{0,nov}) \otimes_{\Lambda_{0,nov}} \Lambda_{nov}$$

is independent of the Hamiltonian diffeomorphism ψ. By combing these, therefore, we have

$$HF(L, b; \Lambda_{nov}) \cong HF((\psi(L), \psi_*(b)), (L, b)); \Lambda_{nov}).$$

The organization of this chapter is in order. We introduce the notions of filtered A_∞ algebras and A_∞ homomorphisms in Section 3.2, and the homotopy unit, the unital or homotopy-unital A_∞ homomorphism in Section 3.3. These are presented in the purely algebraic context and Lagrangian submanifolds do not appear there. After that, we give a geometric realization of the classical A_∞ algebra $(\mathbb{Z}\mathcal{X}_L, \overline{\mathfrak{m}}^L)$ with the homotopy unit on each oriented manifold L. In the following Section 3.5, we will construct the filtered (quantum) A_∞ algebra $(C(L, \Lambda_{0,nov}), \mathfrak{m})$ with homotopy unit associated to a relatively spin Lagrangian submanifold L. We note that throughout in Sections 3.4 and 3.5, we do not assume any unobstructedness. In Section 3.6, we will introduce notions of the bounding cochains and the Maurer-Cartan equation in the context of filtered A_∞ algebras and construct the obstruction classes. We define notions of unobstructedness and weak unobstructedness. We also introduce the potential function $\mathfrak{PO}$ therein and study the relation between the weak unobstructedness condition and existence of Floer cohomology of L. In Section 3.7, we consider a relatively spin pair $(L^{(0)}, L^{(1)})$ of Lagrangian submanifolds. We deform the standard Floer coboundary operator for $(L^{(0)}, L^{(1)})$ using the constructions provided in the previous sections. For this purpose, we introduce the algebraic notions of a filtered A_∞ bimodule structure on a graded filtered $\Lambda_{0,nov}$ module and of A_∞ bimodule homomorphisms in Subsections 3.7.1 and 3.7.2 respectively. We discuss the weak unobstructedness in Subsection 3.7.3. Our main task in Section 3.7 is to construct a left $(C(L^{(1)}, \Lambda_{0,nov}), \mathfrak{m}^{(1)})$ and right $(C(L^{(0)}, \Lambda_{0,nov}), \mathfrak{m}^{(0)})$ filtered A_∞ bimodule structure on $C(L^{(1)}, L^{(0)}; \Lambda_{0,nov})$. This is done for the case that $L^{(0)}$ is transversal to $L^{(1)}$ in Subsection 3.7.4 and for the case that $L^{(0)}$ and $L^{(1)}$ intersect cleanly in Subsection 3.7.5. When we define the A_∞ bimodule structure, it is *not* necessary to assume that the A_∞ algebras $(C(L^{(0)}, \Lambda_{0,nov}), \mathfrak{m}^{(0)})$ and $(C(L^{(1)}, \Lambda_{0,nov}), \mathfrak{m}^{(1)})$ are unobstructed or weakly unobstructed. (Namely filtered A_∞ bimodule is constructed for *arbitrary* relatively spin pair.) If they are unobstructed, then we can obtain the deformed Floer cochain complex $(C(L^{(1)}, L^{(0)}; \Lambda_{0,nov}), \delta_{b_1,b_0})$ by using the A_∞ bimodule structure and bounding cochains b_0, b_1 chosen respectively for $L^{(0)}$, $L^{(1)}$. We will give some simple examples of calculation of Floer cohomology in Subsection 3.7.6. In Section 3.8, we consider the moduli space of pseudo-holomorphic discs with interior marked points in addition. By considering the moduli space of pseudo-holomorphic map from bordered Riemann surface with one interior marked point and no boundary marked point, we will construct a sequence of operators $\mathfrak{p}_k$ and study the properties. Using the operators $\mathfrak{p}$, we study properties of our obstruction classes constructed in Subsection 3.6.2 and Subsection 3.6.3 and give some useful conditions for (weak) unobstructedness in subsections Subsections 3.8.1-3.8.3. Furthermore, by considering the case of several interior marked points in Subsection 3.8.4, we will construct a sequence of operators $\mathfrak{q}$. These operators give a bulk deformation of our filtered A_∞ algebra by elements of $H^2(M; \Lambda_{0,nov}^+)$. We can also construct a relative version of the obstruction classes in Subsection 3.8.5. The outline of the construction of $\mathfrak{q}$ is given in Subsection 3.8.6. This idea is also used in the story of our filtered A_∞ bimodules in Subsection 3.8.7 and we get a sequence of operators $\mathfrak{r}$, whose construction is explained in Subsection 3.8.8. The detail of the construction of these operators will be given in Section 7.4. In the last subsection we generalize the construction of operators $\mathfrak{p}_k$ by combining it with the construction of $\mathfrak{q}$ and obtain a sequence of operators $\mathfrak{p}_{\ell,k}$. We will discuss some properties of it there. These operators will be used in the spectral sequence argument in Chapter 6. We prove several formulas which provides the basic properties of operators $\mathfrak{p}$, $\mathfrak{q}$, $\mathfrak{r}$ in Section 3.8. Those formulas are reinterpreted in Section 7.4 using the language of L_∞ structures and the detail of the construction of them is also given there.

In order to construct the A_∞ algebras geometrically, we need to resolve certain transversality problems. This point will be discussed in Chapter 7 in more details. We need a careful consideration of the sign (or of the orientation). The precise consideration of the signs will be carried out in Chapter 8. So in this chapter, we just state our results in a rigorous manner and prove them modulo the transversality and the sign problems.

We note that our construction in this chapter will be done by choosing and fixing various structures, for example, compatible almost complex structures, Kuranishi structures, multisections, triangulation, countable sets $\mathcal{X}_L, \mathcal{X}(L)$, etc. We have to study the dependence or independence by these choices. This will be done in the following Chapters 4 and 5.

3.2. Algebraic framework on filtered A_∞ algebras

In this section, we introduce the notions of the filtered A_∞ algebra and of the A_∞ homomorphism in a purely algebraic context. So we do not mention Lagrangian submanifolds in this section. We note that our definition of A_∞ algebras is slightly different from the standard one in the literature in ([**Sta63**]) that our coefficient ring is a filtered commutative ring $\Lambda_{0,nov}$. Because of this, in Subsection 3.2.1, we first recall the notion of an A_∞ algebra (without filtrations) and of an A_∞ homomorphism. After that we will introduce our filtered A_∞ algebra and filtered A_∞ homomorphism in the next subsection. To distinguish the ordinary (unfiltered) A_∞ algebra from our filtered A_∞ algebra, we will put 'bar's over the notations for the former.

3.2.1. A_∞ algebras and homomorphisms. Let R be a commutative ring with unit. Let $\overline{C} = \bigoplus_{m \in \mathbb{Z}} \overline{C}^m$ be a free graded R module. We always assume that $\overline{C}$ is generated by countably many elements. We put $(\overline{C}[1])^m = \overline{C}^{m+1}$ and

$$B_k(\overline{C}[1]) = \bigoplus_{m_1, \cdots, m_k} (\overline{C}[1])^{m_1} \otimes \cdots \otimes (\overline{C}[1])^{m_k}.$$

In some literature one denotes by $B_k(\overline{C})$ the right hand side above instead of $B_k(\overline{C}[1])$. However throughout this book, we use the notation $B_k(\overline{C}[1])$. (Sometimes we write $B_k\overline{C}[1]$ in place of $B_k(\overline{C}[1])$.) Suppose that we have a sequence of maps $\overline{\mathfrak{m}} = \{\overline{\mathfrak{m}}_k\}_{k \geq 1}$ of degree $+1$

$$\overline{\mathfrak{m}}_k : B_k(\overline{C}[1]) \to \overline{C}[1], \quad \text{for } k = 1, \cdots.$$

The direct sum $B(\overline{C}[1]) := \bigoplus_k B_k(\overline{C}[1])$ has a structure of graded coalgebra. The coproduct Δ is defined by:

$$\Delta(x_1 \otimes \cdots \otimes x_n) = \sum_{k=0}^{n} (x_1 \otimes \cdots \otimes x_k) \otimes (x_{k+1} \otimes \cdots \otimes x_n).$$

We can extend $\overline{\mathfrak{m}}_k$ uniquely to a coderivation

$$\widehat{\overline{\mathfrak{m}}}_k : \bigoplus_n B_n(\overline{C}[1]) \to \bigoplus_n B_{n-k+1}(\overline{C}[1]),$$

by the formula

$$(3.2.1) \qquad \widehat{\overline{\mathfrak{m}}}_k(x_1 \otimes \cdots \otimes x_n) = \sum_{\ell=1}^{n-k+1} (-1)^{\deg x_1 + \cdots + \deg x_{\ell-1} + \ell - 1} x_1 \otimes \cdots \otimes$$
$$\overline{\mathfrak{m}}_k(x_\ell, \cdots, x_{\ell+k-1}) \otimes \cdots \otimes x_n$$

for $k \leq n$ and $\widehat{\overline{\mathfrak{m}}}_k = 0$ for $k > n$. Here and hereafter $\deg x$ means the degree of x *before* we shift it.

Hereafter for $x \in (\overline{C}[1])^m = \overline{C}^{m+1}$ we put

$$(3.2.2) \qquad\qquad\qquad \deg' x = m = \deg x - 1.$$

Using this notation the sign in (3.2.1) is $(-1)^{\deg' x_1 + \cdots + \deg' x_{\ell-1}}$.

We put $\widehat{\overline{d}} = \sum \widehat{\overline{\mathfrak{m}}}_k$.

DEFINITION 3.2.3. $\overline{\mathfrak{m}} = \{\overline{\mathfrak{m}}_k\}_{k \geq 1}$ defines a structure of A_∞ algebra over R on $\overline{C}$, if $\widehat{\overline{d}} \circ \widehat{\overline{d}} = 0$.

REMARK 3.2.4. (1) The operator $\overline{\mathfrak{m}}_k$ is defined for $k > 0$. ($\overline{\mathfrak{m}}_0 = 0$.) For a *filtered* A_∞ algebra (which we define in the next subsection) we consider $\mathfrak{m}_k$ for $k \geq 0$. Since $\overline{\mathfrak{m}}_0 = 0$, we find that $\overline{\mathfrak{m}}_1 \overline{\mathfrak{m}}_1 = 0$. So we have a cochain complex $(\overline{C}[1], \overline{\mathfrak{m}}_1)$. (See Remark 3.2.21 (1).)

(2) When we regard a differential graded algebra (D.G.A.) over R as an A_∞ algebra, we just put $\overline{\mathfrak{m}}_k = 0$ for $k \geq 3$. But we note that the sign of $\overline{\mathfrak{m}}_2$ is different from that of product in the D.G.A.

$$(3.2.5) \qquad\qquad \begin{aligned} \overline{\mathfrak{m}}_1(x) &= (-1)^{\deg x} dx, \\ \overline{\mathfrak{m}}_2(x, y) &= (-1)^{\deg x(\deg y + 1)} x \cdot y. \end{aligned}$$

Here $x \cdot y$ is the product in the D.G.A. (See also Remark 3.2.21 (2) below.)

Next, we define the notion of an A_∞ homomorphism. Let $(\overline{C}_i, \overline{\mathfrak{m}}^i)$, $i = 1, 2$, be A_∞ algebras over a commutative ring R with unit. For $k = 1, 2, \cdots$, let us consider the family of maps $\bar{f}_k : B_k(\overline{C}_1[1]) \to \overline{C}_2[1]$ of degree 0. These maps induce $\widehat{\bar{f}} : B(\overline{C}_1[1]) \to B(\overline{C}_2[1])$, which on $B_k(\overline{C}_1[1])$ is give by

$$\widehat{\bar{f}}(x_1 \otimes \cdots \otimes x_k) = \sum_{0 < k_1 < \cdots < k_n < k} \bar{f}_{k_1}(x_1, \cdots, x_{k_1}) \otimes \cdots \otimes$$

(3.2.6)
$$\bar{f}_{k_{i+1}-k_i}(x_{k_i+1}, \cdots, x_{k_{i+1}}) \otimes \cdots$$

$$\cdots \cdots \otimes \bar{f}_{k-k_n}(x_{k_n+1}, \cdots, x_k).$$

It is easy to see that $\widehat{\bar{f}} : B(\overline{C}_1[1]) \to B(\overline{C}_2[1])$ is a coalgebra homomorphism. (We remark that $\bar{f}_0 = 0$.)

DEFINITION 3.2.7. We call $\bar{f} = \{\bar{f}_k\}_{k \geq 1}$ an A_∞ *homomorphism from $\overline{C}_1$ to $\overline{C}_2$* if $\widehat{\bar{f}} \circ \widehat{\bar{d}^1} = \widehat{\bar{d}^2} \circ \widehat{\bar{f}}$. We simply write $\bar{f} : \overline{C}_1 \to \overline{C}_2$.

By definition an A_∞ homomorphism $\bar{f}$ from $\overline{C}_1$ to $\overline{C}_2$ induces a homomorphism from $H^*(B(\overline{C}_1[1]), \widehat{\bar{d}^1})$ to $H^*(B(\overline{C}_2[1]), \widehat{\bar{d}^2})$.

Let $\bar{f}_k^i : B_k(\overline{C}_i[1]) \to \overline{C}_{i+1}[1]$ $(i = 1, 2)$ define an A_∞ homomorphism.

DEFINITION 3.2.8. The composition $\bar{f}^2 \circ \bar{f}^1 = \{(\bar{f}^2 \circ \bar{f}^1)_k\}_{k \geq 1}$ of $\bar{f}^1$ and $\bar{f}^2$ is given by the formula

$$(\bar{f}^2 \circ \bar{f}^1)_k(x_1, \cdots, x_k)$$
$$= \sum_m \sum_{k_1 + \cdots + k_m = k} \bar{f}_m^2(\bar{f}_{k_1}^1(x_1, \cdots, x_{k_1}), \cdots, \bar{f}_{k_m}^1(x_{k-k_m+1}, \cdots, x_k)).$$

LEMMA 3.2.9. $\bar{f}^2 \circ \bar{f}^1$ *defines an A_∞ homomorphism from $\overline{C}_1$ to $\overline{C}_3$.*

PROOF. If $\widehat{\bar{f}^1}$ and $\widehat{\bar{f}^2}$ are induced from $\bar{f}_k^1$ and $\bar{f}_k^2$ by (3.2.6) respectively, then the composition $\widehat{\bar{f}^2} \circ \widehat{\bar{f}^1}$ is induced from $(\bar{f}^2 \circ \bar{f}^1)_k$. Lemma 3.2.9 follows immediately. ☐

We remark that
$$\widehat{\bar{f}^2} \circ \widehat{\bar{f}^1} = \widehat{\bar{f}^2 \circ \bar{f}^1}.$$

We find that the degree $+1$ map $\overline{m}_1$ satisfies $\overline{m}_1 \circ \overline{m}_1 = 0$. (See Remark 3.2.4 (1)). Thus we have the complex $(\overline{C}[1], \overline{m}_1)$. An A_∞ homomorphism induces a homomorphism between the cohomology.

DEFINITION 3.2.10. Let $(\overline{C}_i, \overline{m}^i)$ be A_∞ algebras over R. We say that an A_∞ homomorphism $\bar{f} : (\overline{C}_1, \overline{m}^1) \to (\overline{C}_2, \overline{m}^2)$ is a *weak homotopy equivalence* if $\bar{f}_1$ induces a cochain homotopy equivalence.

REMARK 3.2.11. (1) When R is a field or $\mathbb{Z}$, $\bar{f}$ being a weak homotopy equivalence is equivalent to $\bar{f}_1$ being a quasi-isomorphism, i.e., to $\bar{f}_1$ inducing an isomorphism

$$H^*(\overline{C}_1[1], \overline{m}_1^1) \overset{\sim}{\to} H^*(\overline{C}_2[1], \overline{m}_1^2).$$

(Recall that we assume $\overline{C}_i$ are free R modules and countably generated.)

(2) Later in Chapter 4, we will see that the weak homotopy equivalence defines an equivalence relation among the A_∞ algebras. See Corollary 4.2.44 and Theorem 4.2.45.

3.2.2. Filtered A_∞ algebras and homomorphisms. Now we introduce the notion of the filtered A_∞ algebra. Let $\bigoplus_{m \in \mathbb{Z}} C^m$ be a free graded $\Lambda_{0,nov}$ module. There is a filtration $F^\lambda C^m$ on C^m ($\lambda \in \mathbb{R}_{\geq 0}$), such that

(3.2.12.1) $F^\lambda C^m \subset F^{\lambda'} C^m$ if $\lambda > \lambda'$.

(3.2.12.2) $T^{\lambda_0} \cdot F^\lambda C^m \subset F^{\lambda + \lambda_0} C^m$.

(3.2.12.3) $e^k C^m \subset C^{m+2k}$.

(3.2.12.4) C^m is complete with respect to the filtration.

(3.2.12.5) C^m has a basis $\mathbf{v}_i$ such that $\mathbf{v}_i \in F^0 C^m \setminus \bigcup_{\lambda > 0} F^\lambda C^m$.

We call the filtration FC the *energy filtration*. We denote by C the completion of $\bigoplus_{m \in \mathbb{Z}} C^m$ with respect to the energy filtration. (3.2.12.3) means that the degree of e is 2. We consider the shifted complex $C[1]$ defined by $(C[1])^m = C^{m+1}$ and

$$B_k(C[1]) = \bigoplus_{m_1, \cdots, m_k} (C[1])^{m_1} \otimes \cdots \otimes (C[1])^{m_k}.$$

Suppose that we have a sequence of maps $\mathfrak{m} = \{\mathfrak{m}_k\}_{k \geq 0}$ of degree $+1$

$$\mathfrak{m}_k : B_k(C[1]) \to C[1], \quad \text{for } k = 0, 1, \cdots.$$

We note that $\mathfrak{m}_0 : \Lambda_{0,nov} \to C[1]$. We assume that

(3.2.12.6) $\mathfrak{m}_k \left(F^{\lambda_1} C^{m_1} \otimes \cdots \otimes F^{\lambda_k} C^{m_k} \right) \subseteq F^{\lambda_1 + \cdots + \lambda_k} C^{m_1 + \cdots + m_k - k + 2}$

and

(3.2.12.7) $\mathfrak{m}_0(1) \in F^{\lambda'} C[1]$ for some $\lambda' > 0$.

Note that for filtered A_∞ algebra, the operation $\mathfrak{m}_k$ is defined for $k = 0$ also.

Since C is a free $\Lambda_{0,nov}$ module, we have a free R module $\overline{C}$ and an isomorphism

(3.2.13.1) $\overline{C} \otimes_R \Lambda_{0,nov} \cong C.$

We assume that $\overline{C}$ has the following properties, in addition. $\Lambda_{0,nov}$ has the ideal $\Lambda_{0,nov}^+$ such that $\Lambda_{0,nov} / \Lambda_{0,nov}^+ \cong R[e, e^{-1}]$. (See (Conv.4) and (1.37).) We put

(3.2.13.2) $\overline{\mathfrak{m}}_k(x_1, \ldots, x_k) \equiv \mathfrak{m}_k(x_1, \ldots, x_k) \quad \mod \Lambda_{0,nov}^+ C$

for $k = 1, 2, \ldots$. Here $\overline{\mathfrak{m}}_k$ is a homomorphism

$$B_k \overline{C}[1] \otimes_R R[e, e^{-1}] \to \overline{C}[1] \otimes_R R[e, e^{-1}].$$

We *assume* that $\overline{\mathfrak{m}}_k$ is induced by an R module homomorphism

(3.2.13.3) $B_k \overline{C}[1] \to \overline{C}[1].$

In other words, we assume $\overline{\mathfrak{m}}_k$ does not contain e, e^{-1}. We denote the R-module homomorphism (3.2.13.3) by the same symbol $\overline{\mathfrak{m}}_k$.

Now the direct sum $B(C[1]) := \bigoplus_k B_k(C[1])$ has a structure of graded coalgebra. So we regard $B(C[1])$ as a coalgebra and will construct a coderivation on it. The coproduct Δ is defined by:

(3.2.14) $\Delta(x_1 \otimes \cdots \otimes x_n) = \sum_{k=0}^{n} (x_1 \otimes \cdots \otimes x_k) \otimes (x_{k+1} \otimes \cdots \otimes x_n).$

We can uniquely extend $\mathfrak{m}_k$ to a coderivation

$$\hat{\mathfrak{m}}_k : \bigoplus_n B_n(C[1]) \to \bigoplus_n B_{n-k+1}(C[1]),$$

by

(3.2.15)
$$\hat{\mathfrak{m}}_k(x_1 \otimes \cdots \otimes x_n) = \sum_{\ell=1}^{n-k+1} (-1)^{\deg x_1 + \cdots + \deg x_{\ell-1} + \ell - 1} x_1 \otimes \cdots \otimes$$
$$\mathfrak{m}_k(x_\ell, \cdots, x_{\ell+k-1}) \otimes \cdots \otimes x_n$$

for $k \le n$ and $\hat{\mathfrak{m}}_k = 0$ for $k > n$. When $k = 0$, we put $\mathfrak{m}_0(1)$ in the right hand side. Namely we define $\hat{\mathfrak{m}}_0$ by

$$\hat{\mathfrak{m}}_0(x_1 \otimes \cdots \otimes x_n) = \sum_{\ell=1}^{n+1} (-1)^{\deg x_1 + \cdots + \deg x_{\ell-1} + \ell - 1} x_1 \otimes \cdots \otimes x_{\ell-1} \otimes$$
$$\mathfrak{m}_0(1) \otimes x_\ell \otimes \cdots \otimes x_n.$$

We next consider a completion $\widehat{B}(C[1])$ of $B(C[1])$. We define a filtration $F^\lambda B_k(C[1])$ on $B_k(C[1])$ by

$$F^\lambda B_k(C[1]) = \bigcup_{\lambda_1 + \cdots + \lambda_k \ge \lambda} \left(F^{\lambda_1} C^{m_1} \otimes \cdots \otimes F^{\lambda_k} C^{m_k} \right).$$

Let $\widehat{B}_k(C[1])$ be the completion of $B_k(C[1])$ with respect to this filtration. We call this filtration *energy filtration*. There is another filtration of $BC[1]$ that it $\bigoplus_{k \ge k_0} B_k C[1]$, $k_0 = 1, 2, \cdots$. We call it the *number filtration*.

DEFINITION 3.2.16. $\widehat{B}(C[1])$ is the set of all formal sum $\sum_k \mathbf{x}_k$ where $\mathbf{x}_k \in \widehat{B}_k(C[1])$ such that

$$\mathbf{x}_k \in F^{\lambda_k} \widehat{B}_k(C[1])$$

with $\lim_{k \to \infty} \lambda_k \to \infty$.

We define $\hat{d} : \widehat{B}(C[1]) \to \widehat{B}(C[1])$ by $\hat{d} = \sum_{k=0}^\infty \hat{\mathfrak{m}}_k$.

LEMMA 3.2.17. *If* (3.2.12) *is satisfied, then* $\hat{d}$ *is well-defined as a map from* $\widehat{B}(C[1])$ *to* $\widehat{B}(C[1])$.

PROOF. Let $\sum \mathbf{x}_k$ be as in Definition 3.2.16. The $\widehat{B}_k(C[1])$-component of $\hat{d} \sum \mathbf{x}_k$ is $\sum_\ell \hat{\mathfrak{m}}_\ell(\mathbf{x}_{k+\ell-1})$. By (3.2.12) and Definition 3.2.16, we have

$$\hat{\mathfrak{m}}_\ell(\mathbf{x}_{k+\ell-1}) \in F^{\lambda_{k+\ell-1}} \widehat{B}_k(C[1]).$$

Therefore the completeness of $\widehat{B}_k(C[1])$ implies that $\hat{d} \sum \mathbf{x}_k$ converges. The proof of Lemma 3.2.17 is complete. □

Now we introduce the following condition for an element $\mathbf{e}$ of $C^0 = C[1]^{-1}$. (Compare also [**Fuk97II**] Section 11.)

CONDITION 3.2.18.
(3.2.19.1) $\mathfrak{m}_{k+1}(x_1, \cdots, \mathbf{e}, \cdots, x_k) = 0$,   for $k \ge 2$ or $k = 0$.
(3.2.19.2) $\mathfrak{m}_2(\mathbf{e}, x) = (-1)^{\deg x} \mathfrak{m}_2(x, \mathbf{e}) = x$.

DEFINITION 3.2.20. (1) The structure of a *filtered A_∞ algebra* on C is a collection $\mathfrak{m} = \{\mathfrak{m}_k\}_{k\geq 0}$ that satisfy (3.2.12.1) - (3.2.12.7), (3.2.13.1) - (3.2.13.3) and $\widehat{d} \circ \widehat{d} = 0$. We call $\widehat{B}(C[1])$ the (completed) *bar complex* associated to the A_∞ algebra $(C, \mathfrak{m})$.

If $(C, \mathfrak{m})$ is a filtered A_∞ algebra then $(\overline{C}, \overline{\mathfrak{m}}_k)$ as in (3.2.13) is an A_∞ algebra. We call $(\overline{C}, \overline{\mathfrak{m}}_k)$ the *R-reduction* of $(C, \mathfrak{m}_k)$. In this book we frequently denote the R reduction of $(C, \mathfrak{m}_k)$ etc. by $(\overline{C}, \overline{\mathfrak{m}}_k)$ without mentioning.

(2) We say a filtered A_∞ algebra $(C, \mathfrak{m})$ is *strict* if $\mathfrak{m}_0 = 0$.

(3) If a (filtered) A_∞ algebra has an element $\mathbf{e}$ of degree 0 (before shifted) satisfying Condition 3.2.18, we call the A_∞ algebra an (filtered) A_∞ *algebra with unit* and $\mathbf{e}$ a *unit*. Sometimes we simply call it a *unital filtered A_∞ algebra*. For a unital filtered A_∞ algebra $(C, \mathfrak{m})$ we put

$$C_{\mathrm{red}} = C/\Lambda_{0,nov}[\mathbf{e}]$$

and we always assume that there exists a splitting

$$C = C_{\mathrm{red}} \oplus \Lambda_{0,nov}[\mathbf{e}]$$

in this book. For the unfiltered A_∞ algebra $(\overline{C}, \overline{\mathfrak{m}})$ over R, we define the unit and assume the splitting above in the same way. (See Subsections 4.4.4, 4.4.7 as for some discussion on C_{red}.)

REMARK 3.2.21. (1) The equation $\widehat{d} \circ \widehat{d} = 0$ produces infinitely many relations among $\mathfrak{m}_k$'s. For example, the first few relations are given by

$$\mathfrak{m}_1(\mathfrak{m}_0(1)) = 0,$$
$$\mathfrak{m}_2(\mathfrak{m}_0(1), x) + (-1)^{\deg x+1}\mathfrak{m}_2(x, \mathfrak{m}_0(1)) + \mathfrak{m}_1(\mathfrak{m}_1(x)) = 0,$$
$$\mathfrak{m}_3(\mathfrak{m}_0(1), x, y) + (-1)^{\deg x+1}\mathfrak{m}_3(x, \mathfrak{m}_0(1), y)$$
$$+ (-1)^{\deg x+\deg y+2}\mathfrak{m}_3(x, y, \mathfrak{m}_0(1)) + \mathfrak{m}_2(\mathfrak{m}_1(x), y)$$
$$+ (-1)^{\deg x+1}\mathfrak{m}_2(x, \mathfrak{m}_1(y)) + \mathfrak{m}_1(\mathfrak{m}_2(x, y)) = 0,$$
$$\cdots\cdots\cdots$$

In general, it is easy to show that $\widehat{d} \circ \widehat{d} = 0$ is equivalent to that for each k

$$\sum_{k_1+k_2=k+1} \sum_i (-1)^{\deg x_1+\cdots+\deg x_{i-1}+i-1}$$

(3.2.22)

$$\mathfrak{m}_{k_1}(x_1, \cdots, \mathfrak{m}_{k_2}(x_i, \cdots, x_{i+k_2-1}), \cdots, x_k) = 0.$$

We call this identity the A_∞ *formula* or the A_∞ *relation*. If $\mathfrak{m}_0 = 0$, then $\mathfrak{m}_1\mathfrak{m}_1 = 0$. So in this case $\mathfrak{m}_1$ plays the role of a boundary operator.

(2) Suppose $\mathfrak{m}_0 = 0$ and $\mathfrak{m}_3 = \cdots = 0$. Then $\widehat{d} \circ \widehat{d} = 0$ implies

$$(3.2.23) \qquad \mathfrak{m}_2(\mathfrak{m}_2(x, y), z) + (-1)^{\deg x+1}\mathfrak{m}_2(x, \mathfrak{m}_2(y, z)) = 0.$$

(3.2.23) is consistent with (3.2.5) and the associativity of the product in D.G.A.

(3) We put

$$(3.2.24) \qquad \mathfrak{l}_k(x_1, \cdots, x_k) = \frac{1}{k!} \sum_{\sigma \in \mathfrak{S}_k} (-1)^{\epsilon(\sigma)} \mathfrak{m}_k(x_{\sigma(1)}, \cdots, x_{\sigma(k)}),$$

where

(3.2.25) $$\epsilon(\sigma) = \sum_{i<j;\sigma(i)>\sigma(j)} (\deg x_i + 1)(\deg x_j + 1).$$

This can be regarded as a symmetrization of the operators $\mathfrak{m}_k$. The A_∞ formula for $\mathfrak{m}_k$ leads to certain relations among the operators $\mathfrak{l}_k$, which define an L_∞ structure. See Section A3 (and for example [**LaMa95**]) on the symmetrization of an A_∞ structure. The sign convention is slightly different from ours in some of the literatures.

(4) Later in Section 3.5 we will construct a filtered A_∞ algebra associated to a Lagrangian submanifold. This filtered A_∞ algebra does *not* have a unit in the sense of Definition 3.2.20 (3). But in Section 7.3, we will show that it has a *homotopy unit*. We will define the notion of homotopy unit in the A_∞ algebra in Section 3.3.

(5) Note the completion $\widehat{B}C[1]$ is not a coalgebra in the standard sense but there exists an operation

$$\Delta : \widehat{B}C[1] \to \widehat{B}C[1] \widehat{\otimes} \widehat{B}C[1]$$

such that $(\Delta \widehat{\otimes} 1) \circ \Delta = (1 \widehat{\otimes} \Delta) \circ \Delta$. Here and hereafter $\widehat{\otimes}$ denotes a completion of the tensor product over $\Lambda_{0,nov}$. We call such an algebraic structure *formal coalgebra*. (Such a notion appears in the theory of formal group [**Die73**].) Our $\widehat{d}$ is a coderivation of the formal coalgebra.

We next define the gapped condition. Let $G \subset \mathbb{R}_{\geq 0} \times 2\mathbb{Z}$ be a submonoid. We put $G = \{\beta = (\lambda(\beta), \mu(\beta)) \in \mathbb{R}_{\geq 0} \times 2\mathbb{Z} \mid \beta \in G\}$.

DEFINITION 3.2.26. Suppose that G satisfies Condition 3.1.6. We say that a filtered A_∞ algebra $(C, \mathfrak{m})$ is *G-gapped*, if $\mathfrak{m}_k$ has the decomposition

$$\mathfrak{m}_k = \sum_{\beta \in G} T^{\lambda(\beta)} e^{\mu(\beta)/2} \mathfrak{m}_{k,\beta}$$

for some family of R module homomorphisms $\mathfrak{m}_{k,\beta} : B_k \overline{C}[1] \to \overline{C}[1]$ for $k = 0, 1, 2, \cdots$ and $\beta = (\lambda(\beta), \mu(\beta)) \in G$. Here we identify $C = \overline{C} \otimes_R \Lambda_{0,nov}$. $(C, \mathfrak{m})$ is simply said to be *gapped* if it is G-gapped for some G.

Note (3.1.7.2) implies (3.2.13.3).

The gapped condition will be used when we construct a spectral sequence as well as various arguments involving inductive constructions over the filtration. (See Chapters 4, 5 and 6.)

Next, we define the notion of the filtered A_∞ homomorphisms. Let $(C_i, \mathfrak{m}^i)$, $i = 1, 2$, be filtered A_∞ algebras over the ring $\Lambda_{0,nov}$. For $k = 0, 1, 2, \cdots$, we consider the family of $\Lambda_{0,nov}$ module homomorphisms $\mathfrak{f}_k : B_k(C_1[1]) \to C_2[1]$ of degree 0 such that

(3.2.27.1) $$\mathfrak{f}_k(F^\lambda B_k(C_1[1])) \subseteq F^\lambda C_2[1],$$

and

(3.2.27.2) $$\mathfrak{f}_0(1) \in F^{\lambda'} C_2[1] \quad \text{for some } \lambda' > 0.$$

Note that $\mathfrak{f}_0 : \Lambda_{0,nov} \to C_2[1]$ and we do *not* assume $\mathfrak{f}_0(1) = 0$ in this case. These maps induce

$$\widehat{\mathfrak{f}} : \widehat{B}(C_1[1]) \to \widehat{B}(C_2[1]),$$

which on $B_k(C_1[1])$ is given by the formula

$$
\widehat{\mathfrak{f}}(x_1 \otimes \cdots \otimes x_k) = \sum_{0 \leq k_1 \leq \cdots \leq k_n \leq k} \mathfrak{f}_{k_1}(x_1, \cdots, x_{k_1}) \otimes \cdots
$$

(3.2.28)

$$
\cdots \otimes \mathfrak{f}_{k_{i+1}-k_i}(x_{k_i+1}, \cdots, x_{k_{i+1}}) \otimes \cdots
$$

$$
\cdots \otimes \mathfrak{f}_{k-k_n}(x_{k_n+1}, \cdots, x_k),
$$

and (3.2.27) implies that $\widehat{\mathfrak{f}}$ converges. We note that when $\mathfrak{f}_0$ appears in the right hand side of (3.2.28), we put $\mathfrak{f}_0(1)$ there. Thus, in particular, $\widehat{\mathfrak{f}}(1)$ is given by

$$
\widehat{\mathfrak{f}}(1) = 1 + \mathfrak{f}_0(1) + \mathfrak{f}_0(1) \otimes \mathfrak{f}_0(1) + \cdots = e^{\mathfrak{f}_0(1)}
$$

in our notation of exponential function. (See also (3.6.1) below.) We remark that the right hand side converges because of (3.2.27.2). Then it is easy to see that $\widehat{\mathfrak{f}} : \widehat{B}(C_1[1]) \to \widehat{B}(C_2[1])$ is a (formal) coalgebra homomorphism. (See Lemma 3.6.2).

DEFINITION 3.2.29. Let $\mathfrak{f}_k : B_k(C_1[1]) \to C_2[1]$ satisfy (3.2.27) as above. We assume that the $R[e, e^{-1}]$ module homomorphism

$$
\mathfrak{f}_k \mod \Lambda_{0,nov}^+ : B_k\overline{C}[1] \otimes_R R[e, e^{-1}] \to \overline{C}[1] \otimes_R R[e, e^{-1}]
$$

is induced from an R module homomorphism $\overline{\mathfrak{f}}_k : B_k\overline{C}[1] \to \overline{C}[1]$.

(1) We call $\mathfrak{f} = \{\mathfrak{f}_k\}_{k \geq 0}$ a *filtered A_∞ homomorphism from C_1 to C_2* if $\widehat{\mathfrak{f}} \circ \widehat{d}^1 = \widehat{d}^2 \circ \widehat{\mathfrak{f}}$. We simply write $\mathfrak{f} : C_1 \to C_2$.

(2) A filtered A_∞ homomorphism $\mathfrak{f}$ is called *strict* if $\mathfrak{f}_0 = 0$.

(3) Let $G \subset \mathbb{R}_{\geq 0} \times 2\mathbb{Z}$ be a discrete submonoid satisfying Condition 3.1.6. Let C_i ($i = 1, 2$) be gapped filtered A_∞ algebras. We say that $\mathfrak{f}$ is *G-gapped* if there exist $\mathfrak{f}_{k,\beta} : B_k\overline{C}_1[1] \to \overline{C}_2[1]$ for $k = 0, 1, 2, \cdots$, $\beta \in G$ such that

(3.2.30)
$$
\mathfrak{f}_k = \sum \mathfrak{f}_{k,\beta} T^{\lambda(\beta)} e^{\mu(\beta)/2}.
$$

We remark that if G' is another discrete submonoid satisfying Condition 3.1.6 and containing G, then every G-gapped filtered A_∞ homomorphism is G'-gapped. When the submonoid G is not explicitly specified, we just say $\mathfrak{f}$ is *gapped*.

Let $\mathfrak{f}_k^i : B_k(C_i[1]) \to C_{i+1}[1]$ ($i = 1, 2$) define a filtered A_∞ homomorphism.

DEFINITION 3.2.31. The composition $\mathfrak{f}^2 \circ \mathfrak{f}^1 = \{(\mathfrak{f}^2 \circ \mathfrak{f}^1)_k\}$ of $\mathfrak{f}^1$ and $\mathfrak{f}^2$ is defined by the formula

$$
(\mathfrak{f}^2 \circ \mathfrak{f}^1)_k(x_1, \cdots, x_k)
$$
$$
= \sum_m \sum_{k_1 + \cdots + k_m = k} \mathfrak{f}_m^2(\mathfrak{f}_{k_1}^1(x_1, \cdots, x_{k_1}), \cdots, \mathfrak{f}_{k_m}^1(x_{k-k_m+1}, \cdots, x_k)).
$$

LEMMA 3.2.32. *$\mathfrak{f}^2 \circ \mathfrak{f}^1$ defines a filtered A_∞ homomorphism from C_1 to C_3.*

PROOF. By noticing that we have $\widehat{\mathfrak{f}}(1) = e^{\mathfrak{f}_0(1)}$, the proof is similar to that of Lemma 3.2.9. $\square$

Let $(C_i, \mathfrak{m}^i)$ ($i = 1, 2$) be filtered A_∞ algebras over $\Lambda_{0,nov}$ and $\mathfrak{f} : (C_1, \mathfrak{m}^1) \to (C_2, \mathfrak{m}^2)$ a filtered A_∞ homomorphism. Then $\mathfrak{f}$ naturally induces an A_∞ homomorphism $\overline{\mathfrak{f}} : (\overline{C}_1, \overline{\mathfrak{m}}^1) \to (\overline{C}_2, \overline{\mathfrak{m}}^2)$, where $(\overline{C}_i, \overline{\mathfrak{m}}^i)$ is the R-reduction of $(C_i, \mathfrak{m}^i)$.

DEFINITION 3.2.33. Let $(C_i, \mathfrak{m}^i)$ $(i = 1, 2)$ be filtered A_∞ algebras over $\Lambda_{0,nov}$ such that $\overline{\mathfrak{m}}_0^i = 0$. For these filtered A_∞ algebras, we say that a filtered A_∞ homomorphism $\mathfrak{f} : (C_1, \mathfrak{m}^1) \to (C_2, \mathfrak{m}^2)$ is a *weak homotopy equivalence*, if the induced A_∞ homomorphism $\overline{\mathfrak{f}} : (\overline{C}_1, \overline{\mathfrak{m}}^1) \to (\overline{C}_2, \overline{\mathfrak{m}}^2)$ is a weak homotopy equivalence in the sense of Definition 3.2.10. Furthermore, when $(C_i, \mathfrak{m}^i)$ and $\mathfrak{f}$ are G-gapped, we call it a G-*gapped weak homotopy equivalence*.

DEFINITION 3.2.34. For a filtered A_∞ algebra $(C, \mathfrak{m})$, we say that a filtered A_∞ algebra $(C', \mathfrak{m}')$ is *an A_∞-deformation* of $(C, \mathfrak{m})$, if there exists a weak homotopy equivalence $\overline{\mathfrak{f}} : (\overline{C}, \overline{\mathfrak{m}}) \to (\overline{C}', \overline{\mathfrak{m}}')$ between their R-reductions. (We also say that a filtered A_∞ algebra $(C', \mathfrak{m}')$ is *an A_∞-deformation* of an unfiltered A_∞ algebra $(\overline{C}, \overline{\mathfrak{m}})$, if there exists a weak homotopy equivalence $\mathfrak{f} : (\overline{C}, \overline{\mathfrak{m}}) \to (\overline{C}', \overline{\mathfrak{m}}')$.)

3.3. Algebraic framework on the homotopy unit

In Section 3.5 we will construct a filtered A_∞ algebra associated to a Lagrangian submanifold. We do *not* know *in general* whether this filtered A_∞ algebra has a unit in the sense of Definition 3.2.20 (3). In Section 7.3, however, we will see that it has a *homotopy unit*. In this section, we will give an algebraic definition of homotopy unit. A geometric realization of the homotopy unit of our A_∞ algebra associated to a Lagrangian submanifold will be given in Section 7.3. In Subsection 3.3.2, we define the notion of a unital (resp. homotopy-unital) A_∞ homomorphism, which preserves the unit (resp. the homotopy unit).

3.3.1. Definition of the homotopy unit. Let $(C, \mathfrak{m})$ be a filtered A_∞ algebra. (We mainly consider $\Lambda_{0,nov}$ as the coefficient ring, but obviously the following framework is also available for an A_∞ algebra over R without filtration.) We do *not* assume that it has a unit.

Firstly, we prepare some notations. We denote by $B_k(B(C[1]))$ the tensor product of k copies of $B(C[1])$'s and put

$$B(B(C[1])) = \bigoplus_{k \geq 1} B_k(B(C[1])) = B(C[1]) \oplus (B(C[1]) \otimes B(C[1])) \oplus \cdots .$$

Let $\widehat{B}(\widehat{B}(C[1]))$ be a completion of $B(B(C[1]))$ with respect to the energy filtration. To avoid confusion between the tensor product in $B(C[1])$ with the one in $B(B(C[1]))$, we use $\overline{\otimes}$ for the latter, and we use the bold face letter $\mathbf{x}$ etc. to denote elements of $B(C[1])$. Namely, for example, $x_1 \otimes x_2$ is an element of $B_2(C[1])$ and $\mathbf{x}_1 \overline{\otimes} \mathbf{x}_2$ is an element of $B_2(B(C[1]))$. If $\mathbf{x}_i = x_{i,1} \otimes \cdots \otimes x_{i,\ell_i} \in B_{\ell_i}(C[1])$ then $\mathbf{x}_1 \overline{\otimes} \cdots \overline{\otimes} \mathbf{x}_k \in B_k(B(C[1]))$ and $\mathbf{x}_1 \otimes \cdots \otimes \mathbf{x}_k \in B_{\ell_1 + \cdots + \ell_k}(C[1])$. $(\mathbf{x}_1 \otimes \cdots \otimes \mathbf{x}_k = x_{1,1} \otimes x_{1,2} \otimes \cdots \otimes x_{1,\ell_1} \otimes x_{2,1} \otimes \cdots \otimes x_{k,\ell_k}.)$

Now we put

(3.3.1) $$C^+ = C \oplus \Lambda_{0,nov} \mathbf{e}^+ \oplus \Lambda_{0,nov} \mathbf{f},$$

where $\deg \mathbf{e}^+ = 0$, $\deg \mathbf{f} = -1$. (Here deg is a degree before shifted.)

DEFINITION 3.3.2. Let $(C, \mathfrak{m})$ be an A_∞ algebra. We say an element $\mathbf{e} \in C^0 = C[1]^{-1}$ is a *homotopy unit* of $(C, \mathfrak{m})$ if there exist maps

$$\mathfrak{h}_k : B_k(B(C[1])) \to C[1]$$

of degree $3 - 2k$ for $k = 1, 2, \cdots$ which preserve the energy filtration, such that

$$(3.3.3) \qquad\qquad\qquad \mathfrak{h}_1 = \mathfrak{m}$$

and the following $(C^+, \mathfrak{m}^+)$ becomes an A_∞ algebra with unit $\mathbf{e}^+ \in C^+[1]^{-1}$ in the sense of Definition 3.2.20 (3). Here $C^+ = C \oplus \Lambda_{0,nov} \mathbf{e}^+ \oplus \Lambda_{0,nov} \mathbf{f}$ as in (3.3.1) and $\mathfrak{m}^+$ is defined by following:

$$(3.3.4) \qquad \begin{aligned} \mathfrak{m}_2^+(\mathbf{e}^+, x) &= (-1)^{\deg x} \mathfrak{m}_2^+(x, \mathbf{e}^+) = x, \\ \mathfrak{m}_k^+(\cdots, \mathbf{e}^+, \cdots) &= 0, \qquad k \neq 2 \end{aligned}$$

for $x \in C^+$, and

$$(3.3.5.1) \qquad \mathfrak{m}^+(\mathbf{x}_1 \otimes \mathbf{f} \otimes \mathbf{x}_2 \otimes \mathbf{f} \otimes \cdots \otimes \mathbf{f} \otimes \mathbf{x}_k) = \mathfrak{h}_k(\mathbf{x}_1 \overline{\otimes} \cdots \overline{\otimes} \mathbf{x}_k)$$

except for $k = 2$ and $\mathbf{x}_1, \mathbf{x}_2 \in \Lambda_{0,nov}(= \Lambda_{0,nov} \cdot 1)$. For the latter case, we put

$$(3.3.5.2) \qquad\qquad \mathfrak{m}_1^+(\mathbf{f}) = \mathbf{e}^+ - \mathbf{e} + \mathfrak{h}_2(1 \overline{\otimes} 1)$$

with

$$(3.3.5.3) \qquad\qquad \mathfrak{h}_2(1 \overline{\otimes} 1) \equiv 0 \mod \Lambda_{0,nov}^+ C^+.$$

We also assume that $\mathfrak{m}_k^+$ satisfies (3.2.13). In other words, we assume that

$$\mathfrak{h}_k \mod \Lambda_{0,nov}^+ : B_k(B(\overline{C}[1])) \otimes_R R[e, e^{-1}] \to \overline{C}[1] \otimes_R R[e, e^{-1}]$$

is induced by an R module homomorphism

$$(3.3.6) \qquad\qquad \overline{\mathfrak{h}}_k : B_k(B(\overline{C}[1])) \to \overline{C}[1].$$

We call $(C, \mathfrak{m})$ satisfying (3.3.3)-(3.3.6), a *filtered A_∞ algebra with homotopy unit*, or simply, *homotopy-unital filtered A_∞ algebra*.

REMARK 3.3.7. (1) If we count the degree of $\overline{\otimes}$ as $\deg' \overline{\otimes} = -2 (=$ shifted degree of $\mathbf{f}$), the operators $\mathfrak{h}_k$ will always have degree $+1$.

(2) We now explain the geometric origin of our definition of the homotopy unit. Let (X, x_0) be a pointed space. Assume that there exists a product structure $\cdot : X \times X \to X$ such that its restrictions to $\{x_0\} \times X$ and $X \times \{x_0\}$ are homotopic to identity. (In other words X is an H space.) Let $H_1 : \{x_0\} \times X \times [0, 1] \to X$, $H_2 : X \times \{x_0\} \times [0, 1] \to X$ be such homotopies respectively, i.e., satisfy

$$\begin{aligned} H_1(x_0, x, 1) &= H_2(x, x_0, 1) = x, \\ H_1(x_0, x, 0) &= x_0 \cdot x, \qquad H_2(x, x_0, 0) = x \cdot x_0. \end{aligned}$$

Then x_0 is a homotopy unit. We consider the disjoint union $X \cup [0, 1]$ and identify x_0 and 0. Namely we put $X_+ = X \cup [0, 1]/x_0 \sim 0$. We extend $\cdot$ to $\cdot : X_+ \times X_+ \to X_+$ as follows: If $s, s' \in [0, 1]$ and $x, x' \in X$, then

$$s \cdot x' = H_1(x_0, x', s), \quad x \cdot s' = H_2(x, x_0, s').$$

It follows that $1 \cdot x = x \cdot 1 = x$. Namely 1 is a unit. The construction of $(C^+, \mathfrak{m}^+)$ in Definition 3.3.2 is an algebraic version of this construction. More precisely, the observation above provides us with the geometric meaning of the homotopy unit, at least, at the classical level. In this case, the formula involving the term $\mathfrak{h}_2(1 \overline{\otimes} 1)$ in (3.3.5.1), which is nothing but (3.3.5.2), does not appear. In Section 7.3 we will explain the geometric meaning of the term $\mathfrak{h}_2(1 \overline{\otimes} 1)$ in our filtered A_∞ algebra in more detail.

(3) There is an ambiguity of the choice of the maps $\mathfrak{h}$ in Definition 3.3.2. So the A_∞ algebra $(C^+, \mathfrak{m}^+)$ is not uniquely determined from $(C, \mathfrak{m})$. However, we will show that *the homotopy equivalence class as a filtered A_∞ algebra (see Section 4.2) of $(C^+, \mathfrak{m}^+)$ is uniquely determined by $(C, \mathfrak{m})$.* In fact, we will show that $(C^+, \mathfrak{m}^+)$ is homotopy equivalent to $(C, \mathfrak{m})$ as a filtered A_∞ algebra. See Lemma 4.2.55 and Proposition 4.2.52. In this sense, C can be regarded as something similar to a deformation retract of C^+.

The A_∞ formulae for $(C^+, \mathfrak{m}^+)$ imply certain relations between the maps $\mathfrak{h}_k$'s. We now write down these relations explicitly.

We define

$$\hat{\mathfrak{h}}_k : B(B(C[1])) \to B(B(C[1])), \qquad \hat{\mathfrak{h}} : B(B(C[1])) \to B(B(C[1]))$$

as follows: Let $\Delta : B(C[1]) \to B(C[1]) \otimes B(C[1])$ be the coproduct. For $k \geq 2$, we put

$$
\begin{aligned}
&\hat{\mathfrak{h}}_k(\mathbf{x}_1 \overline{\otimes} \cdots \overline{\otimes} \mathbf{x}_n) \\
&= \sum_{a,b,i} (-1)^{\deg' \mathbf{x}_1 + \cdots \deg' \mathbf{x}_{i-1} + \deg' \mathbf{x}'_{i,a}} \, \mathbf{x}_1 \overline{\otimes} \cdots \overline{\otimes} \mathbf{x}_{i-1} \\
&\qquad \overline{\otimes} \left(\mathbf{x}'_{i,a} \otimes \mathfrak{h}_k(\mathbf{x}''_{i,a} \overline{\otimes} \mathbf{x}_{i+1} \overline{\otimes} \cdots \overline{\otimes} \mathbf{x}_{i+k-2} \overline{\otimes} \mathbf{x}'_{i+k-1,b}) \otimes \mathbf{x}''_{i+k-1,b} \right) \\
&\qquad \overline{\otimes} \mathbf{x}_{i+k} \overline{\otimes} \cdots \overline{\otimes} \mathbf{x}_n,
\end{aligned}
$$

where $\Delta \mathbf{x}_i = \sum_a \mathbf{x}'_{i,a} \otimes \mathbf{x}''_{i,a}$. (Note that the homomorphism $\hat{\mathfrak{h}}_k$ maps $B_n(B(C[1]))$ to $B_{n-k+1}(B(C[1]))$, since $\otimes$ in the second line is not $\overline{\otimes}$.) Here $\deg'$ is the degree *after* shifted. Namely, if $\mathbf{x} = x_1 \otimes \cdots \otimes x_m$, then $\deg' \mathbf{x} = \deg x_1 + \cdots + \deg x_m - m$. See (3.2.2). For $k = 1$, we put

$$\hat{\mathfrak{h}}_1(\mathbf{x}_1 \overline{\otimes} \cdots \overline{\otimes} \mathbf{x}_n) = \sum_{a,i} (-1)^{\deg' \mathbf{x}_1 + \cdots \deg' \mathbf{x}_{i-1}} \, \mathbf{x}_1 \overline{\otimes} \cdots \overline{\otimes} \mathbf{x}_{i-1}$$

$$\overline{\otimes} \widehat{d\mathbf{x}}_i \overline{\otimes} \mathbf{x}_{i+1} \overline{\otimes} \cdots \overline{\otimes} \mathbf{x}_n.$$

Here we recall

$$\widehat{d\mathbf{x}}_i = \sum_a (-1)^{\deg' \mathbf{x}^{3;1}_{i,a}} \mathbf{x}^{3;1}_{i,a} \otimes \mathfrak{m}(\mathbf{x}^{3;2}_{i,a}) \otimes \mathbf{x}^{3;3}_{i,a},$$

where we use (Conv.3) (1.34).

We put $\hat{\mathfrak{h}} = \sum \hat{\mathfrak{h}}_k$ and extend it to $\widehat{B}(\widehat{B}(C[1]))$. We also introduce a family of maps $\mathfrak{b}_{k,i} : B_k(B(C[1])) \to B_{k-1}(B(C[1]))$, $(i = 1, \cdots, k-1)$ by

$$
\begin{aligned}
&\mathfrak{b}_{k,i}(\mathbf{x}_1 \overline{\otimes} \cdots \overline{\otimes} \mathbf{x}_k) \\
&= (-1)^{\deg' \mathbf{x}_1 + \cdots + \deg' \mathbf{x}_i} \mathbf{x}_1 \overline{\otimes} \cdots \overline{\otimes} (\mathbf{x}_i \otimes \mathbf{e} \otimes \mathbf{x}_{i+1}) \overline{\otimes} \cdots \overline{\otimes} \mathbf{x}_k
\end{aligned}
$$

for a given $\mathbf{e} \in C^0 = C[1]^{-1}$. (If we count $\deg' \overline{\otimes} = -2$, then $\mathfrak{b}_{k,i}$ is of degree $+1$.)

PROPOSITION 3.3.8. *Let $(C, \mathfrak{m})$ be an A_∞ algebra. Then (3.3.9) is equivalent to (3.3.10).*

(3.3.9)   *The $(C^+, \mathfrak{m}^+)$ defined in Definition 3.3.2 is an A_∞ algebra with unit $\mathbf{e}^+$.*

(3.3.10)   *The maps $\mathfrak{h}_k : B_k(B(C[1])) \to C[1]$ satisfy (3.3.5.2), (3.3.5.3), (3.3.6)
and have the following properties:*

(3.3.10.0) $\mathfrak{h}_1 = \mathfrak{m}.$

(3.3.10.1) $\displaystyle\sum_{\ell=1}^{k} \mathfrak{h}_\ell \circ \hat{\mathfrak{h}}_{k-\ell+1} - \sum_{i=1}^{k-1} \mathfrak{h}_{k-1} \circ \mathfrak{b}_{k,i} + \mathfrak{P}_k = 0.$

Here $\mathfrak{P}_k = 0$ if $k \neq 2$. Moreover, $\mathfrak{P}_2 = 0$ on the complement of

$$\Big(B_0(C[1]) \,\overline{\otimes}\, B_1(C[1])\Big) \oplus \Big(B_1(C[1]) \,\overline{\otimes}\, B_0(C[1])\Big) \subset B_2(B(C[1])).$$

(3.3.10.2) $-\mathfrak{P}_2(x \overline{\otimes} 1) = \mathfrak{P}_2(1 \overline{\otimes} x) = x,$

on $\Big(B_0(C[1]) \,\overline{\otimes}\, B_1(C[1])\Big) \oplus \Big(B_1(C[1]) \,\overline{\otimes}\, B_0(C[1])\Big) \subset B_2(B(C[1])).$

The statement (3.3.10) above enables us to directly formulate the definition of a homotopy unit of $(C, \mathfrak{m})$ in terms of the original A_∞ algebra $(C, \mathfrak{m})$ itself without introducing $(C^+, \mathfrak{m}^+)$.

The proof of Proposition 3.3.8 is a straightforward calculation, which we omit.

3.3.2. Unital (resp. homotopy-unital) A_∞ homomorphisms. In this subsection, we will give the definition of an A_∞ homomorphism preserving unit or homotopy unit.

Let $(C_1, \mathfrak{m}^1)$, $(C_2, \mathfrak{m}^2)$ be filtered A_∞ algebras and $\mathfrak{f} : C_1 \to C_2$ be a filtered A_∞ homomorphism. We first assume that C_i has a unit $\mathbf{e}_i$ $(i = 1, 2)$.

DEFINITION 3.3.11.   We say $\mathfrak{f}$ *preserves unit*, or sometimes call it a *unital A_∞ homomorphism*, if

(3.3.12.1) $\mathfrak{f}_k(x_1, \cdots, x_{i-1}, \mathbf{e}_1, x_{i+1}, \cdots, x_k) = 0$ for $k \geq 2$,
(3.3.12.2) $\mathfrak{f}_1(\mathbf{e}_1) = \mathbf{e}_2.$

Unfiltered version can be defined in the same way.

We next consider the case of A_∞ algebras with homotopy unit. We assume that filtered A_∞ algebras $(C_1, \mathfrak{m}^1)$ and $(C_2, \mathfrak{m}^2)$ have homotopy unit $\mathbf{e}_1$ and $\mathbf{e}_2$, respectively. We then define

$$C_i^+ = C_i \oplus \Lambda_{0,nov} \mathbf{e}_i^+ \oplus \Lambda_{0,nov} \mathbf{f}_i^+$$

as in (3.3.1).

DEFINITION 3.3.13.   We say a filtered A_∞ homomorphism $\mathfrak{f} : C_1 \to C_2$ *preserves homotopy unit*, or call $\mathfrak{f} : C_1 \to C_2$ a *homotopy-unital A_∞ homomorphism*, if it extends to a unital filtered A_∞ homomorphism $\mathfrak{f}^+ : C_1^+ \to C_2^+$.

3.4. A_∞ deformation of the cup product

In this section, we give a geometric construction of the classical A_∞ algebra associated to each oriented, not necessarily relatively spin, Lagrangian submanifold by using the space of metric ribbon trees and the moduli space of constant pseudo-holomorphic discs. (Actually the construction works for any oriented manifold L.) The meaning of "classical" is the A_∞ algebra without filtration. It is defined over

$\mathbb{Z}$. We should note that in our geometric construction of the classical A_∞ algebra, the problem of the transversality at the diagonal plays a crucial role. The proofs related to this transversality will be carried out in Section 7.2. In this section we state the main propositions needed in a precise manner and explain the main geometric ingredients needed for the construction of the deformation.

First, we recall the notion of metric ribbon trees. We refer to [**FuOh97**] for more details, where the idea of using the *metric* ribbon tree in Morse theory and in topological field theory appeared in a rigorous manner for the first time. A *ribbon tree* is a pair (T, i) where T is a tree and $i : T \to D^2$ is an embedding such that

(3.4.1.1)   no vertex of T has 2 edges,
(3.4.1.2)   if $v \in T$ is a vertex with one edge then $i(v) \in \partial D^2$,
(3.4.1.3) $i(T) \cap \partial D^2$ consists of vertices of one edge.

Let G_k be the set of (T, i, v_1) where (T, i) is an isotopy class of ribbon tree such that $\#i(T) \cap \partial D^2 = k$ and that $v_1 \in i(T) \cap \partial D^2$. We call a vertex *exterior* if it lies on ∂D^2 and *interior* otherwise. We order the set of exterior vertices so that v_1 is the first one and that the order is compatible with the counter clockwise orientation on ∂D^2. We call an edge *exterior* if it contains an exterior vertex, and *interior* otherwise.

For each $\mathfrak{t} = (T, i, v_1) \in G_k$, we denote by $C^0_{\text{ext}}(\mathfrak{t})$ the set of all exterior vertices and by $C^0_{\text{int}}(\mathfrak{t})$ the set of all interior vertices. Similarly we denote by $C^1_{\text{ext}}(\mathfrak{t})$, $C^1_{\text{int}}(\mathfrak{t})$ the set of exterior and interior edges respectively.

For each $\mathfrak{t} = (T, i, v_1) \in G_k$, let $Gr(\mathfrak{t})$ be the set of all maps $\ell : C^1_{\text{int}}(\mathfrak{t}) \to \mathbb{R}^+$. We put $Gr_k = \cup_{\mathfrak{t} \in G_k} Gr(\mathfrak{t})$ and call its element a *metric ribbon tree*. We regard $\ell(e)$ as the length of the edge and set the length of exterior edge to be infinite. We refer to [**FuOh97**] for the description of the topology put on Gr_k. Denote the set of all maps $\ell : C^1_{\text{int}}(\mathfrak{t}) \to \mathbb{R}^+ \cup \{\infty\}$ by $\overline{Gr}(\mathfrak{t})$ and their unions by $\overline{Gr}_k$. The space $\overline{Gr}_k$ is a compactification of Gr_k.

We next define a map $\Theta : Gr_k \to \mathcal{M}^{\text{main,reg}}_k$, following Section 10 in [**FuOh97**]. Let $(\mathfrak{t}, \ell) \in Gr_k$. We take an Euclidean rectangle $L_e = [0, \ell(e)] \times [0, 1]$ for each $e \in C^1_{\text{int}}(\mathfrak{t})$ and $L_e = (-\infty, 0] \times [0, 1]$ for $e \in C^1_{\text{ext}}(\mathfrak{t})$. We remove $\{0, \ell(e)\} \times \{1/2\} \subset [0, \ell(e)] \times [0, 1]$, $\{0\} \times \{1/2\} \subset (-\infty, 0] \times [0, 1]$. For given $v \in C^0_{\text{int}}(\mathfrak{t})$, we consider edges e, e' containing v where e' is the edge next to e according to the cyclic order we put on the set of edges containing v. Now if both e and e' are outgoing edges, we glue $\{0\} \times (1/2, 1] \subset \partial L_e$ and $\{0\} \times [0, 1/2) \subset \partial L_{e'}$. We carry out a similar gluing process for other cases of the orientations put on e and e'. See Figure 3.4.1.

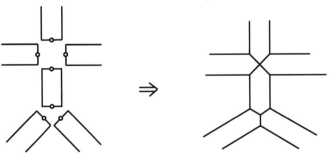

Figure 3.4.1

We have thus obtained a space $X_0(\mathfrak{t}, \ell)$ together with an (incomplete) flat metric. We can conformally fill the holes of $X_0(\mathfrak{t}, \ell)$ and obtain a space $X(\mathfrak{t}, \ell)$

equipped with a complex structure and a singular Riemannian metric. We denote $\Theta(\mathfrak{t}, \ell) := [X(\mathfrak{t}, \ell)]$ which is the isomorphism class of $X(\mathfrak{t}, \ell)$. In Theorem 10.4 [FuOh97], the first and the second named authors proved that the map $\Theta : Gr_k \to \mathcal{M}_k^{\mathrm{main,reg}}$ is a homeomorphism. (Recall that $\mathcal{M}_k^{\mathrm{main,reg}}$ is diffeomorphic to $\mathbb{R}^{k-3}$, see Section 2.1.) We used this homeomorphism to define a smooth structure on Gr_k.

We remark that Θ can be extended to the compactification $\overline{Gr}_k$ of Gr_k and leads to a homeomorphism $\overline{\Theta} : \overline{Gr}_k \to \mathcal{M}_k^{\mathrm{main}}$. We have thus chosen a singular metric on each element of $\mathcal{M}_k^{\mathrm{main,reg}}$. We modify this family of metrics in a neighborhood of singular points and obtain a smooth family of smooth Riemannian metrics. We will use these metrics to define appropriate Sobolev norms in Section 7.1.

Now we are going to construct the classical A_∞ algebra associated to each oriented Lagrangian submanifold L in our symplectic manifold M. Let $\Delta_{k+1} \subset L^{k+1} = L \times \cdots \times L$ ($k + 1$ times direct products of L) be the main diagonal where $\Delta_{k+1} \simeq L$ and let $N_{\Delta_{k+1}} L^{k+1}$ be the normal bundle of Δ_{k+1} in L^{k+1}. We identify $N_{\Delta_{k+1}} L^{k+1}$ with a tubular neighborhood $\mathrm{Tube}_{\Delta_{k+1}} L^{k+1}$ of Δ_{k+1} in L^{k+1}. For $\beta \in \Pi(M, L)$, we denote by $\mathcal{M}_{k+1}^{\mathrm{main}}(\beta)$ the main component of the moduli space of genus 0 stable pseudo-holomorphic maps from $(\Sigma, \partial\Sigma)$ to (M, L) in class β with $k + 1$ marked points on the boundary (see Definition 2.1.27).

For the case
$$\beta_0 = 0, \quad k + 1 > 2,$$
$\mathcal{M}_{k+1}^{\mathrm{main}}(\beta_0)$ is the moduli space of constant maps. This moduli space is transversal, namely it has a correct dimension $k - 2 + n$. However the evaluation map $ev : \mathcal{M}_{k+1}^{\mathrm{main}}(\beta_0) \to L^{k+1}$ is not a submersion. So we take the following Kuranishi structure on it. (See Section A1 for the definition of Kuranishi structure.)

We take $U_{k+1} = \mathrm{Tube}_{\Delta_{k+1}} L^{k+1} \times \overline{Gr}_{k+1}$. We pull back the normal bundle $N_{\Delta_{k+1}} L^{k+1}$ to U_{k+1} and take it as an obstruction bundle E_{k+1}. We can find a section $s_{k+1} : U_{k+1} \to E_{k+1}$ which vanishes only at $\Delta_{k+1} \times \overline{Gr}_{k+1}$ by identifying $\mathrm{Tube}_{\Delta_{k+1}} L^{k+1}$ with $N_{\Delta_{k+1}} L^{k+1}$. Then $(U_{k+1}, E_{k+1}, s_{k+1})$ defines a Kuranishi structure, (with trivial automorphism groups) and $ev = (ev_1, \cdots, ev_k, ev_0) : U_{k+1} \to L^{k+1}$ (which is actually the composition of an open embedding and the projection) is a submersion. It means that ev is weakly submersive (Definition A1.13) with respect to this Kuranishi structure.

Next we have to choose a suitable Kuranishi structure on $\mathcal{M}_{k+1}^{\mathrm{main}}(\beta)$ to construct the filtered A_∞ algebra. This is because of the transversality problem which we mentioned above. We will discuss this point in Chapter 7 Sections 7.1 and 7.2 in details. In this section we just state the following proposition without elaborating the discussion of the Kuranishi structure at this stage.

PROPOSITION 3.4.2. *There exists an oriented Kuranishi structure on the moduli space $\mathcal{M}_{k+1}^{\mathrm{main}}(\beta)$ such that it is compatible with the compactification and the Kuranishi structure on $\mathcal{M}_{k+1}^{\mathrm{main}}(\beta_0)$ coincides with the above Kuranishi structure.*

We will prove Proposition 3.4.2 in Section 7.1, where the precise meaning of the compatibility mentioned in the proposition is given (Proposition 7.1.2). Roughly speaking it means the following. The boundary component that appears in the compactification of $\mathcal{M}_{k+1}^{\mathrm{main}}(\beta)$ can be identified with a fiber product of various other $\mathcal{M}_{k'+1}^{\mathrm{main}}(\beta')$'s. The fiber product of the space with Kuranishi structure has the induced Kuranishi structure (see Section A1.2). The compatibility means that the Kuranishi structure on the boundary induced by the fiber product coincides with the Kuranishi structure induced from that of $\mathcal{M}_{k+1}^{main}(\beta)$ as the boundary.

We next state the main result on the existence of appropriate perturbations of the original s, the Kuranishi map.

We consider a countable set $\mathcal{X}_L$ of smooth singular simplices on L such that if $P \in \mathcal{X}_L$ then each of its face $\partial_i P$ is contained in $\mathcal{X}_L$. We take such a countable set because we use the method of "smooth correspondence" and need the transversality argument for which we have to use the Baire category theorem. This point will be discussed in Chapter 7 in details. We write an element in $\mathcal{X}_L$ as $P = (|P|, f)$. Here $|P|$ is a simplex and f is a smooth map $|P| \to L$. (We write P in place of $|P|$ sometimes by abuse of notation.)

Now, we consider a free $\mathbb{Z}$ module generated by $\mathcal{X}_L$. We write it as $\mathbb{Z}\mathcal{X}_L$. We are going to define the structures of A_∞ algebra on $\mathbb{Z}\mathcal{X}_L$. Let $(P_i, f_i) \in \mathcal{X}_L$. We put

$$(3.4.3)\quad \mathcal{M}_{k+1}^{main}(\beta_0; P_1, \cdots, P_k) = \mathcal{M}_{k+1}^{main}(\beta_0)_{(ev_1,\cdots,ev_k)} \times_{f_1 \times \cdots \times f_k} (P_1 \times \cdots \times P_k).$$

Here the right hand side of (3.4.3) is the fiber product in the sense of the space of Kuranishi structure. We define it in general in Section A1.2 Lemma A1.39. Here we explain what it is in our case. We defined the Kuranishi structure $(U_{k+1}, E_{k+1}, s_{k+1})$ of $\mathcal{M}_{k+1}^{main}(\beta_0)$. The evaluation map

$$ev = (ev_1, \cdots, ev_k, ev_0) : U_{k+1} \to L^{k+1}$$

is a submersion hence the fiber product

$$(3.4.4)\qquad U_{k+1}(P_1, \cdots, P_k) = U_{k+1\,(ev_1,\cdots,ev_k)} \times_{f_1 \times \cdots \times f_k} (P_1 \times \cdots \times P_k)$$

is transversal and is a manifold (with possibly corners) equipped with a smooth triangulation. The bundle $E_{k+1} \to U_{k+1}$ can be pulled back to give a bundle, which we denote by $E_{k+1}(P_1, \cdots, P_k)$. The section s_{k+1} of E_{k+1} (the Kuranishi map) induces a section of $E_{k+1}(P_1, \cdots, P_k)$, which we write $s_{P_1,\cdots,P_k}$. Then, $(U_{k+1}(P_1, \cdots, P_k), E_{k+1}(P_1, \cdots, P_k), s_{P_1,\cdots,P_k})$ defines a Kuranishi structure on the fiber product of the right hand side of (3.4.3), regarded as a topological space.

From now on we regard that $\mathcal{M}_{k+1}^{main}(\beta_0; P_1, \cdots, P_k)$ is a space with Kuranishi structure and $ev_0 : \mathcal{M}_{k+1}^{main}(\beta_0; P_1, \cdots, P_k) \to L$ is defined and is a strongly continuous map. (See Definition A1.13 for its definition).

Now we will prove the following theorem in Section 7.2 (Proposition 7.2.35). We put $\vec{P} = (P_1, \cdots, P_k)$, $P_i \in \mathcal{X}_L$.

PROPOSITION 3.4.5. *There exist a choice of $\mathcal{X}_L$ and a system of perturbations (single valued sections of obstruction bundles) $\mathfrak{s}_{\vec{P}}$ of $\mathcal{M}_{k+1}^{main}(\beta_0; \vec{P})$, such that the following holds.*

(3.4.6.1) $\mathfrak{s}_{\vec{P}}$ *is transversal to 0.*

(3.4.6.2) $\mathfrak{s}_{\vec{P}}$ *is compatible at the compactification.*

(3.4.6.3)   *There is a smooth triangulation of $\mathfrak{s}_{\vec{P}}^{-1}(0)$ so that $(\mathfrak{s}_{\vec{P}}^{-1}(0), ev_0)$ can be regarded as a $\mathbb{Z}$ linear combination of elements of $\mathcal{X}_L$.*

(3.4.6.4)   *The inclusion $\mathbb{Z}\mathcal{X}_L \subset C(L; \mathbb{Q})$ induces an isomorphism of $H(\mathbb{Z}\mathcal{X}_L, \delta)$ to the cohomology $H(L; \mathbb{Q})$ of L.*

Some explanation on (3.4.6.3) is in order. By (3.4.6.1), $\mathfrak{s}_{\vec{P}}^{-1}(0)$ is a smooth manifold. We take a smooth triangulation together with an order of vertices. Each simplex of this triangulation can be canonically identified to the standard simplex by using order of the vertices. We restrict $ev_0 : \mathfrak{s}_{\vec{P}}^{-1}(0) \to L$ to one of the simplices. We then obtain a smooth singular simplex of L. (3.4.6.3) asserts that it is an element of $\mathcal{X}_L$.

Let Δ_a^d, $a \in A$ be the set of all simplices of $\mathfrak{s}_{\vec{P}}^{-1}(0)$ of dimension $d = \dim \mathfrak{s}_{\vec{P}}^{-1}(0)$ Hereafter we write

$$\mathcal{M}_{k+1}^{\mathrm{main}}(\beta_0; P_1, \cdots, P_k)^{\mathfrak{s}} = (\mathfrak{s}_{\vec{P}}^{-1}(0), ev_0) = \sum_{a \in A} \pm (\Delta_a^d, ev_0),$$

which is regarded as a smooth singular chain of L. Here the sign $\pm$ in the above formula is defined as follows. Our moduli space $\mathcal{M}_{k+1}^{\mathrm{main}}(\beta_0; \vec{P})$ has an orientation (Chapter 8). Each of the simplex Δ_a^d is identified with the standard simplex in $\mathbb{R}^d$ with standard orientation. We take $+$ sign if and only if these two orientations coincide. (See Section 7.2 Remark 7.2.15 (3).)

Now we define the operations $\overline{\mathfrak{m}}^L = \{\overline{\mathfrak{m}}_k^L\}_{k=0}^\infty$ which define the A_∞ algebra structure on $\mathbb{Z}\mathcal{X}_L$ as follows:

(3.4.7.1) $\overline{\mathfrak{m}}_0^L = 0,$
(3.4.7.2) $\overline{\mathfrak{m}}_1^L(P) = (-1)^n \partial P,$
(3.4.7.3) $\overline{\mathfrak{m}}_k^L(P_1, \cdots, P_k) = \mathcal{M}_{k+1}^{\mathrm{main}}(\beta_0; P_1, \cdots, P_k)^{\mathfrak{s}},$

where $n = \dim L$. The notation ∂ in (3.4.7.2) is the usual (classical) boundary operator. Here we regarded P as a chain. See Remark 3.5.8 (1). We note that Proposition 3.4.2 and the choice of $\mathcal{X}_L$ yield that we can define the fiber product in the right hand side in (3.4.7.3) in the sense of Kuranishi structure. The orientation of the moduli space in (3.4.7.3) is defined in Definition 8.4.1, Chapter 8. Here we equip $\Delta_k \times \overline{Gr}_{k+1}$ with the orientation transferred from the one on the moduli space $\mathcal{M}_{k+1}^{\mathrm{main}}(\beta_0)$ of constant maps via the identification $\overline{\Theta} : \overline{Gr}_{k+1} \to \mathcal{M}_{k+1}^{\mathrm{main}} \cong \mathcal{M}_{k+1}^{\mathrm{main}}(\beta_0)$. The orientation on $\mathcal{M}_{k+1}^{\mathrm{main}}(\beta_0)$ will be given in Chapter 8, Section 8.6. On the other hand, we have defined another orientation on $\mathcal{M}_{k+1}^{\mathrm{main,reg}}$ in Subsection 2.1.2. By analyzing orientation on $\mathcal{M}_{k+1}^{\mathrm{main}}$ and using the map $\overline{\Theta} : \overline{Gr}_{k+1} \to \mathcal{M}_{k+1}^{\mathrm{main}}$, we can find an orientation on $\Delta_k \times \overline{Gr}_{k+1}$. This orientation might be different from the one defined above as the zero set $\mathfrak{s}_{k+1}^{-1}(0)$. One can see the difference exactly but we omit it, because we do not need it.

Then we can obtain the following theorem.

THEOREM 3.4.8. *Let L be a smooth oriented manifold. Then there exists a countable set $\mathcal{X}_L$ of smooth singular simplices on L which satisfies the following properties:*

(3.4.9.1) *$(\mathbb{Z}\mathcal{X}_L, \overline{\mathfrak{m}}^L)$ is an A_∞ algebra over $\mathbb{Z}$.*
(3.4.9.2) *There is a smooth simplicial decomposition of L by which we regard $PD[L]$ as an element of $\mathbb{Z}\mathcal{X}_L$. (Here PD denotes the Poincaré duality.) Then $PD[L]$ is a homotopy unit of $(\mathbb{Z}\mathcal{X}_L, \overline{\mathfrak{m}}^L)$.*
(3.4.9.3) *The cohomology group of $(\mathbb{Z}\mathcal{X}_L, \overline{\mathfrak{m}}_1^L)$ is isomorphic to the cohomology group (over $\mathbb{Z}$-coefficient) of L.*

Here (3.4.9.1) follows from Proposition 3.4.5 (especially (3.4.6.2)). The detailed proof is given in Subsections 7.2.4-8.

We now explain (3.4.9.2). We take a smooth simplicial decomposition of L and order its vertices. Then each simplex of it can be identified with the standard simplex and hence determines a singular simplex. The sum

$$(3.4.10) \qquad\qquad \sum_a \pm \Delta_a^{\dim L}$$

of all such singular simplices of dimension $\dim L$ represents the fundamental homology class $[L]$. (Here $\pm$ is determined whether the orientation of the standard simplex coincides with the orientation of L or not.) (See Subsection 7.3.2.)

In this book, we regard singular *chain* complex as a *cochain* complex. Hence the sum (3.4.10) above is regarded as an element of $S^0(L; \mathbb{Z})$. We write it as $PD[L]$.

The property (3.4.9.2) will be proved in Section 7.3. (3.4.9.3) follows from (3.4.6.4).

We call $(\mathbb{Z}\mathcal{X}_L, \overline{\mathfrak{m}}^L)$ *the classical A_∞ algebra associated to L.*

We would like to mention that there are works [**McC04, Wil05**] closely related to Theorem 3.4.8.

REMARK 3.4.11. We remark that in Section 7.2 we construct A_∞ structure *not* directly by using the multisections $\mathfrak{s}_{\vec{\beta}}$. Instead, we construct an A_K structure for each K directly using $\mathfrak{s}_{\vec{\beta}}$ (see Definition 4.4.6) and then obtain an A_∞ structure which is A_K homotopy equivalent thereto (Definition 4.4.8). The reason why we can not directly construct an A_∞ structure at once will be explained in Subsection 7.2.3. This point is quite technical. The same remark applies to other constructions of this chapter. However we do not make this remark again. In practice it does not matter whether we construct an A_∞ structure at once or construct an A_K structure for each K and then obtain an A_∞ structure in somewhat indirect way.

In Chapter 4 (as a part of Theorem 4.1.1 proven there) we will find that the weak homotopy equivalence class of the A_∞ algebra $(\mathbb{Z}\mathcal{X}_L, \overline{\mathfrak{m}}^L)$ is uniquely determined by L. Namely, the A_∞ algebra $(\mathbb{Z}\mathcal{X}_L, \overline{\mathfrak{m}}^L)$ is independent of the choices of the perturbed section $\mathfrak{s}^k$ constructed in Theorem 3.4.8 and the countable set $\mathcal{X}_L$, up to weak homotopy equivalence. Moreover, in Section 7.5, we prove that when we put $\mathbb{R}\mathcal{X}_L = \mathbb{Z}\mathcal{X}_L \otimes \mathbb{R}$ and extend $\overline{\mathfrak{m}}^L$ to $\mathbb{R}\mathcal{X}_L$, then $(\mathbb{R}\mathcal{X}_L, \overline{\mathfrak{m}}^L)$ is weak homotopy equivalent to the de Rham complex of L over $\mathbb{R}$ (Theorem X).

3.5. The filtered A_∞ algebra associated to a Lagrangian submanifold

In this section, we show that the construction of Chapter 2 and its generalization lead to a geometric realization of the filtered A_∞ algebra on each relatively spin Lagrangian submanifold L of M. Our main theorem in this section is Theorem 3.5.11. We again emphasize that we do *not* yet impose the condition $[o_k(L)] = 0$ on the obstruction classes $o_k(L)$. In this section we put $R = \mathbb{Q}$.

Let $S^k(L; \mathbb{Q})$ be the free $\mathbb{Q}$ module generated by codimension k smooth singular simplices of L. Let $\mathcal{X}_1(L)$ be a countable set of smooth singular simplices with $\mathcal{X}_1(L) \supset \mathcal{X}_L$, $\mathcal{X}_1(L) \neq \mathcal{X}_L$ where $\mathcal{X}_L$ is as in Theorem 3.4.8. We denote by $C^k(L; \mathbb{Q})$ the submodule of $S^k(L; \mathbb{Q})$ generated by $\mathcal{X}_1(L)$. (As in the previous section, we use the method of "smooth correspondence". For this purpose, we need to use the transversality argument and the Baire category theorem which is why the *countably* generated complex $C^k(L; \mathbb{Q})$ is used. See Section 7.2 for the construction of $C^k(L; \mathbb{Q})$.) We sometimes write an element of $\mathcal{X}_1(L)$ as $P = (|P|, f)$ as in Section 3.4. We define $C^\bullet(L; \Lambda_{0,nov})$ to be the completion of $C^\bullet(L; \mathbb{Q}) \otimes \Lambda_{0,nov}$. For the convenience of notations, we put

$$C^\bullet = C^\bullet(L; \Lambda_{0,nov}) := (C^\bullet(L; \mathbb{Q}) \otimes \Lambda_{0,nov})\hat{\ }.$$

Recall that the element $T^\lambda e^\mu$ in $\Lambda_{0,nov}$ has degree 2μ. Thus the degree in $C^\bullet(L; \Lambda_{0,nov})$ is the sum of the degree in $C^\bullet(L; \mathbb{Q})$ and the degree of the coefficients in $\Lambda_{0,nov}$. Using the filtration on $\Lambda_{0,nov}$, we can uniquely define the filtration on $C^k(L; \Lambda_{0,nov})$ which satisfies the following conditions:

$$C^k(L; \mathbb{Q}) \subset F^0 C^k(L; \Lambda_{0,nov})$$

and

$$C^k(L; \mathbb{Q}) \cap F^\lambda C^k(L; \Lambda_{0,nov}) = \{0\} \quad \text{for } \lambda > 0.$$

We now define the homomorphisms

$$\mathfrak{m}_k : B_k(C(L; \Lambda_{0,nov})[1]) \to C(L; \Lambda_{0,nov})[1]$$

for $k \geq 0$. To do this, we recall that $\mathcal{M}_{k+1}(\beta)$ is the set of pairs $((\Sigma, \vec{z}), w)$ where $(\Sigma, \vec{z}) \in \mathcal{M}_{k+1}$ and $w : (\Sigma, \partial\Sigma) \to (M, L)$ is a pseudo-holomorphic map which represents the class β. Let $\mathcal{M}_{k+1}^{main}(\beta)$ be the subset of $\mathcal{M}_{k+1}(\beta)$ consisting of elements $((\Sigma, \vec{z}), w)$ where $(\Sigma, \vec{z})$ is in the main component. (See Definitions 2.1.20 and 2.1.27.)

Let $P_i \in \mathcal{X}_1(L)$, we consider fiber product

$$(3.5.1) \qquad \mathcal{M}_{k+1}^{main}(\beta) \, {}_{(ev_1, \cdots, ev_k)} \times_{(f_1 \times \cdots \times f_k)} (P_1 \times \cdots \times P_k)$$

as in the last section. Let $\vec{P} = (P_1, \cdots, P_k)$, $P_i \in \mathcal{X}_1(L)$. The fiber product (3.5.1) is a space with Kuranishi structure, we denote (3.5.1) by $\mathcal{M}_{k+1}^{main}(\beta; \vec{P})$.

PROPOSITION 3.5.2. *Suppose that L is a relatively spin Lagrangian submanifold. Then there exist a choice of $\mathcal{X}_1(L)$ and a system of multisections $\mathfrak{s}_{\beta, \vec{P}}$ of $\mathcal{M}_{k+1}^{main}(\beta; \vec{P})$ with the following properties:*

$(3.5.3.1)$ *The (virtual) dimension of $\mathcal{M}_{k+1}^{main}(\beta; \vec{P})$ is given by*

$$n - \sum(g_i - 1) + \mu_L(\beta) - 2,$$

where $n = \dim L$, $(P_i, f_i) \in C^{g_i}(L; \mathbb{Q})$ and $\mu_L(\beta)$ is the Maslov index.
$(3.5.3.2)$ $\mathfrak{s}_{\beta, \vec{P}}$ *is transversal to 0.*
$(3.5.3.3)$ $\mathfrak{s}_{\beta, \vec{P}}$ *is compatible at the boundary.*
$(3.5.3.4)$ $(\mathfrak{s}_{\beta, \vec{P}}^{-1}(0), ev_0)$ *is a $\mathbb{Q}$ linear combination of elements of $\mathcal{X}_1(L)$.*

More precisely (3.5.3.4) is stated as follows. By Lemma A1.26 the set $\mathfrak{s}_{\beta, \vec{P}}^{-1}(0)$ has a smooth triangulation. Take one of such triangulations. We also fix an order of the vertices of this triangulation. Each simplex Δ_a^d of dimension $d = \dim \mathfrak{s}_{\beta, \vec{P}}^{-1}(0)$ of it comes with multiplicity $mul_{\Delta_a^d}$. (See Definition A1.27.) The restriction of ev_0 to Δ_a^d defines a smooth singular simplex (Δ_a^d, ev_0). Then (3.5.3.4) means that each of (Δ_a^d, ev_0) is an element of $\mathcal{X}_1(L)$.

We remark that the virtual fundamental chain $(\mathfrak{s}_{\beta, \vec{P}}^{-1}(0), ev_0)$ is defined to be

$$(\mathfrak{s}_{\beta, \vec{P}}^{-1}(0), ev_0) = \sum_{a \in A} \pm mul_{\Delta_a^d}(\Delta_a^d, ev_0)$$

where $\{\Delta_a^d \mid a \in A\}$ is the set of all simplices of dimension $d = \dim \mathfrak{s}_{\beta,\vec{P}}^{-1}(0)$ and $\pm$ is determined by considering the orientation. (See Definition A1.28.)

REMARK 3.5.4. We should emphasize that the choice of the multisection $\mathfrak{s}_{\beta,\vec{P}}$ depends on β and $\vec{P}$. We have to choose the multisection $\mathfrak{s}_{\beta,\vec{P}}$ satisfying certain compatibility conditions (3.5.3.3). (See Compatibility Conditions 7.2.38 and 7.2.44.) We also need to choose the triangulation of $\mathfrak{s}_{\beta,\vec{P}}^{-1}(0)$ to be compatible for various choices of β, $\vec{P}$. We will discuss these point in Section 7.2 in detail.

PROOF. We will explain our construction of the Kuranishi structure and state Propositions 7.1.1, 7.1.2 and 7.2.35 in Chapter 7 which are about how we choose $C(L;\mathbb{Q})$ and the multisection $\mathfrak{s}$ above. As for the orientations on $\mathcal{M}_{k+1}^{main}(\beta)$ and for the fiber product of Kuranishi structures, see Chapter 8 Sections 8.4 and 8.5. Here we prove only the statement on the dimension in (3.5.3.1). We compute the dimension

$$\mu_L(\beta) + k + 1 - 3 + n - \sum g_i = \mu_L(\beta) + n - \sum(g_i - 1) - 2,$$

as required. $\qquad\qquad\qquad\qquad\qquad\qquad\qquad\qquad\qquad\qquad\qquad\qquad\qquad\qquad\Box$

DEFINITION 3.5.5. Let the multisection $\mathfrak{s}$ and the countably generated submodule $C(L;\mathbb{Q})$ be as in Proposition 3.5.2. We define $\mathcal{M}_{k+1}^{main}(\beta;\vec{P})^{\mathfrak{s}}$ by

$$\mathcal{M}_{k+1}^{main}(\beta;\vec{P})^{\mathfrak{s}} := (\mathfrak{s}_{\beta,\vec{P}}^{-1}(0), ev_0).$$

(As for the orientation of the above moduli space, see Definition 8.4.1 in Chapter 8).

Now we define the maps $\mathfrak{m}_k$. We recall that we have the element $\beta_0 = 0 \in G(L)$, (see (3.1.8) in Section 3.1 for the definition of $G(L)$). It satisfies $\mu_L(\beta_0) = 0$ and $\omega(\beta_0) = 0$.

DEFINITION 3.5.6. (1) For $(P, f) \in C^k(L, \mathbb{Q})$, we define

$$\mathfrak{m}_{0,\beta}(1) = \begin{cases} \mathcal{M}_1(\beta)^{\mathfrak{s}} & \text{for } \beta \neq \beta_0 \\ 0 & \text{for } \beta = \beta_0, \end{cases}$$

$$\mathfrak{m}_{1,\beta}(P, f) = \begin{cases} \mathcal{M}_2^{main}(\beta;P)^{\mathfrak{s}} & \text{for } \beta \neq \beta_0 \\ (-1)^n \partial P & \text{for } \beta = \beta_0, \end{cases}$$

and

$$\mathbf{e} = PD([L]) \in C^0(L) = C[1]^{-1}(L),$$

where $[L]$ is the fundamental cycle of L and PD denotes the Poincaré duality. The notation ∂ in the definition of $\mathfrak{m}_{1,\beta_0}$ is the usual (classical) *boundary* operator.

(2) For each $k \geq 2$ and $P_i \in C^{g_i}(L, \mathbb{Q})$, we define $\mathfrak{m}_{k,\beta}$ by

$$\mathfrak{m}_{k,\beta}(P_1, \ldots, P_k) = \mathfrak{m}_{k,\beta}(P_1 \otimes \cdots \otimes P_k) = \mathcal{M}_{k+1}^{main}(\beta;\vec{P})^{\mathfrak{s}}.$$

(3) Then we define $\mathfrak{m}_k$ $(k \geq 0)$ by

$$(3.5.7) \qquad\qquad \mathfrak{m}_k = \sum_{\beta \in G(L)} \mathfrak{m}_{k,\beta} \otimes T^{\omega(\beta)} e^{\mu_L(\beta)/2}.$$

REMARK 3.5.8. (1) In the definition of $\mathfrak{m}_{1,\beta_0}$ above, we see P as a *chain* and ∂ is the usual boundary operator as we noted. When we see P as a *cochain*, we have to change the sign into the following;

$$\mathfrak{m}_{1,\beta_0}(P) = (-1)^{n+\deg P+1} dP,$$

where $\deg P$ is the degree of P before shifted. Here we use the convention of the sign on the Poincaré duality as follows: For a chain S in L, the Poincaré dual $PD(S)$, regarded as a current, satisfies

$$\int_S \alpha|_S = \int_L PD(S) \wedge \alpha$$

for any $\alpha \in \Omega^{\dim S}(L)$. We note that this convention is consistent with the convention on the orientation of the normal bundle given in Section 8.6. Under this convention, we can see that $PD(\partial S) = (-1)^{\deg S+1} d(PD(S))$.

(2) We note that $\mathfrak{m}_k$ depends on the almost complex structure J and perturbation $\mathfrak{s}$ of Kuranishi map (that is a multisection of the obstruction bundle. See Section A1.) We will study this dependence in detail later in Section 4.6.

(3) We note that the condition (3.2.12.7) is satisfied since $\mathfrak{m}_{0,\beta_0}(1) = 0$.

(4) As in (3.2.13), we can reduce the coefficient $\Lambda_{0,nov}$ of $(C(L, \Lambda_{0,nov}), \mathfrak{m})$ to $\mathbb{Q}$ to get an A_∞ algebra $(\overline{C}, \overline{\mathfrak{m}})$, since Condition (3.2.13.3) is a consequence of (3.1.7.2). Because $\mathfrak{m}_{0,\beta_0} = 0$, we have $\overline{\mathfrak{m}}_0 = 0$ in this case. Furthermore, we should note that $(\overline{C}, \overline{\mathfrak{m}})$ is *not* a D.G.A., but an A_∞ algebra. Let us consider the case $\beta = \beta_0(= 0)$. If $P_1 \neq P_2$, $\mathcal{M}_2^{\mathrm{main}}(\beta_0; P_1, P_2)$ is (as a set) nothing but $P_1 \cap P_2$. But an essential point is that we can *not* define self intersection *at the chain level*. Similarly we can not expect that $\overline{\mathfrak{m}}_k = 0$ for $k \geq 3$, because we do not have the transversality for the diagonal case. We will discuss this problem in more detail at Section 7.2 in Chapter 7. In the previous section Section 3.4, for the Lagrangian submanifold L, we constructed the classical A_∞ algebra $(\mathbb{Z}\mathcal{X}_L, \overline{\mathfrak{m}}^L)$ over $\mathbb{Z}$, admitting the transversality argument. Then we can show that $(C(L, \Lambda_{0,nov}), \mathfrak{m})$ is an A_∞ deformation of $(\mathbb{Q}\mathcal{X}_L, \overline{\mathfrak{m}}^L)$ in the sense of Definition 3.2.34. (See Theorem 3.5.11 below.) We also remark one more point about the sign. According to (3.2.5), we should check

$$(3.5.9) \qquad \mathcal{M}_3^{\mathrm{main}}(\beta_0; P_1, P_2) = (-1)^{\deg P_1(\deg P_2+1)} P_1 \cap P_2,$$

for $\beta = \beta_0(= 0)$. This will be proved in Corollary 8.6.4 in Chapter 8.

LEMMA 3.5.10. *The formal sum (3.5.7) converges and defines a continuous operation*

$$\mathfrak{m}_k : B_k(C(L; \Lambda_{0,nov})[1]) \to C(L; \Lambda_{0,nov})[1].$$

PROOF. $G(L)$ satisfies Condition 3.1.6 by Gromov's compactness theorem. □

Recall we put $\deg \beta = \mu_L(\beta)$ and shift the degree of (P, f) by 1. Then the dimension formula (3.5.3.1) implies that the degree of $\mathfrak{m}_k$ on $B(C[1])$ is $+1$.

The following is the main theorem in this section:

THEOREM 3.5.11. *Suppose that L is a relatively spin Lagrangian submanifold. Then we have the following:*

$(3.5.12.1) \qquad (C(L; \Lambda_{0,nov}), \mathfrak{m})$ *is a filtered A_∞ algebra with homotopy unit* **e**.

(3.5.12.2) $(C(L; \Lambda_{0,nov}), \mathfrak{m})$ *is $G(L)$-gapped.*
(3.5.12.3) $(C(L; \Lambda_{0,nov}), \mathfrak{m})$ *is an A_∞ deformation of the classical A_∞ algebra* $(\mathbb{Q}\mathcal{X}_L, \overline{\mathfrak{m}}^L)$ *in Theorem 3.4.8, in the sense of Definition 3.2.34.*

We note (3.5.12.3) means the following: when we reduce the coefficient ring $\Lambda_{0,nov}$ to $\mathbb{Q}$ as in (3.2.13), we have an A_∞ algebra $(C(L; \mathbb{Q}), \overline{\mathfrak{m}})$ over $\mathbb{Q}$ with $\overline{\mathfrak{m}}_0 = 0$: Then the restriction of $\overline{\mathfrak{m}}$ to $\mathbb{Q}\mathcal{X}_L \subset C(L; \mathbb{Q})$ coincides with $\overline{\mathfrak{m}}^L$ constructed in Section 3.4.

REMARK 3.5.13. As mentioned in Remark 3.4.11, we will *not* directly construct the filtered A_∞ structure out of the multisection $\mathfrak{s}$. Instead, for any energy $E \geq 0$ and k fixed, we will construct an $A_{n,K}$ structure using only the moduli spaces of pseudo-holomorphic discs with energy bounded by E. See Section 7.2.6 for the precise definition of the $A_{n,K}$ structure and details of the constructions are in Sections 7.2.4-8.

PROOF. The properties (3.2.12.1)-(3.2.12.5) follow directly from our construction of $(C(L; \Lambda_{0,nov}), \mathfrak{m})$. We now prove that $\{\mathfrak{m}_k\}_{k \geq 0}$ satisfy the A_∞ formulae, assuming the sign rules in (3.5.17) below. The sign will be precisely checked in Section 8.5. Let us prove that $\widehat{d} \circ \widehat{d} = 0$. This is a consequence of analysis of the boundary of $\mathcal{M}_{k+1}^{\text{main}}(\beta; P_1, \cdots, P_k)$. (See (3.5.1).) We find that its boundary is the sum of

$$\sum_i \mathcal{M}_{k+1}^{\text{main}}(\beta; P_1, \cdots, \partial P_i, \cdots, P_k)$$

and the terms described by Figure 3.5.1 below.

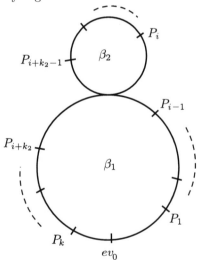

Figure 3.5.1

On the other hand, in order to prove $\widehat{d} \circ \widehat{d} = 0$, we note that it is enough to show that

(3.5.14)
$$\sum_{\beta_1 + \beta_2 = \beta} \sum_{k_1 + k_2 = k+1} \sum_i (-1)^{\deg P_1 + \cdots + \deg P_{i-1} + i - 1}$$
$$\mathfrak{m}_{k_1, \beta_1}(P_1, \cdots, \mathfrak{m}_{k_2, \beta_2}(P_i, \cdots, P_{i+k_2-1}), \cdots, P_k) = 0.$$

(See Remark 3.2.21 (1).) Here we write P_i in place of (P_i, f_i) for simplicity. We divide the left hand side of (3.5.14) into 3 terms, corresponding to the cases $\beta_1 = 0$

and $k_1 = 1$, $\beta_2 = 0$ and $k_2 = 1$, and the others. Then we can rewrite the left hand side of (3.5.14) as follows:

$$
\mathfrak{m}_{1,0}\mathfrak{m}_{k,\beta}(P_1, \cdots, P_k)
$$
$$
+ \sum_i (-1)^{\deg P_1 + \cdots + \deg P_{i-1} + i - 1} \mathfrak{m}_{k,\beta}(P_1, \cdots, \mathfrak{m}_{1,0}(P_i), \cdots, P_k)
$$

(3.5.15)
$$
+ \sum_{\substack{\beta_1 + \beta_2 = \beta, \ k_1 + k_2 = k+1; \\ \beta_1 \neq 0 \text{ or } k_1 \neq 1, \\ \beta_2 \neq 0 \text{ or } k_2 \neq 1}} \sum_i (-1)^{\deg P_1 + \cdots + \deg P_{i-1} + i - 1}
$$
$$
\mathfrak{m}_{k_1, \beta_1}(P_1, \cdots, \mathfrak{m}_{k_2, \beta_2}(P_i, \cdots, P_{i+k_2-1}), \cdots, P_k).
$$

By Definition 3.5.6, we have $\mathfrak{m}_{1,0} = (-1)^n \partial$, where ∂ is the classical boundary map. Hence the first term in (3.5.15) is nothing but

(3.5.16.0)
$$
(-1)^n \partial \mathcal{M}_{k+1}^{\text{main}}(\beta : P_1, \cdots, P_k),
$$

and the second term in (3.5.15) is the sum of

(3.5.16.1)
$$
(-1)^{n + \sum_{j=1}^{i-1}(\deg P_j + 1)} \mathcal{M}_{k+1}^{\text{main}}(\beta : P_1, \cdots, \partial P_i, \cdots, P_k).
$$

The third term in (3.5.15) geometrically corresponds to the moduli spaces described by Figure 3.5.1. This is the sum of

(3.5.16.2)
$$
(-1)^{\sum_{j=1}^{i-1}(\deg P_j + 1)} \mathcal{M}_{k-k_2+2}^{\text{main}}(\beta_1; P_1, \cdots,
$$
$$
\mathcal{M}_{k_2+1}^{\text{main}}(\beta_2; P_i, \cdots, P_{i+k_2-1}), \cdots, P_k).
$$

Moreover, as for the orientations of these spaces, we can show the following:

(3.5.17.1)
$$
(-1)^n \mathcal{M}_{k+1}^{\text{main}}(\beta : P_1, \cdots, \partial P_i, \cdots, P_k)
$$
$$
\subseteq (-1)^{n+1+\sum_{j=1}^{i-1}(\deg P_j + 1)} \partial \mathcal{M}_{k+1}^{\text{main}}(\beta; P_1, \cdots, P_k)
$$

and

(3.5.17.2)
$$
\mathcal{M}_{k-k_2+2}^{\text{main}}(\beta_1; P_1, \cdots, \mathcal{M}_{k_2+1}^{\text{main}}(\beta_2; P_i, \cdots, P_{i+k_2-1}), \cdots, P_k)
$$
$$
\subseteq (-1)^{n+1+\sum_{j=1}^{i-1}(\deg P_j + 1)} \partial \mathcal{M}_{k+1}^{\text{main}}(\beta; P_1, \cdots, P_k).
$$

The proofs of (3.5.17.1) and (3.5.17.2) will be given in Proposition 8.5.1 in Chapter 8. Therefore we find that (3.5.16.0) and the sum of (3.5.16.1) and (3.5.16.2) cancel each other and so (3.5.15) becomes zero. Thus we have proved that $\widehat{d} \circ \widehat{d} = 0$. (3.5.12.2) is immediate from construction.

For the construction of a homotopy unit, we also have to study transversality. The proofs will be postponed until Section 7.3 (and Section 8.10 for the signs).

(3.5.12.3) is immediate from its construction which will be given in Subsections 7.2.4 - 7.2.7, except the sign in (3.5.9) which will be checked in Corollary 8.6.4. $\square$

3.6. Bounding cochains and the A_∞ Maurer-Cartan equation

So far we have constructed a filtered A_∞ algebra for a relatively spin Lagrangian submanifold without assuming any unobstructedness conditions. Because of the presence of $\mathfrak{m}_0$, the operator $\mathfrak{m}_1$ can not define the cohomology in general. In this section, we study the obstruction to deforming $\mathfrak{m}_1$ so that the deformed $\mathfrak{m}_1$ defines the cohomology. For this purpose we first introduce an algebraic notion of bounding cochains (solutions of Maurer-Cartan equation) in a filtered A_∞ algebra in Subsection 3.6.1, and we construct a sequence of the classical cohomology classes in Subsection 3.6.2 which describes the obstruction to the existence of the bounding cochains. Further in Subsection 3.6.3 we introduce a weaker unobstructedness condition by using the unit or the homotopy unit in the A_∞ algebra. These constructions can be done in a purely algebraic manner.

3.6.1. Bounding cochains and deformations. Let $(C, \mathfrak{m})$ be a filtered A_∞ algebra over $\Lambda_{0,nov}$ and $b \in (C[1])^0 = C^1$ with $b \equiv 0 \pmod{\Lambda_{0,nov}^+}$. We put

$$(3.6.1) \qquad e^b := 1 + b + b \otimes b + \cdots + \underbrace{b \otimes \cdots \otimes b}_{k \text{ times}} + \cdots \in \widehat{B}(C[1]).$$

We do not put the factorials here unlike the usual definition of the exponential. This is because we used only the main component among the $k!$ components of $\mathcal{M}_{k+1}$ when we realized the map $\mathfrak{m}_{k,\beta}$ geometrically in Section 3.5. The condition that $b \equiv 0 \pmod{\Lambda_{0,nov}^+}$ implies that the right hand side in (3.6.1) converges with respect to the topology defined by the energy filtration, and so it defines an element of $\widehat{B}(C[1])$.

We remark the following:

LEMMA 3.6.2. *For a non-zero element* $\mathbf{x}$ *of* $\widehat{B}(C[1])$, $\mathbf{x} = e^b$ *for some* $b \in B_1(C[1]) = C[1]$ *if and only if* $\Delta \mathbf{x} = \mathbf{x} \otimes \mathbf{x}$, *where* Δ *is the coproduct on* $\widehat{B}(C[1])$ *defined by* (3.2.14).

PROOF. It is easy to check the statement for "only if" and so we will only prove the one for "if". Write $\mathbf{x} = \sum_{k=0}^\infty \mathbf{x}_k$, $\mathbf{x}_k \in B_k(C[1])$ and assume

$$(3.6.3) \qquad \qquad \Delta \mathbf{x} = \mathbf{x} \,\overline{\otimes}\, \mathbf{x}.$$

Note $\Delta : BC[1] \to BC[1] \,\overline{\otimes}\, BC[1]$ where we write $\overline{\otimes}$ for the tensor product of the right hand side of the above formula. We say the

$$\bigoplus_{k_1+k_2=k} BC_{k_1}[1] \,\overline{\otimes}\, B_{k_2}C[1]$$

component of $BC[1] \,\overline{\otimes}\, BC[1]$, the k-th order term and denote the k-th order term of $\mathbf{y}$ by $(\mathbf{y})_k$. We also write $BC_k[1]$ component of $\mathbf{y} \in BC[1]$ by $(\mathbf{y})_k$.

Using the definition (3.2.14) of the coproduct Δ and comparing the 0-th order term of the two sides of (3.6.3) we get the equation

$$(\mathbf{x}_0)^2 = \mathbf{x}_0, \quad \mathbf{x}_0 \in \Lambda_{0,nov}$$

and hence $\mathbf{x}_0 = 0$ or 1. In case $\mathbf{x}_0 = 1$, comparison of the 1st-order terms of (3.6.3) gives rise to the equation

$$1 \,\overline{\otimes}\, \mathbf{x}_1 + \mathbf{x}_1 \,\overline{\otimes}\, 1 = 1 \,\overline{\otimes}\, \mathbf{x}_1 + \mathbf{x}_1 \,\overline{\otimes}\, 1.$$

In other words, the equation gives no restriction on the 1st-order term. We set $b := \mathbf{x}_1$. Now for the second order terms in general, it is easy to see that the coproduct satisfies

$$(\Delta \mathbf{x}_2)_2 = 1 \,\overline{\otimes}\, \mathbf{x}_2 + \pi(\mathbf{x}_2) + \mathbf{x}_2 \,\overline{\otimes}\, 1.$$

Here $\pi : B_2 C[1] \to B_1 C[1] \,\overline{\otimes}\, B_1 C[1]$ is defined by $\pi(x \otimes y) = x \,\overline{\otimes}\, y$.

Therefore the second order term of (3.6.3) becomes

$$1 \overline{\otimes} \mathbf{x}_2 + \pi(\mathbf{x}_2) + \mathbf{x}_2 \overline{\otimes} 1 = 1 \overline{\otimes} \mathbf{x}_2 + \mathbf{x}_1 \overline{\otimes} \mathbf{x}_1 + \mathbf{x}_2 \overline{\otimes} 1$$

and hence $\mathbf{x}_2 = \mathbf{x}_1 \otimes \mathbf{x}_1 = b \otimes b$.

Repeating this straight-forward order-by-order comparisons of the two sides of (3.6.3), we prove $\mathbf{x} = e^b$. In case $\mathbf{x}_0 = 0$, a similar reasoning proves $\mathbf{x} = 0$. This finishes the proof. $\qquad\square$

DEFINITION 3.6.4. We say that $b \in (C[1])^0$ with $b \equiv 0$ (or mod $\Lambda^+_{0,nov}$) is a *bounding cochain* or a *solution of Maurer-Cartan equation* if $\widehat{d}e^b = 0$. (Recall that $\widehat{d} = \sum \widehat{\mathfrak{m}}_k$ and $\widehat{\mathfrak{m}}_k$ is defined in (3.2.15).) A filtered A_∞ algebra is said to be *unobstructed* if there exists a bounding cochain and *obstructed* otherwise. We denote by $\widehat{\mathcal{M}}(C)$ the set of all bounding cochains b.

REMARK 3.6.5. Our equation $\widehat{d}e^b = 0$ is an inhomogeneous A_∞-*version of the Maurer-Cartan* or the *Batalin-Vilkovisky master equation* [**BaVi93**]. In fact we can write it as

$$\delta b_\beta + \sum_{\substack{k=0,1,2,\cdots \\ \beta_{k+1},\beta_1,\cdots,\beta_k \in G, \\ \beta_{k+1}+\beta_1+\cdots+\beta_k=\beta \\ (k,\beta_{k+1})\neq(1,(0,0))}} \mathfrak{m}_{k,\beta_{k+1}}(b_{\beta_1},\cdots,b_{\beta_k}) = 0$$

where $b = \sum T^{\lambda(\beta)} e^{\mu(\beta)/2} b_\beta$.

The relation of the BV master equation to the deformation theory is discussed in [**ASKZ97, GugSt86, HiSc97, Kon03, Sche98**]. (See also [**Fuk02III**].)

Let $(C, \mathfrak{m})$ be a filtered A_∞ algebra with bounding cochains b_1, b_0. We define $\delta_{b_1,b_0} : C[1] \longrightarrow C[1]$ as follows.

DEFINITION 3.6.6.

$$\delta_{b_1,b_0}(x) = \sum_{k_1,k_0 \geq 0} \mathfrak{m}_{k_1+k_0+1}(\underbrace{b_1,\cdots,b_1}_{k_1}, x, \underbrace{b_0,\cdots,b_0}_{k_0}).$$

Symbolically we may simply write this definition as $\delta_{b_1,b_0}(x) = \mathfrak{m}(e^{b_1} x e^{b_0})$ in an obvious way. It then follows that

$$(3.6.7) \qquad \widehat{d}(e^{b_1} x e^{b_0}) = e^{b_1} \delta_{b_1,b_0}(x) e^{b_0} + \widehat{d}(e^{b_1}) x e^{b_0} + (-1)^{\deg x + 1} e^{b_1} x \widehat{d}(e^{b_0}).$$

The second and the third term vanishes if $\widehat{d}(e^{b_1}) = \widehat{d}(e^{b_0}) = 0$.

LEMMA 3.6.8. *If* $\widehat{d}(e^{b_1}) = \widehat{d}(e^{b_0}) = 0$, *then* $\delta_{b_1,b_0} \circ \delta_{b_1,b_0} = 0$.

PROOF. By (3.6.7) we have

$$0 = \widehat{d}(\widehat{d}(e^{b_1} x e^{b_0})) = \widehat{d}(e^{b_1} \delta_{b_1,b_0}(x) e^{b_0}) = e^{b_1}((\delta_{b_1,b_0} \circ \delta_{b_1,b_0})(x)) e^{b_0},$$

from which the lemma immediately follows. $\qquad\square$

We remark that we can also deform the structure of the filtered A_∞ algebra for any cochain $b \in C[1]^0$ with $b \equiv 0 \mod \Lambda^+_{0,nov}$, which is *not* necessarily a bounding cochain as follows. Later in Subsection 5.2.2, we will discuss deformations of the filtered A_∞ homomorphisms.

DEFINITION 3.6.9. For any cochain $b \in C[1]^0$ with $b \equiv 0 \mod \Lambda_{0,nov}^+$, we put

$$\mathfrak{m}_k^b(x_1, \cdots, x_k)$$
$$= \sum_{\ell_0, \cdots, \ell_k} \mathfrak{m}_{k+\sum \ell_i} (\underbrace{b, \cdots, b}_{\ell_0}, x_1, \underbrace{b, \cdots, b}_{\ell_1}, \cdots, \underbrace{b, \cdots, b}_{\ell_{k-1}}, x_k, \underbrace{b, \cdots, b}_{\ell_k})$$
$$= \mathfrak{m}(e^b x_1 e^b x_2 \cdots x_{k-1} e^b x_k e^b)$$

for $k = 0, 1, 2, \cdots$. We note that $\mathfrak{m}_0^b(1) = \mathfrak{m}(e^b)$.

Then we can easily see the following.

PROPOSITION 3.6.10. $(C, \mathfrak{m}^b)$ is also a filtered A_∞ algebra. And $\mathfrak{m}_0^b = 0$ if and only if b satisfies $\widehat{d}(e^b) = 0$. In this case $\mathfrak{m}_1^b$ is nothing but $\delta_{b,b}$ in Definition 3.6.6.

PROOF. We extend $\mathfrak{m}_k^b$ to $\widehat{d}^b$ as a coderivation on $\widehat{B}(C[1])$ which is given by

$$\widehat{d}^b(x_1, \cdots, x_k) = \sum_{\ell=1}^{k+1} \sum_{\ell'=\ell}^{k+1} (-1)^{\deg x_1 + \cdots + \deg x_{\ell-1} + \ell - 1} x_1 \otimes \cdots \otimes x_{\ell-1}$$
$$\otimes \mathfrak{m}(e^b x_\ell e^b \cdots e^b x_{\ell'-1} e^b) \otimes x_{\ell'} \otimes \cdots \otimes x_k.$$

When $\ell' = \ell$, we put $\mathfrak{m}(e^b)$ in place of $\mathfrak{m}(e^b x_\ell e^b \cdots e^b x_{\ell'-1} e^b)$ in the right hand side. We compare this formula with $\widehat{d} \circ \widehat{d}(e^b x_1 e^b \cdots e^b x_k e^b) = 0$ and obtain the result that $\widehat{d}^b \circ \widehat{d}^b = 0$. Moreover by noticing the following identities

$$\widehat{d}(e^b) = e^b \mathfrak{m}(e^b) e^b = e^b \mathfrak{m}_0^b(1) e^b,$$

we have proven the second assertion. $\square$

DEFINITION 3.6.11. For $b_1, b_0 \in \widehat{\mathcal{M}}(C)$, we put

$$HF(C, b_1, b_0; \Lambda_{0,nov}) = H(C, \delta_{b_1, b_0}).$$

When $b_1 = b_0$, we simply write $HF(C, b; \Lambda_{0,nov}) = H(C, \mathfrak{m}_1^b)$.

We recall that when we consider a homotopy unit in an A_∞ algebra C, we extended C to $C^+ = C \oplus \Lambda_{0,nov} e^+ \oplus \Lambda_{0,nov} \mathbf{f}$ as in (3.3.1). We next study the relationship between bounding cochains of C and of C^+.

PROPOSITION 3.6.12. If $b \in C[1]^0 = C^1$ is a bounding cochain of $(C, \mathfrak{m})$, then it is also a bounding cochain of $(C^+, \mathfrak{m}^+)$. The natural inclusion $(C, \mathfrak{m}^b) \to (C^+, \mathfrak{m}^{+b})$ induces an isomorphism $H(C, \mathfrak{m}_1^b) \to H(C^+, \mathfrak{m}_1^{+b})$.

REMARK 3.6.13. From Theorem 4.2.45, we will find that the second assertion implies that the natural inclusion $(C, \mathfrak{m}^b) \to (C^+, \mathfrak{m}^{+b})$ gives a homotopy equivalence between the two filtered A_∞ algebras. See Section 4.2 for the definition of the notion of the homotopy equivalence between A_∞ algebras.

PROOF. The first half of the assertions is obvious. We prove the second half of the assertions. Clearly the natural inclusion is a cochain map and is injective. The quotient cochain complex is generated by $[\mathbf{e}^+]$ and $[\mathbf{f}]$. Then (3.3.5.2) implies $d[\mathbf{f}] = [\mathbf{e}^+]$. Hence the quotient complex is acyclic. This finishes the proof. $\square$

Now we apply the above discussion to our geometric situation. We have the filtered A_∞ algebra $C(L; \Lambda_{0,nov})$ associated to a relatively spin Lagrangian submanifold L.

DEFINITION 3.6.14. We say that $b \in C(L; \Lambda_{0,nov})[1]^0 \in C^1(L; \Lambda_{0,nov})$ is a *bounding cochain* if $\widehat{d}e^b = 0$. We denote by $\widehat{\mathcal{M}}(L; J, \mathfrak{s})$ the set of all bounding cochains b. We say L is *unobstructed*, if $\widehat{\mathcal{M}}(L; J, \mathfrak{s})$ is nonempty.

The solution set $\widehat{\mathcal{M}}(L; J, \mathfrak{s})$ may depend on the given almost complex structure J and a system $\mathfrak{s}$ of multisections. However, unobstructedness of L is independent of J and $\mathfrak{s}$, which will be proved later in Section 4.6. When no confusion can occur, we write $\widehat{\mathcal{M}}(L; J, \mathfrak{s})$ as $\widehat{\mathcal{M}}(L)$ for simplicity.

3.6.2. Obstruction for the existence of bounding cochain. In the last subsection, we introduced the notion of bounding cochains b and defined the cohomology group $H(C, \mathfrak{m}_1^b)$. For geometric applications, it is important to know when $\widehat{\mathcal{M}}(L)$ is nonempty. This subsection states conditions for $\widehat{\mathcal{M}}(C)$ to be nonempty in terms of the cohomology of $(\overline{C}, \overline{\mathfrak{m}}_1)$, (which is the usual cohomology of L over $\mathbb{Q}$ when $C = C(L; \Lambda_{0,nov})$). For this purpose we algebraically define a sequence of cohomology classes, which we call obstruction classes in $H(\overline{C}, \overline{\mathfrak{m}}_1)$.

Let $G \subset \mathbb{R}_{\geq 0} \times 2\mathbb{Z}$ be a submonoid satisfying Condition 3.1.6. We write $G = \{(\lambda_i, \mu_i)\}$ such that $i < j \Rightarrow \lambda_i \leq \lambda_j$. (Note that $\lambda_0 = \mu_0 = 0$ and $0 < \lambda_1$.) We consider a G-gapped filtered A_∞ algebra C. (See Definition 3.2.26.)

REMARK 3.6.15. We remark that if G' is another submonoid satisfying Condition 3.1.6 and containing G, then every G-gapped filtered A_∞ algebra is also G'-gapped.

DEFINITION 3.6.16. Let $G' \supseteq G$. A G-gapped filtered A_∞ algebra is called to be *unobstructed over G'* if there exists a bounding cochain b written as

$$b = \sum_{i=1}^{\infty} T^{\lambda_i'} e^{\frac{\mu_i'}{2}} b_i$$

for some $b_i \in \overline{C}[1]^{-\mu_i'} = \overline{C}^{1-\mu_i'}$, where we put $G' = \{(\lambda_i', \mu_i') \mid i = 1, 2, \cdots\}$.

LEMMA 3.6.17. *A G-gapped filtered A_∞ algebra is unobstructed if and only if it is unobstructed over G' for some $G' \supseteq G$.*

The proof of the lemma is obvious.
Now the main result of this subsection is the following.

THEOREM 3.6.18. *Let $G = \{(\lambda_i, \mu_i) \mid i = 0, 1, 2, \cdots\}$ such that $\lambda_i \leq \lambda_j$ for $i < j$ and $\lambda_0 = \mu_0 = 0$ as before and $(C, \mathfrak{m})$ be a G-gapped filtered A_∞ algebra. Then there are sequences of cocycles o_k and cochains b_k with the following properties:*

(3.6.19.1) $[o_k] \in H^{2-\mu_k}(\overline{C}, \overline{\mathfrak{m}}_1)$ *and* $b_k \in \overline{C}^{1-\mu_k}$.
(3.6.19.2)   *The cocycle o_k is defined if b_j and o_j for j with $\lambda_j \lneqq \lambda_k$ are defined. The cohomology class $[o_k]$ depends on b_j and o_j for j with $\lambda_j \lneqq \lambda_k$.*
(3.6.19.3)   *The cochain b_k is defined if $[o_k] = 0$.*
(3.6.19.4)   *$(C, \mathfrak{m})$ is unobstructed over G if and only if there exists a choice of b_k inductively such that $[o_k] = 0$ for all k.*

We call $[o_k]$ $(k = 1, 2, \cdots)$ the *obstruction classes* of $(C, \mathfrak{m})$.

PROOF. Since $(C, \mathfrak{m})$ is a G-gapped filtered A_∞ algebra, we can write

$$\mathfrak{m}_k = \sum_{(\lambda_i, \mu_i) \in G} T^{\lambda_i} e^{\frac{\mu_i}{2}} \mathfrak{m}_{k,i}$$

as in Definition 3.2.26. Here $\mathfrak{m}_{k,i} : B_k \overline{C}[1] \to \overline{C}[1]$ and $\mathfrak{m}_{k,0} = \overline{\mathfrak{m}}_k$. To handle the case where some λ_i's coincide, we prepare some notations. When λ_i is the k-th smallest (non zero) number among the set $\{\lambda_j\}$, we write $\lambda_i = \lambda_i^{(k)}$ and put $\lambda^{(k)} = \lambda_i^{(k)}$. For example, if $0 < \lambda_1 = \cdots = \lambda_\ell \lneqq \lambda_{\ell+1}$, we write $\lambda_1^{(1)} = \lambda_1, \cdots, \lambda_\ell^{(1)} = \lambda_\ell$ and $\lambda_{\ell+1}^{(2)} = \lambda_{\ell+1}$. We are going to construct o_i and b_i inductively on (k).

If $\lambda_1^{(1)} = \cdots = \lambda_\ell^{(1)} \lneqq \lambda_{\ell+1}^{(2)}$, we put

$$o_i = \mathfrak{m}_{0,i}(1) \in \overline{C}[1]^{1-\mu_i} = \overline{C}^{2-\mu_i}, \qquad i = 1, \cdots, \ell.$$

Noting $\mathfrak{m}_{0,0} = 0$, we calculate

$$T^{\lambda^{(1)}} \sum_{i=1}^{\ell} e^{\frac{\mu_i}{2}} \mathfrak{m}_{1,0}(o_i) = \sum_{i=1}^{\ell} T^{\lambda_i} e^{\frac{\mu_i}{2}} \mathfrak{m}_{1,0} \mathfrak{m}_{0,i}(1)$$
$$\equiv \mathfrak{m}_1(\mathfrak{m}_0(1)) \mod T^{\lambda^{(1)}} \Lambda_{0,nov}^+$$

which is zero by the A_∞ formula. Since $\mu_i \neq \mu_{i'}$ for $1 \leq i \neq i' \leq \ell$ and $\mathfrak{m}_{1,0} = \overline{\mathfrak{m}}_1$, we have $\overline{\mathfrak{m}}_1(o_i) = 0$ for all $i = 1, \cdots, \ell$. Therefore o_i define the cohomology classes

$$[o_i] \in H^{2-\mu_i}(\overline{C}, \overline{\mathfrak{m}}_1), \qquad i = 1, \cdots, \ell.$$

If $[o_i] = 0$ for all i $(1 \leq i \leq \ell)$, we can choose $b_i \in \overline{C}^{1-\mu_i}$ such that

$$\mathfrak{m}_{1,0}(b_i) + o_i = 0.$$

If we put $b_{(1)} = \sum_{i=1}^{\ell} T^{\lambda_i} e^{\frac{\mu_i}{2}} b_i \in C^1$, we have

$$(3.6.20) \quad \mathfrak{m}(e^{b_{(1)}}) \equiv \sum_{i=1}^{\ell} \left(T^{\lambda_i} e^{\frac{\mu_i}{2}} \mathfrak{m}_{0,i}(1) + T^{\lambda_i} e^{\frac{\mu_i}{2}} \mathfrak{m}_{1,0}(b_i) \right) = 0 \mod T^{\lambda^{(1)}} \Lambda_{0,nov}^+.$$

Now we assume that we have chosen b_i for i with $\lambda_i < \lambda^{(k)}$ inductively so that

$$(3.6.21) \qquad \qquad \mathfrak{m}(e^{b_{(k-1)}}) \equiv 0 \mod T^{\lambda^{(k-1)}} \Lambda_{0,nov}^+,$$

where

$$(3.6.22) \qquad b_{(i)} = \sum_{j=1}^{*_i} T^{\lambda_j} e^{\frac{\mu_j}{2}} b_j \in C^1, \qquad *_i = \max\{j \mid \lambda_j < \lambda^{(i+1)}\}.$$

DEFINITION 3.6.23. When $\lambda_n^{(k)} = \cdots = \lambda_{n+m}^{(k)} \lneqq \lambda_{n+m+1}^{(k+1)}$ (in this case $*_{k-1} = n - 1$), we denote the coefficient of $T^{\lambda_h} e^{\frac{\mu_h}{2}}$ in $\mathfrak{m}(e^{b_{(k-1)}})$ by $o_h \in \overline{C}^{2-\mu_h}$ for each $h = n, \cdots, n+m$.

LEMMA 3.6.24. $\overline{\mathfrak{m}}_1(o_h) = 0$.

PROOF. By the A_∞ formula again, we have

$$0 = (\mathfrak{m} \circ \widehat{d})(e^{b^{(k-1)}})$$

$$\equiv T^{\lambda^{(k)}} \mathfrak{m} \left(\sum_{h=n}^{n+m} e^{\frac{\mu_h}{2}} o_h \right) \equiv \sum_{h=n}^{n+m} T^{\lambda_h} e^{\frac{\mu_h}{2}} \mathfrak{m}_{1,0}(o_h) \mod T^{\lambda^{(k)}} \Lambda_{0,nov}^+.$$

It follows from this that $\mathfrak{m}_{1,0}(o_h) = 0$ for each $h = n, \cdots, n+m$. $\qquad\square$

We have thus defined the cohomology classes $[o_h]$. If they are all zero, we can choose $b_h \in \overline{C}^{1-\mu_h}$ satisfying

$$(3.6.25) \qquad\qquad\qquad \mathfrak{m}_{1,0}(b_h) + o_h = 0.$$

LEMMA 3.6.26.
$$\mathfrak{m}(e^{b_{(k)}}) \equiv 0 \mod T^{\lambda^{(k)}} \Lambda_{0,nov}^+,$$
where $b_{(k)}$ is defined by (3.6.22).

PROOF. We have

$$\mathfrak{m}(e^{b^{(k-1)}}) \equiv \sum_{h=n}^{n+m} T^{\lambda_h} e^{\frac{\mu_h}{2}} o_h \mod T^{\lambda^{(k)}} \Lambda_{0,nov}^+,$$

since $G = \{(\lambda_i, \mu_i) \mid i = 0, 1, 2, \cdots\}$ is a monoid. The lemma then follows from (3.6.25). $\qquad\square$

We have proved (3.6.19.1),(3.6.19.2) and (3.6.19.3) by now. It is easy to see that if all of b_k are defined (and all of $[o_k]$ are zero) then

$$(3.6.27) \qquad\qquad b = \sum T^{\lambda_k} e^{\frac{\mu_k}{2}} b_k = \lim_{k \to \infty} b_{(k)}$$

is a bounding cochain. In fact, it follows from Lemma 3.6.26 that

$$\mathfrak{m}(e^b) \equiv 0 \mod T^{\lambda_k} \Lambda_{0,nov}^+$$

for any k hence $\mathfrak{m}(e^b) = 0$. Therefore $\widehat{d}(e^b) = e^b \mathfrak{m}(e^b) e^b = 0$.

On the contrary, if $(C, \mathfrak{m})$ is unobstructed over G, we can find a bounding cochain b as in (3.6.27). Then we find that b_k satisfies (3.6.21) and (3.6.25). It means that we can define b_k such that all of $[o_k]$ vanishes. The proof of Theorem 3.6.18 is now complete. $\qquad\square$

REMARK 3.6.28. It may happen that $(C, \mathfrak{m})$ is obstructed over some G but is unobstructed over some bigger G'. This phenomenon is related to the existence of the rational point of the moduli space $\widehat{\mathcal{M}}(C)$. (Compare [**Fuk03I**]).

In case $(C, \mathfrak{m}) = (C(L, \Lambda_{0,nov}), \mathfrak{m})$ as in Theorem 3.5.11, we write o_k as $o_k(L)$. We enumerate the elements of $G = G(L)$ as

$$\{(\lambda(\beta_i), \mu(\beta_i)) \mid \beta_0 = 0, \beta_1, \beta_2, \cdots \in \{\beta \in \Pi(L)) \mid \mathcal{M}(\beta) \neq \emptyset\}\}$$

with $\lambda(\beta_i) \leq \lambda(\beta_{i+1})$. Here $\lambda(\beta_i) = \omega[\beta_i]$ and $\mu(\beta_i) = \mu_L(\beta_i)$ are the energy (symplectic area) and the Maslov index, respectively. We put

$$o(L; \beta_i) := o_i(L).$$

3.6.3. Weak unobstructedness and existence of Floer cohomology. It turns out [**Oh93**] Addenda, [**Oh96II**] that the Floer cohomology for the pair $L^{(0)} = L, L^{(1)} = \psi(L)$ with ψ a Hamiltonian diffeomorphism can be defined under the weaker condition on L than the condition needed for a general pair $(L^{(0)}, L^{(1)})$. This fact is important for various applications. In this subsection, we discuss the algebraic counterpart of this phenomenon. See also §3.7.3 below.

DEFINITION 3.6.29.   (1) Suppose that C has a unit $\mathbf{e}$.   An element $b \in (C[1])^0 = C^1$ with $b \equiv 0 \pmod{\Lambda^+_{0,nov}}$ is called a *weak bounding cochain*, or a *weak Maurer-Cartan solution*, if it satisfies

$$(3.6.30) \qquad\qquad \mathfrak{m}(e^b) = c e \, \mathbf{e},$$

for some $c \in \Lambda^{+(0)}_{0,nov}$, where $\Lambda^{+(0)}_{0,nov}$ is the degree 0 part of $\Lambda^+_{0,nov}$. We denote by $\widehat{\mathcal{M}}_{\text{weak}}(C)$ the set of all weak bounding cochains. We say C is *weakly unobstructed* if $\widehat{\mathcal{M}}_{\text{weak}}(C) \neq \emptyset$.

(2) Suppose that C has a homotopy unit. Then as in Definition 3.3.2, we have the associated A_∞ algebra

$$(C^+, \mathfrak{m}^+) = (C \oplus \Lambda_{0,nov}\mathbf{e}^+ \oplus \Lambda_{0,nov}\mathbf{f}, \mathfrak{m}^+)$$

with unit $\mathbf{e}^+$. We say C is *weakly unobstructed* if $\widehat{\mathcal{M}}_{\text{weak}}(C^+) \neq \emptyset$ in the sense of (1) above.

Here we remind readers that the symbol e is the formal parameter encoding the Maslov index which has degree 2.

REMARK 3.6.31.   When C has a strict unit $\mathbf{e}$, we can also regard it as a homotopy unit. Thus we can consider $\widehat{\mathcal{M}}_{\text{weak}}(C^+)$ as well as $\widehat{\mathcal{M}}_{\text{weak}}(C)$. They are related to each other by

$$\widehat{\mathcal{M}}_{\text{weak}}(C) \ni b \longmapsto b + c e \mathbf{f} \in \widehat{\mathcal{M}}_{\text{weak}}(C^+).$$

In fact, when C has a strict unit, we can take $(C^+, \mathfrak{m}^+)$ so that $\mathfrak{h}_k = 0$ for $k \geq 2$ in Definition 3.3.2. Therefore we can see that

$$\mathfrak{m}^+(e^{b+ce\mathbf{f}}) = \mathfrak{m}(e^b) + \mathfrak{m}^+(e^b c e \mathbf{f} e^b) = c e \mathbf{e} + c e \mathfrak{m}^+_1(\mathbf{f}) = c e \mathbf{e} + c e (\mathbf{e}^+ - \mathbf{e}) = c e \mathbf{e}^+.$$

Conversely, let $b^+ \in C^+[1]^0$ be a solution of $\mathfrak{m}^+(e^{b^+}) = c e \mathbf{e}^+$. By the degree reason, we can write as $b^+ = b + c'e\mathbf{f}$ with $c' \in \Lambda^{(0)}_{0,nov}$. (Recall $\deg e^m = 2m$ and $\deg \mathbf{e} = 0$.) The same calculation shows that

$$c e \mathbf{e}^+ = \mathfrak{m}^+(e^{b+c'e\mathbf{f}}) = \mathfrak{m}(e^b) + c' e \mathfrak{m}^+_1(\mathbf{f}) = \mathfrak{m}(e^b) + c' e (\mathbf{e}^+ - \mathbf{e}).$$

Comparing the both hand sides, we have $c = c'$ and $\mathfrak{m}(e^b) = c e \mathbf{e}$.

However, when C just has a homotopy unit (not a strict unit), the above argument does not hold. (Although we might be able to formally consider a set $\widehat{\mathcal{M}}_{\text{weak}}(C)$ of the solutions to the equation $\mathfrak{m}(e^b) = c e \mathbf{e}$ on C itself for the *homotopy unit* $\mathbf{e} \in C$, we *never* consider the equation on C unless C has a *strict unit*.) When C has a homotopy unit, *every statement related to weak unobstructedness of C should be interpreted as one for C^+.* Since C^+ is homotopy equivalent to C (see Remark 3.3.7 (3) and Lemma 4.2.55 in Section 4.2), we *define*

$$\widehat{\mathcal{M}}_{\text{weak}}(C) := \widehat{\mathcal{M}}_{\text{weak}}(C^+)$$

when C has only a homotopy unit. We warn the readers not to get confused that the following lemma may hold for the solutions of the formal equation $\mathfrak{m}(e^b) = c e \mathbf{e}$ on C itself when $\mathbf{e}$ is not a strict unit.

LEMMA 3.6.32. *If $b \in \widehat{\mathcal{M}}_{weak}(C)$ then $\delta_{b,b} \circ \delta_{b,b} = 0$, where $\delta_{b,b}$ is as in Definition 3.6.6.*

PROOF. By using (3.2.19) and (3.6.7), we have

$$
\begin{aligned}
0 &= (\mathfrak{m} \circ \widehat{d})(e^b x e^b) \\
&= \mathfrak{m}(e^b \delta_{b,b}(x) e^b) + \mathfrak{m}(\widehat{d}(e^b) x e^b) + (-1)^{\deg x + 1} \mathfrak{m}((e^b x \widehat{d}(e^b)) \\
&= (\delta_{b,b} \circ \delta_{b,b})(x) + ce\, \mathfrak{m}(e^b \mathbf{e} e^b x e^b) + (-1)^{\deg x + 1} ce\, \mathfrak{m}(e^b x\, e^b \mathbf{e} e^b) \\
&= (\delta_{b,b} \circ \delta_{b,b})(x) + ce\, x + (-1)^{\deg x + 1}(-1)^{\deg x} ce\, x \\
&= (\delta_{b,b} \circ \delta_{b,b})(x).
\end{aligned}
$$

$\square$

DEFINITION 3.6.33. (1) For $b \in \widehat{\mathcal{M}}_{weak}(C)$ we define

$$
HF(C, b) = \frac{\operatorname{Ker}(\delta_{b,b} : C^+ \to C^+)}{\operatorname{Im}(\delta_{b,b} : C^+ \to C^+)}.
$$

(2) We define a function $\mathfrak{PO} : \widehat{\mathcal{M}}_{weak}(C) \longrightarrow \Lambda_{0,nov}^{+(0)}$ by the equation

$$
\mathfrak{m}(e^b) = \mathfrak{PO}(b) e \mathbf{e}.
$$

We call this function a *potential function*.

REMARK 3.6.34. (1) The potential function we have defined here is closely related to the superpotential introduced in the physics literature ([**KKLM00, HoVa00**]). It has been partially calculated in some cases [**ChOh03**]. See also Subsection 3.7.7 for the simplest case. We will use the potential function in §3.7.3. (See also [**FOOO08I,08II**].)

(2) When C has homotopy unit $\delta_{b,b} : C^+ \to C^+$ is defined for $b \in \widehat{\mathcal{M}}_{weak}(C) = \widehat{\mathcal{M}}_{weak}(C^+)$. Lemma 3.6.32 below holds also in this case.

If we assume the following condition in addition

$$
(3.6.35) \qquad
\begin{cases}
\mathfrak{m}(\mathbf{x}_0 \otimes \mathbf{f} \otimes \mathbf{x}_1 \otimes \cdots \otimes \mathbf{x}_{k-1} \otimes \mathbf{f} \otimes \mathbf{x}_k) \in C \;\; (k \neq 0,\, \mathbf{x}_i \in BC[1]), \\
\mathfrak{m}_1(\mathbf{f}) - \mathbf{e}^+ \in C,
\end{cases}
$$

then $\delta_{b,b}$ maps C to C and so its restriction $\delta_{b,b} : C \to C$ is defined. Moreover the natural inclusion $(C, \delta_{b,b}) \to (C^+, \delta_{b,b})$ is a chain homotopy equivalence.

LEMMA 3.6.36. *Let $\mathfrak{f} : C_1 \to C_2$ be a filtered A_∞ homomorphism.*
(1) For any $b \in C_1[1]^0$ with $b \equiv 0 \mod \Lambda_{0,nov}^+$, define

$$
(3.6.37) \qquad \mathfrak{f}_*(b) := \mathfrak{f}(e^b) = \mathfrak{f}_0(1) + \mathfrak{f}_1(b) + \mathfrak{f}_2(b, b) + \cdots.
$$

Here $\mathfrak{f}(e^b) = \left(\sum_{k=0}^\infty \mathfrak{f}_k \right)(e^b)$. Then it induces a map $\mathfrak{f}_* : C_1[1]^0 \to C_2[1]^0$ and $\mathfrak{f}_*(b) \equiv 0 \mod \Lambda_{0,nov}^+$.

(2) Suppose C_i has a unit and let $\mathfrak{f} : C_1 \to C_2$ be a unital filtered A_∞ homomorphism. (See Definition 3.3.11.) Then for any $b \in \widehat{\mathcal{M}}_{weak}(C_1)$, we have $\mathfrak{f}_*(b) = \mathfrak{f}(e^b) \in \widehat{\mathcal{M}}_{weak}(C_2)$. Thus $\mathfrak{f}$ induces a map $\mathfrak{f}_* : \widehat{\mathcal{M}}_{weak}(C_1) \to \widehat{\mathcal{M}}_{weak}(C_2)$.

When C_i is unobstructed, we also have the map $\mathfrak{f}_* : \widehat{\mathcal{M}}(C_1) \to \widehat{\mathcal{M}}(C_2)$ by putting $c = 0$ in the proof below.

(3) Moreover under the situation (2), let $\mathfrak{PO}_i : \widehat{\mathcal{M}}_{\mathrm{weak}}(C_i) \to \Lambda_{0,nov}^{(0)}$ be the potential function. Then we have

$$\mathfrak{PO}_2 \circ \mathfrak{f}_*(b) = \mathfrak{PO}_1(b).$$

PROOF. (1) Since $\mathfrak{f}$ preserves the shifted degree, it is obvious that $\mathfrak{f}_*(b) \in C_2[1]^0$. Since $\bar{\mathfrak{f}}_0 = 0$ and $\mathfrak{f}$ preserves the energy filtration (see (3.2.27.1)) and $b \equiv 0$ mod $\Lambda_{0,nov}^+$, we have $\mathfrak{f}_*(b) \equiv 0 \mod \Lambda_{0,nov}^+$.

(2) Let $\widehat{\mathfrak{f}}$ be the coalgebra homomorphism induced by $\mathfrak{f}$. See (3.2.28). Then applying Lemma 3.6.2, we can write $\widehat{\mathfrak{f}}(e^b)$ as an exponential. In fact, we can check that

(3.6.38) $\widehat{\mathfrak{f}}(e^b) = e^{\mathfrak{f}(e^b)}.$

A straightforward calculation gives rise to

$$\widehat{d}(e^{\mathfrak{f}(e^b)}) = \widehat{d}(\widehat{\mathfrak{f}}(e^b)) = \widehat{\mathfrak{f}}(\widehat{d}(e^b)) = c\widehat{\mathfrak{f}}(e^b \mathbf{e} e^b) = cee^{\mathfrak{f}(e^b)}\mathbf{e}e^{\mathfrak{f}(e^b)}.$$

On the other hand, we also have

$$\widehat{d}(e^{\mathfrak{f}(e^b)}) = e^{\mathfrak{f}(e^b)}\mathfrak{m}(e^{\mathfrak{f}(e^b)})e^{\mathfrak{f}(e^b)}.$$

Comparing the two, we prove $\mathfrak{m}(e^{\mathfrak{f}(e^b)}) = ce\mathbf{e}$ as required. The assertion (3) also follows from the above calculation.   □

When C is a homotopy-unital filtered A_∞ algebra, we can define potential function on

$$\widehat{\mathcal{M}}_{\mathrm{weak}}(C) = \widehat{\mathcal{M}}_{\mathrm{weak}}(C^+).$$

in the same way.

Next we study the analog to Theorem 3.6.18 in the weakly unobstructed case. We work under the following assumption.

ASSUMPTION 3.6.39. We also assume that $H^k(\overline{C}, \overline{\mathfrak{m}}_1) = 0$ for $k < 0$. Moreover $H^0(\overline{C}, \overline{\mathfrak{m}}_1)$ is generated by $[\overline{\mathbf{e}}]$ the equivalence class of the unit.

Let $G \subset \mathbb{R}_{\geq 0} \times 2\mathbb{Z}$ be a submonoid satisfying Condition 3.1.6 and assume that C is G-gapped. We write $G = \{(\lambda_i, \mu_i) \mid i = 0, 1, 2, \cdots\}$ such that $i < j \Rightarrow \lambda_i \leq \lambda_j$ as before.

DEFINITION 3.6.40. A G-gapped A_∞ algebra C is *weakly unobstructed over* G, if there exists a weak bounding cochain b, which can be written as

$$b = \sum_{(\lambda_i, \mu_i) \in G} T^{\lambda_i} e^{\frac{\mu_i}{2}} b_i$$

for some $b_i \in \overline{C}[1]^{-\mu_i} = \overline{C}^{1-\mu_i}$.

Now we put

(3.6.41) $G_{\mu \leq 0} = \{(\lambda, \mu) \in G \mid \mu \leq 0\}.$

By omitting i's with $\mu_i > 0$ from the given enumeration of G, we find a nonde-creasing function $j : \mathbb{Z}_{\geq 0} \to \mathbb{Z}_{\geq 0}$ with $j(0) = 0$ such that

$$(3.6.42) \qquad\qquad G_{\mu \leq 0} = \{(\lambda_{j(i)}, \mu_{j(i)}) \,|\, i = 0, 1, 2, \cdots\}.$$

THEOREM 3.6.43. *Let $(C, \mathfrak{m})$ be a G-gapped filtered A_∞ algebra. Under Assumption 3.6.39, we have $o_k(\text{weak})$ and $b_i(\text{weak})$ with the following properties:*

(3.6.44.1) $[o_k(\text{weak})] \in H^{2-\mu_k}(\overline{C}, \overline{\mathfrak{m}}_1)$ *and* $b_i(\text{weak}) \in \overline{C}^{1-\mu_i}$.
(3.6.44.2)   *The cocycle $o_k(\text{weak})$ is defined if $[o_i(\text{weak})]$ and $b_i(\text{weak})$ for $i < k$ are defined and if $\mu_k \leq 0$. $[o_k(\text{weak})]$ depends on $[o_i(\text{weak})]$ and $b_i(\text{weak})$ for $i < k$.*
(3.6.44.3)   *When $\mu_k \leq 0$, $b_k(\text{weak})$ is defined if $[o_k(\text{weak})]$ is defined and is zero. If $\mu_k > 0$, $b_k(\text{weak})$ exists if $b_i(\text{weak})$ exists for $i < k$.*
(3.6.44.4)   *$(C, \mathfrak{m})$ is weakly unobstructed over G if and only if there exists a choice of b'_i inductively such that $[o_k(\text{weak})]$ for $\mu_k \leq 0$ are all zero.*

In other words, the obstruction classes $[o_k(\text{weak})]$ can be defined if we assume that the cocycle $o_i(\text{weak})$ is defined and $[o_i(\text{weak})] = 0$ in $H^*(\overline{C}, \overline{\mathfrak{m}}_1)$ only for those with $\mu_i \leq 0$, $i < k$.

$o_k(\text{weak})$ is defined by the same formula as o_k (Definition 3.6.23), and $b_k(\text{weak})$ is defined by

$$(3.6.45) \qquad -\mathfrak{m}_{1,0}(b_k(\text{weak})) = \begin{cases} o_k(\text{weak}) & \mu_k \leq 0, \\ o_k + c_k \mathbf{e} & \mu_k = 2, \\ o_k & \mu_k > 2. \end{cases}$$

Note that the existence of such $b_k(\text{weak})$ is automatic for $\mu_k > 0$. (o_k is defined in the same way as Definition 3.6.23.)

Since we will prove a more general result (Theorem 3.8.50) later, the proof is omitted here and left to the readers.

In case $(C, \mathfrak{m}) = (C(L; \Lambda_{0,nov})^+, \mathfrak{m}^+)$, where $(C(L; \Lambda_{0,nov}), \mathfrak{m})$ is as in Section 3.5 and $^+$ is as in Section 3.3, we write $o_k(L; \text{weak})$ in place of $o_k(\text{weak})$.

3.6.4. The superpotential and $\widehat{\mathcal{M}}(C)$. Recall the reason why we assume $b \equiv 0 \mod \Lambda_{0,nov}^+$: we want the formal series $e^b = 1 + b + b \otimes b + \cdots$ to converge. However, if there exists $k(\lambda) \in \mathbb{Z}$ with $\lim_{\lambda \to \infty} k(\lambda) = \infty$ such that if $k > k(\lambda)$ then $\mathfrak{m}_k \equiv 0 \mod T^\lambda$ already, then $\widehat{d}(e^b)$ will converge for any $b \in C^0[1]$. This is indeed the case for the A_∞ algebra that appeared in Chekanov's work [**Chek02**].

In our case such a $k(\lambda)$ do not seem to exist. (See Conjecture 3.6.53 below.) However, we still expect:

CONJECTURE 3.6.46. *We can choose our filtered A_∞ algebra $(C(L), \mathfrak{m})$ so that $\widehat{d}(e^b)$ converges for any $b \in C(L)[1]^0$.*

Compare this conjecture with Conjecture T in introduction.

REMARK 3.6.47. Note that the Conjecture 3.6.46 means that

$$\sum_k \mathfrak{m}_{k,\beta}(b, \cdots, b)$$

converges for any *fixed* β and $b \in C(L; \mathbb{Q})$. A priori, obtaining this convergence should be easier than having the convergence of operators $\mathfrak{m}_k$ after substituting

$T = e^{-1}$, for example. Namely, Conjecture 3.6.46 appears much easier than proving the convergence of the series

$$\sum_{k,\beta} e^{-\omega[\beta]} \mathfrak{m}_{k,\beta}(b, \cdots, b)$$

where we need to sum up over all different β. (See [**Fuk02I, KoSo01**] etc.)

Now we discuss how the Maurer-Cartan equation is expected to behave when $L \subset M$ is a special Lagrangian submanifold (or more generally Lagrangian submanifold with zero Maslov class) in a Calabi-Yau 3-fold.

Firstly, we remark that we can take $C(L) = H(L; \mathbb{Q}) \otimes \Lambda_{0,nov}$. This is a consequence of Theorem 5.4.2, which asserts existence of the *canonical model* of the filtered A_∞ algebra. See Definition 5.4.3. We also take $\overline{C}(L) = H(L; \mathbb{Q})$ as a differential graded algebra. Moreover we can forget the 0-th and 3-rd cohomologies. (See Subsection 5.4.6.) Hence we are left only with $H^1(L; \mathbb{Q})$ and $H^2(L; \mathbb{Q})$.

Secondly, there is a conjecture which is widely believed to be true but not yet proven.

CONJECTURE 3.6.48. We can take an A_∞ structure on $(C(L), \mathfrak{m})$ so it satisfies the following: There exists $\langle \cdot, \cdot \rangle : C(L) \otimes C(L) \to \Lambda_{0,nov}$ induced by the Poincaré duality pairing in homology which satisfies the cyclic symmetry condition

$$\langle x_0, \mathfrak{m}_k(x_1, \cdots, x_k) \rangle = (-1)^{\deg' x_k \times (\deg' x_0 + \cdots + \deg' x_{k-1})} \langle x_k, \mathfrak{m}_k(x_0, x_1, \cdots, x_{k-1}) \rangle.$$

If one could ignore the delicate problems of transversality and sign, Conjecture 3.6.48 could be easily seen. (Achieving the transversality while keeping the required symmetry is a difficult task. See however Section A3 and [**Fuk05II**].) Under these hypotheses, we choose a basis e_i, $i = 1, \cdots, m$ of $H^1(L; \mathbb{Q})$. We define a function $\Psi : \Lambda_{0,nov} \times \cdots \times \Lambda_{0,nov} \to \Lambda_{0,nov}$ by

$$(3.6.49) \qquad \Psi(x_1, \cdots, x_m) = \sum_k \frac{1}{k+1} \langle b, \mathfrak{m}_k(b, \cdots, b) \rangle$$

where $b = \sum x_i e_i$. (See [**Laza01, Tom01**].) This function seems to be widely known in the physics literature and is called the *superpotential*. Conjecture 3.6.46 is needed for the right hand side of (3.6.49) to be well-defined for $b \in C(L; \Lambda_{0,nov})$.

PROPOSITION 3.6.50. *Assume Conjectures* 3.6.46 *and* 3.6.48. *Then* $b = \sum x_i e_i$ *satisfies* $\widehat{d}(e^b) = 0$ *if and only if* $(x_1, \cdots, x_m)$ *is a critical point of* Ψ.

PROOF. Using Conjecture 3.6.48, we find

$$\frac{\partial}{\partial x_i} \Psi(x_1, \cdots, x_m) = \sum_k \langle e_i, \mathfrak{m}_k(b, \cdots, b) \rangle = \langle e_i, \mathfrak{m}(e^b) \rangle.$$

The proposition follows.   □

In a similar way, we can strengthen the statement of this proposition. For this purpose, we define $\mathfrak{m}^b_{i_1, \cdots, i_k, i_0} \in \Lambda^+_{0,nov}$, and $\mathfrak{l}^b_{i_1, \cdots, i_k, i_0} \in \Lambda^+_{0,nov}$ by

$$(3.6.51.1) \qquad \mathfrak{m}^b_{i_1, \cdots, i_k, i_0} = \langle e_{i_0}, \mathfrak{m}(e^b e_{i_1} e^b \cdots e^b e_{i_k} e^b) \rangle$$

and

$$(3.6.51.2) \qquad \mathfrak{l}^b_{i_1,\cdots,i_k,i_0} = \sum_{\sigma \in \mathfrak{S}_k} \mathfrak{m}^b_{i_{\sigma(1)},\cdots,i_{\sigma(k)},i_0} = \frac{1}{k+1} \sum_{\sigma \in \mathfrak{S}_{k+1}} \mathfrak{m}^b_{i_{\sigma(1)},\cdots,i_{\sigma(k)},i_{\sigma(0)}}$$

where $\mathfrak{S}_k$ in the symmetric group of order $k!$. Then $\mathfrak{l}^b_{i_1,\cdots,i_k,i_0}$ are the structure constants of the L_∞ structure obtained by symmetrizing $\mathfrak{m}$. (See Section A3).

PROPOSITION 3.6.52. *We assume Conjectures 3.6.46 and 3.6.48. Then we have:*

$$\frac{\partial^{k+1} \Psi}{\partial x_{i_1} \cdots \partial x_{i_k} \partial x_{i_0}}(b) = \mathfrak{l}^b_{i_1,\cdots,i_k,i_0}.$$

PROOF. If $b_0 = \sum x_i^0 e_i$, $b = \sum x_i e_i$ then we have

$$\Psi(x_1 + x_1^0, \cdots, x_m + x_m^0)$$

$$= \sum \frac{1}{k+1} \langle b_0 + b, \mathfrak{m}_k(b_0 + b, \cdots, b_0 + b) \rangle$$

$$= \sum_{k,\ell_0,\cdots,\ell_k} \frac{1}{k+1+\sum \ell_i} \left\langle b, \mathfrak{m}_{k+\sum \ell_i}(b_0^{\ell_0}, b, b_0^{\ell_1}, \cdots, b_0^{\ell_{k-1}}, b, b_0^{\ell_k}) \right\rangle$$

$$+ \sum_{k,\ell_0,\cdots,\ell_k} \frac{1}{k+1+\sum \ell_i} \left\langle b_0, \mathfrak{m}_{k+\sum \ell_i}(b_0^{\ell_0}, b, b_0^{\ell_1}, \cdots, b_0^{\ell_{k-1}}, b, b_0^{\ell_k}) \right\rangle$$

$$\overset{*}{=} \sum_{k,\ell_0,\cdots,\ell_k} \frac{1}{k+1} \left\langle b, \mathfrak{m}_{k+\sum \ell_i}(b_0^{\ell_0}, b, b_0^{\ell_1}, \cdots, b_0^{\ell_{k-1}}, b, b_0^{\ell_k}) \right\rangle$$

$$= \sum_k \frac{1}{k+1} \langle b_0, \mathfrak{m}_k(b_0, \cdots, b_0) \rangle + \sum_k \frac{1}{k+1} \left\langle b, \mathfrak{m}_k^{b_0}(b, \cdots, b) \right\rangle.$$

For the equality $\overset{*}{=}$ above, we used the cyclic symmetry (Conjecture 3.6.48) in the following way: We consider, for k and ℓ, the sum

$$\sum_{\ell_0+\ell_1+\cdots+\ell_k=\ell} \left\langle b, \mathfrak{m}_{k+\ell}(b_0^{\ell_0}, b, b_0^{\ell_1}, \cdots, b_0^{\ell_{k-1}}, b, b_0^{\ell_k}) \right\rangle.$$

We take its cyclic permutations of variables. Then among $\ell + k + 1$ of them, $k + 1$ are of the form

$$\sum_{\ell_0+\ell_1+\cdots+\ell_k=\ell} \left\langle b, \mathfrak{m}_{k+\ell}(b_0^{\ell_0}, b, b_0^{\ell_1}, \cdots, b_0^{\ell_{k-1}}, b, b_0^{\ell_k}) \right\rangle$$

and ℓ of them are of the form

$$\sum_{\ell_0+\ell_1+\cdots+\ell_{k+1}=\ell-1} \left\langle b_0, \mathfrak{m}_{k+\ell}(b_0^{\ell_0}, b, b_0^{\ell_1}, \cdots, b_0^{\ell_k}, b, b_0^{\ell_{k+1}}) \right\rangle.$$

$\overset{*}{=}$ follows.

Therefore, replacing $\mathfrak{m}_k$ by $\mathfrak{m}_k^{b_0}$, it suffices to prove the proposition at $b = 0$. Then

$$\frac{\partial^{k+1} \Psi}{\partial x_{i_1} \cdots \partial x_{i_k} \partial x_{i_0}}(0) = \frac{1}{k+1} \frac{\partial^{k+1}}{\partial x_{i_1} \cdots \partial x_{i_k} \partial x_{i_0}} \langle b, \mathfrak{m}_k(b, \cdots, b) \rangle \Big|_{b=0} = \mathfrak{l}_{i_1,\cdots,i_k,i_0},$$

as required. $\qquad\qquad\qquad\qquad\qquad\qquad\qquad\qquad\qquad\qquad\qquad\qquad\qquad\qquad\qquad \square$

Now we consider (M, L) a pair of Calabi-Yau 3-fold M and its Lagrangian submanifold $L \subset M$ with zero Maslov class. By taking an appropriate almost complex structure J, we may assume that all somewhere injective holomorphic discs are isolated. Enumerate them by $u_i : (D^2, \partial D^2) \to (M, L)$ and denote

$$\lambda_i = \int_{D^2} u_i^* \omega, \qquad a_{i,j} = [\partial u_i] \cap x_j.$$

CONJECTURE 3.6.53. Let Ψ be the superpotential defined as above. Then

$$\Psi(x_1, \cdots, x_m) = c + \sum_{i=1}^{\infty} \sum_{d=1}^{\infty} \epsilon_{i,d} n_d T^{d\lambda_i} \exp\left(d \sum_{j=1}^{m} a_{i,j} x_j\right).$$

Here $\exp : \mathbb{C} \to \mathbb{C}$ is the usual exponential and n_d is the number depending only on d and describing how to count d fold cover of the disc u_i. (In some literature [OoVa96, KatLi01] there are some results which suggest $n_d = d^{-2}$.) $\epsilon_{i,d} = \pm 1$ is the sign to count the d fold covering of the disc u_i. $c \in \Lambda_{0,nov}$ is independent of $(x_1, \cdots, x_m)$ but may depend of L, J and the perturbation.

We expect to be able to prove some of the conjectures stated of this subsection in a near future using the technique of [Fuk05II].

REMARK 3.6.54. In the toric case the relationship between superpotential and the Floer cohomology is studied in [ChOh03, Cho04II, FOOO08I]. A formula similar to the one in Proposition 3.6.52 was proved by Cho [Cho04II]. In the toric case we can identify the Landau-Ginzburg potential with our potential function by putting $T = \exp(-1)$. The relationship between the superpotential and filtered A_∞ structure in the Calabi-Yau case has a different form that of the toric case: In the Calabi-Yau case (which we discussed in this section) the first derivative of superpotential is related to $\mathfrak{m}_0(1)$. Moreover the k-th derivative of the superpotential is related to the symmetrization of $\mathfrak{m}_{k-1}$. In the toric case, $\mathfrak{m}_0(1)$ is the Landau-Ginzburg potential function itself and its first derivative corresponds to $\mathfrak{m}_1$.

3.7. A_∞ bimodules and Floer cohomology

In this section, we deform the standard Floer's 'coboundary' operator using the constructions given in the previous sections. We first prepare the algebraic frameworks for the filtered A_∞ bimodule structures in Subsection 3.7.1 and for filtered A_∞ bimodule homomorphisms in Subsection 3.7.2. In Subsection 3.7.3, we provide an algebraic definition of our deformed coboundary operator on a filtered A_∞ bimodule when the A_∞ algebras are (weakly) unobstructed. After that, we construct the geometric realization associated to a relatively spin pair of Lagrangian submanifolds $(L^{(0)}, L^{(1)})$ and its Floer cohomology $HF((L^{(1)}, b_1), (L^{(0)}, b_0); \Lambda_{0,nov})$ in Subsection 3.7.4 when $L^{(0)}$ is transversal to $L^{(1)}$, and in Subsection 3.7.5 when $L^{(0)}$ intersects $L^{(1)}$ cleanly. In Subsection 3.7.6, we give a simple example of calculations of Floer cohomologies and discuss the (weak) unobstructedness condition in the examples. In Subsection 3.7.7 a product structure on Floer cohomology is defined.

3.7.1. Algebraic framework.

In this subsection, we introduce some algebraic notions without involving Lagrangian submanifolds. Let $(C_0, \mathfrak{m}^0)$, $(C_1, \mathfrak{m}^1)$ be two filtered A_∞ algebras over $\Lambda_{0,nov}$. Let $\bigoplus_{m \in \mathbb{Z}} D^m$ be a graded free filtered

$\Lambda_{0,nov}$ module and $F^\lambda D^m$ its filtration defined similarly as in (3.2.12). We suppose that the filtration $F^\lambda D^m$ satisfies the same conditions as (3.2.12.1)-(3.2.12.5). We denote by D the completion of $\bigoplus_{m \in \mathbb{Z}} D^m$ with respect to this filtration. We consider a family of operations

$$\mathfrak{n}_{k_1, k_0} : B_{k_1}(C_1[1]) \otimes_{\Lambda_{0,nov}} D[1] \otimes_{\Lambda_{0,nov}} B_{k_0}(C_0[1]) \longrightarrow D[1]$$

of degree $+1$ satisfying

$$
\begin{aligned}
(3.7.1) \quad &\mathfrak{n}_{k_1, k_0} \left(F^{\lambda_1}(C_1[1])^{m_1} \otimes \cdots \otimes F^{\lambda_{k_1}}(C_1[1])^{m_{k_1}} \otimes F^{\lambda_0}(D[1])^{m_0} \right. \\
&\qquad\qquad \left. \otimes F^{\lambda'_1}(C_0[1])^{m'_1} \otimes \cdots \otimes F^{\lambda'_{k_0}}(C_0[1])^{m'_{k_0}} \right) \\
&\subseteq F^{\Sigma \lambda_i + \lambda_0 + \Sigma \lambda'_i}(D[1])^{\Sigma m_i + m_0 + \Sigma m'_i + 1}.
\end{aligned}
$$

We now use condition (3.7.1) to extend $\mathfrak{n}_{k_1, k_0}$ to the completion

$$\widehat{B}(C_1[1]) \,\widehat{\otimes}_{\Lambda_{0,nov}}\, D[1] \,\widehat{\otimes}_{\Lambda_{0,nov}}\, \widehat{B}(C_0[1])$$

of $\bigoplus_{k_1, k_0} B_{k_1}(C_1[1]) \otimes_{\Lambda_{0,nov}} D[1] \otimes_{\Lambda_{0,nov}} B_{k_0}(C_0[1])$. For this purpose we first remark that $\widehat{B}(C_1[1]) \,\widehat{\otimes}_{\Lambda_{0,nov}}\, D[1] \,\widehat{\otimes}_{\Lambda_{0,nov}}\, \widehat{B}(C_0[1])$ is a left $\widehat{B}(C_1[1])$ and right $\widehat{B}(C_0[1])$ (formal) bi-comodule. We then extend $\mathfrak{n}_{k_1, k_0}$ to a bi-coderivation;

$$
\begin{aligned}
\widehat{d} : &\widehat{B}(C_1[1]) \,\widehat{\otimes}_{\Lambda_{0,nov}}\, D[1] \,\widehat{\otimes}_{\Lambda_{0,nov}}\, \widehat{B}(C_0[1]) \\
&\to \widehat{B}(C_1[1]) \,\widehat{\otimes}_{\Lambda_{0,nov}}\, D[1] \,\widehat{\otimes}_{\Lambda_{0,nov}}\, \widehat{B}(C_0[1]),
\end{aligned}
$$

which is defined by

$$
\begin{aligned}
(3.7.2) \quad &\widehat{d}\left(x_{1,1} \otimes \cdots \otimes x_{1,k_1} \otimes y \otimes x_{0,1} \otimes \cdots \otimes x_{0,k_0} \right) \\
&= \sum_{k'_1 \le k_1, k'_0 \le k_0} (-1)^{\deg x_{1,1} + \cdots + \deg x_{1,k_1 - k'_1} + k_1 - k'_1} \\
&\qquad x_{1,1} \otimes \cdots \otimes x_{1,k_1 - k'_1} \otimes \mathfrak{n}_{k'_1, k'_0}\left(x_{1,k_1 - k'_1 + 1}, \cdots, \right. \\
&\qquad\qquad \left. y, \cdots, x_{0,k'_0} \right) \otimes x_{0,k'_0 + 1} \otimes \cdots \otimes x_{0,k_0} \\
&\quad + \widehat{d^1}\left(x_{1,1} \otimes \cdots \otimes x_{1,k_1} \right) \otimes y \otimes x_{0,1} \otimes \cdots \otimes x_{0,k_0} \\
&\quad + (-1)^{\Sigma \deg x_{1,i} + \deg y + k_1 + 1} x_{1,1} \otimes \cdots \otimes x_{1,k_1} \\
&\qquad\qquad\qquad\qquad \otimes y \otimes \widehat{d^0}\left(x_{0,1} \otimes \cdots \otimes x_{0,k_0} \right).
\end{aligned}
$$

Here $\widehat{d^i}$ is defined by $\mathfrak{m}^i$ ($i = 0, 1$). When we use the convention (Conv.2) (1.36), we can simply rewrite (3.7.2) as

$$
\begin{aligned}
(3.7.3) \quad &\widehat{d}(\mathbf{x}_1 \otimes y \otimes \mathbf{x}_0) \\
&= \sum_{a,b} (-1)^{\deg' \mathbf{x}'_{1,a}} \mathbf{x}'_{1,a} \otimes \mathfrak{n}(\mathbf{x}''_{1,a} \otimes y \otimes \mathbf{x}'_{0,b}) \otimes \mathbf{x}''_{0,b} \\
&\quad + \widehat{d^1} \mathbf{x}_1 \otimes y \otimes \mathbf{x}_0 + (-1)^{\deg' \mathbf{x}_1 + \deg' y} \mathbf{x}_1 \otimes y \otimes \widehat{d^0} \mathbf{x}_0.
\end{aligned}
$$

Here $\deg'$ is the degree after shifted as in Section 3.3. Then (3.7.1) implies that (3.7.2) is extended to the completion $\widehat{B}(C_1[1]) \,\widehat{\otimes}_{\Lambda_{0,nov}}\, D[1] \,\widehat{\otimes}_{\Lambda_{0,nov}}\, \widehat{B}(C_0[1])$.

Since D is a free $\Lambda_{0,nov}$ module, we have a free R module $\overline{D}$ and an isomorphism

$$D \cong \overline{D} \otimes_R \Lambda_{0,nov}.$$

Since $D/\Lambda_{0,nov}^+ \cong \overline{D}[e, e^{-1}]$, the operation $\mathfrak{n}_{k_1,k_0}$ induces a homomorphism

$$\overline{\mathfrak{n}}_{k_1,k_0} : B_{k_1}(\overline{C}_1[1]) \otimes_R \overline{D}[1] \otimes_R B_{k_0}(\overline{C}_0[1]) \otimes_R R[e, e^{-1}] \longrightarrow \overline{D}[1] \otimes_R R[e, e^{-1}].$$

We *assume* that $\overline{\mathfrak{n}}_{k_1,k_0}$ is induced by an operation

$$B_{k_1}(\overline{C}_1[1]) \otimes_R \overline{D}[1] \otimes_R B_{k_0}(\overline{C}_0[1]) \longrightarrow \overline{D}[1].$$

We denote this operation by the same symbol $\overline{\mathfrak{n}}_{k_1,k_0}$.

An analog to Condition 3.2.18 is the following.

CONDITION 3.7.4. For an element $\mathbf{e}_i \in C_i[1]$ $(i = 0, 1)$,

$$(3.7.4.1) \qquad \mathfrak{n}_{k_1,k_0}(x_1 \otimes \cdots \otimes \mathbf{e}_1 \otimes \cdots \otimes x_{k_1-1} \otimes y \otimes x_1' \otimes \cdots \otimes x_{k_0}') = 0$$

for $k_1 + k_0 \geq 2$ and

$$(3.7.4.2) \qquad \mathfrak{n}_{k_1,k_0}(x_1 \otimes \cdots \otimes x_{k_1} \otimes y \otimes x_1' \otimes \cdots \otimes \mathbf{e}_0 \otimes \cdots \otimes x_{k_0-1}') = 0$$

for $k_1 + k_0 \geq 2$. And

$$(3.7.4.3) \qquad \mathfrak{n}_{1,0}(\mathbf{e}_1, y) = (-1)^{\deg y} \mathfrak{n}_{0,1}(y, \mathbf{e}_0) = y.$$

DEFINITION 3.7.5. (1) We say that $\mathfrak{n}_{k_1,k_0}$ defines a *left* $(C_1, \mathfrak{m}^1)$ *and right* $(C_0, \mathfrak{m}^0)$ *filtered A_∞ bimodule structure on* D, or simply D is a (C_1, C_0) *filtered A_∞ bimodule*, (or *filtered A_∞ bimodule over* (C_1, C_0)), if it satisfies (3.7.1) and $\widehat{d} \circ \widehat{d} = 0$.

(2) Let $(C_i, \mathfrak{m}^i)$ have a unit $\mathbf{e}_i$. We say that $\{\mathbf{e}_1, \mathbf{e}_0\}$ *acts as a unit* if Condition 3.7.4 is satisfied. In this case we sometimes say that D is a *unital filtered A_∞ bimodule*.

(3) When $(C_i, \mathfrak{m}^i)$ has a homotopy unit $\mathbf{e}_i$, we say that $\{\mathbf{e}_1, \mathbf{e}_0\}$ *acts as a homotopy unit* if there exists a left $(C_1^+, \mathfrak{m}^1)$ and right $(C_0^+, \mathfrak{m}^0)$ filtered A_∞ bimodule structure on D such that $\{\mathbf{e}_1^+, \mathbf{e}_0^+\}$ acts as a unit. Here $C_i^+ = C_i \oplus \Lambda_{0,nov}\mathbf{e}_i^+ \oplus \Lambda_{0,nov}\mathbf{f}_i$ as in (3.3.1) and $\mathbf{e}_i^+ = \mathfrak{m}_1^i(\mathbf{f}_i) + \mathbf{e}_i - \mathfrak{h}_2^i(1 \overline{\otimes} 1)$ as in (3.3.6). We also say that D is *a homotopy-unital A_∞ bimodule* in this case.

(4) For unfiltered A_∞ algebras $(\overline{C}_i, \overline{\mathfrak{m}}^i)$ $(i = 0, 1)$ over R, a $(\overline{C}_1, \overline{C}_0)$ A_∞ bimodule $(\overline{D}, \overline{\mathfrak{n}})$ over R is defined in a similar way. An unfiltered unital (homotopy-unital) A_∞ bimodule is also defined as in (2),(3) above.

If D is a (C_1, C_0) filtered A_∞ bimodule, then $\overline{D}$ is a $(\overline{C}_1, \overline{C}_0)$ A_∞ module. We call it the R *reduction* of D.

(5) Let $G_i \subset \mathbb{R}_{\geq 0} \times 2\mathbb{Z}$ be a monoid satisfying Condition 3.1.6 and $(C_i, \mathfrak{m}^i)$ G_i-gapped filtered A_∞ algebras. Let $G \subset \mathbb{R}_{\geq 0} \times 2\mathbb{Z}$ be another monoid satisfying Condition 3.1.6 such that $G \supseteq G_1, G_0$. We say that a filtered A_∞ bimodule $(D, \mathfrak{n}_{k_1,k_0})$ is G-*gapped*, if there exists

$$\mathfrak{n}_{k_1,k_0,\beta} : B_{k_1}\overline{C}_1[1] \otimes \overline{D}[1] \otimes B_{k_0}\overline{C}_0[1] \to \overline{D}[1]$$

for each k_1, k_0 and $\beta \in G$ such that

$$\mathfrak{n}_{k_1,k_0} = \sum_{\beta \in G} T^{\lambda(\beta)} e^{\mu(\beta)/2} \mathfrak{n}_{k_1,k_0,\beta}.$$

As in Remark 3.6.15, we note that if G' is a monoid satisfying Condition 3.7.4 and containing G above, then every G-gapped filtered A_∞ bimodule is G'-gapped. When we do not necessarily specify G, we say that $(D, \mathfrak{n}_{k_1,k_0})$ is a *gapped* filtered A_∞ bimodule for simplicity.

EXAMPLE 3.7.6. Let $(C, \mathfrak{m})$ be a filtered A_∞ algebra. We can regard C as a left $(C, \mathfrak{m})$ and right $(C, \mathfrak{m})$ filtered A_∞ bimodule. Namely we put

$$\mathfrak{n}_{k_1, k_0}(\mathbf{x} \otimes y \otimes \mathbf{z}) = \mathfrak{m}_{k_1 + k_0 + 1}(\mathbf{x}, y, \mathbf{z}).$$

Here $\mathbf{x} \in B_{k_1} C[1]$, $y \in C[1]$, $\mathbf{z} \in B_{k_0} C[1]$. If C has a unit (resp. homotopy unit), it acts as a unit (resp. homotopy unit) to C (resp. C^+). If C is gapped as a filtered A_∞ algebra, then C is gapped as a filtered A_∞ bimodule.

We will also use Λ_{nov} as a coefficient ring to consider filtered A_∞ bimodules. This is because Floer cohomology of a pair of two different Lagrangian submanifolds remains isomorphic under the Hamiltonian isotopy only over the Λ_{nov}-coefficient. (See Section 5.3.) We define the filtered A_∞ bimodule with the Λ_{nov}-coefficient to be the tensor product (over $\Lambda_{0,nov}$) of a filtered A_∞ bimodule on $\Lambda_{0,nov}$ and Λ_{nov}. (See Subsection 5.2.1.)

3.7.2. A_∞ bimodule homomorphisms. Let C_i and C_i' be filtered A_∞ algebras $(i = 0, 1)$. Let D and D' be (C_1, C_0) and (C_1', C_0') filtered A_∞ bimodules, respectively. Let $\mathfrak{f}^i : C_i \to C_i'$ be filtered A_∞ algebra homomorphisms.

DEFINITION 3.7.7. A *filtered A_∞ bimodule homomorphism $D \to D'$ over the pair* $(\mathfrak{f}^1, \mathfrak{f}^0)$ is a family of $\Lambda_{0,nov}$-module homomorphisms $\varphi = \{\varphi_{k_1, k_0}\}$, which is simply written as $\varphi : D \to D'$,

$$\varphi_{k_1, k_0} : B_{k_1}(C_1[1]) \widehat{\otimes}_{\Lambda_{0,nov}} D[1] \widehat{\otimes}_{\Lambda_{0,nov}} B_{k_0}(C_0[1]) \longrightarrow D'[1]$$

with the following two properties (1) (2) (3):

(1) It respects the energy filtration. Namely

$$\varphi_{k_1, k_0}\left(F^{\lambda_1} B_{k_1}(C_1[1]) \widehat{\otimes} F^\lambda D[1] \widehat{\otimes} F^{\lambda_0} B_{k_0}(C_0[1])\right) \subseteq F^{\lambda_1 + \lambda + \lambda_0} D'[1].$$

(2) Let $\widehat{\varphi} : B(C_1[1]) \widehat{\otimes} D[1] \widehat{\otimes} B(C_0[1]) \to B(C_1'[1]) \widehat{\otimes} D'[1] \widehat{\otimes} B(C_0'[1])$ be the comodule homomorphism induced by φ_{k_1, k_0} and $\mathfrak{f}^i$. Namely, it is defined by

$$(3.7.8) \qquad \widehat{\varphi}(\mathbf{x}_1 \otimes y \otimes \mathbf{x}_0) = \sum_{a,b} \widehat{\mathfrak{f}^1}(\mathbf{x}_{1,a}') \otimes \varphi(\mathbf{x}_{1,a}'' \otimes y \otimes \mathbf{x}_{0,b}') \otimes \widehat{\mathfrak{f}^0}(\mathbf{x}_{0,b}'')$$

for $\mathbf{x}_i \in B(C_i[1])$ and $y \in D[1]$, where $\widehat{\mathfrak{f}^i}$ is induced by $\mathfrak{f}^i$ as in (3.2.28) and we use convention (Conv.2) (1.36). Then the following diagram commutes:

$$
\begin{array}{ccc}
\widehat{B}(C_1[1]) \widehat{\otimes} D[1] \widehat{\otimes} \widehat{B}(C_0[1]) & \xrightarrow{\widehat{d}} & \widehat{B}(C_1[1]) \widehat{\otimes} D[1] \widehat{\otimes} \widehat{B}(C_0[1]) \\
\widehat{\varphi} \downarrow & & \widehat{\varphi} \downarrow \\
\widehat{B}(C_1'[1]) \widehat{\otimes} D'[1] \widehat{\otimes} \widehat{B}(C_0'[1]) & \xrightarrow{\widehat{d'}} & \widehat{B}(C_1'[1]) \widehat{\otimes} D'[1] \widehat{\otimes} \widehat{B}(C_0'[1]).
\end{array}
$$

Diagram 3.7.1

Here $\widehat{d}$ and $\widehat{d'}$ are defined as in (3.7.2) and the tensor product $\widehat{\otimes}$ is taken over $\Lambda_{0,nov}$.

(3) By the property (1) φ_{k_1, k_0} induces

$$\overline{\varphi}_{k_1, k_0} : B_{k_1}(\overline{C}_1[1]) \otimes_R \overline{D}[1] \otimes_R B_{k_0}(\overline{C}_0[1]) \otimes_R R[e, e^{-1}] \longrightarrow \overline{D}'[1] \otimes_R R[e, e^{-1}].$$

We assume that it is induced by

$$B_{k_1}(\overline{C}_1[1]) \otimes_R \overline{D}[1] \otimes_R B_{k_0}(\overline{C}_0[1]) \longrightarrow \overline{D}'[1]$$

and denote it by the same symbol $\overline{\varphi}_{k_1,k_0}$.

We define an *unfiltered A_∞ bimodule homomorphism* $\overline{\varphi} : \overline{D} \to \overline{D}'$ in a similar way so that it satisfies $\widehat{\overline{\varphi}} \circ \widehat{\overline{d}} = \widehat{\overline{d}'} \circ \widehat{\overline{\varphi}}$.

We next discuss the gapped condition.

DEFINITION 3.7.9. We assume that C_i, C_i' are gapped filtered A_∞ algebras and $\mathfrak{f}^{(i)} : C_i \to C_i'$ are G_i-gapped filtered A_∞ homomorphisms. (See Definitions 3.2.26 and 3.2.29). Let $G \subseteq \mathbb{R}_{\geq 0} \times 2\mathbb{Z}$ be a monoid satisfying Condition 3.1.6 and containing G_1, G_0. Let D (resp. D') be G-gapped filtered C_1, C_0 bimodule (resp. C_1', C_0' bimodule). Then a filtered A_∞ bimodule homomorphism $\varphi = \{\varphi_{k_1,k_0}\}$: $D \to D'$ over $(\mathfrak{f}^1, \mathfrak{f}^0)$ is called *G-gapped*, if there exist

$$\varphi_{k_1,k_0,i} : B_{k_1}\overline{C}_1[1] \otimes \overline{D}[1] \otimes B_{k_0}\overline{C}_0[1] \to \overline{D}'[1]$$

such that

$$\varphi_{k_1,k_0} = \sum_i T^{\lambda_i} e^{\mu_i/2} \varphi_{k_1,k_0,i}.$$

Here we identify $D = \overline{D} \otimes_R \Lambda_{0,nov}$ etc. If G' is another monoid satisfying Condition 3.1.6 and contains G, then every G-gapped filtered A_∞ bimodule homomorphism is G'-gapped. When we do not necessarily specify G, we say that φ is *gapped* for simplicity.

We can define compositions of the filtered A_∞ bimodule homomorphisms in an obvious way.

As we mentioned at the end of the previous subsection, when we consider Floer cohomology of a pair of Lagrangian submanifolds, we will also use the ring Λ_{nov} as the coefficient ring to study the invariance property of the Floer cohomology. In this case we will introduce the notion of the *weakly* filtered A_∞ bimodule homomorphism and a certain *gapped condition* for the weakly filtered A_∞ bimodule homomorphisms. See Subsection 5.2.1 in Chapter 5.

DEFINITION 3.7.10. Suppose that C_i and C_i' have unit $\mathbf{e}_i$ and $\mathbf{e}_i'$, respectively, and $\{\mathbf{e}_1, \mathbf{e}_0\}$ acts on D as a unit and $\{\mathbf{e}_1', \mathbf{e}_0'\}$ acts on D' as a unit. Moreover, let $\mathfrak{f}^i : C_i \to C_i'$ be a unital A_∞ homomorphism in the sense of Definition 3.3.11, and $\varphi : D \to D'$ a filtered A_∞ bimodule homomorphism over $(\mathfrak{f}^1, \mathfrak{f}^0)$. We say φ *preserves unit*, or call it a *unital A_∞ bimodule homomorphism* if it satisfies

(3.7.11) $\varphi(\mathbf{x}_1 \otimes \mathbf{e}_1 \otimes \mathbf{x}_2, v, \mathbf{y}) = \varphi(\mathbf{x}, v, \mathbf{y}_1 \otimes \mathbf{e}_0 \otimes \mathbf{y}_2) = 0,$

where $v \in D$, $\mathbf{x}, \mathbf{x}_1, \mathbf{x}_2 \in BC_1[1]$, $\mathbf{y}, \mathbf{y}_1, \mathbf{y}_2 \in BC_0[1]$. Note that (3.7.11) includes the case when $\mathbf{x}_1, \mathbf{x}_2, \mathbf{x}, \mathbf{y}_1, \mathbf{y}_2,$ or $\mathbf{y}$ is equal to 1. For example,

$$\varphi(\mathbf{e}_1, v, \mathbf{y}) = \varphi(1, v, \mathbf{y}_1 \otimes \mathbf{e}_0 \otimes \mathbf{y}_2) = 0,$$
$$\varphi(\mathbf{e}_1, v, 1) = \varphi(1, v, \mathbf{e}_0) = 0.$$

The unfiltered version can be defined in the same way.

We next assume that C_i and C_i' have homotopy units $\mathbf{e}_i$ and $\mathbf{e}_i'$, and they act on D and D' as homotopy unit, respectively. Moreover, let $\mathfrak{f}^i : C_i \to C_i'$ be a homotopy-unital A_∞ homomorphism and $\mathfrak{f}^{i,+} : C_i^+ \to C_i'^+$ its extension as in Definition 3.3.13, which preserves units $\mathbf{e}_i^+$ and $\mathbf{e}_i'^+$.

DEFINITION 3.7.12. Under the situation above, we say a filtered A_∞ bimodule homomorphism $\varphi : D \to D'$ over $(\mathfrak{f}^1, \mathfrak{f}^0)$ *preserves homotopy unit*, or call it a *homotopy-unital A_∞ bimodule homomorphism*, if it extends to a filtered A_∞ bimodule homomorphism φ^+ over $(\mathfrak{f}^{1,+}, \mathfrak{f}^{0,+})$, which preserves unit in the sense of Definition 3.7.10. The unfiltered version can be also defined in the same way.

3.7.3. Weak unobstructedness and deformations. In Section 3.6, we defined the coboundary operator

$$\delta_{b_1, b_0} : C[1] \longrightarrow C[1]$$

for an unobstructed filtered A_∞ algebra C associated to each given pair (b_1, b_0) with $b_i \in \widehat{\mathcal{M}}(C)$ (Definition 3.6.6). When C is weakly unobstructed, we similarly defined the coboundary operator $\delta_{b,b}$ for a given $b \in \widehat{\mathcal{M}}_{\mathrm{weak}}(C)$ (Lemma 3.6.33). In this subsection, we will discuss the A_∞ bimodule version.

Let D be a left $(C_1, \mathfrak{m}^1)$ and right $(C_0, \mathfrak{m}^0)$ filtered A_∞ bimodule. The A_∞ bimodule structure is given by $\mathfrak{n}_{k_1, k_0}$.

First, we deform the filtered A_∞ bimodule structure.

DEFINITION-LEMMA 3.7.13. (1) *For any $b_i \in C_i[1]^0$ with $b_i \equiv 0 \mod \Lambda_{0,nov}^+$ $(i = 0, 1)$, we define a family of operators*

$$^{b_1}\mathfrak{n}_{k_1, k_0}^{b_0}(x_{1,1}, \cdots, x_{1,k_1}, y, x_{0,1}, \cdots, x_{0,k_0})$$
$$= \mathfrak{n}(e^{b_1} x_{1,1} e^{b_1} \cdots x_{1,k_1} e^{b_1}, y, e^{b_0} x_{0,1} e^{b_0} \cdots x_{0,k_0} e^{b_0})$$

for $x_{1,1} \otimes \cdots \otimes x_{1,k_1} \in B_{k_1} C_1[1]$, $y \in D[1]$ and $x_{0,1} \otimes \cdots \otimes x_{0,k_0} \in B_{k_0} C_0[1]$. Then it defines a $((C_1, \mathfrak{m}^{1,b_1}), (C_0, \mathfrak{m}^{0,b_0}))$ filtered A_∞ bimodule structure on D. (See Definition 3.6.9 for the deformed A_∞ algebras.) We denote it by $^{b_1}\mathfrak{n}^{b_0}$ and call it a deformed A_∞ bimodule structure of $\mathfrak{n}$ by b_1, b_0. We also denote by $^{b_1}\widehat{d}^{b_0}$ the induced operator by $^{b_1}\mathfrak{n}^{b_0}$ as in (3.7.3).

(2) *In particular, we put for $y \in D[1]$*

$$\delta_{b_1, b_0}(y) = {}^{b_1}\mathfrak{n}^{b_0}(y) = \mathfrak{n}(e^{b_1} y e^{b_0}) = \sum_{k_1, k_0} \mathfrak{n}_{k_1, k_0}(b_1, \cdots, b_1, y, b_0, \cdots, b_0).$$

The proof of that $^{b_1}\mathfrak{n}^{b_0}$ defines a filtered A_∞ bimodule structure is similar to that of Proposition 3.6.10 so we omit it. Later in Subsection 5.2.2, we will discuss deformations of the filtered A_∞ bimodule homomorphisms.

Now we assume that $(C_1, \mathfrak{m}^1)$ and $(C_0, \mathfrak{m}^0)$ are unobstructed. Let b_1 and b_0 be bounding cochains of $(C_1, \mathfrak{m}^1)$ and $(C_0, \mathfrak{m}^0)$ respectively. We deform the A_∞ bimodule structure by b_1, b_0, so that we obtain a coboundary operator $\delta_{b_1, b_0} : D \to D$ as follows. This corresponds to a deformation of the standard Floer coboundary operator in our geometric context.

LEMMA 3.7.14. *For any bounding cochains b_1, b_0 of $(C_1, \mathfrak{m}^1)$, $(C_0, \mathfrak{m}^0)$ given respectively, we have $\delta_{b_1, b_0} \circ \delta_{b_1, b_0} = 0$.*

The proof of Lemma 3.7.14 is the same as that of Lemma 3.6.8. So we omit the proof.

Next, we assume that C_1 and C_0 have units $\mathbf{e}_1, \mathbf{e}_0$ respectively, and $\{\mathbf{e}_1, \mathbf{e}_0\}$ acts as a unit. Then as in Definition-Lemma 3.7.13, we can deform the filtered A_∞ bimodule structure by b_1, b_0. It is easy to see that $\{\mathbf{e}_1, \mathbf{e}_0\}$ acts as a unit on the deformed filtered A_∞ bimodule as well.

If C_i is weakly unobstructed, we have the potential function

$$(3.7.15) \qquad \mathfrak{PO}_i : \widehat{\mathcal{M}}_{\text{weak}}(C_i) \longrightarrow \Lambda_{0,nov}^{+(0)}$$

for $i = 0, 1$ defined as in Definition 3.6.33 (2). For each $b_i \in \widehat{\mathcal{M}}_{\text{weak}}(C_i)$, we define $\delta_{b_1,b_0} : D \to D$ by

$$(3.7.16) \qquad \delta_{b_1,b_0}(y) = \mathfrak{n}(e^{b_1} y e^{b_0}).$$

PROPOSITION 3.7.17. *For $y \in D$, we have*

$$\delta_{b_1,b_0} \circ \delta_{b_1,b_0}(y) = (-\mathfrak{PO}_1(b_1) + \mathfrak{PO}_0(b_0))ey.$$

In particular, if $\mathfrak{PO}_1(b_1) = \mathfrak{PO}_0(b_0)$, we can define the cohomology of (D, δ_{b_1,b_0}).

PROOF. A straightforward computations gives

$$
\begin{aligned}
\delta_{b_1,b_0}(\delta_{b_1,b_0}(y)) &= \mathfrak{n}(e^{b_1}\mathfrak{n}(e^{b_1}y e^{b_0})e^{b_0}) \\
&= \mathfrak{n}(\widehat{d}(e^{b_1}y e^{b_0})) - \mathfrak{n}(\widehat{d}(e^{b_1})y e^{b_0}) + (-1)^{\deg y}\mathfrak{n}(e^{b_1}y \widehat{d}(e^{b_0})) \\
&= (-\mathfrak{PO}_1(b_1) + \mathfrak{PO}_0(b_0))ey.
\end{aligned}
$$

At the last equality we used (3.7.4.3). $\qquad\qquad\square$

REMARK 3.7.18. When C_i has a homotopy unit $\mathbf{e}_i$ which acts as a homotopy unit and C_i is weakly unobstructed in the sense of Definition 3.6.29 (2), the argument above also holds by considering $C_i^+ = C_i \oplus \Lambda_{0,nov}\mathbf{e}_i^+ \oplus \Lambda_{0,nov}\mathbf{f}_i$ as in (3.3.1). (Note $\delta_{b_1,b_0} : D \to D$ is defined in this case. Compare Remark 3.6.33 (1).) In Subsection 3.7.6, we will give a geometric example of Proposition 3.7.17.

3.7.4. The filtered A_∞ bimodule $C(L^{(1)}, L^{(0)}; \Lambda_{0,nov})$. The main result of this subsection is Theorem 3.7.21. In this subsection we put $R = \mathbb{Q}$.

Let $L^{(0)}, L^{(1)}$ be a relatively spin pair of Lagrangian submanifolds of M. We will first define a $\Lambda_{0,nov}$ module $C(L^{(1)}, L^{(0)}; \Lambda_{0,nov})$ and construct a filtered A_∞ bimodule structure on it. We do *not* need to assume $L^{(i)}$ is unobstructed for this purpose. In this subsection, we assume that they are transverse to each other. In the next subsection, we will treat the case where two Lagrangian submanifolds intersect cleanly.

Let $(C(L^{(0)}; \Lambda_{0,nov}), \mathfrak{m}^{(0)})$ and $(C(L^{(1)}; \Lambda_{0,nov}), \mathfrak{m}^{(1)})$ be the filtered A_∞ algebras constructed in Theorem 3.5.11. We define

$$CF(L^{(1)}, L^{(0)}; \ell_0) = CF(L^{(1)}, L^{(0)}; \ell_0; \mathbb{Q}) = \widehat{\bigoplus_{[\ell_p, w] \in Cr(L^{(0)}, L^{(1)}; \ell_0)}} \mathbb{Q}[\ell_p, w]$$

$$CF(L^{(1)}, L^{(0)}) = \widehat{\bigoplus_{\ell_0 \in \pi_0(\Omega(L^{(1)}, \Omega(L^{(0)})))}} CF(L^{(1)}, L^{(0)}; \ell_0)$$

$$= \widehat{\bigoplus_{[\ell_p, w] \in Cr(L^{(0)}, L^{(1)})}} \mathbb{Q}[\ell_p, w]$$

where $Cr(L^{(0)}, L^{(1)}; \ell_0)$, $Cr(L^{(0)}, L^{(1)})$ are the sets of the equivalence classes $[\ell_p, w]$ which are critical points of our functional $\mathcal{A}$ (see Subsection 2.2.2) and the sum in the second line is taken over all connected components of $\Omega(L^{(0)}, L^{(1)})$. The symbol $\widehat{\oplus}$ denotes the completion of the direct sum. The Γ-equivalence relation is given in Definition 2.2.4, and ℓ_p the constant path to an intersection point $p \in L^{(1)} \cap L^{(0)}$.

We define

$$\widehat{CF}(L^{(1)}, L^{(0)}; \Lambda_{nov}) := CF(L^{(1)}, L^{(0)}) \; \widehat{\otimes}_{\mathbb{Q}} \; \Lambda_{nov}$$

and an equivalence relation $\sim$ on $\widehat{CF}(L^{(1)}, L^{(0)}; \Lambda_{nov})$ as follows: Say

$$T^\lambda e^\mu [\ell_p, w] \sim T^{\lambda'} e^{\mu'} [\ell_{p'}, w']$$

for $T^\lambda e^\mu [\ell_p, w]$, $T^{\lambda'} e^{\mu'} [\ell_{p'}, w'] \in \widehat{CF}(L^{(1)}, L^{(0)}; \Lambda_{nov})$, if and only if the following conditions are satisfied:

(3.7.19.1)
$$p = p'$$

(3.7.19.2)
$$\lambda + \int_w \omega = \lambda' + \int_{w'} \omega$$

(3.7.19.3)
$$2\mu + \mu([\ell_p, w]) = 2\mu' + \mu([\ell_{p'}, w']).$$

Here $\mu([\ell_p, w])$ is the Maslov-Morse index given in Subsection 2.2.2. It is easy to see that these conditions are compatible with the conditions put on the Γ-equivalence (Definition 2.2.12) and so $\sim$ defines an equivalence relation on $\widehat{CF}(L^{(1)}, L^{(0)}; \Lambda_{nov})$. Furthermore we define the *energy filtration* on $\widehat{CF}(L^{(1)}, L^{(0)}; \Lambda_{nov})$ by the following. Let $T^\lambda e^\mu [\ell_p, w]$ be an element of $\widehat{CF}(L^{(1)}, L^{(0)}; \Lambda_{nov})$. We say

$$T^\lambda e^\mu [\ell_p, w] \in F^{\lambda'} \widehat{CF}(L^{(1)}, L^{(0)}; \Lambda_{0,nov})$$

if $\lambda + \int_w \omega \geq \lambda'$.

This filtration obviously induces an energy filtration on $\widehat{CF}(L^{(1)}, L^{(0)}; \Lambda_{nov})/\sim$. Now, we define $C(L^{(1)}, L^{(0)}; \Lambda_{0,nov})$ as follows.

DEFINITION 3.7.20. We denote by $C(L^{(1)}, L^{(0)}; \Lambda_{0,nov})$ the non-negative energy part of the completion of $\widehat{CF}(L^{(1)}, L^{(0)}; \Lambda_{nov})/\sim$ with respect to the energy filtration. Namely

$$C(L^{(1)}, L^{(0)}; \Lambda_{0,nov}) = F^0 CF(L^{(1)}, L^{(0)}; \Lambda_{nov}).$$

Giving the grading of an element $T^\lambda e^\mu [\ell_p, w]$ by $2\mu + \mu([\ell_p, w])$, it becomes a filtered graded free $\Lambda_{0,nov}$ module.

It is easy to see that $C(L^{(1)}, L^{(0)}; \Lambda_{0,nov})$ satisfies the conditions (3.2.12.1) - (3.2.12.5). We also note that $C(L^{(1)}, L^{(0)}; \Lambda_{0,nov})$ is isomorphic to the completion (with respect to the filtration on $\Lambda_{0,nov}$) of the free $\Lambda_{0,nov}$ module generated by the intersection points $p \in L^{(1)} \cap L^{(0)}$. Namely

$$C(L^{(1)}, L^{(0)}; \Lambda_{0,nov}) \cong \widehat{\bigoplus_{p \in L^{(1)} \cap L^{(0)}}} \Lambda_{0,nov}[p]$$

as a $\Lambda_{0,nov}$ module.

Let $\{J_t\}_t = \{J_t\}_{0 \leq t \leq 1}$ be a t-dependent family of almost complex structures as before. The following is the main theorem of this subsection.

THEOREM 3.7.21. *Let $(L^{(0)}, L^{(1)})$ be a relatively spin pair of Lagrangian submanifolds which transversely intersect.*

Then we have a left $(C(L^{(1)}; \Lambda_{0,nov}), \mathfrak{m}^{(1)})$ and right $(C(L^{(0)}; \Lambda_{0,nov}), \mathfrak{m}^{(0)})$ filtered A_∞ bimodule structure on $C(L^{(1)}, L^{(0)}; \Lambda_{0,nov})$, which is $G(L^{(1)}, L^{(0)})$-gapped.

Moreover the pair $\{\mathbf{e}_1, \mathbf{e}_0\}$ of the homotopy units of $(C(L^{(1)}; \Lambda_{0,nov}), \mathfrak{m}^{(1)})$ and $(C(L^{(0)}; \Lambda_{0,nov}), \mathfrak{m}^{(0)})$ acts as a homotopy unit.

We will give the definition of $G(L^{(1)}, L^{(0)})$ in the course of the proof. See (3.7.43).

PROOF. We need to study the transversality problem precisely like as in Theorem 3.5.11. The proof of this point is a minor modification of one in Section 3.5. The discussion on the homotopy unit is similar to the one in Section 7.3. See Section 8.10 for the signs.

Let $[\ell_p, w_1], [\ell_q, w_2] \in Cr(L^{(0)}, L^{(1)})$. To construct the filtered A_∞ bimodule structure on $C(L^{(1)}, L^{(0)}; \Lambda_{0,nov})$, we need to define the relevant moduli space of *marked stable broken Floer trajectories*

$$\mathcal{M}_{k_1,k_0}([\ell_p, w_1], [\ell_q, w_2]) = \mathcal{M}_{k_1,k_0}(L^{(1)}, L^{(0)}; [\ell_p, w_1], [\ell_q, w_2])$$

which are now in order. The special case $\mathcal{M}_{0,0}([\ell_p, w_1], [\ell_q, w_2])$ will coincide with the moduli space $\mathcal{M}([\ell_p, w_1], [\ell_q, w_2]; \{J_t\}_t)$ defined in Section 2.4.2.

Let Σ be $\mathbb{R} \times [0,1]$ possibly with a finite number of tower of sphere components attached (at points on $\mathbb{R} \times (0,1)$). (The way how to handle sphere bubble using the fiber product is the same as [**FuOn99II**]. So we do not repeat its detail here.) Let $u : \Sigma \to M$ be a smooth map and $\tau_j^{(0)} \in \mathbb{R}$ $(j = 1, \cdots, k_0)$, $\tau_j^{(1)} \in \mathbb{R}$, $(j = 1, \cdots, k_1)$. We put

$$\vec{\tau}^{(i)} = (\tau_1^{(i)}, \cdots, \tau_{k_i}^{(i)}), \quad (i = 0, 1) \quad \text{and} \quad \vec{\tau} = (\vec{\tau}^{(0)}, \vec{\tau}^{(1)}).$$

We consider the following conditions for them. (See Figure 3.7.1.):

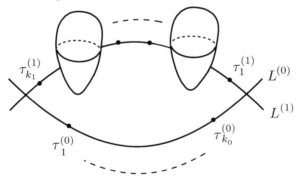

Figure 3.7.1

(3.7.22.1)   On $\mathbb{R} \times [0,1]$, u satisfies

$$\frac{\partial u}{\partial \tau} + J_t \frac{\partial u}{\partial t} = 0.$$

If a bubble tree of spheres is rooted at (τ, t), all the spheres in this bubble tree are J_t-holomorphic.

(3.7.22.2) $u(\mathbb{R} \times \{0\}) \subset L^{(0)}$, $u(\mathbb{R} \times \{1\}) \subset L^{(1)}$.

(3.7.22.3) $\lim_{\tau \to -\infty} u = p$ and $\lim_{\tau \to \infty} u = q$.

(3.7.22.4) $\tau_j^{(0)} < \tau_{j+1}^{(0)}, j = 1, \cdots, k_0 - 1, \tau_j^{(1)} > \tau_{j+1}^{(1)}, j = 1, \cdots, k_1 - 1.$

(3.7.22.5) $w_1 \# u \sim w_2.$

(3.7.22.6) $((\Sigma, \vec{\tau}), u)$ is stable, i.e., the set of automorphisms $\varphi : \Sigma \to \Sigma$ with $\varphi(\tau_j^{(i)}) = \tau_j^{(i)}$, $u \circ \varphi = u$ is finite.

In (3.7.22.5), we use the notation of Definition 2.2.4 for the equivalence relation $\sim$ and $w_1 \# u$ is the obvious concatenation of w_1 and u (see Section 2.2.1).

REMARK 3.7.23. (1) We would like to remark that we give the structure of a *left* $(C(L^{(1)}; \Lambda_{0,nov}), \mathfrak{m}^{(1)})$ and *right* $(C(L^{(0)}; \Lambda_{0,nov}), \mathfrak{m}^{(0)})$ filtered A_∞ bimodule to $C(L^{(1)}, L^{(0)}; \Lambda_{0,nov})$. At first sight, it might seem natural to construct a *right* $(C(L^{(1)}; \Lambda_{0,nov}), \mathfrak{m}^{(1)})$ and *left* $(C(L^{(0)}; \Lambda_{0,nov}), \mathfrak{m}^{(0)})$ structure. The reason the left and right is as in Theorem 3.7.21 is as follows: We consider the space of path from $L^{(0)}$ to $L^{(1)}$. Hence the natural boundary condition for $u : \Sigma \to M$ is as in (3.7.22.2). (See Figure 3.7.2.)

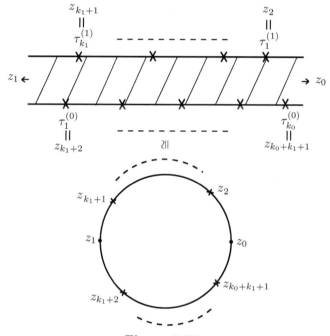

Figure 3.7.2

But the standard way of putting the orientation on the circle as a boundary of the disc is the *counter clockwise* order.

Therefore, the natural order of the marked points $(\tau_j^{(i)}, i)$ ($i = 0, 1$; $j = 1, \cdots, k_i$) and $-\infty$ is $(\tau_1^{(1)}, 1), \cdots, (\tau_{k_1}^{(1)}, 1), -\infty, (\tau_1^{(0)}, 0), \cdots, (\tau_{k_0}^{(0)}, 0)$.

Therefore, if we define $\mathfrak{n}$ using the space $\mathcal{M}_{k_1,k_0}(L^{(1)}, L^{(0)}; [\ell_p, w_1], [\ell_q, w_2])$ as below, the chains of $L^{(1)}$ should come first and then $[\ell_p, w_1]$ and finally the chains of $L^{(0)}$.

(2) When we describe the map u as a map from the unit disc D^2 instead of $\mathbb{R} \times [0, 1]$, the points $-\infty$ and $+\infty$ correspond to the points -1 and $+1$ on the boundary of the unit disc respectively. In the later argument, these points will be assigned to the first and 0-th marked points z_1, z_0 respectively. See Sections 8.7 and 8.8. The order of the marked points on the boundary is important when we

consider the orientation problem. We like to keep the notations z_0 and z_1 as $+1$ and -1. In Sections 8.1 and 8.8 we put $z_2 = (\tau_1^{(1)}, 1), \cdots, z_{k_1+1} = (\tau_{k_1}^{(1)}, 1)$ and $z_{k_0+2} = (\tau_1^{(0)}, 0), \cdots, z_{k_0+k_1+1} = (\tau_{k_0}^{(0)}, 0)$. See also Figure 3.7.2 above.

We consider the $\mathbb{R}$-action defined by $u(\cdot, \cdot) \to u(\cdot + \tau_0, \cdot)$ for $\tau_0 \in \mathbb{R}$ which induces a natural equivalence relation $\sim_\mathbb{R}$ among the set of solution u's of (3.7.22).

DEFINITION 3.7.24. We denote by

$$\overset{\circ}{\mathcal{M}}_{k_1,k_0}([\ell_p, w_1], [\ell_q, w_2]) = \overset{\circ}{\mathcal{M}}_{k_1,k_0}(L^{(1)}, L^{(0)}; [\ell_p, w_1], [\ell_q, w_2])$$

the totality of the $\sim_\mathbb{R}$ equivalence classes of $((\Sigma, \vec{\tau}), u)$ satisfying (3.7.22).

We have the evaluation map

(3.7.25)
$$ev = (ev^{(1)}, ev^{(0)}) = ((ev_1^{(1)}, \ldots, ev_{k_1}^{(1)}), (ev_1^{(0)}, \ldots, ev_{k_0}^{(0)}))$$
$$: \overset{\circ}{\mathcal{M}}_{k_1,k_0}([\ell_p, w], [\ell_q, w']) \to \left(L^{(1)}\right)^{k_1} \times \left(L^{(0)}\right)^{k_0}$$

which is defined by

$$ev_j^{(i)}((\Sigma, \vec{\tau}), u) = u(\tau_j^{(i)}, i) \in L^{(i)}, \quad (i = 0, 1).$$

To state the next proposition we need to explain some notations. We recall that the Kuranishi structure on $\mathcal{M}_k(\beta)$ was constructed for $\beta \in \Pi(M; L)$ in Proposition 3.4.2. ($\Pi(M; L)$ is defined in Definition 2.4.17.) The moduli space $\mathcal{M}_k^{\text{main}}(\beta)$ together with its Kuranishi structure depends on the choice of L, β as well as a compatible almost structure J. To specify the choice we write $\mathcal{M}_k^{\text{main}}(L; \beta; J)$.

PROPOSITION 3.7.26. Let $(L^{(0)}, L^{(1)})$ be a relatively spin pair of Lagrangian submanifolds which are transversal to each other, and $[\ell_p, w_1], [\ell_q, w_2]$ be elements of $Cr(L^{(1)}, L^{(0)})$.

Then $\overset{\circ}{\mathcal{M}}_{k_1,k_0}(L^{(1)}, L^{(0)}; [\ell_p, w_1], [\ell_q, w_2])$ has a compactification which we denote by $\mathcal{M}_{k_1,k_0}(L^{(1)}, L^{(0)}; [\ell_p, w_1], [\ell_q, w_2])$. The evaluation map (3.7.25) is extended to the compactification so that it is weakly submersive and strongly continuous and smooth.

$\mathcal{M}_{k_1,k_0}(L^{(1)}, L^{(0)}; [\ell_p, w_1], [\ell_q, w_2])$ has an oriented Kuranishi structure, which is compatible to each other and with the Kuranishi structures of the moduli spaces $\mathcal{M}_k^{\text{main}}(L^{(0)}; \beta^{(0)}; J_0)$ and $\mathcal{M}_k^{\text{main}}(L^{(1)}; \beta^{(1)}; J_1)$ constructed in Proposition 3.4.2.

The compatibility in the statement of Proposition 3.7.26 means the compatibility at the end of the moduli spaces via fiber product. (See Subsection 7.1.1.)

PROOF. We here only describe the compactification $\mathcal{M}_{k_1,k_0}(L^{(1)}, L^{(0)}; [\ell_p, w_1], [\ell_q, w_2])$. Construction of the Kuranishi structure thereon is the same as the other cases discussed in Section 7.1.

To describe compactification of the moduli space, we need to prepare some notations.

DEFINITION 3.7.27. Let l_0, l_1, m_0, m_1 and $m_{0,1}, \cdots, m_{0,l_0}, m_{1,1}, \cdots, m_{1,l_1}$ be nonnegative integers such that

$$k_i = m_i + \sum_{a=1}^{l_i} m_{i,a},$$

for $i = 0, 1$. We consider a subset

$$A_i \subseteq \{1, \cdots, m_i + l_i\}, \quad \#A_i = l_i,$$

and put

$$A_i = \{\sigma_i(1), \cdots, \sigma_i(l_i)\}, \quad \sigma_i(a) < \sigma_i(a+1).$$

Let $\pi_{i,1} : (L^{(i)})^{k_i+l_i} \to (L^{(i)})^{l_i}$ be the projection

$$\pi_{i,1}(x_1, \cdots, x_{k_i+l_i}) = (x_{\sigma_i(1)}, \cdots, x_{\sigma_i(l_i)}).$$

Let $\pi_{i,2} : (L^{(i)})^{k_i+l_i} \to (L^{(i)})^{k_i}$ be the projection to the other factors.

We denote by A the data, $l_0, l_1, m_0, m_1, m_{0,1}, \cdots, m_{0,l_0}, m_{1,1}, \cdots, m_{1,l_1}$ and A_0, A_1.

We put

$$
\begin{aligned}
&\mathcal{M}^A_{k_1,k_0}([\ell_p, w_1], [\ell_q, w_2]) \\
(3.7.28) \quad &= \bigcup_{w_2' \# \sum \beta_{1,a} \# \sum \beta_{0,b} = w_2} \overset{\circ}{\mathcal{M}}_{l_1+m_1, l_0+m_0}([\ell_p, w_1], [\ell_q, w_2']) \\
&\qquad {}_{(\pi_{1,1}, \pi_{0,1}) \circ ev} \times_{\vec{ev}_0} \\
&\left(\prod_{a=1}^{l_1} \mathcal{M}^{\mathrm{main}}_{m_{1,a}+1}(L^{(1)}; \beta_{1,a}; J_1) \times \prod_{b=1}^{l_0} \mathcal{M}^{\mathrm{main}}_{m_{0,b}+1}(L^{(0)}; \beta_{0,b}; J_0) \right),
\end{aligned}
$$

(where $\vec{ev}_0 = (ev_0, \cdots, ev_0)$) and

$$(3.7.29) \qquad \mathcal{M}^{\mathrm{unbr}}_{k_1,k_0}([\ell_p, w_1], [\ell_q, w_2]) = \bigcup_A \mathcal{M}^A_{k_1,k_0}([\ell_p, w_1], [\ell_q, w_2]).$$

Here 'unbr' stands for 'unbroken'. Elements of $\mathcal{M}^{\mathrm{unbr}}_{k_1,k_0}([\ell_p, w_1], [\ell_q, w_2])$ are called *unbroken Floer trajectory with marked points on the boundary*. See Figure 3.7.3. (We remark that $\tau_j^{(0)}$, $\tau_j^{(1)}$ in the figure are positions of the marked points of the $\overset{\circ}{\mathcal{M}}_{l_1+m_1, l_0+m_0}([\ell_p, w_1], [\ell_q, w_2'])$ factor of elements in (3.7.28).)

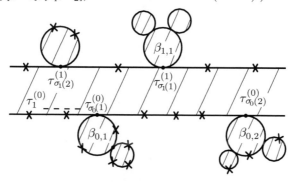

Figure 3.7.3

For each element of $\mathcal{M}^A_{k_1,k_0}([\ell_p, w_1], [\ell_q, w_2])$ there are k_1 (resp. k_0) marked points which are mapped to $L^{(1)}$ (resp. $L^{(0)}$) after taking fiber product. In fact m_1 (resp. m_0) of them are on the principal component and $\sum m_{1,j}$ (resp. $\sum m_{0,j}$) of them are on the bubbles.

We renumber them according to the counter clockwise order and use it to define evaluation maps. Thus we defined an evaluation map

(3.7.30) $ev : \mathcal{M}^A_{k_1,k_0}([\ell_p, w_1], [\ell_q, w_2]) \to (L^{(1)})^{k_1} \times (L^{(0)})^{k_0}.$

We next put

(3.7.31)
$$\mathcal{M}_{k_1,k_0}([\ell_p, w_1], [\ell_q, w_2])$$
$$= \coprod_K \coprod_{w(1),\cdots,w(K)} \coprod_{p(0),\cdots,p(K)} \coprod_{k_{1,1},\cdots,k_{1,K}} \coprod_{k_{0,1},\cdots,k_{0,K}}$$
$$\prod_{a=1}^{K-1} \mathcal{M}^{unbr}_{k_{1,a},k_{0,a}}([\ell_{p(a)}, w(a)], [\ell_{p(a+1)}, w(a+1)]).$$

Here the disjoint union in the right hand side is taken over all $K, w(\cdot), p(\cdot), k_{0,*}, k_{1,*}$ such that

(3.7.32.1) $p(0) = p,\ p(K) = q,$
(3.7.32.2) $[\ell_{p(a)}, w(a)] \in Cr(L^{(0)}, L^{(1)}),$
(3.7.32.3) $k_{1,1} + \cdots + k_{1,K} = k_1,\ k_{0,1} + \cdots + k_{0,K} = k_0.$

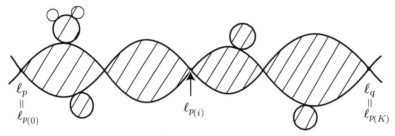

Figure 3.7.4

The map (3.7.30) induces the evaluation map

(3.7.33) $ev : \mathcal{M}_{k_1,k_0}([\ell_p, w_1], [\ell_q, w_2]) \to (L^{(1)})^{k_1} \times (L^{(0)})^{k_0}$

in an obvious way.

We can define a topology on $\mathcal{M}_{k_1,k_0}([\ell_p, w_1], [\ell_q, w_2])$ and prove that it is Hausdorff and compact in the same way as Subsection 7.1.4. The construction of the Kuranishi structure is also similar to the argument in Section 7.1 given for other cases. The orientation on $\mathcal{M}_{k_1,k_0}(L^{(1)}, L^{(0)}; [\ell_p, w_1], [\ell_q, w_2])$ is defined in Section 8.7.

Proposition 3.7.26 is proved.   □

Now as in Section 3.5, let $S^k(L^{(0)}; \mathbb{Q})$ (resp. $S^k(L^{(1)}; \mathbb{Q})$) be the free $\mathbb{Q}$ module generated by codimension k smooth singular simplices on $L^{(0)}$ (resp. $L^{(1)}$).

We consider the submodules $C(L^{(i)}; \mathbb{Q})$ $(i = 0, 1)$ of $S(L^{(i)}; \mathbb{Q})$ generated by the countable set $\mathcal{X}_1(L^{(i)})$ respectively, as mentioned in Section 3.5. Let $(P^{(i)}_j, f^{(i)}_j) \in \mathcal{X}_1(L^{(i)})$, $j = 1, \cdots, k_i$ and consider the fiber product

(3.7.34)
$$\mathcal{M}_{k_1,k_0}(L^{(1)}, L^{(0)}; [\ell_p, w_1], [\ell_q, w_2])$$
$$ev \times_{f^{(1)}_1 \times \cdots \times f^{(0)}_{k_0}} \left(\prod_{i=1}^{k_1} P^{(1)}_i \times \prod_{i=1}^{k_0} P^{(0)}_i \right).$$

We put $\vec{P}^{(i)} = (P_1^{(i)}, \cdots, P_{k_i}^{(i)})$ and denote (3.7.34) by

$$(3.7.35) \qquad \mathcal{M}_{k_1,k_0}(L^{(1)}, L^{(0)}; [\ell_p, w_1], [\ell_q, w_2]; \vec{P}^{(1)}, \vec{P}^{(0)}).$$

It has a Kuranishi structure by Proposition 3.7.26.

We write

$$\mathcal{M}_k(L^{(i)}; \beta^{(i)}; J_i; \vec{P}^{(i)}), \quad \mathcal{M}_{k_1,k_0}(L^{(1)}, L^{(0)}; [\ell_p, w_1], [\ell_q, w_2]; \vec{P}^{(1)}, \vec{P}^{(0)}; \{J_t\}_t)$$

in place of

$$\mathcal{M}_k(\beta^{(i)}; \vec{P}^{(i)}), \quad \mathcal{M}_{k_1,k_0}(L^{(1)}, L^{(0)}; [\ell_p, w_1], [\ell_q, w_2]; \vec{P}^{(1)}, \vec{P}^{(0)}),$$

respectively, in case we need to specify the choice of J_i etc. We remark that we have chosen a system of multisections of $\mathcal{M}_k(L^{(i)}; \beta^{(i)}; J_i; \vec{P}^{(i)})$ (as well as the countable set $\mathcal{X}_1(L^{(i)})$) in Section 3.5 to define our filtered A_∞ algebra associated to $L^{(i)}$. We denote by $\mathfrak{s}_{\beta^{(i)}, \vec{P}^{(i)}}$ the multisections determined there.

PROPOSITION 3.7.36. *In the situation above, there exists a system of multisections* $\mathfrak{s}_{[\ell_p, w_1], [\ell_q, w_2], \vec{P}^{(1)}, \vec{P}^{(0)}}$ *on the moduli space* $\mathcal{M}_{k_1,k_0}(L^{(1)}, L^{(0)}; [\ell_p, w_1], [\ell_q, w_2]; \vec{P}^{(1)}, \vec{P}^{(0)})$ *with the following properties:*

(3.7.37.1)   *The virtual dimension of the moduli space*

$$\mathcal{M}_{k_1,k_0}(L^{(1)}, L^{(0)}; [\ell_p, w_1], [\ell_q, w_2]; \vec{P}^{(1)}, \vec{P}^{(0)})$$

is given by

$$(3.7.38) \qquad \mu([\ell_q, w_2]) - \mu([\ell_p, w_1]) - \sum_{i=1}^{k_0} \deg P_i^{(0)} - \sum_{i=1}^{k_1} \deg P_i^{(1)} + k_0 + k_1 - 1.$$

Here $\deg P_i^{(0)}$ *and* $\deg P_i^{(1)}$ *are the degree of* $P_i^{(0)}$ *and* $P_i^{(1)}$ *as cochains before shifted.*
(3.7.37.2)   *The multisection* $\mathfrak{s}_{[\ell_p, w_1], [\ell_q, w_2], \vec{P}^{(1)}, \vec{P}^{(0)}}$ *are transversal to* 0.
(3.7.37.3)   *The multisection* $\mathfrak{s}_{[\ell_p, w_1], [\ell_q, w_2], \vec{P}^{(1)}, \vec{P}^{(0)}}$ *are compatible with other multisections* $\mathfrak{s}_{[\ell_{p'}, w_1'], [\ell_{q'}, w_2'], \vec{P}^{(1)'}, \vec{P}^{(0)'}}$ *and with* $\mathfrak{s}_{\beta^{(0)}, \vec{P}^{(0)}}$, $\mathfrak{s}_{\beta^{(1)}, \vec{P}^{(1)}}$ *at the boundary.*

Proof. The proof is the same as the case of filtered A_∞ algebras (Proposition 3.5.2) whose details are given in Section 7.2. The dimension can be calculated in the way similar to the one in Section 2.3 and in Proposition 3.5.2.   □

DEFINITION 3.7.39. We denote

$$\mathcal{M}_{k_1,k_0}(L^{(1)}, L^{(0)}; [\ell_p, w_1], [\ell_q, w_2]; \vec{P}^{(1)}, \vec{P}^{(0)})^{\mathfrak{s}} := \left(\mathfrak{s}_{[\ell_p, w_1], [\ell_q, w_2], \vec{P}^{(1)}, \vec{P}^{(0)}} \right)^{-1}(0).$$

As for the orientation of the moduli space in the above formula, we refer to Definition 8.7.1 in Chapter 8.

We remark that $\left(\mathfrak{s}_{[\ell_p, w_1], [\ell_q, w_2], \vec{P}^{(1)}, \vec{P}^{(0)}} \right)^{-1}(0)$ is a space with triangulation together with rational weights on each simplex of top dimension. (See Section 6 **[FuOn99II]** or Definition A1.28.) If the dimension (3.7.38) is 0, it consists of a finite number of points with a weight $\in \mathbb{Q}$ assigned at each point. When dimension (3.7.38) is 1, it is an (oriented) graph with a weight $\in \mathbb{Q}$ assigned at each edge.

REMARK 3.7.40. We do not take any particular evaluation map on the perturbed moduli space $\mathcal{M}_{k_1,k_0}(L^{(1)}, L^{(0)}; [\ell_p, w_1], [\ell_q, w_2]; \vec{P}^{(1)}, \vec{P}^{(0)})^{\mathfrak{s}}$ in this subsection. So it is not regarded as a singular chain in this subsection. However it is more natural to regard it as a singular chain on the zero dimensional space $\{q\} \subset L^{(1)} \cap L^{(0)}$. This point becomes clearer in the next subsection where we deal with the case when $L^{(1)} \cap L^{(0)}$ is a union of finite dimensional manifolds.

Using the spaces $\mathcal{M}_{k_1,k_0}(L^{(1)}, L^{(0)}; [\ell_p, w_1], [\ell_q, w_2]; \vec{P}^{(1)}, \vec{P}^{(0)})^{\mathfrak{s}}$, we now define a family of operators $\mathfrak{n}_{k_1,k_0}$ which will define the structure of filtered A_∞ bimodules on $C(L^{(1)}, L^{(0)}; \Lambda_{0,nov})$.

DEFINITION 3.7.41. Consider the case of the dimension (3.7.38) being 0. Let

$$T^{\lambda_i^{(0)}} e^{\mu_i^{(0)}} P_i^{(0)} \in C(L^{(0)}, \Lambda_{0,nov}), \quad T^{\lambda_i^{(1)}} e^{\mu_i^{(1)}} P_i^{(1)} \in C(L^{(1)}, \Lambda_{0,nov})$$

and

$$T^\lambda e^\mu [\ell_p, w_1] \in C(L^{(1)}, L^{(0)}; \Lambda_{0,nov}).$$

Then we define $\mathfrak{n}_{k_1,k_0}$ by the following formula.

$$\mathfrak{n}_{k_1,k_0}(T^{\lambda_1^{(1)}} e^{\mu_1^{(1)}} P_1^{(1)} \otimes \cdots \otimes T^{\lambda_{k_1}^{(1)}} e^{\mu_{k_1}^{(1)}} P_{k_1}^{(1)} \otimes T^\lambda e^\mu [\ell_p, w_1] \otimes$$
$$T^{\lambda_1^{(0)}} e^{\mu_1^{(0)}} P_1^{(0)} \otimes \cdots \otimes T^{\lambda_{k_0}^{(0)}} e^{\mu_{k_0}^{(0)}} P_{k_0}^{(0)})$$
$$= \sum_{[\ell_q, w_2] \in Cr(L^{(0)}, L^{(1)})} \#\left(\mathcal{M}_{k_1,k_0}(L^{(1)}, L^{(0)}; [\ell_p, w_1], [\ell_q, w_2]; \vec{P}^{(1)}, \vec{P}^{(0)})^{\mathfrak{s}}\right)$$
$$T^{\lambda'} e^{\mu'} [\ell_q, w_2],$$

where

$$\lambda' = \sum_{i=1}^{k_0} \lambda_i^{(0)} + \lambda + \sum_{i=1}^{k_1} \lambda_i^{(1)}, \qquad \mu' = \sum_{i=1}^{k_0} \mu_i^{(0)} + \mu + \sum_{i=1}^{k_1} \mu_i^{(1)}.$$

Here $\#$ is the sum of weights assigned to each points. We note that for a pseudo-holomorphic map $u : \Sigma \to M$ satisfying (3.7.22), we have

$$\int_{w_2} \omega - \int_{w_1} \omega = \int_\Sigma u^* \omega \geq 0$$

by (3.7.22.5). Thus we find that the energy of $T^{\lambda'} e^{\mu'} [\ell_q, w_2]$ is

$$(3.7.42) \qquad \lambda' + \int_{w_2} \omega \geq \left(\sum_{i=1}^{k_0} \lambda_i^{(0)}\right) + \left(\sum_{i=1}^{k_1} \lambda_i^{(1)}\right) + \left(\lambda + \int_{w_1} \omega\right),$$

which is non negative, since each of the summands is non negative. So it defines an element of $C(L^{(1)}, L^{(0)}; \Lambda_{0,nov})$. Hence the maps $\mathfrak{n}_{k_1,k_0}$ define

$$\mathfrak{n}_{k_1,k_0} : B_{k_1}(C(L^{(1)}, \Lambda_{0,nov})[1]) \otimes_{\Lambda_{0,nov}} C(L^{(1)}, L^{(0)}; \Lambda_{0,nov})[1]$$
$$\otimes_{\Lambda_{0,nov}} B_{k_0}(C(L^{(0)}, \Lambda_{0,nov})[1]) \longrightarrow C(L^{(1)}, L^{(0)}; \Lambda_{0,nov})[1].$$

Since the sum in Definition 3.7.41 is taken over $[\ell_q, w_2]$ such that (3.7.38) is equal to 0, it follows that the degree of $\mathfrak{n}_{k_1,k_0}$ is $+1$. Moreover from (3.2.12.1) the inequality (3.7.42) implies that the maps $\mathfrak{n}_{k_1,k_0}$ satisfy the condition (3.7.1).

Let us prove the gapped condition. We denote by $G(L^{(1)}, L^{(0)})_0 \subset \mathbb{R}_{\geq 0} \times 2\mathbb{Z}$ the submonoid generated by the set

$$\{(\omega[B], \mu(p, q; B)) \mid p, q \in L^{(0)} \cap L^{(1)}, B \in \pi_2(p, q), \mathcal{M}(p, q; B) \neq \emptyset\}.$$

See Subsection 2.3.1 for the notations. We define

$$(3.7.43) \quad G(L^{(1)}, L^{(0)}) = \{\beta^{(1)} + \alpha + \beta^{(0)} \mid \beta^{(i)} \in G(L^{(i)}), \alpha \in G(L^{(1)}, L^{(0)})_0\}.$$

Then $G(L^{(1)}, L^{(0)}) \supseteq G(L^{(1)}), G(L^{(0)})$ is also a submonoid and by Gromov's compactness theorem $G(L^{(1)}, L^{(0)})$ satisfies Condition 3.1.6. Our operator is obviously $G(L^{(1)}, L^{(0)})$-gapped by definition.

Now let $\widehat{d}$ be the map obtained from the $\mathfrak{n}_{k_1,k_2}$ by the formula (3.7.2). To prove Theorem 3.7.21 it suffices to show the following.

LEMMA 3.7.44. *The homomorphism $\widehat{d}$ defined in (3.7.2) satisfies $\widehat{d} \circ \widehat{d} = 0$.*

PROOF. Consider the moduli space

$$\mathcal{M}_{k_1,k_0}(L^{(1)}, L^{(0)}; [\ell_p, w_1], [\ell_q, w_2]; \vec{P}^{(1)}, \vec{P}^{(0)})^{\mathfrak{s}}$$

when its dimension is 1. The boundary of this moduli space is described by one of the following Figures 3.7.5-3.7.7.

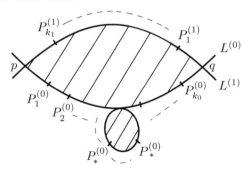

Figure 3.7.5

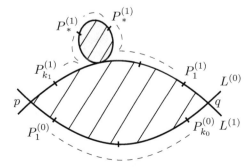

Figure 3.7.6

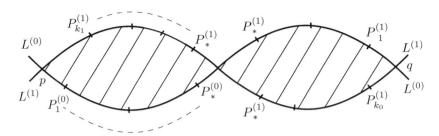

Figure 3.7.7

The terms corresponding to Figure 3.7.5 are

$$\mathfrak{n}\left(\widehat{d}^{(1)}(P_1^{(1)} \otimes \cdots \otimes P_{k_1}^{(1)}) \otimes [\ell_p, w_1] \otimes P_1^{(0)} \otimes \cdots P_{k_0}^{(0)}\right).$$

Here $\widehat{d}^{(1)}$ is defined in $(C(L^{(1)}, \Lambda_{0,nov}), \mathfrak{m}^{(1)})$. The terms corresponding to Figure 3.7.6 are

$$\mathfrak{n}\left(P_1^{(1)} \otimes \cdots \otimes P_{k_1}^{(1)} \otimes [\ell_p, w_1] \otimes \widehat{d}^{(0)}(P_1^{(0)} \otimes \cdots P_{k_0}^{(0)})\right).$$

Here $\widehat{d}^{(0)}$ is defined in $(C(L^{(0)}, \Lambda_{0,nov}), \mathfrak{m}^{(0)})$. The terms corresponding to Figure 3.7.7 are

$$\mathfrak{n}\left(P_1^{(1)} \otimes \cdots \cdots \mathfrak{n}(\cdots \otimes P_{k_1}^{(1)} \otimes [\ell_p, w_1] \otimes P_1^{(0)} \otimes \cdots) \cdots \otimes P_{k_0}^{(0)}\right).$$

Combing the argument in Sections 8.5 and 8.7, we can check the signs in a similar way. Therefore we find that these three terms cancel each other. Hence the proof of Lemma 3.7.44 is complete. $\qquad\square$

Thus we have finished the construction of a left $(C(L^{(1)}; \Lambda_{0,nov}), \mathfrak{m}^{(1)})$ and right $(C(L^{(0)}; \Lambda_{0,nov}), \mathfrak{m}^{(0)})$ filtered A_∞ bimodule structure on $C(L^{(1)}, L^{(0)}; \Lambda_{0,nov})$ and hence the proof of Theorem 3.7.21. $\qquad\square$

Now, we assume that $(C(L^{(0)}; \Lambda_{0,nov}), \mathfrak{m}^{(0)})$ and $(C(L^{(1)}; \Lambda_{0,nov}), \mathfrak{m}^{(1)})$ are unobstructed. Then by Definition-Lemma 3.7.13 and Lemma 3.7.14 in the previous subsection, we can define the coboundary operator

$$\delta_{b_1, b_0} : C(L^{(1)}, L^{(0)}; \Lambda_{0,nov}) \longrightarrow C(L^{(1)}, L^{(0)}; \Lambda_{0,nov})$$

for any bounding cochains $b_i \in \widehat{\mathcal{M}}(L^{(i)}; J_i; \mathfrak{s}_i)$. (Definition 3.6.14.) This gives rise to a deformation of the standard Floer coboundary operator. Thus the following theorem is an immediate consequence of Lemma 3.7.14 and Theorem 3.7.21.

THEOREM 3.7.45. *Let $(L^{(0)}, L^{(1)})$ be a relatively spin pair of Lagrangian submanifolds which are transversal to each other. Let $b_0 \in \widehat{\mathcal{M}}(L^{(0)}; J_0; \mathfrak{s}_0)$ and $b_1 \in \widehat{\mathcal{M}}(L^{(1)}; J_1; \mathfrak{s}_1)$. Then there exists a cohomology*

$$HF((L^{(1)}, b_1), (L^{(0)}, b_0); \Lambda_{0,nov}) = \frac{\operatorname{Ker} \delta_{b_1, b_0}}{\operatorname{Im} \delta_{b_1, b_0}},$$

which we call the Floer cohomology of $(L^{(0)}, L^{(1)})$ deformed by b_0, b_1.

Of course, when $(C(L^{(0)}; \Lambda_{0,nov}), \mathfrak{m}^{(0)})$ and $(C(L^{(1)}; \Lambda_{0,nov}), \mathfrak{m}^{(1)})$ are weakly unobstructed (with respect to the homotopy unit), we can apply Proposition 3.7.17

and define Floer cohomology deformed by $b_i \in \widehat{\mathcal{M}}_{\text{weak}}(L^{(i)}; J_i; \mathfrak{s}_i)$ which satisfy the condition $\mathfrak{PO}_0(b_0) = \mathfrak{PO}_1(b_1)$.

REMARK 3.7.46. We define

$$C(L^{(1)}, L^{(0)}; \ell_0; \Lambda_{nov}) = (C(L^{(1)}, L^{(0)}; \ell_0; \mathbb{Q}) \otimes \Lambda_{nov}) / \sim$$

in the same way as in Definition 3.7.20 and put

$$C(L^{(1)}, L^{(0)}; \ell_0; \Lambda_{0,nov}) = F^0(C(L^{(1)}, L^{(0)}; \ell_0; \Lambda_{nov})).$$

Then, it is easy to see from the construction that the decomposition

$$C(L^{(1)}, L^{(0)}; \Lambda_{0,nov}) = \widehat{\bigoplus_{[\ell_0] \in \pi_0(\Omega(L^{(0)}, L^{(1)}))}} C(L^{(1)}, L^{(0)}; \ell_0; \Lambda_{0,nov})$$

is the completion of the direct sum of filtered A_∞ bimodule. It follows that we have a decomposition of the Floer cohomology

$$
(3.7.47) \quad
\begin{aligned}
&HF((L^{(1)}, b_1), (L^{(0)}, b_0); \Lambda_{0,nov}) \\
&\cong \widehat{\bigoplus_{[\ell_0] \in \pi_0(\Omega(L^{(0)}, L^{(1)}))}} HF((L^{(1)}, b_1), (L^{(0)}, b_0); \ell_0; \Lambda_{0,nov})
\end{aligned}
$$

into the completed direct sum over $\pi_0(\Omega(L^{(0)}, L^{(1)}))$. The same remark applies in the Bott-Morse case discussed in the next subsection.

3.7.5. The Bott-Morse case. In this subsection, we generalize the results in the previous subsection to the case of clean intersection (the Bott-Morse analogue of Lagrangian intersection Floer theory). (See Subsection 2.3.3 for earlier works on Bott-Morse theory in Floer homology.) We start with the following situation. Let $(L^{(0)}, L^{(1)})$ be a relatively spin pair of Lagrangian submanifolds. We assume that they intersect cleanly in the following sense.

DEFINITION 3.7.48. We say that $L^{(0)}$ and $L^{(1)}$ *intersect cleanly* if the following holds. Let $L^{(1)} \cap L^{(0)} = \bigcup_{h \in \pi_0(L^{(0)} \cap L^{(1)})} R_h$ be the decomposition into the connected components of $L^{(1)} \cap L^{(0)}$. We assume that R_h is a smooth submanifold and

$$N_{L^{(1)}/R_h} \oplus N_{L^{(0)}/R_h} \oplus TR_h = (TL^{(1)} + TL^{(0)})|_{R_h}$$

for each component R_h, where $N_{L^{(0)}/R_h}$ and $N_{L^{(1)}/R_h}$ are normal bundles of R_h in $L^{(0)}$ and $L^{(1)}$, respectively.

We note that the case $L^{(0)} = L^{(1)}$ is a special case of clean intersections.

Let d_h be the dimension of R_h. If $L^{(1)} \cap L^{(0)}$ is disconnected, we need to fix some additional data on each component. We first fix a base point p_h on each R_h. We next consider the map $w : [0,1] \times [0,1] \to M$ such that

(3.7.49.1) $w(0, t) = \ell_0(t).$
(3.7.49.2) $w(s, 0) \in L^{(0)}, \; w(s, 1) \in L^{(1)}$ for all $0 \le s \le 1.$
(3.7.49.3) $w(1, t) \equiv p_h.$

Here ℓ_0 is a based path that we fixed for each connected component of the path space $\Omega(L^{(0)}, L^{(1)})$. (See Section 2.2.) We define the equivalence relation on w's as in Definition 2.2.4. Let $\widetilde{\pi}_0(L^{(0)} \cap L^{(1)})$ be the set of all equivalence classes of pairs $[h, w]$.

DEFINITION 3.7.50. We put

$$\widetilde{\pi}_0(L^{(0)} \cap L^{(1)})_{h_0} = \left\{ [h, w] \in \widetilde{\pi}_0(L^{(0)} \cap L^{(1)}) \ \middle| \ h = h_0 \right\},$$

and

$$\Lambda_{h_0} = \mathrm{Span}_{\mathbb{Q}} \left\{ [h, w_i] \ \middle| \ [h, w_i] \in \widetilde{\pi}_0(L^{(0)} \cap L^{(1)})_{h_0} \right\}.$$

In the Bott-Morse theory of finite dimension, we should take local systems on critical submanifolds into account as follows. Let $f : X \to \mathbb{R}$ be a Bott-Morse function on a finite dimensional manifold X such that its critical point set is decomposed as $Cr(f) = \sum R_h$. Then there exists a spectral sequence

$$E_2^{ij} = \bigoplus_{\dim R_h = i} H^j(R_h, \Theta_{R_h}^-) \Rightarrow H^{i+j}(X; \mathbb{Z}).$$

Here Θ_j^- is the determinant (real) line bundle of the unstable bundle over R_j. (This is Theorem 2.1 [**Fuk96II**] in which the first named author overlooked putting $\Theta_{R_i}^-$ there. This statement is in principle known to Bott. See Subsection 7.2.2 also.)

In our case where we need to replace the space X by its Novikov covering $\widetilde{\Omega}(L^{(0)}, L^{(1)})$ and f by the action functional $\mathcal{A}$, we need a similar data as the local system Θ_j^- above. If $L^{(1)}$ is considered as a cross section of the cotangent bundle of $L^{(0)}$, then the same local system as in the Bott-Morse case is what we need. In general, we define the local system as follows. Define a vector bundle V_h on R_h by

$$(3.7.51) \qquad V_h = \{(TL^{(1)} + TL^{(0)})/(TL^{(1)} + TL^{(0)})^{\perp_\omega}\}|_{R_h},$$

which is a symplectic vector bundle. Denote by U and U' the image of $TL^{(0)}$ and $TL^{(1)}$ in V_h which form Lagrangian subbundles of V_h. We consider a path λ of Lagrangian subspaces in V_h from U to U' so that the path $\lambda \oplus TR_h$ is a path of oriented Lagrangian subspaces in TM from $T_pL^{(0)}$ to $T_pL^{(1)}$. Then, we consider the index of the Dolbeault operator on the half disc with Lagrangian boundary condition, which we will discuss more in Chapter 8. See Proposition 8.8.1 of Subsection 8.8. In this way, we get a family of operators on the space of paths λ. The orientation bundle of the family index of these operators descends to a local system on R_h, which we denote by $\Theta_{R_h}^-$.

We will define the Maslov index $\mu([h, w]) \in \mathbb{Z}$ for $[h, w] \in \widehat{\pi}_0(L^{(0)} \cap L^{(1)})$ in Definition 3.7.62 below.

Let $S^{*-\mu([h,w])}(R_h; \Theta_{R_h}^-)$ be a cochain complex of smooth singular simplices with coefficients in the local system $\Theta_{R_h}^- \otimes \det TR_h$. Namely if $\Theta_{R_h}^-$ is induced by the representation $\rho_h : \pi_1(R_h) \to \{\pm 1\}$, then using the notation of Section A2 Definition A2.1, we put

$$S^*(R_h; \Theta_{R_h}^-) = S^*(R_h; \rho_h; \mathbb{Q}).$$

(Note in our situation R_h may not be orientable. So we need $\det TR_h$ to regard a chain as a cochain.)

We will take a countably generated subcomplex $C(R_h; \Theta_{R_h}^-)$ thereof later in Proposition 3.7.59. (We assume that it is independent of w up to degree.)

We define $\widehat{CF}_{BM}(L^{(1)}, L^{(0)}; \Lambda_{nov})$ to be a completion of

$$\bigoplus_h \left(C(R_h; \Theta_{R_h}^-) \otimes_{\mathbb{Q}} \Lambda_h \right) \otimes_{\mathbb{Q}} \Lambda_{nov},$$

where Λ_h is defined in Definition 3.7.50.

For $S \otimes [h,w] \otimes T^\lambda e^\mu \in \widehat{CF}^k_{BM}(L^{(1)}, L^{(0)}; \Lambda_{nov})$ with $S \in C^\ell(R_h; \Theta^-_{R_h})$, we define the energy by $\int_w \omega + \lambda$ and the degree by $k = \ell + \mu([h,w]) + 2\mu$. For a codimension ℓ chain S in R_h labelled by $[h,w]$, we define

$$\deg S = \ell + \mu([h,w]).$$

In a way similar to (3.7.19) in Subsection 3.7.4, we can define an equivalence relation $\sim$ on $\widehat{CF}_{BM}(L^{(1)}, L^{(0)}; \Lambda_{nov})$ by using the energy and the degree. Furthermore, we can similarly define the energy filtration thereon which also induces the filtration on $\widehat{CF}_{BM}(L^{(1)}, L^{(0)}; \Lambda_{nov})/\sim$.

DEFINITION 3.7.52. We denote by $C(L^{(1)}, L^{(0)}; \Lambda_{0,nov})$ the non-negative energy part of the completion of $\widehat{CF}_{BM}(L^{(1)}, L^{(0)}; \Lambda_{nov})/\sim$ with respect to the energy filtration.

Giving the grading as above, it becomes a filtered graded free $\Lambda_{0,nov}$ module and satisfies (3.2.12.1) - (3.2.12.5).

REMARK 3.7.53. If $S = (|S|, f, \xi)$, where $f : |S| \to R_h$ is an immersion of a simplex and ξ is a trivialization of $\det N_{R_h/S} \otimes \Theta^-_{R_h}$, then we obtain an element $[S, w]$ in $C^*(L^{(1)}, L^{(0)}; \Lambda_{0,nov})$. (We take the Poincaré dual of the local system $\Theta^-_{R_h}$ coefficient.)

Next we will define a $((C(L^{(1)}; \Lambda_{0,nov}), \mathfrak{m}^{(1)}), (C(L^{(0)}; \Lambda_{0,nov}), \mathfrak{m}^{(0)})$ filtered A_∞ bimodule structure on $C(L^{(1)}, L^{(0)}; \Lambda_{0,nov})$. In order to do so, we will introduce the following moduli space of pseudo-holomorphic maps. Let R_h, $R_{h'}$ be connected components of $L^{(1)} \cap L^{(0)}$ and $\{J_t\}_t = \{J_t\}_{0 \le t \le 1}$ a one parameter family connecting J_0 and J_1, and $S \in C(R_h; \Theta^-_h)$.

Let Σ be $\mathbb{R} \times [0,1]$ plus sphere bubbles as in Subsection 3.7.4. Let $u : \Sigma \to M$, $\tau^{(i)}_j \in \mathbb{R}$ $(i = 0, 1)$ and we put $\vec{\tau} = (\vec{\tau}^{(0)}, \vec{\tau}^{(1)})$ with $\vec{\tau}^{(i)} = (\tau^{(i)}_1, \cdots, \tau^{(i)}_{k_i})$. We consider the following conditions for them.

(3.7.54.1) u satisfies

$$\frac{\partial u}{\partial \tau} + J_t \frac{\partial u}{\partial t} = 0,$$

on $\mathbb{R} \times [0,1]$. If the bubble tree of spheres is rooted at (τ, t), all the spheres are J_t-holomorphic.

(3.7.54.2) $u(\mathbb{R} \times \{0\}) \subset L^{(0)}$, $u(\mathbb{R} \times \{1\}) \subset L^{(1)}$.

(3.7.54.3) u converges to a point in R_h as $\tau \to -\infty$ and u converges to a point in $R_{h'}$ as $\tau \to +\infty$.

(3.7.54.4) $\tau^{(0)}_j < \tau^{(0)}_{j+1}, j = 1, \cdots, k_0 - 1$, $\tau^{(1)}_j > \tau^{(1)}_{j+1}, j = 1, \cdots, k_1 - 1$.

(3.7.54.5) $w \# u(\Sigma) \sim w'$. Here $\#$ is an obvious concatenation.

(3.7.54.6) $((\Sigma, \vec{\tau}), u)$ is stable.

We consider the obvious $\mathbb{R}$-action of τ-translations and denote by $\sim_\mathbb{R}$ the corresponding equivalence relation. We denote by

$$\overset{\circ}{\mathcal{M}}_{k_1, k_0}(L^{(1)}, L^{(0)}; [h,w], [h', w']; \{J_t\}_t) = \overset{\circ}{\mathcal{M}}_{k_1, k_0}([h,w], [h', w'])$$
$$= \{\text{The } \sim_\mathbb{R} \text{ equivalence classes of } ((\Sigma, \vec{\tau}), u) \text{ satisfying (3.7.54)}\}.$$

We have the evaluation map

$$ev = (ev^{(1)}, ev^{(0)})) = ((ev_1^{(1)}, \ldots, ev_{k_1}^{(1)}), (ev_1^{(0)}, \ldots, ev_{k_0}^{(0)}))$$

$$: \overset{\circ}{\mathcal{M}}_{k_1,k_0}([h,w],[h',w']) \to \left(L^{(1)}\right)^{k_1} \times \left(L^{(0)}\right)^{k_0}$$

which is defined by

$$ev_j^{(i)}((\Sigma,\vec{\tau}),u) = u(\tau_j^{(i)},i) \in L^{(i)}, \quad (i = 0,1).$$

We also define

$$ev_{-\infty} : \overset{\circ}{\mathcal{M}}_{k_1,k_0}([h,w],[h',w']) \to R_h, \ ev_{+\infty} : \overset{\circ}{\mathcal{M}}_{k_1,k_0}([h,w],[h',w']) \to R_{h'},$$

by $ev_{\pm\infty}((\Sigma,\vec{\tau}),u) = \lim_{\tau\to\pm\infty} u(\tau,t)$. Then we can prove the following.

PROPOSITION 3.7.55. *We can compactify the moduli space*

$$\overset{\circ}{\mathcal{M}}_{k_1,k_0}([h,w],[h',w'];\{J_t\}_t)$$

to

$$\mathcal{M}_{k_1,k_0}([h,w],[h',w'];\{J_t\}_t).$$

It has a Kuranishi structure compatible to each other and to the Kuranishi structures on $\mathcal{M}_k^{\mathrm{main}}(L^{(0)};\beta^{(0)};J_0)$ and on $\mathcal{M}_k^{\mathrm{main}}(L^{(1)};\beta^{(1)};J_1)$ in Proposition 3.4.2. Moreover we can extend the evaluation map to

$$(ev_{-\infty}, ev, ev_{+\infty}) : \mathcal{M}_{k_1,k_0}([h,w],[h',w']) \to R_h \times \left(L^{(1)}\right)^{k_1} \times \left(L^{(0)}\right)^{k_0} \times R_{h'}$$

which is weakly submersive.

PROOF. We first define $\mathcal{M}_{k_1,k_0}^{\mathrm{unbr}}([h,w],[h',w'])$ in a way similar to (3.7.29), using $\overset{\circ}{\mathcal{M}}_{k_1,k_0}([h,w],[h',w'])$. Then we define

$$\mathcal{M}_{k_1,k_0}([h,w],[h',w'])$$

(3.7.56)
$$= \coprod_K \coprod_{w(1),\cdots,w(K)} \coprod_{h(0),\cdots,h(K)} \coprod_{k_{1,1},\cdots,k_{1,K}} \coprod_{k_{0,1},\cdots,k_{0,K}}$$

$$\mathcal{M}_{k_{1,1},k_{0,1}}^{\mathrm{unbr}}([h(1),w(1)],[h(2),w(2)])$$

$$\times_{R_{h(2)}} \mathcal{M}_{k_{1,2},k_{0,2}}^{\mathrm{unbr}}([h(2),w(2)],[h(3),w(3)])$$

$$\times_{R_{h(3)}} \cdots \times_{R_{h(i)}} \cdots$$

$$\times_{R_{h(K-1)}} \mathcal{M}_{k_{1,K-1},k_{0,K-1}}^{\mathrm{unbr}}([h(K-1),w(K-1)],[h(K),w(K)])$$

where the disjoint union in (3.7.56) is taken over all $K, h(\cdot), w(\cdot), k_{i,\cdot}$ such that

(3.7.57.1)　$h(1) = h, h(K) = h'$,
(3.7.57.2)　$[h(i),w(i)] \in Cr(L^{(0)}, L^{(1)})$,
(3.7.57.3)　$k_{1,1} + \cdots + k_{1,K} = k_1, k_{0,1} + \cdots + k_{0,K} = k_0$.

We remark that in (3.7.56) we take fiber product over $R_{h(i)}$. (In (3.7.33) we took direct product.)

We can define a topology on $\mathcal{M}_{k_1,k_0}([h,w],[h',w'])$ and can prove that it is Hausdorff and compact in the same way as Section 7.1. The construction of Kuranishi structure is also similar to the discussion in Section 7.1.　□

We remark that the moduli space $\mathcal{M}_{k_1,k_0}([h,w],[h',w'])$ may *not* be oriented even when $(L^{(0)}, L^{(1)})$ is a relatively spin pair. See Lemma 3.7.70 below for the precise statement on this issue and we will discuss the details on the orientation problem for the Bott-Morse case in Section 8.8.

We next consider submodules $C(L^{(0)}; \mathbb{Q})$, $C(L^{(1)}; \mathbb{Q})$ of $S(L^{(0)}; \mathbb{Q})$, $S(L^{(1)}; \mathbb{Q})$ generated by the countable sets $\mathcal{X}_1(L^{(0)})$, $\mathcal{X}_1(L^{(1)})$ in Section 3.5 respectively.

Let O_{R_h} be the orientation (real line) bundle of the tangent bundle of R_h. (Namely $O_{R_h} = \det T R_h$.) We will also take (in the course of the proof of the next proposition) a countable set $\mathcal{X}_1(R_h)$ of smooth chains $S = (|S|, f)$ equipped with trivialization of $f^* O_{R_h} \otimes f^* \Theta_{R_h}^-$. An element S of $\mathcal{X}_1(R_h)$ represents a $\Theta_{R_h}^-$-valued cochain in R_h. We denote it by the same symbol S. They generate a submodule $C(R_h; \Theta_{R_h}^-)$ of $S(R_h; \Theta_{R_h}^-)$.

REMARK 3.7.58. The countable set of smooth singular simplices $\mathcal{X}_1(L^{(i)})$ was already taken and fixed at the time when we define filtered A_∞ algebras. Here in the course of the proof of Proposition 3.7.59, we make a choice of $\mathcal{X}_1(R_h)$ to define $C(R_h; \Theta_{R_h}^-)$. The argument for it is similar to one in Section 7.2.

Let $(P_j^{(i)}, f_j^{(i)}) \in \mathcal{X}_1(L^{(i)})$, $j = 1, \cdots, k_i$ and $S = (|S|, f) \in \mathcal{X}_1(R_h)$. We take the fiber product

$$\mathcal{M}_{k_1,k_0}(L^{(1)}, L^{(0)}; [h,w], [h',w'])\,_{(ev^{(1)}, ev_{-\infty}, ev^{(0)})}$$

$$\times_{f_1^{(1)} \times \cdots f_{k_1}^{(1)} \times f \times f_1^{(0)} \cdots \times f_{k_0}^{(0)}} \left(\prod_{j=1}^{k_1} P_j^{(1)} \times S \times \prod_{j=1}^{k_0} P_j^{(0)} \right),$$

which we denote by

$$\mathcal{M}_{k_1,k_0,(+\infty)}(L^{(1)}, L^{(0)}; [h,w], [h',w']; \vec{P}^{(1)}, S, \vec{P}^{(0)}).$$

Here we put $\vec{P}^{(i)} = (P_1^{(i)}, \cdots, P_{k_i}^{(i)})$.

By Proposition 3.7.55, $\mathcal{M}_{k_1,k_0,(+\infty)}(L^{(1)}, L^{(0)}; [h,w], [h',w']; \vec{P}^{(1)}, S, \vec{P}^{(0)})$ has a Kuranishi structure. Moreover the evaluation map

$$ev_{+\infty} : \mathcal{M}_{k_1,k_0,(+\infty)}(L^{(1)}, L^{(0)}; [h,w], [h',w']; \vec{P}^{(1)}, S, \vec{P}^{(0)}) \to R_{h'}$$

is weakly submersive. As usual, the dimension will be provided by the index of certain Cauchy-Riemann type operator with a suitable boundary condition which is obtained by linearizing the equation (3.7.54). Postponing its topological definition shortly, we first state the following proposition.

PROPOSITION 3.7.59. *In the above situation, we assume that $(L^{(0)}, L^{(1)})$ is a relatively spin pair in addition.*

Then for each $h \in \pi_0(L^{(0)} \cap L^{(1)})$ there exist a countable set of smooth singular simplices $\mathcal{X}_1(R_h)$ and a set of integers $\mu([h,w]) \in \mathbb{Z}$ assigned to each $[h,w]$ so that we can find a system of multisections $\mathfrak{s}_{[h,w],[h',w'],\vec{P}^{(1)},S,\vec{P}^{(0)}}$ on

$$\mathcal{M}_{k_1,k_0,(+\infty)}(L^{(1)}, L^{(0)}; [h,w], [h',w']; \vec{P}^{(1)}, S, \vec{P}^{(0)}),$$

that satisfy the following properties:

(3.7.60.1)   *The (virtual) dimension of the fiber product*

$$\mathcal{M}_{k_1,k_0,(+\infty)}(L^{(1)}, L^{(0)}; [h, w], [h', w']; \vec{P}^{(1)}, S, \vec{P}^{(0)})$$

is given by

$$\dim S + d_{h'} - d_h + \mu([h', w']) - \mu([h, w]) - \sum_{j=1}^{k_0} \deg P_j^{(0)} - \sum_{j=1}^{k_1} \deg P_j^{(1)} + k_0 + k_1 - 1.$$

Here $d_h = \dim R_h$ and $\deg P_j^{(0)}$ and $\deg P_j^{(1)}$ are the degrees of $P_j^{(0)}$ and $P_j^{(1)}$ as cochains before shifted.

(3.7.60.2)   *The multisection $\mathfrak{s}_{[h,w],[h',w'],\vec{P}^{(1)},S,\vec{P}^{(0)}}$ is transversal to 0.*

(3.7.60.3)   *The multisection $\mathfrak{s}_{[h,w],[h',w'],\vec{P}^{(1)},S,\vec{P}^{(0)}}$ is compatible with other multisections $\mathfrak{s}_{[h'',w''],[h''',w'''],\vec{P}^{(1)'},S',\vec{P}^{(0)'}}$ and with $\mathfrak{s}_{\beta^{(0)},\vec{P}^{(0)}}$, $\mathfrak{s}_{\beta^{(1)},\vec{P}^{(1)}}$.*

(3.7.60.4)   *$((\mathfrak{s}_{[h,w],[h',w'],\vec{P}^{(1)},S,\vec{P}^{(0)}})^{-1}(0), ev_{+\infty})$ is an element of the chain complex $C(R_{h'}; \Theta_{R_{h'}}^-)$.*

We remark that to make the statement (3.7.60.4) more precise we need to take a triangulation and an order of its vertices to regard the virtual fundamental chain

$$((\mathfrak{s}_{[h,w],[h',w'],\vec{P}^{(1)},S,\vec{P}^{(0)}})^{-1}(0), ev_{+\infty})$$

as a singular chain similarly to what we did just after (3.5.3.4). Since this is the same as what did for (3.5.3.4) we do not repeat it here.

The proof of this proposition is similar to that of Proposition 3.7.36. There are, however, three new points to discuss. One is a choice of $\mathcal{X}_1(R_h)$, which can be handled in the same way as in Section 7.2. The other two are the issues of the degree $\mu([h, w])$ and of the orientation(flat) bundle $\Theta_{R_h}^-$. We will explain these two issues below.

To give the dimension formula, we need to provide the description of the linearized operator of (3.7.54.1). We first give the description of this linearization problem.

We recall from Subsection 2.2.2 that we fixed a base path $\ell_0 : [0, 1] \to M$ (where $\ell_0(0) \in L^{(0)}$, $\ell_0(1) \in L^{(0)}$) of the space of paths $\Omega(L^{(0)}, L^{(1)})$. We also took $t \mapsto \lambda^0(t)$ such that $\lambda^0(t)$ is an oriented Lagrangian linear subspace of $T_{\ell_0(t)}M$ and

$$\lambda^0(0) = T_{\ell_0(0)}L^{(0)}, \quad \lambda^0(1) = T_{\ell_0(1)}L^{(1)}$$

as oriented linear spaces.

For $p_h \in R_h \subseteq L_0 \cap L_1$, we consider a path space of Lagrangian subspaces

$$\mathcal{P}_{R_h}(T_{p_h}L_0, T_{p_h}L_1) = \{\lambda : [0, 1] \to \Lambda^{ori}(T_{p_h}M) \mid \lambda(0) = T_{p_h}(L_0), \lambda(1) = T_{p_h}(L_1)\}.$$

Here $\Lambda^{ori}(T_{p_h}M)$ is the oriented Lagrangian Grassmanian of $T_{p_h}M$.

Using the above path λ^0 and the map w as in (3.7.49) we will define a (homotopy class) of an element of $\mathcal{P}_{R_h}(T_{p_h}L_0, T_{p_h}L_1)$ as follows. Since $[0, 1]^2$ is contractible we have an isomorphism $w^*TM \cong [0, 1]^2 \times T_pM$. Then for

$$(s, t) \in (\{0\} \times [0, 1]) \cup ([0, 1] \times \{0, 1\}) \stackrel{homeo}{\cong} [0, 1]$$

we define

$$\lambda(0, t) = \lambda^0(t), \quad \lambda(i, s) = T_{w(i,s)}L^{(i)}.$$

We denote this path by λ_{w,λ^0}.

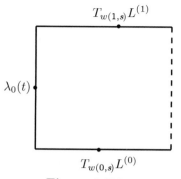

$$T_{w(1,s)}L^{(1)}$$

$$\lambda_0(t) \bullet$$

$$T_{w(0,s)}L^{(0)}$$

Figure 3.7.8

We put

$$Z_- = \{z \in \mathbb{C} \mid |z| \le 1\} \cup \{z \in \mathbb{C} \mid \mathrm{Re}\, z \ge 0, |\mathrm{Im}\, z| \le 1\}$$
$$Z_+ = \{z \in \mathbb{C} \mid \mathrm{Re}\, z \le 0, |\mathrm{Im}\, z| \le 1\} \cup \{z \in \mathbb{C} \mid |z| \le 1\}.$$

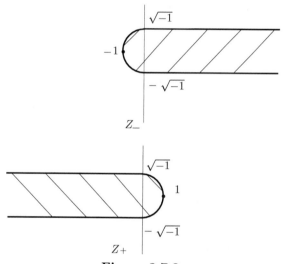

Figure 3.7.9

We put $z = \tau + \sqrt{-1}t$. For each $\lambda \in \mathcal{P}_{R_h}(T_{p_h}L^{(0)}, T_{p_h}L^{(1)})$, we are going to define a Fredholm operator as follows. Let $W^{1,p}_\lambda(Z_+; T_{p_h}M)$, (resp. $W^{1,p}_\lambda(Z_-; T_{p_h}M)$) be the Banach space consisting of locally $L^{1,p}$ maps $\zeta_+ : Z_+ \to T_{p_h}M$ (resp. $\zeta_- : Z_- \to T_{p_h}M$) such that

(3.7.61.1) $\zeta_+(\tau, i) \in T_{p_h}L^{(i)}$. (resp. $\zeta_-(\tau, i) \in T_{p_h}L^{(i)}$). Here $i = 0, 1$.

(3.7.61.2) $\zeta_+(z_+(t)) \in \lambda(t)$, (resp. $\zeta_-(z_-) \in \lambda(t)$ $(i = 0, 1)$) where we put $z_\pm(t) = e^{\pi\sqrt{-1}(-1/2\pm t)} \in \partial Z_\pm$.

(3.7.61.3)

$$\int_{Z_\pm} e^{\delta|\tau|} \left(|\nabla \zeta_\pm|^p + |\zeta_\pm|^p \right) d\tau dt < \infty.$$

Let $L^p(Z_\pm; T_{p_h}M \otimes \Lambda^{0,1}(Z_\pm))$ be the Banach space of locally L^p sections $\zeta_\pm$ of the bundle $T_{p_h}M \otimes \Lambda^{0,1}(Z_\pm)$ such that

$$\int_{Z_\pm} e^{\delta|\tau|}|\zeta_\pm|^p d\tau dt < \infty.$$

The Dolbeault operator induces a bounded linear map

$$\overline{\partial}_{\lambda,Z_\pm} : W_\lambda^{1,p}(Z_\pm; T_{p_h}M) \to L^p(Z_\pm; T_{p_h}M \otimes \Lambda^{0,1}(Z_\pm)).$$

It is by now well-known that $\overline{\partial}_{\lambda,Z_\pm}$ is a Fredholm operator.

DEFINITION 3.7.62. We denote

$$\mu_{\lambda^0}^{anal}([h,w]) = \operatorname{Index} \overline{\partial}_{\lambda_{w,\lambda^0},Z_-}.$$

In Lemma 3.7.69, we will prove that this analytical index coincides with the generalized Maslov-Morse index $\mu([h,w]; \lambda_0)$.

Now we are ready to give the proof of Proposition 3.7.59.

PROOF OF PROPOSITION 3.7.59. We set $\mu([h,w]) = \mu_{\lambda^0}^{anal}([h,w])$. With this choice made, we first verify (3.7.60.1). Let $u \in \mathcal{M}(L^{(1)}, L^{(0)}; [h,w], [h',w'])$. ($u(\tau,t): \mathbb{R} \times [0,1] \to M$ is a pseudo-holomorphic map.)

We consider the Banach space $W_\delta^{1,p}(\mathbb{R} \times [0,1]; u^*TM, u^*TL^{(1)}, u^*TL^{(0)})$ consisting of all sections ζ of u^*TM of locally $L^{1,p}$ class such that

(3.7.63.1) $\zeta(\tau,i) \in T_{p_h}L^{(i)}$ $(i = 0, 1)$.
(3.7.63.2)

$$\int_{\mathbb{R} \times [0,1]} e^{\delta|\tau|}\left(|\nabla\zeta|^p + |\zeta|^p\right) d\tau dt < \infty.$$

Let $L^p(\mathbb{R} \times [0,1]; u^*TM \otimes \Lambda^{0,1}(\mathbb{R} \times [0,1]))$ be the Banach space of all locally L^p sections ζ of the bundle $u^*TM \otimes \Lambda^{0,1}(\mathbb{R} \times [0,1])$ such that

$$\int_{\mathbb{R} \times [0,1]} e^{\delta|\tau|}|\zeta|^p d\tau dt < \infty.$$

The Dolbeault operator induces a bounded linear map

$$\begin{aligned}\overline{\partial}_u : &W_\delta^{1,p}(\mathbb{R} \times [0,1]; u^*TM, u^*TL^{(1)}, u^*TL^{(0)})\\ &\to L^p(\mathbb{R} \times [0,1]; u^*TM \otimes \Lambda^{0,1}(\mathbb{R} \times [0,1])).\end{aligned}$$

Since $w\#u \sim w'$, a standard result (the index sum formula) implies:

LEMMA 3.7.64.

$$\operatorname{Index} \overline{\partial}_{\lambda_{w,\lambda^0},Z_-} + \operatorname{Index} \overline{\partial}_u = \operatorname{Index} \overline{\partial}_{\lambda_{w',\lambda^0},Z_-} + d_h.$$

PROOF. When $\tau \to +\infty$ the operator $\overline{\partial}_{\lambda_{w,\lambda^0},Z_-}$ is a product type (that is of the form $\frac{\partial}{\partial\tau} + P_\tau$) and the number of zero eigenvalues of $\lim_{\tau \to +\infty} P_\tau$ is exactly $d_h = \dim R_h$.

The operator $\operatorname{Index} \overline{\partial}_u$ when $\tau \to -\infty$ has a similar form and the number of zero eigenvalues is d_h. Using an obvious modification of Theorem 3.10 [APS75], the lemma follows from these facts. $\square$

LEMMA 3.7.65.

$$\dim \mathcal{M}(L^{(1)}, L^{(0)}; [h, w], [h', w']) = \text{Index}\, \overline{\partial}_u + d_h + d_{h'} - 1.$$

PROOF. The operator $\overline{\partial}_u$ has the same symbol as the linearization operator $D_u \overline{\partial}$ of nonlinear Cauchy-Riemann equation at u. Since we assumed (3.7.63.2) the section ζ goes to zero in the exponential order as $|\tau| \to \infty$. Therefore the index of $\overline{\partial}_u$ is the virtual dimension of the moduli space of pseudo-holomorphic strips which converges to *fixed* points $p_h \in R_h$, $p_{h'} \in R_{h'}$ as $\tau \to -\infty, +\infty$. Note that the boundary condition for $v \in \mathcal{M}(L^{(1)}, L^{(0)}; [h, w], [h', w'])$ at $\tau \to \pm\infty$ is that v converges to *some* points in R_h, and in $R_{h'}$ as $\tau \to -\infty$ and $\tau \to +\infty$, respectively. Also we divide the moduli space by the $\mathbb{R}$ action. Hence $\dim \mathcal{M}(L^{(1)}, L^{(0)}; [h, w], [h', w'])$ is as asserted. (See Subsection 7.1.2 for the Fredholm theory in the case $R_h = L^{(0)} = L^{(1)}$. Its generalization to the case of arbitrary pair $(L^{(0)}, L^{(1)})$ of clean intersection, which we are studying here, is straightforward.) □

Now we are ready to wrap-up the proof of (3.7.60.1). The moduli space

$$\mathcal{M}_{k_1, k_0, (+\infty)}(L^{(1)}, L^{(0)}; [h, w], [h', w']; \vec{P}^{(1)}, S, \vec{P}^{(0)})$$

is obtained from $\mathcal{M}(L^{(1)}, L^{(0)}; [h, w], [h', w'])$ by taking fiber products with several chains. The process taking a fiber product with S decreases the dimension by $d_h - \dim S$. The process taking a fiber product with $P_i^{(j)}$ decreases the dimension by $\deg P_i^{(j)}$. We put $k_1 + k_0$ boundary points, and so we have extra dimension $k_1 + k_0$. Therefore

$$\dim \mathcal{M}_{k_1, k_0, (+\infty)}(L^{(1)}, L^{(0)}; [h, w], [h', w']; \vec{P}^{(1)}, S, \vec{P}^{(0)})$$
$$= \dim \mathcal{M}(L^{(1)}, L^{(0)}; [h, w], [h', w']) + \dim S - d_h$$
$$- \sum_{j=1}^{k_0} \deg P_j^{(0)} - \sum_{j=1}^{k_1} \deg P_j^{(1)} + k_0 + k_1.$$

Lemmas 3.7.64 and 3.7.65 imply

$$\dim \mathcal{M}(L^{(1)}, L^{(0)}; [h, w], [h', w']) = \mu_{\lambda^0}([h', w']) - \mu_{\lambda^0}([h, w]) + d_{h'} - 1.$$

Hence (3.7.60.1) follows. (We like to remark that all the dimensions above are the virtual dimensions, that is, by definition, the dimensions in the sense of Kuranishi structure.)

REMARK 3.7.66. Formula (3.7.60.1) determines the integers $\mu([h, w])$ modulo the addition by a constant. These integers depend on the connected component of the path space $\Omega(L^{(0)}, L^{(1)})$. (In the above discussion the connected component was determined by ℓ_0.) This ambiguity of constant will not become an issue as long as we define them to provide the dimension formula (3.7.60.1).

However, we emphasize that we will need to use a canonical choice of $\mu([h, w])$ i.e., an absolute degree (depending only on λ^0) for the construction of bimodule, especially for the study of the orientations of relevant moduli spaces. The above analytical index $\mu_{\lambda_0}^{anal}([h, w])$ given in Definition 3.7.62 will provide one such canonical choice.

For example, in Formula (3.7.2), $\deg y$ (that is $\deg S$ (see (8.8.8)) in our geometric situation) appears in the third term of the right hand side. It does not appear in the second term. If we change $\mu([h,w])$ by overall constant then $\deg S = \deg y$ changes. But $\deg x_{i,j} = \deg P_j^{(i)}$ that appears in the second term does not change. As a consequence, (3.7.2) will no longer hold unless we suitably normalize the choice of integers $\mu([h,w])$. In fact in Chapter 8, the orientations that we put on the moduli space $\mathcal{M}(L^{(1)}, L^{(0)}; [h,w], [h',w'])$ will depend on the choice of the reference Lagrangian path λ^0 and so the signs appearing in the operators $\mathfrak{n}$ depend on λ^0.

For the case of transversal pairs of Lagrangian submanifolds, we stated in Section 2.2 that the analytical index coincides with the topological index $\mu([h,w]; \lambda^0)$ (Definition 2.2.12) which we call the Maslov-Morse index. We next generalize its definition to the Bott-Morse case and prove the coincidence in this generalized context.

Let us consider the situation of Proposition 3.7.59, where the intersection $L^{(0)} \cap L^{(1)}$ is clean. We fix an element $h \in \pi_0(L^{(0)} \cap L^{(1)})$ and let $p_h \in L^{(0)} \cap L^{(1)}$ be its representative.

Let $w : [0,1]^2 \to M$, ℓ_0, λ^0 be a smooth map satisfying (3.7.49). For $(s,0), (s,1) \in \partial[0,1]^2$, we denote

$$\lambda_w(s,i) = T_{w(s,i)}L^{(i)}, \quad i = 0, 1.$$

We now complete these Lagrangian paths into a bundle pair. For this purpose, we need to take a Lagrangian path α_h in $\Lambda(T_{p_h}M)$ such that

$$(3.7.67.1) \qquad \alpha_h(0) = T_{p_h}L^{(0)}, \quad \alpha_h(1) = T_{p_h}L^{(1)}.$$

We choose $\alpha_h(t)$ so that it defines a path of oriented Lagrangian subspace of $T_{p(h)}M$ that extends the given orientations on the Lagrangian subspaces (3.7.67.1). As in Section 2.1, the homotopy class of such paths is not unique and so we will fix a homotopy class of α_h by putting a condition on the path α_h similar to (2.1.4.3).

For this purpose, we also require the following

$$(3.7.67.2) \qquad \alpha_h(t) \cap T_{p_h}L^{(1)} = T_{p_h}L^{(0)} \cap T_{p_h}L^{(1)}$$

for all $0 \le t < 1$. Then if we identify $T_{p_h}M = \mathbb{C}^n = \mathbb{C}^{d_h} \oplus \mathbb{C}^{n-d_h}$ where $\mathbb{C}^{d_h} = T_{p_h}R_h \otimes \mathbb{C}$, we can decompose $\alpha_h(t)$ such that it decompose to

$$(3.7.67.3) \qquad \alpha_h(t) = T_{p_h}R_h \oplus \alpha_h^2(t).$$

We assume that

$$(3.7.67.4) \qquad \alpha_h^2(t) \in U_0(\alpha_h^2(0)) \quad \text{for small } t$$

where the right hand side is as in (2.1.2) applied to $\mathbb{C}^{n-d_h}$.

We define a symplectic bundle pair $(w^*TM, \lambda_{\ell_0, \lambda^0, h})$. (Definition 2.1.13.) Here $\lambda_{\ell_0, \lambda^0, h}$ is $\lambda^0(t)$, $\alpha_h(t)$, or $\lambda_w(s,i)$ at $(0,t), (1,t), (s,i)$, respectively. We then define:

$$(3.7.68) \qquad \mu([h,w]; \lambda^0) := \mu(w^*TM, \lambda_{\ell_0, \lambda^0, h}).$$

We remark that this definition reduces to Definition 2.2.12 in the case when $L^{(0)}$ is transversal to $L^{(1)}$. Now we prove

LEMMA 3.7.69. *Let w be as above and $\partial_{\lambda_{w,\lambda^0};Z_-}$ be the Dolbeault operator satisfying (3.7.61). Then we have*

$$\mu([h,w]; \lambda^0) = \mu_{\lambda^0}^{anal}([h,w])(= \operatorname{Index} \overline{\partial}_{\lambda_{w,\lambda^0};Z_-}).$$

PROOF. We note that under the trivialization $w^*TM \cong [0,1]^2 \times T_{p_h}M$ the Lagrangian subbundle $\lambda_{\ell_0,\lambda^0,h}$ defines a Lagrangian loop, which we still denote by $\lambda_{\ell_0,\lambda^0,h}$. The Maslov index of the loop is invariant under the symplectic transformations and under the homotopy. We will consider homotopy of the loop that is fixed on the boundary $\{(1,t) \mid t \in [0,1]\} \subset \partial[0,1]^2$. We then elongate $[0,1) \times [0,1] \cong \mathbb{R} \times [0,1]$ by a cut-off function $\chi : [0,\infty) \to [0,1]$ as given in Section 2.1. Under this elongation the operator $\overline{\partial}_{\lambda_{w,\lambda^0};Z_-}$ becomes the product type as $\tau \to \infty$ and its index is invariant under the continuous deformations of coefficients and of the boundary conditions fixing the asymptotic condition, by the homotopy invariance of the Fredholm index.

Therefore it suffices to consider the following special case (See Appendix [**Oh99**] for the detailed explanation on this kind of reduction.):

$$T_{p_h}M = \mathbb{C}^n, \qquad T_{p_h}L^{(0)} = \mathbb{R}^n, \qquad T_{p_h}L^{(1)} = \mathbb{R}^{d_h} \oplus \sqrt{-1}\mathbb{R}^{n-d_h}$$

and

$$\alpha_h(t) = \mathbb{R}^{d_h} \oplus e^{\pi\sqrt{-1}t/2}\mathbb{R}^{n-d_h}$$

together with the path $\lambda_{w,\lambda^0} : \partial[0,1]^2 \setminus \{(1,t)\} \to \mathbb{C}^n$ given by

$$\lambda_{w,\lambda^0}(s,0) \equiv \mathbb{R}^n,$$

$$\lambda_{w,\lambda^0}(s,1) \equiv \mathbb{R}^{d_h} \oplus \sqrt{-1}\mathbb{R}^{n-d_h}$$

$$\lambda_{w,\lambda^0}(0,t) = \mathbb{R}^{d_h} \oplus (e^{-(l_1+1/2)\pi\sqrt{-1}t}\mathbb{R} \oplus \cdots \oplus e^{-(l_{n-d_h}+1/2)\pi\sqrt{-1}t}\mathbb{R})$$

with $l_j \in \mathbb{Z}$. Then we have the Lagrangian loop $\lambda_{\ell_0,\lambda^0,h} = \lambda_{w,\lambda^0} \cup \alpha_h$.

Now the index problem splits into one-dimensional problems of the types

$$\begin{cases} \overline{\partial}\zeta = 0 \\ \zeta(\tau,0) \in \mathbb{R}, \quad \zeta(\tau,1) \in \sqrt{-1}\mathbb{R} \\ \zeta(0,t) \in e^{-(l+1/2)\pi\sqrt{-1}t}\mathbb{R} \end{cases}$$

or the one with the boundary condition $\zeta(\partial[0,1]^2) \subset \mathbb{R}$ for the constant Lagrangian path $t \mapsto \mathbb{R}$ arising from the $\mathbb{R}^{d_h}$-factor. For the first type, the corresponding Lagrangian loop $\lambda_{\ell_0,\lambda^0,h}$ defined above defined on $\partial[0,1]^2$ becomes

$$(s,0) \mapsto \mathbb{R}, \quad (0,t) \mapsto e^{-(l+1/2)\pi\sqrt{-1}t}\mathbb{R}$$
$$(s,1) \mapsto \sqrt{-1}\mathbb{R}, \quad (1,t) \mapsto e^{\pi\sqrt{-1}t/2}\mathbb{R}.$$

This loop travelled in the positive direction along $\partial[0,1]^2$ is homotopic to the concatenated Lagrangian path that is $t \in [0,1] \mapsto e^{(l+1/2)\pi\sqrt{-1}(1-t)}\mathbb{R})$ followed by $t \in [0,1] \mapsto e^{\pi\sqrt{-1}t/2}\mathbb{R}$. This concatenated path defines a loop which has the Maslov index $l+1$. Summing-up these, we obtain the Maslov index

$$\mu(\lambda_{\ell_0,\lambda^0,h}) = \sum_{j=1}^{n-d_j}(l_j+1).$$

On the other hand for the corresponding Fredholm index, the one dimensional problem can be explicitly solved by the complex one variable Fourier analysis. For example, the index was computed in (A.12) [**Oh99**] to be $l+1$. On the other hand for the constant path $t \mapsto \mathbb{R}$ coming from $\mathbb{C}^{d_h}$, the obvious constant solutions do not live in the weighted Sobolev space $W^{1,p}_\delta$ whose elements are required to have exponential decay due to the weight factor $e^{\delta|\tau|}$ in the weighted Sobolev space $W_\delta^{1,p}$. And the corresponding cokernel can be easily shown to be zero. This proves

$$\text{Index}\,\overline{\partial}_{\lambda_{w,\lambda^0},Z_-} = \sum_{j=1}^{n-d_j} (l_j + 1).$$

Comparing the last two index formulae we have finished the proof. $\square$

We next discuss orientation (flat) bundle $\Theta_{R_h}^-$ which we need to prove (3.7.60.4). We will discuss this in detail in Section 8.8.

We remark that $\mathcal{M}_{k_1,k_0,(+\infty)}(L^{(1)}, L^{(0)}; [h, w], [h', w']; \vec{P}^{(1)}, S, \vec{P}^{(0)})$ may *not* be orientable in the sense of Kuranishi structure. This is the reason why we need orientation bundle $\Theta_{R_h}^-$. Consider the fiber product

$$\mathcal{M}_{k_1,k_0}(L^{(1)}, L^{(0)}; [h, w], [h', w'])\ {}_{ev}\times_{(f_1^{(1)}\times\cdots\times f_{k_0}^{(0)})}\left(\prod_{j=1}^{k_1} P_j^{(1)} \times \prod_{j=1}^{k_0} P_j^{(0)}\right),$$

which we denote by $\mathcal{M}_{k_1,k_0}(L^{(1)}, L^{(0)}; [h, w], [h', w']; \vec{P}^{(1)}, \vec{P}^{(0)})$. The signs in the A_∞-structure and for the boundary operators in the Floer theory are determined by the orientation bundle of the moduli space

$$\mathcal{M}_{k_1,k_0}(L^{(1)}, L^{(0)}; [h, w], [h', w']; \vec{P}^{(1)}, \vec{P}^{(0)}),$$

and the local systems $\{\Theta_{R_h}^-\}$. More precisely we have the following. Put $O_{R_{h'}} = \det TR_{h'}$.

LEMMA 3.7.70. *The Kuranishi structure of*

$$\mathcal{M}_{k_1,k_0}(L^{(1)}, L^{(0)}; [h, w], [h', w']; \vec{P}^{(1)}, \vec{P}^{(0)})$$

has a tangent bundle. We consider the Kuranishi structure of the moduli space $\mathcal{M}_{k_1,k_0}(L^{(1)}, L^{(0)}; [h, w], [h', w']; \vec{P}^{(1)}, \vec{P}^{(0)})$. *Let* $U_p = V_p/\Gamma_p$ *and* E_p *be as in the definition of Kuranishi structure (Definition A1.1). Then,* $ev_{\pm\infty}$ *extends to* U_p *as submersions* ($ev_{\pm\infty}$ *are weakly submersive). Then there exists an isomorphism*

$$\det(E_p^*) \otimes \det(TV_p) \cong ev_{+\infty}^*\Theta_{R_{h'}}^- \otimes ev_{+\infty}^* O_{R_{h'}} \otimes ev_{-\infty}^*\Theta_{R_h}^-,$$

which is compatible with the isomorphism

$$\det(E_p^*)|_{V_{pq}} \otimes \det(TV_p)|_{V_{pq}} \cong \det(E_q^*) \otimes \det(TV_q)$$

for $q \in \psi_p(s_p^{-1}(0))$ *obtained from the existence of a tangent bundle. Here*

$$ev_{-\infty}\ :\ \mathcal{M}_{k_1,k_0}(L^{(1)}, L^{(0)}; [h, w], [h', w']; \vec{P}^{(1)}, \vec{P}^{(0)}) \to R_h$$
$$ev_{+\infty}\ :\ \mathcal{M}_{k_1,k_0}(L^{(1)}, L^{(0)}; [h, w], [h', w']; \vec{P}^{(1)}, \vec{P}^{(0)}) \to R_{h'}$$

are defined similarly as before.

Note that $\det(E_p^*) \otimes \det(TV_p)$ is the orientation bundle

$$O_{\mathcal{M}_{k_1,k_0}(L^{(1)}, L^{(0)};[h,w],[h',w'];\vec{P}^{(1)},\vec{P}^{(0)})}$$

of the space $\mathcal{M}_{k_1,k_0}(L^{(1)}, L^{(0)}; [h,w], [h',w']; \vec{P}^{(1)}, \vec{P}^{(0)})$ in the sense of Kuranishi structure. Moreover, since M is oriented, it follows that there is a canonical isomorphism as $\{\pm 1\}$-flat bundles

$$\Theta_{R_{h'}}^+ \cong O_{R_{h'}} \otimes \Theta_{R_{h'}}^-.$$

A detailed argument will be given in Section 8.8 (Proposition 8.8.6, Definition 8.8.11). (In Section 8.8, we study the fiber product of $\mathcal{M}(L^{(1)}, L^{(0)}; [h,w], [h',w'])$ and the singular simplex S with coefficients in $O_{R_h} \otimes \Theta_{R_h}^-$. The orientation on $\mathcal{M}_{k_1,k_0,(+\infty)}(L^{(1)}, L^{(0)}; [h,w], S, [h',w'])$ is given in Definition 8.8.11. We can also interpret this moduli space as the fiber product of $\mathcal{M}_{k_1,k_0}(L^{(1)}, L^{(0)}; [h,w], [h',w'])$ and S by an appropriate sign change rule concerning the exchange of factors. Then we can formulate the result as in Lemma 3.7.70.)

We use Lemma 3.7.70 to study the orientation in (3.7.60.4) as follows. See the proof of Proposition 8.8.7 for detail. Let $(\phi : S \to R_h) \in \mathcal{X}_1(R_h)$ equipped with a flat section s of $O_{R_h} \otimes \Theta_{R_h}^- \otimes O_S$. Here $O_S = \det TS$. We find that

$$\det(E_p^*) \otimes \det(T(V_p \times_{R_h} S)) \cong (-1)^{r_h} ev_{+\infty}^* \Theta_{R_{h'}}^+ \otimes ev_{-\infty}^* \Theta_{R_h}^- \otimes O_{R_h} \otimes O_S.$$

Here $r_h = \dim R_h$. (See also the proof of Proposition 8.8.7 for the reason why the factor $(-1)^{r_h}$ appears.) Thus we have

$$ev_{+\infty}^* \Theta_{R_{h'}}^+ \otimes (\det E_p^*) \otimes \det(T(V_p \times_{R_h} S))$$
$$\cong (-1)^{r_h \cdot (\mu(h,w)+1)} ev_{-\infty}^* (O_{R_h} \otimes \Theta_{R_h}^-) \otimes O_S.$$

Hence the flat section s of $\phi^*(O_{R_h} \otimes \Theta_{R_h}^-) \otimes O_S$ induces a flat section of $ev_{+\infty}^* \Theta_{R_{h'}}^+ \otimes (\det E_p^*) \otimes \det(T(V_p \times_{R_h} S))$. This implies that

$$((\mathfrak{s}_{[h,w],[h',w'],\vec{P}^{(1)},S,\vec{P}^{(0)}})^{-1}(0), ev_{+\infty})$$

is a chain in $R_{h'}$ with coefficients in $O_{R_{h'}} \otimes \Theta_{R_{h'}}^- \cong \Theta_{R_{h'}}^+$. This is the orientation part of the proof of (3.7.60.4).

Proposition 3.7.59 is now proved modulo the points deferred to later chapters.□

We now put

$$\mathcal{M}_{k_1,k_0,(+\infty)}(L^{(1)}, L^{(0)}; [h,w], [h',w']; \vec{P}^{(1)}, S, \vec{P}^{(0)})^{\mathfrak{s}}$$
$$:= ((\mathfrak{s}_{[h,w],[h',w'],\vec{P}^{(1)},S,\vec{P}^{(0)}})^{-1}(0), ev_{+\infty}).$$

We refer to Definition 8.8.11 for the orientation of the above moduli space. (We need to take triangulation and an order of its vertices to regard the virtual fundamental chain (the right hand side) as a singular chain. See Definition A1.28.)

DEFINITION 3.7.71. For $S \in \mathcal{X}_1(R_h)$ we write $S \otimes [h,w]$ for the corresponding element in $C(L^{(0)}, \mathbb{Q})$. Let

$$T^{\lambda_i^{(0)}} e^{\mu_i^{(0)}} P_i^{(0)} \in C(L^{(0)}, \Lambda_{0,nov}), \quad T^{\lambda_i^{(1)}} e^{\mu_i^{(1)}} P_i^{(1)} \in C(L^{(1)}, \Lambda_{0,nov})$$

and

$$T^\lambda e^\mu [S; h, w] \in C(R_h; \Theta_{R_h}^-) \otimes \Lambda_{0,nov}.$$

We define $\mathfrak{n}_{k_1,k_0}$ by

$$\mathfrak{n}_{k_1,k_0}(T^{\lambda_1^{(1)}} e^{\mu_1^{(1)}} P_1^{(1)} \otimes \cdots \otimes T^{\lambda_{k_1}^{(1)}} e^{\mu_{k_1}^{(1)}} P_{k_1}^{(1)} \otimes T^\lambda e^\mu (S \otimes [h,w])$$

$$\otimes T^{\lambda_1^{(0)}} e^{\mu_1^{(0)}} P_1^{(0)} \otimes \cdots \otimes T^{\lambda_{k_0}^{(0)}} e^{\mu_{k_0}^{(0)}} P_{k_0}^{(0)})$$

$$= \sum_{[h',w']} T^{\lambda'} e^{\mu'} \mathcal{M}_{k_1,k_0,(+\infty)}(L^{(1)}, L^{(0)}; [h,w], [h',w']; \vec{P}^{(1)}, S, \vec{P}^{(0)})^\mathfrak{s} \otimes [h',w'],$$

where

$$\lambda' = \sum_{i=1}^{k_0} \lambda_i^{(0)} + \lambda + \sum_{i=1}^{k_1} \lambda_i^{(1)}, \quad \mu' = \sum_{i=1}^{k_0} \mu_i^{(0)} + \mu + \sum_{i=1}^{k_1} \mu_i^{(1)}.$$

In case $(k_1, k_0) \neq (0,0)$. In case $(k_1, k_0) = (0,0)$ we add extra term

$$(-1)^{d_h + \mu([h,w])} \partial S \otimes [h,w].$$

We remark that the sum in Definition 3.7.71 contains the case when $[h,w] = [h',w'], \lambda = \lambda', \mu = \mu', (k_1, k_0) \neq (0,0)$. In such a case the corresponding term is

$$\overline{\mathfrak{m}}_{k_1+1+k_0}((P_1^{(1)} \cap R_h), \cdots, (P_{k_1}^{(1)} \cap R_h), S, (P_1^{(0)} \cap R_h), \cdots, (P_{k_0}^{(0)} \cap R_h))$$

where $\overline{\mathfrak{m}}_{k_1+1+k_0}$ is an A_∞ deformation of the cup product on R_h. In fact the moduli space we use to define such a term consists of constant maps to R_h. We also remark that we can choose our countable set of chains on $L^{(0)}$, $L^{(1)}$ so that they are transversal to R_h. (Otherwise the above equality does not hold. However for the transversality of our moduli space we do not need to choose so.)

We also remarks that $\deg S = d_h - \dim S$, $\deg P_j^{(i)} = n - \dim P_j^{(i)}$. Hence (3.7.60.1) implies

$$d_{h'} - \dim \mathcal{M}_{k_1,k_0,(+\infty)}(L^{(1)}, L^{(0)}; [h,w], [h',w']; \vec{P}^{(1)}, S, \vec{P}^{(0)})^\mathfrak{s}$$

$$= \sum \deg' P_j^{(0)} + \sum \deg' P_j^{(1)} + \mu([h,w]) - \mu([h',w']) + \deg S + 1.$$

Hence $\mathfrak{n}_{k_1,k_0}$ increase the (shifted) degree by 1.

Now we can show the following.

THEOREM 3.7.72. *The* $\mathfrak{n}_{k_1,k_0}$ *above defines a left* $(C(L^{(1)}, \Lambda_{0,nov}), \mathfrak{m}^{(1)})$ *and right* $(C(L^{(0)}, \Lambda_{0,nov}), \mathfrak{m}^{(0)})$ *filtered* A_∞ *bimodule structure on* $C(L^{(1)}, L^{(0)}; \Lambda_{0,nov})$.

It is $G(L^{(0)}, L^{(1)})$-*gapped. Furthermore the pair of the homotopy units* $\{\mathbf{e}_1, \mathbf{e}_0\}$ *of* $(C(L^{(1)}; \Lambda_{0,nov}), \mathfrak{m}^{(1)})$ *and* $(C(L^{(0)}; \Lambda_{0,nov}), \mathfrak{m}^{(0)})$ *acts as a homotopy unit.*

The proof is a straight-forward generalization of the proof of Theorem 3.7.21 in Subsection 3.7.4 and hence is omitted.

Now we assume that the A_∞ algebras

$$(C(L^{(0)}, \Lambda_{0,nov}), \mathfrak{m}^{(0)}) \quad \text{and} \quad (C(L^{(1)}, \Lambda_{0,nov}), \mathfrak{m}^{(1)})$$

are unobstructed. Let b_0 and b_1 be bounding cochains of $(C(L^{(0)}; \Lambda_{0,nov}), \mathfrak{m}^{(0)})$ and $(C(L^{(1)}; \Lambda_{0,nov}), \mathfrak{m}^{(1)})$ respectively. Then by Lemma 3.7.14 and Theorem 3.7.72 we obtain a cochain complex

(3.7.73) $$(C(L^{(1)}, L^{(0)}; \Lambda_{0,nov}), \delta_{b_1,b_0})$$

by the same way as in Subsection 3.7.4.

DEFINITION 3.7.74. We call the cohomology of (3.7.73) the *Floer cohomology deformed by* b_0, b_1 and write it as $HF((L^{(1)}, b_1), (L^{(0)}, b_0); \Lambda_{0,nov})$.

This cochain complex (3.7.73) coincides with the one defined in Subsection 2.1.2 if $L^{(0)}$ is transverse to $L^{(1)}$. When $L^{(0)} = L^{(1)}$ we have the following.

PROPOSITION 3.7.75. *Assume that* $L = L^{(0)} = L^{(1)}$. *We also assume that* J_t *is independent of* t. *Then, the filtered* A_∞ *bimodule defined in Theorem* 3.7.72 *can be taken to be the same as the one we obtain from Example* 3.7.6.

PROOF. Note that there is only one component $L^{(1)} \cap L^{(0)}$, which is L. The orientability of L and M implies that the local system Θ_L^- is trivial in this case. Then, by inspecting the proofs, we may take $\mathcal{X}_1(R_h) = \mathcal{X}_1(L)$, where $\mathcal{X}_1(L)$ is as in Section 3.5 and $\mathcal{X}_1(R_h)$ is as in Proposition 3.7.55. Moreover we can take

$$
(3.7.76) \qquad \begin{aligned} \mathcal{M}_{k_1, k_0, (+\infty)} & (L^{(1)}, L^{(0)}; [h, w], [h, w']; \vec{P}^{(1)}, S, \vec{P}^{(0)}) \\ & = \mathcal{M}_{k_1 + k_0 + 1}(L; \beta; \vec{P}^{(1)}, S, \vec{P}^{(0)}), \end{aligned}
$$

where the left hand side is an in Proposition 3.7.55 and the right hand side is as in Proposition 3.7.59 and $w' = w \# \beta$. Then we can take multisections in Proposition 3.5.2 which are identified with those in Proposition 3.5.2 via (3.7.76). The equality

$$
\mathfrak{n}_{k_1, k_0}(\mathbf{x} \otimes y \otimes \mathbf{z}) = \mathfrak{m}_{k_1 + k_0 + 1}(\mathbf{x}, y, \mathbf{z})
$$

now follows from construction. Our conventions and definitions concerning the orientation ensure that the orientations on the both hand sides of (3.7.76) indeed coincide. See Sections 8.5 and 8.8. Thus the above equality holds with signs. □

Thus Proposition 3.7.75 yields that

$$
(3.7.77) \qquad HF(L, b; \Lambda_{0,nov}) \cong HF((L, b), (L, b), \Lambda_{0,nov}),
$$

where the left hand side is defined by Definition 3.6.11 or Definition 3.6.33 (1) (weakly unobstructed case) from the filtered A_∞ algebra $(C(L; \Lambda_{0,nov}), \mathfrak{m})$ and the right hand side is defined from the filtered A_∞ bimodule as in this subsection. Furthermore, Proposition 3.7.75 together with independence of

$$
HF((L^{(1)}, b_1), (L^{(0)}, b_0); \Lambda_{nov}) := HF((L^{(1)}, b_1), (L^{(0)}, b_0); \Lambda_{0,nov}) \otimes_{\Lambda_{0,nov}} \Lambda_{nov}
$$

under the Hamiltonian isotopy (which we prove as Theorem 5.3.14 and Theorem 4.1.5 in Section 5.3) enable us to use spectral sequence (which we establish in Chapter 6) to study Floer cohomology of L and its Hamiltonian deformation. In particular, if $L^{(1)} = \psi^1(L^{(0)})$ is a Hamiltonian deformation of $L^{(0)}$, we will see that

$$
(3.7.78) \qquad HF(L, b; \Lambda_{nov}) \cong HF((\psi^1(L), \psi_*^1(b)), (L, b), \Lambda_{nov}).
$$

See examples in the next subsection.

3.7.6. Examples. In this subsection, we give simple but instructive examples of calculations of Floer cohomology and explain how we can geometrically see the relation between the existence of Floer cohomology and the potential function $\mathfrak{PO}$ discussed in Subsections 3.6.3 and 3.7.3. Moreover we will exhibit how the choice of the coefficient rings $\Lambda_{0,nov}$ and Λ_{nov} affects the invariance of or the dependence of Floer cohomology under the Hamiltonian isotopy. More examples are given in [**FOOO08I,08II,09I,09II**].

Consider an embedded circle L in $S^2 \simeq \mathbb{C}P^1$. There are two simple holomorphic discs bounding the circle. We denote them by D_u and D_ℓ. (Actually there are multiple covers of them. However we can show that they do not contribute to the Floer cohomology by the degree reason.) In case they have the same area, e.g., when L is an equator, they belong to the same class β in $\Pi(L) = \Pi(S^2; L) \cong \mathbb{Z}$. See Definition 2.4.17 for the notation. Otherwise they belong to two different classes in $\Pi(S^2; L) \cong \mathbb{Z} \oplus \mathbb{Z}$. We denote the classes by β_u and β_ℓ respectively. It is easy to see that

(3.7.79) $$\mu_L(\beta) = \mu_L(\beta_u) = \mu_L(\beta_\ell) = 2.$$

We write by S^1_{eq} for the circle such that $\Pi(S^1_{eq}) = \mathbb{Z}$ and S^1_{neq} for the circle such that $\Pi(S^1_{neq}) = \mathbb{Z} \oplus \mathbb{Z}$. From (3.7.79), we note that any Lagrangian circle L in S^2 is weakly unobstructed. The obstruction classes live only in $H^0(L; \mathbb{Q})$.

Case I. *The case where $L^{(1)}$ is a Hamiltonian deformation of $L^{(0)}$.*

We denote by ψ_1 a Hamiltonian isotopy such that $L^{(1)} = \psi_1(L^{(0)})$.

Case I-a. *The case for $L^{(0)} = S^1_{eq}$.*

Firstly, we calculate the first obstruction class $[o_1(S^1_{eq})]$. As we mentioned above, we have two holomorphic discs D_u and D_ℓ with the same area. There is an anti-symplectic involution τ on S^2 such that τ fixes S^1_{eq} and $\tau(D_u) = D_\ell$. When we define the obstruction class, we consider both $\mathcal{M}_1(S^1_{eq}; \beta)$ and $\mathcal{M}_1(S^1_{eq}; \tau_*\beta)$ which are the moduli spaces of pseudo-holomorphic discs with one marked point. Therefore, to calculate the obstruction class precisely, we need to analyze how τ respects the orientation on the moduli spaces of pseudo-holomorphic discs with marked points. They are studied in [**FOOO09I**]. There we find that $\tau_* : \mathcal{M}_1(S^1_{eq}; \beta) \to \mathcal{M}_1(S^1_{eq}; \tau_*\beta)$ preserves the orientation, because of the fact that $\mu_L(\beta) = 2$ and the number of the marked point is one. Therefore the two holomorphic discs D_u and D_ℓ have the same contribution to the obstruction class $[o_1(S^1_{eq})] = [o(S^1_{eq}; \overline{\beta})]$. (Here $\overline{\beta} = [\beta] = [\tau_*\beta] \in \Pi(S^1_{eq})$.) Hence we have

(3.7.80) $$[o(S^1_{eq}; \overline{\beta})] = 2[S^1_{eq}] \quad \text{in} \quad H^0(S^1; \mathbb{Q}).$$

Secondly, since there is no holomorphic discs with negative Maslov indices (in fact this is the monotone case), the Floer cohomology can be defined. (Namely $S^1_{eq} \subset S^2$ is weakly unobstructed.) Moreover 0 is an element of $\mathcal{M}_{\text{weak}}(S^1_{eq})$. Hereafter we drop 0 from the notation in the rest of this subsection.

Thirdly, we calculate $HF(L^{(0)}, L^{(0)}; \Lambda_{nov})$ using the Bott-Morse theory. (Here $L^{(0)} = S^1_{eq}$.) The boundary map $\mathfrak{m}_{1,\beta}$ for $\beta \neq 0$ is induced by the moduli space $\mathcal{M}_2(L^{(0)}; \beta; J)$. According to the results from [**FOOO09I**] we obtain

$$ev_*([\mathcal{M}_2(L^{(0)}; \beta; J)]) = -ev_*([\mathcal{M}_2(L^{(0)}; \tau_*\beta; J)]).$$

since in this case the number of the marked points is two so τ_* is orientation *reversing*. Therefore we have

(3.7.81) $$HF(L^{(0)}, L^{(0)}; \Lambda_{0,nov}) \cong \Lambda_{0,nov} \oplus \Lambda_{0,nov}.$$

(Alternatively we can say that the spectral sequence which will be constructed in Chapter 6 degenerates at E_2 level.)

Let us compare (3.7.81) with $HF(L^{(1)}, L^{(0)}; \Lambda_{nov})$ where $L^{(1)} = \psi_1(L^{(0)})$ is Hamiltonian isotopic to $L^{(0)}$. Let us take a Hamiltonian isotopy such that $\psi_1(L^{(0)}) \cap L^{(0)} = \{p, q\}$. (Note that $\#(\psi_1(S_{eq}^1) \cap S_{eq}^1) \geq 2$, in general.) The moduli space of connecting orbits from p to q (or q to p) with minimal area has two components, respectively.

On the other hand, the invariance of Floer cohomology of Hamiltonian isotopy and by (3.7.81), we find that

$$(3.7.82.1) \qquad HF(\psi_1(S_{eq}^1), S_{eq}^1; \Lambda_{nov}) \cong \Lambda_{nov} \oplus \Lambda_{nov}.$$

It follows that the two have different contribution cancels each other. (We can also prove it directly by comparing it with the moduli space of gradient trajectories of a Morse function on $L^{(0)} = S^1$ with two critical points $\{p, q\}$.) The contribution of the pseudo-holomorphic strip with non-minimal energy is 0 by degree reason. Thus we have

$$(3.7.82.2) \qquad HF(\psi_1(S_{eq}^1), S_{eq}^1; \Lambda_{0,nov}) \cong \Lambda_{0,nov} \oplus \Lambda_{0,nov}.$$

Case I-b. *The case for* $L^{(0)} = S_{neq}^1$.

In this case, the two holomorphic discs D_u and D_ℓ which bound $L^{(0)} = S_{neq}^1$ have different symplectic areas. We have $[o(S_{neq}^1; \beta_u)]$ and $[o(S_{neq}^1; \beta_\ell)]$ that are obstruction classes corresponding to β_u and β_ℓ which generate $\Pi(S^2; S_{neq}^1) \cong \mathbb{Z} \oplus \mathbb{Z}$. We can find that

$$(3.7.83) \qquad [o(S_{neq}^1; \beta_u)] = [o(S_{neq}^1; \beta_\ell)] = [S_{neq}^1] \in H^0(S^1; \mathbb{Q}).$$

Let us calculate the Floer cohomology $HF(\psi_1(S_{neq}^1), S_{neq}^1)$. We like to emphasize that, in general, the Floer cohomology over $\Lambda_{0,nov}$ *depends* on the Hamiltonian diffeomorphism ψ_1 but one over Λ_{nov} is always *independent* of the Hamiltonian diffeomorphism. This point will be proved as Theorem 5.3.14 in Section 5.3. Here we will elaborate the phenomena by this example.

We first note that there exists a large Hamiltonian isotopy $\{\psi_t\}_{0 \leq t \leq 1}$ with $\psi_1(S_{neq}^1) \cap S_{neq}^1 = \emptyset$. In this case, we have

$$HF(\psi_1(S_{neq}^1), S_{neq}^1; \Lambda_{0,nov}) = 0.$$

Obviously, it also vanishes over Λ_{nov}.

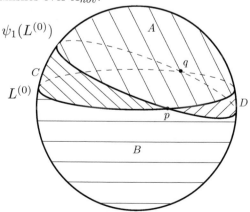

Figure 3.7.10

On the other hand, let us consider the case $\psi_1(L^{(0)}) \cap L^{(0)} = \{p, q\}$. In this case, the complement $\mathbb{C}P^1 \setminus (\psi_1(L^{(0)}) \cup L^{(0)})$ consists of 4 components. We denote their symplectic areas by A, B, C and D, respectively. Since ψ_1 is a Hamiltonian diffeomorphism, we have $C = D$ or $A = B$. (Since $L^{(0)}$ is not an equator, the case that $A = B$ and $C = D$ is not our case.) See Figure 3.7.10.

We can find that the orientation on the moduli space of the connecting orbit form p to q (resp. from q to p) with the area A (resp. C) is opposite to one corresponding to having the area B (resp. D). We can prove this using the fact that the orientation of the moduli space appearing here is the same as the one in I-a. (Alternatively, we can use the reduction to the Morse (Novikov) theory.) When $C = D$, the two connecting orbits from p to q are in different orbits under the deck transformation $\Pi(S^2; S^1_{neq})$, while those from q to p cancels each other. The case $A = B$ is similar. Therefore, the coboundary operator δ is given by

(3.7.84.1) $[p] \mapsto T^A[q] - T^B[q], \qquad [q] \mapsto 0,$

or

(3.7.84.2) $[p] \mapsto 0, \qquad [q] \mapsto T^C[p]e - T^D[p]e.$

(Here we are considering the degree of $[q]$ is one bigger than that of $[p]$ and recall that the indeterminate e has degree 2 in our convention.) The contribution to the coboundary operator from the other components of the moduli space of pseudo-holomorphic discs vanish by degree reason. Hence we obtain $\delta \circ \delta = 0$. So the Floer cohomology $HF(\psi_1(S^1_{neq}), S^1_{neq}; \Lambda_{0,nov})$ can be also defined, but it is not zero for this case. This is a *torsion group*. (In fact it is $\Lambda_{0,nov}/T^C\Lambda_{0,nov}$ if $C < D$.) This example shows that $HF(\psi_1(S^1_{neq}), S^1_{neq}; \Lambda_{0,nov})$ actually depends on the Hamiltonian diffeomorphism. However, when we consider the Floer cohomology over Λ_{nov}, we find that

(3.7.85) $HF(\psi_1(S^1_{neq}), S^1_{neq}; \Lambda_{nov}) = 0,$

because $T^A - T^B$ is invertible in Λ_{nov} in the case $C = D$ and $T^C - T^D$ is invertible in Λ_{nov} in the case $A = B$. In fact, if $A < B$, then

$$(T^A - T^B)^{-1} = T^{-A}(1 - T^{B-A})^{-1} = T^{-A} \sum_{j=0}^{\infty} T^{(B-A)j}.$$

This result coincides with the Floer cohomology for the case $\psi_1(S^1_{neq}) \cap S^1_{neq} = \emptyset$ over Λ_{nov}.

Case II. *The case where $L^{(1)}$ is not a Hamiltonian deformation of $L^{(0)}$.*

Let us consider the case $L^{(1)} \cap L^{(0)} = \{p, q\}$. As in the Case I-b, we can find that the coboundary operator should be

$$[p] \mapsto T^A[q] - T^B[q], \qquad [q] \mapsto T^C[p]e - T^D[p]e.$$

But since $L^{(1)}$ is not a Hamiltonian deformation of $L^{(0)}$, $A \neq B$ and $C \neq D$ in this case. Therefore we have $\delta \circ \delta \neq 0$ and hence Floer cohomology is not defined.

REMARK 3.7.86. In Subsections 3.6.1 (unobstructed case) and in Subsections 3.6.3 (weakly unobstructed case), we defined the Floer cohomology $HF(L, b; \Lambda_{0,nov})$ (see Definition 3.6.11 and Definition 3.6.33 (1)). On the other hand, in Definition 3.7.74 Subsection 3.7.5, we defined $HF((L, b), (L, b); \Lambda_{0,nov})$, as a special case of the Floer cohomology for a pair of Lagrangian submanifolds in the Bott-Morse situation. Then Proposition 3.7.75 says that they are isomorphic over $\Lambda_{0,nov}$. However, as we saw in the above example, they are *not* isomorphic over $\Lambda_{0,nov}$ in general to the Floer cohomology of the pair $((L, b), (\psi(L), \psi_*(b))$ for a Hamiltonian diffeomorphism $\psi \neq id$, while they are isomorphic over Λ_{nov}. This will be proved as Theorem 4.1.5 in Section 5.3 Chapter 5. Moreover, the dependence of the Floer cohomology $HF((\psi(L), \psi_*(b)), (L, b); \Lambda_{0,nov})$ on ψ appears in the torsion parts of the Floer cohomology. In Subsection 6.5.3, we will study the torsion part and use this in relation to the study of Hofer's distance of some Hamiltonian isotopies.

3.7.7. The multiplicative structure on Floer cohomology. In this subsection, we prove some purely algebraic results which will be used to prove (B.2) in Theorem B and (G.5) in Theorem G in Subsection 3.8.10.

PROPOSITION 3.7.87. (1) *Let C be a filtered A_∞ algebra and $b_i \in \widehat{\mathcal{M}}(C)$, then we have an operation*

$$(3.7.88) \qquad \mathfrak{m}_2 : H(C, \delta_{b_0,b_1}) \otimes H(C, \delta_{b_1,b_2}) \to H(C, \delta_{b_0,b_2})$$

which is associative up to the sign. Namely

$$(3.7.89) \qquad \mathfrak{m}_2(\mathfrak{m}_2(x, y), z) = (-1)^{\deg' x} \mathfrak{m}_2(x, \mathfrak{m}_2(y, z)).$$

(2) *If C is unital then the same conclusion holds for $b_i \in \widehat{\mathcal{M}}_{\text{weak}}(C)$ with $\mathfrak{PO}(b_1) = \mathfrak{PO}(b_0)$.*

PROOF. Let $x_{ij} \in C$. We put

$$(3.7.90) \qquad \tilde{\mathfrak{m}}_2(x_{ij}, x_{jk}) = \mathfrak{m}(e^{b_i}, x_{ij}, e^{b_j}, x_{jk}, e^{b_k}).$$

It is easy to see from A_∞ formula that

$$(3.7.91) \qquad \begin{aligned} &- (\delta_{b_i,b_k} \circ \tilde{\mathfrak{m}}_2)(x_{ij}, x_{ik}) \\ &= \tilde{\mathfrak{m}}_2(\delta_{b_i,b_j} x_{ij}, x_{jk}) + (-1)^{\deg' x_{ij}} \tilde{\mathfrak{m}}_2(x_{ij}, \delta_{b_j,b_k} x_{jk}). \end{aligned}$$

Therefore (3.7.90) induces (3.7.88). We next put

$$\tilde{\mathfrak{m}}_3(x_{hi}, x_{ij}, x_{jk}) = \mathfrak{m}(e^{b_h}, x_{hi}, e^{b_i}, x_{ij}, e^{b_j}, x_{jk}, e^{b_k}).$$

Then we can prove the following formula if $\delta_{b_u,b_v}(x_{uv}) = 0$.

$$\begin{aligned} -(\delta_{b_h,b_k} \circ \tilde{\mathfrak{m}}_3)(x_{hi}, x_{ij}, x_{ik}) = &\tilde{\mathfrak{m}}_2(\tilde{\mathfrak{m}}_2(x_{hi}, x_{ij}), x_{jk}) \\ &+ (-1)^{\deg' x_{ij}} \tilde{\mathfrak{m}}_2(x_{hi}, \tilde{\mathfrak{m}}_2(x_{ij}, x_{jk})). \end{aligned}$$

(3.7.89) follows from this. The proof of 'weak' version is the same. $\qquad\square$

We remark that (3.7.89) induces product on $H(C, \delta_{b,b})$ defined by

$$(3.7.92) \qquad x \cup y = (-1)^{\deg x(\deg y+1)} \mathfrak{m}_2(x, y).$$

PROPOSITION 3.7.93. (1) *Let C_1, C_0 be the filtered A_∞ algebra and D is be a (C_1, C_0) filtered A_∞ bimodule. Let $b_i \in \widehat{\mathcal{M}}(C_i)$. Then $H(D, \delta_{b_1, b_0})$ is a $H(C, \delta_{b_1, b_1})$-$H(C, \delta_{b_0, b_0})$ bimodule.*

(2) If C_i are unital and D is unital then the same holds for $b_i \in \widehat{\mathcal{M}}_{\text{weak}}(C_i)$ with $\mathfrak{PO}(b_1) = \mathfrak{PO}(b_0)$.

PROOF. We define $\tilde{n}_{1,0} : C_1 \otimes D \to D$ by $\tilde{n}_{1,0}(x, v) = \mathfrak{n}(e^{b_1} x e^{b_1}, v, e^{b_0})$. It is easy to see that $\tilde{n}_{1,0}$ induces a left $H(C, \delta_{b_1, b_1})$ module structure on $H(D, \delta_{b_1, b_0})$. The other part of the proof is similar. $\qquad\square$

3.8. Inserting marked points in the interior

In this section, we will construct the operators $\mathfrak{p}, \mathfrak{q}$, and $\mathfrak{r}$ considering the moduli spaces of pseudo-holomorphic discs with some marked points in the interior. They are useful to study the relationship of the obstruction class or of the Floer cohomology to the homomorphism $i^* : H^k(M) \to H^k(L)$ and the Gysin homomorphism $i_! : H^k(L) \to H^{n+k}(M)$. The results in this section will be also used to study the differential in the spectral sequence to be constructed in Chapter 6 and in the proofs of the Theorems H, I.

3.8.1. The operator $\mathfrak{p}$. We recall that the Gysin homomorphism is defined by
$$i_! = PD_M \circ i_* \circ PD_L \;:\; H^k(L) \to H^{n+k}(M),$$
where PD's are the Poincaré duality maps in M and L, and $i : L \to M$ is the natural inclusion.

Let $(C(L; \Lambda_{0,nov}), \mathfrak{m})$ be the filtered A_∞ algebra constructed by Theorem 3.5.11 and $(S^*(M; \mathbb{Z}), \delta)$ be the smooth singular chain complex of M. Identifying a codimension k chain as a degree k cochain, we regard $S^*(M; \mathbb{Z})$ as a cochain complex. We put $S^*(M; R) = S^*(M; \mathbb{Z}) \otimes R$ where R is a commutative ring. The Gysin homomorphism is induced by the cochain map $i_! : S^k(L; R) \to S^{k+n}(M; R)$, given by $i_!(|P|, f) = (|P|, i \circ f)$.

To precisely state the main technical result (Theorem 3.8.9), we need to recall a piece of Gromov-Witten theory. Let $0 \neq \tilde{\beta} \in \pi_2(M)$. We consider the moduli space $\widetilde{\mathcal{M}}_{0,2}^{\text{reg}}(M; \tilde{\beta})$ consisting of the set of all $((S^2, (z_0^+, z_1^+)), w)$ where $w : S^2 \to M$ is a pseudo-holomorphic map whose homotopy class is $\tilde{\beta}$ and (z_0^+, z_1^+) is a pair of distinct points on S^2. We divide $\mathcal{M}_{0,2}(M; \tilde{\beta})$ by the action of $PSL(2; \mathbb{C})$ and compactify the quotient via the stable maps. Let us denote by $\mathcal{M}_{0,2}(M; \tilde{\beta})$ the resulting moduli space. The suffix 0 in the notation $\mathcal{M}_{0,2}(M; \tilde{\beta})$ stands for the genus of the domain of pseudo-holomorphic maps. We have two evaluation maps at the marked points z_1^+, z_0^+:
$$ev = (ev_1, ev_0) : \mathcal{M}_{0,2}(M; \tilde{\beta}) \to M^2.$$

We consider a chain

(3.8.1) $$ev_{0*}(\mathcal{M}_{0,2}(M; \tilde{\beta})_{ev_1} \times_M L)$$

in M. it has a Kuranishi structure as constructed in [**FuOn99II**]. We denote its virtual fundamental chain by
$$GW_{0,1}(M; \tilde{\beta})(L) \in S^*(M; \mathbb{Q}).$$

Here the degree $*$ (= the codimension) is calculated by $* = n - 2c_1(M)[\tilde\beta] + 2$. Precisely speaking, we fix a triangulation on $\mathcal{M}_{0,2}(M;\tilde\beta)_{ev_1} \times_M L$ and an order of the vertices to identify (3.8.1) as a smooth singular chain in M. (See Definition A1.28.)

We then define a $\Lambda_{0,nov}$-cochain

$$(3.8.2) \quad GW_{0,1}(M)(L) = \sum_{\tilde\beta} T^{\omega[\tilde\beta]} e^{c_1(M)[\tilde\beta]} GW_{0,1}(M;\tilde\beta)(L) \in S^{n+2}(M;\Lambda_{0,nov}).$$

We next introduce a *cyclic bar complex* $B_k^{cyc}C[1]$. Let C be a filtered A_∞ algebra and define an automorphism

$$\mathrm{cyc} : B_k C[1] \to B_k C[1]$$

by

$$\mathrm{cyc}(x_1 \otimes \cdots \otimes x_k) = (-1)^{\deg' x_k \times (\sum_{i=1}^{k-1} \deg' x_i)} x_k \otimes x_1 \otimes \cdots \otimes x_{k-1}.$$

It induces a $\mathbb{Z}_k$ action on $B_k C[1]$. Let $B_k^{cyc}C[1]$ be the invariant set of cyc and $B^{cyc}C[1] = \widehat{\bigoplus}_k B_k^{cyc}C[1]$ the completed direct sum of them.

REMARK 3.8.3. The notion of the cyclic bar complex which sometimes appear in the literature (for example in [**GeJo90**]) is the symmetrization with respect to the symmetric group $\mathfrak{S}_k$ acting on $B_k C[1]$. Here we symmetrize it only by the cyclic group $\mathbb{Z}_k$. We denote the symmetrization by $\mathfrak{S}_k$ action by $E_k C$. (See Definition 3.8.30.)

LEMMA & DEFINITION 3.8.4. *Let $(C,\mathfrak{m})$ be an A_∞ algebra and $(BC[1],\widehat{d})$ the associated bar complex. Then $B^{cyc}C[1]$ is preserved under the map $\widehat{d}$. Thus we define*

$$\widehat{d}^{cyc} := \widehat{d}|_{B^{cyc}C[1]}.$$

PROOF. Let $x_1 \otimes \cdots \otimes x_k \in B_k C[1]$ and consider the element

$$(3.8.5) \qquad [x_1 \otimes \cdots \otimes x_k] = \sum_{i=1}^k \mathrm{cyc}^i(x_1 \otimes \cdots \otimes x_k) \in B_k^{cyc}C[1].$$

Then we have

$$\widehat{d}([x_1 \otimes \cdots \otimes x_k])$$

$$(3.8.6) \quad = \sum_{i \le j+1} \sum_{\ell=1}^k (-1)^{\deg' x_\ell + \cdots + \deg' x_{\ell+i-2} + \alpha_\ell}$$

$$x_\ell \otimes \cdots \otimes \mathfrak{m}_{j-i+1}(x_{\ell+i-1}, \cdots, x_{\ell+j-1}) \otimes \cdots \otimes x_{\ell-1},$$

where $\alpha_\ell = \sum_{a<\ell\le b} \deg' x_a \deg' x_b$. Here we use the convention $x_{k+m} = x_m$. It is easy to check that the right hand side of (3.8.6) is in $B^{cyc}C[1]$.

If $\mathbb{Q} \subseteq R$, then since elements of the form $[x_1 \otimes \cdots \otimes x_k]$ span $B_k^{cyc}C[1]$, we have finished the proof of Lemma 3.8.4.

For general R, the elements of the form $[x_1 \otimes \cdots \otimes x_k]$ do not span $B_k^{cyc}C[1]$. So we need to proceed differently. It is enough to consider the case when the coefficient is $\mathbb{Z}$. Let us assume

$$x_1 \otimes \cdots \otimes x_k = \underbrace{\mathbf{x} \otimes \cdots \otimes \mathbf{x}}_{m' \text{ times}},$$

where $\mathbf{x} \in B_m C[1]$ and $mm' = k$. Then we have

$$\operatorname{cyc}^m(x_1 \otimes \cdots \otimes x_k) = (-1)^{(m'-1)\deg' \mathbf{x}} x_1 \otimes \cdots \otimes x_k,$$

where $\deg' \mathbf{x} = \sum_{i=1}^m \deg' x_i$. We consider

$$[x_1 \otimes \cdots \otimes x_k]^{(m)} = \sum_{i=1}^m \operatorname{cyc}^i(x_1 \otimes \cdots \otimes x_k).$$

Then

$$\widehat{d}([x_1 \otimes \cdots \otimes x_k]^{(m)})$$

(3.8.7)
$$= \sum_{i \leq j+1} \sum_{\ell=1}^m (-1)^{\deg' x_\ell + \cdots + \deg' x_{\ell+i-2} + \alpha_\ell}$$

$$x_\ell \otimes \cdots \otimes \mathfrak{m}_{j-i+1}(x_{\ell+i-1}, \cdots, x_{\ell+j-1}) \otimes \cdots \otimes x_{\ell-1}.$$

Since $x_{m+k} = x_k$, it follows that (3.8.7) is in $B^{\mathrm{cyc}}C[1]$. Since elements of the form $[x_1 \otimes \cdots \otimes x_k]^{(m)}$ generate $B_k^{\mathrm{cyc}}C[1]$ we obtain the lemma. (Though the algebra works over the torsion coefficients, we can prove our main geometric result Theorem 3.8.9 only over the rational coefficients so far.) $\qquad \square$

REMARK 3.8.8. We do not need any kind of extra symmetry to define $\widehat{d}^{\mathrm{cyc}}$. The problem of cyclic symmetry of $\langle x_0, \mathfrak{m}_k(x_1, \cdots, x_k) \rangle$ for the Poincaré duality pairing (see Conjecture 3.6.48) is a different kind from that of defining the operator $\widehat{d}^{\mathrm{cyc}}$.

Now a main result of this section is:

THEOREM 3.8.9. *For any ring $R \supseteq \mathbb{Q}$, there exists a sequence of operators*

$$\mathfrak{p}_k : B_k^{\mathrm{cyc}}C(L; \Lambda_{0,nov})[1] \longrightarrow S^*(M; \Lambda_{0,nov})$$

$(k = 0, 1, 2, \cdots)$ *of degree $n+1$ with the following properties. Let*

$$\mathfrak{p} : B^{\mathrm{cyc}}C(L; \Lambda_{0,nov})[1] \longrightarrow S^*(M; \Lambda_{0,nov})$$

be the operator whose restriction on $B_k^{\mathrm{cyc}}C(L; \Lambda_{0,nov})[1]$ is $\mathfrak{p}_k$. We denote by δ_M the $\Lambda_{0,nov}$-coefficient coboundary operator on $S^*(M; \Lambda_{0,nov})$, which is an obvious extension of the classical coboundary operator on M. Then we have

(3.8.10.1) $\mathfrak{p}_1 \equiv i_! \mod \Lambda_{0,nov}^+$,

(3.8.10.2) $\mathfrak{p} \circ \widehat{d}^{\mathrm{cyc}} + \delta_M \circ \mathfrak{p}_k = 0$, *for $k > 0$*,

(3.8.10.3) $\mathfrak{p}_1 \circ \mathfrak{m}_0(1) + \delta_M \circ \mathfrak{p}_0(1) + GW_{0,1}(M)(L) = 0$.

We can further extend $\mathfrak{p}_k$ to

$$\mathfrak{p}_k^+ : B_k^{\mathrm{cyc}}C(L; \Lambda_{0,nov})^+[1] \longrightarrow S^*(M; \Lambda_{0,nov})$$

incorporating the homotopy unit so that the same formula as (3.8.10.2) holds after replacing $\mathfrak{p}$, $\widehat{d}^{\mathrm{cyc}}$ by $\mathfrak{p}^+$, $\widehat{d}^{+\mathrm{cyc}}$, respectively. (Here $\widehat{d}^{+\mathrm{cyc}}$ is defined from $\mathfrak{m}^+$ in the same way as $\widehat{d}^{\mathrm{cyc}}$.) Moreover we have

(3.8.10.4) $\mathfrak{p}_k^+[\mathbf{e}^+, x_1, \cdots, x_{k-1}] = 0$ *for $k \neq 1, 2$*,

(3.8.10.5) $\mathfrak{p}_1^+(\mathbf{e}^+) = PD([L])$,

(3.8.10.6) $\mathfrak{p}_2^+(\mathbf{e}^+, x) = x$.

Here $C(L; \Lambda_{0,nov})^+ = C(L; \Lambda_{0,nov}) \oplus \Lambda_{0,nov}\mathbf{e}^+ \oplus \Lambda_{0,nov}\mathbf{f}$ as in Section 3.3 and $[L]$ is the fundamental cycle of L.

The proof of Theorem 3.8.9 will be given in Subsection 3.8.3 and Section 7.4. (To show (3.8.10.4)-(3.8.10.6) we also need to use the argument in Section 7.3.) As for the orientation problem related to (3.8.10.3), see Proposition 8.10.6 in Subsection 8.10.2.

3.8.2. Applications to vanishing of the obstruction classes $o_k(L)$. In this subsection, we discuss some applications of Theorem 3.8.9. Let

$$[GW_{0,1}(M)(L)] \in H^*(M; \mathbb{Q}) \otimes \Lambda_{0,nov}$$

be the cohomology class of $GW_{0,1}(M)(L)$.

In the next theorem PD_M denotes the Poincaré duality

$$PD_M : H_*(M; \mathbb{Q}) \to H^{2n-*}(M; \mathbb{Q}).$$

THEOREM 3.8.11. *Let $L \subset M$ be a relatively spin Lagrangian submanifold.*

(3.8.12.1) *If $[GW_{0,1}(M)(L)] \neq 0$, then $\widehat{\mathcal{M}}(L) = \emptyset$.*

(3.8.12.2) *If $[GW_{0,1}(M)(L)] = 0$, then the obstruction $[o_i(L)]$ lies in the kernel of the Gysin homomorphism $i_! : H^{2-\mu_i}(L; \mathbb{Q}) \to H^{n+2-\mu_i}(M; \mathbb{Q})$.*

(3.8.12.3) *If $[GW_{0,1}(M)(L)]$ is not of the form $c\, PD_M[L]$ then $\widehat{\mathcal{M}}_{\text{weak}}(L) = \emptyset$.*

(3.8.12.4) *If $[GW_{0,1}(M)(L)] = c\, PD_M[L]$ then*

$$o_i(L; \text{weak}) \in \text{Ker}(i_! : H^{2-\mu_i}(L; \mathbb{Q}) \to H^{n+2-\mu_i}(M; \mathbb{Q})).$$

(3.8.12.5) *Suppose $[GW_{0,1}(M)(L)] = c\, PD_M[L]$, $b \in \widehat{\mathcal{M}}_{\text{weak}}(L)$, and $[L] \neq 0$ in $H(M; \mathbb{Q})$. Then, we have*

$$c = \mathfrak{PO}(b).$$

PROOF. We recall that $G(L)$ is a monoid generated by

$$G_0(L) = \{(\omega[\beta], \mu(\beta)) \mid \beta \in \Pi(L), \mathcal{M}(L; \beta) \neq \emptyset\}.$$

Let $G \supset G(L)$ be a monoid satisfying Condition 3.1.6. We put

$$G = \{(\lambda_i, \mu_i) \mid i = 0, 1, 2 \cdots\}$$

with $\lambda_i \leq \lambda_{i+1}$, and $\lambda_i = \lambda_{i+1} \Rightarrow \mu_i < \mu_{i+1}$. For simplicity of notation, we assume that $\lambda_i < \lambda_{i+1}$ for any i. Other cases can be handled after an obvious modification. (See the proof of Theorem 3.6.18 in Subsection 3.6.2).

Suppose that $[o_j(L)] = 0$ for $j = 1, \cdots, i-1$. It means that we can choose

$$b_{(i-1)} = \sum_{j=1}^{i-1} T^{\lambda_j} e^{\frac{\mu_j}{2}} b_j$$

such that

$$\mathfrak{m}(e^{b_{(i-1)}}) \equiv 0 \quad \mod T^{\lambda_{i-1}} \Lambda_{0,nov}^+.$$

We remark that

$$\widehat{d}(e^{b_{(i-1)}}) \equiv T^{\lambda_i} o_i(L) \quad \mod T^{\lambda_i} \Lambda_{0,nov}^+.$$

We also remark that $e^{b_{(i-1)}}$ is invariant under the cyc operation and

$$\widehat{d}^{\text{cyc}}(e^{b_{(i-1)}}) = e^{b_{(i-1)}} \otimes \mathfrak{m}(e^{b_{(i-1)}}) \otimes e^{b_{(i-1)}}.$$

Now we calculate using (3.8.10.2) and (3.8.10.3) to obtain

$$\mathfrak{p}(\widehat{d}^{\text{cyc}}(e^{b_{(i-1)}})) = -\delta_M(\mathfrak{p}(e^{b_{(i-1)}})) - GW_{0,1}(M)(L).$$

Using (3.8.10.1), we have

(3.8.13.1) $T^{\lambda_i} i_!(o_i(L)) \equiv -\delta_M(\mathfrak{p}(e^{b_{(i-1)}})) - GW_{0,1}(M)(L) \mod T^{\lambda_i}\Lambda^+_{0,nov}.$

Since $GW_{0,1}(M)(L)$ defines a $\Lambda_{0,nov}$-coefficient cocycle in M, (3.8.13.1) gives us an equality on cohomology classes:

(3.8.13.2) $T^{\lambda_i} i_!([o_i(L)]) \equiv -[GW_{0,1}(M)(L)] \mod T^{\lambda_i}\Lambda^+_{0,nov}.$

Hence if $[o_i(L)] = 0$ for all i then $[GW_{0,1}(M)(L)] \equiv 0 \mod T^{\lambda_i}\Lambda^+_{0,nov}$ for all i. Therefore we have $[GW_{0,1}(M)(L)] = 0$.

On the other hand, if $[GW_{0,1}(M)(L)] = 0$, it follows from (3.8.13.2) that $i_!([o_i(L)]) = 0$.

The statement about $[o_i(L; \text{weak})]$ can be proved in a similar way using Formulae (3.8.10.4) and (3.8.10.5). The proof of Theorem 3.8.11 is now complete. □

Theorem 3.8.11 yields several concrete corollaries. Let us start with the following lemma.

LEMMA 3.8.14. *If* $[GW_{0,1}(M; \tilde{\beta})(L)] \in H^*(M; \mathbb{Q})$ *with* $* = 2n$ *or* $2n - 1$, *then we have* $[GW_{0,1}(M; \tilde{\beta})(L)] = 0$.

PROOF. We have degree $* = n - 2c_1(M)[\tilde{\beta}] + 2$, since $\dim \mathcal{M}_{0,2}(M; \tilde{\beta}) = 2n + 2c_1(M)[\tilde{\beta}] - 2$. Therefore the virtual dimension of $\mathcal{M}_{0,1}(M; \tilde{\beta})$, which is similarly defined as $\mathcal{M}_{0,2}(M; \tilde{\beta})$, is $2n - 4 + 2c_1(M)[\tilde{\beta}] = 3n - * - 2$. Thus, by the assumption,

$$\dim \mathcal{M}_{0,1}(M; \tilde{\beta}) = n - 2 \quad \text{or} \quad n - 1.$$

Hence the fiber product $\mathcal{M}_{0,1}(M; \tilde{\beta})\,_{ev_0} \times_M L$ is empty. We may take the perturbation of $\mathcal{M}_{0,2}(M; \tilde{\beta})$ compatible with the forgetful map and obtain an evaluation map $\mathcal{M}_{0,2}(M; \tilde{\beta}) \to \mathcal{M}_{0,1}(M; \tilde{\beta})$ and ev_0 is compatible with this evaluation map. (See Section 23 [**FuOn99II**].) Therefore we can conclude $[GW_{0,1}(M; \tilde{\beta})(L)] = 0$.□

REMARK 3.8.15. The argument here is simpler than a similar argument in Section 7.3 (construction of homotopy unit). This is because when we deal with Gromov-Witten invariant, we can work in the cohomology level and do not need to work in the chain level.

COROLLARY 3.8.16. *If* $[o_i(L)]$ *is defined and in* $H^n(L; \mathbb{Q})$, *then* $[o_i(L)] = 0$. *If* $[o_i(L)]$ *is in* $H^{n-1}(L)$, *then* $i_!([o_i(L)]) = 0$. *The same applies to* $[o_i(L; \text{weak})]$.

PROOF. We remark that $i_! : H^n(L) \to H^{2n}(M)$ is injective. The result then follows from Theorem 3.8.11 and Lemma 3.8.14.   □

COROLLARY 3.8.17. *Suppose that* $\dim_{\mathbb{R}} M = 6$ *and* $c_1(M) = 0$, *and let* L *be a relatively spin Lagrangian submanifold. If* $i_* : H_*(L; \mathbb{Q}) \to H_*(M; \mathbb{Q})$ *is injective, L is unobstructed.*

The proof is immediate from Theorem 3.8.11 and Lemma 3.8.14. The next corollary also follows from Corollary 3.8.16 and Theorem 3.6.43.

COROLLARY 3.8.18. *Any relatively spin Lagrangian submanifold which is a rational homology sphere is weakly unobstructed.*

We remark that Theorem 3.8.11 also gives some new information on the relation of Gromov-Witten invariant and homology class of L. For example, we have:

COROLLARY 3.8.19. *Let M be a symplectic manifold with $c_1(M) = 0$ and L a relatively spin Lagrangian submanifold with vanishing Maslov class. We assume that $H^2(L; \mathbb{Q}) = 0$. Then $[GW_{0,1}(M)(L)] = 0$.*

The proof is obvious from Theorem 3.8.11. This, for example, implies in case $n = 4$ that a certain middle dimensional homology class $\in H_4(M; \mathbb{Z})$ can not be realized by a relatively spin Lagrangian rational homology S^4 in 8 dimensional symplectic manifold M with $c_1(M) = 0$. To obtain more explicit result we need to calculate Gromov-Witten invariant.

REMARK 3.8.20. In the preprint 2000 version [**FOOO00**] of this book, we asserted that L is unobstructed if $H_*(L; \mathbb{Q}) \to H_*(M; \mathbb{Q})$ is injective. This statement does not seem correct. We overlooked the term $GW_{0,1}(M)(L)$ which appears in the right hand side of (3.8.10.3). In the next section we will explain why such term appears. However, this trouble is partially overcome by using operators $\mathfrak{q}$ and $\mathfrak{p}_{\ell,k}$ which we introduce in Subsections 3.8.4 and 3.8.9 below. (See Corollary 3.8.43, for example.) In particular, 'Theorem B' in [**FOOO00**] (that is Theorem I in this book) is proved as was stated in [**FOOO00**]. (See Subsection 6.5.2.)

In Chapter 6, we will also use operators $\mathfrak{p}$ to prove that the image of the differential of the spectral sequence in Theorem D lies in the kernel of $i_! : H^*(L; \mathbb{Q}) \to H^{*+n}(M; \mathbb{Q})$.

3.8.3 Outline of the construction of the operator $\mathfrak{p}$. The main idea of the construction of $\mathfrak{p}$ is to use the space $\mathcal{M}_{k,1}^{\mathrm{main}}(L; \beta)$. Here $\beta \in \pi_2(M, L)$, $k = 0, 1, 2, \cdots$, and $\mathcal{M}_{k,1}^{\mathrm{main}}(L; \beta)$ is defined as follows. Let $\widetilde{\mathcal{M}}_{k,1}^{\mathrm{main}}(L; \beta)$ be the set of $(w, \vec{z}, z^+) = ((\Sigma, \vec{z}, z^+), w)$ where $(\Sigma, \vec{z}, z^+) \in \mathcal{M}_{k,1}^{\mathrm{main}}$, $\vec{z} = (z_1, \cdots, z_k)$, $z_i \in \partial\Sigma$, z^+ is an interior marked point and $w : \Sigma \to M$ is pseudo-holomorphic with $w(\partial\Sigma) \subset L$, $[w] = \beta$. (Σ is a disc D^2 plus possibly sphere bubbles.) We divide it by a $PSL(2; \mathbb{R})$ action and compactify the quotient by adding stable maps to obtain $\mathcal{M}_{k,1}^{\mathrm{main}}(L; \beta)$. See Definition 2.1.24. $\mathcal{M}_{0,1}^{\mathrm{main}}(L; \beta)$ needs a special attention in its compactification as we will explain later in this subsection.

PROPOSITION 3.8.21. *If $k \geq 1$ then $\mathcal{M}_{k,1}^{\mathrm{main}}(L; \beta)$ has a Kuranishi structure with corners.*

We remark that there exists an action of $\mathbb{Z}_k$ on $\mathcal{M}_{k,1}^{\mathrm{main}}(L; \beta)$ given by the cyclic change of the marked points. Namely

$$\mathrm{cyc} : (w, (z_1, \cdots, z_k), z^+) \mapsto (w, (z_k, z_1, \cdots, z_{k-1}), z^+).$$

PROPOSITION 3.8.22. *The action cyc preserves the Kuranishi structure. It is orientation preserving (in the sense of Kuranishi structure) if and only if k is odd.*

The proofs of these two propositions are closely tied to the transversality question. We postpone them till Section 7.4. Constructing a virtual fundamental chain by perturbing the Kuranishi map, while keeping the cyclic symmetry, is a nontrivial matter.

Let

$$ev = (ev_\partial, ev_0) = (ev_1, \cdots, ev_k, ev_0) : \mathcal{M}_{k,1}^{\mathrm{main}}(L; \beta) \to L^k \times M$$

be the evaluation map defined by

$$ev(w, (z_1, \cdots, z_k), z^+) = (w(z_1), \cdots, w(z_k), w(z^+)).$$

Let $P_i = (|P_i|, f_i)$ be a singular chain representing one of the generators of $C(L)$. We put

$$\mathcal{M}_{k,1}^{\mathrm{main}}(L; \beta; P_1, \cdots, P_k) = \mathcal{M}_{k,1}^{\mathrm{main}}(L; \beta) \; {}_{ev_\partial} \times_{(f_1 \times \cdots \times f_k)} (P_1 \times \cdots \times P_k).$$

Then $\mathcal{M}_{k,1}(\beta; P_1, \cdots, P_k)$ has a Kuranishi structure and we take an appropriate multisection $\mathfrak{s}$ to define its virtual fundamental chain. We will carry out the detail of this construction at Section 7.4. We then define the map $\mathfrak{p}$ as follows.

DEFINITION 3.8.23. We put

$$\mathfrak{p}_{k,\beta}(P_1, \cdots, P_k) = ev_{0*} \left(\mathcal{M}_{k,1}^{\mathrm{main}}(L; \beta; P_1, \cdots, P_k) \right),$$

and define

(3.8.24) $$\mathfrak{p}_k = \sum_\beta T^{\omega[\beta]} e^{\frac{\mu(\beta)}{2}} \mathfrak{p}_{k,\beta}.$$

The convergence of the right hand side of (3.8.24) follows from Gromov's compactness in the usual way.

LEMMA 3.8.25. *We may choose a multisection $\mathfrak{s}$ so that the following cyclic property of $\mathfrak{p}_{k,\beta}$ holds:*

$$\mathfrak{p}_{k,\beta}(P_1, \cdots, P_k) = (-1)^{\deg' P_k \times (\sum_{i=1}^{k-1} \deg' P_i)} \mathfrak{p}_{k,\beta}(P_k, P_1, \cdots, P_{k-1}).$$

In this book we do not prove a similar cyclic symmetry for our operator $\mathfrak{m}_k$ (see Remark 3.8.8). The proof of Lemma 3.8.25 will be given at Section 7.4 with the relevant orientation problem analyzed in Subsection 8.10.2.

Now we prove (3.8.10). The proof of (3.8.10.1) is easy. In fact the moduli space $\mathcal{M}_{1,1}^{\mathrm{main}}(L; \beta_0)$ (where $\beta_0 = 0$) is transverse and identified with L itself. Therefore we do not need to perturb it and so $\mathfrak{p}_{1,\beta_0}(P) = P$, which implies (3.8.10.1).

We next prove (3.8.10.2). To see the term $\delta_M \circ \mathfrak{p}_k$, we consider the boundary of $\mathcal{M}_{k,1}^{\mathrm{main}}(L; \beta; P_1, \cdots, P_k)$. If $((w^{(m)}, \vec{z}^{(m)}, z^{+(m)}), (p_1^{(m)}, \cdots, p_k^{(m)}), z^{+(m)})$ is a diverging sequence, then one of the following occurs:

(3.8.26.1)   Some $p_i^{(m)}$ goes to the boundary of P_i.

(3.8.26.2) $w^{(m)} : \Sigma \to M$ goes to a map from union of two genus zero bordered Riemann surfaces $w^{(\infty)} : \Sigma_1 \cup \Sigma_2 \to M$ glued at boundary.

We remark that there may be, of course, a sphere bubble. But this does not contribute to the boundary since sphere bubble occurs in codimension two. (When we are studying stable maps, sphere bubble always occurs in real codimension two).

(3.8.26.1) corresponds to $\mathfrak{p}_{k,\beta}(P_1, \cdots, \partial P_i, \cdots, P_k)$, where ∂ is the classical boundary operator on $C(L)$, which satisfies $\mathfrak{m}_{1,0} = (-1)^n \partial$. (See Definition 3.5.6.)

Let us study (3.8.26.2). Let $((p_1^{(\infty)}, \cdots, p_k^{(\infty)}), z^{+(\infty)})$ be the limit points of marked points. We may number Σ_1 and Σ_2 so that $z^{+(\infty)} \in \Sigma_2$. There are several cases.

(3.8.26.2.1)   There exists $a \le b$ such that $p_a^{(\infty)}, \cdots, p_b^{(\infty)}$ are on $\partial\Sigma_1$ and other $p_i^{(\infty)}$ are on $\partial\Sigma_2$.

(3.8.26.2.2)   There exists $a \le b$ such that $p_{b+1}^{(\infty)}, \cdots, p_k^{(\infty)}, p_1^{(\infty)}, \cdots, p_{a-1}^{(\infty)}$ are on $\partial\Sigma_1$ and other $p_i^{(\infty)}$ are on $\partial\Sigma_2$.

(3.8.26.2.3)   The case there are no $p_i^{(\infty)}$ on $\partial\Sigma_1$.

See Figures 3.8.1 - 3.8.3. Then (3.8.26.2.1) (Figure 3.8.1) corresponds to

$$\mathfrak{p}(P_1, \cdots, \mathfrak{m}(P_a, \cdots, P_b), \cdots, P_k),$$

(3.8.26.2.2) (Figure 3.8.2) corresponds to

$$\mathfrak{p}(P_a, \cdots, P_b, \mathfrak{m}(P_{b+1}, \cdots, P_k, P_1, \cdots, P_{a-1})),$$

and (3.8.26.2.3) (Figure 3.8.3) corresponds to

$$\mathfrak{p}(P_1, \cdots, P_i, \mathfrak{m}_0(1), P_{i+1}, \cdots, P_k).$$

Taking the cyclic symmetry (Lemma 3.8.25) into account, (3.8.10.2) follows from the argument similar to the proof of Theorem 3.5.11.

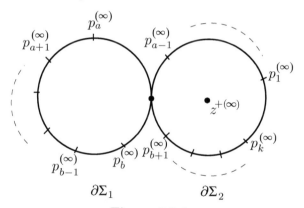

Figure 3.8.1

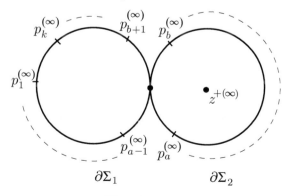

Figure 3.8.2

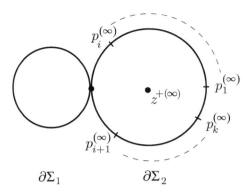

Figure 3.8.3

Now we prove (3.8.10.3). For this purpose, we need to point out the following: Consider the exact sequence

$$H_2(M) \xrightarrow{i_*} H_2(M, L) \xrightarrow{\partial} H_1(L).$$

We need to include *unstable* maps to compactify $\mathcal{M}_{0,1}(L;\beta)$ when $\partial\beta = 0 \in H_1(L)$.

Suppose $\partial\beta = 0$. Then we have $\beta = i_*(\tilde\beta)$ for some $\tilde\beta \in H_2(M)$. There could be more than one such $\tilde\beta$. We consider the element $(w, (z_0^+, z_1^+)) \in \mathcal{M}_{0,2}(M;\tilde\beta)$ such that $w(z_0^+) \in L$. (We like to note that the reader should not be confused with the notation $\mathcal{M}_{0,2}(M;\tilde\beta)$ with $\mathcal{M}_{0,2}(L;\beta)$. The suffix $0,2$ in $\mathcal{M}_{0,2}(M;\tilde\beta)$ denotes the genus ($= 0$) of the domain (closed Riemann surface) and the number of (interior) marked points ($= 2$). The suffix $0,2$ in $\mathcal{M}_{0,2}(L;\beta)$ is the number of boundary marked points ($= 0$) and the number of interior marked points ($= 2$).) We consider the map $\mathrm{const}_{w(z_0^+)} : D^2 \to M$ such that $\mathrm{const}_{w(z_0^+)}(x) \equiv w(z_0^+)$. We glue D^2 with S^2 at $0 \in D^2$ and $z_0^+ \in S^2$ to obtain Σ. Then we consider $((\Sigma, z_1^+), w \# \mathrm{const}_{w(z_0^+)})$. This is not a stable map in the standard sense, since $\mathrm{Aut}(D^2, 0) \cong U(1)$ and so $\mathrm{Aut}(D^2, 0)$ is not finite. However, this object appears as a limit of the element of $\mathcal{M}_{0,1}(L;\beta)$. (See the proof of Proposition 3.8.27 given later in Section 7.4.) We remark that such $((\Sigma, z_1^+), w \# \mathrm{const}_{w(z_0^+)})$ corresponds one to one to $\mathcal{M}_{0,2}(M;\tilde\beta) \times_M L$. Summing up we have the following:

PROPOSITION 3.8.27. *We consider*

$$\mathcal{M}_{0,1}(L;\beta) \cup \bigcup_{\tilde\beta \,;\, i_*(\tilde\beta) = \beta} (\mathcal{M}_{0,2}(M;\tilde\beta) \times_M L).$$

We can define a topology on it so that it is compact and Hausdorff. It then has an oriented Kuranishi structure with boundary. Here $\mathcal{M}_{0,2}(M;\tilde\beta) \times_M L$ lies in its boundary and the Kuranishi structure of $\mathcal{M}_{0,2}(M;\tilde\beta) \times_M L$ is compatible with the Kuranishi structure of $\mathcal{M}_{0,1}(L;\beta) \cup \bigcup_{\tilde\beta}(\mathcal{M}_{0,2}(M;\tilde\beta) \times_M L)$.

We will prove this proposition in Subsection 7.4.1. The essential point is that sphere bubbles (which corresponds to $\mathcal{M}_{0,2}(M;\tilde\beta) \times_M L$) occur in codimension one in this case. This is because the constant disc with the sphere bubble in question has automorphism group of dimension 1.

From now on we write $\mathcal{M}_{0,1}(L;\beta) \cup (\mathcal{M}_{0,2}(M;(i_*)^{-1}(\beta)) \times_M L)$ in place of $\mathcal{M}_{0,1}(L;\beta) \cup \bigcup_{\tilde\beta}(\mathcal{M}_{0,2}(M;\tilde\beta) \times_M L)$ to simplify the notation. We use this moduli space to define $\mathfrak{p}_{0,\beta}$ in the same way as Definition 3.8.23.

Now we are ready to prove of (3.8.10.3). We note that the boundary of

$$\mathcal{M}_{0,1}(L;\beta) \cup (\mathcal{M}_{0,2}(M;(i_*)^{-1}(\beta)) \times_M L)$$

is the union of the fiber product $\mathcal{M}_{0,2}(M;(i_*)^{-1}(\beta)) \times_M L$ and

$$\sum_{\beta_1+\beta_2=\beta} \mathcal{M}_1(L;\beta_1) \times_L \mathcal{M}_{1,1}(L;\beta_2).$$

Thus we have

$$\delta_M(\mathfrak{p}_{0,\beta}(1)) + \sum_{\beta_1+\beta_2=\beta} \mathfrak{p}_{1,\beta_2}(\mathfrak{m}_{0,\beta_1}(1)) + \sum_{\tilde\beta;i_*(\tilde\beta)=\beta} ev_{0*}(\mathcal{M}_{0,2}(M;\tilde\beta) \times_M L) = 0.$$

(3.8.10.3) follows. The proofs of (3.8.10.4), (3.8.10.5) are combination of the arguments in Sections 7.2 and 7.3. □

3.8.4. The operator $\mathfrak{q}$. We have constructed the operator $\mathfrak{p}$ by moving the last (0-th) boundary marked point into the interior. We will construct operator $\mathfrak{q}$ by moving 1-st, ... , k-th boundary marked points into the interior. This construction enables us to relax the condition for Floer cohomology to be defined as we will discuss in the next subsection. For example, this construction is used to prove Theorem I stated in the introduction. We remark that [**Ono96, Sei02, OzSa04**] also use the idea of cutting down the moduli space of pseudo-holomorphic discs via the cycle of the ambient symplectic manifold.

To precisely state our main technical result Theorem 3.8.32, we need to prepare some notations. For the rest of this subsection, we put $R = \mathbb{Q}$.

Take a countable set $\mathcal{X}_1(L)$ of smooth singular simplices on L as in Section 3.5 and let $C_1(L;\Lambda_{0,nov})$ be the cochain complex generated by $\mathcal{X}_1(L)$. Our filtered A_∞ structure $\mathfrak{m}$ in Section 3.5 is constructed on this complex.

Let $S(M)$ be the smooth singular chain complex of M, which we regard as a cochain complex. We choose a countable set $\mathcal{X}(M)$ of smooth singular simplices on M. Let $C(M)$ be the $\mathbb{Q}$ submodule generated by $\mathcal{X}(M)$ in $S(M)$. We put $C(M;\Lambda_{0,nov}) = C(M)\widehat\otimes\Lambda_{0,nov}$.

ASSUMPTION 3.8.28.
(3.8.29.1) $C(M)$ is a cochain subcomplex of $S(M)$.
(3.8.29.2)   The natural inclusion $C(M) \to S(M)$ induces an isomorphism of cohomology $H(C(M),\delta_M) \cong H(M)$.
(3.8.29.3)   Each element $Q \in \mathcal{X}(M)$ is transversal to L and $L \cap Q$ has a smooth triangulation. It defines an element of $\mathcal{X}_1(L)$.
(3.8.29.4)   Moreover the triangulation of $\partial_i Q \cap L$ coincides with the restriction of the triangulation of $Q \cap L$. Here $\partial_i Q$ is the i-th face of Q.

We define $i^\sharp : C(M) \to C(L)$ by $i^\sharp(Q) = L \cap Q$. Here we fix a triangulation of $L \cap Q$ so that (3.8.29.3) holds. Then $L \cap Q$ defines an element of $C(L)$.

Then (3.8.29.4) implies that $i^\sharp$ is a cochain homomorphism. Clearly it induces a natural homomorphism $H^*(M) \to H^*(L)$ (induced by the inclusion).

We shift the degree of elements of $C(M; \Lambda_{0,nov})$ by 2 and consider the shifted complex $C(M; \Lambda_{0,nov})[2]$. We also consider its associated bar complex

$$BC(M; \Lambda_{0,nov})[2].$$

We define an action of the symmetric group $\mathfrak{S}_k$ on $B_k C(M; \Lambda_{0,nov})[2]$ as follows: We put

$$\sigma(y_1 \otimes \cdots \otimes y_k) = (-1)^{\epsilon(\sigma)} y_{\sigma(1)} \otimes \cdots \otimes y_{\sigma(k)}$$

for $\sigma \in \mathfrak{S}_k$, where $\epsilon(\sigma) = \sum_{i<j;\sigma(i)>\sigma(j)} \deg y_i \deg y_j$. (Here we note that the degree is shifted by 2 and so we do not need to use the shifted degrees.)

DEFINITION 3.8.30. $E_k C(M; \Lambda_{0,nov})[2]$ is the subspace of $BC(M; \Lambda_{0,nov})[2]$ consisting of elements which are invariant of the $\mathfrak{S}_k$ action. We put

$$\widehat{E}C(M; \Lambda_{0,nov})[2] = \widehat{\bigoplus} E_k C(M; \Lambda_{0,nov})[2].$$

The coproduct Δ on $BC(M; \Lambda_{0,nov})[2]$ induces one on $\widehat{E}C(M; \Lambda_{0,nov})[2]$;

$$(3.8.31) \qquad \Delta : \widehat{E}C(M; \Lambda_{0,nov})[2] \to \widehat{E}C(M; \Lambda_{0,nov})[2] \,\widehat{\otimes}\, \widehat{E}C(M; \Lambda_{0,nov})[2].$$

(Namely the restriction of Δ to $\widehat{E}C(M; \Lambda_{0,nov})[2]$ is contained in the right hand side of (3.8.31).) The coboundary operator δ_M on $C(M; \Lambda_{0,nov})$ induces a coderivation $\widehat{\delta}_M$ on $\widehat{E}C(M; \Lambda_{0,nov})[2]$ by

$$\widehat{\delta}_M(y_1 \otimes \cdots \otimes y_k) = \sum_{i=1}^{k} (-1)^{\deg y_1 + \cdots + \deg y_{i-1}} y_1 \otimes \cdots \otimes \delta_M y_i \otimes \cdots \otimes y_k.$$

(See Section A3.)

Let $\mathbf{y} \in EC(M)[2]$ and $\mathbf{x} \in BC(L)[1]$. We put

$$\Delta^{k-1}\mathbf{y} = \sum_{c_1} \mathbf{y}_{c_1}^{(k;1)} \otimes \cdots \otimes \mathbf{y}_{c_1}^{(k;k)},$$

$$\Delta^{k-1}\mathbf{x} = \sum_{c_2} \mathbf{x}_{c_2}^{(k;1)} \otimes \cdots \otimes \mathbf{x}_{c_2}^{(k;k)}.$$

We use this notation throughout this section.

Now the following is the main result of this subsection.

THEOREM 3.8.32. *There exists a countable set of smooth singular simplices* $\mathcal{X}_{1+}(L)$ *containing* $\mathcal{X}_1(L)$, *and a structure of a filtered* A_∞ *algebra on* $C_{1+}(L; \Lambda_{0,nov})$ *generated by* $\mathcal{X}_{1+}(L)$ *such that* $(C_{1+}(L; \Lambda_{0,nov}), \mathfrak{m})$ *satisfies the following properties:*

(1) *The filtered* A_∞ *algebra structure on* $C_{1+}(L; \Lambda_{0,nov})$ *extends the filtered* A_∞ *algebra structure on* $C_1(L; \Lambda_{0,nov})$.

(2) *There exists a sequence of operators*

$$\mathfrak{q}_{\ell,k} : E_\ell C(M; \Lambda_{0,nov})[2] \otimes B_k C_{1+}(L; \Lambda_{0,nov})[1] \to C_{1+}(L; \Lambda_{0,nov})[1]$$

$(k = 0, 1, 2, \cdots, \ell = 0, 1, 2, \cdots)$ *of degree* $+1$ *satisfying the following relations*

$$(3.8.33) \quad \mathfrak{q}_{\ell,k}(\widehat{\delta}_M(\mathbf{y}) \otimes \mathbf{x}) + \sum_{c_1,c_2} (-1)^{\deg \mathbf{y}_{c_1}^{(2;2)} \deg' \mathbf{x}_{c_2}^{(3;1)} + \deg' \mathbf{x}_{c_2}^{(3;1)} + \deg' \mathbf{y}_{c_1}^{(2;1)}}$$

$$\mathfrak{q}(\mathbf{y}_{c_1}^{(2;1)} \otimes (\mathbf{x}_{c_2}^{(3;1)} \otimes \mathfrak{q}(\mathbf{y}_{c_1}^{(2;2)} \otimes \mathbf{x}_{c_2}^{(3;2)}) \otimes \mathbf{x}_{c_2}^{(3;3)})) = 0.$$

If $\ell \neq 0$, then we have

$$(3.8.34.1) \qquad \mathfrak{q}_{\ell,k} \equiv \begin{cases} i^{\sharp} \mod \Lambda^+_{0,nov} & \ell = 1 \ and \ k = 0, \\ 0 \mod \Lambda^+_{0,nov} & otherwise. \end{cases}$$

For $\ell = 0$, we have

$$(3.8.34.2) \qquad \mathfrak{q}_{0,k} = \mathfrak{m}_k$$

on $B_k C_{1+}(L; \Lambda_{0,nov})[1]$.
    (3) Furthermore, we can extend $\mathfrak{q}_{\ell,k}$ to

$$\mathfrak{q}^+_{\ell,k} : E_\ell C(M; \Lambda_{0,nov})[2] \otimes B_k C_{1+}(L; \Lambda_{0,nov})^+[1] \longrightarrow C_{1+}(L; \Lambda_{0,nov})^+[1]$$

which satisfies the same formula as (3.8.33) after replacing $\mathfrak{q}$ by $\mathfrak{q}^+$. It also satisfies the following:

$$(3.8.35.1) \qquad \mathfrak{q}^+_{\ell,k}(\mathbf{y} \otimes (\mathbf{x}_1 \otimes \mathbf{e}^+ \otimes \mathbf{x}_2)) = 0, \qquad \ell \geq 1$$

$$(3.8.35.2) \qquad \mathfrak{q}^+_{0,k} = \mathfrak{m}^+_k.$$

    (4) Moreover we have the following. We put $\tilde{\mathbf{e}} = PD[M]$ (the Poincaré dual to the fundamental class), and

$$C(M; \Lambda_{0,nov})^+ = C(M; \Lambda_{0,nov}) \oplus \Lambda_{0,nov}[\tilde{\mathbf{f}}] \oplus \Lambda_{0,nov}[\tilde{\mathbf{e}}^+].$$

Here $\deg \tilde{\mathbf{f}} = -1$ and $\deg \tilde{\mathbf{e}}^+ = 0$. We can then further extend $\mathfrak{q}^+_{\ell,k}$ to

$$\mathfrak{q}^{++}_{\ell,k} : E_\ell C(M; \Lambda_{0,nov})^+[2] \otimes B_k C_{1++}(L; \Lambda_{0,nov})^+[1] \longrightarrow C_{1++}(L; \Lambda_{0,nov})^+[1]$$

which satisfies the same formula as (3.8.33) after replacing $\mathfrak{q}$ with $\mathfrak{q}^{++}$ and (3.8.35) after replacing $\mathfrak{q}^+$ with $\mathfrak{q}^{++}$. It also satisfies

$$(3.8.36.1) \qquad \mathfrak{q}^{++}_{\ell+1,k}(\mathbf{y} \otimes \tilde{\mathbf{e}}^+, \mathbf{x}) = 0$$

for $(\ell, k) \neq (0,0)$ and

$$(3.8.36.2) \qquad \mathfrak{q}^{++}_{1,0}(\tilde{\mathbf{e}}^+, 1) = \mathbf{e}^+,$$

$$(3.8.36.3) \qquad \delta_M(\tilde{\mathbf{f}}) = \mathbf{e}^+ - \mathbf{e},$$

$$(3.8.36.4) \qquad \mathfrak{q}^{++}_{1,0}(\tilde{\mathbf{f}}, 1) \equiv \mathbf{f} \mod \Lambda^+_{0,nov}.$$

We will sketch the proof of Theorem 3.8.32 in Subsection 3.8.6. The detail of the proof is given in Section 7.4 and Subsection 7.3.3.
    Note $\mathfrak{q}^+_{\ell,k}$ is obtained from an extension of $\mathfrak{h}$ (in Definition 3.3.3) to

$$\mathfrak{h}^{+M}_k : EC(M; \Lambda_{0,nov})[2] \otimes B_k(BC_{1+}(L; \Lambda_{0,nov})[1]) \longrightarrow C_{1+}(L; \Lambda_{0,nov})[1]$$

by

$$(3.8.35.3) \qquad \mathfrak{q}^+(\mathbf{y} \otimes (\mathbf{x}_1 \otimes \mathbf{f} \otimes \mathbf{x}_2 \otimes \mathbf{f} \otimes \cdots \otimes \mathbf{f} \otimes \mathbf{x}_k)) = \mathfrak{h}^{+M}_k(\mathbf{y}, \mathbf{x}_1 \overline{\otimes} \cdots \overline{\otimes} \mathbf{x}_k)$$

unless $\ell = 0$, $k = 2$ and $\mathbf{x}_1, \mathbf{x}_2 \in \Lambda_{0,nov}$. (In the case when $\ell = 0$, $k = 2$ and $\mathbf{x}_1, \mathbf{x}_2 \in \Lambda_{0,nov}$, we have

$$(3.8.35.4) \qquad \mathfrak{q}^+_{0,1}(1 \otimes \mathbf{f}) = \mathfrak{m}^+_1(\mathbf{f}) = \mathbf{e}^+ - \mathbf{e} + \mathfrak{h}^{+M}_2(1, 1\overline{\otimes}1),$$

which is consistent with (3.8.35.2).) Here $C_{1+}(L; \Lambda_{0,nov})^+[1]$, $\mathbf{e}^+$ and $\mathbf{f}$ as in Section 3.3.

(3.8.33) is a rather complicated formula. We introduce several algebraic structures (L_∞ structures) in Section 7.4 and use them to rewrite Theorem 3.8.32. It is Theorem Y in the introduction and Theorems 7.4.102.

A related algebraic discussion can also be found in [**KaSt05**] for example.

3.8.5. Bulk deformation of the filtered A_∞ structures. We can use Theorem 3.8.32 to define a deformation of the A_∞ structure $\mathfrak{m}$ on $C_{1+}(L; \Lambda_{0,nov})$. Elements of $H^2(M; \Lambda_{0,nov}^+)$ induces an extended deformation of symplectic structure, and this deformation is the one used for the deformation defined in this subsection. In this sense we can call this deformation *the bulk deformation*.

Let $\mathfrak{b} \in C^2(M; \Lambda_{0,nov}^+) = C(M; \Lambda_{0,nov}^+)[2]^0$. We assume that $\mathfrak{b} \equiv 0 \mod \Lambda_{0,nov}^+$. We put

$$e^{\mathfrak{b}} = \sum_{k=0}^{\infty} \overbrace{\mathfrak{b} \otimes \cdots \otimes \mathfrak{b}}^{k \text{ times}} \in \widehat{E}C(M; \Lambda_{0,nov})[2].$$

We remark (see Lemma 3.6.2)

$$(3.8.37) \qquad\qquad \Delta(e^{\mathfrak{b}}) = e^{\mathfrak{b}} \otimes e^{\mathfrak{b}}.$$

We remark that

$$e^{\mathfrak{b}} \neq \sum_{k=1}^{\infty} \frac{1}{k!} \mathfrak{b}^{\otimes k}$$

even though we symmetrized $B_k C[2]$ to obtain $E_k C[2]$. This is justified by (3.8.37). In fact if we choose different convention to define Δ (coproduct) on $EC[2]$, then we will need the coefficient $1/k!$ in the definition of $e^{\mathfrak{b}}$. Actually, instead, we put $1/\ell!$ in (3.8.68) in the definition of $\mathfrak{q}$.

DEFINITION 3.8.38. For $\mathfrak{b} \in C^2(M; \Lambda_{0,nov}^+)$ with $\mathfrak{b} \equiv 0 \mod \Lambda_{0,nov}^+$ and $b \in C_{1+}^1(L; \Lambda_{0,nov}^+)$, we define

$$\mathfrak{m}_k^{\mathfrak{b},b}(x_1, \cdots, x_k) = \mathfrak{q}(e^{\mathfrak{b}} \otimes e^b x_1 e^b \cdots e^b x_k e^b), \quad k = 0, 1, 2, \cdots.$$

Similarly we define

$$\mathfrak{m}_k^{+\mathfrak{b},b}(x_1, \cdots, x_k) = \mathfrak{q}^+(e^{\mathfrak{b}} \otimes e^b x_1 e^b \cdots e^b x_k e^b), \quad k = 0, 1, 2, \cdots.$$

LEMMA 3.8.39. *Suppose* $\delta_M \mathfrak{b} = 0$. *Then* $\mathfrak{m}_k^{\mathfrak{b},b}$ *defines a structure of a filtered A_∞ algebra on $C_{1+}(L; \Lambda_{0,nov})$. Moreover,* $\mathfrak{m}_0^{\mathfrak{b},b} = 0$ *if and only if* $\mathfrak{q}(e^{\mathfrak{b}} \otimes e^b) = 0$. *Similarly* $\mathfrak{m}_k^{+\mathfrak{b},b}$ *defines a filtered A_∞ algebra with unit on $C_{1+}(L; \Lambda_{0,nov})^+$ and* $\mathfrak{m}_0^{+\mathfrak{b},b} = 0$ *is equivalent to* $\mathfrak{q}^+(e^{\mathfrak{b}} \otimes e^b) = 0$.

PROOF. By assumption $\widehat{\delta}_M e^{\mathfrak{b}} = 0$. Combining (3.8.33) and (3.8.34) we have

$$0 = \sum_{0 \leq i \leq j \leq k} (-1)^{\deg' x_1 + \cdots \deg' x_i} \mathfrak{q}(e^{\mathfrak{b}} \otimes e^b x_1 e^b \cdots e^b x_i e^b$$

$$\mathfrak{q}(e^{\mathfrak{b}} \otimes e^b x_{i+1} e^b \cdots e^b x_j e^b) e^b x_{j+1} e^b \cdots e^b x_k e^b),$$

which turns out to be the A_∞ relation of $\mathfrak{m}_k^{\mathfrak{b},b}$. The version for $\mathfrak{m}_k^{+\mathfrak{b},b}$ is similar. $\square$

Now we study the obstruction for the equation $\mathfrak{m}_0^{\mathfrak{b},b} = 0$ having a solution.

DEFINITION 3.8.40. (1) We say L is *unobstructed after bulk deformation* if $\mathfrak{m}_0^{\mathfrak{b},b} = 0$ has a solution. We write $\widehat{\mathcal{M}}_{\mathrm{def}}(L)$ the set of all $(\mathfrak{b}, b)$ such that $\mathfrak{m}_0^{\mathfrak{b},b} = 0$. For a fixed $\mathfrak{b}$ with $\delta_M \mathfrak{b} = 0$ we put

$$\widehat{\mathcal{M}}^{\mathfrak{b}}(L) = \{b \in C^1(L; \Lambda_{0,nov}^+) \mid (\mathfrak{b}, b) \in \widehat{\mathcal{M}}_{\mathrm{def}}(L)\}.$$

(2) We say L is *weakly unobstructed after bulk deformation* if

$$\mathfrak{m}_0^{+\mathfrak{b},b}(1) = cee^+$$

with $c \in \Lambda_{0,nov}^{(0)}$ (the degree zero part) has a solution. Here $\mathfrak{m}^+$ defines the filtered A_∞ structure on $C_{1+}(L; \Lambda_{0,nov})^+$ and $\mathbf{e}^+$ is its unit. We write

$$\widehat{\mathcal{M}}_{\mathrm{weak,def}}(L) = \{(\mathfrak{b}, b) \mid \mathfrak{m}_0^{+\mathfrak{b},b} = cee^+\}.$$

We define $\widehat{\mathcal{M}}_{\mathrm{weak}}^{\mathfrak{b}}(L)$ in a similar way.

(3) Furthermore we define the *potential function*

$$\mathfrak{PO} : \widehat{\mathcal{M}}_{\mathrm{weak,def}}(L) \longrightarrow \Lambda_{0,nov}^{(0)}$$

by the equation

$$\mathfrak{m}_0^{+\mathfrak{b},b}(1) = \mathfrak{PO}(\mathfrak{b}, b)ee^+.$$

An analog of Lemma 3.6.36 will be given later. See Theorem 4.6.52 and Corollary 4.6.53 for the precise statement.

We remark that $\widehat{\mathcal{M}}^{\mathfrak{b}}(L)$ is the set of bounding cochains of the filtered A_∞ algebra $(C(L; \Lambda_{0,nov}), \mathfrak{m}^{(\mathfrak{b},0)})$. Namely $\widehat{\mathcal{M}}^{\mathfrak{b}}(L) = \widehat{\mathcal{M}}((C(L; \Lambda_{0,nov}), \mathfrak{m}^{(\mathfrak{b},0)}))$.

Now we have the following analog to Theorem 3.6.18. We recall $G(L)$ is a monoid generated by

$$G_0(L) = \{(\omega[\beta], \mu_L(\beta)) \mid \beta \in \Pi(L), \mathcal{M}(L; \beta) \neq \emptyset\}.$$

Let $G \supset G(L)$ be a monoid satisfying Condition 3.1.6. We enumerate as $G = \{(\lambda_i, \mu_i) \mid i = 0, 1, 2 \cdots\}$ with $\lambda_i \leq \lambda_{i+1}$, and $\lambda_i = \lambda_{i+1} \Rightarrow \mu_i < \mu_{i+1}$.

THEOREM 3.8.41. *There exists a sequence of obstruction classes*

$$[o_k(L; \mathrm{def})] \in \frac{H^{2-\mu_k}(L; \mathbb{Q})}{\mathrm{Im}(i^* : H^{2-\mu_k}(M; \mathbb{Q}) \to H^{2-\mu_k}(L; \mathbb{Q}))}, \quad k = 1, 2, \cdots$$

and $b_k \in C^{1-\mu_k}(L; \mathbb{Q})$, $\mathfrak{b}_k \in C^{2-\mu_k}(M; \mathbb{Q})$, $(\delta_M \mathfrak{b}_k = 0$ *and* μ_k *is the Maslov index which is even), with the following properties:*

(3.8.42.1) *The cocycle* $o_k(L; \mathrm{def})$ *is defined if* b_j, $\mathfrak{b}_j$ *and* o_j *for* j *with* $\lambda_j \lneq \lambda_k$ *are defined.* $[o_k(L; \mathrm{def})]$ *depends on* b_j, $\mathfrak{b}_j$ *and* o_j *for* j *with* $\lambda_j \lneq \lambda_k$.
(3.8.42.2) b_k *and* $\mathfrak{b}_k$ *are defined if* $[o_k(L; \mathrm{def})] = 0$.
(3.8.42.3) L *is unobstructed after bulk deformation if all the obstruction classes* $[o_k(L; \mathrm{def})]$ *are defined and are zero.*

The next corollary follows immediately from Theorem 3.8.41.

COROLLARY 3.8.43. *If* $i^* : H^{2k}(M; \mathbb{Q}) \to H^{2k}(L; \mathbb{Q})$ *is surjective for all* k, *then* L *is unobstructed after bulk deformation.*

PROOF OF THEOREM 3.8.41. We will prove the theorem by induction over k. As in the proof of Theorem 3.8.11, we assume that $\lambda_i < \lambda_{i+1}$ for any i to simplify the notation. Other cases can be handled after an obvious modification. (See §3.6.2). We now state the induction hypothesis precisely. Put

$$\mathfrak{b}_{(i)} = \sum_{j=1}^{i} T^{\lambda_j} e^{\frac{\mu_j}{2}} \mathfrak{b}_j, \qquad b_{(i)} = \sum_{j=1}^{i} T^{\lambda_j} e^{\frac{\mu_j}{2}} b_j$$

and assume that $b_i, \mathfrak{b}_i$ for $i < k$ satisfy $\delta_M \mathfrak{b}_i = 0$ and

(3.8.44) $\qquad \mathfrak{q}(e^{\mathfrak{b}_{(i)}} \otimes e^{b_{(i)}}) \equiv 0 \mod T^{\lambda_i} \Lambda_{0,nov}^+ \qquad$ for $i < k$.

Under this assumption, we will construct a cochain $o_k(L; \text{def})$ which is indeed a cocycle. Moreover, if the cohomology class $[o_k(L; \text{def})]$ vanishes, we will prove that b_k and $\mathfrak{b}_k$ are defined and satisfy

$$\mathfrak{q}(e^{\mathfrak{b}_{(k)}} \otimes e^{b_{(k)}}) \equiv 0 \mod T^{\lambda_k} \Lambda_{0,nov}^+.$$

We now define $o_k(L; \text{def})$ by the equation

(3.8.45) $\qquad T^{\lambda_k} e^{\frac{\mu_k}{2}} o_k(L; \text{def}) \equiv \mathfrak{q}(e^{\mathfrak{b}_{(k-1)}} \otimes e^{b_{(k-1)}}) \mod T^{\lambda_k} \Lambda_{0,nov}^+.$

LEMMA 3.8.46. $o_k(L; \text{def})$ is a cocycle in $C(L; \mathbb{Q})$.

PROOF. We apply (3.8.33) to $e^{\mathfrak{b}_{(k-1)}} \otimes e^{b_{(k-1)}}$. Then we have

$$\mathfrak{q}(e^{\mathfrak{b}_{(k-1)}} \otimes e^{b_{(k-1)}} \mathfrak{q}(e^{\mathfrak{b}_{(k-1)}} \otimes e^{b_{(k-1)}}) e^{b_{(k-1)}}) = 0.$$

By (3.8.45) we have

$$T^{\lambda_k} e^{\frac{\mu_k}{2}} \mathfrak{q}(e^{\mathfrak{b}_{(k-1)}} \otimes e^{b_{(k-1)}} o_k(L; \text{def}) e^{b_{(k-1)}}) \equiv 0 \mod T^{\lambda_k} \Lambda_{0,nov}^+.$$

Using (3.8.34.2) and $\mathfrak{b}_{(k)} \equiv b_{(k)} \equiv 0 \mod \Lambda_{0,nov}^+$, we have $\overline{\mathfrak{m}}_1(o_k(L; \text{def})) = 0$ as required. $\qquad\square$

We define $[o_k(L; \text{def})]$ the class induced by $o_k(L; \text{def})$ in

$$\frac{H^{2-\mu_k}(L; \mathbb{Q})}{\text{Im}(i^* : H^{2-\mu_k}(M; \mathbb{Q}) \to H^{2-\mu_k}(L; \mathbb{Q}))}.$$

Now suppose $[o_k(L; \text{def})] = 0$. It means that there exist $b_k \in C_2^{1-\mu_k}(L; \mathbb{Q})$ and $\mathfrak{b}_k \in C^{2-\mu_k}(M; \mathbb{Q})$ such that

(3.8.47) $\qquad i^\sharp \mathfrak{b}_k + \overline{\mathfrak{m}}_1(b_k) + o_k(L; \text{def}) = 0, \qquad \delta_M(\mathfrak{b}_k) = 0.$

We calculate $\mathfrak{q}(e^{\mathfrak{b}_{(k)}} \otimes e^{b_{(k)}})$. We find

(3.8.48)
$$\mathfrak{q}(e^{\mathfrak{b}_{(k)}} \otimes e^{b_{(k)}}) - \mathfrak{q}(e^{\mathfrak{b}_{(k-1)}} \otimes e^{b_{(k-1)}})$$
$$\equiv T^{\lambda_k} e^{\frac{\mu_k}{2}} (\mathfrak{q}_{1,0}(\mathfrak{b}_k \otimes 1) + \mathfrak{q}_{0,1}(1 \otimes b_k)) \mod T^{\lambda_k} \Lambda_{0,nov}^+.$$

The right hand side is equal to $T^{\lambda_k} e^{\frac{\mu_k}{2}} (i^\sharp \mathfrak{b}_k + \overline{\mathfrak{m}}_1 b_k) \mod T^{\lambda_k} \Lambda_{0,nov}^+$ by (3.8.34.1) and (3.8.34.2). Hence

(3.8.49) $\qquad \mathfrak{q}(e^{\mathfrak{b}_{(k)}} \otimes e^{b_{(k)}}) \equiv 0 \mod T^{\lambda_k} \Lambda_{0,nov}^+$

as required. Thus we have proved (3.8.42.1) and (3.8.42.2). Then the proof of (3.8.42.3) is now similar to one of (3.6.19.4) in Theorem 3.6.18. $\qquad\square$

Next we generalize Theorem 3.8.41 to the version of the weakly unobstructed case after bulk deformation. This can be regarded as an analog of Theorem 3.6.43. As before, the monoid $G \supset G(L)$ is enumerated as $G = \{(\lambda_i, \mu_i) \mid i = 0, 1, 2 \cdots \}$ with $\lambda_i \leq \lambda_{i+1}$, and $\lambda_i = \lambda_{i+1} \Rightarrow \mu_i < \mu_{i+1}$. Then as in Subsection 3.6.3, we put

$$G_{\mu \leq 0} = \{(\lambda_i, \mu_i) \in G \mid \mu_i \leq 0\}.$$

By omitting i's with $\mu_i > 0$ from the given enumeration of G, we find the nondecreasing function $j : \mathbb{Z}_{\geq 0} \to \mathbb{Z}_{\geq 0}$ with $j(0) = 0$ such that

$$G_{\mu \leq 0} = \{(\lambda_{j(i)}, \mu_{j(i)}) \mid i = 0, 1, 2, \cdots \}.$$

See (3.6.42). Obviously Assumption 3.6.39 is satisfied in our geometric situation. We note that the proof of Theorem 3.6.43 can be immediately reduced to one given below by ignoring the bulk deformation.

THEOREM 3.8.50. *There exists a sequence of obstruction classes*

$$[o_k(L; \text{weak,def})] \in \frac{H^{2-\mu_k}(L; \mathbb{Q})}{\operatorname{Im}(i^* : H^{2-\mu_k}(M; \mathbb{Q}) \to H^{2-\mu_k}(L; \mathbb{Q}))}, \quad k = 1, 2, \cdots$$

and $b_k \in C_2^{1-\mu_k}(L; \mathbb{Q})$, $\mathfrak{b}_k \in C^{2-\mu_k}(M; \mathbb{Q})$, ($\delta_M \mathfrak{b}_k = 0$ and μ_k is the Maslov index which is even), with the following properties.

(3.8.51.1) $[o_k(L; \text{weak,def})]$ *is defined if $o_i(L; \text{weak,def})$ and $b_i, \mathfrak{b}_i$ for $i < k$ are defined and $\mu_k \leq 0$. $[o_k(L; \text{weak,def})]$ depends on $o_i(L; \text{weak,def})$ and $b_i, \mathfrak{b}_i$ for $i < k$.*

(3.8.51.2) *When $\mu_k \leq 0$, b_k and $\mathfrak{b}_k$ are defined if $[o_k(L; \text{weak,def})]$ is defined and is zero. If $\mu_k > 0$, b_k and $\mathfrak{b}_k$ are defined if b_i and $\mathfrak{b}_i$ exist for $i < k$.*

(3.8.51.3) *L is weakly unobstructed after bulk deformation if all the obstruction classes $[o_k(L; \text{weak,def})]$ for $\mu_k \leq 0$ are defined and are zero.*

PROOF. The proof goes in a way similar to that of Theorem 3.8.41. As in the proof of Theorem 3.8.41, we assume that $\lambda_i < \lambda_{i+1}$ for any i to simplify the notation and put

$$\mathfrak{b}_{(i)} = \sum_{j=1}^{i} T^{\lambda_j} e^{\frac{\mu_j}{2}} \mathfrak{b}_j, \qquad b_{(i)} = \sum_{j=1}^{i} T^{\lambda_j} e^{\frac{\mu_j}{2}} b_j.$$

If $\ell \in \operatorname{Im}(j)$ for any $\ell \leq k$, then the argument for $[o_k(L; \text{weak,def})]$ and b_k, $\mathfrak{b}_k$ is exactly the same as in Theorem 3.8.41 and the induction goes to the next step. The main problem to be discussed is the following case. The other cases can be handled similarly. We assume that $\ell \in \operatorname{Im}(j)$ for any $\ell < k$ and $k \notin \operatorname{Im}(j)$. Hence we have $\mu_k \geq 2$ because μ_k is an even integer. Recall that $\mathbf{e} = PD[L]$ is the homotopy unit of our filtered A_∞ algebra and consider

$$C_{1+}(L; \Lambda_{0,nov})^+ = C_{1+}(L; \Lambda_{0,nov}) \oplus \Lambda_{0,nov}\mathbf{e}^+ \oplus \Lambda_{0,nov}\mathbf{f}$$

with $\deg \mathbf{e}^+ = 0$ and $\deg \mathbf{f} = -1$ as in Section 3.3. Note that since $\overline{\mathfrak{m}}_1^+(\mathbf{f}) \equiv \mathbf{e}^+ - \mathbf{e}$ mod $\Lambda_{0,nov}^+$ from (3.3.5.2), we have $H(L; \mathbb{Q}) \cong H(C(L; \mathbb{Q})^+, \overline{\mathfrak{m}}_1^+)$. Together with this, the operators $\mathfrak{q}$ is also extended to $\mathfrak{q}^+$ by Theorem 3.8.32.

Under the situation above, we will prove the following: We assume that we have $b_i \in C_{1+}(L; \mathbb{Q})^+, \mathfrak{b}_i \in C(M; \mathbb{Q})$ for $i < k$ satisfying $\delta_M \mathfrak{b}_i = 0$ and

$$\mathfrak{q}^+ \left(e^{\mathfrak{b}_{(i)}(\text{weak})} \otimes e^{b_{(i)}(\text{weak})} \right) \equiv c_i \mathbf{e} \mathbf{e}^+ \mod T^{\lambda_i} \Lambda_{0,nov}^+ \qquad \text{for } i < k$$

with $c_i \in \Lambda_{0,nov}^{(0)}$. Under this assumption we will construct obstruction cochains $o_k(L; \text{weak,def})$ and also b_k, $\mathfrak{b}_k$ such that $o_k(L; \text{weak, def})$ is a cocycle and they satisfy

$$\mathfrak{q}^+(e^{\mathfrak{b}(k)} \otimes e^{b(k)}) \equiv c_k e e^+ \quad \mod T^{\lambda_k} \Lambda_{0,nov}^+$$

for some $c_k \in \Lambda_{0,nov}^{(0)}$.

We define $o_k(L; \text{weak,def})$ by the equation

$$T^{\lambda_k} e^{\frac{\mu_k}{2}} o_k(L; \text{weak,def}) \equiv \mathfrak{q}^+(e^{\mathfrak{b}(k-1)} \otimes e^{b(k-1)}) \quad \mod T^{\lambda_k} \Lambda_{0,nov}^+$$

as before. Then we can similarly show the following.

LEMMA 3.8.52. $o_k(L; \text{weak,def})$ *is an* $\overline{\mathfrak{m}}_1^+$-*cocycle in* $C^{2-\mu_k}(L; \mathbb{Q})^+$.

PROOF. If $\mathbf{e} = PD[L]$ is a strict unit, then we do not have to consider the extended ones like $C(L; \Lambda_{0,nov})^+$ and $\mathfrak{q}^+$, etc. In this case the assertion can be shown by the same argument as Lemma 3.8.46. If $PD[L]$ is a homotopy unit, Definition 3.8.37 and Lemma 3.8.38 imply that $(C(L; \Lambda_{0,nov})^+, \mathfrak{m}^{+\mathfrak{b}})$ is the filtered A_∞ algebra with unit for any $\mathfrak{b} \in C^2(M; \Lambda_{0,nov}^+)$ with $\delta_M \mathfrak{b} = 0$. Then we can prove the assertion in a way similar to the case of strict unit as before. $\qquad \square$

Firstly we consider the case that $\mu_k > 2$. Since we assume that L is oriented, we have $\mu_k \geq 4$. Then $o_k(L; \text{weak,def})$ is automatically cohomologous to zero by degree reason. Namely $o_k(L; \text{weak,def})$ is a cycle of (homology) dimension $> \dim L$. (Note that $\deg \mathbf{f} = -1$. Moreover even if $\mu_k = 3$, we find that any element of degree -1 in $C(L; Q)^+$ is not a cocycle over $\mathbb{Q}$, because $\overline{\mathfrak{m}}_1^+(\mathbf{f}) \equiv \mathbf{e}^+ - \mathbf{e} \neq 0 \mod \Lambda_{0,nov}^+$ from (3.3.5.2).) We put $\mathfrak{b}_k = 0$ and can find b_k such that $\delta b_k = o_k(L; \text{weak,def})$. Then obviously we have

$$\mathfrak{q}^+(e^{\mathfrak{b}(k)} \otimes e^{b(k)}) \equiv c_k e e^+ \quad \mod T^{\lambda_k} \Lambda_{0,nov}^+$$

with $c_k = c_{k-1}$ as required.

If $\mu_k = 2$, then we can write

$$o_k(L; \text{weak,def}) = \bar{c}_{k,1} PD[L] + \bar{c}_{k,2} \mathbf{e}^+ \in C^0(L; \mathbb{Q})^+ = C^0(L; \mathbb{Q}) \oplus \mathbb{Q}\mathbf{e}^+$$

for some $\bar{c}_{k,i} \in \mathbb{Q}$. In this case of $\mu_k = 2$, we *do not assume* that

$$[o_k(L; \text{weak,def})] = 0 \in \frac{H^0(L; \mathbb{Q})}{\text{Im}(i^* : H^0(M; \mathbb{Q}) \to H^0(L; \mathbb{Q}))}.$$

We define

(3.8.53.1) $b_k = \bar{c}_{k,1} \mathbf{f},$

(3.8.53.2) $\mathfrak{b}_k = 0.$

Noticing (3.3.5.2) and (3.8.35.4), the argument similar to that in the proof of Theorem 3.8.41 gives

$$\mathfrak{q}^+(e^{\mathfrak{b}(k)} \otimes e^{b(k)}) - \mathfrak{q}^+(e^{\mathfrak{b}(k-1)} \otimes e^{b(k-1)})$$
$$\equiv \mathfrak{q}_{0,1}(1 \otimes T^{\lambda_k} e^{\frac{\mu_k}{2}} b_k) = \bar{c}_{k,1}(\mathbf{e}^+ - \mathbf{e})T^{\lambda_k} e^{\frac{\mu_k}{2}} \quad \mod T^{\lambda_k} \Lambda_{0,nov}^+,$$

because $\mathfrak{h}_2^{+M}(1, 1\overline{\otimes}1) \equiv 0 \mod \Lambda_{0,nov}^+$. Therefore we obtain

$$\mathfrak{q}^+(e^{\mathfrak{b}(k)} \otimes e^{b(k)}) \equiv o_k(L; \text{weak, def})T^{\lambda_k}e^{\frac{\mu_k}{2}} + \bar{c}_{k,1}(\mathbf{e}^+ - \mathbf{e})T^{\lambda_k}e^{\frac{\mu_k}{2}}$$
$$\equiv (\bar{c}_{k,1} + \bar{c}_{k,2})T^{\lambda_k}e\mathbf{e}^+ = c_k e\mathbf{e}^+ \mod T^{\lambda_k}\Lambda_{0,nov}^+$$

with $c_k = (\bar{c}_{k,1} + \bar{c}_{k,2})T^{\lambda_k}$ as required. Therefore the induction works. The other part is similar. In fact, if we put

$$b = \lim_{k\to\infty} b_{(k)}, \quad \mathfrak{b} = \lim_{k\to\infty} \mathfrak{b}_{(k)}, \quad c = \lim_{k\to\infty} c_k,$$

then they converge in the completion with respect to the energy filtration and they satisfy the equation $\mathfrak{m}_0^{+\mathfrak{b},b} = ce\mathbf{e}^+$. This finishes the proof of Theorem 3.8.50. $\quad\square$

We next use (3.8.36) to prove Proposition 3.8.54 below. Here we write $\mathfrak{q}$ and $C(L; \Lambda_{0,nov})^+$ in place of $\mathfrak{q}_{++}$ and $C_{++}(L; \Lambda_{0,nov})^+$ respectively.

PROPOSITION 3.8.54. *Let* $\mathfrak{b} \in C^2(L; \Lambda_{0,nov}^+)^+$ *and* $c \in \Lambda_{0,nov}^+$ *with* $\deg c = 0$. *We put* $\mathfrak{b}' = \mathfrak{b} - ce\tilde{\mathbf{e}}_+$. *Then we have the following.*

(3.8.55.1) $\quad \widehat{\mathcal{M}}_{\text{weak}}^{\mathfrak{b}}(L) = \widehat{\mathcal{M}}_{\text{weak}}^{\mathfrak{b}'}(L).$

(3.8.55.2) $\quad$ *If* b *is an element of the above set, then* $\mathfrak{m}_k^{\mathfrak{b}',b} = \mathfrak{m}_k^{\mathfrak{b},b}$ *for* $k \neq 0$.

(3.8.55.3) $\quad \mathfrak{m}_0^{\mathfrak{b}',b}(1) = \mathfrak{m}_0^{\mathfrak{b},b}(1) - ce\mathbf{e}^+$. *In particular*

$$\mathfrak{PO}(\mathfrak{b}', b) = \mathfrak{PO}(\mathfrak{b}, b) - ce.$$

PROOF. Let $\mathbf{x} \in B_k C(L; \Lambda_0)$ with $k \neq 0$. Using (3.8.36.1), (3.8.36.2) we calculate

(3.8.56.1) $\qquad \mathfrak{q}(e^{\mathfrak{b}'}, \mathbf{x}) = \mathfrak{q}(e^{\mathfrak{b}}, \mathbf{x}) - ce\mathfrak{q}(e^{\mathfrak{b}}\tilde{\mathbf{e}}^+, \mathbf{x}) + \cdots = \mathfrak{q}(e^{\mathfrak{b}}, \mathbf{x}).$

On the other hand,

$$\mathfrak{q}(e^{\mathfrak{b}'}, 1) = \mathfrak{q}(e^{\mathfrak{b}}, 1) - ce\mathfrak{q}(\tilde{\mathbf{e}}^+, 1) - ce\mathfrak{q}((e^{\tilde{\mathfrak{b}}} - 1)\tilde{\mathbf{e}}^+, 1)$$

(3.8.56.2) $\qquad\qquad\qquad + c^2 e^2 \mathfrak{q}(e^{\tilde{\mathfrak{b}}}(\tilde{\mathbf{e}}^+)^2, 1) + \cdots$

$$= \mathfrak{q}(e^{\mathfrak{b}}, 1) - ce\mathbf{e}^+.$$

(3.8.55) follows from (3.8.56) easily. $\qquad\qquad\qquad\qquad\qquad\qquad\qquad\qquad\square$

COROLLARY 3.8.57. *If* $b \in \widehat{\mathcal{M}}_{\text{weak}}^{\mathfrak{b}}(L)$, *there exists some* $\mathfrak{b}'$ *for which* $b \in \widehat{\mathcal{M}}^{\mathfrak{b}'}(L)$.

PROOF. We have only to choose $\mathfrak{b}' = \mathfrak{b} - \mathfrak{PO}(\mathfrak{b}, b)e\tilde{\mathbf{e}}^+$. $\qquad\qquad\qquad\qquad\square$

Now we assume that L is unobstructed after bulk deformation. Let

$$(\mathfrak{b}, b), (\mathfrak{b}, b') \in \widehat{\mathcal{M}}_{\text{def}}(L).$$

(We remark that the first factor $\mathfrak{b}$ is the same while the second may be different. Namely $b, b' \in \widehat{\mathcal{M}}^{\mathfrak{b}}(L)$.) We define a cochain complex $CF((L; (\mathfrak{b}, b)), (L; (\mathfrak{b}, b')))$ as follows.

DEFINITION 3.8.58. (1) When L is unobstructed after bulk deformation, we put $CF((L;(\mathfrak{b},b)),(L;(\mathfrak{b},b'))) = C(L;\Lambda_{0,nov})$ as a graded module. Its differential $\delta_{(\mathfrak{b},b),(\mathfrak{b},b)}$ is defined by

$$(3.8.59.1) \qquad \delta_{(\mathfrak{b},b),(\mathfrak{b},b')}(x) = \mathfrak{m}_1^{\mathfrak{b},b,b'}(x) := \mathfrak{q}(e^{\mathfrak{b}}, e^b x e^{b'})$$

for $(\mathfrak{b},b) \in \widehat{\mathcal{M}}_{\mathrm{def}}(L)$.

(2) When L is weakly unobstructed after bulk deformation, we put

$$CF((L;(\mathfrak{b},b)),(L;(\mathfrak{b},b'))) = C(L;\Lambda_{0,nov})$$

as in Section 3.3 and its differential $\delta_{(\mathfrak{b},b),(\mathfrak{b},b)}^+$, (we will sometimes write as $\delta_{(\mathfrak{b},b),(\mathfrak{b},b)}$ for simplicity, when no confusion can occur), is defined by

$$(3.8.59.2) \qquad \delta_{(\mathfrak{b},b),(\mathfrak{b},b')}^+(x) = \mathfrak{m}_1^{+\mathfrak{b},b,b'}(x) := \mathfrak{q}^+(e^{\mathfrak{b}}, e^b x e^{b'})$$

for $(\mathfrak{b},b) \in \widehat{\mathcal{M}}_{\mathrm{weak,def}}(L)$. We remark that the right hand side is contained in $C(L;\Lambda_{0,nov})$ ($\subset C(L;\Lambda_{0,nov})^+$) by construction. Therefore we can apply Remark 3.6.34 (2).

When $b = b'$ in both cases, we will simply write as

$$\delta_{(\mathfrak{b},b)}(x) = \mathfrak{m}_1^{\mathfrak{b},b}(x) = \mathfrak{q}(e^{\mathfrak{b}}, e^b x e^b), \text{ or } \delta_{(\mathfrak{b},b)}^+(x) = \mathfrak{m}_1^{+\mathfrak{b},b}(x) = \mathfrak{q}^+(e^{\mathfrak{b}}, e^b x e^b).$$

LEMMA 3.8.60. (1) *If L is unobstructed after bulk deformation, then we have* $\delta_{(\mathfrak{b},b),(\mathfrak{b},b')} \circ \delta_{(\mathfrak{b},b),(\mathfrak{b},b')} = 0$ *for* $(\mathfrak{b},b), (\mathfrak{b},b') \in \widehat{\mathcal{M}}_{\mathrm{def}}(L)$.

(2) *If L is weakly unobstructed after bulk deformation, then we have* $\delta_{(\mathfrak{b},b),(\mathfrak{b},b')}^+ \circ \delta_{(\mathfrak{b},b),(\mathfrak{b},b')}^+ = 0$ *for* $(\mathfrak{b},b), (\mathfrak{b},b') \in \widehat{\mathcal{M}}_{\mathrm{weak,def}}(L)$, *whenever*

$$\mathfrak{PO}(\mathfrak{b},b) = \mathfrak{PO}(\mathfrak{b},b').$$

PROOF. Lemma 3.8.60 follows from Lemmas 3.8.39, 3.6.8 and Remark 3.6.34 (2). $\qquad \square$

DEFINITION 3.8.61. (1) We define the Floer cohomology

$$HF((L;(\mathfrak{b},b)),((L;\mathfrak{b},b'));\Lambda_{0,nov})$$

deformed by $(\mathfrak{b},b),(\mathfrak{b},b') \in \widehat{\mathcal{M}}_{\mathrm{def}}(L)$ to be the cohomology group of the cochain complex:

$$HF((L;(\mathfrak{b},b)),((L;\mathfrak{b},b'));\Lambda_{0,nov}) = H(C((L;(\mathfrak{b},b)),((L;\mathfrak{b},b'))),\delta_{(\mathfrak{b},b),(\mathfrak{b},b')}).$$

(2) For the case when L is weakly unobstructed after bulk deformation, we define $HF((L;(\mathfrak{b},b)),((L;\mathfrak{b},b'));\Lambda_{0,nov})$ for $(\mathfrak{b},b),(\mathfrak{b},b') \in \widehat{\mathcal{M}}_{\mathrm{weak,def}}(L)$ with $\mathfrak{PO}(\mathfrak{b},b) = \mathfrak{PO}(\mathfrak{b},b')$ in a similar way.

When $b = b'$ in both cases, we will simply write as $HF(L;(\mathfrak{b},b);\Lambda_{0,nov})$.

We will study how the Floer cohomology depends on $(\mathfrak{b},b)$ in the next chapter. The relation of it to mirror symmetry was mentioned in Section 1.4.

We turn to another application of Theorem 3.8.32.

THEOREM 3.8.62. *For each $(\mathfrak{b}, b) \in \widehat{\mathcal{M}}_{\mathrm{def}}(L)$, there exists a homomorphism*

$$i^*_{\mathrm{qm},(\mathfrak{b},b)} : H^*(M; \Lambda_{0,nov}) \longrightarrow HF((L; (\mathfrak{b}, b)), (L; (\mathfrak{b}, b)); \Lambda_{0,nov}).$$

(Here $H^*(M; \Lambda_{0,nov})$ is the usual cohomology group with $\Lambda_{0,nov}$ coefficient.) The homomorphism above is induced by a cochain homomorphism

$$i^\sharp_{\mathrm{qm},(\mathfrak{b},b)} : C(M; \Lambda_{0,nov}) \longrightarrow C_{1+}(L; \Lambda_{0,nov})$$

such that

(3.8.63) $$i^\sharp_{\mathrm{qm},(\mathfrak{b},b)} \equiv \pm i^\sharp \mod \Lambda^+_{0,nov}.$$

The same also holds for the case when L is weakly unobstructed after bulk deformation.

PROOF. Let $x \in C(M; \Lambda_{0,nov})$. We define

$$i^\sharp_{\mathrm{qm},(\mathfrak{b},b)}(x) = (-1)^{\deg x} \mathfrak{q}(e^{\mathfrak{b}} x e^{\mathfrak{b}} \otimes e^b).$$

We plug in $e^{\mathfrak{b}} x e^{\mathfrak{b}} \otimes e^b$ to (3.8.33) and take $B_1 C_{1+}(L)$ component of it. We then obtain

$$(-1)^{\deg' x} \mathfrak{q}(e^{\mathfrak{b}} x e^{\mathfrak{b}} \otimes \mathfrak{q}(e^{\mathfrak{b}} \otimes e^b)) + \mathfrak{q}(e^{\mathfrak{b}} \delta_M(x) e^{\mathfrak{b}} \otimes e^b)$$
$$+ \mathfrak{q}(e^{\mathfrak{b}} \otimes e^b \mathfrak{q}(e^{\mathfrak{b}} x e^{\mathfrak{b}} \otimes e^b) e^b) = 0.$$

The first term is zero since $(\mathfrak{b}, b) \in \widehat{\mathcal{M}}_{\mathrm{def}}(L)$. Hence we have

(3.8.64) $$i^\sharp_{\mathrm{qm},(\mathfrak{b},b)}(\delta_M(x)) = \pm \delta_{(\mathfrak{b},b),(\mathfrak{b},b)}(i^\sharp_{\mathrm{qm},(\mathfrak{b},b)}(x)).$$

It implies that $i^\sharp_{\mathrm{qm},(\mathfrak{b},b)}$ is a cochain homomorphism. (3.8.63) follows from (3.8.34.1).

We can handle weakly unobstructed case by using (3.8.35.1). □

A part of Theorem 3.8.62 can be restated in the language of the spectral sequence we will construct in Chapter 6.

3.8.6. Outline of the construction of the operator $\mathfrak{q}$. One delicate point of the proof of Theorem 3.8.32 is the choice of a countable set of smooth singular simplices $\mathcal{X}_{1+}(L)$. We postpone this choice to Section 7.4 (which is based on the discussion of Section 7.2). In this subsection, we explain an outline of the construction of the operator $\mathfrak{q}$ and the proofs of the formulae (3.8.33) and (3.8.34), assuming the existence of such a choice of $\mathcal{X}_{1+}(L)$.

Let us consider the moduli space $\mathcal{M}^{\mathrm{main}}_{k+1,\ell}(L, \beta)$ introduced in Subsection 2.1.2. We denote the $(k+1)$ boundary marked points by $z_0, \cdots, z_k$ and the ℓ interior marked points by $z_1^+, \cdots, z_\ell^+$. We put $\vec{z} = (z_1, \cdots, z_k)$, $\vec{z}^+ = (z_1^+, \cdots, z_\ell^+)$. The evaluation map

$$ev = (ev_{\mathrm{int}}, ev_\partial, ev_0) : \mathcal{M}^{\mathrm{main}}_{k+1,\ell}(L, \beta) \to M^\ell \times L^{k+1}$$

is defined by

$$ev(w, (\vec{z}^+, \vec{z}, z_0)) = (w(z_1^+), \cdots, w(z_\ell^+), w(z_1), \cdots, w(z_k), w(z_0)).$$

For given $Q_i \in \mathcal{X}(M)$ ($i = 1, \cdots, \ell$) and $P_i \in \mathcal{X}_{1+}(L)$ ($i = 1, \cdots, k$), we define the fiber product

$$\mathcal{M}^{\mathrm{main}}_{k+1,\ell}(L, \beta; \vec{Q}, \vec{P}) = \mathcal{M}^{\mathrm{main}}_{k+1,\ell}(L, \beta)\ {}_{ev_{\mathrm{int}}, ev_\partial} \times_{M^\ell \times L^k} (Q_1 \times \cdots \times Q_\ell) \times (P_1 \times \cdots \times P_k).$$

(Here $\vec{Q} = (Q_1, \cdots, Q_\ell)$, $\vec{P} = (P_1, \cdots, P_k)$.)

The following propositions are proved in Subsection 7.1.4 and Section 7.4, respectively.

PROPOSITION 3.8.65. $\mathcal{M}_{k+1,\ell}^{\mathrm{main}}(L, \beta; \vec{Q}, \vec{P})$ *has a Kuranishi structure which is compatible with the Kuranishi structures of* $\mathcal{M}_{k'+1}^{\mathrm{main}}(L, \beta'; \vec{P'})$ *(introduced in* (3.5.1)) *and* $\mathcal{M}_{k'+1,\ell'}^{\mathrm{main}}(L, \beta'; \vec{Q'}, \vec{P'})$ *at the boundary.*

PROPOSITION 3.8.66. *We can make a choice of* $\mathcal{X}_{1+}(L)$ *so that there exists a system of multisections* $\mathfrak{s}_{\beta, \vec{Q}, \vec{P}}$ *compatible to* $\mathfrak{s}_{\beta', \vec{P'}}$ *and compatible to one another at the end and so that*

$$(\mathfrak{s}_{\beta, \vec{Q}, \vec{P}}^{-1}(0), ev_0) \in C_{1+}(L).$$

Here we take an appropriate triangulation and an order of its vertices to regard $(\mathfrak{s}_{\beta, \vec{Q}, \vec{P}}^{-1}(0), ev_0)$ as a smooth singular chain.

We remark that we have to use such $\mathfrak{s}_{\beta, \vec{P}}$ for $P_i \in \mathcal{X}_{1+}(L) \setminus \mathcal{X}_1(L)$ also in the proof of Proposition 3.8.65 as well. We denote

$$\mathcal{M}_{k+1,\ell}^{\mathrm{main}}(L, \beta; \vec{Q}, \vec{P})^{\mathfrak{s}} = (\mathfrak{s}_{\beta, \vec{Q}, \vec{P}}^{-1}(0), ev_0).$$

LEMMA 3.8.67. *We assume* $R \supseteq \mathbb{Q}$. *Then we can choose* $\mathfrak{s}_{\beta, \vec{Q}, \vec{P}}$ *so that for each* $\sigma \in \mathfrak{S}_\ell$ *we have*

$$\mathcal{M}_{k+1,\ell}^{\mathrm{main}}(L, \beta; \sigma(\vec{Q}), \vec{P})^{\mathfrak{s}_{\beta, \sigma(\vec{Q}), \vec{P}}} = (-1)^{\epsilon(\sigma)} \mathcal{M}_{k+1,\ell}^{\mathrm{main}}(L, \beta; \vec{Q}, \vec{P})^{\mathfrak{s}_{\beta, \vec{Q}, \vec{P}}},$$

where

$$\sigma(\vec{Q}) = (Q_{\sigma(1)}, \cdots, Q_{\sigma(k)}), \quad \epsilon(\sigma) = \sum_{i < j; \sigma(i) > \sigma(j)} \deg Q_i \deg Q_j.$$

We now define

(3.8.68)
$$\begin{cases} \mathfrak{q}_{\ell,k,\beta}((Q_1, \cdots, Q_\ell) \otimes (P_1, \cdots, P_k)) = \dfrac{1}{\ell!} \mathcal{M}_{k+1,\ell}^{\mathrm{main}}(L, \beta; \vec{Q}, \vec{P})^{\mathfrak{s}}, \\ \mathfrak{q}_{\ell,k} = \displaystyle\sum_{\beta \in \pi_2(M,L)} T^{\omega[\beta]} e^{\mu_L(\beta)/2} \mathfrak{q}_{\ell,k,\beta}. \end{cases}$$

We now check (3.8.33). We study the boundary of $\mathcal{M}_{k+1,\ell}^{\mathrm{main}}(L, \beta; \vec{Q}, \vec{P})$ for this purpose. Let $((w^{(m)}, \vec{z}^{+(m)}, \vec{z}^{(m)}, z_0^{(m)}), (\vec{p}_{\mathrm{int}}^{(m)}, \vec{p}_\partial^{(m)}))$ be a divergent sequence of points of $\mathcal{M}_{k+1,\ell}^{\mathrm{main}}(L, \beta; \vec{Q}, \vec{P})$. Here $\vec{p}_{\mathrm{int}}^{(m)} = (p_{\mathrm{int},1}^{(m)}, \cdots, p_{\mathrm{int},\ell}^{(m)})$, $p_{\mathrm{int},i}^{(m)} \in Q_i$, and $\vec{p}_\partial^{(m)} = (p_{\partial,1}^{(m)}, \cdots, p_{\partial,k}^{(m)})$, $p_{\partial,i}^{(m)} \in P_i$. Then there are three cases.

(3.8.69.1) $\lim_{m \to \infty} p_{\partial,i}^{(m)} \in \partial P_i$.

(3.8.69.2) $\lim_{m \to \infty} p_{\mathrm{int},i}^{(m)} \in \partial Q_i$.

(3.8.69.3) $w^{(m)} : \Sigma \to M$ converges to a map from union of two genus zero bordered Riemann surfaces $w^{(\infty)} : \Sigma_1 \cup \Sigma_2 \to M$ glued at boundary. See Figure 3.8.4.

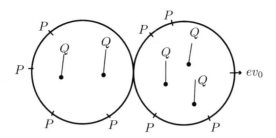

Figure 3.8.4

Let us consider the case (3.8.69.3). We may take Σ_1, Σ_2 so that $z_0^{(\infty)} \in \Sigma_2$. Now for each partition $A_1 \cup A_2 = \{1, \cdots, \ell\}$ with $A_1 \cap A_2 = \emptyset$, we have corresponding components of (3.8.69.3) that is $Q_i \in \Sigma_j$ if and only if $i \in A_j$. We call such components $\partial_{A_1, A_2} \mathcal{M}_{k+1, \ell}^{\mathrm{main}}(L, \beta; \vec{Q}, \vec{P})$.

For $i \leq j$ we put $\vec{P}_{i,j} = (P_i, \cdots, P_j)$. $\vec{P}_{\leq i} = (P_1, \cdots, P_i)$, $\vec{P}_{>j} = (P_{j+1}, \cdots, P_k)$. Let $m_{A_1, 1} < \cdots < m_{A_1, \#A_1}$ be elements of A_1 and $m_{A_2, i}$ $(i = 1, \cdots, \#A_2)$ are defined in the same way. We put

$$\sigma(\vec{Q}; A_j)_i = Q_{\sigma(m_{A_j, i})},$$
$$\sigma(\vec{Q}; A_j) = (Q_{\sigma(m_{A_j, 1})}, \cdots, Q_{\sigma(m_{A_j, \#A_j})}),$$

and

$$Q_{A_j} = (Q_{m_{A_j, 1}}, \cdots, Q_{m_{A_j, \#A_j}}).$$

Then we have

$$\frac{1}{\ell!} \sum_{(A_1, A_2)} \sum_{\sigma \in \mathfrak{S}_\ell} (-1)^{\epsilon(\sigma)} \partial_{A_1, A_2} \mathcal{M}_{k+1, \ell}^{\mathrm{main}}(L, \beta; \sigma(\vec{Q}), \vec{P})^{\mathfrak{s}}$$

$$= \frac{1}{\ell!} \sum_{\sigma \in \mathfrak{S}_\ell} \sum_{\substack{\beta_1 + \beta_2 = \beta \\ \beta_j \neq 0}} \sum_{(A_1, A_2)} \sum_{0 \leq i \leq j \leq k} (-1)^{\epsilon(\sigma)} \mathcal{M}_{k-j+i, \#A_2}^{\mathrm{main}}(L; \beta_2; \sigma(\vec{Q}; A_2)$$

$$; \vec{P}_{\leq i}, \mathcal{M}_{j-i+1, \#A_1}^{\mathrm{main}}(L, \beta_1; \sigma(\vec{Q}; A_1); \vec{P}_{i,j})^{\mathfrak{s}}, \vec{P}_{>j}).$$

Using Lemma 3.8.67 we can see that the above formula is equal to the following.

$$\sum_{(A_1, A_2)} \sum_{\beta_1 + \beta_2 = \beta, \beta_j \neq 0} \sum_{0 \leq i \leq j \leq k} \sum_{\sigma_1 \in \mathfrak{S}_{\#A_1}} \sum_{\sigma_2 \in \mathfrak{S}_{\#A_2}} (-1)^{\epsilon_{i,j, A_1, A_2}} \frac{1}{\#A_1! \#A_2!}$$

$$\mathcal{M}_{k-j+i, \#A_2}^{\mathrm{main}}(L; \beta_2; \sigma_2(\vec{Q}_{A_2}); \vec{P}_{\leq i}, \mathcal{M}_{j-i+1, \#A_1}^{\mathrm{main}}(L, \beta_1; \sigma_1(\vec{Q}_{A_1}); \vec{P}_{i,j})^{\mathfrak{s}}, \vec{P}_{>j}).$$

We put

$$[\vec{Q}] = \sum_{\sigma \in \mathfrak{S}_\ell} \sigma(\vec{Q})$$

for $\vec{Q} = (Q_1, \cdots, Q_\ell)$. Then we have

$$\frac{1}{\ell!} \sum_{(A_1, A_2)} \sum_{\sigma \in \mathfrak{S}_\ell} (-1)^{\epsilon(\sigma)} \partial_{A_1, A_2} \mathcal{M}_{k+1, \ell}^{\mathrm{main}}(L, \beta; \sigma(\vec{Q}), \vec{P})^{\mathfrak{s}}$$

(3.8.70)

$$= \sum_{(A_1, A_2)} \sum_{\beta_1 + \beta_2 = \beta, \beta_j \neq 0} \sum_{0 \leq i \leq j \leq k} \mathfrak{q}_{\#A_2, \ell_2, k-j+i, \beta_2}([\vec{Q}_{A_2}] \otimes$$

$$\vec{P}_{\leq i}, \mathfrak{q}_{\#A_1, j-i+1, \beta_1}([\vec{Q}_{A_1}] \otimes \vec{P}_{i,j}), \vec{P}_{>j}).$$

We remark that

$$\Delta \vec{Q} = \sum_{A_1 < A_2} Q_{A_1} \otimes Q_{A_2}$$

where we write $A_1 < A_2$ if $i < j$ for any $i \in A_1$, $j \in A_2$. Hence

$$\Delta[\vec{Q}] = \sum_{(A_1, A_2)} [Q_{A_1}] \otimes [Q_{A_2}].$$

Therefore, (3.8.70) gives the terms of (3.8.33) except those involving the classical boundary operator. The terms of (3.8.70) involving the classical boundary operator either come from (3.8.69.1), (3.8.69.2) or $\partial \mathcal{M}_{k+1,\ell}^{\mathrm{main}}(L, \beta; \vec{Q}, \vec{P})$. The proof of (3.8.33) is now complete.

We next prove (3.8.34). (3.8.34.2) is obvious from our construction. To prove (3.8.34.1), we remark that $\mathcal{M}_{k+1,1}^{\mathrm{main}}(L, \beta_0)$ consists of constant maps to L. (Recall $\beta_0 = 0 \in \pi_2(M, L)$.) Hence in case $k = 0$, we have

$$\mathcal{M}_{1,1}^{\mathrm{main}}(L, \beta_0, Q) = L \cap Q.$$

So we obtain the case $k = 0, \ell = 1$ of (3.8.34.1). For $k > 0, \ell = 1$ we remark that the support of $\mathcal{M}_{k+1,1}(L, \beta_0; Q, \vec{P})$ is in

$$\sum_i \mathfrak{m}_{k+1}^L(P_1, \cdots, P_i, L \cap Q, P_{i+1}, \cdots, P_k).$$

On the other hand,

$$\deg \mathfrak{m}_{k+1}^L(P_1, \cdots, P_i, L \cap Q, P_{i+1}, \cdots, P_k) = \deg \mathfrak{q}_{1,k}(Q \otimes (P_1, \cdots, P_k)) + 1.$$

Hence we set

$$\mathfrak{q}_{1,k,\beta_0}(Q \otimes (P_1, \cdots, P_k)) = 0.$$

The case $\ell > 1$ can be handled in the same way. See Remark 7.2.172 (3).

The proof of (3.8.35) and (3.8.36) are combination of the above argument with one in Section 7.3. See the end of Section 7.3. □

3.8.7. The operator $\mathfrak{r}$ and the A_∞ bimodule. To prove Theorem I, we need to combine the story of Subsection 3.8.5 to that of filtered A_∞ bimodules. Let $(L^{(0)}, L^{(1)})$ be a relatively spin pair of Lagrangian submanifolds of M. We take $\mathcal{X}_{1+}(L^{(1)})$, $\mathcal{X}_{1+}(L^{(0)})$, $\mathcal{X}(M)$ as in Subsection 3.8.5. We remark that we use the same $\mathcal{X}(M)$ for both $L^{(0)}$ and $L^{(1)}$. We assume that $L^{(0)}$ and $L^{(1)}$ intersect cleanly and decompose $L^{(1)} \cap L^{(0)} = \cup_h R^h$. (We consider the Bott-Morse case only since it includes the transversal case.) We take countable sets $\mathcal{X}_1(R_h)$ of chains and define $C(R_h, \Lambda_{0,nov})$ in the same way as in Subsection 3.7.5, and put $C^k(L^{(1)}, L^{(0)}; \Lambda_{0,nov})$ as in Subsection 3.7.5. Now we have

THEOREM 3.8.71. *There exists a countable set of smooth singular simplices $\mathcal{X}_{1+}(R_h) \supset \mathcal{X}_1(R_h)$ which generates the free $\Lambda_{0,nov}$ module $C_{1+}(L^{(1)}, L^{(0)}; \Lambda_{0,nov})$ on which we can extend the filtered A_∞ bimodule structure constructed in §3.7.5. And there exists a sequence of operators*

$$\mathfrak{r}_{\ell;k_1,k_0} : E_\ell C(M; \Lambda_{0,nov})[2] \otimes B_{k_1} C_{1+}(L^{(1)}; \Lambda_{0,nov})[1]$$
$$\otimes C_{1+}(L^{(1)}, L^{(0)}; \Lambda_{0,nov})[1]$$
$$\otimes B_{k_0} C_{1+}(L^{(0)}; \Lambda_{0,nov})[1] \longrightarrow C_{1+}(L^{(1)}, L^{(0)}; \Lambda_{0,nov})[1]$$

of degree $+1$ such that

$$0 = \mathfrak{r}_{\ell;k_1,k_0}\big(\widehat{\delta}_M(\mathbf{y}) \otimes \mathbf{x} \otimes v \otimes \mathbf{z}\big)$$

$$+ \sum_{c_1,c_2} (-1)^{\deg \mathbf{y}_{c_1}^{(2;2)} \deg' \mathbf{x}_{c_2}^{(3;1)} + \deg' \mathbf{x}_{c_2}^{(3;1)} + \deg \mathbf{y}_{c_1}^{(2;1)}}$$

$$\mathfrak{r}(\mathbf{y}_{c_1}^{(2;1)} \otimes (\mathbf{x}_{c_2}^{(3;1)} \otimes \mathfrak{q}(\mathbf{y}_{c_1}^{(2;2)} \otimes \mathbf{x}_{c_2}^{(3;2)}) \otimes \mathbf{x}_{c_2}^{(3;3)}) \otimes v \otimes \mathbf{z})$$

(3.8.72)
$$+ \sum_{c_1,c_2,c_3} (-1)^{\deg \mathbf{y}_{c_1}^{(2;2)} \deg' \mathbf{x}_{c_2}^{(2;1)} + \deg' \mathbf{x}_{c_2}^{(2;1)} + \deg \mathbf{y}_{c_1}^{(2;1)}}$$

$$\mathfrak{r}(\mathbf{y}_{c_1}^{(2;1)} \otimes \mathbf{x}_{c_2}^{(2;1)} \otimes \mathfrak{r}(\mathbf{y}_{c_1}^{(2;2)} \otimes \mathbf{x}_{c_2}^{(2;2)} \otimes v \otimes \mathbf{z}_{c_3}^{(2;1)})) \otimes \mathbf{z}_{c_3}^{(2;2)})$$

$$+ \sum_{c_1,c_3} (-1)^{(\deg \mathbf{y}_{c_1}^{(2;2)}+1)(\deg' \mathbf{x}+\deg' v+\deg' \mathbf{z}_{c_3}^{(3;1)})+\deg \mathbf{y}_{c_1}^{(2;1)}}$$

$$\mathfrak{r}(\mathbf{y}_{c_1}^{(2;1)} \otimes (\mathbf{x} \otimes v \otimes (\mathbf{z}_{c_3}^{(3;1)} \otimes \mathfrak{q}(\mathbf{y}_{c_1}^{(2;2)} \otimes \mathbf{z}_{c_3}^{(3;2)}) \otimes \mathbf{z}_{c_3}^{(3;3)}))).$$

Here $\widehat{\delta}_M$ is defined in Subsection 3.8.4. Moreover we have

(3.8.73.1) $\qquad\qquad \mathfrak{r}_{0;k_1,k_0} = \mathfrak{n}_{k_1,k_0},$

(3.8.73.2) $\qquad\qquad \mathfrak{r}_{\ell;k_1,k_0} \equiv 0 \mod \Lambda^+_{0,nov} \qquad$ *for $\ell \neq 0$.*

Furthermore, we can extend $\mathfrak{r}$ to

$$\mathfrak{r}^+_{\ell;k_1,k_0} : E_\ell C(M; \Lambda_{0,nov})[2] \otimes B_{k_1} C_{1+}(L^{(1)}; \Lambda_{0,nov})^+[1]$$

$$\otimes C_{1+}(L^{(1)}, L^{(0)}; \Lambda_{0,nov})[1]$$

$$\otimes B_{k_0} C_{1+}(L^{(0)}; \Lambda_{0,nov})^+[1] \longrightarrow C_{1+}(L^{(1)}, L^{(0)}; \Lambda_{0,nov})[1].$$

It satisfies the same formula as (3.8.72) after replacing $\mathfrak{r},\mathfrak{q}$ by $\mathfrak{r}^+,\mathfrak{q}^+$, respectively. It also satisfies:

$$\mathfrak{r}^+_{\ell;k_1,k_0}(\mathbf{y} \otimes x_1 \otimes \cdots \otimes \mathbf{e}^+_1 \otimes \cdots \otimes x_{k_1-1} \otimes v \otimes z_1 \otimes \cdots \otimes z_{k_0}) = 0,$$

$$\mathfrak{r}^+_{\ell;k_1,k_0}(\mathbf{y} \otimes x_1 \otimes \cdots \otimes x_{k_1} \otimes v \otimes z_1 \otimes \cdots \otimes \mathbf{e}^+_0 \otimes \cdots \otimes z_{k_0-1}) = 0$$

for $k_1 + k_0 \geq 2$. Here $\mathbf{e}^+_i$ is the unit in $C_{1+}(L^{(i)}; \Lambda_{0,nov})^+ = C_{1+}(L^{(i)}; \Lambda_{0,nov}) \oplus \Lambda_{0,nov}\mathbf{e}^+_i \oplus \Lambda_{0,nov}\mathbf{f}_i$ as in Section 3.3. Moreover

$$\mathfrak{r}^+_{0;k_1,k_0} = \mathfrak{n}^+_{k_1,k_0}$$

where $\mathfrak{n}^+_{k_1,k_0}$ is the filtered $C_{1+}(L^{(1)}; \Lambda_{0,nov})^+$, $C_{1+}(L^{(0)}; \Lambda_{0,nov})^+$ bimodule structure on $C_+(L^{(1)}, L^{(0)}; \Lambda_{0,nov})$.

We sketch the proof in the next subsection. The detail of the proof is given in Sections 7.4.8-9. There we reinterpret Theorem 3.8.71 (especially Formula (3.8.72)) using the language of L_∞ module homomorphism. See Theorem 7.4.154.

Now let $\mathfrak{b} \in C^2(M; \Lambda^+_{0,nov})$ with $\delta_M \mathfrak{b} = 0$. We define

$$\mathfrak{n}^{\mathfrak{b}}_{k_1,k_0} : B_{k_1} C_{1+}(L^{(1)}; \Lambda_{0,nov})[1] \otimes C_{1+}(L^{(1)}, L^{(0)}; \Lambda_{0,nov})$$

$$\otimes B_{k_0} C_{1+}(L^{(0)}; \Lambda_{0,nov})[1] \longrightarrow C_{1+}(L^{(1)}, L^{(0)}; \Lambda_{0,nov})$$

by

$$\mathfrak{n}^{\mathfrak{b}}_{k_1,k_0}(\mathbf{x} \otimes v \otimes \mathbf{z}) = \mathfrak{r}(e^{\mathfrak{b}} \otimes \mathbf{x} \otimes v \otimes \mathbf{z}).$$

Moreover, as in Definition-Lemma 3.7.13, for $b_i \in C_{1+}(L^{(i)}; \Lambda_{0,nov})$ with $b_i \equiv 0$ mod $\Lambda_{0,nov}^+$, we define

$$
\begin{aligned}
{}^{(\mathfrak{b},b_1)}\mathfrak{n}^{(\mathfrak{b},b_0)} & (\mathbf{x} \otimes v \otimes \mathbf{z}) \\
& = \mathfrak{r}(e^{\mathfrak{b}} \otimes e^{b_1} \otimes x_1 \otimes e^{b_1} \cdots e^{b_1} \otimes x_{k_1} \otimes e^{b_1} \otimes v \otimes e^{b_0} \\
& \qquad\qquad \otimes z_1 \otimes e^{b_0} \cdots e^{b_0} \otimes z_{k_0} \otimes e^{b_0})
\end{aligned}
$$

with $\mathbf{x} = x_1 \otimes \cdots \otimes x_{k_1}$ and $\mathbf{z} = z_1 \otimes \cdots \otimes z_{k_0}$.

LEMMA 3.8.74. (1) *The operators* $\mathfrak{n}_{k_1,k_0}^{\mathfrak{b}}$ *define a*

$$
((C(L^{(1)}; \Lambda_{0,nov}), \mathfrak{m}^{(\mathfrak{b},0)}), (C(L^{(0)}; \Lambda_{0,nov}), \mathfrak{m}^{(\mathfrak{b},0)}))
$$

filtered A_∞ *bimodule structure on* $C_{1+}(L^{(1)}, L^{(0)}; \Lambda_{0,nov})$.

(2) *The operator* ${}^{(\mathfrak{b},b_1)}\mathfrak{n}^{(\mathfrak{b},b_0)}$ *also defines a left* $(C(L^{(1)}; \Lambda_{0,nov}), \mathfrak{m}^{(\mathfrak{b},b_1)})$ *and right* $(C(L^{(0)}; \Lambda_{0,nov}), \mathfrak{m}^{(\mathfrak{b},b_0)})$ *filtered* A_∞ *bimodule structure on* $C_{1+}(L^{(1)}, L^{(0)}; \Lambda_{0,nov})$.

PROOF. The proof is a straightforward calculation based on (3.8.72). $\square$

Lemma 3.8.74 implies that $\mathfrak{n}_{k_1,k_0}^{\mathfrak{b}}$ defines a *filtered* A_∞ *bimodule structure deformed by* $\mathfrak{b}$. And ${}^{(\mathfrak{b},b_1)}\mathfrak{n}^{(\mathfrak{b},b_0)}$ can be regarded as a deformed filtered A_∞ bimodule structure after the bulk deformation. In particular, we consider

$$
\delta_{(\mathfrak{b},b_1),(\mathfrak{b},b_0)} : C_{1+}^k(L^{(1)}, L^{(0)}; \Lambda_{0,nov}) \longrightarrow C_{1+}^{k+1}(L^{(1)}, L^{(0)}; \Lambda_{0,nov})
$$

defined by

$$
\delta_{(\mathfrak{b},b_1),(\mathfrak{b},b_0)}(v) = \mathfrak{r}(e^{\mathfrak{b}} \otimes e^{b_1} \otimes v \otimes e^{b_0}).
$$

Then we have

LEMMA-DEFINITION 3.8.75. (1) *If* $b_0 \in \widehat{\mathcal{M}}^{\mathfrak{b}}(L^{(0)})$ *and* $b_1 \in \widehat{\mathcal{M}}^{\mathfrak{b}}(L^{(1)})$, *we have*

$$
\delta_{(\mathfrak{b},b_1),(\mathfrak{b},b_0)} \circ \delta_{(\mathfrak{b},b_1),(\mathfrak{b},b_0)} = 0.
$$

Thus we can define the Floer cohomology group

$$
HF((L^{(1)}, (\mathfrak{b}, b_1)), (L^{(0)}, (\mathfrak{b}, b_0)); \Lambda_{0,nov})
$$

to be the cohomology of the complex $(C_{1+}(L^{(1)}, L^{(0)}; \Lambda_{0,nov}), \delta_{(\mathfrak{b},b_1),(\mathfrak{b},b_0)})$.

(2) *If* $L^{(i)}$ ($i = 0, 1$) *are weakly unobstructed after bulk deformation (see Definition 3.8.39), then for any* $(\mathfrak{b}, b_i) \in \widehat{\mathcal{M}}_{weak,def}(L^{(i)})$ *satisfying*

$$
\mathfrak{PD}_{L^{(0)}}(\mathfrak{b}, b_0) = \mathfrak{PD}_{L^{(1)}}(\mathfrak{b}, b_1),
$$

we define

$$
\delta_{(\mathfrak{b},b_1),(\mathfrak{b},b_0)}^+(v) = \mathfrak{r}^+(e^{\mathfrak{b}} \otimes e^{b_1} \otimes v \otimes e^{b_0}).
$$

Then we have $\delta_{(\mathfrak{b},b_1),(\mathfrak{b},b_0)}^+ \circ \delta_{(\mathfrak{b},b_1),(\mathfrak{b},b_0)}^+ = 0$. *Thus we can define the Floer cohomology group*

$$
HF((L^{(1)}, (\mathfrak{b}, b_1)), (L^{(0)}, (\mathfrak{b}, b_0)); \Lambda_{0,nov})
$$

to be the cohomology of the complex $(C_{1+}(L^{(1)}, L^{(0)}; \Lambda_{0,nov}), \delta_{(\mathfrak{b},b_1),(\mathfrak{b},b_0)}^+)$.

In Lemma-Definition 3.8.75 (2), we can also define the deformed filtered A_∞ bimodule structure after bulk deformation in a similar way as follows:

$$^{(\mathfrak{b},b_1)}\mathfrak{n}^{+(\mathfrak{b},b_0)}(\mathbf{x} \otimes v \otimes \mathbf{z})$$
$$= \mathfrak{r}^+(e^\mathfrak{b} \otimes e^{b_1} \otimes x_1 \otimes e^{b_1} \cdots e^{b_1} \otimes x_{k_1} \otimes e^{b_1}$$
$$\otimes v \otimes e^{b_0} \otimes z_1 \otimes e^{b_0} \cdots e^{b_0} \otimes z_{k_0} \otimes e^{b_0}).$$

3.8.8. Construction of the operator $\mathfrak{r}$. In this subsection, we discuss the proof of Theorem 3.8.71. The proof is a straight forward combination of the construction we have already discussed. We take a one parameter family $\{J_t\}_t$ of almost complex structures. Let us consider the set of $((\Sigma, \vec{\tau}, \vec{z}^+), u)$ such that

(3.8.76.1) $((\Sigma, \vec{\tau}), u)$ satisfies the same condition as an element of the moduli space $\mathcal{M}_{k_1,k_0}(L^{(1)}, L^{(0)}; [h, w], [h', w'])$ except it may have unstable component.
(3.8.76.2) $\vec{z}^+ = (z_1^+, \cdots, z_\ell^+)$ are interior points on Σ.
(3.8.76.3) $((\Sigma, \vec{\tau}, \vec{z}^+), u)$ is stable. Namely the group of its automorphisms is of finite order.

Here $\vec{\tau} = (\vec{\tau}^{(0)}, \vec{\tau}^{(1)})$ with $\vec{\tau}^{(i)} = (\tau_1^{(i)}, \cdots, \tau_{k_i}^{(i)})$ $(i = 0, 1)$ as in Subsection 3.7.5. Let

$$\mathcal{M}_{k_1,k_0;\ell}(L^{(1)}, L^{(0)}; [h, w], [h', w'])$$

be the moduli space of such system

$$((\Sigma, \vec{\tau}, \vec{z}^+), u).$$

We define evaluation maps

$$(ev_{\text{int}}, ev^{(1)}, ev^{(0)}) : \mathcal{M}_{k_1,k_0;\ell}(L^{(1)}, L^{(0)}; [h, w], [h', w'])$$
$$\to M^\ell \times (L^{(1)})^{k_1} \times (L^{(0)})^{k_0}$$

by

$$(ev_{\text{int}}, ev^{(1)}, ev^{(0)})(((\Sigma, \vec{\tau}, \vec{z}^+), u))$$
$$= (u(z_1^+), \cdots, u(z_\ell^+), u((\tau_1^{(1)}), 1), \cdots, u((\tau_{k_0}^{(0)}), 0))$$

and

$$ev_{-\infty} : \mathcal{M}_{k_1,k_0;\ell}(L^{(1)}, L^{(0)}; [h, w], [h', w']) \to R_h$$
$$ev_{+\infty} : \mathcal{M}_{k_1,k_0;\ell}(L^{(1)}, L^{(0)}; [h, w], [h', w']) \to R_{h'},$$

by $ev_{\pm\infty}(((\Sigma, \vec{\tau}, \vec{z}^+), u)) = \lim_{\tau \to \pm\infty} u(\tau, t)$.

Let $Q_i \in \mathcal{X}(M)$, $P_i^{(j)} \in \mathcal{X}_{1+}(L^{(j)})$ and $S \in \mathcal{X}_{1+}(R_h)$. We define

$$\mathcal{M}_{k_1,k_0;\ell}(L^{(1)}, L^{(0)}; [h, w], [h', w']; \vec{Q}, \vec{P}^{(1)}, S, \vec{P}^{(0)})$$
$$= \mathcal{M}_{k_1,k_0;\ell}(L^{(1)}, L^{(0)}; [h, w], [h', w'])$$
$$_{(ev_{\text{int}}, ev^{(1)}, ev_{-\infty}, ev^{(0)})} \times \left(\prod Q_i \times \prod P_i^{(1)} \times S \times \prod P_i^{(0)}\right).$$

See Figure 3.8.5.

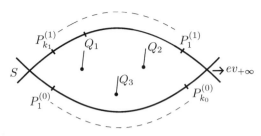

Figure 3.8.5

It has a Kuranishi structure and we can define a multisection $\mathfrak{s}$ on it compatible at the end. We then put

$$\mathcal{M}_{k_1,k_0;\ell}(L^{(1)}, L^{(0)}; [h,w], [h',w']; \vec{Q}, \vec{P}^{(1)}, S, \vec{P}^{(0)})^\mathfrak{s} = (-1)^\epsilon ev_{+\infty}(\mathfrak{s}^{-1}(0)),$$

which is a chain on $R_{h'}$. Here the sign $(-1)^\epsilon$ is the same as one just before Definition 3.7.71 in Subsection 3.7.5. We can choose $\mathcal{X}_{1+}(R_h)$ so that the virtual fundamental chain $\mathcal{M}_{k_1,k_0;\ell}(L^{(1)}, L^{(0)}; [h,w], [h',w']; \vec{Q}, \vec{P}^{(1)}, S, \vec{P}^{(0)})^\mathfrak{s}$ again is contained in it. Now we take

$$\mathfrak{r}_{k_1,k_0;\ell}(Q_1 \otimes \cdots Q_\ell \otimes P_1^{(1)} \otimes \cdots \otimes P_{k_1}^{(1)} \otimes [S,w] \otimes P_1^{(0)} \otimes \cdots \otimes P_{k_0}^{(0)})$$
$$= \sum_{[h',w']} \frac{1}{\ell!} \mathcal{M}_{k_1,k_0;\ell}(L^{(1)}, L^{(0)}; [h,w], [h',w']; \vec{Q}, \vec{P}^{(1)}, S, \vec{P}^{(0)})^\mathfrak{s}.$$

The proofs of (3.8.72) and (3.8.73) are now straightforward.   □

3.8.9. Generalization of the operator $\mathfrak{p}$. We generalize the operator $\mathfrak{p}_k$ by combining it with $\mathfrak{q}$ to obtain an operator $\mathfrak{p}_{\ell,k}$. (The difference between operators $\mathfrak{p}$ and $\mathfrak{q}$ is as follows: For the moduli space used to define $\mathfrak{p}$ the 0-th marked point is an interior marked point: On the other hand, for the moduli space used to define $\mathfrak{q}$, the 0-th marked point is a boundary marked point.) The operator $\mathfrak{p}_{\ell,k}$ will be used in Chapter 6 to describe the image of the differential of the spectral sequence constructed there.

Since the construction of $\mathfrak{p}_{\ell,k}$ is a straightforward analogue of ones discussed already in this section, we write the conclusion only. We first recall Gromov-Witten invariant a bit more. Let $\mathcal{M}_{0,\ell+2}(M; \tilde{\beta})$ be the moduli space of pseudo-holomorphic spheres with $(\ell+2)$ marked points, whose homology class $\tilde{\beta} \in H_2(M)$. We can define an obvious evaluation map

$$ev = (ev_1, \cdots, ev_{\ell+1}, ev_0) : \mathcal{M}_{0,\ell+2}(M; \tilde{\beta}) \to M^{\ell+2}.$$

For each chains $Q_i \subset M$, $i = 1, \cdots, \ell+1$ we put

$$\mathcal{M}_{0,\ell+2}(M; \tilde{\beta}; \vec{Q}) = \mathcal{M}_{0,\ell+2}(M; \tilde{\beta})_{(ev_1, \cdots, ev_{\ell+1})} \times (Q_1 \times \cdots \times Q_{\ell+1})$$

and define

$$(3.8.77) \qquad GW_{0,\ell+1}(M)(\vec{Q}) = \sum_{\tilde{\beta}} T^{\omega[\tilde{\beta}]} e^{c_1(M)(\tilde{\beta})} ev_{0*}(\mathcal{M}_{0,\ell+2}(M; \tilde{\beta}; \vec{Q})).$$

We remark that (3.8.77) is a generalization of (3.8.2). (We regard the right hand as an element of $S^*(M; \Lambda_{0,nov})$ by taking an appropriate triangulation.)

We next remark that $\mathfrak{q}$ induces

$$\hat{\mathfrak{q}}^{\mathrm{cyc}} : EC(M; \Lambda_{0,nov})[2] \otimes B^{\mathrm{cyc}} C_{1+}(L; \Lambda_{0,nov})[1] \to B^{\mathrm{cyc}} C_{1+}(L; \Lambda_{0,nov})[1]$$

in the same way as $\mathfrak{m}_k$ induces $\hat{d}^{\,\mathrm{cyc}}$ in Lemma 3.8.4.

PROPOSITION 3.8.78. *In case $R = \mathbb{Q}$, there exists a sequence of operators*

$$\mathfrak{p}_{\ell,k} : E_\ell C(M; \Lambda_{0,nov})[2] \otimes B_k^{\mathrm{cyc}} C_{1+}(L; \Lambda_{0,nov})[1] \longrightarrow S^*(M; \Lambda_{0,nov})$$

$(k = 0, 1, 2, \cdots, \ell = 0, 1, 2, \cdots)$ *of degree $n + 1$ with the following properties:*

(3.8.79.1) $\mathfrak{p}_{0,k} = \mathfrak{p}_k$.
(3.8.79.2) $\mathfrak{p}_{\ell,k} \equiv 0 \mod \Lambda_{0,nov}^+$ *for $\ell > 0$.*
(3.8.79.3) *For $k > 0$ we have*

$$\mathfrak{p}_{\ell,k}(\hat{\delta}_M(\mathbf{y}) \otimes \mathbf{x}) + \delta_M(\mathfrak{p}_{\ell,k}(\mathbf{y} \otimes \mathbf{x}))$$
$$+ \sum_{c_1, c_2} \mathfrak{p}(\mathbf{y}_{c_1}^{(2;1)} \otimes (\hat{\mathfrak{q}}^{\mathrm{cyc}}(\mathbf{y}_{c_1}^{(2;2)} \otimes \mathbf{x}))) = 0.$$

Here the notations are the same as in Theorem 3.8.32.

(3.8.79.4)
$$\mathfrak{p}_{\ell,0}(\hat{\delta}_M(\mathbf{y}) \otimes 1) + \delta_M(\mathfrak{p}_{\ell,0}(\mathbf{y} \otimes 1))$$
$$+ \sum_{c_1} (-1)^{\deg \mathbf{y}_{c_1}^{(2;1)}} \mathfrak{p}(\mathbf{y}_{c_1}^{(2;1)} \otimes (\mathfrak{q}(\mathbf{y}_{c_1}^{(2;2)} \otimes 1)))$$
$$+ \frac{1}{\ell!} GW_{0,\ell+1}(M)(\mathbf{y} \otimes L) = 0.$$

Here the last term on the left hand side is defined as in (3.8.77). Namely, $Q_i = y_i, (i = 1, \cdots, \ell)$, where $\mathbf{y} = y_1 \otimes \cdots \otimes y_\ell$ and $L = Q_{\ell+1}$.
We can furthermore extend $\mathfrak{p}_{\ell,k}$ to

$$\mathfrak{p}_{\ell,k}^+ : E_\ell C(M; \Lambda_{0,nov})[2] \otimes B_k^{\mathrm{cyc}} C_{1+}(L; \Lambda_{0,nov})^+[1] \longrightarrow S^*(M; \Lambda_{0,nov})$$

satisfying

(3.8.79.5) $\mathfrak{p}_{0,k}^+ = \mathfrak{p}_k^+$

and a similar compatible condition as in (3.8.35.1) − (3.8.35.3). In particular,

(3.8.79.6) $\mathfrak{p}_{\ell,k}^+(\mathbf{y} \otimes [\mathbf{e}^+, x_1, \cdots, x_{k-1}]) = 0$ *for $\ell \neq 0$ and any k.*

Here $C_{1+}(L; \Lambda_{0,nov})^+ = C_{1+}(L; \Lambda_{0,nov}) \oplus \Lambda_{0,nov}\mathbf{e}^+ \oplus \Lambda_{0,nov}\mathbf{f}$ as in Section 3.3.

The construction of the operator $\mathfrak{p}_{\ell,k}$ uses the moduli space $\mathcal{M}_{k,\ell+1}^{\mathrm{main}}(L, \beta)$ where the last (0-th) marked point is the *interior* marked point. (Recall that the last marked point in the case of defining $\mathfrak{p}$ is the *interior* point, while one in the case of $\mathfrak{q}$ is the *boundary* marked point.) See Figure 3.8.6 below. For example Figure 3.8.7 gives

$$\mathfrak{p}((Q_3 \otimes Q_4) \otimes (\mathfrak{q}((Q_1 \otimes Q_2) \otimes (P_6 \otimes P_1 \otimes P_2)) \otimes P_3 \otimes P_4 \otimes P_5).$$

It is one of the terms of the last term in the left hand side of (3.8.79.3).

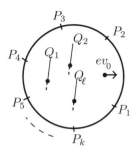

$$\mathfrak{p}_{\ell,k}((Q_1 \otimes \cdots \otimes Q_\ell) \otimes (P_1 \otimes \cdots \otimes P_k))$$

Figure 3.8.6

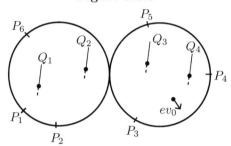

Figure 3.8.7

The reason we have the term $GW_{0,\ell+1}(M)(\mathbf{y} \otimes L)$ in (3.8.79.4) is the same as the case of $\mathfrak{p}$. The detail of the proof of Proposition 3.8.78 is a combination of the arguments we have already discussed. It will be discussed in Subsection 7.4.11 in detail. $\square$

We remark Proposition 3.8.78 will be reinterpreted in Sections 7.4.10-11 using L_∞ structure. See Theorem 7.4.192.

EXAMPLE 3.8.80. Let us consider $(M, \omega_M) = (\mathbb{C}P^1, \omega) \times (\mathbb{C}P^1, -\omega)$, and $L =$ diagonal, which is oriented so that the first factor projection respects the orientation. We take $p = (z_0, w_0) \in M$ and consider $PD[p] \in H^{2n}(M; \mathbb{Q})$. We put $\mathbf{y} = PD[p]$ in (3.8.79.4) and get

$$(3.8.81) \quad \begin{aligned} &\delta_M(\mathfrak{p}_{1,0}(PD[p] \otimes 1)) + \mathfrak{p}_{1,1}(PD[p] \otimes \mathfrak{m}_0(1)) \\ &+ \mathfrak{p}_{0,1}(1 \otimes \mathfrak{q}_{1,0}(PD[p] \otimes 1)) + GW(M)_{0,2}(PD[p] \otimes [L]) = 0. \end{aligned}$$

By dimension counting we have $\mathfrak{m}_0(1) = 0$ as chain. Hence (3.8.81) implies

$$(3.8.82) \quad [\mathfrak{p}_{0,1}(1 \otimes \mathfrak{q}_{1,0}(PD[p] \otimes 1)))] = -[GW_{0,2}(M)(PD[p] \otimes [L])].$$

Let us check the leading term of Formula (3.8.82) directly.

We put $H^2(M; \mathbb{Z}) = \mathbb{Z} \oplus \mathbb{Z}$. We take the complex structure $J_M = J_{\mathbb{C}P^1} \oplus -J_{\mathbb{C}P^1}$ on M. Then $\tilde{\beta}_1 = (1, 0)$ and $\tilde{\beta}_2 = (0, -1)$ are both represented by pseudo-holomorphic spheres of minimal symplectic area. We find

$$\mathcal{M}_{0,3}(M; \tilde{\beta}_1) \times_M (\{p\} \times L) \cong S^2,$$

and its evaluation map image is

$$ev_0(\mathcal{M}_{0,3}(M; \tilde{\beta}_1) \times_M (\{p\} \times L)) = \{(z, w_0) \mid z \in \mathbb{C}P^1\}.$$

Hence

$$(3.8.83.1) \qquad GW_{0,2}(M; \tilde{\beta}_1)(PD[p] \otimes [L]) = \mathbb{C}P^1 \times \{w_0\}.$$

On the other hand, taking $\tilde{\beta}_1 \cap L = -\tilde{\beta}_2 \cap L$ into account, we find

$$(3.8.83.2) \qquad GW_{0,2}(M; \tilde{\beta}_2)(PD[p] \otimes [L]) = \{z_0\} \times \mathbb{C}P^1.$$

Here we note that the orientation of $\mathbb{C}P^1$ on the right hand side of (3.8.83.2) is opposite to that of the pseudo-holomorphic sphere representing $\tilde{\beta}_2$. Hence

$$(3.8.84) \qquad [GW_{0,2}(M)(PD[p] \otimes [L])] \equiv T^{\omega[\mathbb{C}P^1]}(1,1) \mod T^{\omega[\mathbb{C}P^1]}\Lambda^+_{0,nov}.$$

We next calculate the left hand side of (3.8.82). Let $\beta \in H_2(M, L; \mathbb{Z})$ be the image of $\tilde{\beta}_i$. ($\tilde{\beta}_1$ and $\tilde{\beta}_2$ go to the same element of $H_2(M, L; \mathbb{Z})$.) We identify $\mathbb{C}P^1 = \mathbb{C} \cup \{\infty\}$ and $z_0 = 0$, $w_0 = \infty$. Then

$$(3.8.85) \qquad \mathcal{M}^{\mathrm{main,reg}}_{0,1}(L; \beta) \;_{ev} \times \{p\} \cong (0, \infty)$$

and $r \in (0, \infty)$ is identified with a holomorphic map $u_r : D^2 \to M$ defined by $u_r(z) = (rz, r/\bar{z})$. (Note $u_r(0) = p$ and $u_r(\partial D^2) \subseteq L$.) (See Figure 3.8.8.) It follows that $\mathcal{M}^{\mathrm{reg}}_{1,1}(L; \beta) \;_{ev} \times \{p\} \cong \mathbb{R} \times S^1$ and

$$[ev_0(\mathcal{M}^{\mathrm{main}}_{1,1}(L; \beta) \;_{ev} \times \{p\})] = \pm[L].$$

Namely

$$\mathfrak{q}_{1,0}(PD[p] \otimes 1) \equiv \pm T^{\omega[\mathbb{C}P^1]}[L] \mod T^{\omega[\mathbb{C}P^1]}\Lambda^+_{0,nov}.$$

Thus we have

$$(3.8.86) \qquad [\mathfrak{p}_{0,1}(1 \otimes \mathfrak{q}_{1,0}(PD[p] \otimes 1))] \equiv \pm T^{\omega[\mathbb{C}P^1]}[L] \mod T^{\omega[\mathbb{C}P^1]}\Lambda^+_{0,nov}.$$

This is consistent with (3.8.82), (3.8.84). (We do not try to check the sign here.)

We remark that the two ends of the moduli space (3.8.85) correspond to the trivial disc plus sphere bubble. Those bubbles correspond to (3.8.83.1) and (3.8.83.2), respectively.

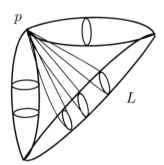

Figure 3.8.8

Now let $\mathfrak{b} \in C^2(M; \Lambda^+_{0,nov})$, with $\delta_M \mathfrak{b} = 0$. We define

$$\mathfrak{p}^{\mathfrak{b}}_k : B^{\mathrm{cyc}}_k C_{1+}(L; \Lambda_{0,nov})[1] \longrightarrow S^*(M; \Lambda_{0,nov})$$

by

$$\mathfrak{p}^{\mathfrak{b}}_k(\mathbf{x}) = \sum_{\ell} \mathfrak{p}_{\ell,k}(\mathfrak{b}^\ell \otimes \mathbf{x}) = \mathfrak{p}(e^{\mathfrak{b}} \otimes \mathbf{x}).$$

We then have

(3.8.87.1) $\mathfrak{p}_1^\mathfrak{b} \equiv i_! \mod \Lambda_{0,nov}^+$.

(3.8.87.2) $\mathfrak{p}^\mathfrak{b} \circ \widehat{d}^{\mathfrak{b},\mathrm{cyc}} + \delta_M \circ \mathfrak{p}_k^\mathfrak{b} = 0$, for $k > 0$.

(3.8.87.3) $\mathfrak{p}_1^\mathfrak{b} \circ \mathfrak{m}_0^\mathfrak{b}(1) + \delta_M \circ \mathfrak{p}_0^\mathfrak{b}(1) + \sum_\ell \dfrac{1}{\ell!} GW_{0,\ell+1}(M)(\mathfrak{b}^{\otimes \ell} \otimes L) = 0$.

This is the same formula as (3.8.10.1),(3.8.10.2),(3.8.10.3). In other words, we can use $\mathfrak{p}_k^\mathfrak{b}$ in place of $\mathfrak{p}_k$ when we study $HF((L,(\mathfrak{b},b)),(L,(\mathfrak{b},b'));\Lambda_{0,nov})$.

We can generalize Theorem 3.8.11 as follows. We recall from Definition 3.8.40 that

$$\widehat{\mathcal{M}}^\mathfrak{b}(L) = \{b \in C(L;\Lambda_{0,nov}^+) \mid (\mathfrak{b},b) \in \widehat{\mathcal{M}}_{\mathrm{def}}(L)\}$$

and $\widehat{\mathcal{M}}_{\mathrm{weak}}^\mathfrak{b}(L)$ is defined in a similar way.

Let $[o_i(L;\mathfrak{b})]$ be the obstruction classes for $\mathcal{M}^\mathfrak{b}(L)$ being nonempty. (See Theorem 3.6.18.) $[o_i(L;\mathfrak{b};\mathrm{weak})]$ is defined in a similar way. (See Theorem 3.6.43.)

THEOREM 3.8.88. *Let $L \subset M$ be a relatively spin Lagrangian submanifold and $\mathfrak{b} \in H^2(M;\Lambda_{0,nov}^+)$.*

(3.8.89.1)   *If*

$$(3.8.90) \qquad \sum_{\ell=0}^\infty \frac{1}{\ell!}[GW_{0,\ell+1}(M)(\mathfrak{b}^{\otimes \ell} \otimes L)] \neq 0,$$

then $\widehat{\mathcal{M}}^\mathfrak{b}(L) = \emptyset$.

(3.8.89.2)   *If the left hand side of the formula (3.8.90) is 0, then the obstruction $[o_i(L;\mathfrak{b})]$ lies in the kernel of the Gysin homomorphism*

$$i_! : H^{2-\mu_i}(L;\mathbb{Q}) \to H^{n+2-\mu_i}(M;\mathbb{Q}).$$

(3.8.89.3)   *If the left hand side of the formula (3.8.90) is not of the form $c\,PD_M[L]$ then $\widehat{\mathcal{M}}_{\mathrm{weak}}^\mathfrak{b}(L) = \emptyset$.*

(3.8.89.4)   *If the left hand side of (3.8.90) is of the form $c\,PD_M[L]$ then*

$$o_i(L;\mathfrak{b};\mathrm{weak}) \in \mathrm{Ker}(i_! : H^{2-\mu_i}(L;\mathbb{Q}) \to H^{n+2-\mu_i}(M;\mathbb{Q})).$$

(3.8.89.5)   *If the left hand side of (3.8.90) is $c\,PD_M[L]$, $b \in \widehat{\mathcal{M}}_{\mathrm{weak}}^\mathfrak{b}(L)$, and $[L] \neq 0$ in $H(M;\mathbb{Q})$, then*

$$c = \mathfrak{PD}(\mathfrak{b},b).$$

The proof of Theorem 3.8.88 is the same as the proof of Theorem 3.8.11 using (3.8.87) and is omitted.

REMARK 3.8.91. We remark that we can not generalize Lemma 3.8.14 to our situation. Namely the left hand side of (3.8.90) may have a nontrivial $H^*(M;\mathbb{Q}) \otimes \Lambda_{0,nov}^+$ component with $* = 2n, 2n-1$.

In fact if $\mathfrak{b} \in H^n(M;\mathbb{Q}) \otimes \Lambda_{0,nov}^+$ with $\mathfrak{b} \cap L \neq 0$ then

$$GW_{0,2}(M;\tilde{\beta}_0)(\mathfrak{b},L) = PD_M(\mathfrak{b} \cap L) \neq 0.$$

Here $\tilde{\beta}_0 = 0$, and $PD_M : H_d(M;\mathbb{Q}) \otimes \Lambda_{0,nov} \to H^{2n-d}(M;\mathbb{Q}) \otimes \Lambda_{0,nov}$ is the Poincaré duality of M.

We can partially generalize Lemma 3.8.14 as follows.

LEMMA 3.8.92. *Let* $B_j \in H(M; \mathbb{Q})$, $j = 1, \cdots, \ell$. *We assume*

$$GW_{0,\ell+1}(M, \tilde{\beta})(B_1, \cdots, B_\ell, L) \in H^*(M; \mathbb{Q}) \otimes \Lambda^+_{0,nov}$$

with $* = 2n$ *or* $2n - 1$. *We assume, in addition, that one of the following conditions is satisfied.*

(3.8.93.1) $\tilde{\beta} \neq 0$ *in* $H_2(M; \mathbb{Z})$.
(3.8.93.2) $\ell \neq 1$.

Then $GW_{0,\ell+1}(M, \tilde{\beta})([B_1, \cdots, B_\ell, L]) = 0$.

PROOF. We put $d_j = \deg B_j = 2n - \dim B_j$. We have

$$* = n - 2c_1(M)[\tilde{\beta}] + 2 + \sum_{j=1}^{\ell}(d_j - 2),$$

since $\dim \mathcal{M}_{0,\ell+2}(M; \tilde{\beta}) = 2n + 2c_1(M)[\tilde{\beta}] - 2 + 2\ell$. This implies that the virtual dimension of the moduli space

(3.8.94) $$\mathcal{M}_{0,\ell+1}(M; \tilde{\beta}) \times_{M^\ell} (B_1 \times \cdots \times B_\ell)$$

is $2n - 4 + 2c_1(M)[\tilde{\beta}] + \sum_{j=1}^{\ell}(2 - d_j) = 3n - * - 2$. Thus, by the assumption,

$$\dim \mathcal{M}_{0,\ell+1}(M; \tilde{\beta}) \times_{M^\ell} (B_1 \times \cdots \times B_\ell) = n - 2 \quad \text{or} \quad n - 1.$$

Therefore the fiber product

$$\mathcal{M}_{0,\ell+1}(M; \tilde{\beta}) \times_{M^{\ell+1}} (B_1 \times \cdots \times B_\ell \times L)$$

is empty. We may take the perturbation of

(3.8.95) $$\mathcal{M}_{0,\ell+2}(M; \tilde{\beta}) \times_{M^{\ell+1}} (B_1 \times \cdots \times B_\ell \times L)$$

compatible with the forgetful map

$$\mathcal{M}_{0,\ell+2}(M; \tilde{\beta}) \times_{M^{\ell+1}} (B_1 \times \cdots \times B_\ell \times L)$$
$$\to \mathcal{M}_{0,\ell+1}(M; \tilde{\beta}) \times_{M^{\ell+1}} (B_1 \times \cdots \times B_\ell \times L),$$

and ev_0 is compatible with evaluation map. (See Section 23 [**FuOn99II**].) Note we use our assumption (3.8.93) here. In fact in the case $\tilde{\beta} = \tilde{\beta}_0 = 0$ and $\ell = 1$, $\mathcal{M}_{0,2}(M; \tilde{\beta}_0)$ is empty since constant map from sphere with two marked points is unstable. (On the other hand, $\mathcal{M}_{0,3}(M; \tilde{\beta}_0)$ is M and is nonempty.)

Since (3.8.95) is an emptyset under the given hypothesis we have

$$[GW_{0,\ell+1}(M, \tilde{\beta})([B_1, \cdots, B_\ell, L])] = 0.$$

$\square$

Let $\Pi^d : H(M; \Lambda_{0,nov}) \to H^d(M; \mathbb{Q}) \otimes \Lambda_{0,nov}$ be the projection. We use Lemma 3.8.92 and (3.8.87.3) to find

$$\Pi^* \left(\mathfrak{p}_1^{\mathfrak{b}} \circ \mathfrak{m}_0^{\mathfrak{b}}(1) + \delta_M \circ \mathfrak{p}_0^{\mathfrak{b}}(1) \right) = \Pi^*(PD_M([L] \cap \mathfrak{b}))$$

for $* = 2n - 1$ or $* = 2n$. We can use it to prove the following Corollary 3.8.96 which generalize Corollary 3.8.16.

COROLLARY 3.8.96. *We assume either*

(a) $\Pi^n(PD_L(\mathfrak{b} \cap L)) = 0$, *or*
(b) $\Pi^{n-1}(PD_L(\mathfrak{b} \cap L)) = 0$.

(Here $PD_L : H_d(L; \mathbb{Q}) \otimes \Lambda_{0,nov} \to H^{n-d}(L; \mathbb{Q}) \otimes \Lambda_{0,nov}$ is the Poincaré duality in L.)

(1) *We assume* (a) *and that the obstruction class $[o_i(L; \mathfrak{b})]$ is defined and in $H^n(L; \mathbb{Q})$. Then we have $[o_i(L; \mathfrak{b})] = 0$.*
(2) *We assume* (b). *If $[o_i(L; \mathfrak{b})] \in H^{n-1}(L; \mathbb{Q})$ then $i_!(o_i(L; \mathfrak{b})) = 0$.*

The same applies to $[o_i(L; \mathfrak{b}; \text{weak})]$.

We can use Corollary 3.8.96 to prove the following two corollaries which partially generalize Corollary 3.8.19.

COROLLARY 3.8.97. *Let L be a relatively spin Lagrangian submanifold which is a rational homology sphere. Let*

$$\mathfrak{b} \in \bigoplus_{*\geq 2} H^*(M; \mathbb{Q}) \otimes \Lambda^+_{0,nov}.$$

We assume $\Pi^n(PD_L(\mathfrak{b} \cap L)) = 0$. We assume in addition that there exists no pseudo-holomorphic disc of nonnegative Maslov index which bounds L. Then

$$(3.8.98) \qquad \sum_{\ell=0}^{\infty} \frac{1}{\ell!} [GW_{0,\ell+1}(M)(\mathfrak{b}^{\otimes \ell} \otimes L)] = 0.$$

PROOF. Since L is a rational homology sphere $[o_i(L; \mathfrak{b})]$ lies either in $H^n(L; \mathbb{Q})$ or in $H^0(L; \mathbb{Q})$. Non-existence of pseudo-holomorphic disc with nonnegative Maslov index which bounds L and $\mathfrak{b}$ having degree ≥ 2 imply that

$$\mathfrak{m}_0^{\mathfrak{b}}(1) \in \bigoplus_{*\geq 2} H^*(M; \mathbb{Q}) \otimes \Lambda^+_{0,nov}.$$

Therefore $[o_i(L; \mathfrak{b})]$ does not lie in $H^0(L; \mathbb{Q})$. Then $[o_i(L; \mathfrak{b})] = 0$ follows from Corollary 3.8.96. Now Theorem 3.8.88 (1) implies Corollary 3.8.97. $\qquad \square$

COROLLARY 3.8.99. *Let L be a relatively spin Lagrangian submanifold with vanishing Maslov index. Let $\mathfrak{b} \in H^2(M; \mathbb{Q}) \otimes \Lambda^+_{0,nov}$. Assume $H^2(L; \mathbb{Q}) = 0$.*
Then (3.8.98) *holds.*

PROOF. We can prove that $[o_i(L; \mathfrak{b})]$ lies in $H^2(M; \mathbb{Q})$ by degree counting. Therefore by assumption $\widehat{\mathcal{M}}^{\mathfrak{b}}(L) \neq \emptyset$. Corollary 3.8.99 follows from Theorem 3.8.88 (1). $\qquad \square$

3.8.10. Proof of parts of Theorems B, C and G. Now we summarize the results so far and see that they imply Theorem B (B.2), Theorem C, and Theorem G (G.1),(G.5) (and the construction of Floer cohomologies in Theorems B and G).

The construction of the Floer cohomology of Theorem B is a consequence of Proposition 3.7.17 and Definition 3.8.40. (B.2) then is a consequence of Proposition 3.7.87 (2) and Definition 3.8.38.

Theorem C follows from Theorem 3.8.50 and Corollary 3.8.96. Namely the statements of Theorem C except $m_k < \dim L/2$ are consequences of Theorem 3.8.50.

We will use Corollary 3.8.96 to prove $o_k^{\dim L}(L; \mathrm{def}) = 0$ as follows. We put $n = \dim L$.

We consider the proof of Theorem 3.8.41. We will prove by induction that we can choose $\mathfrak{b}_{(i)}$ such that $\Pi^n(\mathfrak{b}_{(i)}) = 0$. Namely the $H^n(M; \mathbb{Q}) \otimes \Lambda^+_{0,nov}$ component of $\mathfrak{b}_{(i)}$.

Suppose we have chosen such $\mathfrak{b}_{(i)}$ for $i < k$. Then we can apply Corollary 3.8.96 (1). Therefore if $o_k(L : \mathrm{weak}, \mathrm{def}) \in H^n(L; \mathbb{Q})$ then it is automatically 0. This implies that when we choose $\mathfrak{b}_k$ such that (3.8.47) is satisfied, we may choose $\mathfrak{b}_k = 0$ if $o_k(L : \mathrm{weak}, \mathrm{def}) \in H^n(L; \mathbb{Q})$. Note $\mathfrak{b}_k \in H^n(M; Q)$ if and only if $o_k(L : \mathrm{weak}, \mathrm{def}) \in H^n(L; \mathbb{Q})$. Thus induction works.

We proved at the same time that if $o_k(L : \mathrm{weak}, \mathrm{def}) \in H^n(L; \mathbb{Q})$ then $o_k(L : \mathrm{weak}, \mathrm{def}) = 0$. This is what we wanted to prove.

Note also that the condition $o_k^{\dim L}(L; \mathrm{def}) = 0$ is equivalent to the condition $o_k^{\dim L}(L; \mathrm{weak}, \mathrm{def}) = 0$ by Proposition 3.8.54.

The existence of Floer cohomology in Theorem G is also a consequence of Proposition 3.7.17 and Definition 3.8.58. (G.1) follows from Proposition 3.7.75 and its analog which asserts that operation $\mathfrak{r}, \mathfrak{r}^+$ coincides with $\mathfrak{q}, \mathfrak{q}^+$ in case $L^{(1)} = L^{(0)}$. (The proof of this fact is similar to the proof of Proposition 3.7.75.) (G.5) is a consequence of Proposition 3.7.93.

CHAPTER 4

Homotopy equivalence of A_∞ algebras

4.1. Outline of Chapters 4 and 5

In Chapter 3, we have constructed the filtered A_∞ algebra $(C(L; \Lambda_{0,nov}), \mathfrak{m})$ associated to a relatively spin Lagrangian submanifold L and the filtered A_∞ bimodule $C(L^{(1)}, L^{(0)}; \Lambda_{0,nov})$ for a relatively spin pair $(L^{(0)}, L^{(1)})$. In this chapter and the next, we study dependence of the filtered A_∞ algebra $C(L; \Lambda_{0,nov})$, the filtered A_∞ bimodule $C(L^{(1)}, L^{(0)}; \Lambda_{0,nov})$ and the Floer cohomology on the Hamiltonian deformations, other parameters involved in the definitions: that is, the compatible almost complex structure J, the perturbation (multisection) $\mathfrak{s}$, triangulation of $\mathfrak{s}^{-1}(0)$, and the choice of countable set of smooth singular simplices. Among them, we define the gauge equivalence relation on the set of the bounding cochains b (the solutions of the Maurer-Cartan equation) and study dependence of the Floer cohomology on the choice of the bounding cochain b. Throughout these two chapters, we assume that a Lagrangian submanifold L is orientable and relatively spin, and that a pair of two Lagrangian submanifolds is relatively spin. (See Definition 3.1.1 in Section 3.1.)

First we explain the reason why the Floer cohomology depends on various choices (especially on the bounding cochain b). We recall that the basic trouble being discussed in this book in defining the Floer cohomology of Lagrangian submanifolds lies in the fact that in general the moduli space of pseudo-holomorphic discs has codimension one boundary. It means that the fundamental cycle of the moduli space of pseudo-holomorphic discs may not be well-defined in the usual sense.

A similar phenomenon was found by Donaldson [**Don86II**] in his study of the moduli space of solutions of ASD equation on 4-manifolds with $b_2^+ = 1$. In that case, Donaldson observed that if we consider one parameter family of perturbations (especially the perturbation of Riemannian metric), then the homology class of the moduli space may jump at some point. This phenomenon is called the *wall crossing*. We recall how the wall crossing occurs for the case, for simplicity, where the virtual dimension of the moduli space is 0. The order, counted with sign, of the moduli space is the invariant (Donaldson invariant). If we consider one parameter family of perturbations, we have one parameter family $\mathcal{M}_s$ of moduli spaces ($s \in [0,1]$) whose union $\cup_s \{s\} \times \mathcal{M}_s$ is a one dimensional manifold. Independence of the invariant under the perturbation could be proved by a cobordism argument if $\cup_s \{s\} \times \mathcal{M}_s$ were compact for a generic one parameter family, in which case its boundary would become $-\mathcal{M}_0 \cup \mathcal{M}_1$. However in the case where the bubbling phenomenon is of codimension one, we cannot completely avoid bubbling even for a generic one parameter family and so the parameterized moduli space $\cup_s \{s\} \times \mathcal{M}_s$ is not compact in general. Therefore the cobordism argument cannot prove independence of the invariant thus constructed on the perturbation involved.

191

In the gauge theory, Donaldson introduced the "chamber structure" to handle this trouble. In that case, the trouble has a nice feature that we can control where the wall crossing occurs, in terms of the abelian gauge theory which is nothing but the cohomology theory. Namely the wall crossing occurs at the points where there exists a nonzero anti-self-dual harmonic 2 form whose cohomology class is integral. In particular, if we take a perturbation which does not change the abelian gauge theory (especially the perturbation which does not change the Riemannian metric) then the wall crossing does not occur. So the Donaldson invariant is well-defined, for example, if we fix a Riemannian metric. The problem is similar in the case of Seiberg-Witten invariant of 4-manifolds with $b_2^+ = 1$.

In our situation, the problem is more non trivial, because we do not have any control where the wall crossing might occur. So we are forced to consider the whole family of perturbations to obtain something invariant under the perturbations. To carry out this, we will investigate infinitesimal structure of the moduli space of (unobstructed) Lagrangian submanifolds. Let us take and fix a Lagrangian submanifold L of M. (We also fix a compatible almost complex structure J.) We are going to find a formal neighborhood of L in the extended moduli space of Lagrangian submanifolds. For another Lagrangian submanifold L' near L, we say that $L \sim L'$ if there exists a Hamiltonian isotopy ψ_s such that $L' = \psi_1(L)$. One can see that the set of $\sim$ equivalence classes of such Lagrangian submanifolds is isomorphic to a neighborhood of 0 in the first cohomology group $H^1(L; \mathbb{R})$. (There exists a trouble related to the Hausdorffness of the moduli space of Lagrangian submanifolds. We do not discuss this since we concern only with the local problem here. See Section 1 [**Fuk02I**].)

Because of various reasons (especially because of the presence of relative homology class $H_2(M; L)$ of nonzero Maslov-index), we want to extend this parameter space to $H^{odd}(L; \mathbb{R})$. Only $H^1(L; \mathbb{R})$-direction of this extended space $H^{odd}(L; \mathbb{R})$ has direct geometric meaning. But one can still define deformations of "Floer (co)homology" to other directions. As we will explain below, our construction is similar to that of deformations of the cup product using the genus 0 Gromov-Witten invariant: Let M be a symplectic manifold. The space $H^2(M; \mathbb{R})$ parameterizes (locally) the moduli space of symplectic structures of M. The Gromov-Witten theory and the Frobenius structure obtained from it is regarded as a family of deformations of the cup product of M parameterized by $H^{even}(M; \mathbb{R})$, which is the "extended moduli space of symplectic structures on M". The deformations to $H^2(M; \mathbb{R})$-direction have obvious geometric meaning, that is the deformation of symplectic forms. This deformation space is extended to $H^{even}(M; \mathbb{R})$ direction also by using the Gromov-Witten potential. One may extend it to $H^{odd}(M; \mathbb{R})$ direction by regarding this parameter space as a super space. (See [**ASKZ97, Dub96, KoMa94, Man99, Ran96**].)

The extended moduli space of Lagrangian submanifolds which we mentioned above is a natural analog to the extended moduli space that appeared in the Frobenius structure and Gromov-Witten potentials. We consider the formal neighborhood of a Lagrangian submanifold L in this extended moduli space, which is the zero set of a formal power series expansion of the defining equation of the moduli space or of the Kuranishi map. (The convergence of this formal power series is not known yet.) In other words, we are studying our moduli space as a formal scheme. The set of bounding cochains $\widehat{\mathcal{M}}(L)$ we introduced in the last chapter, after dividing it out by appropriate gauge equivalence which we will define in this chapter, will turn out to be this formal scheme $\mathcal{M}(L)$. See Sections 1.4 and 5.4.

One important fact on the Gromov-Witten potential is that the extended moduli space of deformations of the symplectic structure is *not obstructed*. Namely the full neighborhood of zero in $H^{even}(M, \mathbb{R})$ locally parameterizes the extended moduli space. The group $H^{odd}(M, \mathbb{R})$ in principle is the obstruction group. However the obstruction map or the Kuranishi map is identically zero for the case of the Gromov-Witten potential. This fact is consistent with the mirror symmetry in the following way: Let $M^{\vee}$ be the mirror of M. Then a part of $H^{odd}(M; \mathbb{C})$ will be isomorphic to $H^2(M^{\vee}, TM^{\vee})$ which is the vector space where the obstruction to the Kodaira-Spencer deformation theory lives. In other words, this is the space where the Kuranishi map (of the deformation theory of complex structure) takes its value. However the Kuranishi map is automatically 0 for the Calabi-Yau manifold. For the classical direction $H^1(M^{\vee}, TM^{\vee})$ this fact was proved by Bogomolov-Tian-Todorov [**Bog78, Tia87, Tod89**]. For the other extended directions $H^k(M^{\vee}, \Omega^{odd-k}M^{\vee})$, this fact was proved by Baranikov-Kontsevich [**BaKo98**].

On the other hand, our extended moduli space of Lagrangian submanifolds is indeed *obstructed* in general. The corresponding obstruction map or the Kuranishi map is exactly our obstruction class. Thus, finding a formal neighborhood of extended moduli space of (unobstructed) Lagrangian submanifolds is equivalent to studying the behavior of the obstruction class in a neighborhood of L. Our problem of understanding dependence of the obstruction class and of the Floer cohomology on the perturbation is closely related to this study. The obstruction phenomenon we mentioned above is directly related to the wall crossing phenomenon we mentioned before. Namely wall crossing occurs because the parametrized version of the obstruction class is nonzero.

Now we describe the contents of Chapters 4 and 5. Chapter 4 is devoted to studying the homotopy equivalence of filtered A_{∞} algebras and Chapter 5 to that of filtered A_{∞} bimodules. These two chapters contain both algebraic and geometric discussions. The algebraic part is a homotopical (homological) algebra of A_{∞} structures. There are various references about it. (See for example [**Fuk02II,03II, Kel01, Lef03, MSS02, Smi00, Sei06**].) However we include self contained discussions in this book, since there is no discussion in the case of a *filtered A_{∞} algebra* in the literature. Moreover the relation to the gauge equivalence of the bounding cochains is not so transparent in the literature, and we need to include discussion about (homotopy) unit and to handle the case over torsion coefficient for the application in [**FOOO09I**].

The first four sections Sections 4.2-4.5 are of purely algebraic nature. (In Subsection 4.3.3 we discuss the gauge equivalence on $\widehat{\mathcal{M}}_{weak,def}(L)$. In Chapter 3, when we introduced the notion of bulk deformation we used the operator $\mathfrak{q}$ which is defined geometrically. However, the results also holds for any filtered A_{∞} algebra which has an operator $\mathfrak{q}$ satisfying the conclusion of Theorem 3.8.32.) In Section 4.2, we introduce the notion of two (filtered) A_{∞} homomorphisms to be *homotopic* each other and establish basic properties about homotopy between (filtered) A_{∞} homomorphisms. This allows us to define two (filtered) A_{∞} algebras are *homotopy equivalent*. In Definition 3.2.33, we introduced a notion that a (filtered) A_{∞} homomorphism is a *weak homotopy equivalence*. In fact, a (filtered) A_{∞} homomorphism is a homotopy equivalence if and only if it is a weak homotopy equivalence

(Theorem 4.2.45 proved in Section 4.5). This gives a nice criterion for an A_∞ homomorphism to be a homotopy equivalence. The key result (Theorem 4.2.34) to prove basic properties of homotopy of A_∞ homomorphisms is proved in Section 4.4.

In Section 4.3, we introduce the notion that two bounding cochains are *gauge equivalent*, and establish its basic properties. It is an equivalence relation and we divide the set of bounding cochains $\widehat{\mathcal{M}}(C)$ by this gauge equivalence relation to get a set $\mathcal{M}(C)$. (Later on in Section 5.4 we will define a structure on $\mathcal{M}(C)$.) We show that it is invariant of the homotopy type of the filtered A_∞ algebra C.

In Section 4.6, we will consider our geometric situation and show that the homotopy type (in the sense of Section 4.3) of our filtered A_∞ algebra $(C(L; \Lambda_{0,nov}), \mathfrak{m})$ associated to a relatively spin Lagrangian submanifold L is independent of various choices involved. More precisely, we will prove the following Theorem 4.1.1.

Let (M, ω), (M', ω') be symplectic manifolds and $L \subset M$ and $L' \subset M'$ Lagrangian submanifolds. Let $\psi : M \to M'$ be a symplectic diffeomorphism such that $\psi(L) = L'$. We fix various choices we made (compatible almost complex structures, perturbations, triangulation, and countable sets of smooth singular simplices), for M, L and M', L' to define $(C(L; \Lambda_{0,nov}), \mathfrak{m})$ and $(C(L'; \Lambda_{0,nov}), \mathfrak{m})$.

THEOREM 4.1.1. *In the above situation, there exists a homotopically unital filtered A_∞ homomorphism $\psi_* : (C(L; \Lambda_{0,nov}), \mathfrak{m}) \to (C(L'; \Lambda_{0,nov}), \mathfrak{m})$ induced by ψ, which is a homotopy equivalence of the filtered A_∞ algebras.*

If we consider the case when $M = M'$ and $L = L'$, Theorem 4.1.1 implies that our filtered A_∞ algebra $(C(L; \Lambda_{0,nov}), \mathfrak{m})$ is invariant of various choices involved up to homotopy equivalence.

Moreover we will prove that the homotopy equivalence ψ_* in Theorem 4.1.1 is independent of various choices involved up to homotopy. Namely we will prove:

THEOREM 4.1.2. *In the situation of Theorem 4.1.1, we take a one parameter family $\{\psi_s\}_s$ $(0 \le s \le 1)$ of symplectic diffeomorphisms such that $\psi_s(L) = L'$ for each s. Then ψ_{0*} is homotopic to ψ_{1*} as homotopically unital filtered A_∞ homomorphisms.*

These two theorems together with algebraic results in sections Sections 4.2-4.5 imply that the set $\mathcal{M}(L)$ of the gauge equivalence classes of the bounding cochains is independent of various choices involved up to canonical isomorphism. It also implies that the Floer cohomology $HF((L, b_1), (L, b_0); \Lambda_{0,nov})$ depends only on the gauge equivalence classes of b_i. More precisely, we have the following.

THEOREM 4.1.3. *In the situation of Theorem 4.1.1, there exists a bijection $\psi_* : \mathcal{M}(L) \to \mathcal{M}(L')$ which depends only of the homotopy class of ψ (in the sense of Theorem 4.1.2).*

Moreover, if $b_0, b_1 \in \widehat{\mathcal{M}}(L)$, $b'_0, b'_1 \in \widehat{\mathcal{M}}(L')$ and $\psi_*[b_i] = [b'_i] \in \mathcal{M}(L')$, then there exists a canonical isomorphism

$$\psi_* : HF((L, b_1), (L, b_0); \Lambda_{0,nov}) \to HF((L', b'_1), (L', b'_0); \Lambda_{0,nov}).$$

Theorem B (B.3) and (B.4) in the introduction follows from Theorem 4.1.3 and its 'def,weak' version. See Subsection 4.6.5.

Chapter 5 deals with the case when there are two Lagrangian submanifolds or (filtered) A_∞ bimodules. In Section 5.1, we discuss relations of various Novikov rings which appear in the theory of Floer cohomologies. In Section 5.2, we study homotopy between (filtered) A_∞ bimodule homomorphisms, in a way similar to the case of (filtered) A_∞ algebras. Namely we define *homotopy between (filtered) A_∞ bimodule homomorphisms* and define *homotopy equivalence of A_∞ bimodules*, etc.

Section 5.3 is devoted to the geometric part of the construction. We will construct homotopy equivalence between filtered A_∞ bimodules associated to a relatively spin pair of Lagrangian submanifolds $(L^{(0)}, L^{(1)})$ defined in Section 3.7. It implies that Floer cohomology $HF((L^{(1)}, b^{(1)}), (L^{(0)}, b^{(0)}))$ between two Lagrangian submanifolds is independent of various choices involved in the construction (but *depends* on the gauge equivalence classes of $b^{(0)}, b^{(1)}$), and of Hamiltonian perturbations of $L^{(0)}, L^{(1)}$.

To be precise, there are two different cases, which we have to discuss in a different way. One is the case when we move two Lagrangian submanifolds $L^{(0)}$ and $L^{(1)}$ by the *same symplectic diffeomorphism*, the other is the case when we move $L^{(0)}$ and $L^{(1)}$ by *different Hamiltonian isotopies*. In the first case, Floer cohomology over $\Lambda_{0,nov}$ is preserved, while in the second case, only the Floer cohomology over Λ_{nov} (see (Conv.4) in Chapter 1) is preserved. We will discuss this point in Section 5.3 and again in Chapter 6 when we prove Theorem J. More precisely, we have the following two theorems.

We first consider the following situation. Let $(L^{(0)}, L^{(1)})$ and $(L^{(0)\prime}, L^{(1)\prime})$ be relatively spin pairs of Lagrangian submanifolds of symplectic manifolds M and M' respectively. Let $\psi : M \to M'$ be a symplectic diffeomorphism such that $\psi(L^{(0)}) = L^{(0)\prime}$, $\psi(L^{(1)}) = L^{(1)\prime}$ and preserving relative spin structure. We fix families of compatible almost complex structures J_t, J_t' as well as other choices to define the filtered A_∞ bimodules $C(L^{(1)}, L^{(0)}; \Lambda_{0,nov})$, $C(L^{(1)\prime}, L^{(0)\prime}; \Lambda_{0,nov})$ in Section 3.7.

THEOREM 4.1.4. *Let* $b^{(0)} \in \widehat{\mathcal{M}}(L^{(0)})$, $b^{(1)} \in \widehat{\mathcal{M}}(L^{(1)})$, $b^{(0)\prime} \in \widehat{\mathcal{M}}(L^{(0)\prime})$, *and* $b^{(1)\prime} \in \widehat{\mathcal{M}}(L^{(1)\prime})$. *Suppose that* $\psi_*([b^{(0)}]) = [b^{(0)\prime}]$ *and* $\psi_*([b^{(1)}]) = [b^{(1)\prime}]$. *Then there exists an isomorphism*

$$\psi_* : HF((L^{(1)}, b^{(1)}), (L^{(0)}, b^{(0)}); \Lambda_{0,nov}) \cong HF((L^{(1)\prime}, b^{(1)\prime}), (L^{(0)\prime}, b^{(0)\prime}); \Lambda_{0,nov}).$$

Moreover, if $\{\psi_s\}_s$ $(0 \le s \le 1)$ *is an isotopy of symplectic diffeomorphisms such that* $\psi_s(L^{(0)}) = L^{(0)\prime}$, $\psi_s(L^{(1)}) = L^{(1)\prime}$ *for each* s, *then* ψ_{0*} *is equal to* ψ_{1*}.

If we consider the case when $M = M'$ and $L^{(i)} = L^{(i)\prime}$ $(i = 0, 1)$ in Theorem 4.1.4, then it implies that Floer cohomology does not depend on the various choices involved in the definition.

For example, let us consider the case when $\dim_{\mathbb{R}} M = 4$, $c_1(M) = 0$ and the Maslov indices of $L^{(0)}$ and $L^{(1)}$ vanish. Then for generic compatible almost complex structures on M, there is no pseudo-holomorphic disc bounding $L^{(0)}, L^{(1)}$. Hence our filtered A_∞ structure is equal to the classical one. In particular, we can simply take $b_0 = 0, b_1 = 0$ as their bounding cochains. However the Floer cohomology

$$HF((L^{(1)}, 0), (L^{(0)}, 0); \Lambda_{0,nov})$$

depends on the choice of the almost complex structure. We can explain this phenomenon using Theorems 4.1.1, 4.1.4 as follows. If we change almost complex structures from J to J', then we have a filtered A_∞ homomorphism

$$\mathfrak{f} : (C(L^{(i)}; \Lambda_{0,nov}), \mathfrak{m}) \longrightarrow (C(L^{(i)}; \Lambda_{0,nov}), \mathfrak{m}).$$

(Note that since quantum effects are both zero, our filtered A_∞ algebras do not depend on J.) The induced homomorphism $\mathfrak{f}_* : \widehat{\mathcal{M}}(L^{(i)}) \to \widehat{\mathcal{M}}(L^{(i)})$ is in general *non trivial*. Hence by Theorem 4.1.4 we have an isomorphism

$$HF((L^{(1)}, 0), (L^{(0)}, 0); \Lambda_{0,nov}) \cong HF((L^{(1)}, \mathfrak{f}_*(0)), (L^{(0)}, \mathfrak{f}_*(0)); \Lambda_{0,nov}).$$

This is an example of the wall crossing phenomenon we mentioned at the beginning of this section.

Theorem 4.1.4 is deduced from Theorem 5.3.1 in Subsection 5.3.1 using an algebraic argument explained in Subsection 5.3.7. We next consider the following situation. Let $(L^{(0)}, L^{(1)})$ and $(L^{(0)\prime}, L^{(1)\prime})$ be relative spin pairs of Lagrangian submanifolds of a symplectic manifold M. Let $\{\psi_\rho^{(0)}\}_\rho$ and $\{\psi_\rho^{(1)}\}_\rho$ ($0 \le \rho \le 1$) be Hamiltonian isotopies such that $\psi_0^{(0)} = \psi_0^{(1)} = id$, $\psi_1^{(0)}(L^{(0)}) = L^{(0)\prime}$ and $\psi_1^{(1)}(L^{(1)}) = L^{(1)\prime}$.

THEOREM 4.1.5. *Let* $b^{(0)} \in \widehat{\mathcal{M}}(L^{(0)})$, $b^{(1)} \in \widehat{\mathcal{M}}(L^{(1)})$, $b^{(0)\prime} \in \widehat{\mathcal{M}}(L^{(0)\prime})$, *and* $b^{(1)\prime} \in \widehat{\mathcal{M}}(L^{(1)\prime})$. *Suppose that* $\psi_{1*}^{(0)}([b^{(0)}]) = [b^{(0)\prime}]$ *and* $\psi_{1*}^{(1)}([b^{(1)}]) = [b^{(1)\prime}]$. *We consider the Floer cohomology over* Λ_{nov}-*coefficients instead of* $\Lambda_{0,nov}$. *Then there exists an isomorphism*

$$(\{\psi_\rho^{(1)}\}_\rho, \{\psi_\rho^{(0)}\}_\rho)_* : HF((L^{(1)}, b^{(1)}), (L^{(0)}, b^{(0)}); \Lambda_{nov})$$
$$\cong HF((L^{(1)\prime}, b^{(1)\prime}), (L^{(0)\prime}, b^{(0)\prime}); \Lambda_{nov}).$$

Moreover, if $\{\psi_{\rho,s}^{(i)}\}_{\rho,s}$ ($i = 0, 1$) *be a two parameter family of hamiltonian isotopies such that* $\psi_{0,s}^{(i)} = id$ *and* $\psi_{1,s}^{(i)}(L^{(i)}) = L^{(i)\prime}$ *for each* s, *then we have*

$$(\{\psi_{\rho,0}^{(1)}\}_\rho, \{\psi_{\rho,0}^{(0)}\}_\rho)_* = (\{\psi_{\rho,1}^{(1)}\}_\rho, \{\psi_{\rho,1}^{(0)}\}_\rho)_*.$$

Here we restrict ourselves to Hamiltonian isotopies, because we need to show the energy estimate in Subsection 5.3.5.

There are versions of Theorems 4.1.1-4.1.5 including unit (or homotopy unit) and also the versions which include the deformation by elements of $H^2(M; \Lambda_{0,nov}^+)$ we introduced in Section 3.8. We will state them later in Subsection 5.3.7 where we prove them. Theorem G (G.3) then will follow from it.

The proof of Theorems A and F is completed in Section 5.4.

The main part of Section 5.4 is devoted to more discussion on an algebraic side of the story. The main result there is Theorem W (= Theorem 5.4.2) and Theorem 5.4.18, which are proved in Subsection 5.4.4. Another purpose of Section 5.4 is to describe our $\mathcal{M}(L)$ as a zero set of a certain formal map *(Kuranishi map)*. Namely we will prove Theorem M in Section 5.4. We also show that Floer cohomology can be regarded as an object of derived category of coherent sheaves on the product $\mathcal{M}(L^{(1)}) \times \mathcal{M}(L^{(0)})$ regarded as formal scheme. Namely we prove Theorem N in Subsection 5.4.6. We also show that under certain assumption on Maslov class of L the Floer cohomology is defined on a ring a bit smaller than $\Lambda_{0,nov}$. Especially it is defined on Λ_0 defined in Subection 1.4 in case the Maslov class L is trivial. We use it in Subsection 5.4.6 to show Corollaries O and P.

From now on we put $\psi_* = (\psi^{-1})^*$ where $(\psi^{-1})^* : H^*(X) \to H^*(Y)$ is the induced by the diffeomorphism $\psi : X \to Y$.

4.2. Homotopy equivalence of A_∞ algebras: the algebraic framework

4.2.1. Models of $[0,1] \times C$. In the next subsection, we define two (filtered) A_∞ homomorphisms to be homotopic each other. There are various ways to define it and there are various references ([**Kel01, MSS02, Smi00**]) about it. To unify several approaches we proceed as follows. In algebraic topology, homotopy between two maps f, $f' : X \to Y$ is defined by a map $H : [0,1] \times X \to Y$. So we start with defining an algebraic analog of the operation $[0,1] \times$, taking the product with $[0,1]$, for the context of (filtered) A_∞ algebras.

Let R be a commutative ring with unit. Let $\overline{C}$ be an A_∞ algebra over R and let C be a filtered A_∞ algebra over $\Lambda_{0,nov}(R)$. Here $\Lambda_{0,nov}(R)$ is the universal Novikov ring over R. See (Conv.4) in Chapter 1. We always assume that $\overline{C}$ and C are *free* and *countably generated* over R or $\Lambda_{0,nov}(R)$ and $\overline{C}$ is a R reduction of C (Definition 3.2.20). Hereafter we write $\Lambda_{0,nov}$ in place of $\Lambda_{0,nov}(R)$ in case no confusion can occur.

DEFINITION 4.2.1. An A_∞ algebra $\overline{\mathfrak{C}}$ together with A_∞ homomorphisms

$$\overline{\mathrm{Incl}} : \overline{C} \to \overline{\mathfrak{C}}, \quad \overline{\mathrm{Eval}}_{s=0} : \overline{\mathfrak{C}} \to \overline{C}, \quad \overline{\mathrm{Eval}}_{s=1} : \overline{\mathfrak{C}} \to \overline{C}$$

is said to be a *model of* $[0,1] \times \overline{C}$ if the following holds:

(4.2.2.1) $\overline{\mathrm{Incl}}_k : B_k\overline{C}[1] \to \overline{\mathfrak{C}}[1]$ is zero unless $k = 1$. The same holds for $\overline{\mathrm{Eval}}_{s=0}$ and $\overline{\mathrm{Eval}}_{s=1}$.
(4.2.2.2) $\overline{\mathrm{Eval}}_{s=0} \circ \overline{\mathrm{Incl}} = \overline{\mathrm{Eval}}_{s=1} \circ \overline{\mathrm{Incl}} = \mathrm{identity}$.
(4.2.2.3) $\overline{\mathrm{Incl}}_1 : (\overline{C}, \overline{m}) \to (\overline{\mathfrak{C}}, \overline{m})$ is a cochain homotopy equivalence and $(\overline{\mathrm{Eval}}_{s=0})_1$, $(\overline{\mathrm{Eval}}_{s=1})_1 : (\overline{\mathfrak{C}}, \overline{m}) \to (\overline{C}, \overline{m})$ are cochain homotopy equivalences.
(4.2.2.4) The (cochain) homomorphism $(\overline{\mathrm{Eval}}_{s=0})_1 \oplus (\overline{\mathrm{Eval}}_{s=1})_1 : \overline{\mathfrak{C}} \to \overline{C} \oplus \overline{C}$ is surjective.

When $\overline{C}, \overline{\mathfrak{C}}, \overline{\mathrm{Incl}}, \overline{\mathrm{Eval}}_{s=0}$, and $\overline{\mathrm{Eval}}_{s=1}$ are unital, we call $\overline{\mathfrak{C}}$ a *unital model* of $[0,1] \times \overline{C}$.

A filtered A_∞ algebra $\mathfrak{C}$ together with filtered A_∞ homomorphisms

$$\mathrm{Incl} : C \to \mathfrak{C}, \quad \mathrm{Eval}_{s=0} : \mathfrak{C} \to C, \quad \mathrm{Eval}_{s=1} : \mathfrak{C} \to C$$

is said to be a *model of* $[0,1] \times C$ if the following holds.

(4.2.3.1) $\mathrm{Incl}_k : B_kC[1] \to \mathfrak{C}$ is zero unless $k = 1$. The same holds for $\mathrm{Eval}_{s=0}$ and $\mathrm{Eval}_{s=1}$.
(4.2.3.2) $\mathrm{Eval}_{s=0} \circ \mathrm{Incl} = \mathrm{Eval}_{s=1} \circ \mathrm{Incl} = \mathrm{identity}$.
(4.2.3.3) Incl_1 induces a cochain homotopy equivalence of the complex $(\overline{C}, \overline{m}) \to (\overline{\mathfrak{C}}, \overline{m})$, and $(\mathrm{Eval}_{s=0})_1$, $(\mathrm{Eval}_{s=1})_1$ induce cochain homotopy equivalences of the complex $(\overline{\mathfrak{C}}, \overline{m}) \to (\overline{C}, \overline{m})$.
(4.2.3.4) The homomorphism $(\mathrm{Eval}_{s=0})_1 \oplus (\mathrm{Eval}_{s=1})_1 : \mathfrak{C} \to C \oplus C$ is surjective.

When $C, \mathfrak{C}, \mathrm{Incl}, \mathrm{Eval}_{s=0}$, and $\mathrm{Eval}_{s=1}$ are unital, we call $\mathfrak{C}$ a *unital model* of $[0,1] \times C$.

REMARK 4.2.4. (1) We remark that in most of the cases (for example if R is a field or $\mathbb{Z}$), (4.2.2.3) is equivalent to the condition that $\overline{\mathrm{Incl}}_1$, $(\overline{\mathrm{Eval}}_{s=0})_1$, $(\overline{\mathrm{Eval}}_{s=1})_1$ induce isomorphisms on $\overline{m}_1$ cohomology. (Similar remark applies to (4.2.3.3).) Here we note that we assume $\overline{C}$ is *free* and *countably generated* R modules. Hence the map $(\overline{\mathrm{Eval}}_{s=0})_1 \oplus (\overline{\mathrm{Eval}}_{s=1})_1$ in (4.2.2.4) turns out to be *split* surjective.

(2) We remark that in (4.2.3.3) we only assume the cochain homotopy equivalences after reducing the coefficient ring $\Lambda_{0,nov}$ to R. This is because $\mathfrak{m}_1 \circ \mathfrak{m}_1$ may be nonzero.

(3) In the case of the models which we will construct below, we have: $\mathrm{Incl}_1 = \overline{\mathrm{Incl}}_1$, $\mathrm{Eval}_1 = \overline{\mathrm{Eval}}_1$. We do not take it as a part of the definition.

EXAMPLE 4.2.5. Let X be a smooth manifold. We take $\overline{C} = \Lambda(X)$ the de Rham complex of smooth forms on X and $\overline{\mathfrak{C}} = \Lambda(\mathbb{R} \times X)$ be the de Rham complex of smooth forms on $\mathbb{R} \times X$. Let $I_i : X \to \mathbb{R} \times X$ $(i = 0, 1)$ be the inclusion $I_i(x) = (i, x)$ and $\pi : \mathbb{R} \times X \to X$ be the projection. We take $\overline{\mathrm{Incl}}_1 = \pi^*$ and $(\overline{\mathrm{Eval}}_{s=i})_1 = I_i^*$. Then clearly $\overline{\mathfrak{C}}$ satisfies Conditions (4.2.2.1) – (4.2.2.4).

In the rest of this subsection, we will construct the models of $[0, 1] \times C$ for any filtered A_∞ algebra C over $\Lambda_{0,nov}(R)$.

Firstly, we will give an example of the model when $R \supseteq \mathbb{Q}$. This model works for the most cases of our purpose. After that, we will construct the model of $[0, 1] \times C$ over general R, which leads us to be able to define the notion of homotopy equivalence over general R (for instance, over $\mathbb{Z}$ or $\mathbb{Z}/2\mathbb{Z}$).

Now we begin to discuss the case that $R \supseteq \mathbb{Q}$. The construction below is an A_∞ analog to the model given in [**GrMo81**] Chapter X for the case of differential graded algebras. Let $(C, \mathfrak{m})$ be a filtered A_∞ algebra. We consider 'formal power series'

$$(4.2.6) \qquad x(s) = \sum_i x_i(s) T^{\lambda_i}, \qquad y(s) = \sum_i y_i(s) T^{\lambda_i},$$

where $\lambda_i \geq 0$, $\lim_{i \to \infty} \lambda_i = \infty$. (We remark that λ_i are real numbers and is not necessary an integer. This is the reason we put 'formal power series' in the quote.) We assume that the coefficient functions

$$x_i : [0, 1] \to C^k[1] = C^{k+1}, \qquad y_i : [0, 1] \to C^{k-1}[1] = C^k$$

satisfy one of the following conditions.

(4.2.7.1) $x_i(s)$, $y_i(s)$ are polynomials of the variable s.
(4.2.7.2) $x_i(s)$, $y_i(s)$ are smooth functions of $s \in [0, 1]$.
(4.2.7.3) $x_i(s)$ is a continuous piecewise polynomial function of $s \in [0, 1]$. $y_i(s)$ is a piecewise polynomial function of $s \in [0, 1]$ and is not necessarily continuous.
(4.2.7.4) $x_i(s)$ is a continuous piecewise smooth function of $s \in [0, 1]$. $y_i(s)$ is a piecewise smooth function of $s \in [0, 1]$ and is not necessarily continuous.

For the cases of (4.2.7.2) and (4.2.7.4), we assume $R = \mathbb{R}$ or $\mathbb{C}$.

REMARK 4.2.8. Note that we do not equip the vector space C with any particular topology other than the one induced by the energy filtration. By smoothness in the above definition we mean that each of the coefficients with respect to a basis is smooth.

DEFINITION 4.2.9. We define $Poly([0, 1], C)$ to be the graded module such that

$$Poly([0, 1], C)^{k+1} = Poly([0, 1], C)[1]^k \cong Poly([0, 1], C[1])^k$$

is the set of all pairs (x, y) satisfying (4.2.7.1). We define the modules $C^\infty([0, 1], C)$, $PPoly([0, 1], C)$ or $PC^\infty([0, 1], C)$ similarly with the condition (4.2.7.1) replaced by (4.2.7.2), (4.2.7.3) or (4.2.7.4) respectively.

Let $\overline{C}$ be an A_∞ algebra. We define $Poly([0, 1], \overline{C})$ to be the graded module such that

$$Poly([0, 1], \overline{C})^{k+1} = Poly([0, 1], \overline{C})[1]^k \cong Poly([0, 1], \overline{C}[1])^k$$

is the set of all pairs (x, y) such that $x = x(s)$ is a $\overline{C}[1]^k = \overline{C}^{k+1}$ valued polynomial, $y = y(s)$ is a $\overline{C}[1]^{k-1} = \overline{C}^k$ valued polynomial. $C^\infty([0, 1], \overline{C})$, $PPoly([0, 1], \overline{C})$ or $PC^\infty([0, 1], \overline{C})$ are defined similarly.

REMARK 4.2.10. In the definition of $Poly([0, 1], C)^k$ we do *not* assume that the degree of $x_i(s)$ (as a polynomial of s) is bounded over i. So if we rewrite (4.2.6) as

(4.2.11)
$$x(s) = \sum_{k=0}^{\infty} x_{(k)}(T)s^k$$

where $x_{(k)}(T) \in C$, then the right hand side is not a finite sum. However it holds that $x_{(k)}(T) \in F^{\lambda_k} C$ and $\lim_{k \to \infty} \lambda_k = \infty$. In other words, $x(s)$ is in the strictly convergent power series ring $\Lambda_{0,nov}\langle\langle s \rangle\rangle$ (see [**BGR84**] 1.4.1 Definition 1).

We next define a structure of filtered A_∞ algebra on $Map([0, 1], C)$. From now on, Map stands for one of $Poly$, C^∞, $PPoly$ or PC^∞:

$$Map = Poly, \ C^\infty, \ PPoly \text{ or } PC^\infty.$$

We first define $\mathfrak{m}_k$, $k \geq 1$. Let $\mathbf{x}^i = (x^{(i)}, y^{(i)}) \in Map([0, 1], C)^{d_i}$ with $(x^{(i)}, y^{(i)})$ as in Definition 4.2.9. In particular, d_i is the unshifted degree of $x^{(i)}(s) \in C$. We consider the pair $(\tilde{x}, \tilde{y}) \in Map([0, 1], C)^{d_i+1}$ defined by

$$\tilde{x}(s) = \mathfrak{m}_k(x^{(1)}(s), \cdots, x^{(k)}(s)),$$

and

(4.2.12.1) $$\tilde{y}(s) = \sum_{j=1}^{k} (-1)^{d_1 + \cdots + d_{j-1} + j} \mathfrak{m}_k(x^{(1)}(s), \cdots, y^{(j)}(s), \cdots, x^{(k)}(s)),$$

for $k \neq 1$ and

(4.2.12.2) $$\tilde{y}(s) = \frac{\partial x(s)}{\partial s} - \mathfrak{m}_1(y(s)),$$

for $k = 1$. We then define

(4.2.12.3) $$\mathfrak{m}_k(\mathbf{x}^1, \cdots, \mathbf{x}^k) = (\tilde{x}, \tilde{y}) \qquad \text{for } k \geq 1.$$

Let $x_0 = \mathfrak{m}_0(1) \in C$. (Here $\mathfrak{m}_0$ is a part of the A_∞ structure of C). We then define $\mathfrak{m}_0$ on $Map([0, 1], C)$ by

(4.2.12.4) $$\mathfrak{m}_0(1) = (x_0, 0) \in Map([0, 1], C).$$

In case $\overline{C}$ is an A_∞ algebra we define $\overline{\mathfrak{m}}_k$ on $Map([0, 1], \overline{C})$ by the same formulas as (4.2.12.1)-(4.2.12.3) and $\overline{\mathfrak{m}}_0 = 0$. Then we can show the following.

LEMMA 4.2.13. $(Map([0,1], C), \mathfrak{m})$ *(resp.* $(Map([0,1], \overline{C}), \overline{\mathfrak{m}})$*) is a filtered* A_∞
algebra (resp. an A_∞ *algebra). If* C *has a strict unit,* $(Map([0,1], C), \mathfrak{m})$ *also has
a strict unit. The same holds for* $\overline{C}$ *and* $(Map([0,1], \overline{C}), \overline{\mathfrak{m}})$*.*

PROOF. We prove the case of a filtered A_∞ algebra only. We need to calculate

$$(\widehat{x}, \widehat{y}) := (\mathfrak{m} \circ \widehat{d})(\mathbf{x}^{(1)}, \cdots, \mathbf{x}^{(k)}).$$

It easily follows from the A_∞ formula of $(C, \mathfrak{m})$ that $\widehat{x} = 0$. We now calculate
$\widehat{y} = \widehat{y}(s)$. We put

$$_{(j)}\mathbf{x}(s) = x^{(1)}(s) \otimes \cdots \otimes x^{(j-1)}(s),$$
$$\mathbf{x}_{(j)}(s) = x^{(j+1)}(s) \otimes \cdots \otimes x^{(k)}(s),$$

and

$$\Delta^{m-1}\mathbf{x} = \sum_a \mathbf{x}_a^{(1)} \otimes \cdots \otimes \mathbf{x}_a^{(m)},$$
$$\Delta^{m-1}{}_{(j)}\mathbf{x} = \sum_a {}_{(j)}\mathbf{x}_a^{(1)} \otimes \cdots \otimes {}_{(j)}\mathbf{x}_a^{(m)},$$
$$\Delta^{m-1}\mathbf{x}_{(j)} = \sum_a \mathbf{x}_{(j)a}^{(1)} \otimes \cdots \otimes \mathbf{x}_{(j)a}^{(m)}.$$

Then we have

$$\widehat{y}(s) = \sum_a \sum_j (-1)^{\epsilon_1(a)+1} \mathfrak{m}\left({}_{(j)}\mathbf{x}_a^{(1)}(s), \mathfrak{m}\left({}_{(j)}\mathbf{x}_a^{(2)}(s) \right), \right.$$
$$\left. {}_{(j)}\mathbf{x}_a^{(3)}(s), y^{(j)}(s), \mathbf{x}_{(j)}(s) \right)$$
$$+ \sum_a \sum_j (-1)^{\epsilon_2(a)+1} \mathfrak{m}\left({}_{(j)}\mathbf{x}(s), y^{(j)}(s), \mathbf{x}_{(j)a}^{(1)}(s), \right.$$
$$\left. \mathfrak{m}\left(\mathbf{x}_{(j)a}^{(2)}(s) \right), \mathbf{x}_{(j)a}^{(3)}(s) \right)$$
(4.2.14)
$$+ \sum_a \sum_b \sum_j (-1)^{\epsilon_3(a)} \mathfrak{m}\left({}_{(j)}\mathbf{x}_a^{(1)}(s), \mathfrak{m}\left({}_{(j)}\mathbf{x}_a^{(2)}(s), \right. \right.$$
$$\left. \left. y^{(j)}(s), \mathbf{x}_{(j)b}^{(1)}(s) \right), \mathbf{x}_{(j)b}^{(2)}(s) \right)$$
$$- \sum_j \mathfrak{m}\left({}_{(j)}\mathbf{x}(s), \frac{\partial x^{(j)}(s)}{\partial s}, \mathbf{x}_{(j)}(s) \right)$$
$$+ \frac{\partial}{\partial s}\mathfrak{m}_k(x^{(1)}(s), \cdots, x^{(k)}(s)),$$

where

$$\epsilon_1(a) = \deg' {}_{(j)}\mathbf{x}_a^{(1)} + \deg' {}_{(j)}\mathbf{x}_a^{(1)} + \deg' {}_{(j)}\mathbf{x}_a^{(2)} + 1 + \deg' {}_{(j)}\mathbf{x}_a^{(3)}$$
$$= \deg' {}_{(j)}\mathbf{x} + \deg' {}_{(j)}\mathbf{x}_a^{(1)} + 1,$$
$$\epsilon_2(a) = \deg' {}_{(j)}\mathbf{x} + \deg y^{(j)}(s) + 1 + \deg' \mathbf{x}_{(j)a}^{(1)} + \deg'_{(j)} \mathbf{x},$$
$$\epsilon_3(a) = \deg' {}_{(j)}\mathbf{x}_a^{(1)} + \deg' {}_{(j)}\mathbf{x}_a^{(2)} + \deg' {}_{(j)}\mathbf{x}_a^{(1)},$$
$$= \deg' {}_{(j)}\mathbf{x} + \deg' {}_{(j)}\mathbf{x}_a^{(1)}.$$

Here $\deg'$ is the shifted degree. The sum of the first three lines of (4.2.14) is zero by the A_∞ formula for $(C, \mathbf{m})$. The last two lines of (4.2.14) cancel each other. We have thus verified the A_∞ formulae.

If $\mathbf{e}$ is a unit of C, then $(\mathbf{e}, 0)$ is a unit of $Map([0,1], C)$. The proof of Lemma 4.2.13 is complete. $\square$

DEFINITION-PROPOSITION 4.2.15. *If $R \supseteq \mathbb{Q}$, then $(Map([0,1], C), \mathbf{m})$ is a model of $[0,1] \times C$ and $(Map([0,1], \overline{C}), \overline{\mathbf{m}})$ a model of $[0,1] \times \overline{C}$.*

PROOF. We take $s_0 \in [0,1]$ and define an A_∞ homomorphism

$$\mathrm{Eval}_{s=s_0} : Map([0,1], C) \to C$$

by $(\mathrm{Eval}_{s=s_0})_1(\mathbf{x}) = x(s_0) \in C$ for $\mathbf{x} = (x, y)$ and $(\mathrm{Eval}_{s_0})_k = 0$ for $k \neq 1$.

We remark that (4.2.11) is not a polynomial but is a formal power series of s. But we can still put $x(s_0)$. This is because the right hand side of (4.2.11) converges in the adic topology of $\Lambda_{0,nov}$ as was remarked in Remark 4.2.10.

It is easy to check that $\mathrm{Eval}_{s=s_0}$ is a filtered A_∞ homomorphism. We next define $\mathrm{Incl}_1 : C[1] \to Map([0,1], C[1])$, by regarding an element of $C[1]$ as a constant map contained in $Map([0,1], C[1])$. It is easy to see that by putting $\mathrm{Incl}_k = 0$ for $k \neq 1$, we obtain a filtered A_∞ homomorphism.

We define $\overline{\mathrm{Eval}}_{s=s_0}$ and $\overline{\mathrm{Incl}}$ in the same way. It is easy to check (4.2.3.1), (4.2.3.2), (4.2.3.4), (4.2.2.1), (4.2.2.2), (4.2.2.4). Hence to prove Proposition 4.2.15, it suffices to show the following lemma. $\square$

LEMMA 4.2.16. *If $R \supseteq \mathbb{Q}$, then $\overline{\mathrm{Incl}}$ induces an isomorphism of $\overline{\mathbf{m}}_1$ cohomology: $H(\overline{C}, \overline{\mathbf{m}}_1) \to H(Map([0,1], \overline{C}), \overline{\mathbf{m}}_1)$.*

PROOF. The image of the map $\overline{\mathrm{Incl}}_1$ is a sub-complex of $(Map([0,1], \overline{C}), \overline{\mathbf{m}}_1)$ and the quotient complex $Map([0,1], \overline{C})/\mathrm{Im}\,\overline{\mathrm{Incl}}_1$ is isomorphic to the sub-complex of $Map([0,1], \overline{C})$ that consists of the elements $\mathbf{x}$ of the type $\mathbf{x}(s) = (sx(s), y(s))$. We denote this sub-complex by $(Map'([0,1], \overline{C}), \overline{\mathbf{m}}_1)$.

Now we consider the case of $(Poly'([0,1], \overline{C}), \overline{\mathbf{m}}_1)$. (The other case is similar.) We have an exact sequence

$$0 \to (\overline{C}, \overline{\mathbf{m}}_1) \otimes \mathbb{Q}[s] \xrightarrow{i} (Poly'([0,1], \overline{C}), \overline{\mathbf{m}}_1) \xrightarrow{\pi} (\overline{C}, \overline{\mathbf{m}}_1) \otimes \mathbb{Q}[s] \to 0.$$

Diagram 4.2.1

Here $\mathbb{Q}[s]$ is the ring of polynomials. The maps i and π are defined by $i(x(s)) = (0, -x(s))$, $\pi(sx(s), y(s)) = x(s)$. It follows from (4.2.12.2) that the connecting homomorphism of the long exact sequence induced by Diagram 4.2.1 is given by

$$(4.2.17) \qquad x(s) \mapsto -\frac{\partial}{\partial s}(sx(s)).$$

This map is an isomorphism on $\mathbb{Q}[s]$. *We remark that this is the place where we need to assume $\mathbb{Q} \subseteq R$, because the inverse of (4.2.17) involves integration*, i.e, is given by $g \mapsto \frac{1}{s}\int_0^s g(t)\, dt$. This proves the lemma for the case of $Poly$. The other cases can be proved in a similar way. The proof of Lemma 4.2.16 is complete. $\square$

We have thus constructed an example of the model of $[0,1] \times C$ in the case $R \supseteq \mathbb{Q}$. The model $Poly([0,1], C)$ works for the most cases of our purpose. However this model cannot be used if R has a torsion. So we will construct another model in general. From now on, we *do not assume* that $R \supseteq \mathbb{Q}$ in the rest of this subsection.

We put

$$C^{[0,1]} = C \oplus C[-1] \oplus C.$$

We define $\mathfrak{I}_0, \mathfrak{I}_1 : C \to C^{[0,1]}$ and $\mathfrak{J} : C \to C^{[0,1]}$ by

$$\mathfrak{I}_0(x) = (x, 0, 0), \qquad \mathfrak{I}_1(x) = (0, 0, x), \qquad \mathfrak{J}(x) = (0, x, 0).$$

Note that $\mathfrak{I}_0, \mathfrak{I}_1$ preserve degree and $\mathfrak{J}$ is of degree $+1$. We extend $\mathfrak{I}_0, \mathfrak{I}_1$ to $BC[1] \to BC^{[0,1]}[1]$ and denote it by the same symbol. We are going to define an A_∞ structure on $C^{[0,1]}$, which will give another model of C. In the course of the construction of a filtered A_∞ algebra on $C^{[0,1]}$, we denote a filtered A_∞ structure on $C^{[0,1]}$ by $\mathfrak{M}_k$ and a filtered A_∞ structure on C by $\mathfrak{m}_k$.

We define

(4.2.18)
$$\begin{cases} \mathfrak{M}_1(\mathfrak{I}_0(x)) = \mathfrak{I}_0(\mathfrak{m}_1 x) + (-1)^{\deg' x} \mathfrak{J}(x), \\ \mathfrak{M}_1(\mathfrak{I}_1(x)) = \mathfrak{I}_1(\mathfrak{m}_1 x) - (-1)^{\deg' x} \mathfrak{J}(x), \\ \mathfrak{M}_1(\mathfrak{J}(x)) = \mathfrak{J}(\mathfrak{m}_1 x), \end{cases}$$

and

(4.2.19)
$$\begin{cases} (\text{Eval}_{s=0})_1(x, y, z) = x, \quad (\text{Eval}_{s=1})_1(x, y, z) = z, \\ (\text{Incl})_1(x) = \mathfrak{I}_0(x) + \mathfrak{I}_1(x) = (x, 0, x), \end{cases}$$

(4.2.20)
$$\mathfrak{M}_0(1) = (\text{Incl})_1(\mathfrak{m}_0(1)).$$

REMARK 4.2.21. (1) $C^{[0,1]}$ has the following geometric origin. We consider the case $C = C(L)$. Then we consider the locally finite singular chain of $(-\epsilon, 1+\epsilon) \times L$ of the form $(-\epsilon, 1/2] \times \sigma$, $[1/2, 1+\epsilon) \times \sigma$, $\{1/2\} \times \sigma$ with $\sigma \in C(L)$. The set of such chains defines a chain complex which is isomorphic to our $C^{[0,1]}$. (We put $\mathfrak{m}_0 = 0$ in this remark.) But if we consider product structure (cup product) in this geometric model, we are in trouble since the chains are not transversal to one another. (For example $\{1/2\} \times \sigma$ is not transversal to $\{1/2\} \times \sigma'$.) To define a product structure we need to somehow break the symmetry as we will do in Chapter 7. The construction below might be regarded as its algebraic analog.

(2) We remark although we write $(-\epsilon, 1+\epsilon) \times L$, not $L \times (-\epsilon, 1+\epsilon)$ above, the sign we put in (4.2.18) etc. are ones in case we consider $L \times (-\epsilon, 1+\epsilon)$.

Now we define $\mathfrak{M}_k$ for $k \geq 2$ on $C^{[0,1]}$. It suffices to define the operators on the elements of the form $\mathfrak{I}_0(x)$, $\mathfrak{I}_1(x)$ and $\mathfrak{J}(x)$. Let $\mathbf{x} \in B_k C, \mathbf{z} \in B_\ell C, y \in C$. $(k, \ell = 0, 1, 2, \cdots.)$ We define

(4.2.22)
$$\mathfrak{M}_{k+\ell+1}(\mathfrak{I}_0(\mathbf{x}), \mathfrak{J}(y), \mathfrak{I}_1(\mathbf{z})) = (-1)^{\deg' \mathbf{z}} \mathfrak{J}(\mathfrak{m}_{k+\ell+1}(\mathbf{x}, y, \mathbf{z})),$$

and

(4.2.23)
$$\mathfrak{M}_k(\mathfrak{I}_0(\mathbf{x})) = \mathfrak{I}_0(\mathfrak{m}_k(\mathbf{x})), \quad \mathfrak{M}_\ell(\mathfrak{I}_1(\mathbf{z})) = \mathfrak{I}_1(\mathfrak{m}_\ell(\mathbf{z})),$$

for $k, \ell \geq 2$. The operator $\mathfrak{M}_k$ has values zero for all the elements except those given in (4.2.18), (4.2.20), (4.2.22), (4.2.23). This means the following

(4.2.24.1) $$\mathfrak{M}(\cdots, \mathfrak{J}(y_1), \cdots, \mathfrak{J}(y_2), \cdots) = 0,$$

(4.2.24.2) $$\mathfrak{M}(\cdots, \mathfrak{J}(y_1), \cdots, \mathfrak{J}_0(x), \cdots) = 0,$$

(4.2.24.3) $$\mathfrak{M}(\cdots, \mathfrak{J}_1(z), \cdots, \mathfrak{J}(y), \cdots) = 0,$$

(4.2.24.4) $$\mathfrak{M}(\cdots, \mathfrak{J}_1(z), \cdots, \mathfrak{J}_0(x), \cdots) = 0,$$

(4.2.24.5) $$\mathfrak{M}_{k+\ell}(\mathfrak{J}_0(x), \mathfrak{J}_1(z)) = 0.$$

Then we can show the following.

LEMMA 4.2.25. $(C^{[0,1]}, \mathfrak{M}_k)$ is a filtered A_∞ algebra.

PROOF. We will check the A_∞ relation $\mathfrak{M} \circ \widehat{d} = 0$. We use (Conv.3) at the end of Chapter 1. Firstly we calculate

$$(\mathfrak{M} \circ \widehat{d})(\mathfrak{J}_0(\mathbf{x}), \mathfrak{J}(y), \mathfrak{J}_1(\mathbf{z}))$$
$$= \sum_{c_1, c_2} (-1)^{\deg' \mathbf{x}_{c_1}^{(2;1)} + \deg' \mathbf{z}_{c_2}^{(2;1)}} \mathfrak{M}(\mathfrak{J}_0(\mathbf{x}_{c_1}^{(2;1)}), \mathfrak{J}(\mathfrak{m}(\mathbf{x}_{c_1}^{(2;2)}, y, \mathbf{z}_{c_2}^{(2;1)})), \mathfrak{J}_1(\mathbf{z}_{c_2}^{(2;2)}))$$
$$+ \sum_c (-1)^{\deg' \mathbf{x}_c^{(3;1)}} \mathfrak{M}(\mathfrak{J}_0(\mathbf{x}_c^{(3;1)}), \mathfrak{M}(\mathfrak{J}_0(\mathbf{x}_c^{(3;2)})), \mathfrak{J}_0(\mathbf{x}_c^{(3;3)}), \mathfrak{J}(y), \mathfrak{J}_1(\mathbf{z}))$$
$$+ \sum_c (-1)^{\deg' \mathbf{z}_c^{(3;1)} + \deg' \mathbf{x} + \deg' y + 1}$$
$$\mathfrak{M}(\mathfrak{J}_0(\mathbf{x}), \mathfrak{J}(y), \mathfrak{J}_1(\mathbf{z}_c^{(3;1)}), \mathfrak{M}(\mathfrak{J}_1(\mathbf{z}_c^{(3;2)})), \mathfrak{J}_1(\mathbf{z}_c^{(3;3)})).$$

Here in the power of (-1) on the last line, $+1$ stands for $\deg \mathfrak{J} = +1$. Thus we obtain

$$(\mathfrak{M} \circ \widehat{d})(\mathfrak{J}_0(\mathbf{x}), \mathfrak{J}(y), \mathfrak{J}_1(\mathbf{z}))$$
$$= \sum_{c_1, c_2} (-1)^{\deg' \mathbf{x}_{c_1}^{(2;1)} + \deg' \mathbf{z}} \mathfrak{J} \circ \mathfrak{m}(\mathbf{x}_{c_1}^{(2;1)}, \mathfrak{m}(\mathbf{x}_{c_1}^{(2;2)}, y, \mathbf{z}_{c_2}^{(2;1)}), \mathbf{z}_{c_2}^{(2;2)})$$
$$+ \sum_c (-1)^{\deg' \mathbf{x}_c^{(3;1)} + \deg' \mathbf{z}} \mathfrak{J} \circ \mathfrak{m}(\mathbf{x}_c^{(3;1)}, \mathfrak{m}(\mathbf{x}_c^{(3;2)}), \mathbf{x}_c^{(3;3)}, y, \mathbf{z})$$
$$+ \sum_c (-1)^{\deg' \mathbf{z}_c^{(3;1)} + \deg' \mathbf{x} + \deg' y - 1 + \deg' \mathbf{z} + 1}$$
$$\mathfrak{J} \circ \mathfrak{m}(\mathbf{x}, y, \mathbf{z}_c^{(3;1)}, \mathfrak{m}(\mathbf{z}_c^{(3;2)}), \mathbf{z}_c^{(3;3)}).$$

Here on the last line, $\deg' \mathbf{z} + 1 = \deg(\mathbf{z}_c^{(3;1)}, \mathfrak{m}(\mathbf{z}_c^{(3;2)}), \mathbf{z}_c^{(3;3)})$. Then this is zero by the A_∞ relation on C.

REMARK 4.2.26. We remark that $\mathfrak{M}(\mathfrak{J}_0(\mathbf{x}_c^{(3;2)}))$ in the third line of the first equality above contains the case when $\mathbf{x}_c^{(3;2)} \in B_1 C$ or $\in B_0(C)$. In such case $\mathfrak{M}(\mathfrak{J}_0(\mathbf{x}_c^{(3;2)})) \neq \mathfrak{J}_0(\mathfrak{m}(\mathbf{x}_c^{(3;2)}))$. However using (4.2.24) the term involving

$$\mathfrak{M}(\mathfrak{J}_0(\mathbf{x}_c^{(3;2)})) - \mathfrak{J}_0(\mathfrak{m}(\mathbf{x}_c^{(3;2)}))$$

vanishes.

We next calculate $(\mathfrak{M} \circ \widehat{d})(\mathfrak{I}_0(\mathbf{x}))$. We put $\mathbf{x} = \mathbf{x}_- \otimes x_{\text{last}}$ where $x_{\text{last}} \in B_1 C[1]$. Then we have:

$$
\begin{aligned}
&(\mathfrak{M} \circ \widehat{d})(\mathfrak{I}_0(\mathbf{x})) \\
&= \sum_c (-1)^{\deg' \mathbf{x}_c^{(3;1)}} \mathfrak{M}(\mathfrak{I}_0(\mathbf{x}_c^{(3;1)}), \mathfrak{I}_0(\mathfrak{m}(\mathbf{x}_c^{(3;2)})), \mathfrak{I}_0(\mathbf{x}_c^{(3;3)})) \\
&\quad + (-1)^{\deg' \mathbf{x}_- + \deg' x_{\text{last}}} \mathfrak{M}(\mathfrak{I}_0(\mathbf{x}_-), \mathfrak{J}(x_{\text{last}})) \\
&= \sum_c (-1)^{\deg' \mathbf{x}_c^{(3;1)}} \mathfrak{I}_0(\mathfrak{m}(\mathbf{x}_c^{(3;1)}, \mathfrak{m}(\mathbf{x}_c^{(3;2)}), \mathbf{x}_c^{(3;3)})) \\
&\quad + (-1)^{\deg' \mathbf{x}_- + \deg' x_{\text{last}}} \mathfrak{J}(\mathfrak{m}(\mathbf{x}_-, x_{\text{last}})) \\
&\quad + (-1)^{\deg' \mathfrak{m}(\mathbf{x})} \mathfrak{J}(\mathfrak{m}(\mathbf{x})).
\end{aligned}
$$
(4.2.27)

Here the last line comes from the case when $\mathbf{x}_c^{(3;2)} = \mathbf{x}$ in the the first line. The last two lines cancel to each other. Hence (4.2.27) is zero.

We next calculate $(\mathfrak{M} \circ \widehat{d})(\mathfrak{I}_1(\mathbf{z}))$. We put $\mathbf{z} = z_{\text{first}} \otimes \mathbf{z}_-$ where $z_{\text{first}} \in B_1 C[1]$. Then we have:

$$
\begin{aligned}
&(\mathfrak{M} \circ \widehat{d})(\mathfrak{I}_1(\mathbf{z})) \\
&= \sum_c (-1)^{\deg' \mathbf{z}_c^{(3;1)}} \mathfrak{M}(\mathfrak{I}_1(\mathbf{z}_c^{(3;1)}), \mathfrak{I}_1(\mathfrak{m}(\mathbf{z}_c^{(3;2)})), \mathfrak{I}_1(\mathbf{z}_c^{(3;3)})) \\
&\quad - (-1)^{\deg' z_{\text{first}}} \mathfrak{M}(\mathfrak{J}(z_{\text{first}}), \mathfrak{I}_1(\mathbf{z}_-)) \\
&= \sum_c (-1)^{\deg' \mathbf{z}_c^{(3;1)}} \mathfrak{I}_1(\mathfrak{m}(\mathbf{z}_c^{(3;1)}, \mathfrak{m}(\mathbf{z}_c^{(3;2)}), \mathbf{z}_c^{(3;3)})) \\
&\quad - (-1)^{\deg' z_{\text{first}} + \deg' \mathbf{z}_-} \mathfrak{J}(\mathfrak{m}(z_{\text{first}}, \mathbf{z}_-)) \\
&\quad - (-1)^{\deg' \mathfrak{m}(\mathbf{z})} \mathfrak{J}(\mathfrak{m}(\mathbf{z})).
\end{aligned}
$$
(4.2.28)

Here the last line comes from the case when $\mathbf{x}_c^{(3;2)} = \mathbf{x}$ in the the first line. The last two lines cancel to each other. Hence (4.2.28) is zero.

Finally we calculate $(\mathfrak{M} \circ \widehat{d})(\mathfrak{I}_0(\mathbf{x}), \mathfrak{I}_1(\mathbf{z}))$ for $\mathbf{x} \in B_k C[1]$, $\mathbf{z} \in B_\ell C[1]$, $k, \ell > 0$. We have:

$$
\begin{aligned}
&(\mathfrak{M} \circ \widehat{d})(\mathfrak{I}_0(\mathbf{x}), \mathfrak{I}_1(\mathbf{z})) \\
&= (-1)^{\deg' \mathbf{x}_- + \deg' x_{\text{last}}} \mathfrak{M}(\mathfrak{I}_0(\mathbf{x}_-), \mathfrak{J}(x_{\text{last}}), \mathfrak{I}_1(\mathbf{z})) \\
&\quad - (-1)^{\deg' \mathbf{x} + \deg' z_{\text{first}}} \mathfrak{M}(\mathfrak{I}_0(\mathbf{x}), \mathfrak{J}(z_{\text{first}}) \mathfrak{I}_1(\mathbf{z}_-)) \\
&= (-1)^{\deg' \mathbf{x}_- + \deg' x_{\text{last}} + \deg' \mathbf{z}} \mathfrak{J}(\mathfrak{m}(\mathbf{x}_-, x_{\text{last}}, \mathbf{z})) \\
&\quad - (-1)^{\deg' \mathbf{x} + \deg' z_{\text{first}} + \deg' \mathbf{z}_-} \mathfrak{J}(\mathfrak{m}(\mathbf{x}, z_{\text{first}}, \mathbf{z}_-)) \\
&= 0.
\end{aligned}
$$
(4.2.29)

The proof of Lemma 4.2.25 is complete. $\square$

DEFINITION-LEMMA 4.2.30. $(C^{[0,1]}, \mathfrak{M}_k)$ *is a model of* $[0,1] \times C$. *If C has a unit then* $(C^{[0,1]}, \mathfrak{M}_k)$ *also has a unit.*

PROOF. We defined $\text{Eval}_{s=i}$ and Incl already. It is easy to see that they induce cochain homotopy equivalences.

If $\mathbf{e}$ is a unit of C, then $(\mathbf{e}, 0, \mathbf{e})$ is a unit of $(C^{[0,1]}, \mathfrak{M}_k)$. $\square$

We can define $(\overline{C}^{[0,1]}, \overline{\mathfrak{M}}_k)$ in the same way. It is a model of $[0,1] \times \overline{C}$. We have thus proved

THEOREM 4.2.31. *The model $\overline{\mathfrak{C}}$ (resp. $\mathfrak{C}$) of $[0,1] \times \overline{C}$ (resp. $[0,1] \times C$) always exists. If C is gapped, then $\mathfrak{C}$ can be taken as a gapped one. If $\overline{C}$ (resp. C) has a unit, then $\overline{\mathfrak{C}}$ (resp. $\mathfrak{C}$) can be taken as a unital model.*

REMARK 4.2.32. We have defined $C^{[0,1]}$ by directly defining its operations. We can also prove Theorem 4.2.31 by proving the existence of the operations inductively via the obstruction theory.

REMARK 4.2.33. We remark that the A_∞ algebra $Poly([0,1], \overline{C})$ is better than $\overline{C}^{[0,1]}$ in various sense. For example, in case $\overline{C}$ is a (graded) commutative D.G.A., then the A_∞ algebra $Poly([0,1], \overline{C})$ is also graded commutative D.G.A. On the other hand, $\overline{C}^{[0,1]}$ is always noncommutative. The authors do not know how to construct a model of $[0,1] \times \overline{C}$ over the torsion coefficient preserving commutativity.

We remark that $\overline{C}^{[0,1]}$ is somewhat similar to the model used by D. Sullivan in the context of D.G.A. [**Sul78**]. However the model used by Sullivan is commutative and works only for the case of the *minimal* D.G.A.

The following is the key result to establish basic properties of homotopy between (filtered) A_∞ homomorphisms.

THEOREM 4.2.34. *Let C_1, C_2 be gapped filtered A_∞ algebras and $\mathfrak{C}_1, \mathfrak{C}_2$ be any of the models of $[0,1] \times C_1$, $[0,1] \times C_2$, which are gapped. Let $\mathfrak{f} : C_1 \to C_2$ be a gapped filtered A_∞ homomorphism. Then there exists a gapped filtered A_∞ homomorphism $\mathfrak{F} : \mathfrak{C}_1 \to \mathfrak{C}_2$ such that*

$$\mathrm{Eval}_{s=s_0} \circ \mathfrak{F} = \mathfrak{f} \circ \mathrm{Eval}_{s=s_0}$$

for $s_0 = 0, 1$ and

$$\mathrm{Incl} \circ \mathfrak{f} = \mathfrak{F} \circ \mathrm{Incl}.$$

The unfiltered version also holds. If $\mathfrak{f}$ is unital, then so is $\mathfrak{F}$. If $\mathfrak{f}$ is strict, then so is $\mathfrak{F}$.

$$
\begin{array}{ccccc}
C_1 & \xrightarrow{\mathrm{Incl}} & \mathfrak{C}_1 & \xrightarrow{\mathrm{Eval}_{s=0} \oplus \mathrm{Eval}_{s=1}} & C_1 \oplus C_1 \\
\downarrow{\scriptstyle\mathfrak{f}} & & \downarrow{\scriptstyle\mathfrak{F}} & & \downarrow{\scriptstyle\mathfrak{f} \oplus \mathfrak{f}} \\
C_2 & \xrightarrow{\mathrm{Incl}} & \mathfrak{C}_2 & \xrightarrow{\mathrm{Eval}_{s=0} \oplus \mathrm{Eval}_{s=1}} & C_2 \oplus C_2
\end{array}
$$

Diagram 4.2.2

We say that $\mathfrak{F}$ is *compatible with* Incl *and* Eval *over* $\mathfrak{f} : C_1 \to C_2$, if these two relations hold. We will prove Theorem 4.2.34 later in Section 4.4.

4.2.2. Homotopies between A_∞ homomorphisms. From now on we assume that all filtered A_∞ algebras and filtered A_∞ homomorphisms are gapped.

DEFINITION 4.2.35. Let C_1, C_2 be filtered A_∞ algebras and $\mathfrak{f}, \mathfrak{g} : C_1 \to C_2$ filtered A_∞ homomorphisms between them. Let $\mathfrak{C}_2$ be a model of $[0,1] \times C_2$.

We say $\mathfrak{f}$ is *homotopic to* $\mathfrak{g}$ *via* $\mathfrak{C}_2$ and write $\mathfrak{f} \sim_{\mathfrak{C}_2} \mathfrak{g}$, if there exists a filtered A_∞ homomorphism $\mathfrak{F} : C_1 \to \mathfrak{C}_2$ such that $\mathrm{Eval}_{s=0} \circ \mathfrak{F} = \mathfrak{f}$, $\mathrm{Eval}_{s=1} \circ \mathfrak{F} = \mathfrak{g}$.

We call $\mathfrak{F}$ the *homotopy* between $\mathfrak{f}$ and $\mathfrak{g}$.

LEMMA 4.2.36. $\sim_{\mathfrak{C}_2}$ is independent of the choice of $\mathfrak{C}_2$.

PROOF. Let $\mathfrak{C}_2'$ be another model of $[0,1] \times C_2$. We assume $\mathfrak{f} \sim_{\mathfrak{C}_2} \mathfrak{g}$ and $\mathfrak{F}$ is as in Definition 4.2.35. We apply Theorem 4.2.34 to the identity $C_2 \to C_2$ and obtain $\mathfrak{ID} : \mathfrak{C}_2 \to \mathfrak{C}_2'$ which commutes with Eval. Now we put $\mathfrak{F}' = \mathfrak{ID} \circ \mathfrak{F}$. It is easy to see that $\mathrm{Eval}_{s=0} \circ \mathfrak{F}' = \mathfrak{f}$, $\mathrm{Eval}_{s=1} \circ \mathfrak{F}' = \mathfrak{g}$. Hence $\mathfrak{f} \sim_{\mathfrak{C}_2'} \mathfrak{g}$ as required. □

From now one we write $\sim$ in place of $\sim_{\mathfrak{C}_2}$.

PROPOSITION 4.2.37. $\sim$ is an equivalence relation.

PROOF. $\mathfrak{f} \sim \mathfrak{f}$ is obvious.

Let $\mathfrak{f}^{(m)} : C_1 \to C_2$ be filtered A_∞ homomorphisms. We assume $\mathfrak{f}^{(1)} \sim \mathfrak{f}^{(2)}$. Let $\mathfrak{C}_2$ be a model of $[0,1] \times C_2$ and $\mathfrak{F} : C_1 \to \mathfrak{C}_2$ a homotopy from $\mathfrak{f}^{(1)}$ to $\mathfrak{f}^{(2)}$. We consider another model $\mathfrak{C}_2'$ of $[0,1] \times C_2$ as follows. $\mathfrak{C}_2' = \mathfrak{C}_2$ as an filtered A_∞ algebra. We use the same Incl but we exchange $\mathrm{Eval}_{s=0}$ with $\mathrm{Eval}_{s=1}$. Namely $\mathrm{Eval}_{s=0}$ of $\mathfrak{C}_2'$ is $\mathrm{Eval}_{s=1}$ of $\mathfrak{C}_2$ and vice versa. Then $\mathfrak{F}$ regarded an a filtered A_∞ homomorphism from C_1 to $\mathfrak{C}_2'$ is a homotopy from $\mathfrak{f}^{(2)}$ to $\mathfrak{f}^{(1)}$. Namely $\mathfrak{f}^{(2)} \sim \mathfrak{f}^{(1)}$.

Next we assume that $\mathfrak{f}^{(1)} \sim \mathfrak{f}^{(2)}$ and $\mathfrak{f}^{(2)} \sim \mathfrak{f}^{(3)}$. Let $\mathfrak{F}^{(m)} : C_1 \to \mathfrak{C}_2$ be homotopies from $\mathfrak{f}^{(m)}$ to $\mathfrak{f}^{(m+1)}$. We are going to show $\mathfrak{f}^{(1)} \sim \mathfrak{f}^{(3)}$. We define a filtered A_∞ algebra $\mathfrak{C}_2'$ as follows.

$$\begin{cases} \mathfrak{C}_2' = \{(x,y) \in \mathfrak{C}_2 \oplus \mathfrak{C}_2 \mid \deg x = \deg y, \; \mathrm{Eval}_{s=1}(x) = \mathrm{Eval}_{s=0}(y)\}. \\ \mathfrak{m}_k((x_1, y_1), \cdots, (x_k, y_k)) = (\mathfrak{m}_k(x_1, \cdots, x_k), \mathfrak{m}_k(y_1, \cdots, y_k)). \\ \mathrm{Eval}_{s=0}(x,y) = \mathrm{Eval}_{s=0}(x), \quad \mathrm{Eval}_{s=1}(x,y) = \mathrm{Eval}_{s=1}(y), \\ \mathrm{Incl}(x) = (\mathrm{Incl}(x), \mathrm{Incl}(x)). \end{cases}$$

It is easy to see that $\mathfrak{C}_2'$ is a model of $[0,1] \times C_2$. We put $\mathfrak{F}^{(1)} \# \mathfrak{F}^{(2)} : C_1 \to \mathfrak{C}_2'$ by

$$(\mathfrak{F}^{(1)} \# \mathfrak{F}^{(2)})(z) = (\mathfrak{F}^{(1)}(z), \mathfrak{F}^{(2)}(z)).$$

It is easy to see that $\mathfrak{F}^{(1)} \# \mathfrak{F}^{(2)}$ is a filtered A_∞ homomorphism and is a homotopy from $\mathfrak{f}^{(1)}$ to $\mathfrak{f}^{(3)}$. The proof of Proposition 4.2.37 is now completed. □

REMARK 4.2.38. The result similar to Proposition 4.2.37 is proved in the case of differential graded algebra in Corollary 10.7 [GrMo81]. However in the category of differential graded algebra and differential graded homomorphism, the result is correct only under additional assumption that C_1 is minimal. Working in the category of (filtered) A_∞ algebra thus makes the story simpler.

Now we make a brief comparison of our definition with other definitions in the literature. Let us take $\overline{C}_2^{[0,1]}$ as a model of $\overline{C}_2$. Let $\overline{\mathfrak{F}} : \overline{C}_1 \to \overline{C}_2^{[0,1]}$ be an A_∞ homomorphism such that $\overline{\mathfrak{f}}^{(m)} = \overline{\mathrm{Eval}}_{s=m} \circ \mathfrak{F}$. We recall that

$$\overline{C}_2^{[0,1]} = \overline{\mathfrak{J}}_0(\overline{C}_2) \oplus \overline{\mathfrak{J}}(\overline{C}_2) \oplus \overline{\mathfrak{J}}_1(\overline{C}_2).$$

Since we assume $\overline{\mathrm{Eval}}_{s=m} \circ \overline{\mathfrak{F}} = \overline{\mathfrak{f}}^{(m)}$, it follows that there exists $\overline{\mathfrak{h}}_k' : B_k C_1[1] \to C_2[1]$ of degree $+1$ such that

$$\overline{\mathfrak{F}}_k = (\overline{\mathfrak{J}}_0 \circ \overline{\mathfrak{f}}_k^{(0)}) \oplus (\overline{\mathfrak{J}} \circ \overline{\mathfrak{h}}_k') \oplus (\overline{\mathfrak{J}}_1 \circ \overline{\mathfrak{f}}_k^{(1)}).$$

We put

$$\overline{\mathfrak{h}}_k(\mathbf{x}) = (-1)^{\deg' \mathbf{x}} \overline{\mathfrak{h}}_k'(\mathbf{x}).$$

From the definition of A_∞ structure of $\mathfrak{C}$, we derive that $\mathfrak{F}$ is an A_∞ homomorphism if and only if the following holds.

(4.2.39)
$$\sum_c (-1)^{\deg' \mathbf{x}_c^{(3;1)}} \overline{\mathfrak{m}}(\widehat{\bar{\mathfrak{f}}}^{(0)}(\mathbf{x}_c^{(3;1)}), \overline{\mathfrak{h}}(\mathbf{x}_c^{(3;2)}), \widehat{\bar{\mathfrak{f}}}^{(1)}(\mathbf{x}_c^{(3;3)}))$$
$$= \bar{\mathfrak{f}}^{(0)}(\mathbf{x}) - \bar{\mathfrak{f}}^{(1)}(\mathbf{x}) - \sum_c (-1)^{\deg' \mathbf{x}_c^{(3;1)}} \overline{\mathfrak{h}}(\mathbf{x}_c^{(3;1)}, \overline{\mathfrak{m}}(\mathbf{x}_c^{(3;2)}), \mathbf{x}_c^{(3;3)}).$$

((4.2.39) is obtained by taking $\overline{\mathfrak{J}}(\overline{C}_2)$ component of $(\widehat{\overline{\mathfrak{F}}} \circ \widehat{\bar{d}} - \widehat{\bar{d}} \circ \widehat{\overline{\mathfrak{F}}})(\mathbf{x}) = 0$.)

Hence, we have proved the following:

PROPOSITION 4.2.40. *An A_∞ homomorphism $\bar{\mathfrak{f}}^{(0)} : \overline{C}_1 \to \overline{C}_2$ is homotopic to $\bar{\mathfrak{f}}^{(1)} : \overline{C}_1 \to \overline{C}_2$ if and only if there exists a sequences of homomorphisms $\overline{\mathfrak{h}}_k : B_k\overline{C}_1[1] \to \overline{C}_2[1]$ of degree -1 satisfying (4.2.39). The same holds for the filtered versions.*

(4.2.39) is indeed the definition of homotopy between A_∞ homomorphisms which has been used in several literatures. (For example, in section 4.1 [**Smi00**]. It was also used in Section A5 of the preprint version [**FOOO00**] of this book.)

In [**Fuk02II**], the first named author studied homotopy equivalence of A_∞ categories. A_∞ category with one object is an A_∞ algebra. We also find easily that A_∞ functor between two A_∞ categories with one object is an A_∞ homomorphism. If we apply the definition of two A_∞ functors being homotopic given in Definition 8.5 [**Fuk02II**], it is easy to see that the definition is also equivalent to the existence of $\overline{\mathfrak{h}}_k$ satisfying (4.2.39). (In fact two A_∞ functors are defined to be homotopic if there is a natural transformation satisfying appropriate properties. The homomorphism $\overline{\mathfrak{h}}_k$ above is such a natural transformation.)

We next write down the condition for two filtered A_∞ homomorphisms to be homotopic when we use the model $Poly([0,1], C_2)$.

An A_∞ homomorphism $\overline{\mathfrak{h}} : \overline{C}_1 \to Poly([0,1], \overline{C}_2)$ can be written as $\overline{\mathfrak{h}} = (\bar{\mathfrak{f}}(s), \overline{\mathfrak{g}}(s))$, where $\bar{\mathfrak{f}}(s) : B\overline{C}_1[1] \to \overline{C}_2[1][s]$, $\overline{\mathfrak{g}}(s) : B\overline{C}_1[1] \to \overline{C}_2[1][s]$ and $\bar{\mathfrak{f}}(s), \overline{\mathfrak{g}}(s)$ preserve the degree. The condition that $\overline{\mathfrak{h}}$ is an A_∞ homomorphism can be written as

(4.2.41.1) $\bar{\mathfrak{f}}(s_0)$ is an A_∞ homomorphism : $\overline{C}_1 \to \overline{C}_2$ for each $s_0 \in [0,1]$.

(4.2.41.2)
$$\frac{\partial \bar{\mathfrak{f}}(s)}{\partial s} = \mathfrak{m} \circ (\widehat{\bar{\mathfrak{f}}}(s) \otimes \widehat{\overline{\mathfrak{g}}}(s) \otimes \widehat{\bar{\mathfrak{f}}}(s)) \circ \Delta^2 - \overline{\mathfrak{g}}(s) \circ \widehat{d}.$$

We do not check (4.2.41) here since we do not use it.

We now turn to the study of basic properties of the homotopy. We know from Lemma 4.2.36 that the homotopy relation is independent of the choice of a model of $[0,1] \times C$. So, from now on, we use the script letter $\mathfrak{C}$ for the model of $[0,1] \times C$ without specifying the choice. (We will check this independence of the choice, only when it is not manifest.)

DEFINITION 4.2.42. *An A_∞ homomorphism $\bar{\mathfrak{f}} : \overline{C}_1 \to \overline{C}_2$ is called a homotopy equivalence if there exists an A_∞ homomorphism $\overline{\mathfrak{g}} : \overline{C}_2 \to \overline{C}_1$ such that $\bar{\mathfrak{f}} \circ \overline{\mathfrak{g}}$ and $\overline{\mathfrak{g}} \circ \bar{\mathfrak{f}}$ are homotopic to identity.*

Two A_∞ algebras are homotopy equivalent to each other if there exists a homotopy equivalence between them.

The homotopy equivalences between (gapped) filtered A_∞ algebras can be defined in a similar way.

To show that the homotopy equivalence of A_∞ algebras is an equivalence relation we need the following lemma.

LEMMA 4.2.43. *Let* $\mathfrak{f}^{(m)}, \mathfrak{f}^{(m)\prime} : C_m \to C_{m+1}$ *be filtered* A_∞ *homomorphisms. We assume* $\mathfrak{f}^{(m)} \sim \mathfrak{f}^{(m)\prime}$. *Then we have* $\mathfrak{f}^{(2)} \circ \mathfrak{f}^{(1)} \sim \mathfrak{f}^{(2)\prime} \circ \mathfrak{f}^{(1)\prime}$.

The same holds for filtered A_∞ *homomorphisms.*

PROOF. It is easy to see that $\mathfrak{f}^{(2)} \circ \mathfrak{f}^{(1)} \sim \mathfrak{f}^{(2)\prime} \circ \mathfrak{f}^{(1)}$. Hence we may assume $\mathfrak{f}^{(2)} = \mathfrak{f}^{(2)\prime}$. We apply Theorem 4.2.34 to $\mathfrak{f}^{(2)}$ and obtain a filtered A homomorphism $\mathfrak{F}^{(2)} : \mathfrak{C}_2 \to \mathfrak{C}_3$ such that $\text{Eval}_{s=s_0} \circ \mathfrak{F}^{(2)} = \mathfrak{f}^{(2)} \circ \text{Eval}_{s=s_0}$. Now let $\mathfrak{F} : C_1 \to \mathfrak{C}_2$ be the homotopy between $\mathfrak{f}^{(1)}$ and $\mathfrak{f}^{(1)\prime}$. Then $\mathfrak{F}^{(2)} \circ \mathfrak{F}$ is a homotopy from $\mathfrak{f}^{(2)} \circ \mathfrak{f}^{(1)}$ to $\mathfrak{f}^{(2)} \circ \mathfrak{f}^{(1)\prime}$.   □

The following corollary is immediate.

COROLLARY 4.2.44. (1) *A composition of homotopy equivalences is a homotopy equivalence.*

(2) *The homotopy equivalence is an equivalence relation.*

We will prove the following theorem in Section 4.5. We recall that an A_∞ homomorphism between unfiltered A_∞ algebras is said to be a weak homotopy equivalence if it induces a chain homotopy equivalence and a filtered A_∞ homomorphism $\mathfrak{f} : C_1 \to C_2$ between filtered A_∞ algebras (satisfying $\overline{\mathfrak{m}}_0 = 0$) is said to be a weak homotopy equivalence if $\overline{\mathfrak{f}} : \overline{C}_1 \to \overline{C}_2$ is a weak homotopy equivalence (Definitions 3.2.10 and 3.2.33). A filtered A_∞ homomorphism $\mathfrak{f}$ is called strict if $\mathfrak{f}_0 = 0$ (Definition 3.2.29).

THEOREM 4.2.45. (Whitehead theorem for A_∞ algebras) (1) *A weak homotopy equivalence of* A_∞ *algebra is a homotopy equivalence.*

(2) *A gapped weak homotopy equivalence between gapped filtered* A_∞ *algebras is a homotopy equivalence. The homotopy inverse of a strict weak homotopy equivalence can be taken to be strict.*

A similar result appears in the literature which leads that, for any weak homotopy equivalence $\overline{\mathfrak{f}} : \overline{C}_1 \to \overline{C}_2$ there exists an A_∞ homomorphism $\overline{\mathfrak{g}} : \overline{C}_2 \to \overline{C}_1$ which induces inverse in the $\overline{\mathfrak{m}}_1$ cohomology. We remark that Theorem 4.2.45 (1) is slightly sharper than this statement, since A_∞ homomorphism which induces identity on $\overline{\mathfrak{m}}_1$ cohomology may not be homotopic to identity.

In a similar way we can define homotopy between (filtered) A_∞ homomorphisms of (filtered) A_∞ bimodules. We will discuss this later in Section 5.2 Chapter 5.

4.2.3. The unital or homotopy-unital cases. In this subsection, we specialize our study of homotopy to the cases of unital or homotopy-unital (filtered) A_∞ homomorphisms. (See Subsection 3.3.2 for the definitions of unital or homotopy-unital A_∞ homomorphisms.) The main purpose of the subsection is to fix some notations and derive basic facts on them, which will be used in later sections. Although we explicitly discuss only the filtered version here, all the corresponding discussions equally apply to the unfiltered cases without change. We also assume that all filtered A_∞ algebras and filtered A_∞ homomorphisms are gapped.

Let C_1, C_2 be two unital filtered A_∞ algebras. We take models $\mathfrak{C}_i$ of $[0, 1] \times C_i$. We may assume that they are unital.

DEFINITION 4.2.46. We say that unital filtered A_∞ homomorphisms $\mathfrak{f}, \mathfrak{g}$: $C_1 \to C_2$ are *unitally homotopic* to each other and write $\mathfrak{f} \sim \mathfrak{g}$ (or $\mathfrak{f} \sim_u \mathfrak{g}$) if there exists a unital filtered A_∞ homomorphism $\mathfrak{h} : C_1 \to \mathfrak{C}_2$ such that $\mathrm{Eval}_{s=0} \circ \mathfrak{h} = \mathfrak{f}$, $\mathrm{Eval}_{s=1} \circ \mathfrak{h} = \mathfrak{g}$. We call $\mathfrak{h}$ a *unital homotopy* between $\mathfrak{f}$ and $\mathfrak{g}$.

We define a *strict unital homotopy* between strict filtered A_∞ algebras in the same way. We will use symbol $\sim_{su}$ for it.

We sometimes say, for short, *u-homotopic, su-homotopic, u-homotopy, su-homotopy* in place of unitally homotopic, strictly-unitally homotopic, unital homotopy, strictly unital homotopy.

LEMMA 4.2.47. $\sim_u$ *is independent of the choice of the model* $\mathfrak{C}_2$ *and is an equivalence relation. If* $\mathfrak{f} \sim_u \mathfrak{f}'$ *then* $\mathfrak{f} \circ \mathfrak{g} \sim_u \mathfrak{f}' \circ \mathfrak{g}$ *and* $\mathfrak{g}' \circ \mathfrak{f} \sim_u \mathfrak{g}' \circ \mathfrak{f}'$. *The strict version is similar.*

The proof is the same as the proof of Lemma 4.2.36, Proposition 4.2.37 and Lemma 4.2.43. We can now define the notion of *unital homotopy equivalence (u-homotopy equivalence)* in an obvious way.

THEOREM 4.2.45a. *The unital version of Theorem 4.2.45 holds. Moreover, if* $\mathfrak{f} : C_1 \to C_2$ *is a unital filtered A_∞ homomorphism and a homotopy equivalence, then it is a u-homotopy equivalence. The strict unital version also holds.*

We remark that the second half follows from the first half. The proof of the first half is given in Section 4.5.

Let C_1, C_2 be two homotopy-unital filtered A_∞ algebras. We take C_i^+ as in Section 8.1. We take a model $\mathfrak{C}_2^+$ of $[0, 1] \times C_2^+$, which is unital.

REMARK 4.2.48. It is possible to show that there exists a model of $[0, 1] \times C_2$ which is homotopy-unital and is unique in a sense similar to Theorem 4.2.34. Then we might use this model to define the homotopy-unital homotopy. However in the way we take here we do not need to prove it.

DEFINITION 4.2.49. We say that homotopically unital filtered A_∞ homomorphisms $\mathfrak{f}, \mathfrak{g}$: $C_1 \to C_2$ are *homotopy-unitally homotopic* and write $\mathfrak{f} \sim \mathfrak{g}$ (or $\mathfrak{f} \sim_{hu} \mathfrak{g}$), if there exists a unital filtered A_∞ homomorphism $\mathfrak{h} : C_1^+ \to \mathfrak{C}_2^+$ such that $\mathrm{Eval}_{s=0} \circ \mathfrak{h} = \mathfrak{f}^+$, $\mathrm{Eval}_{s=1} \circ \mathfrak{h} = \mathfrak{g}^+$. Here $\mathfrak{f}^+, \mathfrak{g}^+ : C_1^+ \to C_2^+$ are as in Definition 3.3.13. We call $\mathfrak{h}$ a *homotopy-unital homotopy* between $\mathfrak{f}$ and $\mathfrak{g}$.

We sometimes call *hu-homotopic* or *hu-homotopy* in place of homotopy-unitally homotopic or homotopy-unital homotopy. The strict version can be defined in a similar way and abbreviated by *shu-homotopic* or *shu-homotopy*.

LEMMA 4.2.50. $\sim_{hu}$ *is independent of the choice of the model* $\mathfrak{C}_2$ *and is an equivalence relation. If* $\mathfrak{f} \sim_{hu} \mathfrak{f}'$ *then* $\mathfrak{f} \circ \mathfrak{g} \sim_{hu} \mathfrak{f}' \circ \mathfrak{g}$ *and* $\mathfrak{g}' \circ \mathfrak{f} \sim_{hu} \mathfrak{g}' \circ \mathfrak{f}'$. *The same holds for* $\sim_{shu}$

The proof is the same as that of Lemma 4.2.47. We can now define the notion of *homotopy-unital homotopy equivalence (hu-homotopy equivalence)* in an obvious way.

THEOREM 4.2.45b. *The homotopy-unital version of Theorem 4.2.45 holds.*
Moreover, if $\mathfrak{f} : C_1 \to C_2$ *is a hu-filtered A_∞ homomorphism and a homotopy equivalence, then it is a hu-homotopy equivalence. The strict and/or homotopy-unital version also holds.*

The proof will be given in Section 4.5. Before going further, let us remind one technical but delicate issue which is likely to be confused.

REMARK 4.2.51. We have defined a homotopy-unital filtered A_∞ homomorphism $\mathfrak{f} : C_1 \to C_2$ as a unital filtered A_∞ homomorphism $\mathfrak{f}^+ : C_1^+ \to C_2^+$. This means that there are several choices of $\mathfrak{f}^+$ to a given $\mathfrak{f} : C_1 \to C_2$. Moreover the different $\mathfrak{f}^+$ (with the same $\mathfrak{f}$) are regarded as a *different* homotopy unital filtered A_∞ homomorphisms. The authors do not know whether different choice $\mathfrak{f}^{+\prime} : C_1^+ \to C_2^+$ is always unitally homotopic to $\mathfrak{f}^+$ or not. (It is easy to show that $\mathfrak{f}^{+\prime}$ is homotopic to $\mathfrak{f}^+$.)

In case we regard a unital filtered A_∞ homomorphism $\mathfrak{f}$ as a homotopy-unital filtered A_∞ homomorphism, we take a canonical choice of $\mathfrak{f}^+$ such that $\mathfrak{f}^+(\cdots \otimes \mathbf{f} \otimes \cdots) = 0$.

By the choice specified in Remark 4.2.51, we can define a functor

$$\mathcal{I}_{\text{unit}} : [\text{unital filtered } A_\infty \text{ algebra}] \to [\text{homotopy-unital filtered } A_\infty \text{ algebra}].$$

On the other hand $C \mapsto C^+$ defines a functor

$$\mathcal{I}_+ : [\text{homotopy-unital filtered } A_\infty \text{ algebra}] \to [\text{unital filtered } A_\infty \text{ algebra}].$$

PROPOSITION 4.2.52. *$\mathcal{I}_{\text{unit}}$ and $\mathcal{I}_+$ induce equivalences of categories*

$$[\text{unital filtered } A_\infty \text{ algebra};$$
$$\text{u-homotopy class of unital filtered } A_\infty \text{ homomorphisms}]$$
$$\cong \quad [\text{homotopy-unital filtered } A_\infty \text{ algebra};$$
$$\text{hu-homotopy class of homotopy-unital filtered } A_\infty \text{ homomorphisms}].$$

The same holds for the strict version.

PROOF. We first prove the following lemma.

LEMMA 4.2.53. *Let $\mathfrak{f}, \mathfrak{g} : C \to C'$ be two unital filtered A_∞ homomorphisms between unital filtered A_∞ algebras. They are homotopy-unitally homotopic, if and only if they are unitally homotopic.*

For the proof we use the following sublemma.

SUBLEMMA 4.2.54. *If C is a unital filtered A_∞ algebra, then there exists a strict unital and filtered A_∞ homomorphism $\mathfrak{ret} : C^+ \to C$ such that the composition $\mathfrak{ret} \circ i : C \to C$ is identity, where $i : C \to C^+$ is the canonical embedding.*

PROOF OF SUBLEMMA 4.2.54. We put $\mathfrak{ret}_1(\mathbf{e}^+) = \mathbf{e}$, $\mathfrak{ret}_1(\mathbf{f}) = 0$, $\mathfrak{ret}_k = 0$ for $k \neq 1$. We also put $\mathfrak{ret}_1 = id$ on $C \subseteq C^+$. It is easy to see that $\mathfrak{ret}$ has the required property. $\qquad\square$

We remark that i is not unital.

PROOF OF LEMMA 4.2.53. Applying Theorem 4.2.45a we choose a unital homotopy inverse $\mathfrak{ret}^{-1} : C \to C^+$ (resp. $\mathfrak{ret}'^{-1} : C' \to C'^+$) of $\mathfrak{ret}$ (resp. $\mathfrak{ret}'$). Now suppose $\mathfrak{f} \sim_{hu} \mathfrak{g}$. Then $\mathfrak{f}^+ \sim_u \mathfrak{g}^+$. Hence

$$\mathfrak{f} \sim_u \mathfrak{f} \circ \mathfrak{ret} \circ \mathfrak{ret}^{-1} = \mathfrak{ret}' \circ \mathfrak{f}^+ \circ \mathfrak{ret}^{-1} \sim_u \mathfrak{ret}' \circ \mathfrak{g}^+ \circ \mathfrak{ret}^{-1} = \mathfrak{g} \circ \mathfrak{ret} \circ \mathfrak{ret}^{-1} \sim_u \mathfrak{g}.$$

Here the equality $\mathfrak{f} \circ \mathfrak{ret} = \mathfrak{ret}' \circ \mathfrak{f}^+$ follows from the choice of $\mathfrak{f}^+$ we specified in Remark 4.2.51 and by the definition of $\mathfrak{ret}$ above. We next suppose $\mathfrak{f} \sim_u \mathfrak{g}$. Then we have

$$\mathfrak{f}^+ \sim_u \mathfrak{ret}'^{-1} \circ \mathfrak{ret}' \circ \mathfrak{f}^+ = \mathfrak{ret}'^{-1} \circ \mathfrak{f} \circ \mathfrak{ret} \sim_u \mathfrak{ret}'^{-1} \circ \mathfrak{g} \circ \mathfrak{ret} = \mathfrak{ret}'^{-1} \circ \mathfrak{ret}' \circ \mathfrak{g}^+ \sim_u \mathfrak{g}^+.$$

Hence $\mathfrak{f} \sim_{hu} \mathfrak{g}$. $\qquad \square$

Lemma 4.2.53 implies that $\mathcal{I}_{\text{unit}}$ induces an injective functor on the homotopy category. On the other hand, it is easy to see that $\mathcal{I}_+$ induces a functor between homotopy categories. Hence to complete the proof of Proposition 4.2.52 it suffices to show the following lemma. (In fact Lemma 4.2.55 implies that $\mathcal{I}_{\text{unit}} \circ \mathcal{I}_+$ is equivalent to the identity functor.)

LEMMA 4.2.55. *If C be a homotopy-unital filtered A_∞ algebra, then C is hu-homotopy equivalent to C^+.*

PROOF. We extend $i : C \to C^+$ to a unital filtered A_∞ homomorphism $i^+ : C^+ \to C^{++}$ as follows. We write

$$C^+ = C \oplus \Lambda_{0,nov}\mathbf{e}^+ \oplus \Lambda_{0,nov}\mathbf{f},$$
$$C^{++} = C^+ \oplus \Lambda_{0,nov}\mathbf{e}^{++} \oplus \Lambda_{0,nov}\mathbf{f}^+,$$

and put $i_1^+(x) = x$ for $x \in C$, $i_1^+(\mathbf{e}^+) = \mathbf{e}^{++}$, $i_1^+(\mathbf{f}) = \mathbf{f}^+ + \mathbf{f}$. We also set $i_k^+ = 0$ for $k \neq 1$. It is easy to check that i^+ is a unital filtered A_∞ homomorphism. (Note that the unit of C^+ is $\mathbf{e}^+$ and the unit of C^{++} is $\mathbf{e}^{++}$.) Therefore i is homotopy unital. It then follows from Theorem 4.2.45b that i is a hu-filtered homotopy equivalence. $\square$

The proof of Proposition 4.2.52 is now complete. $\qquad \square$

We can reduce most of algebraic discussions of homotopy-unital filtered A_∞ algebras to unital ones, by using Proposition 4.2.52. So we discuss homotopy-unital filtered A_∞ algebras only when we absolutely need to.

4.3. Gauge equivalence of bounding cochains

In this section we define an equivalence relation $\sim$ on the set of bounding cochains $\widehat{\mathcal{M}}(C)$ and show that the quotient space $\mathcal{M}(C) = \widehat{\mathcal{M}}(C)/\sim$ is an invariant of the homotopy type of filtered A_∞ algebras C.

4.3.1. Basic properties and the category $\mathfrak{H}\mathfrak{A}_\infty$. Let C be a filtered A_∞ algebra and $\mathfrak{C}$ a model of $[0,1] \times C$.

DEFINITION 4.3.1. Let $b_0, b_1 \in \widehat{\mathcal{M}}(C)$. We say b_0 is $\mathfrak{C}$-*gauge equivalent* to b_1 and write $b_0 \sim_{\mathfrak{C}} b_1$ if there exists $\tilde{b} \in \widehat{\mathcal{M}}(\mathfrak{C})$ such that $\text{Eval}_{s=0*}(\tilde{b}) = b_0$, $\text{Eval}_{s=1*}(\tilde{b}) = b_1$. We say such $\tilde{b}$, a *homotopy* from b_0 to b_1.

REMARK 4.3.2. We define the set $\widehat{\mathcal{M}}(C)$ and an equivalence relation $\sim$ on it only for the filtered A_∞ algebra. In fact, for the unfiltered A_∞ algebra the set of solutions b of the Maurer-Cartan equation $\widehat{d}(e^b) = 0$ does not make sense, since in general $\widehat{d}(e^b)$ is an infinite sum. Therefore the set of all bounding cochains $\widehat{\mathcal{M}}(\overline{C})$ does not make sense. However we can still define $\widehat{\mathcal{M}}(\overline{C})$ as a functor from the category of Artin rings ([**Schl68**]). See for example [**Fuk03II**] Section 2.1.

LEMMA 4.3.3. $\sim_{\mathfrak{C}}$ is independent of the choice of the model $\mathfrak{C}$ of $[0,1] \times C$.

PROOF. The proof is the same as the proof of Lemma 4.2.36. $\square$

From now on, we write $\sim$ in place of $\sim_{\mathfrak{C}}$ and just say 'gauge equivalent' in place of '$\mathfrak{C}$-gauge equivalent'.

LEMMA 4.3.4. The gauge equivalence $\sim$ on the set of bounding cochains is an equivalence relation.

PROOF. The proof is the same as the proof of Proposition 4.2.37. $\square$

Let us describe the gauge equivalence more explicitly. Let us first take $\mathfrak{C} = Poly([0,1], C)$. Then we have

PROPOSITION 4.3.5. $b_0 \in \widehat{\mathcal{M}}(C)$ is gauge equivalent to $b_1 \in \widehat{\mathcal{M}}(C)$ if and only if there exists $\tilde{b} = (b(s), c(s)) \in Poly([0,1], C)^1$ such that

(4.3.6.1)
$$\frac{\partial b(s)}{\partial s} = \delta_{b(s)} c(s)$$

(4.3.6.2)
$$b(0) = b_0, \quad b(1) = b_1.$$

PROOF. Let $\tilde{b}$ be a homotopy from b_0 to b_1. We put $\tilde{b} = (b(s), c(s))$. Then the condition $\tilde{b} \in \widehat{\mathcal{M}}(Poly([0,1], C))$ is equivalent to (4.3.6.1) and $\mathrm{Eval}_{s=0*}(\tilde{b}) = b_0$, $\mathrm{Eval}_{s=1*}(\tilde{b}) = b_1$ is equivalent to (4.3.6.2). $\square$

For the case of a differential graded algebras $(C; d, \circ)$ where d is a derivation and $\circ$ is an associative product, we can prove that if b is gauge equivalent to b' there exists g such that

$$b' = g^{-1} \circ d(g) + g^{-1} \circ b \circ g.$$

In other words, b' is gauge equivalent to b in the usual sense. We do not prove this since we do not need it. (See Lemma 2.2.2 [**Fuk03II**].)

We also remark the following:

LEMMA 4.3.7. If $(b(s), c(s))$ satisfies (4.3.6.1) and if $b(0)$ is a bounding cochain, then $b(s)$ is also a bounding cochain for each s.

PROOF. Using (4.3.6.1), we calculate

$$\frac{\partial}{\partial s}\mathfrak{m}(e^{b(s)}) = \mathfrak{m}\left(e^{b(s)}, \delta_{b(s)}(c(s)), e^{b(s)}\right) = \delta_{b(s)}(\delta_{b(s)}(c(s))) = 0.$$

Lemma 4.3.7 follows. $\square$

REMARK 4.3.8. The conclusion of Proposition 4.3.5 is an analog of the corresponding definition in the literature concerning D.G.A. (See [**GoMi88, Sche98, Kon03**]). In [**Kon03**] a similar definition is proposed for the case of L_∞ algebras. However we did not find a proof of Lemmas 4.3.3 and 4.3.4 in the literature.

Next we take $\mathfrak{C} = C^{[0,1]}$.

PROPOSITION 4.3.9. *Two bounding cochains b_0 and b_1 are gauge equivalent to each other if and only if there exists $c \in C[1]^{-1}$ such that*

$$(4.3.10) \qquad\qquad b_1 - b_0 = \mathfrak{m}(e^{b_0} c e^{b_1}).$$

PROOF. If $\tilde{b} \in \widehat{\mathcal{M}}(C^{[0,1]})$ be a homotopy from b_0 to b_1, then we can write it as $\tilde{b} = (b_0, c, b_1)$. The equation (4.3.10) is equivalent to the condition that $\tilde{b} \in \widehat{\mathcal{M}}(C^{[0,1]})$. □

DEFINITION 4.3.11. Let $(C, \mathfrak{m})$ be a filtered A_∞ algebra. We define $\mathcal{M}(C, \mathfrak{m})$ as the set of all $\sim$ equivalence classes of $\widehat{\mathcal{M}}(C, \mathfrak{m})$. We sometimes write them as $\mathcal{M}(C)$, $\widehat{\mathcal{M}}(C)$ for simplicity.

DEFINITION 4.3.12. For a relatively spin Lagrangian submanifold of a symplectic manifold M, we associated a filtered A_∞ algebra $(C(L; \Lambda_{0,nov}), \mathfrak{m})$ in Section 3.5. We denote by $\mathcal{M}(L)$ the set $\mathcal{M}(C(L; \Lambda_{0,nov}), \mathfrak{m})$.

One of the main results of this chapter is that $\mathcal{M}(C(L; \Lambda_{0,nov}), \mathfrak{m})$ is invariant of the various choices involved (Theorem 4.1.3). The next theorem is an algebraic part of its proof. Let

$$\mathfrak{H}\mathfrak{A}_\infty = [\text{filtered } A_\infty \text{algebra; homotopy class of filtered } A_\infty \text{ homomorphism}]$$

be a category whose object is a filtered A_∞ algebra and whose morphism is a homotopy class of a filtered A_∞ homomorphism.

THEOREM 4.3.13. *The assignment $(C, \mathfrak{m}) \mapsto \mathcal{M}(C, \mathfrak{m})$ defines a covariant functor $\mathfrak{H}\mathfrak{A}_\infty \longrightarrow [\text{set}]$.*

Corollary 4.3.14 below is a filtered A_∞ algebra analog of a result by Goldman-Millson [**GoMi88,90**].

COROLLARY 4.3.14. *If $\mathfrak{f} : (C_1, \mathfrak{m}^1) \to (C_2, \mathfrak{m}^2)$ is a homotopy equivalence, then it induces a bijection $\mathfrak{f}_* : \mathcal{M}(C_1, \mathfrak{m}^1) \to \mathcal{M}(C_2, \mathfrak{m}^2)$.*

To prove Theorem 4.3.13 it suffices to show the following Lemma 4.3.15. For a filtered A_∞ homomorphism $\mathfrak{f} : (C_1, \mathfrak{m}^1) \to (C_2, \mathfrak{m}^2)$ we defined a map $\mathfrak{f}_* : \widehat{\mathcal{M}}(C_1, \mathfrak{m}^1) \to \widehat{\mathcal{M}}(C_2, \mathfrak{m}^2)$ by $\mathfrak{f}_*(b) = \mathfrak{f}(e^b)$. See Lemma 3.6.36.

LEMMA 4.3.15. (1) *If $b_0 \sim b_1$ in $\widehat{\mathcal{M}}(C_1, \mathfrak{m}^1)$, then $\mathfrak{f}_*(b_0) \sim \mathfrak{f}_*(b_1)$.*
(2) *If $\mathfrak{f}$ is homotopic to $\mathfrak{f}'$, then $\mathfrak{f}_*(b) \sim \mathfrak{f}'_*(b)$ for any $b \in \widehat{\mathcal{M}}(C_1, \mathfrak{m}^1)$.*

PROOF. Let $\mathfrak{C}_i$ $(i = 1, 2)$ be a model of $[0, 1] \times C_i$.
(1) We apply Theorem 4.2.34 to $\mathfrak{f}$ and obtain a filtered A_∞ homomorphism $\mathfrak{F} : \mathfrak{C}_1 \to \mathfrak{C}_2$, such that $\text{Eval}_{s=s_0} \circ \mathfrak{F} = \mathfrak{f} \circ \text{Eval}_{s=s_0}$. Let $\tilde{b} \in \widehat{\mathcal{M}}(\mathfrak{C}_1)$ be a homotopy from b_0 to b_1. Then $\mathfrak{F}_*(\tilde{b})$ is a homotopy from $\mathfrak{f}_*(b_0)$ to $\mathfrak{f}_*(b_1)$. Thus $\mathfrak{f}_*(b_0) \sim \mathfrak{f}_*(b_1)$.
(2) Let $\mathfrak{H} : C_1 \to \mathfrak{C}_2$ be a homotopy from $\mathfrak{f}$ to $\mathfrak{f}'$. Then $\mathfrak{H}_* b$ is a bounding cochain such that $\text{Eval}_{s=0}\mathfrak{H}_* b = \mathfrak{f}_*(b)$ and $\text{Eval}_{s=1}\mathfrak{H}_* b = \mathfrak{f}'_*(b)$. Hence $\mathfrak{f}_*(b) \sim \mathfrak{f}'_*(b)$. □

In the proof of the next proposition, we will use Theorem 4.2.45 which will be proved in Section 4.5.

PROPOSITION 4.3.16. *If $b_0 \sim b_1$ in $\widehat{\mathcal{M}}(C, \mathfrak{m})$, there exists a strict homotopy equivalence $\mathfrak{f} : (C, \mathfrak{m}^{b_0}) \to (C, \mathfrak{m}^{b_1})$ such that $\bar{\mathfrak{f}} \equiv id \mod \Lambda^+_{0,nov}$. Here $\mathfrak{m}^{b_i}$ is the deformed A_∞ structure defined by Definition 3.6.9.*

PROOF. Let $\mathfrak{C}$ be a model of $[0, 1] \times C$ and $\tilde{b}$ as in Definition 4.3.1. Then, $\mathrm{Eval}_{s=0}$ and $\mathrm{Eval}_{s=1}$ define strict filtered A_∞ homomorphisms

$$\mathrm{Eval}_{s=0} : (\mathfrak{C}, \mathfrak{m}^{\tilde{b}}) \to (C, \mathfrak{m}^{b_0}), \qquad \mathrm{Eval}_{s=1} : (\mathfrak{C}, \mathfrak{m}^{\tilde{b}}) \to (C, \mathfrak{m}^{b_1}).$$

Using Theorem 4.2.45, we can prove that they are strict homotopy equivalences. Hence we obtain $\mathfrak{f}$. We will check the property $\bar{\mathfrak{f}} \equiv id \mod \Lambda^+_{0,nov}$ later at the end of Section 4.5. □

REMARK 4.3.17. For any $b \in \widehat{\mathcal{M}}(C, \mathfrak{m})$, the filtered A_∞ algebra $(C, \mathfrak{m}^b)$ is homotopy equivalent to $(C, \mathfrak{m})$. In fact, we define $i^b : (C, \mathfrak{m}^b) \to (C, \mathfrak{m})$ by $i^b_0(1) = b$, $i^b_1 = id$, $i^b_k = 0$ for $k \geq 2$. It is a homotopy equivalence by Theorem 4.2.45. However, note that i^b is *not strict* in the sense of Definition 3.2.29.

The following proposition is a special case when $L = L^{(0)} = L^{(1)}$ in Corollary 5.2.40.

PROPOSITION 4.3.18. *Let $b_0, b_1, b'_0, b'_1 \in \widehat{\mathcal{M}}(C, \mathfrak{m})$. We assume $b_0 \sim b_1$ and $b'_0 \sim b'_1$. Then there exists a canonical isomorphism $H^*(C; \delta_{b_0,b'_0}) \cong H^*(C; \delta_{b_1,b'_1})$.*

PROOF. Let $\tilde{b}, \tilde{b}' \in C^{[0,1]}$ be bounding cochains such that $\mathrm{Eval}_{s=i}\tilde{b} = b_i$ and $\mathrm{Eval}_{s=i}\tilde{b}' = b'_i$ for $i = 0, 1$. We consider the following exact sequence of graded modules:

$$0 \to C[-1] \oplus C \to C^{[0,1]} \to C^{[0,1]}/(C[-1] \oplus C) \to 0,$$

where the second homomorphism is the inclusion. Note that $C[-1] \oplus C$ is closed under $\delta_{\tilde{b},\tilde{b}'}$ as well as $\mathfrak{m}_{1,0}$. ($\overline{C}[-1] \oplus \overline{C}$ is a subcomplex of $(\overline{C}^{[0,1]}, \overline{\mathfrak{m}}_1)$.) It is also easy to see that $(\overline{C}[-1] \oplus \overline{C}, \overline{\mathfrak{m}}_1)$ is an acyclic complex, hence $(C[-1] \oplus C, \mathfrak{m}_{1,0})$ is acyclic. We show that $(C[-1] \oplus C, \delta_{\tilde{b},\tilde{b}'})$ is acyclic.

Let $c = \sum_{j=0}^\infty c_j e^{\nu_j} T^{\lambda_j} \in C[-1] \oplus C$ be a $\delta_{\tilde{b},\tilde{b}'}$-cocycle. For simplicity, we assume that λ_j is strictly monotone increasing: $0 = \lambda_0 < \lambda_1 < \lambda_2 < \cdots$. Since $\delta_{\tilde{b},\tilde{b}'} \equiv \overline{\mathfrak{m}}_1 \mod \Lambda^+_{0,nov}$, $c_0 \in \overline{C}[-1] \oplus \overline{C}$ is a $\overline{\mathfrak{m}}_1$-cocycle. Recall that $\overline{C}[-1] \oplus \overline{C}$ is $\overline{\mathfrak{m}}_1$-acyclic, there is $a_0 \in \overline{C}[-1] \oplus \overline{C}$ such that $c_0 = \overline{\mathfrak{m}}_1 a_0$. Consider $c' = c - \delta_{\tilde{b},\tilde{b}'}(a_0)$, which is a $\delta_{\tilde{b},\tilde{b}'}$-cocycle. (Recall that $\mu_0 = 0$ by our assumption on $\Lambda_{0,nov}$.) Note that the energy level of c' is strictly higher than c, i.e., $c' \in F^\lambda C$ for some $\lambda > 0$. Because of the gapped condition, we can repeat the above procedure to write c as a $\delta_{\tilde{b},\tilde{b}'}$-coboundary. Thus $C[-1] \oplus C$ is $\delta_{\tilde{b},\tilde{b}'}$-acyclic.

Since the quotient complex $C^{[0,1]}/(C[-1] \oplus C)$ with the coboundary operator induced from $\delta_{\tilde{b},\tilde{b}'}$ is naturally isomorphic to the complex (C, δ_{b_0,b'_0}), we obtain $H^*(C^{[0,1]}; \delta_{\tilde{b},\tilde{b}'}) \cong H^*(C; \delta_{b_0,b'_0})$. Similarly, we have $H^*(C^{[0,1]}; \delta_{\tilde{b},\tilde{b}'}) \cong H^*(C; \delta_{b_1,b'_1})$. Hence we obtain Proposition 4.3.18. □

Proposition 4.3.18, in particular, implies that the Floer cohomology group $HF((L, b), (L, b'); \Lambda_{0,nov})$ depends only on gauge equivalence classes of b, b'.
We study $\mathcal{M}(C, \mathfrak{m})$ more in Sections 5.3 and 5.4.

4.3.2. $\mathcal{M}_{\mathrm{weak}}(C)$ and its homotopy invariance. Let C be a unital filtered A_∞ algebra. We defined the set $\widehat{\mathcal{M}}_{\mathrm{weak}}(C)$ in Subsection 3.6.3. Namely $b \in C^1 = C[1]^0$ is in $\widehat{\mathcal{M}}_{\mathrm{weak}}(C)$ if and only if $\mathfrak{m}(e^b) = c\mathbf{ee}$ for some $c \in \Lambda_{0,nov}^{+(0)}$. We called such b a weak bounding cochain. See Definition 3.6.29. Further we recall that a unital filtered A_∞ homomorphism $\mathfrak{f} : C_1 \to C_2$ induces

$$\mathfrak{f}_* : \widehat{\mathcal{M}}_{\mathrm{weak}}(C_1) \to \widehat{\mathcal{M}}_{\mathrm{weak}}(C_2)$$

so that $\mathfrak{f}_*(b) = \mathfrak{f}(e^b)$. See Lemma 3.6.36.

Let $\mathfrak{C}$ be a unital model of $[0,1] \times C$.

DEFINITION 4.3.19. Let $b_0, b_1 \in \widehat{\mathcal{M}}_{\mathrm{weak}}(C)$. We say that b_0 is *gauge equivalent* to b_1 and write $b_0 \sim b_1$, if there exists $\tilde{b} \in \widehat{\mathcal{M}}_{\mathrm{weak}}(\mathfrak{C})$ such that $\mathrm{Eval}_{s=0*} \tilde{b} = b_0$, $\mathrm{Eval}_{s=1*} \tilde{b} = b_1$.

LEMMA 4.3.20. $\sim$ *is independent of the choice of the model of* $[0,1] \times C$ *and it is an equivalence relation.*

The proof is the same as the proofs of Lemmas 4.3.3 and 4.3.4.

DEFINITION 4.3.21. Let $(C, \mathfrak{m})$ be a unital filtered A_∞ algebra. We define $\mathcal{M}_{\mathrm{weak}}(C, \mathfrak{m})$ as the set of all $\sim$ equivalence classes of $\widehat{\mathcal{M}}_{\mathrm{weak}}(C, \mathfrak{m})$.

The next theorem can be proved in the same way as Theorem 4.3.13.

THEOREM 4.3.22. *The assignment* $(C, \mathfrak{m}) \mapsto \mathcal{M}_{\mathrm{weak}}(C, \mathfrak{m})$ *defines a covariant functor*

$$\mathfrak{H}\mathfrak{A}_{\infty u} := [\text{unital filtered } A_\infty \text{ algebra};$$
$$\text{u-homotopy class of unital filtered } A_\infty \text{ homomorphisms}]$$
$$\longrightarrow [\text{set}].$$

If $\mathfrak{f} : (C_1, \mathfrak{m}^1) \to (C_2, \mathfrak{m}^2)$ *is a unital homotopy equivalence, then it induces a bijection* $\mathfrak{f}_* : \mathcal{M}_{\mathrm{weak}}(C_1, \mathfrak{m}^1) \to \mathcal{M}_{\mathrm{weak}}(C_2, \mathfrak{m}^2)$.

In Subsection 3.6.3 we introduced the potential function $\mathfrak{PO} : \widehat{\mathcal{M}}_{\mathrm{weak}}(C) \to \Lambda_{0,nov}^{+(0)}$ by $\mathfrak{m}(e^b) = \mathfrak{PO}(b)\mathbf{ee}$. (Definition 3.6.33.) Then we can show the following.

LEMMA 4.3.23. $\mathfrak{PO}(b)$ *depends only on the gauge equivalence class of* $b \in \widehat{\mathcal{M}}_{\mathrm{weak}}(C)$. *Namely* $\mathfrak{PO}$ *induces* $\mathfrak{PO} : \mathcal{M}_{\mathrm{weak}}(C) \to \Lambda_{0,nov}^{+(0)}$. *Moreover if* C_i *is a unital filtered* A_∞ *algebra and* $\mathfrak{f} : C_1 \to C_2$ *is a unital filtered* A_∞ *homomorphism, we have*

$$\mathfrak{PO}_2 \circ \mathfrak{f}_*(b) = \mathfrak{PO}_1(b)$$

for $b \in \mathcal{M}_{\mathrm{weak}}(C_1)$, *where* $\mathfrak{PO}_i$ *is the potential function for* C_i.

PROOF. Let $b_0 \sim b_1$ in $\widehat{\mathcal{M}}_{\mathrm{weak}}(C)$ and $\tilde{b}$ a homotopy from b_0 to b_1 as in Definition 4.3.1. Then by Lemma 3.6.36 (3) we have

$$\mathfrak{PO}(b_0) = \mathfrak{PO}(\mathrm{Eval}_{s=0*}\tilde{b}) = \mathfrak{PO}(\tilde{b}) = \mathfrak{PO}(\mathrm{Eval}_{s=1*}\tilde{b}) = \mathfrak{PO}(b_1),$$

which proves the first assertion. The second assertion also follows from Lemma 3.6.36 (3). $\square$

When C is a homotopy-unital filtered A_∞ algebra, we *define*

$$(4.3.24) \qquad \mathcal{M}_{\text{weak}}(C) = \mathcal{M}_{\text{weak}}(C^+).$$

It is independent of the hu-homotopy type of C. We can define the potential function in the same way for this case. The potential function is defined as a function on $\mathcal{M}_{\text{weak}}(C) = \mathcal{M}_{\text{weak}}(C^+)$. Also we can define a category $\mathfrak{H}\mathfrak{A}_{\infty hu}$ in a similar way.

Now let us consider the case of filtered A_∞ bimodules. Let C_0, C_1 be unital filtered A_∞ algebras and D a left C_1 and right C_0 unital filtered A_∞ bimodule. (Definition 3.7.5). For $b_0 \in \widehat{\mathcal{M}}_{\text{weak}}(C_0)$ and $b_1 \in \widehat{\mathcal{M}}_{\text{weak}}(C_1)$, we defined $\delta_{b_1,b_0} : D \to D$ in Definition-Lemma 3.7.13. Namely $\delta_{b_1,b_0}(x) = \mathfrak{n}(e^{b_1} x e^{b_0})$. We denote by $\mathfrak{PO}_i, (i = 0,1)$ the potential function of C_i. Proposition 3.7.17 shows that

$$\delta_{b_1,b_0} \circ \delta_{b_1,b_0}(x) = (-\mathfrak{PO}_1(b_1) + \mathfrak{PO}_0(b_0))ex.$$

Thus if $\mathfrak{PO}_0(b_0) = \mathfrak{PO}_1(b_1)$, we can define the cohomology of (D, δ_{b_1,b_0}).

PROPOSITION 4.3.25. *Under the situation above, let $b_0, b_0' \in \widehat{\mathcal{M}}_{\text{weak}}(C_0)$ and $b_1, b_1' \in \widehat{\mathcal{M}}_{\text{weak}}(C_1)$. Assume that $\mathfrak{PO}(b_0) = \mathfrak{PO}(b_1)$. If $b_0 \sim b_0'$ and $b_1 \sim b_1'$, then*

$$H(D, \delta_{b_1,b_0}) \cong H(D, \delta_{b_1',b_0'}).$$

The isomorphism is canonical. The homotopy-unital version also holds.

The proof will be given in Subsection 5.2.4 (Corollary 5.2.40).

4.3.3. $\mathcal{M}_{\text{weak,def}}(L)$ and its homotopy invariance. In Section 3.8 we introduced the infinitesimal deformations (bulk deformations) by using cocycles $\mathfrak{b}$ in the ambient symplectic manifold M. We recall that

$$\widehat{\mathcal{M}}_{\text{weak,def}}(L) = \{(\mathfrak{b}, b) \in C^2(M; \Lambda_{0,nov}^+) \times C^1(L; \Lambda_{0,nov}^+)$$
$$| \; \delta_M \mathfrak{b} = 0, \; \mathfrak{m}_0^{+\mathfrak{b},b} = cee^+\}.$$

See Definition 3.8.40.

We fix $\mathcal{H}^2(M; \Lambda_{0,nov}^+) \subset C(M; \Lambda_{0,nov}^+)$ representing $H^2(M; \Lambda_{0,nov}^+)$.

DEFINITION 4.3.26. Let $(\mathfrak{b}, b_0), (\mathfrak{b}, b_1) \in \widehat{\mathcal{M}}_{\text{weak,def}}(L)$, $\mathfrak{b} \in \mathcal{H}^2(M; \Lambda_{0,nov}^+)$. We say that $(\mathfrak{b}, b_0)$ is *gauge equivalent* to $(\mathfrak{b}, b_1)$ and write $(\mathfrak{b}, b_0) \sim (\mathfrak{b}, b_1)$, if b_0 is gauge equivalent to b_1 in $(C(M; \Lambda_{0,nov}^+), \mathfrak{m}^\mathfrak{b})$ in the sense of Definition 4.3.19. Then $\sim$ obviously defines an equivalence relation and we define $\mathcal{M}_{\text{weak,def}}(L)$ as the set of all gauge equivalence classes of such $(\mathfrak{b}, b)$.

We will prove in Subsection 4.6.4 that $\mathcal{M}_{\text{weak,def}}(L)$ is independent of the choice of the space $\mathcal{H}^2(M; \Lambda_{0,nov}^+)$. Theorem 4.6.47 proven there also implies that the filtered A_∞ algebra $(C(M; \Lambda_{0,nov}^+), \mathfrak{m}^\mathfrak{b})$ depends only on the homology class of $\mathfrak{b}$ up to strict homotopy equivalence. Then, in Definition 4.6.50, we will generalize the Definition 4.3.26 to the pair $(\mathfrak{b}_0, b_0), (\mathfrak{b}_1, b_1)$ where $\mathfrak{b}_0$ is homologous to but may not be equal to $\mathfrak{b}_1$.

By definition we have the well-defined map

$$(4.3.27) \qquad \pi_{\text{amb}} : \mathcal{M}_{\text{weak,def}}(L) \ni (\mathfrak{b}, b) \longmapsto [\mathfrak{b}] \in H^2(M; \Lambda_{0,nov}^+)$$

which we mentioned in Theorem B in Chapter 1. Now we have:

LEMMA 4.3.28. *The potential function $\mathfrak{PO}(\mathfrak{b}, b)$ defined in Definition 3.8.40 depends only on the gauge equivalence class of the bounding cochain*

$$b \in \widehat{\mathcal{M}}_{\text{weak,def}}(C(M; \Lambda^+_{0,nov}), \mathfrak{m}^{\mathfrak{b}}).$$

Namely $\mathfrak{PO}$ induces

$$\mathfrak{PO} : \mathcal{M}_{\text{weak,def}}(L) \to \Lambda^{+(0)}_{0,nov}.$$

PROOF. The lemma follows from Lemma 4.3.23 applied to the filtered A_∞ algebra $(C(M; \Lambda^+_{0,nov}), \mathfrak{m}^{\mathfrak{b}})$. $\qquad\qquad\qquad\qquad\qquad\qquad\qquad \Box$

We will prove $\mathfrak{PO}$ is independent of the choice of $\mathcal{H}^2(M; \Lambda^+_{0,nov})$ later. (See Subsection 4.6.4 Lemma 4.6.51.) We refer Corollary 4.6.53 for the relevant property of the potential function related to a symplectic diffeomorphism $\psi : M \to M'$.

Now we consider the case of filtered A_∞ bimodules as in Subsection 3.8.7. Here we use the same notations as in Subsection 3.8.7. The following is an analog of Proposition 4.3.18 and Proposition 4.3.25. The proof will be also given in Subsection 5.2.4 (Corollary 5.2.40).

PROPOSITION 4.3.29. *Under the situation in Subsection 3.8.7, let*

$$(\mathfrak{b}, b_0), (\mathfrak{b}, b'_0) \in \widehat{\mathcal{M}}_{\text{weak,def}}(L^{(0)}) \quad and \quad (\mathfrak{b}, b_1), (\mathfrak{b}, b'_1) \in \widehat{\mathcal{M}}_{\text{weak,def}}(L^{(1)}).$$

Assume the equality

$$\mathfrak{PO}((\mathfrak{b}, b_0)) = \mathfrak{PO}((\mathfrak{b}, b_1)).$$

If $(\mathfrak{b}, b_0) \sim (\mathfrak{b}, b'_0)$ and $(\mathfrak{b}, b_1) \sim (\mathfrak{b}, b'_1)$, then we have an isomorphism between the Floer cohomologies

$$HF((L^{(1)}, (\mathfrak{b}, b_1)), (L^{(0)}, (\mathfrak{b}, b_0)); \Lambda_{0,nov})$$
$$\cong HF((L^{(1)}, (\mathfrak{b}, b'_1)), (L^{(0)}, (\mathfrak{b}, b'_0)); \Lambda_{0,nov}).$$

The isomorphism is canonical.

This proposition implies that the Floer cohomology is well defined and is parametrized by the pair of the gauge equivalence classes of

$$(\mathfrak{b}, b_0), (\mathfrak{b}, b_1) \in \mathcal{M}_{\text{weak,def}}(L)$$

such that

$$\pi_{\text{amb}}(\mathfrak{b}, b_0) = \pi_{\text{amb}}(\mathfrak{b}, b_1) \quad and \quad \mathfrak{PO}(\mathfrak{b}, b_0) = \mathfrak{PO}(\mathfrak{b}, b_1).$$

This is nothing but Theorem B (B.1) in Chapter 1.

From now on, we will simply denote by the same symbol $(\mathfrak{b}, b) \in \mathcal{M}_{\text{weak,def}}(L)$ the gauge equivalence class of $(\mathfrak{b}, b) \in \widehat{\mathcal{M}}_{\text{weak,def}}(L)$, if no confusion can occur.

4.4. Uniqueness of the model of $[0,1] \times C$

This section is devoted to the proof of Theorem 4.2.34 which plays the fundamental role to study the homotopy equivalence of filtered A_∞ algebras.

4.4.1. Induction on the number filtration I. In Subsections 4.4.1-4.4.4, we first prove the case of unfiltered A_∞ algebras. Namely we consider the following situation. Let $\overline{C}_1, \overline{C}_2$ be A_∞ algebras and $\overline{\mathfrak{C}}_1, \overline{\mathfrak{C}}_2$ models of $[0,1] \times \overline{C}_1$ and of $[0,1] \times \overline{C}_2$ respectively. Let $\bar{\mathfrak{f}} : \overline{C}_1 \to \overline{C}_2$ be an A_∞ homomorphism. We will construct an A_∞ homomorphism $\overline{\mathfrak{F}}$ from $\overline{\mathfrak{C}}_1$ to $\overline{\mathfrak{C}}_2$ such that

(4.4.1.1) $\widehat{\overline{\mathrm{Eval}}}_{s=s_0} \circ \widehat{\overline{\mathfrak{F}}} = \widehat{\bar{\mathfrak{f}}} \circ \widehat{\overline{\mathrm{Eval}}}_{s=s_0}, \quad$ where $s_0 = 0, 1,$

(4.4.1.2) $\widehat{\overline{\mathrm{Incl}}} \circ \widehat{\bar{\mathfrak{f}}} = \widehat{\overline{\mathfrak{F}}} \circ \widehat{\overline{\mathrm{Incl}}}.$

Here $\hat{}$ stands for the induced coalgebra homomorphism on the bar complex. See (3.2.6). We say that $\overline{\mathfrak{F}}$ is *compatible with* $\overline{\mathrm{Incl}}$ *and* $\overline{\mathrm{Eval}}$ *over* $\bar{\mathfrak{f}}$, if (4.4.1) is satisfied.

Recall that an A_∞ homomorphism $\overline{\mathfrak{F}}$ consists of a sequence

$$\overline{\mathfrak{F}}_i \; : \; B_i\overline{\mathfrak{C}}[1] \to \overline{\mathfrak{C}}_2[1], \quad \text{for } i = 1, 2, 3, \cdots$$

satisfying the condition given in Definition 3.2.7. If $\overline{\mathfrak{F}}_i$ $i = 1, \cdots, k$ are defined and (4.4.1.1),(4.4.1.2) hold on $\oplus_{i=1}^k B_i\overline{\mathfrak{C}}_1[1]$, we say that it is *compatible with* $\overline{\mathrm{Incl}}$ *and* $\overline{\mathrm{Eval}}$.

The construction of $\overline{\mathfrak{F}}$ is by induction on the number filtration. Namely we will construct $\overline{\mathfrak{F}}_k : B_k\overline{\mathfrak{C}}_1[1] \to \overline{\mathfrak{C}}_2[1]$ inductively on k. We start the induction with the following:

LEMMA 4.4.2. *There exists a cochain homomorphism* $\overline{\mathfrak{F}}_1 : \overline{\mathfrak{C}}_1 \to \overline{\mathfrak{C}}_2$ *compatible with* $\overline{\mathrm{Incl}}$ *and* $\overline{\mathrm{Eval}}$.

PROOF. We first remark that there exists a cochain map $\overline{\mathfrak{F}}_1'$ which satisfies (4.4.1.2) (on $B_1\overline{C}_1 = \overline{C}_1$) but not necessarily (4.4.1.1). (For example we may put $\overline{\mathfrak{F}}_1' = \overline{\mathrm{Incl}}_1 \circ \bar{\mathfrak{f}}_1 \circ (\overline{\mathrm{Eval}}_{s=1})_1$.) Now we put

$$\overline{\mathrm{Err1}}_{s_0} = (\overline{\mathrm{Eval}}_{s=s_0})_1 \circ \overline{\mathfrak{F}}_1' - \bar{\mathfrak{f}}_1 \circ (\overline{\mathrm{Eval}}_{s=s_0})_1$$

and

$$\overline{\mathrm{Err1}} = (\overline{\mathrm{Err1}}_0, \overline{\mathrm{Err1}}_1) \in Hom(\overline{\mathfrak{C}}_1, \overline{C}_2) \oplus Hom(\overline{\mathfrak{C}}_1, \overline{C}_2).$$

Then $\overline{\mathrm{Err1}}$ is a cochain map. In other words $\delta_1\overline{\mathrm{Err1}} = 0$, where δ_1 is a coboundary operator of $Hom(\overline{\mathfrak{C}}_1, \overline{C}_2) \oplus Hom(\overline{\mathfrak{C}}_1, \overline{C}_2)$ induced by $\hat{\overline{\mathfrak{m}}}_1$ and $\overline{\mathfrak{m}}_1$ on $\overline{\mathfrak{C}}_1$ and $\overline{C}_2$. We derive

$$\overline{\mathrm{Err1}} \circ \overline{\mathrm{Incl}} = (\overline{\mathrm{Eval}}_{s=s_0})_1 \circ \overline{\mathfrak{F}}_1' \circ \overline{\mathrm{Incl}} - \bar{\mathfrak{f}}_1 \circ (\overline{\mathrm{Eval}}_{s=s_0})_1 \circ \overline{\mathrm{Incl}} = 0,$$

since $\overline{\mathfrak{F}}_1'$ satisfies (4.4.1.2). The following lemma will be used several times in this section.

LEMMA 4.4.3. *Let* $(\overline{D}_j, d)$, $j = 1, 2, 3$ *be cochain complexes over* R, *and* $i : \overline{D}_1 \to \overline{D}_2$ *be a cochain homomorphism. Suppose that* i *is a cochain homotopy equivalence that is split injective as an* R *module homomorphism.*

Let $A \in Hom_R(\overline{D}_2, \overline{D}_3)$ *such that* $dA = 0$, $A \circ i = 0$. *Then there exists* $B \in Hom_R(\overline{D}_2, \overline{D}_3)$ *such that* $dB = A$ *and* $B \circ i = 0$.

PROOF. By assumption $i^* : H^*(Hom_R(\overline{D}_2, \overline{D}_3)) \to H^*(Hom_R(\overline{D}_1, \overline{D}_3))$ is an isomorphism. Hence there exists $B' \in Hom_R(\overline{D}_2, \overline{D}_3)$ such that $dB' = A$. Then, by assumption $d(B' \circ i) = 0$. Therefore, there exists $\alpha \in Hom_R(\overline{D}_2, \overline{D}_3)$, $\beta \in Hom_R(\overline{D}_1, \overline{D}_3)$ such that $B' \circ i = \alpha \circ i + d\beta$ and $d\alpha = 0$. Since i is split injective, there exists $\tilde{\beta} \in Hom_R(\overline{D}_2, \overline{D}_3)$ such that $\tilde{\beta} \circ i = \beta$. It is easy to see that $B = B' - \alpha - d\tilde{\beta}$ has required properties. $\square$

We return to the proof of Lemma 4.4.2. We apply Lemma 4.4.3 to $A = \overline{\mathrm{Err1}}$ and obtain $\overline{\mathrm{Corr}}'$ such that $\overline{\mathrm{Err1}} = \delta\overline{\mathrm{Corr}}'$ and $\overline{\mathrm{Corr}}' \circ \overline{\mathrm{Incl}}_1 = 0$.

Since the homomorphism

$$(\overline{\mathrm{Eval}}_{s=0})_1 \oplus (\overline{\mathrm{Eval}}_{s=1})_1 : \mathfrak{C}_2 \longrightarrow \overline{C}_2 \oplus \overline{C}_2$$

is split surjective by (4.2.2.4) and Remark 4.2.4 and since $\overline{\mathrm{Incl}}_1 : \overline{C}_1 \to \mathfrak{C}_1$ is split injective, it follows that we have $\overline{\mathrm{Corr}} \in Hom(\mathfrak{C}_1, \mathfrak{C}_2)$ such that

(4.4.4.1) $$((\overline{\mathrm{Eval}}_{s=0})_1, (\overline{\mathrm{Eval}}_{s=1})_1) \circ \overline{\mathrm{Corr}} = \overline{\mathrm{Corr}}'$$

and

(4.4.4.2) $$\overline{\mathrm{Corr}} \circ \overline{\mathrm{Incl}}_1 = 0.$$

Now we put

$$\overline{\mathfrak{F}}_1 = \overline{\mathfrak{F}}'_1 - \delta\overline{\mathrm{Corr}}.$$

It is easy to see that it has required properties. $\square$

Hence we have finished the first step of the induction. To proceed further we introduce the notion of A_K structures.

4.4.2. A_K structures and homomorphisms. To define A_K structure, we need some more notations. Let $\overline{C}$ be a graded R module and $m_1 < m_2$ be natural numbers. We put

(4.4.5) $$B_{m_1 \cdots m_2}\overline{C}[1] \cong \frac{\bigoplus_{k=1}^{m_2} B_k \overline{C}[1]}{\bigoplus_{k=1}^{m_1-1} B_k \overline{C}[1]}.$$

We consider a series of degree 1 homomorphisms $\overline{\mathrm{m}}_k : B_k\overline{C}[1] \to \overline{C}[1]$, for $k = 1, \cdots, K$. It induces a coderivation $\widehat{\overline{\mathrm{m}}}_k : B_{1 \cdots K}\overline{C}[1] \to B_{1 \cdots K}\overline{C}[1]$ by (3.2.1). We put $\widehat{\overline{d}}_{1 \cdots K} = \sum_{k=1}^{K} \widehat{\overline{\mathrm{m}}}_k$.

DEFINITION 4.4.6. $\overline{\mathrm{m}} = \{\overline{\mathrm{m}}_1, \cdots, \overline{\mathrm{m}}_K\}$ defines a structure of A_K *algebra* over R if $\widehat{\overline{d}}_{1 \cdots K} \circ \widehat{\overline{d}}_{1 \cdots K} = 0$.

REMARK 4.4.7. We do not try to generalize the notion of A_K algebras to one for the filtered A_∞ algebra in this section. Because m_0 does not preserve $B_{1 \cdots K}C[1]$, the definition thereof is more involved. We will introduce the filtered $A_{n,K}$ algebras in Subsection 7.2.6, where we use them.

Let $(\overline{C}_i, \overline{\mathrm{m}})$, $i = 1, 2$ be A_K algebras. We consider a sequence of R module homomorphisms $\overline{\mathfrak{f}}_k : B_k\overline{C}_1[1] \to \overline{C}_2[1]$ of degree 0, for $k = 1, 2, 3, \cdots, K$. It induces coalgebra homomorphisms $\widehat{\overline{\mathfrak{f}}}_k : B_{1 \cdots K}\overline{C}_1[1] \to B_{1 \cdots K}\overline{C}_2[1]$, by (3.2.6). We put $\widehat{\overline{\mathfrak{f}}}_{1 \cdots K} = \sum_{k=1}^{K} \widehat{\overline{\mathfrak{f}}}_k$.

DEFINITION 4.4.8. We call $\bar{\mathfrak{f}} = \{\bar{\mathfrak{f}}_1, \cdots, \bar{\mathfrak{f}}_K\}$ an A_K *homomorphism from* $\overline{C}_1$ *to* $\overline{C}_2$ if $\widehat{\bar{\mathfrak{f}}}_{1\cdots K} \circ \widehat{\bar{d}}_{1\cdots K} = \widehat{\bar{d}}_{1\cdots K} \circ \widehat{\bar{\mathfrak{f}}}_{1\cdots K}$. The composition of two A_K homomorphisms are defined in the same way as in Definition 3.2.8. Further, the notions of the A_K *homotopy* between A_K homomorphisms and the A_K *homotopy equivalence* are defined in a similar way in Subsection 4.2.2.

We remark that an A_K structure induces an $A_{K'}$ structure for $K' \leq K \leq \infty$. We state the following two lemmas which will be used in the next subsection.

LEMMA 4.4.9. *If* $(\overline{C}, \overline{\mathfrak{m}})$ *is an* A_K *algebra and* $m_2 - m_1 < K$, *then* $\overline{\mathfrak{m}}$ *induces a homomorphism* $\widehat{\bar{d}}_{m_1\cdots m_2} : B_{m_1\cdots m_2}\overline{C}[1] \to B_{m_1\cdots m_2}\overline{C}[1]$ *such that* $\widehat{\bar{d}}_{m_1\cdots m_2} \circ \widehat{\bar{d}}_{m_1\cdots m_2} = 0$.

LEMMA 4.4.10. *If* $\widehat{\bar{\mathfrak{f}}} : \overline{C}_1 \to \overline{C}_2$ *is an* A_K *homomorphism and if* $m_2 - m_1 < K$, *then* $\bar{\mathfrak{f}}$ *induces a homomorphism* $\widehat{\bar{\mathfrak{f}}}_{m_1\cdots m_2} : B_{m_1\cdots m_2}\overline{C}[1] \to B_{m_1\cdots m_2}\overline{C}[1]$ *such that* $\widehat{\bar{\mathfrak{f}}}_{m_1\cdots m_2} \circ \widehat{\bar{d}}_{m_1\cdots m_2} = \widehat{\bar{d}}_{m_1\cdots m_2} \circ \widehat{\bar{\mathfrak{f}}}_{m_1\cdots m_2}$.

The proofs are easy and omitted.

4.4.3. Induction on the number filtration II. Now we prove the following proposition by induction on K. We consider the situation of Theorem 4.2.34.

PROPOSITION 4.4.11. *For any given* A_{K-1} *homomorphism* $\overline{\mathfrak{F}}^{(K-1)}$ *compatible with* $\overline{\mathrm{Incl}}$ *and* $\overline{\mathrm{Eval}}$ *over* $\bar{\mathfrak{f}}$, *there exists an* A_K *homomorphism* $\overline{\mathfrak{F}}^{(K)}$ *from* $\overline{\mathfrak{C}}_1$ *to* $\overline{\mathfrak{C}}_2$ *compatible with* $\overline{\mathrm{Incl}}$ *and* $\overline{\mathrm{Eval}}$ *over* $\bar{\mathfrak{f}}$. *Moreover if we regard* $\overline{\mathfrak{F}}^{(K)}$ *as an* A_{K-1} *homomorphism, it coincides with* $\overline{\mathfrak{F}}^{(K-1)}$.

PROOF. The proof is by induction on K. The case of $K = 1$ is already taken care of in Lemma 4.4.2. Assume that Proposition 4.4.11 is proved for $K - 1$. Then $\overline{\mathfrak{F}}^{(K-1)}$ induces a coalgebra homomorphism

$$\widehat{\overline{\mathfrak{F}}}^{(K-1)} : B\overline{\mathfrak{C}}_1[1] \to B\overline{\mathfrak{C}}_2[1].$$

We consider the restriction of

$$\tag{4.4.12} \widehat{\bar{d}} \circ \widehat{\overline{\mathfrak{F}}}^{(K-1)} - \widehat{\overline{\mathfrak{F}}}^{(K-1)} \circ \widehat{\bar{d}}$$

to $B_{1\cdots K}\overline{\mathfrak{C}}_1[1]$ and denote it by $\overline{\mathrm{Err}}_K$.

LEMMA 4.4.13. *The restriction of* $\overline{\mathrm{Err}}_K$ *to* $B_{1\cdots K-1}\overline{\mathfrak{C}}_1[1]$ *vanishes. The image of* $\overline{\mathrm{Err}}_K$ *is in* $B_1\overline{\mathfrak{C}}_2[1] = \overline{\mathfrak{C}}_2[1]$.

PROOF. It is easy to see that the restriction of $\widehat{\overline{\mathfrak{F}}}^{(K-1)}$ to $B_{1\cdots K-1}\overline{\mathfrak{C}}_1[1]$ is $\widehat{\overline{\mathfrak{F}}}_{1\cdots K-1}$. The first statement then follows from Lemma 4.4.10. $\widehat{\overline{\mathfrak{F}}}^{(K-1)}$ induces $\widehat{\overline{\mathfrak{F}}}_{2\cdots K}$ on $Hom(B_{2\cdots K}\overline{\mathfrak{C}}_1[1], B_{2\cdots K}\overline{\mathfrak{C}}_2[1])$. Then the second half also follows from Lemma 4.4.10. $\square$

By Lemma 4.4.13, we may regard

$$\overline{\mathrm{Err}}_K \in Hom(B_K\overline{\mathfrak{C}}_1[1], \overline{\mathfrak{C}}_2[1])).$$

The coboundary operator $\overline{\mathfrak{m}}_1$ induces

$$\delta_1 : Hom(B_K\overline{\mathfrak{C}}_1[1], \overline{\mathfrak{C}}_2[1])) \to Hom(B_K\overline{\mathfrak{C}}_1[1], \overline{\mathfrak{C}}_2[1]))$$

by

$$\delta_1(A) = \overline{\mathfrak{m}}_1 \circ A - (-1)^{\deg A} A \circ \widehat{\overline{\mathfrak{m}}}_1.$$

LEMMA 4.4.14. $\delta_1 \overline{\text{Err}}_K = 0$.

PROOF. Note that $\widehat{\overline{d}}$ induces a coboundary operator on $Hom(B\overline{\mathfrak{C}}_1[1], B\overline{\mathfrak{C}}_2[1]))$ by

$$\phi \mapsto \widehat{\overline{d}}(\phi) = \widehat{\overline{d}} \circ \phi - (-1)^{\deg \phi} \phi \circ \widehat{\overline{d}}.$$

By definition, $\overline{\text{Err}}_K$ is a restriction of $\widehat{\overline{d}}(\overline{\mathfrak{F}}^{(K-1)})$ to $B_K\overline{\mathfrak{C}}_1[1]$. Hence, by Lemma 4.4.13, the restriction of $\widehat{\overline{d}}(\widehat{\overline{d}}(\overline{\mathfrak{F}}^{(K-1)}))) = 0$ to $B_K\overline{\mathfrak{C}}_1[1]$ is $\delta_1 \overline{\text{Err}}_K$. The lemma follows. $\qquad\square$

LEMMA 4.4.15. $\overline{\text{Err}}_K \in \text{Im}\, \delta_1$ in $Hom(B_K\overline{\mathfrak{C}}_1[1], \overline{\mathfrak{C}}_2[1])$.

PROOF. Let $\widehat{\overline{\mathfrak{f}}}^{(K-1)} : B\overline{C}_1[1] \to B\overline{C}_2[1]$ be the coalgebra homomorphism induced by $\widehat{\overline{\mathfrak{f}}}_1, \cdots, \widehat{\overline{\mathfrak{f}}}_{K-1}$. Then since $\overline{\mathfrak{f}}$ is an A_∞ homomorphism, it follows from the A_∞ formula that

$$\widehat{\overline{d}} \circ \widehat{\overline{\mathfrak{f}}}^{(K-1)} - \widehat{\overline{\mathfrak{f}}}^{(K-1)} \circ \widehat{\overline{d}} + \delta_1(\overline{\mathfrak{f}}_K) = 0$$

on $B_{1\cdots K}\overline{C}_1$. Here $\delta_1 : Hom(B_K\overline{C}_1[1], \overline{C}_2[1])) \to Hom(B_K\overline{C}_1[1], \overline{C}_2[1]))$ is induced by $\overline{\mathfrak{m}}_1$.

Now, we calculate, using the compatibility of $\overline{\mathfrak{F}}^{(K-1)}$ with $\overline{\text{Incl}}$, to obtain the following formula in $Hom(B_k\overline{C}_1[1], \overline{\mathfrak{C}}_2[1])$:

$$\overline{\text{Err}}_K \circ \widehat{\overline{\text{Incl}}} = (\overline{\mathfrak{m}} \circ \widehat{\overline{\mathfrak{F}}}^{(K-1)} - \overline{\mathfrak{F}}^{(K-1)} \circ \widehat{\overline{d}}) \circ \widehat{\overline{\text{Incl}}}$$

(4.4.16)
$$= \overline{\text{Incl}}_1 \circ (\overline{\mathfrak{m}} \circ \widehat{\overline{\mathfrak{f}}}^{(K-1)} - \overline{\mathfrak{f}}^{(K-1)} \circ \widehat{\overline{d}})$$

$$= -\delta_1(\overline{\text{Incl}}_1 \circ \widehat{\overline{\mathfrak{f}}}_K).$$

The lemma then follows from the fact that $\overline{\text{Incl}}_1$ is a cochain homotopy equivalence. $\qquad\square$

Lemma 4.4.15 implies there exists $\overline{\mathfrak{F}}'_K \in Hom(B_K\overline{\mathfrak{C}}_1[1], \overline{\mathfrak{C}}_2[1])$ such that

$$\delta_1(\overline{\mathfrak{F}}'_K) + \overline{\text{Err}}_K = 0.$$

LEMMA 4.4.17. *We may choose $\overline{\mathfrak{F}}'_K$ such that $\overline{\mathfrak{F}}'_K \circ \overline{\text{Incl}}_1 = \overline{\text{Incl}}_1 \circ \overline{\mathfrak{f}}_K$ in addition.*

PROOF. Let us first take any $\overline{\mathfrak{F}}''_K$ such that $\delta_1(\overline{\mathfrak{F}}''_K) + \overline{\text{Err}}_K = 0$. (4.4.16) then implies

$$\delta_1 \left(\overline{\mathfrak{F}}''_K \circ \widehat{\overline{\text{Incl}}} - \overline{\text{Incl}}_1 \circ \overline{\mathfrak{f}}_K \right) = 0.$$

Here there exist $\alpha \in Hom(B_K\overline{\mathfrak{C}}_1[1], \overline{\mathfrak{C}}_2[1])$ and $\beta \in Hom(B_K\overline{C}_1[1], \overline{\mathfrak{C}}_2[1])$ such that $\delta_1 \alpha = 0$ and

$$\overline{\mathfrak{F}}''_K \circ \widehat{\overline{\text{Incl}}} - \overline{\text{Incl}}_1 \circ \overline{\mathfrak{f}}_K = \alpha \circ \widehat{\overline{\text{Incl}}} + \delta_1 \beta.$$

We have $\widetilde{\beta}$ such that $\widetilde{\beta} \circ \widehat{\overline{\mathrm{Incl}}} = \beta$. We put

$$\overline{\mathfrak{F}}'_K = \overline{\mathfrak{F}}''_K - \alpha - \delta_1 \widetilde{\beta}.$$

Then it is easy to check that $\overline{\mathfrak{F}}'_K$ has required properties. $\square$

By definition, $\overline{\mathfrak{F}}^{(K-1)}$ together with $\overline{\mathfrak{F}}'_K$ defines an A_K homomorphism compatible with $\overline{\mathrm{Incl}}$.

LEMMA 4.4.18. *We can modify $\overline{\mathfrak{F}}'_K$ to $\overline{\overline{\mathfrak{F}}}_K$ so that the A_K homomorphism $\overline{\mathfrak{F}}^{(K)}$ obtained from $\overline{\mathfrak{F}}^{(K-1)}$ and $\overline{\overline{\mathfrak{F}}}_K$ is compatible with $\overline{\mathrm{Incl}}$ and $\overline{\mathrm{Eval}}$ over $\bar{\mathfrak{f}}$.*

PROOF. Let us use $\overline{\mathfrak{F}}'_K$ to obtain an A_K homomorphism $\overline{\mathfrak{F}}^{(K)\prime}$. We put

(4.4.19) $$\overline{\mathrm{Err}}_K^{(s_0)} = \overline{\mathrm{Eval}}_{s=s_0} \circ \overline{\mathfrak{F}}^{(K)\prime} - \bar{\mathfrak{f}} \circ \widehat{\overline{\mathrm{Eval}}}_{s=s_0} \quad \text{for } s_0 = 0, 1.$$

Since $\overline{\mathfrak{F}}^{(K-1)}$ is compatible with $\overline{\mathrm{Eval}}$ by induction hypothesis, it follows that the restriction of $\overline{\mathrm{Err}}_K^{(s_0)}$ to $B_{1\cdots K-1}\overline{\mathfrak{C}}_1[1]$ is zero. Moreover the image of its restriction to $B_{1\cdots K}\overline{\mathfrak{C}}_1[1]$ is in $B_1\overline{C}_2[1] = \overline{C}_2[1]$. Namely we have

$$(\overline{\mathrm{Err}}_K^{(0)}, \overline{\mathrm{Err}}_K^{(1)}) \in Hom(B_K\overline{\mathfrak{C}}_1[1], \overline{C}_2[1] \oplus \overline{C}_2[1]).$$

Since $\overline{\mathfrak{F}}^{(K)\prime}$ and $\bar{\mathfrak{f}}$ both are A_K homomorphisms, it follows that

$$\delta_1(\overline{\mathrm{Err}}_K^{(0)}, \overline{\mathrm{Err}}_K^{(1)}) = 0.$$

Moreover using the compatibility with $\overline{\mathrm{Incl}}$ we have

$$\overline{\mathrm{Err}}_K^{(s_0)} \circ \widehat{\overline{\mathrm{Incl}}} = 0.$$

Now we apply Lemma 4.4.3 to $A = (\overline{\mathrm{Err}}_K^{(0)}, \overline{\mathrm{Err}}_K^{(1)})$. Then, there exists

$$(\overline{\mathrm{Cor1}}_K^{(0)}, \overline{\mathrm{Cor1}}_K^{(1)}) \in Hom(B_K\overline{\mathfrak{C}}_1[1], \overline{C}_2[1] \oplus \overline{C}_2[1])$$

such that

(4.4.20.1) $$\delta_1(\overline{\mathrm{Cor1}}_K^{(0)}, \overline{\mathrm{Cor1}}_K^{(1)}) = (\overline{\mathrm{Err}}_K^{(0)}, \overline{\mathrm{Err}}_K^{(1)}),$$

(4.4.20.2) $$\overline{\mathrm{Cor1}}_K^{(s_0)} \circ \widehat{\overline{\mathrm{Incl}}} = 0.$$

Using the property (4.2.2.4) we find $\overline{\mathrm{Cor2}}_K \in Hom(B_K\overline{\mathfrak{C}}_1[1], \overline{\mathfrak{C}}_2[1])$ such that

(4.4.21.1) $$(\overline{\mathrm{Eval}}_{s=s_0})_1 \circ (\overline{\mathrm{Cor2}}_K) = \overline{\mathrm{Cor1}}_K^{(s_0)},$$

(4.4.21.2) $$\overline{\mathrm{Cor2}}_K \circ \widehat{\overline{\mathrm{Incl}}} = 0.$$

We put $\overline{\overline{\mathfrak{F}}}_K = \overline{\mathfrak{F}}'_K - \overline{\mathrm{Cor2}}_K$. Then (4.4.20.1), (4.4.21.1) and (4.4.21.2) imply that $\overline{\overline{\mathfrak{F}}}_K$ satisfies the required properties. $\square$

Therefore we have now finished the proof of Proposition 4.4.11. $\square$

Proposition 4.4.11 immediately implies the unfiltered version of Theorem 4.2.34.

4.4.4. Unital case I: the unfiltered version. Before proceeding to the filtered version, we explain how we can modify the argument above to treat the unital case. Suppose $\bar{\mathfrak{f}}$ is unital. We will construct $\overline{\widehat{\mathfrak{F}}}$ that is compatible with $\overline{\text{Incl}}$ and $\overline{\text{Eval}}$ over $\bar{\mathfrak{f}}$ and also is unital. We consider an A_∞ algebra $\overline{C}$ with unit $\mathbf{e}$.

DEFINITION 4.4.22. We define the *partially reduced bar complex* denoted by $\widehat{B}^{\mathrm{red}}\overline{C}[1]$ as follows. Putting $\overline{C}_{\mathrm{red}} = \overline{C}/R[\mathbf{e}]$, we define

$$(4.4.23) \qquad B_k^{\mathrm{red}}\overline{C}[1] = \begin{cases} \overline{C}[1] \otimes B_{k-2}\overline{C}_{\mathrm{red}}[1] \otimes \overline{C}[1], & \text{if } k \geq 2, \\ \overline{C}[1], & \text{if } k = 1, \end{cases}$$

and $\widehat{B}^{\mathrm{red}}\overline{C}[1] = \widehat{\bigoplus}_{k \geq 1} B_k^{\mathrm{red}}\overline{C}[1]$.

LEMMA-DEFINITION 4.4.24. $\widehat{\hat{d}} : B\overline{C}[1] \to B\overline{C}[1]$ *induces a differential* $\widehat{\hat{d}}^{\mathrm{red}}$ *on* $\widehat{B}^{\mathrm{red}}\overline{C}[1]$.

PROOF. Let us consider an element $\mathbf{x}_1 \otimes \mathbf{e} \otimes \mathbf{x}_2 \in B\overline{C}[1]$ with $\mathbf{x}_i \in B_{k_i}\overline{C}[1]$, $k_i \geq 1$. We write $\mathbf{x}_1 = \mathbf{x}_{1-} \otimes x_{\mathrm{last}}$, $\mathbf{x}_2 = x_{\mathrm{first}} \otimes \mathbf{x}_{2-}$. Then we have

$$\widehat{\hat{d}}(\mathbf{x}_1 \otimes \mathbf{e} \otimes \mathbf{x}_2) = (-1)^{\deg' \mathbf{x}_{1-}} \mathbf{x}_{1-} \otimes \mathfrak{m}_2(x_{\mathrm{last}}, \mathbf{e}) \otimes \mathbf{x}_2$$
$$+ (-1)^{\deg' \mathbf{x}} \mathbf{x} \otimes \mathfrak{m}_2(\mathbf{e}, x_{\mathrm{first}}) \otimes \mathbf{x}_{2-} = 0$$

in $\widehat{B}^{\mathrm{red}}\overline{C}[1]$ by Condition 3.2.18. Hence the lemma follows. $\qquad \square$

We remark that $\widehat{\hat{d}} : \widehat{B\overline{C}}_{\mathrm{red}}[1] \to \widehat{B\overline{C}}_{\mathrm{red}}[1]$ is *not* well defined.

Next we define operators $s_{\mathrm{left}}, s_{\mathrm{right}} : B_k^{\mathrm{red}}\overline{C}[1] \to B_{k+1}^{\mathrm{red}}\overline{C}[1]$ by

$$s_{\mathrm{left}}(\mathbf{x}) = \mathbf{e} \otimes \mathbf{x}, \qquad s_{\mathrm{right}}(\mathbf{x}) = (-1)^{\deg \mathbf{x}} \mathbf{x} \otimes \mathbf{e}.$$

LEMMA 4.4.25. $\widehat{\hat{d}}^{\mathrm{red}} \circ s_{\mathrm{left}} + s_{\mathrm{left}} \circ \widehat{\hat{d}}^{\mathrm{red}} = \widehat{\hat{d}}^{\mathrm{red}} \circ s_{\mathrm{right}} + s_{\mathrm{right}} \circ \widehat{\hat{d}}^{\mathrm{red}} = \text{identity}.$

The proof is an easy calculation using Condition 3.2.18.

Let $\overline{C}_1$, $\overline{C}_2$ be unital A_∞ algebras. Suppose we have a sequence of homomorphisms $\bar{\mathfrak{f}}_{k,\mathrm{red}} : B_k^{\mathrm{red}}\overline{C}_1[1] \to \overline{C}_2[1]$ of degree 0, with $\bar{\mathfrak{f}}_{1,\mathrm{red}}(\mathbf{e}) = \mathbf{e}$. It induces

$$(4.4.26) \qquad \widehat{\bar{\mathfrak{f}}}_{\mathrm{red}} : \widehat{B}^{\mathrm{red}}\overline{C}_1[1] \longrightarrow \widehat{B\overline{C}}_2[1]$$

as follows. (We remark that right hand side is the usual bar complex and is not the reduced one.) We choose a splitting

$$(4.4.27) \qquad \overline{C} = \overline{C}_{\mathrm{red}} \oplus R[\mathbf{e}].$$

See Definition 3.2.20 (3). We use (4.4.27) to regard $B_k\overline{C}_{1\mathrm{red}}[1] \subset \widehat{B}_k^{\mathrm{red}}\overline{C}_1[1]$. The we define $\widehat{\bar{\mathfrak{f}}}$ by the same formula as (3.2.28) on $\widehat{B}\overline{C}_{1\mathrm{red}}$. Finally we put

$$\widehat{\bar{\mathfrak{f}}}_{\mathrm{red}}(\mathbf{e} \otimes \mathbf{x}) = \mathbf{e} \otimes \widehat{\bar{\mathfrak{f}}}_{\mathrm{red}}(\mathbf{x}), \quad \widehat{\bar{\mathfrak{f}}}_{\mathrm{red}}(\mathbf{x} \otimes \mathbf{e}) = \widehat{\bar{\mathfrak{f}}}_{\mathrm{red}}(\mathbf{x}) \otimes \mathbf{e},$$
$$\widehat{\bar{\mathfrak{f}}}_{\mathrm{red}}(\mathbf{e} \otimes \mathbf{x} \otimes \mathbf{e}) = \mathbf{e} \otimes \widehat{\bar{\mathfrak{f}}}_{\mathrm{red}}(\mathbf{x}) \otimes \mathbf{e}, \quad \widehat{\bar{\mathfrak{f}}}_{\mathrm{red}}(\mathbf{e}) = \mathbf{e},$$

for $\mathbf{x} \in \widehat{B}\overline{C}_{1\mathrm{red}}$. We also define $\widehat{\bar{\mathfrak{f}}} : \widehat{B\overline{C}}_1[1] \to \widehat{B\overline{C}}_2[1]$ by putting

$$(4.4.28) \qquad \widehat{\bar{\mathfrak{f}}}(\mathbf{x}_1 \otimes \mathbf{e} \otimes \cdots \otimes \mathbf{e} \otimes \mathbf{x}_\ell) = \widehat{\bar{\mathfrak{f}}}_{\mathrm{red}}(\mathbf{x}_1) \otimes \mathbf{e} \otimes \cdots \otimes \mathbf{e} \otimes \widehat{\bar{\mathfrak{f}}}_{\mathrm{red}}(\mathbf{x}_\ell)$$

for $\mathbf{x}_i \in B_{k_i}\overline{C}_{1\mathrm{red}}[1]$. We use (4.4.27) to regard $B_k\overline{C}_{1\mathrm{red}}[1] \subset \widehat{B}_k^{\mathrm{red}}\overline{C}_1[1]$ and put $\widehat{\overline{\mathfrak{f}}}_{\mathrm{red}}(1) = 1$ for $1 \in B_0\overline{C}_{1\mathrm{red}}[1]$ which is not contained in $\widehat{B}^{\mathrm{red}}\overline{C}_1[1]$.

REMARK 4.4.29. We remark that $\overline{C}_{\mathrm{red}}$ is not an A_∞ subalgebra in general. Namely the image of the restriction of $\mathfrak{m}_k$ to $B_k\overline{C}_{\mathrm{red}}$ may be ce. Moreover the splitting (4.4.27) is not necessarily canonical in the algebraic situation. (In our geometric situation there is a canonical splitting but we do not use it.)

LEMMA 4.4.30. *Let* $\overline{\mathfrak{f}}_{k,\mathrm{red}}$ *be a sequence of homomorphisms as in* (4.4.26). *We assume*

$$(4.4.31.1) \quad \widehat{\overline{\mathfrak{f}}}_{\mathrm{red}} \circ \widehat{\overline{d}}^{\mathrm{red}} = \widehat{\overline{d}} \circ \widehat{\overline{\mathfrak{f}}}_{\mathrm{red}}.$$

Then the homomorphism (4.4.28) *is a unital A_∞ homomorphism. Moreover every unital A_∞ homomorphism is obtained from a sequence* $\overline{\mathfrak{f}}_{k,\mathrm{red}}$ *satisfying* (4.4.31.1) *and*

$$(4.4.31.2) \quad \overline{\mathfrak{f}}_{k,\mathrm{red}} \circ s_{\mathrm{left}} = \overline{\mathfrak{f}}_{k,\mathrm{red}} \circ s_{\mathrm{right}} = 0.$$

PROOF. Let us assume (4.4.31). We calculate, for $\mathbf{x}_i \in B_{k_i}\overline{C}_{1\mathrm{red}}[1]$,

$$(4.4.32) \quad \begin{aligned} &\overline{\mathfrak{m}}(\widehat{\overline{\mathfrak{f}}}(\mathbf{x}_1 \otimes \mathbf{e} \otimes \cdots \otimes \mathbf{e} \otimes \mathbf{x}_\ell)) \\ &= \overline{\mathfrak{m}}(\widehat{\overline{\mathfrak{f}}}_{\mathrm{red}}(\mathbf{x}_1) \otimes \mathbf{e} \otimes \cdots \otimes \mathbf{e} \otimes \widehat{\overline{\mathfrak{f}}}_{\mathrm{red}}(\mathbf{x}_\ell)). \end{aligned}$$

Case 1: If $k_1, k_\ell > 0$, then (4.4.32) is zero. Also we have

$$(4.4.33) \quad (\overline{\mathfrak{f}} \circ \widehat{d})(\mathbf{x}_1 \otimes \mathbf{e} \otimes \cdots \otimes \mathbf{e} \otimes \mathbf{x}_\ell)) = 0.$$

Case 2: If $\ell > 2$, then (4.4.32) is zero. (4.4.33) also holds.
Case 3: If $\ell = 1$, then

$$(\widehat{\overline{d}} \circ \widehat{\overline{\mathfrak{f}}})(\mathbf{x}_1) = (\widehat{\overline{d}} \circ \widehat{\overline{\mathfrak{f}}}_{\mathrm{red}})(\mathbf{x}_1) = (\widehat{\overline{\mathfrak{f}}}_{\mathrm{red}} \circ \widehat{\overline{d}}^{\mathrm{red}})(\mathbf{x}_1).$$

By taking its component we have

$$(\overline{\mathfrak{m}} \circ \widehat{\overline{\mathfrak{f}}})(\mathbf{x}_1) = (\overline{\mathfrak{f}} \circ \widehat{\overline{d}})(\mathbf{x}_1),$$

since $B_1 C_2[1]$ component of $\widehat{\overline{\mathfrak{f}}}_{\mathrm{red}}$ is $\overline{\mathfrak{f}}$.
Case 4: If $\ell = 2$, $k_1 = 0$, we have

$$\overline{\mathfrak{m}}(\widehat{\overline{\mathfrak{f}}}(\mathbf{e} \otimes \mathbf{x})) = \overline{\mathfrak{m}}(\mathbf{e} \otimes \widehat{\overline{\mathfrak{f}}}_{\mathrm{red}}(\mathbf{x})) = \overline{\mathfrak{m}}_2(\mathbf{e} \otimes \overline{\mathfrak{f}}(\mathbf{x})) = \overline{\mathfrak{f}}(\mathbf{x}).$$

On the other hand, since $\widehat{\overline{d}}(\mathbf{e} \otimes \mathbf{x}) = \mathbf{x} - \mathbf{e} \otimes \widehat{\overline{d}}(\mathbf{x})$, we have

$$\overline{\mathfrak{f}}(\widehat{\overline{d}}(\mathbf{e} \otimes \mathbf{x})) = \overline{\mathfrak{f}}(\mathbf{x}).$$

Case 5: $\ell = 2$, $k_2 = 0$. Similar to Case 4.

Thus we proved that $\widehat{\overline{\mathfrak{f}}}$ is a cochain homomorphism. On the other hand, (4.4.28) implies that $\widehat{\overline{\mathfrak{f}}}$ is a coalgebra homomorphism. We proved that $\widehat{\overline{\mathfrak{f}}}$ is a filtered A_∞ homomorphism. It is easy to see that it is unital. The converse is easy. $\square$

Now we are ready to give the proof of the unfiltered unital version of Theorem 4.2.34. Let $\overline{\mathfrak{f}}_{k,\mathrm{red}}$ be as in Lemma 4.4.30, and let $\overline{\mathfrak{C}}_1$, $\overline{\mathfrak{C}}_2$ be models of $[0,1] \times \overline{C}_1$ and

$[0,1] \times \overline{C}_2$ respectively. We take a splitting (4.4.27) which is compatible with $\overline{\mathrm{Incl}}$ and $\overline{\mathrm{Eval}}$.

PROPOSITION 4.4.34. *For $k = 1, \cdots, K$, there exists $\overline{\mathfrak{F}}_{k,\mathrm{red}} : B_k \overline{\mathfrak{C}}_{1,\mathrm{red}}[1] \to \overline{\mathfrak{C}}_2[1]$ satisfying (4.4.31) so that the induced unital A_K homomorphism $\overline{\mathfrak{F}}^{(K)} : \mathfrak{C}_1 \to \mathfrak{C}_2$ is compatible with $\overline{\mathrm{Incl}}$ and $\overline{\mathrm{Eval}}$ over $\overline{\mathfrak{f}}$.*

PROOF. The proof goes in a similar way as that of Proposition 4.4.11. So we discuss only the point which needs modification. The first step of induction is the same as the proof of Lemma 4.4.2. The only point to check is that $\overline{\mathfrak{F}}_{1,\mathrm{red}}$ satisfies $\overline{\mathfrak{F}}_{1,\mathrm{red}}(\mathbf{e}) = \mathbf{e}$. This follows automatically from the compatibility with $\overline{\mathrm{Incl}}$.

We suppose that Proposition 4.4.34 is proved for $K-1$. Namely we have $\overline{\mathfrak{F}}_{k,\mathrm{red}}$ for $k = 1, \cdots, K-1$. We then obtain $\overline{\mathfrak{F}}^{(K-1)}$ which induces

$$\widehat{\overline{\mathfrak{F}}}_{\mathrm{red}}^{(K-1)} : B_{1\cdots K}^{\mathrm{red}} \overline{\mathfrak{C}}_1[1] \to B_{1\cdots K} \overline{\mathfrak{C}}_2[1].$$

We consider

$$\overline{\mathrm{Err}}_K = \widehat{\overline{d}} \circ \widehat{\overline{\mathfrak{F}}}_{\mathrm{red}}^{(K-1)} - \widehat{\overline{\mathfrak{F}}}_{\mathrm{red}}^{(K-1)} \circ \widehat{\overline{d}}^{\mathrm{red}} \in Hom(B_{1\cdots K}^{\mathrm{red}} \overline{\mathfrak{C}}_1[1], B_{1\cdots K} \overline{\mathfrak{C}}_2[1]).$$

In the same way as the proof of Proposition 4.4.11 we can prove

$$\overline{\mathrm{Err}}_K \in Hom(B_K^{\mathrm{red}} \overline{\mathfrak{C}}_1[1], \overline{\mathfrak{C}}_2[1]),$$

$$\overline{\mathrm{Err}}_K = \overline{\mathfrak{m}} \circ \widehat{\overline{\mathfrak{F}}}_{\mathrm{red}}^{(K-1)} - \widehat{\overline{\mathfrak{F}}}_{\mathrm{red}}^{(K-1)} \circ \widehat{\overline{d}}^{\mathrm{red}} \in Hom(B_{1\cdots K}^{\mathrm{red}} \overline{\mathfrak{C}}_1[1], B_{1\cdots K} \overline{\mathfrak{C}}_2[1])$$

and

$$\delta_1(\overline{\mathrm{Err}}_K) = 0, \quad \overline{\mathrm{Err}}_K \in \mathrm{Im}\,\delta_1.$$

Here, $\overline{\mathfrak{F}}_{\mathrm{red}}^{(K-1)}$ is a homomorphism $B_{1\cdots K}^{\mathrm{red}} \overline{\mathfrak{C}}_1[1] \to \overline{\mathfrak{C}}_2[1]$ which is $\overline{\mathfrak{F}}_{\mathrm{red},k}$ on $B_k^{\mathrm{red}} \overline{\mathfrak{C}}_1[1]$ $(k = 1, \cdots, K)$ and is 0 on $B_K^{\mathrm{red}} \overline{\mathfrak{C}}_1[1]$. The new point to check is the following.

LEMMA 4.4.35. $\overline{\mathrm{Err}}_K \circ s_{\mathrm{left}} = \overline{\mathrm{Err}}_K \circ s_{\mathrm{right}} = 0.$

PROOF. We first calculate

$$(4.4.36) \quad \begin{aligned} (\widehat{\overline{\mathfrak{F}}}_{\mathrm{red}}^{(K-1)} \circ s_{\mathrm{right}})(\mathbf{x}) &= (-1)^{\deg \mathbf{x}} \widehat{\overline{\mathfrak{F}}}_{\mathrm{red}}^{(K-1)}(\mathbf{x}) \otimes \mathfrak{F}_{1,\mathrm{red}}(\mathbf{e}) \\ &= (s_{\mathrm{right}} \circ \widehat{\overline{\mathfrak{F}}}_{\mathrm{red}}^{(K-1)})(\mathbf{x}) \end{aligned}$$

by (4.4.31.2). Hence using Lemma 4.4.25 and (4.4.36), we have

$$(4.4.37) \quad \begin{aligned} &\overline{\mathrm{Err}}_K \circ s_{\mathrm{right}} \\ &= \overline{\mathfrak{m}} \circ \widehat{\overline{\mathfrak{F}}}_{\mathrm{red}}^{(K-1)} \circ s_{\mathrm{right}} - \widehat{\overline{\mathfrak{F}}}_{\mathrm{red}}^{(K-1)} \circ \widehat{\overline{d}}^{\mathrm{red}} \circ s_{\mathrm{right}} \\ &= \overline{\mathfrak{m}} \circ s_{\mathrm{right}} \circ \widehat{\overline{\mathfrak{F}}}_{\mathrm{red}}^{(K-1)} + \overline{\mathfrak{F}}_{\mathrm{red}}^{(K-1)} \circ s_{\mathrm{right}} \circ \widehat{\overline{d}}^{\mathrm{red}} - \overline{\mathfrak{F}}_{\mathrm{red}}^{(K-1)}. \end{aligned}$$

From (4.4.31.2) we have $\overline{\mathfrak{F}}_{\mathrm{red}}^{(K-1)} \circ s_{\mathrm{right}} = 0$. (Note there is no 'hat' in this formula.) On the other hand, by the definition of s_{right} we have

$$(4.4.38) \quad (\overline{\mathfrak{m}} \circ s_{\mathrm{right}} \circ \widehat{\overline{\mathfrak{F}}}_{\mathrm{red}}^{(K-1)})(\mathbf{x}) = (-1)^{\deg \mathbf{x}} \overline{\mathfrak{m}}(\widehat{\overline{\mathfrak{F}}}_{\mathrm{red}}^{(K-1)}(\mathbf{x}) \otimes \mathbf{e}).$$

In the right hand side, only the term in $B_1\overline{\mathfrak{C}}_2[1] \otimes \mathbf{e}$ is nonzero. Hence (4.4.38) is equal to $\overline{\mathfrak{F}}_{\mathrm{red}}^{(K-1)}(\mathbf{x})$. Therefore (4.4.37) is zero. The proof of $\overline{\mathrm{Err}}_K \circ s_{\mathrm{left}} = 0$ is similar. □

Now the rest of the proof is similar to the proof of Proposition 4.4.11. Using Lemma 4.4.35, we may regard

$$\overline{\mathrm{Err}}_K \in Hom(B_K\overline{\mathfrak{C}}_{1\mathrm{red}}[1], \overline{\mathfrak{C}}_2[1]).$$

We can define a coboundary operator δ_1 on $Hom(B_K\overline{\mathfrak{C}}_{1\mathrm{red}}[1], \overline{\mathfrak{C}}_2[1])$ using $\overline{\mathfrak{m}}_1$. (We can not use $\overline{\mathfrak{m}}_2$ etc. to define operators on $B\overline{\mathfrak{C}}_{\mathrm{red}}[1]$.)

So we can apply the argument of the proof of Proposition 4.4.11 to show that $\overline{\mathrm{Err}}_K$ is in the image of δ_1. Hence we have $\overline{\mathrm{Err}}_K = \delta_1\overline{\mathfrak{F}}'_{K,\mathrm{red}}$ with $\overline{\mathfrak{F}}'_{K,\mathrm{red}} \in Hom(B_K\overline{\mathfrak{C}}_{1\mathrm{red}}[1], \overline{\mathfrak{C}}_2[1])$. It can be identified with a homomorphism : $B_K^{\mathrm{red}}\overline{\mathfrak{C}}_1[1] \to \overline{\mathfrak{C}}_1[1]$ satisfying (4.4.31.2). Using it we obtain a unital A_K homomorphism : $\overline{\mathfrak{C}}_1 \to \overline{\mathfrak{C}}_2$. We can modify it so that it is compatible with $\overline{\mathrm{Incl}}$ and $\overline{\mathrm{Eval}}$ in exactly the same way as in the proof of Proposition 4.4.11. The proof of Proposition 4.4.34 is now complete. □

Proposition 4.4.34 immediately implies that the unital unfiltered version of Theorem 4.2.34 also holds.

4.4.5. Coderivation and Hochschild cohomology. Now we proceed to the proof of Theorem 4.2.34 for filtered A_∞ algebras. The proof will be done by induction on the energy filtration.

We start with introducing some notations. Let $\overline{C}_i[1]$, $i = 1, 2$ be free graded R modules. The free graded R module $B\overline{C}_i[1] = \bigoplus_{k=0}^{\infty} B_k\overline{C}_i[1]$ has a coalgebra structure of Δ by (3.2.14). Let $\widehat{\overline{\mathfrak{f}}} : B\overline{C}_1[1] \to B\overline{C}_2[1]$ be a coalgebra homomorphism of degree 0 and put

$$\varphi = (\varphi_0, \varphi_1, \varphi_2, \cdots) \in \prod_{k=0}^{\infty} Hom(B_k\overline{C}_1[1], \overline{C}_2[1]),$$

where $\deg\varphi_k = \deg\varphi$ is independent of k. We define $\widehat{\varphi} : B\overline{C}_1[1] \to B\overline{C}_2[1]$ as follows. We use (Conv.3) (1.35) below.

We define $\widehat{\varphi} : B\overline{C}_1[1] \to B\overline{C}_2[1]$ by

$$(4.4.39) \qquad \widehat{\varphi}(\mathbf{x}) = \sum_a (-1)^{\deg\varphi\, \deg'\mathbf{x}_a^{(3;1)}}\widehat{\overline{\mathfrak{f}}}(\mathbf{x}_a^{(3;1)}) \,\widehat{\otimes}\, \varphi(\mathbf{x}_a^{(3;2)}) \,\widehat{\otimes}\, \widehat{\overline{\mathfrak{f}}}(\mathbf{x}_a^{(3;3)})$$

where $\varphi : B\overline{C}_1[1] \to C_2[1]$ is a homomorphism which restricts to φ_k on $B_k\overline{C}_1[1]$. We can easily check that $\widehat{\varphi}$ is a coderivation, i.e., satisfies

$$(4.4.40) \qquad ((\widehat{\varphi} \,\widehat{\otimes}\, \widehat{\overline{\mathfrak{f}}}) + (\widehat{\overline{\mathfrak{f}}} \,\widehat{\otimes}\, \widehat{\varphi})) \circ \Delta = \Delta \circ \widehat{\varphi}.$$

Here $\widehat{\otimes}$ is a graded tensor product defined by

$$(\widehat{\overline{\mathfrak{f}}} \,\widehat{\otimes}\, \widehat{\varphi})(\mathbf{x} \otimes \mathbf{y}) = (-1)^{\deg\varphi\, \deg'\mathbf{x}}\widehat{\overline{\mathfrak{f}}}(\mathbf{x}) \otimes \widehat{\varphi}(\mathbf{y}).$$

We remark that the image of $\widehat{\varphi}$ is in $B_{1\cdots\infty}\overline{C}_2[1]$. Namely its $B_0\overline{C}_2[1] = R$ component is zero.

We put

$$B_{1\cdots\infty}\overline{C}_i[1] = \bigoplus_{k=1}^{\infty} B_k\overline{C}_i[1].$$

DEFINITION 4.4.41. We denote by $\mathrm{Der}(B\overline{C}_1[1], B\overline{C}_2[1]; \bar{\mathfrak{f}})$ the set of all graded coderivations $\widehat{\varphi}$ whose images lie in $B_{1\cdots\infty}\overline{C}_2[1]$.

The assignment $\varphi \mapsto \widehat{\varphi}$ determines a homomorphism

$$(4.4.42) \qquad \prod_{k=0}^{\infty} Hom(B_k\overline{C}_1[1], \overline{C}_2[1]) \to \mathrm{Der}(B\overline{C}_1[1], B\overline{C}_2[1]; \bar{\mathfrak{f}}).$$

Then we can show the following.

LEMMA 4.4.43. (4.4.42) *is an isomorphism.*

PROOF. Let $\widehat{\varphi} \in \mathrm{Der}(B\overline{C}_1[1], B\overline{C}_2[1]; \bar{\mathfrak{f}})$ and $\varphi_k \in Hom(B_k\overline{C}_1[1], B_1\overline{C}_2[1]; \bar{\mathfrak{f}})$ be its component. Thus we obtain a homomorphism

$$(4.4.44) \qquad \mathrm{Der}(B\overline{C}_1[1], B\overline{C}_2[1]; \bar{\mathfrak{f}}) \to \prod_{k=0}^{\infty} Hom(B_k\overline{C}_1[1], \overline{C}_2[1]).$$

It is easy to see the composition of (4.4.42) followed by (4.4.44) is the identity $\prod_{k=0}^{\infty} Hom(B_k\overline{C}_1[1], \overline{C}_2[1]) \to \prod_{k=0}^{\infty} Hom(B_k\overline{C}_1[1], \overline{C}_2[1])$. Hence it is enough to show that (4.4.44) is an injection.

Now we suppose that $\widehat{\varphi} \in \mathrm{Der}(B\overline{C}_1[1], B\overline{C}_2[1]; \widehat{\bar{\mathfrak{f}}})$ is in the kernel of (4.4.44). Let $\pi_{1\cdots n} : B\overline{C}_2[1] \to B_{1\cdots n}\overline{C}_2[1]$ be the projection. We will prove that $\pi_{1\cdots n} \circ \widehat{\varphi} = 0$ for all n by induction. (Note $\pi_0 \circ \widehat{\varphi} = 0$ by Definition 4.4.41.)

The case $n = 1$ is immediate from the assumption that $\widehat{\varphi}$ is in the kernel of (4.4.44). Assuming $\pi_{1\cdots n} \circ \widehat{\varphi} = 0$, we will prove $\pi_{1\cdots n+1} \circ \widehat{\varphi} = 0$. Let $\pi_k : B\overline{C}_i[1] \to B_k\overline{C}_i[1]$ be the projection. By the induction hypothesis, we have

$$(4.4.45) \qquad (\pi_{1\cdots\infty} \otimes \pi_{1\cdots\infty}) \circ \Delta \circ \pi_{1\cdots n+1} \circ \widehat{\varphi} = \sum_{k=0}^{n+1} (\pi_k \otimes \pi_{n+1-k}) \circ \Delta \circ \widehat{\varphi}.$$

On the other hand, we have

$$\sum_{k=1}^{n} (\pi_k \otimes \pi_{n+1-k}) \circ \Delta \circ \widehat{\varphi} = \sum_{k=1}^{n} (\pi_k \otimes \pi_{n+1-k}) \circ ((\widehat{\varphi} \,\widehat{\otimes}\, \widehat{\bar{\mathfrak{f}}}) + (\widehat{\bar{\mathfrak{f}}} \,\widehat{\otimes}\, \widehat{\varphi})) \circ \Delta.$$

The right hand side vanishes by the induction hypothesis.

Moreover, since $\pi_0 \circ \widehat{\varphi} = 0$, it follows that

$$(\pi_0 \otimes \pi_{n+1} + \pi_{n+1} \otimes \pi_0) \circ \Delta \circ \widehat{\varphi} = \Delta \circ (\pi_0 \otimes \pi_{n+1} + \pi_{n+1} \otimes \pi_0) \circ \widehat{\varphi} = 0.$$

The proof of Lemma 4.4.43 is now complete. $\qquad\qquad\square$

Now we assume that $\overline{C}_i$ has the structure of an A_∞ algebra and let $\widehat{\bar{d}}$ be the coboundary operator on $B\overline{C}[1]$. We also assume that $\widehat{\bar{\mathfrak{f}}}$ is induced by an A_∞ homomorphism $\bar{\mathfrak{f}}$. Hence $\widehat{\bar{\mathfrak{f}}}$ is a $\widehat{\bar{d}}$ cochain map.

LEMMA & DEFINITION 4.4.46. *If $\widehat{\overline{\varphi}} \in \mathrm{Der}(B\overline{C}_1[1], B\overline{C}_2[1]; \overline{\mathfrak{f}})$, then*

$$\widehat{\overline{d}} \circ \widehat{\overline{\varphi}} - (-1)^{\deg \widehat{\overline{\varphi}}} \widehat{\overline{\varphi}} \circ \widehat{\overline{d}} \in \mathrm{Der}(B\overline{C}_1[1], B\overline{C}_2[1]; \overline{\mathfrak{f}}).$$

We define

$$\delta : \mathrm{Der}(B\overline{C}_1[1], B\overline{C}_2[1]; \overline{\mathfrak{f}}) \to \mathrm{Der}(B\overline{C}_1[1], B\overline{C}_2[1]; \overline{\mathfrak{f}})$$

by $\delta(\widehat{\overline{\varphi}}) = \widehat{\overline{d}} \circ \widehat{\overline{\varphi}} - (-1)^{\deg \widehat{\overline{\varphi}}} \widehat{\overline{\varphi}} \circ \widehat{\overline{d}}$.

The proof is standard and omitted. It is easy to see that $\delta \circ \delta = 0$.

DEFINITION 4.4.47. We define $HH(\overline{C}_1, \overline{C}_2; \overline{\mathfrak{f}}) = \mathrm{Ker}\,\delta / \mathrm{Im}\,\delta$ and call it the *Hochschild cohomology* of an A_∞ homomorphism $\overline{\mathfrak{f}}$.

We remark that the left hand side of (4.4.42) is independent of $\overline{\mathfrak{f}}$. However, the right hand side does depend on $\overline{\mathfrak{f}}$. So the Hochschild cohomology depends on $\overline{\mathfrak{f}}$ in general.

Let $\overline{\mathfrak{g}} : \overline{C}_1' \to \overline{C}_1$ and $\overline{\mathfrak{g}}' : \overline{C}_2 \to \overline{C}_2'$ be A_∞ homomorphisms. In an obvious way they induce a cochain map denoted by $(\overline{\mathfrak{g}}, \overline{\mathfrak{g}}')_*$

$$(\overline{\mathfrak{g}}, \overline{\mathfrak{g}}')_* \; : \; \mathrm{Der}(B\overline{C}_1[1], B\overline{C}_2[1]; \overline{\mathfrak{f}}) \to \mathrm{Der}(B\overline{C}_1'[1], B\overline{C}_2'[1]; \overline{\mathfrak{g}}' \circ \overline{\mathfrak{f}} \circ \overline{\mathfrak{g}}).$$

We denote the map induced by $(\overline{\mathfrak{g}}, \overline{\mathfrak{g}}')_*$ on the Hochschild cohomology by the same symbol.

PROPOSITION 4.4.48. *If $\overline{\mathfrak{g}}$ and $\overline{\mathfrak{g}}'$ are homotopy equivalences, then the homomorphism $(\overline{\mathfrak{g}}, \overline{\mathfrak{g}}')_* : HH(\overline{C}_1, \overline{C}_2; \overline{\mathfrak{f}}) \to HH(\overline{C}_1', \overline{C}_2'; \overline{\mathfrak{g}}' \circ \overline{\mathfrak{f}} \circ \overline{\mathfrak{g}})$ is an isomorphism.*

PROOF. Let $\overline{\mathfrak{C}}_1$, $\overline{\mathfrak{C}}_2$ be models of $[0,1] \times \overline{C}_1$, $[0,1] \times \overline{C}_2$, respectively. $\overline{\mathrm{Incl}}$ induces homomorphisms

$$(\overline{\mathrm{Incl}}, id)_* : HH(\overline{\mathfrak{C}}_1, \overline{C}_2) \to HH(\overline{C}_1, \overline{C}_2)$$

and

$$(id, \overline{\mathrm{Incl}})_* : HH(\overline{C}_1, \overline{C}_2) \to HH(\overline{C}_1, \overline{\mathfrak{C}}_2).$$

LEMMA 4.4.49. $(\overline{\mathrm{Incl}}, id)_*$ *and* $(id, \overline{\mathrm{Incl}})_*$ *are isomorphisms.*

PROOF. We first prove the case of $(\overline{\mathrm{Incl}}, id)_*$. Since

$$(\overline{\mathrm{Incl}}, id)_* \circ (\overline{\mathrm{Eval}}_{s=0}, id)_* = id,$$

it follows that $(\overline{\mathrm{Incl}}, id)_*$ is surjective. We will prove its injectivity.

Let

$$\varphi = (\varphi_0, \varphi_1, \cdots) \in \bigoplus_k Hom(B_k \overline{\mathfrak{C}}_1[1], \overline{C}_2[1])$$

such that $\delta \varphi = 0$ and $\varphi \circ \widehat{\overline{\mathrm{Incl}}} = \delta \psi$. Then

$$\delta\left(\varphi - \delta(\psi \circ \widehat{\overline{\mathrm{Eval}}}_{s=0})\right) = 0$$

and

$$\left(\varphi - \delta(\psi \circ \widehat{\overline{\mathrm{Eval}}}_{s=0})\right) \circ \widehat{\overline{\mathrm{Incl}}} = 0.$$

Therefore it suffices to consider φ such that

(4.4.50) $\delta\varphi = 0, \qquad \varphi \circ \widehat{\overline{\mathrm{Incl}}} = 0,$

and prove the following sublemma.

SUBLEMMA 4.4.51. *If $\varphi = (\varphi_0, \varphi_1, \cdots)$ satisfies (4.4.50) and if φ is an element of $\bigoplus_{\ell=k}^{\infty} Hom(B_\ell \overline{\mathfrak{C}}_1[1], \overline{C}_2[1])$, then there exists an element*

$$\psi \in \bigoplus_{\ell=k}^{\infty} Hom(B_\ell \overline{\mathfrak{C}}_1[1], \overline{C}_2[1])$$

such that

$$\varphi - \delta\psi \in \bigoplus_{\ell=k+1}^{\infty} Hom(B_\ell \overline{\mathfrak{C}}_1[1], \overline{C}_2[1])$$

and that $\varphi - \delta\psi$ satisfies (4.4.50).

PROOF. We remark that

$$\widehat{\overline{\mathrm{Incl}}} : Hom(B_k \overline{\mathfrak{C}}_1[1], \overline{C}_2[1]) \to Hom(B_k \overline{C}_1[1], \overline{C}_2[1])$$

satisfies

$$\delta_1 \circ \widehat{\overline{\mathrm{Incl}}} = \widehat{\overline{\mathrm{Incl}}} \circ \delta_1,$$

and induces an isomorphism on δ_1 cohomology. (Note $\delta_1(A) = \overline{\mathfrak{m}}_1 \circ A - (-1)^{\deg A} A \circ \hat{\overline{\mathfrak{m}}}_1$.)

Since $\hat{\varphi} = 0$ and

$$\varphi \in \bigoplus_{\ell=k}^{\infty} Hom(B_\ell \overline{\mathfrak{C}}_1[1], \overline{C}_2[1]),$$

it follows that $\delta_1(\varphi_k) = 0$. Moreover, by assumption $\varphi_k \circ \widehat{\overline{\mathrm{Incl}}} = 0$. Therefore, there exists $\psi'_k \in Hom(B_k \overline{\mathfrak{C}}_1[1], \overline{C}_2[1])$ such that $\varphi_k = \delta_1(\psi'_k)$. We put

$$\psi' = (0, \cdots, 0, \psi'_k, 0, \cdots) \in \bigoplus_{\ell=k}^{\infty} Hom(B_\ell \overline{\mathfrak{C}}_1[1], \overline{C}_2[1])$$

and

$$\psi = \psi' - \psi' \circ \widehat{\overline{\mathrm{Incl}}} \circ \widehat{\overline{\mathrm{Eval}}}_{s=0}.$$

We can check that ψ has the required property by an easy calculation.   □

Lemma 4.4.49 follows immediately from Sublemma 4.4.51 for the case of $(\overline{\mathrm{Incl}}, id)_*$.

We next prove the case of $(id, \overline{\mathrm{Incl}})_*$. Since

$$(id, \overline{\mathrm{Eval}}_{s=0})_* \circ (id, \overline{\mathrm{Incl}})_* = id,$$

it follows that $(id, \overline{\mathrm{Incl}})_*$ is injective. Thus it suffices to show its surjectivity.

Let

$$\psi \in \bigoplus_{k} Hom(B_k \overline{C}_1[1], \overline{\mathfrak{C}}_2[1])$$

be a δ-cocycle, i.e., $\delta\psi = 0$. More concretely, $\overline{\mathfrak{m}}_1 \circ \psi - (-1)^{\deg \psi} \psi \circ \hat{\overline{d}} = 0$. Note that $\overline{\mathrm{Eval}}_{s=0} \circ \psi$ is a δ-cocycle in $\bigoplus_k Hom(B_k \overline{C}_1[1], \overline{C}_2[1])$. Since $\overline{\mathrm{Incl}} \circ \overline{\mathrm{Eval}}_{s=0}$ is chain homotopic to the identity, i.e.,

$$id - \overline{\mathrm{Incl}} \circ \overline{\mathrm{Eval}}_{s=0} = \overline{\mathfrak{m}}_1 \circ h + h \circ \overline{\mathfrak{m}}_1,$$

where h is a chain homotopy, we find that

$$
\begin{aligned}
\psi - \overline{\mathrm{Incl}} \circ \overline{\mathrm{Eval}}_{s=0} \circ \psi &= (\overline{\mathrm{m}}_1 \circ h + h \circ \overline{\mathrm{m}}_1)\psi \\
&= \overline{\mathrm{m}}_1(h \circ \psi) + (-1)^{\deg \psi}(h \circ \psi) \circ \hat{\bar{d}} \\
&= \overline{\mathrm{m}}_1(h \circ \psi) - (-1)^{\deg h \circ \psi}(h \circ \psi) \circ \hat{\bar{d}}.
\end{aligned}
$$

Thus we have

$$
\psi = \overline{\mathrm{Incl}}(\overline{\mathrm{Eval}}_{s=0} \circ \psi) + \delta(h \circ \psi).
$$

Hence $(id, \overline{\mathrm{Incl}})_* : HH(\overline{C}_1, \overline{C}_2) \to HH(\overline{C}_1, \overline{\mathfrak{C}}_2)$ is surjective. The proof of Lemma 4.4.49 is now complete. $\qquad\square$

Using Lemma 4.4.49, we can prove easily that $(\overline{\mathfrak{g}}, \overline{\mathfrak{g}}')_* : HH(\overline{C}_1, \overline{C}_2; \overline{\mathfrak{f}}) \to HH(\overline{C}'_1, \overline{C}'_2; \overline{\mathfrak{g}}' \circ \overline{\mathfrak{f}} \circ \overline{\mathfrak{g}})$ depends only on homotopy classes of $\overline{\mathfrak{g}}$ and $\overline{\mathfrak{g}}'$. This implies Proposition 4.4.48. $\qquad\square$

4.4.6. Induction on the energy filtration. In this subsection and the next, we complete the proof of Theorem 4.2.34. We use the notations of Theorem 4.2.34. We take $G \subseteq \mathbb{R}_{\geq 0} \times 2\mathbb{Z}$ satisfying Condition 3.1.6 and assume that all filtered A_∞ algebras and filtered A_∞ homomorphisms we consider are G-gapped. We can enumerate the image of the projection of G to $\mathbb{R}_{\geq 0}$ denoted by $\mathrm{Spec}(G) = \{\lambda_0, \lambda_1, \cdots\}$ so that $\lambda_i < \lambda_{i+1}$, $\lim_{i \to \infty} \lambda_i = \infty$, because $\mathrm{Spec}(G)$ is discrete by Condition 3.1.6. We will construct

$$
\mathfrak{F}_{k,i} : B_k \overline{\mathfrak{C}}_1[1] \to \overline{\mathfrak{C}}_2[1], \qquad k = 0, 1, 2 \cdots, \ i = 0, 1, 2, \cdots,
$$

and define

$$
\mathfrak{F}_k^{(n)} = \sum_{i=0}^{n} \mathfrak{F}_{k,i} T^{\lambda_i} : B_k \mathfrak{C}_1[1] \to \mathfrak{C}_2[1], \qquad k = 0, 1, 2 \cdots.
$$

(We assume $\mathfrak{F}_{0,0} = 0$.) We extend $\sum_k \mathfrak{F}_k^{(n)}$ to a coalgebra homomorphism $\widehat{\mathfrak{F}}^{(n)} : \widehat{B}\mathfrak{C}_1[1] \to \widehat{B}\mathfrak{C}_2[1]$. Now we show the following by induction on n.

PROPOSITION 4.4.52. *For any $n = 0, 1, 2, \cdots$, there exists $\mathfrak{F}_{k,i}$ for $i \leq n$ such that*

(4.4.53.1) $$\qquad\qquad \hat{d} \circ \widehat{\mathfrak{F}}^{(n)} \equiv \widehat{\mathfrak{F}}^{(n)} \circ \hat{d} \quad \mathrm{mod}\ T^{\lambda_{n+1}},$$

(4.4.53.2) $$\qquad\qquad \widehat{\mathrm{Incl}} \circ \hat{\mathfrak{f}} \equiv \widehat{\mathfrak{F}}^{(n)} \circ \widehat{\mathrm{Incl}} \quad \mathrm{mod}\ T^{\lambda_{n+1}},$$

(4.4.53.3) $$\qquad \widehat{\mathrm{Eval}}_{s=s_0} \circ \widehat{\mathfrak{F}}^{(n)} \equiv \hat{\mathfrak{f}} \circ \widehat{\mathrm{Eval}}_{s=s_0} \quad \mathrm{mod}\ T^{\lambda_{n+1}} \ for\ s_0 = 0, 1.$$

Moreover we have

(4.4.53.4) $$\qquad\qquad\qquad \widehat{\mathfrak{F}}^{(n)} - \widehat{\mathfrak{F}}^{(n-1)} \equiv 0. \quad \mathrm{mod}\ T^{\lambda_n}.$$

PROOF. We apply the unfiltered version of Theorem 4.2.34 to $\bar{f}$ and get $\overline{\mathfrak{F}}_k$. We put $\mathfrak{F}_{k,0} = \overline{\mathfrak{F}}_k$. Thus, we proved the case of $n = 0$.

We assume Proposition 4.4.52 for n and will prove it for $n + 1$. By induction hypothesis (4.4.53), we have

$$\mathrm{Err1}_n \in \mathrm{Der}(B\overline{\mathfrak{C}}_1[1], B\overline{\mathfrak{C}}_2[1]),$$
$$\mathrm{Err2}_n \in \mathrm{Der}(B\overline{C}_1[1], B\overline{\mathfrak{C}}_2[1]),$$
$$\mathrm{Err3}_n \in \mathrm{Der}(B\overline{\mathfrak{C}}_1[1], B\overline{C}_2[1]),$$

such that

(4.4.54.1) $\widehat{d} \circ \widehat{\mathfrak{F}}^{(n)} - \widehat{\mathfrak{F}}^{(n)} \circ \widehat{d} - T^{\lambda_{n+1}} \mathrm{Err1}_n \equiv 0 \mod T^{\lambda_{n+2}}$,

(4.4.54.2) $\widehat{\mathrm{Incl}} \circ \widehat{f} - \widehat{\mathfrak{F}}^{(n)} \circ \widehat{\mathrm{Incl}} - T^{\lambda_{n+1}} \mathrm{Err2}_n \equiv 0 \mod T^{\lambda_{n+2}}$,

(4.4.54.3) $\widehat{\mathrm{Eval}}_{s=s_0} \circ \widehat{\mathfrak{F}}^{(n)} - \widehat{f} \circ \widehat{\mathrm{Eval}}_{s=s_0} - T^{\lambda_{n+1}} \mathrm{Err3}_n \equiv 0 \mod T^{\lambda_{n+2}}$.

We note that

(4.4.55) $$\widehat{d} \equiv \widehat{\overline{d}} \mod T^{\lambda_1}.$$

Since $\overline{\mathrm{Incl}}$ is split injective, we can take $\mathrm{Err2}_n^{\sim} \in \mathrm{Der}(B\overline{\mathfrak{C}}_1[1], B\overline{\mathfrak{C}}_2[1])$ such that $\mathrm{Err2}_n^{\sim} \circ \widehat{\mathrm{Incl}} = \mathrm{Err2}_n$. We replace $\widehat{\mathfrak{F}}^{(n)}$ by $\widehat{\mathfrak{F}}^{(n)} - T^{\lambda_{n+1}} \mathrm{Err2}_n^{\sim}$. Then after changing the choices of $\mathrm{Err1}_n$ and $\mathrm{Err3}_n$, if necessary, we may assume that (4.4.54.1) and (4.4.54.3) hold and

(4.4.54.2+) $$\widehat{\mathrm{Incl}} \circ \widehat{f} - \widehat{\mathfrak{F}}^{(n)} \circ \widehat{\mathrm{Incl}} \equiv 0 \mod T^{\lambda_{n+2}}.$$

We use (4.4.54.2+) and (4.4.54.3) to obtain

(4.4.56) $$\mathrm{Err3}_n \circ \widehat{\mathrm{Incl}} = 0 \in \mathrm{Der}(B\overline{C}_1[1], B\overline{C}_2[1]).$$

Using the fact that $((\overline{\mathrm{Eval}}_{s=0})_1, (\overline{\mathrm{Eval}}_{s=1})_1)$ is surjective and $\overline{\mathrm{Incl}}_1$ is split injective together with (4.4.56) and Lemma 4.4.43, we find a coderivation $\mathrm{Err3}_n^{\sim} \in \mathrm{Der}(B\overline{\mathfrak{C}}_1[1], B\overline{\mathfrak{C}}_2[1])$ such that

(4.4.57.1) $(\widehat{\overline{\mathrm{Eval}}}_{s=0} \circ \mathrm{Err3}_n^{\sim}, \widehat{\overline{\mathrm{Eval}}}_{s=1} \circ \mathrm{Err3}_n^{\sim}) = \mathrm{Err3}_n$,

(4.4.57.2) $\mathrm{Err3}_n^{\sim} \circ \widehat{\mathrm{Incl}} = 0$.

We replace $\widehat{\mathfrak{F}}_{(n)}$ by $\widehat{\mathfrak{F}}_{(n)} - T^{\lambda_{n+1}} \mathrm{Err3}_n^{\sim}$. Then, (4.4.54.1), (4.4.54.2+) and

(4.4.54.3+) $$\widehat{\mathrm{Eval}}_{s=s_0} \circ \widehat{\mathfrak{F}}_{(n)} - \widehat{f} \circ \widehat{\mathrm{Eval}}_{s=s_0} \equiv 0 \mod T^{\lambda_{n+2}}$$

hold. Now we have

LEMMA 4.4.58. $\delta(\mathrm{Err1}_n) = 0$. *Here δ is as in* Definition 4.4.46.

PROOF. By definition

$$\widehat{\overline{d}} \circ \mathrm{Err1}_n + \mathrm{Err1}_n \circ \widehat{\overline{d}} = 0.$$

Then the lemma follows from (4.4.55). $\qquad \square$

By (4.4.54.2+), (4.4.54.3+) we have

(4.4.59.1) $$\mathrm{Err1}_n \circ \overline{\mathrm{Incl}}_1 = 0,$$

(4.4.59.2) $$\overline{\mathrm{Eval}}_{s=s_0} \circ \mathrm{Err1}_n = 0.$$

We put
$$\overline{D}_3 = \operatorname{Ker}\overline{\operatorname{Eval}}_{0*} \cap \operatorname{Ker}\overline{\operatorname{Eval}}_{1*} \subseteq \overline{\mathfrak{C}}_2[1].$$
We can now apply Lemma 4.4.3 and Lemma 4.4.49 to $A = \operatorname{Err1}_n$ to obtain
$$\mathfrak{F}_{k,n+1} \in Hom(B_k\overline{\mathfrak{C}}_1[1], \overline{D}_3) \subseteq Der(B\overline{\mathfrak{C}}_1[1], B\overline{\mathfrak{C}}_2[1])$$
$k = 0, 1, 2, \cdots$ such that

(4.4.60.1) $\mathfrak{F}_{*,n+1} \circ \widehat{\operatorname{Incl}_1} = 0,$

(4.4.60.2) $\delta(\mathfrak{F}_{*,n+1}) + \operatorname{Err1}_n = 0.$

It is easy to see that $\mathfrak{F}_{k,n+1}$ has the required properties. The proof of Proposition 4.4.52 is now complete.   □

To prove Theorem 4.2.34 from Proposition 4.4.52, we only need additional arguments in the case when $\mathfrak{f}$ is strict and/or unital.

In the case when $\mathfrak{f}$ is strict, we can take $\mathfrak{F}_{k,i}$ such that $\mathfrak{F}_{0,i}$ is zero, inductively as follows. Suppose $\mathfrak{F}_{0,i}$ is zero for $i \leq n$. Then since $\mathfrak{f}$ is strict, $\operatorname{Err1}_n$, $\operatorname{Err2}_n$, $\operatorname{Err3}_n$ is zero on $B_0\overline{C}_1$ or $B_0\overline{\mathfrak{C}}_1$. Hence when we modify $\widehat{\mathfrak{F}}_{(n)}$ so that (4.4.54.2+) and (4.4.54.3+) will be satisfied, we may still assume $\mathfrak{F}_{0,i} = 0$. Hence $\operatorname{Err1}_n$ is zero on $B_0\overline{\mathfrak{C}}_1$. Therefore we may take $\mathfrak{F}_{0,n+1} = 0$ by construction.

The case where $\mathfrak{f}$ is unital is treated in the next subsection.

4.4.7. Unital case II: the filtered version. In this subsection we prove the unital filtered version of Proposition 4.4.52. Let $(C, \mathfrak{m})$ be a unital filtered A_∞ algebra.

DEFINITION 4.4.61. We define *partially reduced bar complex* $\widehat{B}^{\mathrm{red}}C[1]$ as follows. Putting $C_{\mathrm{red}} = C/\Lambda_{0,nov}[\mathbf{e}]$, we define

(4.4.62) $B_k^{\mathrm{red}}C[1] = \begin{cases} C[1] \otimes B_{k-2}C_{\mathrm{red}}[1] \otimes C[1], & \text{if } k \geq 2, \\ C[1], & \text{if } k = 1, \\ \Lambda_{0,nov}, & \text{if } k = 0, \end{cases}$

and $\widehat{B}^{\mathrm{red}}C[1] = \widehat{\bigoplus}_k B_k^{\mathrm{red}}C[1]$.

$\widehat{d} : BC[1] \to BC[1]$ induces a differential $\widehat{d}^{\mathrm{red}}$ on $\widehat{B}^{\mathrm{red}}C[1]$. (We can prove it in the same way as Lemma 4.4.24.)

We define operators $s_{\mathrm{left}}, s_{\mathrm{right}} : B_k^{\mathrm{red}}C[1] \to B_{k+1}^{\mathrm{red}}C[1]$ by
$$s_{\mathrm{left}}(\mathbf{x}) = \mathbf{e} \otimes \mathbf{x}, \qquad s_{\mathrm{right}}(\mathbf{x}) = (-1)^{\deg \mathbf{x}} \mathbf{x} \otimes \mathbf{e},$$
for $k \geq 1$ and $s_{\mathrm{left}} = s_{\mathrm{right}} = 0$ on $B_0^{\mathrm{red}}C[1]$.

LEMMA 4.4.63. $\widehat{d}^{\mathrm{red}} \circ s_{\mathrm{left}} + s_{\mathrm{left}} \circ \widehat{d}^{\mathrm{red}} = \widehat{d}^{\mathrm{red}} \circ s_{\mathrm{right}} + s_{\mathrm{right}} \circ \widehat{d}^{\mathrm{red}} = id$, on $\widehat{\bigoplus}_{k \geq 1} B_k^{\mathrm{red}}$.

The proof is an easy calculation so omitted. We choose a splitting

(4.4.64) $C = C_{\mathrm{red}} \oplus \Lambda_{0,nov}[\mathbf{e}].$

Let $\mathfrak{f}_{k,\mathrm{red}} : B_k^{\mathrm{red}}C_1[1] \to C_2[1]$, $k = 0, 1, 2, \cdots$ be a series of homomorphisms. We define $\widehat{\mathfrak{f}}_{\mathrm{red}} : BC_1[1] \to BC_2[1]$ in a way similar to (4.4.28) by
$$\widehat{\mathfrak{f}}_{\mathrm{red}}(\mathbf{x}_1 \otimes \mathbf{e} \otimes \cdots \otimes \mathbf{e} \otimes \mathbf{x}_k) = \mathfrak{f}_{k,\mathrm{red}}(\mathbf{x}_1) \otimes \mathbf{e} \otimes \cdots \otimes \mathbf{e} \otimes \mathfrak{f}_{k,\mathrm{red}}(\mathbf{x}_k),$$

where $\mathbf{x}_i \in B_{k_i} C_{1,\mathrm{red}}[1] \subset B_{k_i} C_1[1]$.

LEMMA 4.4.65. *A series of operators* $\mathfrak{f}_{k,\mathrm{red}} : B_k^{\mathrm{red}} C_1[1] \to C_2[1]$, $k = 0, 1, \cdots$ *satisfying the following conditions* (4.4.66) *which corresponds one to one to the unital filtered A_∞ homomorphism $C_1 \to C_2$.*

(4.4.66.1) $\widehat{\mathfrak{f}}_{\mathrm{red}} \circ \widehat{d}^{\mathrm{red}} = \widehat{d} \circ \widehat{\mathfrak{f}}_{\mathrm{red}}.$

(4.4.66.2) $\mathfrak{f}_{k,\mathrm{red}} \circ s_{\mathrm{left}} = \mathfrak{f}_{k,\mathrm{red}} \circ s_{\mathrm{right}} = 0.$

(4.4.66.3) $\mathfrak{f}_{1,\mathrm{red}}(\mathbf{e}) = \mathbf{e}.$

(4.4.66.4) $\mathfrak{f}_{0,\mathrm{red}} \equiv 0 \mod \Lambda_{0,nov}^+.$

The proof is straightforward and is analogous to the proof of Lemma 4.4.30. Now we prove a unital version of Proposition 4.4.52. Namely suppose we have

$$\mathfrak{F}_{k,i} : B_k^{\mathrm{red}} \overline{\mathfrak{C}}_1[1] \to \overline{\mathfrak{C}}_2[1], \qquad k = 0, 1, 2 \cdots, \ i = 0, 1, 2, \cdots, n$$

which induces

$$\mathfrak{F}_k^{(n)} = \sum_{i=0}^{n} \mathfrak{F}_{k,i} T^{\lambda_i} : B_k^{\mathrm{red}} \mathfrak{C}_1[1] \to \mathfrak{C}_2[1],$$

satisfying (4.4.66.2), (4.4.66.3), (4.4.66.4). We extend it to a coalgebra homomorphism

$$\widehat{\mathfrak{F}}^{(n)\mathrm{red}} : \widehat{B}^{\mathrm{red}} \mathfrak{C}_1[1] \to \widehat{B} \mathfrak{C}_2[1],$$

which induces a unital homomorphism

$$\widehat{\mathfrak{F}}^{(n)} : \widehat{B} \mathfrak{C}_1[1] \to \widehat{B} \mathfrak{C}_2[1].$$

We assume that it satisfies (4.4.53.1), (4.4.53.2), (4.4.53.3). We then want to find $\mathfrak{F}_{k,n+1}$. (We remark that the case $n = 0$ is already proved in Subsection 4.4.4.)

We define

$$\mathrm{Err}1_n \in \mathrm{Der}(B\overline{\mathfrak{C}}_1[1], B\overline{\mathfrak{C}}_2[1]),$$

$$\mathrm{Err}2_n \in \mathrm{Der}(B\overline{C}_1[1], B\overline{\mathfrak{C}}_2[1]),$$

$$\mathrm{Err}3_n \in \mathrm{Der}(B\overline{\mathfrak{C}}_1[1], B\overline{C}_2[1]),$$

by formulas (4.4.54.1), (4.4.54.2), (4.4.54.3).

LEMMA 4.4.67. *For $* = 1, 2, 3$, the operators $\mathrm{Err} *_n$ are induced by those on $B^{\mathrm{red}} \overline{C}_1 \oplus B_0 \overline{C}_1$ or $B^{\mathrm{red}} \overline{\mathfrak{C}}_1 \oplus B_0 \overline{\mathfrak{C}}_1$. We also have: $\mathrm{Err} *_n \circ s_{\mathrm{left}} = \mathrm{Err} *_n \circ s_{\mathrm{right}} = 0.$*

PROOF. For $\mathrm{Err}2_n$ and $\mathrm{Err}3_n$, the lemma is immediate from definition. For $\mathrm{Err}3_n$, the proof is similar to that of Lemma 4.4.35. $\square$

Using Lemma 4.4.67, the rest of the proof goes in the same way as that of Proposition 4.4.52. Hence we have proved the unital filtered version of Theorem 4.2.34. Therefore the proof of Theorem 4.2.34 is now complete. $\square$

4.5. Whitehead theorem in A_∞ algebras

In this section we prove Theorem 4.2.45. The strategy of the proof is similar to that of Theorem 4.2.34. Namely we will construct the required homotopy inverse by an induction on the number and the energy filtrations. To make the exposition transparent we develop a kind of obstruction theory. Then the proof looks quite similar to the proof of the well-known Whitehead theorem in algebraic topology.

4.5.1. Extending A_K homomorphisms to A_{K+1} homomorphisms. The main result of this subsection is the following Theorem 4.5.1. Let $\overline{C}_i$ be A_{K+1} algebras and $\bar{\mathfrak{f}} : \overline{C}_1 \to \overline{C}_2$ an A_K homomorphism. We consider an R module $Hom(B_{K+1}\overline{C}_1[1], \overline{C}_2[1])$. A coboundary operator δ_1 on $Hom(B_{K+1}\overline{C}_1[1], \overline{C}_2[1])$ is defined by

$$\delta_1(\varphi) = \overline{\mathfrak{m}}_1 \circ \varphi + (-1)^{\deg \varphi + 1} \varphi \circ \widehat{\overline{\mathfrak{m}}}_1,$$

where $\widehat{\overline{\mathfrak{m}}}_1 : B\overline{C}_1[1] \to B\overline{C}_1[1]$ is a coderivation induced by $\overline{\mathfrak{m}}_1$ on $\overline{C}_1$. (See (3.2.1).) We denote by

$$H(Hom(B_{K+1}\overline{C}_1[1], \overline{C}_2[1]), \delta_1)$$

the set of δ_1-cohomology classes.

THEOREM 4.5.1. *There exists $o_{K+1}(\bar{\mathfrak{f}}) \in Hom(B_{K+1}\overline{C}_1[1], \overline{C}_2[1])$ of degree 1, such that the following holds.*

(4.5.2.1) $\delta_1(o_{K+1}(\bar{\mathfrak{f}})) = 0.$

(4.5.2.2) $[o_{K+1}(\bar{\mathfrak{f}})] = 0$ *as a δ_1-cohomology class if and only if there exists an A_{K+1} homomorphism extending $\bar{\mathfrak{f}}$.*

(4.5.2.3) *If $\bar{\mathfrak{f}}'$ is A_K homotopic to $\bar{\mathfrak{f}}$, then*

$$[o_{K+1}(\bar{\mathfrak{f}})] = [o_{K+1}(\bar{\mathfrak{f}}')] \in H(Hom(B_{K+1}\overline{C}_1[1], \overline{C}_2[1]), \delta_1).$$

(4.5.2.4) *If $\bar{\mathfrak{g}} : \overline{C}_1' \to \overline{C}_1$, $\bar{\mathfrak{g}}' : \overline{C}_2 \to \overline{C}_2'$ are A_{K+1} homomorphisms, then*

$$[o_{K+1}(\bar{\mathfrak{g}}' \circ \bar{\mathfrak{f}} \circ \bar{\mathfrak{g}})] = (\bar{\mathfrak{g}}_1')_* \circ [o_{K+1}(\bar{\mathfrak{f}})] \circ (\bar{\mathfrak{g}}_1 \otimes \cdots \otimes \bar{\mathfrak{g}}_1)_*$$

in $H(Hom(B_{K+1}\overline{C}_1'[1], \overline{C}_2'[1]), \delta_1)$. Here

$$\bar{\mathfrak{g}}_1 \otimes \cdots \otimes \bar{\mathfrak{g}}_1 : B_{K+1}\overline{C}_1'[1] \to B_{K+1}\overline{C}_1[1]$$

is induced by $\bar{\mathfrak{g}}_1 : \overline{C}_1'[1] \to \overline{C}_1[1]$. It induces homomorphism $(\bar{\mathfrak{g}}_1 \otimes \cdots \otimes \bar{\mathfrak{g}}_1)_*$ on δ_1 cohomology.

REMARK 4.5.3. In fact, we already used a similar results in the course of the proof of Theorem 4.2.34. Since the notion of homotopy appears in the statement of Theorem 4.5.1, we repeat the arguments here in order to make clear that our argument is not circular.

PROOF OF THEOREM 4.5.1. We first take $\bar{\mathfrak{f}}_{K+1}' = 0$ and consider

$$\widehat{\bar{\mathfrak{f}}}_{1\cdots K+1} \in Hom(B_{1\cdots K+1}\overline{C}_1[1], B_{1\cdots K+1}\overline{C}_2[1]).$$

It induces cochain homomorphisms $\widehat{\bar{\mathfrak{f}}}_{2\cdots K+1}$ and $\widehat{\bar{\mathfrak{f}}}_{1\cdots K}$ by Lemmas 4.4.9 and 4.4.10. Therefore $\widehat{\bar{d}}_{1\cdots K+1} \circ \widehat{\bar{\mathfrak{f}}}_{1\cdots K+1} - \widehat{\bar{\mathfrak{f}}}_{1\cdots K+1} \circ \widehat{\bar{d}}_{1\cdots K+1}$ is zero on $B_{1\cdots K}\overline{C}_1[1]$ and its image is in $B_1\overline{C}_2[1] = \overline{C}_2[1]$. We define

$$o_{K+1}(\bar{\mathfrak{f}}) = \widehat{\bar{d}}_{1\cdots K+1} \circ \widehat{\bar{\mathfrak{f}}}_{1\cdots K+1} - \widehat{\bar{\mathfrak{f}}}_{1\cdots K+1} \circ \widehat{\bar{d}}_{1\cdots K+1} \in Hom(B_{K+1}\overline{C}_1[1], \overline{C}_2[1]).$$

Then $o_{K+1}(\bar{\mathfrak{f}})$ satisfies

$$\delta_1(o_{K+1}(\bar{\mathfrak{f}})) = \overline{\mathfrak{m}}_1 \circ o_{K+1}(\bar{\mathfrak{f}}) - o_{K+1}(\bar{\mathfrak{f}}) \circ \widehat{\overline{\mathfrak{m}}}_1 = 0.$$

This gives (4.5.2.1).

To prove (4.5.2.2), we only need to remark that $\bar{f}_i$, $i = 1, \cdots, K$ together with $\bar{f}_{K+1}$ define an A_{K+1} homomorphism if and only if $\delta_1(\bar{f}_{K+1}) = -o_{K+1}(\bar{f})$.

Let us prove (4.5.2.4). We consider the coalgebra homomorphisms

$$\hat{\bar{g}} : BC'_{1\cdots K+1} \to BC_{1\cdots K+1} \quad \text{and} \quad \hat{\bar{g}}' : BC'_{2\cdots K+1} \to BC_{2\cdots K+1}$$

which are induced by $\hat{\bar{g}}_i$ $i = 1, \cdots, K$. Then the process to take hat commutes with composition. Now we consider the commutator

$$\{\hat{d}, \hat{\bar{g}}' \circ \hat{\bar{f}} \circ \hat{\bar{g}}\} = \{\hat{d}, \hat{\bar{g}}'\} \circ \hat{\bar{f}} \circ \hat{\bar{g}} + \hat{\bar{g}}' \circ \{\hat{d}, \hat{\bar{f}}\} \circ \hat{\bar{g}} + \hat{\bar{g}}' \circ \hat{\bar{f}} \circ \{\hat{d}, \hat{\bar{g}}\}.$$

The $Hom(B_{K+1}\overline{C}'_1[1], \overline{C}'_2[1])$ component of the left hand side is $[o_{K+1}(\hat{\bar{g}}' \circ \hat{\bar{f}} \circ \hat{\bar{g}})]$. The first term of the right hand side is $-\delta_1 \bar{g}'_{K+1} \circ \bar{f}_1^{\otimes K+1} \circ \bar{g}_1^{\otimes K+1}$ and is a δ_1 boundary. The second term of the right hand side is $\bar{g}'_1 \circ o_{K+1}(\bar{f}) \circ (\bar{g}_1 \otimes \cdots \otimes \bar{g}_1)$. The third term of the right hand side is $-\bar{g}'_1 \circ \bar{f}_1 \circ \delta_1 \bar{g}_{K+1}$ and is a δ_1 boundary. (4.5.2.4) follows.

To prove (4.5.2.3) we need the following lemma.

LEMMA 4.5.4. *If* $\bar{f} : \overline{C}_1 \to \overline{C}_2$ *is* A_1 *homotopic to* $\bar{g} : \overline{C}_1 \to \overline{C}_2$, *then*

$$\bar{f}_* = \bar{g}_* : H^*(\overline{C}_1; \overline{m}_1) \to H^*(\overline{C}_2; \overline{m}_1).$$

PROOF. Let $\mathfrak{h} : \overline{C}_1 \to \overline{\mathfrak{C}}_2$ be an A_1 homotopy between $\bar{f}$ and $\bar{g}$. By (4.2.2.3), $\overline{\text{Incl}}$ induces an isomorphism on $\overline{m}_1$-cohomology. On the other hand, by (4.2.2.2), $\overline{\text{Eval}}_{s=s_0} \circ \overline{\text{Incl}}$ is identity for any s_0. Hence

$$\overline{\text{Eval}}_{s=0*} = \overline{\text{Eval}}_{s=1*} : H^*(\overline{\mathfrak{C}}_2, \overline{m}_1) \to H^*(\overline{C}_2, \overline{m}_1).$$

Therefore $\bar{f}_* = \overline{\text{Eval}}_{s=0*} \circ \mathfrak{h}_* = \overline{\text{Eval}}_{s=1*} \circ \mathfrak{h}_* = \bar{g}_*$, as required. $\square$

Now we prove (4.5.2.3). Let $\overline{\mathfrak{h}} : \overline{C}_1 \to \overline{\mathfrak{C}}_2$ be an A_K homotopy between $\bar{f}$ and $\bar{f}'$. By (4.5.2.4) and Lemma 4.5.4, we have

$$[o_{K+1}(\bar{f})] = [o_{K+1}(\overline{\text{Eval}}_{s=0} \circ \overline{\mathfrak{h}})] = \overline{\text{Eval}}_{s=0*}[o_{K+1}(\overline{\mathfrak{h}})]$$
$$= \overline{\text{Eval}}_{s=1*}[o_{K+1}(\overline{\mathfrak{h}})] = [o_{K+1}(\overline{\text{Eval}}_{s=1} \circ \overline{\mathfrak{h}})] = [o_{K+1}(\bar{f}')].$$

The proof of Theorem 4.5.1 is now complete. $\square$

We will use the following corollary in the next subsection.

COROLLARY 4.5.5. *Let* $\bar{f} : \overline{C}_1 \to \overline{C}_2$ *be an* A_{K+1} *homomorphism,* $\bar{g} : \overline{C}_1 \to \overline{C}_2$ *an* A_K *homomorphism, and let* $\overline{\mathfrak{h}} : \overline{C}_1 \to \overline{\mathfrak{C}}_2$ *be an* A_K *homotopy from* $\bar{f}$ *to* $\bar{g}$. *Then* $\bar{g}$ *is extended to an* A_{K+1} *homomorphism* $\bar{g}'$ *and* $\overline{\mathfrak{h}}$ *is extended to an* A_{K+1} *homotopy from* $\bar{f}$ *to* $\bar{g}'$.

PROOF. Since $(\overline{\text{Eval}}_{s=0})_{1*}[o_{K+1}(\overline{\mathfrak{h}})] = [o_{K+1}(\bar{f})] = 0$ by (4.5.2.2) and (4.5.2.4) and $(\overline{\text{Eval}}_{s=0})_{1*}$ induces an isomorphism on cohomology, it follows that $\overline{\mathfrak{h}}$ is extended to an A_{K+1} homomorphism. To prove the corollary we need to extend $\overline{\mathfrak{h}}$ with some additional properties. So we proceed as follows.

We consider $\overline{\mathfrak{h}}'_{K+1} = \overline{\text{Incl}} \circ \bar{f}_{K+1}$. Then we find

$$(\overline{\text{Eval}}_{s=0})_1(o_{K+1}(\overline{\mathfrak{h}}) + \delta_1(\overline{\mathfrak{h}}'_{K+1})) = 0$$

and

$$(\overline{\mathrm{Eval}}_{s=0})_1 \circ \overline{\mathfrak{h}}'_{K+1} = \overline{\mathfrak{f}}_{K+1}.$$

Since the kernel of $\overline{\mathrm{Eval}}_{s=0,*}$ is δ_1-acyclic, it follows that we have $\Delta\overline{\mathfrak{h}}_{K+1}$ such that

$$o_{K+1}(\overline{\mathfrak{h}}) + \delta_1(\overline{\mathfrak{h}}'_{K+1}) = \delta_1(\Delta\overline{\mathfrak{h}}_{K+1})$$

and

$$(\overline{\mathrm{Eval}}_{s=0})_1(\Delta\overline{\mathfrak{h}}_{k+1}) = 0.$$

We put $\overline{\mathfrak{h}}_{K+1} = \overline{\mathfrak{h}}'_{K+1} - \Delta\overline{\mathfrak{h}}_{K+1}$. Then $\overline{\mathfrak{h}}_k$, $k = 1, \cdots, K + 1$ define an A_{K+1} homomorphism denoted by $\widetilde{\overline{\mathfrak{h}}}$. We define $\overline{\mathfrak{g}}' = (\overline{\mathrm{Eval}}_{s=1})_1 \circ \widetilde{\overline{\mathfrak{h}}}$. It is easy to see that $\overline{\mathfrak{g}}'$ is an A_{K+1} homomorphism which extends $\overline{\mathfrak{g}}$. Moreover since $(\overline{\mathrm{Eval}}_{s=0})_1 \circ \overline{\mathfrak{h}}'_{K+1} = \overline{\mathfrak{f}}_{K+1}$, it follows that $\widetilde{\overline{\mathfrak{h}}}$ is an A_{K+1} homotopy between $\overline{\mathfrak{f}}$ and $\overline{\mathfrak{g}}'$. $\square$

4.5.2. Proof of Theorem 4.2.45 I: the number filtration. Let $\overline{\mathfrak{f}} : \overline{C}_1 \to \overline{C}_2$ be a weak homotopy equivalence.

PROPOSITION 4.5.6. *Let* $\overline{\mathfrak{g}}^{(K)} : \overline{C}_2 \to \overline{C}_1$ *be an* A_K *homomorphism and* $\overline{\mathfrak{h}}^{(K)} :$ $\overline{C}_1 \to \overline{\mathfrak{C}}_1$ *an* A_K *homotopy from identity to* $\overline{\mathfrak{g}}^{(K)} \circ \overline{\mathfrak{f}}$. *Then* $\overline{\mathfrak{g}}^{(K)}$ *can be extended to an* A_{K+1} *homomorphism* $\overline{\mathfrak{g}}^{(K+1)}$ *and* $\overline{\mathfrak{h}}^{(K)}$ *is extended to an* A_{K+1} *homotopy* $\overline{\mathfrak{h}}^{(K+1)}$ *from identity to* $\overline{\mathfrak{g}}^{(K+1)} \circ \overline{\mathfrak{f}}$.

$$
\begin{array}{ccccccc}
\overline{C}_1 & \xleftarrow{\overline{\mathrm{Eval}}_{s=0}} & \overline{\mathfrak{C}}_1 & \xrightarrow{\overline{\mathrm{Eval}}_{s=1}} & \overline{C}_1 & \xleftarrow{\overline{\mathfrak{g}}^{(K)}} & \overline{C}_2 \\
\| & & \uparrow \overline{\mathfrak{h}} & & \| & & \| \\
\overline{C}_1 & = & \overline{C}_1 & = & \overline{C}_1 & \xrightarrow{\overline{\mathfrak{f}}} & \overline{C}_2
\end{array}
$$

Diagram 4.5.1

PROOF. By Corollary 4.5.5, we have $\overline{\mathfrak{h}}'_{K+1}$ such that $\overline{\mathfrak{h}}_k$, $k = 1, 2, \cdots, K$ and $\overline{\mathfrak{h}}'_{K+1}$ define an A_{K+1} homomorphism $\overline{\mathfrak{h}}^{(K+1)'}$ from $\overline{C}_1$ to $\overline{\mathfrak{C}}_1$ and $\overline{\mathrm{Eval}}_{s=0} \circ \overline{\mathfrak{h}}^{(K+1)'} = id.$ Moreover $\overline{\mathrm{Eval}}_{s=1} \circ \overline{\mathfrak{h}}'_{K+1}$ extends $\overline{\mathfrak{g}}^{(K)} \circ \overline{\mathfrak{f}}$ to an A_{K+1} homomorphism. Namely we have

$$(4.5.7) \qquad o_{K+1}(\overline{\mathfrak{g}}^{(K)} \circ \overline{\mathfrak{f}}) = -\delta_1(\overline{\mathrm{Eval}}_{s=1} \circ \overline{\mathfrak{h}}'_{K+1}).$$

Since $\overline{\mathfrak{f}} : \overline{C}_1 \to \overline{C}_2$ is a weak homotopy equivalence, it follows from (4.5.2.4) and (4.5.7) that $[o_{K+1}(\overline{\mathfrak{g}}^{(K)})] = 0$. Hence we have $\overline{\mathfrak{g}}'_{K+1}$ such that

$$(4.5.8) \qquad o_{K+1}(\overline{\mathfrak{g}}^{(K)}) = -\delta_1(\overline{\mathfrak{g}}'_{K+1}).$$

We define

$$\Xi = \overline{\mathfrak{g}}'_{K+1} \circ (\overline{\mathfrak{f}}_1)^{\otimes K+1} - \overline{\mathrm{Eval}}_1 \circ \overline{\mathfrak{h}}'_{K+1} \in Hom(B_{K+1}\overline{C}_1[1], \overline{C}_1[1]).$$

By (4.5.7) we have $\delta_1(\Xi) = 0$. Since $\overline{\mathfrak{f}}$ is a weak homotopy equivalence, there exists a δ_1-cocycle $\Delta\overline{\mathfrak{g}}'_{K+1} \in Hom(B_{K+1}\overline{C}_2[1], \overline{C}_1[1])$ such that $[\Xi + (\Delta\overline{\mathfrak{g}}'_{K+1} \circ \overline{\mathfrak{f}}_1^{\otimes K+1})] = 0$. Therefore, there exists $\Delta_1\overline{\mathfrak{h}}_{K+1} \in Hom(B_{K+1}\overline{C}_1[1], \overline{C}_1[1])$ such that

$$(4.5.9) \qquad \delta_1(\Delta_1\overline{\mathfrak{h}}_{K+1}) = (\overline{\mathfrak{g}}'_{K+1} + \Delta\overline{\mathfrak{g}}'_{K+1}) \circ \overline{\mathfrak{f}}_1^{\otimes K+1} - (\overline{\mathrm{Eval}}_{s=1})_1 \circ \overline{\mathfrak{h}}'_{K+1}.$$

Using (4.2.2.4), we find $\Delta\overline{\mathfrak{h}}_{K+1} \in Hom(B_{K+1}\overline{C}_1[1], \overline{\mathfrak{C}}_1[1])$ such that

$$(4.5.10) \qquad (\overline{\mathrm{Eval}}_{s=0})_1 \circ \Delta\overline{\mathfrak{h}}_{K+1} = 0, \qquad (\overline{\mathrm{Eval}}_{s=1})_1 \circ \Delta\overline{\mathfrak{h}}_{K+1} = \Delta_1\overline{\mathfrak{h}}_{K+1}.$$

We now put $\overline{\mathfrak{g}}_{K+1} = \overline{\mathfrak{g}}'_{K+1} + \Delta\overline{\mathfrak{g}}'_{K+1}$, $\overline{\mathfrak{h}}_{K+1} = \overline{\mathfrak{h}}'_{K+1} + \delta_1(\Delta\overline{\mathfrak{h}}_{K+1})$. Let us check that they have the required properties.

Since $\Delta\overline{\mathfrak{g}}'_{K+1}$ is a δ_1-cocycle, it follows from (4.5.8) that

$$o_{K+1}(\overline{\mathfrak{g}}^{(K)}) = -\delta_1(\overline{\mathfrak{g}}_{K+1}).$$

Namely $\overline{\mathfrak{g}}_{K+1}$ gives an extension of $\overline{\mathfrak{g}}^{(K)}$ to an A_{K+1} homomorphism $\overline{\mathfrak{g}}^{(K+1)}$. Similarly, $\overline{\mathfrak{h}}_{K+1}$ extends $\overline{\mathfrak{h}}^{(K)}$ to an A_{K+1} homomorphism $\overline{\mathfrak{h}}^{(K+1)}$.

By (4.5.10), we have

$$(\overline{\mathrm{Eval}}_{s=0})_1 \circ \overline{\mathfrak{h}}^{(K+1)} = (\overline{\mathrm{Eval}}_{s=0})_1 \circ \overline{\mathfrak{h}}^{(K+1)'} = id.$$

Finally by (4.5.9) and (4.5.10), we obtain

$$(\overline{\mathrm{Eval}}_{s=1})_1 \circ \overline{\mathfrak{h}}_{K+1} = (\overline{\mathrm{Eval}}_{s=1})_1 \circ \overline{\mathfrak{h}}'_{K+1} + \delta_1(\Delta_1\overline{\mathfrak{h}}_{K+1}) = \overline{\mathfrak{g}}_{K+1} \circ \overline{\mathfrak{f}}_1^{\otimes K+1}.$$

Thus $\overline{\mathfrak{h}}^{(K+1)}$ is an A_{K+1} homotopy from id to $\overline{\mathfrak{g}}^{(K+1)} \circ \overline{\mathfrak{f}}$. $\qquad\square$

Now we are ready to complete the proof of Theorem 4.2.45 (1). Let $\overline{\mathfrak{f}} : \overline{C}_1 \to \overline{C}_2$ be a weak homotopy equivalence. Since $\overline{\mathfrak{f}}_1 : (\overline{C}_1, \overline{\mathfrak{m}}_1) \to (\overline{C}_2, \overline{\mathfrak{m}}_1)$ is a cochain homotopy equivalence, there exists a cochain map $\overline{\mathfrak{g}}_1 : (\overline{C}_2, \overline{\mathfrak{m}}_1) \to (\overline{C}_1, \overline{\mathfrak{m}}_1)$ such that $\overline{\mathfrak{g}}_1 \circ \overline{\mathfrak{f}}_1$ is cochain homotopic to identity. $\overline{\mathfrak{g}}_1$ defines an A_1 homomorphism: $\overline{\mathfrak{g}}^{(1)} : \overline{C}_2 \to \overline{C}_1$. Let $\overline{\mathfrak{h}}_1^a : \overline{C}_1 \to \overline{C}_1$ be a cochain homotopy from identity to $\overline{\mathfrak{g}}_1 \circ \overline{\mathfrak{f}}_1$. We use (4.2.2.4) to obtain $\overline{\mathfrak{h}}_1^b : \overline{C}_1 \to \overline{\mathfrak{C}}_1$ such that

$$(\overline{\mathrm{Eval}}_{s=1})_1 \circ \overline{\mathfrak{h}}_1^b = \overline{\mathfrak{h}}_1^a, \qquad (\overline{\mathrm{Eval}}_{s=0})_1 \circ \overline{\mathfrak{h}}_1^b = 0.$$

We put

$$\overline{\mathfrak{h}}_1 = (\overline{\mathrm{Incl}})_1 + \overline{\mathfrak{m}}_1 \circ \overline{\mathfrak{h}}_1^b + \overline{\mathfrak{h}}_1^b \circ \overline{\mathfrak{m}}_1 : \overline{C}_1 \to \overline{\mathfrak{C}}_1.$$

It is easy to check that $\overline{\mathfrak{h}}_1$ defines an A_1 homotopy from id to $\overline{\mathfrak{g}}^{(1)} \circ \overline{\mathfrak{f}}$.

We now apply Proposition 4.5.6 inductively and obtain an A_∞ homomorphism $\overline{\mathfrak{g}} : \overline{C}_2 \to \overline{C}_1$ and an A_∞ homotopy $\overline{\mathfrak{h}}$ from id to $\overline{\mathfrak{g}} \circ \overline{\mathfrak{f}}$.

We finally prove that $\overline{\mathfrak{f}} \circ \overline{\mathfrak{g}}$ is homotopic to identity. We remark that $\overline{\mathfrak{g}}$ is a weak homotopy equivalence because $\overline{\mathfrak{g}}_1$ is chain homotopic to a chain homotopy inverse of $\overline{\mathfrak{f}}_1$. So we apply the above argument to obtain an A_∞ homomorphism $\overline{\mathfrak{f}}'$ such that $\overline{\mathfrak{f}}' \circ \overline{\mathfrak{g}}$ is homotopic to identity. Therefore $\overline{\mathfrak{f}}' \circ \overline{\mathfrak{g}} \circ \overline{\mathfrak{f}}$ is homotopic to $\overline{\mathfrak{f}}$ by Lemma 4.2.43. On the other hand, since $\overline{\mathfrak{g}} \circ \overline{\mathfrak{f}}$ is homotopic to identity, Lemma 4.2.43 again implies that $\overline{\mathfrak{f}}' \circ \overline{\mathfrak{g}} \circ \overline{\mathfrak{f}}$ is homotopic to $\overline{\mathfrak{f}}'$. Thus we proved that $\overline{\mathfrak{f}}'$ is homotopic to $\overline{\mathfrak{f}}$.

Then, since $\overline{\mathfrak{f}}' \circ \overline{\mathfrak{g}}$ is homotopic to identity, $\overline{\mathfrak{f}} \circ \overline{\mathfrak{g}}$ is homotopic to identity. The proof of Theorem 4.2.45 (1) is now complete. $\qquad\square$

4.5.3. Unital case: the unfiltered version. We prove the unfiltered versions of Theorem 4.2.45a and 4.2.45b in this subsection. As for unfiltered versions of Theorem 4.2.45a the proof is parallel to the proof of Theorem 4.2.45 (1). The main difference is that we replace Theorem 4.5.1 by the following Theorem 4.5.1a. Let $\overline{\mathfrak{f}} : \overline{C}_1 \to \overline{C}_2$ be a unital A_K homomorphism.

Let us recall

$$B_k \overline{C}_{1,\mathrm{red}}[1] = \underbrace{\overline{C}_1[1]/R[\mathbf{e}] \otimes \cdots \otimes \overline{C}_1[1]/R[\mathbf{e}]}_{k \text{ times}}.$$

Since $\overline{\mathfrak{m}}_1 \mathbf{e} = 0$, it follows that $\hat{\overline{\mathfrak{m}}}_1$ induces an operator on $B_k \overline{C}_{1,\mathrm{red}}[1]$. We denote it also by $\hat{\overline{\mathfrak{m}}}_1$. Hence $\hat{\overline{\mathfrak{m}}}_1$ and $\overline{\mathfrak{m}}_1 : \overline{C}_2[1] \to \overline{C}_2[1]$ induce a differential δ_1 on $Hom(B_k \overline{C}_{1,\mathrm{red}}[1], \overline{C}_2[1])$.

THEOREM 4.5.1a. *There exists* $o_{K+1}^{\mathrm{red}}(\bar{\mathfrak{f}}) \in Hom(B_{K+1}\overline{C}_{1,\mathrm{red}}[1], \overline{C}_2[1])$ *of degree 1, such that the following holds.*

(4.5.2a.1) $\delta_1(o_{K+1}^{\mathrm{red}}(\bar{\mathfrak{f}})) = 0$.

(4.5.2a.2) $[o_{K+1}^{\mathrm{red}}(\bar{\mathfrak{f}})] = 0$ *as a δ_1-cohomology class if and only if there exists an* A_{K+1} *homomorphism extending* $\bar{\mathfrak{f}}$.

(4.5.2a.3)   *If* $\bar{\mathfrak{f}}'$ *is A_K homotopic to* $\bar{\mathfrak{f}}$, *then* $[o_{K+1}^{\mathrm{red}}(\bar{\mathfrak{f}})] = [o_{K+1}^{\mathrm{red}}(\bar{\mathfrak{f}}')]$ *as δ_1-cohomology class.*

(4.5.2a.4)   *If* $\bar{\mathfrak{g}} : \overline{C}_1' \to \overline{C}_1$ *and* $\bar{\mathfrak{g}}' : \overline{C}_2 \to \overline{C}_2'$ *are unital A_{K+1} homomorphisms, then*

$$[o_{K+1}^{\mathrm{red}}(\bar{\mathfrak{g}}' \circ \bar{\mathfrak{f}} \circ \bar{\mathfrak{g}})] = (\bar{\mathfrak{g}}_1')_* \circ [o_{K+1}^{\mathrm{red}}(\bar{\mathfrak{f}})] \circ (\bar{\mathfrak{g}}_1 \otimes \cdots \otimes \bar{\mathfrak{g}}_1)_*$$

in $H(Hom(B_{K+1}\overline{C}_{1,\mathrm{red}}[1], \overline{C}_2[1]), \delta_1)$. *Here*

$$\bar{\mathfrak{g}}_1 \otimes \cdots \otimes \bar{\mathfrak{g}}_1 : B_{K+1}\overline{C}_1'^{\mathrm{red}}[1] \to B_{K+1}\overline{C}_1^{\mathrm{red}}[1]$$

is induced by $\bar{\mathfrak{g}}_1 : \overline{C}_1'^{\mathrm{red}}[1] \to \overline{C}_1^{\mathrm{red}}[1]$.

PROOF. We use Lemma 4.4.30 (or its A_K analogue) to associate an R module homomorphism $\hat{\bar{\mathfrak{f}}}_{k,\mathrm{red}} : B_k^{\mathrm{red}}\overline{C}_1[1] \to \overline{C}_2[1]$ for $k = 1, \cdots, K$. They induce

$$\hat{\bar{\mathfrak{f}}}_{1\cdots K+1}^{\mathrm{red}} \in Hom(B_{1\cdots K+1,\mathrm{red}}\overline{C}_1[1], B_{1\cdots K+1}\overline{C}_2[1])$$

by putting $\hat{\bar{\mathfrak{f}}}_{K+1,\mathrm{red}}' = 0$. We then consider

$$o_{K+1}^{\mathrm{red},0}(\bar{\mathfrak{f}}) = \hat{\bar{d}}_{1\cdots K+1} \circ \hat{\bar{\mathfrak{f}}}_{1\cdots K+1} - \hat{\bar{\mathfrak{f}}}_{1\cdots K+1} \circ \hat{\bar{d}}_{1\cdots K+1} \in Hom(B_{K+1}^{\mathrm{red}}\overline{C}_1[1], \overline{C}_2[1]).$$

We can show that $o_{K+1}^{\mathrm{red},0} \circ s_{\mathrm{left}} = o_{K+1}^{\mathrm{red},0} \circ s_{\mathrm{right}} = 0$ in a way similar to the proof of Lemma 4.4.35. Hence we obtain $o_{K+1}^{\mathrm{red}}(\bar{\mathfrak{f}}) \in Hom(B_{K+1}\overline{C}_{1,\mathrm{red}}[1], \overline{C}_2[1])$. Then it is a straightforward analog to the proof of Theorem 4.5.1 to check that it has required properties.   □

We use Theorem 4.5.1a in place of Theorem 4.5.1 and the rest of the proof goes in the same way. We thus proved the unfiltered version of Theorem 4.2.45a.   □

We next turn to the unfiltered version of Theorem 4.2.45b. We start with a homotopy-unital A_∞ homomorphism $\overline{C}_1 \to \overline{C}_2$ which is, by definition, a unital A_∞ homomorphism $\bar{\mathfrak{f}}^+ : \overline{C}_1^+ \to \overline{C}_2^+$ such that

(4.5.11) $\bar{\mathfrak{f}}_k^+ (B_k(\overline{C}_1[1])) \subseteq \overline{C}_2[1]$.

We then need to find a homotopy inverse $\bar{\mathfrak{g}}^+ : \overline{C}_2^+[1] \to \overline{C}_1^+[1]$ such that

(4.5.12) $\bar{\mathfrak{g}}_k^+ (B_k(\overline{C}_2[1])) \subseteq \overline{C}_1[1]$.

So we need some additional argument to apply Theorem 4.2.45a to $\overline{\mathfrak{f}}^+$.

Let $\overline{\mathfrak{C}}_1^{(+)}$ be a model of $[0,1] \times \overline{C}_1^+$ which is unital. We put

$$(4.5.13) \qquad \overline{\mathfrak{C}}_1 = (\overline{\mathrm{Eval}}_{s=0})_1^{-1}(C_1) \cap (\overline{\mathrm{Eval}}_{s=1})_1^{-1}(C_1).$$

Since $(\overline{\mathrm{Eval}}_{s=s_0})_k = 0$ for $k \neq 1$, it follows that $\overline{\mathfrak{C}}_1$ is an A_∞ subalgebra. (We remark that C_1 is an A_∞ subalgebra of C_1^+.) It is easy to see that $\overline{\mathfrak{C}}_1$ is a model of $[0,1] \times \overline{C}_1$.

Now we prove the following by induction on K.

PROPOSITION 4.5.6b. *Let* $\overline{\mathfrak{f}}^+ : \overline{C}_1^+ \to \overline{C}_2^+$ *be a unital weak homotopy equivalence satisfying* (4.5.11) *and* $\overline{\mathfrak{g}}^{+(K)} : \overline{C}_2^+ \to \overline{C}_1^+$ *a unital A_K homomorphism satisfying* (4.5.12). *Let* $\overline{\mathfrak{h}}^{+(K)} : \overline{C}_1^+ \to \overline{\mathfrak{C}}_1^{(+)}$ *be a unital A_K homotopy from identity to* $\overline{\mathfrak{g}}^{+(K)} \circ \overline{\mathfrak{f}}^+$ *such that*

$$(4.5.14) \qquad \overline{\mathfrak{h}}_k^+(B_k(\overline{C}_1[1])) \subseteq \overline{\mathfrak{C}}_1.$$

Then $\overline{\mathfrak{g}}^{+(K)}$ *can be extended to a unital A_{K+1} homomorphism* $\overline{\mathfrak{g}}^{+(K+1)}$ *satisfying* (4.5.12) *and* $\overline{\mathfrak{h}}^{+(K)}$ *is extended to a unital A_{K+1} homotopy* $\overline{\mathfrak{h}}^{+(K+1)}$ *from identity to* $\overline{\mathfrak{g}}^{(K+1)} \circ \overline{\mathfrak{f}}^+$ *satisfying* (4.5.14).

PROOF. The proof is parallel to that of Theorem 4.5.1a after we remark the following two points.

First, the A_∞ algebra $\overline{C}_i^+$ has a *canonical* splitting $\overline{C}_i^+ = \overline{C}_i^{+\mathrm{red}} \oplus R\mathbf{e}$, where $\overline{C}_i^{+\mathrm{red}} = \overline{C}_i \oplus R\mathbf{f}$.

Second, to keep Conditions (4.5.12) and (4.5.14), we modify the obstruction theory Theorem 4.5.1a a bit. Namely, for example, the obstruction $o_{K+1}^{\mathrm{red}}(\overline{\mathfrak{g}}^{+(K)})$ for $\overline{\mathfrak{g}}^{+(K)}$ to be extended to a unital A_{K+1} homomorphism satisfying (4.5.12) lies in the group $Hom(B_{K+1}\overline{C}_1^{+\mathrm{red}}[1], \overline{C}_2[1])$ in place of the group $Hom(B_{K+1}\overline{C}_1^{+\mathrm{red}}[1], \overline{C}_2^+[1])$.

The proof now goes in the same way. The proof of Proposition 4.5.6b and the unfiltered version of Theorem 4.2.45b is now complete. □

4.5.4. Extending filtered A_∞ homomorphism modulo T^{λ_i} to modulo $T^{\lambda_{i+1}}$.

We next proceed to the proof of Theorem 4.2.45 (2). We will use the induction on the energy filtration for this purpose. Let $G \subset \mathbb{R}_{\geq 0} \times 2\mathbb{Z}$ satisfy Condition 3.1.6 and we assume all filtered A_∞ algebras as well as filtered A_∞ homomorphisms we consider are G-gapped. As in Subsection 4.4.6 we can enumerate the image of the projection of G to $\mathbb{R}_{\geq 0}$ denoted by $\mathrm{Spec}(G) = \{\lambda_0, \lambda_1, \cdots\}$ so that $\lambda_i < \lambda_{i+1}$, $\lim_{i \to \infty} \lambda_i = \infty$. Let

$$\mathfrak{f}_k : B_k C_1[1] \to C_2[1], \quad k = 0, 1, 2, \cdots$$

be a sequence of degree 0 homomorphisms which satisfy (3.2.27). They induce a coalgebra homomorphism $\widehat{\mathfrak{f}} : \widehat{B}C_1[1] \to \widehat{B}C_2[1]$ as in (3.2.28).

DEFINITION 4.5.15. We say $\mathfrak{f}$ is a *filtered A_∞ homomorphism modulo T^{λ_i}* if

$$\widehat{d} \circ \widehat{\mathfrak{f}} - \widehat{\mathfrak{f}} \circ \widehat{d} \equiv 0 \mod T^{\lambda_i}.$$

Here $i = 1, 2, \cdots$

Let $\mathfrak{f}$, $\mathfrak{g}$ be filtered A_∞ homomorphisms modulo T^{λ_i} from C_1 to C_2 and $\mathfrak{C}_2$ a model of $[0,1] \times C_2$. We say that they are *homotopic modulo* T^{λ_i} if there is a filtered A_∞ homomorphism $\mathfrak{h}$ modulo T^{λ_i} from C_1 to $\mathfrak{C}_2$ and such that

$$\mathrm{Eval}_{s=0} \circ \mathfrak{h} \equiv \mathfrak{f} \mod T^{\lambda_i}, \qquad \mathrm{Eval}_{s=1} \circ \mathfrak{h} \equiv \mathfrak{g} \mod T^{\lambda_i}.$$

We can define the composition of filtered A_∞ homomorphisms modulo T^{λ_i} in an obvious way. We remark that a filtered A_∞ homomorphism $\mathfrak{f} : C_1 \to C_2$ modulo T^{λ_i} induces an A_∞ homomorphism $\overline{\mathfrak{f}} : \overline{C}_1 \to \overline{C}_2$.

Now we are ready to start the proof of Theorem 4.2.45 (2).

DEFINITION-PROPOSITION 4.5.16. *Assume that $\mathfrak{f}^{(i)}$ is a filtered A_∞ homomorphism modulo T^{λ_i} in the sense of Definition 4.5.15. Then there exists a Hochschild cohomology class $[o_{\lambda_i}(\mathfrak{f}^{(i)})] \in HH(\overline{C}_1, \overline{C}_2; \overline{\mathfrak{f}}^{(i)})$ with the following properties.*

(4.5.17.1) $[o_{\lambda_i}(\mathfrak{f}^{(i)})] = 0$ *if and only if there exists $\mathfrak{f}^{(i)\prime}$ such that:*
    (4.5.17.1.1) $\mathfrak{f}^{(i)\prime}$ *is a filtered A_∞ homomorphism modulo $T^{\lambda_{i+1}}$.*
    (4.5.17.1.2) $\mathfrak{f}^{(i)\prime} \equiv \mathfrak{f}^{(i)} \mod T^{\lambda_i}$.
(4.5.17.2)   *If $\mathfrak{f}^{(i)\prime}$ is a filtered A_∞ homomorphism modulo T^{λ_i} homotopic to $\mathfrak{f}^{(i)}$ modulo T^{λ_i}, then we have*

$$[o_{\lambda_i}(\mathfrak{f}^{(i)})] = [o_{\lambda_i}(\mathfrak{f}^{(i)\prime})].$$

(4.5.17.3)   *If $\mathfrak{g} : C_1' \to C_1$, $\mathfrak{g}' : C_2 \to C_2'$ be filtered A_∞ homomorphisms modulo $T^{\lambda_{i+1}}$, then*

$$[o_{\lambda_i}(\mathfrak{g}' \circ \mathfrak{f}^{(i)} \circ \mathfrak{g})] = (\overline{\mathfrak{g}}, \overline{\mathfrak{g}}')_*[o_{\lambda_i}(\mathfrak{f}^{(i)})].$$

REMARK 4.5.18. We need some explanation on the meaning of (4.5.17.2). Since we assume that $\overline{\mathfrak{f}}^{(i)}, \overline{\mathfrak{f}}^{(i)\prime} : \overline{C}_1 \to \overline{C}_2$ are homotopic by a homotopy $\overline{\mathfrak{h}} : \overline{C}_1 \to \overline{\mathfrak{C}}_2$, we have a canonical isomorphism

$$HH(\overline{C}_1, \overline{C}_2; \overline{\mathfrak{f}}^{(i)}) \cong HH(\overline{C}_1, \overline{C}_2; \overline{\mathfrak{f}}^{(i)\prime}).$$

Therefore the equality (4.5.17.2) makes sense under the identification via this canonical isomorphism. The proof of this isomorphism follows from the fact that the homomorphisms $(\overline{\mathrm{Eval}}_{s=0})_1$ and $\overline{\mathrm{Incl}}_1$ induce an isomorphism

$$HH(\overline{C}_1, \overline{\mathfrak{C}}_2; \overline{\mathfrak{h}}) \cong HH(\overline{C}_1, \overline{C}_2; \overline{\mathfrak{f}})$$

and $(\overline{\mathrm{Eval}}_{s=1})_1$ and $\overline{\mathrm{Incl}}_1$ induce an isomorphism

$$HH(\overline{C}_1, \overline{\mathfrak{C}}_2; \overline{\mathfrak{h}}) \cong HH(\overline{C}_1, \overline{C}_2; \overline{\mathfrak{f}}').$$

This follows from Proposition 4.4.48.

PROOF OF PROPOSITION 4.5.16. By assumption, there exists

$$o_{\lambda_i}(\mathfrak{f}^{(i)}) \in Hom(B\overline{C}_1[1], B\overline{C}_2[1])$$

such that

$$\widehat{d} \circ \widehat{\mathfrak{f}}^{(i)} - \widehat{\mathfrak{f}}^{(i)} \circ \widehat{d} \equiv T^{\lambda_i} o_{\lambda_i}(\mathfrak{f}^{(i)}) \mod T^{\lambda_{i+1}}.$$

Since $\widehat{d}$ is a coderivation and $\widehat{\mathfrak{f}}^{(i)}$ is a coalgebra homomorphism, it easily follows that $o_{\lambda_i}(\mathfrak{f}^{(i)})$ is a coderivation. Moreover, since

$$\widehat{d}(\widehat{d} \circ \widehat{\mathfrak{f}}^{(i)} - \widehat{\mathfrak{f}}^{(i)} \circ \widehat{d}) + (\widehat{d} \circ \widehat{\mathfrak{f}}^{(i)} - \widehat{d} \circ \widehat{\mathfrak{f}}^{(i)})\widehat{d} = 0,$$

we have $\delta(o_{\lambda_i}(\mathfrak{f}^{(i)})) = 0$. Therefore it defines $[o_{\lambda_i}(\mathfrak{f}^{(i)})] \in HH(\overline{C}_1, \overline{C}_2; \widehat{\mathfrak{f}}^{(i)})$. We can check the properties (4.5.17.1), (4.5.17.2), (4.5.17.3) in a way similar to the proof of Theorem 4.5.1. □

4.5.5. Proof of Theorem 4.2.45 II: the energy filtration. Now we go back to the proof of Theorem 4.2.45 (2). We take G and λ_i as in the last subsection. Let C_i be G-gapped filtered A_∞ algebras, and $\mathfrak{f}: C_1 \to C_2$ be a G-gapped filtered A_∞ homomorphism. We assume that $\mathfrak{f}$ is a weak homotopy equivalence, i.e., the unfiltered A_∞ homomorphism $\bar{\mathfrak{f}}: \overline{C}_1 \to \overline{C}_2$ induced by $\mathfrak{f}$ defines an isomorphism in $\overline{\mathfrak{m}}_1$-cohomology. Then $\bar{\mathfrak{f}}$ is a homotopy equivalence by Theorem 4.2.45 (1), which we already proved.

We prove the following proposition by induction on n.

PROPOSITION 4.5.19. *Let $\mathfrak{g}^{(n)} : C_2 \to C_1$ be a filtered A_∞ homomorphism modulo T^{λ_n} and let $\mathfrak{h}^{(n)} : C_1 \to \mathfrak{C}_1$ be a filtered A_∞ homotopy modulo T^{λ_n} between id and $\mathfrak{g}^{(n)} \circ \mathfrak{f}$. Then there exists $\mathfrak{g}^{(n+1)} : C_2 \to C_1$ a filtered A_∞ homomorphism modulo $T^{\lambda_{n+1}}$ and $\mathfrak{h}^{(n+1)} : C_1 \to \mathfrak{C}_1$ a filtered A_∞ homotopy modulo $T^{\lambda_{n+1}}$ between id and $\mathfrak{g}^{(n+1)} \circ \mathfrak{f}$. Moreover we have $\mathfrak{g}^{(n+1)} \equiv \mathfrak{g}^{(n)} \mod T^{\lambda_n}$ and $\mathfrak{h}^{(n+1)} \equiv \mathfrak{h}^{(n)} \mod T^{\lambda_n}$.*

$$C_1 \xleftarrow{\text{Eval}_{s=0}} \mathfrak{C}_1 \xrightarrow{\text{Eval}_{s=1}} C_1 \xleftarrow{\mathfrak{g}^{(n)}} C_2$$
$$\| \qquad \qquad \uparrow^{\mathfrak{h}} \qquad \qquad \|$$
$$C_1 === C_1 === C_1 \xrightarrow{\mathfrak{f}} C_2$$

Diagram 4.5.2

PROOF. We consider $o_{\lambda_n}(\mathfrak{h}^n)$. Since $(\overline{\text{Eval}}_0, id)_*[o_{\lambda_n}(\mathfrak{h}^n)] = o_{\lambda_n}(id) = 0$, we have $[o_{\lambda_n}(\mathfrak{h}^n)] = 0$ by Proposition 4.4.48 and (4.5.2.4). Indeed, we can prove more. Namely, we remark that $o_{\lambda_n}(\mathfrak{h}^n)$ lies in:

(4.5.20) $\mathfrak{K} := \text{Ker}\left((\overline{\text{Eval}}_{s=0}, id)_* : \text{Der}(B\overline{C}_1[1], B\overline{\mathfrak{C}}_2[1]) \to \text{Der}(B\overline{C}_1[1], B\overline{C}_2[1])\right).$

We also remark that $\mathfrak{K}$ is an acyclic complex by Proposition 4.4.48 and (4.2.3.3). Thus there exists $\mathfrak{h}'_{n+1} \in \mathfrak{K}$ such that $-\delta(\mathfrak{h}'_{n+1}) = o_{\lambda_n}(\mathfrak{h}^n)$ and

$$(\overline{\text{Eval}}_{s=0}, id)_*(\mathfrak{h}'_{n+1}) = 0.$$

It is easy to see that $\mathfrak{h}'^{(n+1)} = \mathfrak{h}^n + T^{\lambda_{n+1}}\mathfrak{h}'_{n+1}$ is an A_∞ homomorphism modulo $T^{\lambda_{n+1}}$.

Since

$$-\delta((\overline{\text{Eval}}_{s=1}, id)_*(\mathfrak{h}'_{n+1})) = (\overline{\text{Eval}}_{s=1}, id)_* o_{\lambda_n}(\mathfrak{h}^{(n)}) = o_{\lambda_n}(\mathfrak{g}^{(n)} \circ \mathfrak{f})$$

and $\bar{\mathfrak{f}}$ induces an isomorphism on the Hochschild cohomology (Proposition 4.4.48), there exists $\mathfrak{g}'_{n+1} \in \text{Der}(B\overline{C}_2[1], B\overline{C}_1[1])$ such that $\delta(\mathfrak{g}'_{n+1}) = o_{\lambda_n}(\mathfrak{g}^{(n)})$. Then we have

$$\delta((\overline{\text{Eval}}_{s=1}, id)_*(\mathfrak{h}'_{n+1}) - (id, \bar{\mathfrak{f}})_*(\mathfrak{g}'_{n+1})) = 0.$$

Moreover since $\bar{\mathfrak{f}}$ induces an isomorphism on the Hochschild cohomology (Proposition 4.4.48), there exist

$$\Delta\mathfrak{g}_{n+1} \in \mathrm{Der}(B\overline{C}_2[1], B\overline{C}_1[1]) \quad \text{and} \quad \Delta_1\mathfrak{h}_{n+1} \in \mathrm{Der}(B\overline{C}_2[1], B\overline{C}_1[1])$$

such that

$$(id, \bar{\mathfrak{f}})_*(\mathfrak{g}_{K+1}) + (id, \bar{\mathfrak{f}})_*(\Delta\mathfrak{g}_{n+1}) - (\overline{\mathrm{Eval}}_1, id)_*(\mathfrak{h}'_{n+1}) = \delta(\Delta_1\mathfrak{h}_{n+1}).$$

By (4.2.3.3) and Lemma 4.4.43 we have $\Delta\mathfrak{h}_{n+1} \in \mathrm{Der}(B\overline{C}_2[1], B\overline{\mathfrak{C}}_1[1])$ such that

$$\widehat{\overline{\mathrm{Eval}}}_{s=1} \circ \Delta\mathfrak{h}_{n+1} = \Delta_1\mathfrak{h}_{n+1}, \quad \widehat{\overline{\mathrm{Eval}}}_{s=0} \circ \Delta\mathfrak{h}_{n+1} = 0.$$

We put $\mathfrak{g}_{n+1} = \mathfrak{g}'_{n+1} + \Delta\mathfrak{g}'_{n+1}$, $\mathfrak{h}_{n+1} = \mathfrak{h}'_{n+1} + \delta(\Delta\mathfrak{h}_{n+1})$. Then it is easy to check that they satisfy the required properties.   □

Now we are ready to complete the proof of Theorem 4.2.45 (2). We remark that Theorem 4.2.45 (1) which we proved in Subsection 4.5.2 implies that the assumption of Proposition 4.5.19 holds for $n = 1$. Therefore suppose we have $\mathfrak{g}^{(n)}$ and $\mathfrak{h}^{(n)}$ by induction. Since $\mathfrak{g}^{(n+1)} \equiv \mathfrak{g}^{(n)} \mod T^{\lambda_n}$ and $\mathfrak{h}^{(n+1)} \equiv \mathfrak{h}^{(n)} \mod T^{\lambda_n}$, it follows that $\lim \mathfrak{g}^{(n)}, \lim \mathfrak{h}^{(n)}$ exist. Hence we have $\mathfrak{g}$ such that $\mathfrak{g} \circ \mathfrak{f}$ is homotopic to the identity. The proof that $\mathfrak{f} \circ \mathfrak{g} \sim id$ goes as in the last step of the proof of Theorem 4.2.45 (1). The proof of Theorem 4.2.45 is now complete.   □

For the unital or the homotopy-unital version Theorem 4.2.45a, 4.2.45b, the argument is a modification of the above. Since the required modification of the proof is similar to those of Subsection 4.5.3 and Subsection 4.4.7, we omit the details.   □

PROOF OF PROPOSITION 4.3.16. We prove the property $\bar{\mathfrak{f}} \equiv id \mod \Lambda^+_{0,nov}$. We use the notation in the proof at Section 4.3. We remark that if we reduce the coefficient of $(\mathfrak{C}, \mathfrak{m}^{\bar{b}})$ to R then we have a model of $[0,1] \times \overline{C}$. Hence we can use $\overline{\mathrm{Incl}}$ to start the induction of the construction of the homotopy inverse of $\mathrm{Eval}_{s=0}$: $(\mathfrak{C}, \mathfrak{m}^{\bar{b}}) \to (C, \mathfrak{m}^{b_0})$. Therefore the homotopy equivalence $\mathfrak{f} : (C, \mathfrak{m}^{b_0}) \to (C, \mathfrak{m}^{b_1})$ has a property $\bar{\mathfrak{f}} = \overline{\mathrm{Eval}}_{s=1} \circ \overline{\mathrm{Incl}} = id$ as required.   □

4.6. Homotopy equivalence of A_∞ algebras: the geometric realization

4.6.1. Construction of A_∞ homomorphisms.
The aim of this section is to prove that the filtered A_∞ algebra constructed in Theorem 3.5.11 is independent of various choices involved. More precisely we prove the following Theorem 4.6.1 (and Theorem 4.1.1). We recall the notations from Section 4.1. Let (M, ω), (M', ω') be symplectic manifolds and $L \subset M$ and $L' \subset M'$ be n dimensional Lagrangian submanifolds. Let $\psi : M \longrightarrow M'$ be a symplectic diffeomorphism such that $\psi(L) = L'$. Let J be a compatible almost complex structure on M. We use J to construct the moduli spaces $\mathcal{M}^{\mathrm{main}}_{k+1}(\beta)$ as in Section 3.5. To specify the choices of L and J we write $\mathcal{M}^{\mathrm{main}}_{k+1}((L, J), \beta)$. Let J' be a compatible almost structure on M'. We then define $\mathcal{M}^{\mathrm{main}}_{k+1}((L', J'), \beta)$ in a similar way. (We remark that we do not assume any genericity condition on J, J'. The transversality we need will be achieved by abstract perturbations, *not* by perturbation of J.)

In Section 3.5 we took a countable set $\mathcal{X}_1(L)$ of smooth singular simplices and considered a subcomplex of $S(L; \mathbb{Q})$ spanned by it. We denote this subcomplex by $C_1(L; \mathbb{Q})$. For $P_i \in \mathcal{X}_1(L)$ we considered also the fiber product

$$\mathcal{M}_{k+1}^{\mathrm{main}}((L, J), \beta; \vec{P}) = \mathcal{M}_{k+1}^{\mathrm{main}}((L, J), \beta)_{ev} \times (P_1 \times \cdots \times P_k).$$

It is a space with Kuranishi structure. Proposition 3.5.2 (whose proof will be completed in Section 7.2) asserts that we can choose $\mathcal{X}_1(L)$ and a system of multisections $\mathfrak{s}$ on $\mathcal{M}_{k+1}((L, J), \beta; \vec{P})$ such that

$$\mathcal{M}_{k+1}^{\mathrm{main}}((L, J), \beta; \vec{P})^{\mathfrak{s}} = (\mathfrak{s}^{-1}(0), ev_0)$$

is contained in $C_1(L; \mathbb{Q})$ for any $P_i \in \mathcal{X}_1(L)$, by taking appropriate triangulation of $\mathfrak{s}^{-1}(0)$.

Proposition 3.5.2 also asserts that the multisections $\mathfrak{s}$ are compatible in the compactification of $\mathcal{M}_{k+1}^{\mathrm{main}}((L, J), \beta; \vec{P})$. We then defined

$$\mathfrak{m}_{k,\beta}(P_1, \cdots, P_k) = \mathcal{M}_{k+1}^{\mathrm{main}}((L, J), \beta; \vec{P})^{\mathfrak{s}}.$$

To specify the choices of J and $\mathfrak{s}$ we write $\mathfrak{m}_{k,\beta}^{J,\mathfrak{s}}$. These maps define a structure of filtered A_∞ algebra on $C_1(L; \Lambda_{0,nov})$.

We make similar choices for L', J', and obtain a countably set of smooth singular simplices $\mathcal{X}_2(L')$ which generates a subcomplex $C_2(L'; \mathbb{Q})$ and a moduli space $\mathcal{M}_{k+1}^{\mathrm{main}}((L', J'), \beta; \vec{P}')^{\mathfrak{s}'}$ for $P_i' \in \mathcal{X}_2(L')$. It induces a structure of filtered A_∞ algebra on $C_2(L'; \Lambda_{0,nov})$. We denote it by $\mathfrak{m}_{k,\beta}^{J',\mathfrak{s}'}$.

We recall that we chose $C_1(L; \mathbb{Q})$ and $C_2(L'; \mathbb{Q})$ so that their cohomology groups are isomorphic to the cohomology groups of L and L' respectively.

THEOREM 4.6.1. *There exists a countable set of smooth singular simplices $\mathcal{X}_3(L')$ which generates a subcomplex $C_3(L'; \mathbb{Q})$ of $S(L'; \mathbb{Q})$, a structure of filtered A_∞ algebra $\mathfrak{m}_{k,\beta}^{J',\mathfrak{s}''}$ on $C_3(L'; \Lambda_{0,nov})$, and a gapped filtered A_∞ homomorphism*

$$\mathfrak{f}: C_1(L; \Lambda_{0,nov}) \to C_3(L'; \Lambda_{0,nov})$$

with the following properties:

(4.6.2.1) $\mathfrak{s}''$ *is a system of multisections on $\mathcal{M}_{k+1}^{\mathrm{main}}((L', J'), \beta; \vec{P})$ which is compatible at their boundaries. Here $P_i \in C_3(L'; \mathbb{Q})$.*

(4.6.2.2) $\mathcal{X}_3(L') \supset \mathcal{X}_2(L')$. *Moreover, if $P_i \in \mathcal{X}_2(L')$, then $\mathfrak{s}'' = \mathfrak{s}'$ on the moduli space $\mathcal{M}_{k+1}^{\mathrm{main}}((L', J'), \beta; \vec{P})$.*

(4.6.2.3) *The cohomology of $C_3(L'; \mathbb{Q})$ (with respect to the usual coboundary operator) is isomorphic to the cohomology of L'.*

(4.6.2.4) *The homomorphism*

$$(\bar{\mathfrak{f}}_1)_* = \psi^{-1*} : H^*(C_1(L; \mathbb{Q}), \overline{\mathfrak{m}}_1) \cong H^*(L; \mathbb{Q}) \to H^*(C_3(L'; \mathbb{Q}), \overline{\mathfrak{m}}_1) \cong H^*(L'; \mathbb{Q})$$

induced by $\mathfrak{f}$ coincides with the isomorphism ψ^{-1*} induced by the diffeomorphism ψ^{-1}.

COROLLARY 4.6.3. *The filtered A_∞ algebras $(C_1(L; \Lambda_{0,nov}), \mathfrak{m}_k^{J,\mathfrak{s}})$ is homotopy equivalent to $(C_2(L'; \Lambda_{0,nov}), \mathfrak{m}_k^{J',\mathfrak{s}'})$.*

Corollary 4.6.3 is a restatement of Theorem 4.1.1.

PROOF OF THEOREM 4.6.1 $\Rightarrow$ COROLLARY 4.6.3. By (4.6.2.4), $\mathfrak{f}$ is a weak homotopy equivalence. Hence by Theorem 4.2.45 it is a homotopy equivalence. On the other hand, by (4.6.2.2) the natural inclusion $C_2(L';\mathbb{Q}) \subset C_3(L';\mathbb{Q})$ induces a filtered A_∞ homomorphism. It is a homotopy equivalence by (4.6.2.3) and Theorem 4.2.45. Corollary 4.6.3 now follows from Corollary 4.2.44. $\square$

The proof of Theorem 4.6.1 occupies the rest of this subsection. Strictly speaking, we presume Proposition 4.6.14 holds in this subsection, which is related to how to choose the countable set $\mathcal{X}_3(L')$ and will be proved in Section 7.2. So presuming Proposition 4.6.14, we will complete the proof of Theorem 4.6.1 in this subsection. We start with preparing more notations.

Let $J^\psi = \psi_* J$. Since the set of compatible almost complex structures are contractible, we can find a family of compatible almost complex structures $\{J_\rho\}_\rho = \{J_\rho \mid \rho \in [0,1]\}$ such that

$$J_0 = J^\psi(= \psi_* J), \quad J_1 = J'.$$

We remark that the diffeomorphism $\psi : L \to L'$ induces an isomorphism between the vector spaces of smooth singular chains on L and ones on L'. We denote by $\mathcal{X}_1(L')$ and by $C_1(L';\mathbb{Q})$ the images of $\mathcal{X}_1(L)$ and $C_1(L;\mathbb{Q})$ by this isomorphism respectively. Using J^ψ we obtain a moduli space $\mathcal{M}_{k+1}^{main}((L',J^\psi),\beta;\vec{P}')$. If $P_i' = \psi(P_i)$, then obviously we have

$$(4.6.4) \qquad \mathcal{M}_{k+1}^{main}((L',J^\psi),\beta;\vec{P}') \cong \mathcal{M}_{k+1}^{main}((L,J),\beta;\vec{P})$$

as spaces with Kuranishi structures. Therefore a system of multisections $\mathfrak{s}$ on $\mathcal{M}_{k+1}^{main}((L,J),\beta;\vec{P})$ induces a system of multisections on $\mathcal{M}_{k+1}^{main}((L',J^\psi),\beta;\vec{P}')$. We denote it by $\mathfrak{s}^\psi$.

We thus obtain a structure of filtered A_∞ algebra on $C_1(L';\Lambda_{0,nov})$. We denote it by $\mathfrak{m}_k^{J^\psi,\mathfrak{s}^\psi}$. It follows from (4.6.4) that ψ induces (not only a homotopy equivalence but also) a canonical isomorphism

$$\psi_* : (C_1(L;\Lambda_{0,nov}),\mathfrak{m}_k^{J,\mathfrak{s}}) \longrightarrow (C_1(L';\Lambda_{0,nov}),\mathfrak{m}_k^{J^\psi,\mathfrak{s}^\psi})$$

of filtered A_∞ algebras.

REMARK 4.6.5. By the discussion above we may replace $L, J, \mathfrak{s}$ by $L', J^\psi, \mathfrak{s}^\psi$ and may assume $\psi = id$ in the proof of Theorem 4.6.1. However we do not do so, since in the next subsection we show that the homotopy equivalence constructed in Theorem 4.6.1 is independent of the symplectic isotopy of ψ, where we need to consider a non-constant family of isomorphisms (4.6.4).

Now to construct $\mathfrak{f}$ in Theorem 4.6.1 we use another moduli space of bordered pseudo-holomorphic curves of genus zero. Here we need to consider the case where components are pseudo-holomorphic with respect to the compatible almost complex structure which may *vary* on the components. Defining such a moduli space is our next task.

Let $(\Sigma, \vec{z})$ be an element of $\mathcal{M}_{k+1}^{main}$. Let $\{\Sigma_\alpha \mid \alpha \in \mathfrak{A}\}$ be the set of the components of Σ. (When Σ has sphere bubbles, we include each of the tree of sphere bubbles to the disc component where it is rooted. In particular the boundary $\partial\Sigma_\alpha$ of each component Σ_α is S^1.) We define a partial order on $\mathfrak{A}$ as follows: Let

$\alpha_1, \alpha_2 \in \mathfrak{A}$, and let $\Sigma_{\alpha_1}, \Sigma_{\alpha_2}$ be the corresponding components of Σ. Let Σ_{α_0} be the component containing the 0-th marked point.

DEFINITION 4.6.6. We say $\alpha_1 \leq \alpha_2$ if every path joining Σ_{α_1} to Σ_{α_0} intersects with Σ_{α_2}.

It is easy to see that Definition 4.6.6 defines a partial order on $\mathfrak{A}$. (α_0 is maximum among α's.) Now we consider the system $((\Sigma, \vec{z}), (u_\alpha), (\rho_\alpha))$ with the following properties:

(4.6.7.1) $u_\alpha : (\Sigma_\alpha, \partial\Sigma_\alpha) \to (M', L')$ is J_{ρ_α} holomorphic.
(4.6.7.2) $\rho_\alpha \in [0, 1]$. If $\alpha_1 \leq \alpha_2$, then $\rho_{\alpha_1} \leq \rho_{\alpha_2}$.
(4.6.7.3) $((\Sigma, \vec{z}), (u_\alpha))$ is stable in the sense of Definition 2.1.24.
(4.6.7.4)   The homology class of u_α is $\beta(\alpha)$ and $\sum_{\alpha \in \mathfrak{A}} \beta(\alpha) = \beta$.
(4.6.7.5)   If $z \in \Sigma_\alpha \cap \Sigma_{\alpha'}$, then $u_\alpha(z) = u_{\alpha'}(z)$.

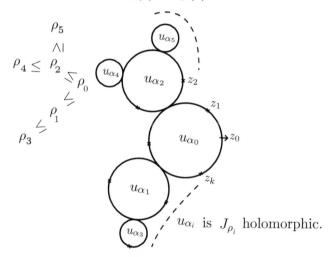

Figure 4.6.1

We identify two such systems if there exists an isomorphism between them in an obvious sense. We remark that Definition 4.6.6 is similar to the "time ordered product" which appears in quantum field theory.

DEFINITION 4.6.8. We define $\mathcal{M}_{k+1}^{\text{main}}(M', L', \{J_\rho\}_\rho : \beta; \text{top}(\rho))$ to be the set of all equivalence classes $((\Sigma, \vec{z}), (u_\alpha), (\rho_\alpha))$ satisfying (4.6.7).

Here and hereafter $\text{top}(\rho)$ in the symbol $\mathcal{M}_{k+1}^{\text{main}}(M', L', \{J_\rho\}_\rho : \beta; \text{top}(\rho))$ means that we are taking **time ordered product** with respect to the ρ-parameter in the sense mentioned above. We are considering family of almost complex structures parametrized by several variables and consider moduli spaces using it. In the later argument, we take either time ordered product as above or take fiber product at each time (**time-wise product**). For the latter case we use the notation $\text{twp}(s)$ to specify which kind of product we take there. These two moduli spaces are related to two methods to prove independence of Floer cohomologies of various choices, respectively. See the discussion right after (2.3.13) and also Subsection 7.2.14.

As usual, our moduli space $\mathcal{M}_{k+1}^{\text{main}}(M', L', \{J_\rho\}_\rho : \beta; \text{top}(\rho))$ has a Kuranishi structure with boundary. A sequence of elements $((\Sigma^{(i)}, \vec{z}^{(i)}), (u_\alpha^{(i)}), (\rho_\alpha^{(i)}))$ of

$\mathcal{M}_{k+1}^{\mathrm{main}}(M', L', \{J_\rho\}_\rho : \beta; \mathrm{top}(\rho))$ goes to the boundary in the sense of Kuranishi structure if one of the following occurs.

(4.6.9.1)   One of the components $\Sigma_\alpha^{(i)}$ splits into two components.
(4.6.9.2) $\lim_{i \to \infty} \rho_\alpha^{(i)} = \lim_{i \to \infty} \rho_{\alpha'}^{(i)}$, where $\Sigma_\alpha^{(i)} \cap \Sigma_{\alpha'}^{(i)} \neq \emptyset$.
(4.6.9.3) $\lim_{i \to \infty} \rho_\alpha^{(i)} = 0$.
(4.6.9.4) $\lim_{i \to \infty} \rho_\alpha^{(i)} = 1$.

(See Figure 4.6.2-4.6.5.)

Each of the boundary components corresponding to (4.6.9.1)–(4.6.9.4) is described as a fiber product of moduli spaces. (See Section A1.2 for the definition of the fiber product of spaces with Kuranishi structure.)

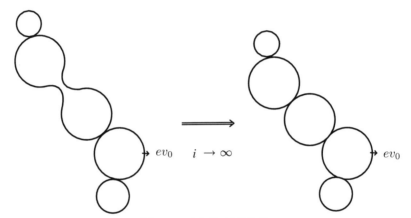

Figure 4.6.2 (4.6.9.1)

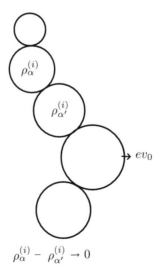

Figure 4.6.3 (4.6.9.2)

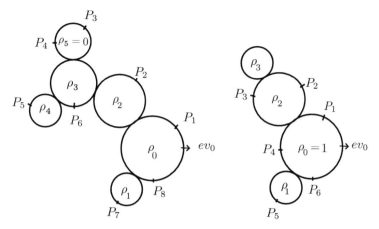

Figure 4.6.4 (4.6.9.3)   **Figure 4.6.5** (4.6.9.4)

We observe that (4.6.9.1) cancels with (4.6.9.2). Therefore we only need to consider (4.6.9.3) and (4.6.9.4). We remark that the moduli space describing (4.6.9.3) is a fiber product of the moduli spaces $\mathcal{M}^{\mathrm{main}}_{\ell+1}(M', L', \{J_\rho\}_\rho : \beta'; \mathrm{top}(\rho))$ for $\beta' \leq \beta$ and of $\mathcal{M}^{\mathrm{main}}_{\ell'+1}((L', J^\psi), \beta'')$, since $J_0 = J^\psi$. Similarly the moduli space describing (4.6.9.4) is a fiber product of the moduli spaces $\mathcal{M}^{\mathrm{main}}_{\ell+1}(M', L', \{J_\rho\}_\rho : \beta'; \mathrm{top}(\rho))$ for $\beta' \leq \beta$ and of $\mathcal{M}^{\mathrm{main}}_{\ell'+1}((L', J'), \beta'')$. (We go back to this point, which is the main idea of the proof of Theorem 4.6.1, at the end of the proof.)

We define

$$ev = (ev_1, \cdots, ev_k, ev_0) : \mathcal{M}^{\mathrm{main}}_{k+1}(M', L', \{J_\rho\}_\rho : \beta; \mathrm{top}(\rho)) \to L^k \times L'$$

by

$$\begin{cases} ev_0(((\Sigma, \vec{z}), (u_\alpha), (\rho_\alpha))) = u(z_0), \\ ev_i(((\Sigma, \vec{z}), (u_\alpha), (\rho_\alpha))) = \psi^{-1}(u(z_i)), \qquad (i = 1, \cdots, k). \end{cases}$$

DEFINITION 4.6.10. For $P_i \in \mathcal{X}_1(L)$, we define

$$\mathcal{M}^{\mathrm{main}}_{k+1}(M', L', \{J_\rho\}_\rho : \beta; \mathrm{top}(\rho); \vec{P})$$

$$= \mathcal{M}^{\mathrm{main}}_{k+1}(M', L', \{J_\rho\}_\rho : \beta; \mathrm{top}(\rho))_{(ev_1, \cdots, ev_k)} \times \left(\prod_{i=1}^{k} P_i \right),$$

where the right hand side is the fiber product over L^k.

Let $\mathfrak{s}^{\mathrm{top}(\rho)}$ be a system of multisections of the space $\mathcal{M}^{\mathrm{main}}_{k+1}(M', L', \{J_\rho\}_\rho : \beta; \mathrm{top}(\rho); \vec{P})$. (We will describe the properties which $\mathfrak{s}^{\mathrm{top}(\rho)}$ satisfies in Proposition 4.6.14 below.) We put

(4.6.11) $$\mathcal{M}^{\mathrm{main}}_{k+1}(M', L', \{J_\rho\}_\rho : \beta; \mathrm{top}(\rho); \vec{P})^{\mathfrak{s}^{\mathrm{top}(\rho)}} = ((\mathfrak{s}^{\mathrm{top}(\rho)})^{-1}(0), ev_0).$$

Here the right hand side is regarded as a singular chain by taking an appropriate triangulation. See Definition A1.28. (As for the orientation of this space, see Section 8.9.) We now define:

DEFINITION 4.6.12.

(4.6.13.1) $\mathfrak{f}_{1,\beta_0}(P) = \psi(P)$.

(4.6.13.2) $\mathfrak{f}_{k,\beta}(P_1, \cdots, P_k) = \mathcal{M}_{k+1}^{\mathrm{main}}(M', L', \{J_\rho\}_\rho : \beta; \mathrm{top}(\rho); \vec{P})^{\mathfrak{s}^{\mathrm{top}(\rho)}}$, for (k, β)
$\neq (1, \beta_0)$.

(4.6.13.3) $\mathfrak{f}_k(P_1, \cdots, P_k) = \sum_\beta \mathfrak{f}_{k,\beta}(P_1, \cdots, P_k) \otimes T^{E(\beta)} e^{\mu_L(\beta)/2}$.

We remark that the set of β for which

$$\mathcal{M}_{k+1}^{\mathrm{main}}(M', L', \{J_\rho\}_\rho : \beta; \mathrm{top}(\rho)) \neq \emptyset$$

and $E(\beta) < E_0$ is finite for any E_0 by the Gromov compactness. Therefore
$\mathfrak{f}_k(P_1, \cdots, P_k)$ is well defined and $\mathfrak{f}$ is gapped.

In order to prove Theorem 4.6.1 we need to clarify where the right hand side
of (4.6.13) belongs. This is related to the choice of the countable set $\mathcal{X}_3(L')$. We
will prove this point in detail in Subsection 7.2.9 (see Proposition 7.2.100). Now
we can state the properties we need for $\mathfrak{s}^{\mathrm{top}(\rho)}$.

PROPOSITION 4.6.14. *We can find* $\mathcal{X}_3(L')$, $\mathfrak{s}''$ *and* $\mathfrak{s}^{\mathrm{top}(\rho)}$ *with the following
properties:*

(4.6.15.1)   (4.6.2.1), (4.6.2.2), (4.6.2.3) *are satisfied.*
(4.6.15.2)   *For any* $P_i \in \mathcal{X}_1(L)$, *the* $\mathbb{Q}$ *chain* $\mathfrak{f}_{k,\beta}(P_1, \cdots, P_k)$ *defined by* (4.6.13)
is in $C_3(L', \mathbb{Q})$. *In other words,* $\mathfrak{f}_k(P_1, \cdots, P_k) \in C_3(L', \Lambda_{0,nov})$. *In particular,*
$\psi(P) \in C_3(L', \Lambda_{0,nov})$ *for each* $P \in \mathcal{X}_1(L)$.
(4.6.15.3) $\mathfrak{s}^{\mathrm{top}(\rho)}$ *is compatible with* $\mathfrak{s}^\psi$ *at the boundary of* $\mathcal{M}_{k+1}^{\mathrm{main}}(M', L', \{J_\rho\}_\rho :
\beta; \mathrm{top}(\rho); \vec{P})$ *corresponding to* (4.6.9.3).
(4.6.15.4) $\mathfrak{s}^{\mathrm{top}(\rho)}$ *is compatible with* $\mathfrak{s}''$ *at the boundary of* $\mathcal{M}_{k+1}^{\mathrm{main}}(M', L', \{J_\rho\}_\rho :
\beta; \mathrm{top}(\rho); \vec{P})$ *corresponding to* (4.6.9.4).

We will prove Proposition 4.6.14 in Subsection 7.2.9. Precisely speaking, in
Subsection 7.2.9 we fix E_0 and prove Proposition 4.6.14 only for β with $\omega[\beta] \leq
E_0$. It defines filtered $A_{n,K}$ homomorphism (in the sense defined in Subsection
7.2.6) for any n, K. Then using homological algebra we will construct filtered A_∞
homomorphism in Subsection 7.2.11. Compare this also with Remark 3.5.13.

Here we complete the proof of Theorem 4.6.1 assuming Proposition 4.6.14. For
this purpose we only need to check that $\mathfrak{f}$ is a filtered A_∞ homomorphism.

Let $P_j \in \mathcal{X}_1(L)$. We put $P_j = (|P_j|, f_j)$, where $|P_j|$ is a simplex and $f_j : |P_j| \to
L$ is a smooth map. We consider the boundary of the chains $\mathfrak{f}_{k,\beta}(P_1, \cdots, P_k)$. Let
$((\Sigma^{(i)}, \vec{z}^{(i)}), (u_\alpha^{(i)}), (\rho_\alpha^{(i)}))$ be a sequence and $x_j^{(i)} \in |P_j|$ such that

$$ev_j((\Sigma^{(i)}, \vec{z}^{(i)}), (u_\alpha^{(i)}), (\rho_\alpha^{(i)})) = f_j(x_j^{(i)})$$

for $j = 1, \cdots, k$. We thus have a sequence

$$(((\Sigma^{(i)}, \vec{z}^{(i)}), (u_\alpha^{(i)}), (\rho_\alpha^{(i)})); x_1^{(i)}, \cdots, x_k^{(i)})$$

of elements of the moduli space $\mathcal{M}_{k+1}^{\mathrm{main}}(M', L', \{J_\rho\}_\rho : \beta; \mathrm{top}(\rho); \vec{P})$. Now this
sequence will go to the boundary if one of the following happens.

(4.6.16.1)   (4.6.9.1) occurs.
(4.6.16.2)   (4.6.9.2) occurs.
(4.6.16.3)   (4.6.9.3) occurs.

(4.6.16.4)   (4.6.9.4) occurs.

(4.6.16.5)   One of $x_j^{(i)}$ goes to the boundary of P_j.

(4.6.16.1) cancels with (4.6.16.2) as we remarked before. (4.6.16.3) corresponds to the sum

$$
(4.6.17) \qquad \sum_{\ell,m} \sum_{\beta_1,\beta_2 \neq 0; \beta=\beta_1+\beta_2} \mathfrak{f}_{k+\ell-m,\beta_1}(P_1, \cdots, P_{\ell-1},
$$
$$
\mathfrak{m}_{m-\ell+1,\beta_2}^{J,\mathfrak{s}}(P_\ell, \cdots, P_m), P_{m+1}, \cdots, P_k).
$$

For example, Figure 4.6.4 corresponds

$$
\mathfrak{f}_7(P_1, P_2, \mathfrak{m}_2(P_3, P_4), P_5, P_6, P_7, P_8).
$$

(4.6.16.4) corresponds to the sum

$$
(4.6.18) \qquad \sum_{m,1=\ell_1 \leq \ell_2 \cdots \leq \ell_m = k+1} \sum_{\beta_1,\beta_{2,i} \neq 0; \beta=\beta_1+\sum_{i=1}^{m-1}\beta_{2,i}}
$$
$$
\mathfrak{m}_{m-1,\beta_1}^{J',\mathfrak{s}'}\Big(\mathfrak{f}_{\ell_2-\ell_1,\beta_{2,1}}(P_1, \cdots, P_{\ell_2-1}), \cdots \mathfrak{f}_{\ell_{i+1}-\ell_i,\beta_{2,i}}(P_{\ell_i}, \cdots
$$
$$
\cdots, P_{\ell_{i+1}-1}), \mathfrak{f}_{\ell_m-\ell_{m-1},\beta_{2,m-1}}(P_{\ell_{m-1}}, \cdots, P_{\ell_m-1})\Big).
$$

For example Figure 4.6.5 corresponds to

$$
\mathfrak{m}_5(\psi(P_1), \mathfrak{f}_2(P_2, P_3), \psi(P_4), \mathfrak{f}_1(P_5), \psi(P_6)).
$$

(We remark that $\psi(P) = \mathfrak{f}_{1,\beta_0}(P)$.)

(4.6.16.5) corresponds to the sum

$$
(4.6.19) \qquad \sum_j \mathfrak{f}_{k,\beta}(P_1, \cdots, \overline{\mathfrak{m}}_1(P_j), \cdots, P_k).
$$

Thus we find that $\overline{\mathfrak{m}}_1(\mathfrak{f}_{k,\beta}(P_1, \cdots, P_k))$ is sum of (4.6.17), (4.6.18) and (4.6.19). (We do not discuss sign here. The sign is discussed in Section 8.9.) This implies that $\mathfrak{f}$ is a filtered A_∞ homomorphism. $\qquad \square$

REMARK 4.6.20. In the discussion above, we need to perturb the moduli space $\mathcal{M}_{k+1}^{main}(M', L', \{J_\rho\}_\rho : \beta; \mathrm{top}(\rho); \vec{P})$ by our multisection and use the perturbed moduli space $\mathcal{M}_{k+1}^{main}(M', L', \{J_\rho\}_\rho : \beta; \mathrm{top}(\rho); \vec{P})^\mathfrak{s}$. However the compatibility of the multisections asserted in Proposition 4.6.14 is designed so that the argument above goes through including the perturbations induced by $\mathfrak{s}^{\mathrm{top}(\rho)}$ and etc.

4.6.2. Homotopies between A_∞ homomorphisms. The purpose of this subsection is to prove that the homotopy class of the filtered A_∞ homomorphism $\mathfrak{g}$ obtained in Corollary 4.6.3 is independent of various choices we made and of a symplectic isotopy of ψ. Namely we will prove Theorem 4.1.2. We continue to use the notations in the last subsection. To specify the dependence of $\mathfrak{f}$ on $\psi, \{J_\rho\}_\rho$ and $\mathfrak{s}^{\mathrm{top}(\rho)}$ we write $\mathfrak{f}^{\psi,\{J_\rho\}_\rho,\mathfrak{s}^{\mathrm{top}(\rho)}}$ in place of $\mathfrak{f}$. We have constructed the filtered A_∞ homomorphism

$$
(4.6.21) \qquad \mathfrak{f}^{\psi,\{J_\rho\}_\rho,\mathfrak{s}^{\mathrm{top}(\rho)}} : (C_1(L; \Lambda_{0,nov}), \mathfrak{m}_k^{J,\mathfrak{s}}) \to (C_3(L'; \Lambda_{0,nov}), \mathfrak{m}_k^{J',\mathfrak{s}''})
$$

in the previous subsection. We compose this with the homotopy inverse of the filtered A_∞ homomorphism

$$(C_2(L'; \Lambda_{0,nov}), \mathfrak{m}_k^{J', \mathfrak{s}'}) \to (C_3(L'; \Lambda_{0,nov}), \mathfrak{m}_k^{J', \mathfrak{s}''})$$

induced by the natural inclusion $C_2(L'; \mathbb{Q}) \subset C_3(L'; \mathbb{Q})$ (see (4.6.2.2)) and obtain

$$(4.6.22) \qquad \mathfrak{g}^{\psi, \{J_\rho\}_\rho, \mathfrak{s}^{\mathrm{top}(\rho)}} : (C_1(L; \Lambda_{0,nov}), \mathfrak{m}_k^{J, \mathfrak{s}}) \to (C_2(L'; \Lambda_{0,nov}), \mathfrak{m}_k^{J', \mathfrak{s}'}).$$

$\mathfrak{g}^{\psi, \{J_\rho\}_\rho, \mathfrak{s}^{\mathrm{top}(\rho)}}$ gives a homotopy equivalence. Hereafter in this subsection we write $\mathfrak{s}''_{s=0}$, $\mathfrak{s}^{\mathrm{top}(\rho)}_{s=0}$ in place of $\mathfrak{s}''$, $\mathfrak{s}^{\mathrm{top}(\rho)}$. We also write $C_3^{s=0}(L'; \Lambda_{0,nov})$, $\chi_3^{s=0}(L')$. We write $\mathfrak{g}^{\psi, \{J_\rho^{s=0}\}_\rho, \mathfrak{s}^{\mathrm{top}(\rho)}_{s=0}}_{s=0}$, $\mathfrak{f}^{\psi, \{J_\rho^{s=0}\}_\rho, \mathfrak{s}^{\mathrm{top}(\rho)}_{s=0}}_{s=0}$, also.

Let $\psi_s : M \to M'$, $s \in [0, 1]$ be a symplectic isotopy with $\psi_0 = \psi$, $\psi_1 = \psi'$. (In order to clarify which we are considering on the source or the target space of ψ_s, we denote the target space by M' instead of M.) We write $\psi = \{\psi_s\}_s$. We assume

$$(4.6.23) \qquad\qquad\qquad \psi_s(L) = L'$$

for each s. We apply the construction of the last subsection to $\psi_1 = \psi'$ in place of $\psi_0 = \psi$ and obtain the following:

(4.6.24.1) $\{J_\rho^{s=1}\}_\rho$, a homotopy of compatible almost complex structures on M' from J^{ψ_1} to J'.

(4.6.24.2) $\mathcal{X}_3^{s=1}(L')$, a countable set of smooth singular chains which generates a subcomplex $C_3^{s=1}(L', \mathbb{Q})$ of $S(L')$.

(4.6.24.3) $\mathfrak{s}''_{s=1}$, $\mathfrak{s}^{\mathrm{top}(\rho)}_{s=1}$. Here $\mathfrak{s}^{\mathrm{top}(\rho)}_{s=1}$ is a system of multisections of the moduli spaces $\mathcal{M}_{k+1}^{\mathrm{main}}(M', L, \{J_\rho^{s=1}\}_\rho : \beta; \mathrm{top}(\rho); \vec{P})$ and $\mathfrak{s}''_{s=1}$ is a system of multisections of $\mathcal{M}_{k+1}^{\mathrm{main}}((L', J'), \beta; \vec{P}')$ for $P_i' \in \mathcal{X}_3^{s=1}(L')$.

They satisfy (4.6.15) and hence induce filtered A_∞ homomorphisms. We denote them by

$$\mathfrak{f}_{s=1}^{\psi_1, \{J_\rho^{s=1}\}_\rho, \mathfrak{s}^{\mathrm{top}(\rho)}_{s=1}} : (C_1(L; \Lambda_{0,nov}), \mathfrak{m}_k^{J, \mathfrak{s}}) \to (C_3^{s=1}(L'; \Lambda_{0,nov}), \mathfrak{m}_k^{J', \mathfrak{s}''_{s=1}})$$

and

$$\mathfrak{g}_{s=1}^{\psi_1, \{J_\rho^{s=1}\}_\rho, \mathfrak{s}^{\mathrm{top}(\rho)}_{s=1}} : (C_1(L; \Lambda_{0,nov}), \mathfrak{m}_k^{J, \mathfrak{s}}) \to (C_2(L'; \Lambda_{0,nov}), \mathfrak{m}_k^{J', \mathfrak{s}'}).$$

Now our main result of this subsection is:

THEOREM 4.6.25. $\mathfrak{g}_{s=0}^{\psi_0, \{J_\rho^{s=0}\}_\rho, \mathfrak{s}^{\mathrm{top}(\rho)}_{s=0}}$ is homotopic to $\mathfrak{g}_{s=1}^{\psi_1, \{J_\rho^{s=1}\}_\rho, \mathfrak{s}^{\mathrm{top}(\rho)}_{s=1}}$.

PROOF. We use a homotopy between two homotopies $\{J_\rho^{s=1}\}_\rho$, $\{J_\rho^{s=0}\}_\rho$ of compatible almost complex structures. Namely we consider a two-parameter family $\{J_{\rho,s}\}_{\rho,s}$ of compatible almost complex structures such that

(4.6.26.1) $\{J_{\rho,0}\}_\rho$ coincides with the family $\{J_\rho^{s=0}\}_\rho$.

(4.6.26.2) $\{J_{\rho,1}\}_\rho$ coincides with the family $\{J_\rho^{s=1}\}_\rho$.

(4.6.26.3) $J_{0,s} = (\psi_s)_* J$ for any $s \in [0.1]$.

(4.6.26.4) $J_{1,s} = J'$ for any $s \in [0, 1]$.

The contractibility of the set of compatible almost complex structures implies that there exists such a homotopy $\{J_{\rho,s}\}_{\rho,s}$. We also denote this two parameter family by $\{J_{\rho,s}\}_{\rho,s}$.

For each fixed s, we have a family of compatible almost complex structures $\rho \mapsto J_{\rho,s}$, which we denote by $\{J_{\rho,s}\}_\rho$. Using $\{J_{\rho,s}\}_\rho$ we obtain moduli spaces $\mathcal{M}_{k+1}^{\mathrm{main}}(M', L', \{J_{\rho,s}\}_\rho : \beta; \mathrm{top}(\rho))$. We put

(4.6.27)
$$\mathcal{M}_{k+1}^{\mathrm{main}}(M', L', \{J_{\rho,s}\}_{\rho,s} : \beta; \mathrm{top}(\rho), \mathrm{twp}(s))$$
$$= \bigcup_{s \in [0,1]} \{s\} \times \mathcal{M}_{k+1}^{\mathrm{main}}(M', L', \{J_{\rho,s}\}_\rho : \beta; \mathrm{top}(\rho)).$$

We define evaluation maps

$$ev_0 : \mathcal{M}_{k+1}^{\mathrm{main}}(M', L', \{J_{\rho,s}\}_{\rho,s} : \beta; \mathrm{top}(\rho), \mathrm{twp}(s)) \to L'$$
$$ev_i : \mathcal{M}_{k+1}^{\mathrm{main}}(M', L', \{J_{\rho,s}\}_{\rho,s} : \beta; \mathrm{top}(\rho), \mathrm{twp}(s)) \to L, \quad i = 1, \cdots, k$$

and

$$ev_{\mathrm{s}} : \mathcal{M}_{k+1}^{\mathrm{main}}(M', L', \{J_{\rho,s}\}_{\rho,s} : \beta; \mathrm{top}(\rho), \mathrm{twp}(s)) \to [0,1]$$

as follows.

Let $((\Sigma, \vec{z}), (u_\alpha), (\rho_\alpha)) \in \mathcal{M}_{k+1}^{\mathrm{main}}(M', L', \{J_{\rho,s}\}_\rho : \beta; \mathrm{top}(\rho))$. We put

(4.6.28.1) $\quad ev_0(((\Sigma, \vec{z}), (u_\alpha), (\rho_\alpha)), s) = u_{\alpha_0}(z_0),$
(4.6.28.2) $\quad ev_i(((\Sigma, \vec{z}), (u_\alpha), (\rho_\alpha)), s) = \psi_s^{-1}(u_{\alpha_i}(z_i)),$
(4.6.28.3) $\quad ev_{\mathrm{s}}(((\Sigma, \vec{z}), (u_\alpha), (\rho_\alpha)), s) = s.$

For $P_i \in \mathcal{X}_1(L)$ $(i = 1, \cdots, k)$ we use ev_i to define

(4.6.29)
$$\mathcal{M}_{k+1}^{\mathrm{main}}(M', L', \{J_{\rho,s}\}_{\rho,s} : \beta; \mathrm{top}(\rho), \mathrm{twp}(s); \vec{P})$$
$$= \mathcal{M}_{k+1}^{\mathrm{main}}(M', L', \{J_{\rho,s}\}_{\rho,s} : \beta; \mathrm{top}(\rho), \mathrm{twp}(s))_{(ev_1, \cdots, ev_k)} \times \left(\prod_{i=1}^{k} P_i \right).$$

The idea of the proof of Theorem 4.6.25 is to use these moduli spaces to construct a filtered A_∞ homomorphism from $(C_1(L'; \Lambda_{0,nov}), \mathfrak{m}_k^{J,s})$ to a filtered A_∞ algebra defined on the module of smooth singular chains on $[0,1] \times L'$. To define this filtered A_∞ algebra we need more notations.

Note we will use homomorphisms $\mathrm{Eval}_{s=s_0} : C([0,1] \times L') \to C(L')$ for appropriate subcomplexes of singular chain complexes on $[0,1] \times L'$ and on L'. The homomorphism $\mathrm{Eval}_{s=s_0}$ induces a homomorphism $H^*([0,1] \times L') \to H^*(L')$ which coincides with the one induced by the inclusion $L' \to \{s_0\} \times L' \subset [0,1] \times L'$. We remark that we are working with cohomology groups rather than homology groups. We use singular *chains* to represent elements of *cohomology* group. In other words, we use Poincaré duality. The Poincaré dual to the homomorphism $H^*([0,1] \times L') \to H^*(L')$ is the composition

$$H_*([0,1] \times L'; \{0,1\} \times L') \to H_{*-1}(\{0,1\} \times L') \to H_{*-1}(\{s_0\} \times L')$$

of the connecting homomorphism $H_*([0,1] \times L'; \{0,1\} \times L') \to H_{*-1}(\{0,1\} \times L')$ and the projection to the $H_{*-1}(\{s_0\} \times L')$ factor. We are going to define chain complexes $C([0,1] \times L')$, $C(L')$ so that the connecting homomorphism can be defined *in the chain level*.

From now on, we use the script letter $\mathcal{P}$ for singular simplices on $[0,1] \times L'$ and roman letter P, P' for singular simplices on L, L'.

DEFINITION 4.6.30. Let $\mathcal{P} = (|\mathcal{P}|, f)$ $(f : |\mathcal{P}| \to [0,1] \times L')$ be a smooth singular simplex. We say $\mathcal{P}$ is *adapted* if the following condition are satisfied for $s_0 = 0, 1$.

(4.6.31.1) $f^{-1}(\{s_0\} \times L') \cap |\mathcal{P}|$ is either $|\mathcal{P}|$, empty or consists of a single face (of arbitrary codimension).

(4.6.31.2)   If $f^{-1}(\{0\} \times L') \cap |\mathcal{P}|$ is nonempty then $|\mathcal{P}| \subset [0, 1/3) \times L'$. If $f^{-1}(\{1\} \times L') \cap |\mathcal{P}|$ is nonempty then $|\mathcal{P}| \subset (2/3, 1] \times L'$.

(4.6.31.3)   If Δ_a^m is a face of $|\mathcal{P}|$ and $\Delta_b^{m'}$ be another face containing Δ_a^m. We assume $x \in \Delta_a^m \subset f^{-1}(\{s_0\} \times L')$ and $\Delta_b^{m'}$ is not contained in $f^{-1}(\{s_0\} \times L')$. Then, for any vector $N \in T_x \Delta_b^{m'} \setminus T_x(\partial \Delta_b^{m'})$, the $[0,1]$ component of $f_*(N)$ is nonzero.

A singular simplex of dimension m on $[0,1] \times L'$ is regarded as a cochain of degree $d = 1 + \dim L' - m$. We write $S_+^d([0,1] \times L')$ the abelian group of adapted cochains of degree d. It is easy to see that it is a cochain complex. The smooth singular chain complex $S(\{0,1\} \times L')$ is a subcomplex of it. We define

$$S([0,1] \times L') = \frac{S_+([0,1] \times L')}{S(\{0,1\} \times L')}.$$

$S([0,1] \times L')$ is free on the basis of singular simplices which satisfy Condition 4.6.30 and which are not contained in $\{0,1\} \times L'$.

We define $\mathrm{Eval}_{s=s_0} : S([0,1] \times L') \to S(L')$ as follows. (Here $S(L')$ is the smooth singular chain complex of L'.) If $f^{-1}(\{s_0\} \times L') \cap |\mathcal{P}|$ is not codimension one in $|\mathcal{P}|$, then

(4.6.32.1) $\mathrm{Eval}_{s=s_0}(\mathcal{P}) = 0.$

If $f^{-1}(\{s_0\} \times L') \cap |\mathcal{P}|$ is codimension one in $|\mathcal{P}|$, then

(4.6.32.2) $\mathrm{Eval}_{s=s_0}(\mathcal{P}) = \pm(f^{-1}(\{s_0\} \times L') \cap |\mathcal{P}|, f).$

See Subsection 7.2.10 for the sign $\pm$. In Lemma 7.2.136 Section 7.2, we will prove that $\mathrm{Eval}_{s=s_0} : S([0,1] \times L') \to S(L')$ is a cochain map and is a cochain homotopy equivalence.

We also consider the following condition for $\mathcal{P} \in S([0,1] \times L')$.

CONDITION 4.6.33. $\mathrm{Eval}_{s=s_0}(\mathcal{P}) \in C_3^{s=s_0}(L', \mathbb{Q})$.

We next define $\mathrm{Incl}_{1,\beta_0} : S(L') \to S([0,1] \times L')$ by the following formula.

$$\mathrm{Incl}_{1,\beta_0}(|P|, f) = ([0,1] \times |P|, id \times f),$$

where we take an appropriate prism type simplicial decomposition of $[0,1] \times |P|$ to regard the right hand side as a singular chain. (See Subsection 7.2.10 for detail.)

We will construct a structure of filtered A_∞ algebra on a cochain complex which is generated by countably many adapted smooth singular simplices. For this purpose we use another parametrized version of moduli space of pseudo-holomorphic discs. For the family $\{J_{\rho,s}\}_{\rho,s}$ satisfying (4.6.26), we put $\rho = 1$. Then we have a family $\{J_{1,s}\}_s$ of compatible almost complex structures $J_{1,s}$, $s \in [0,1]$. From

(4.6.26.4) this is a constant family for $\rho = 1$. Namely $J_{1,s} = J'$ for each s. Using $\{J_{1,s}\}_s$, we obtain the moduli space $\mathcal{M}_{k+1}^{\mathrm{main}}((L', J_{1,s}), \beta)$. We now put

(4.6.34)
$$
\begin{aligned}
&\mathcal{M}_{k+1}^{\mathrm{main}}(M', L', \{J_{1,s}\}_s : \beta; \mathrm{twp}(s)) \\
&= \bigcup_{s \in [0,1]} \{s\} \times \mathcal{M}_{k+1}^{\mathrm{main}}((L', J_{1,s}), \beta) = [0,1] \times \mathcal{M}_{k+1}^{\mathrm{main}}((L', J'), \beta).
\end{aligned}
$$

We remark that we have defined $\mathcal{M}_{k+1}^{\mathrm{main}}(M', L', \{J_{1,s}\}_s : \beta; \mathrm{twp}(s))$ using the moduli spaces $\mathcal{M}_{k+1}^{\mathrm{main}}((L', J_{1,s}), \beta)$ "time-wise". So this is *different* from the moduli space $\mathcal{M}_{k+1}^{\mathrm{main}}(M', L', \{J_{1,s}\}_s : \beta; \mathrm{top}(s))$ for the family $s \mapsto J_{1,s}$. Namely, $\mathcal{M}_{k+1}^{\mathrm{main}}(M', L', \{J_{1,s}\}_s : \beta; \mathrm{top}(s))$ is a moduli space of pseudo-holomorphic maps from semi stable genus zero bordered Riemann surface with respect to the almost complex structure *depending on the component*. But an element of the moduli space $\mathcal{M}_{k+1}^{\mathrm{main}}(M', L', \{J_{1,s}\}_s : \beta; \mathrm{twp}(s))$ is a pseudo-holomorphic map from a semi stable bordered Riemann surface with respect to some $J_{1,s}$ where s is *independent of the component*.

We can define evaluation maps

$$
ev_i : \mathcal{M}_{k+1}^{\mathrm{main}}(M', L', \{J_{1,s}\}_s : \beta; \mathrm{twp}(s)) \to L', \qquad \text{for } i = 0, \cdots, k,
$$
$$
ev_{\mathrm{s}} : \mathcal{M}_{k+1}^{\mathrm{main}}(M', L', \{J_{1,s}\}_s : \beta; \mathrm{twp}(s)) \to [0,1],
$$

by

(4.6.35.1) $ev_i((\Sigma, \vec{z}), (u_\alpha)), s) = u_{\alpha_i}(z_i),$

(4.6.35.2) $ev_{\mathrm{s}}((\Sigma, \vec{z}), (u_\alpha)), s) = s.$

(Here we note that ev_i for $i = 0, \cdots, k$ maps to L'.) We put $ev_i^+ = (ev_{\mathrm{s}}, ev_i)$. For $\mathcal{P}_i \in \overline{S}([0,1] \times L')$, $(i = 1, \cdots, k)$, we define

$$
\begin{aligned}
&\mathcal{M}_{k+1}^{\mathrm{main}}(M', L', \{J_{1,s}\}_s : \beta; \mathrm{twp}(s); \vec{\mathcal{P}}) \\
&= \mathcal{M}_{k+1}^{\mathrm{main}}(M', L', \{J_{1,s}\}_s : \beta; \mathrm{twp}(s))_{(ev_1^+, \cdots, ev_k^+)} \times \left(\prod_{i=1}^{k} \mathcal{P}_i \right).
\end{aligned}
$$

Here the fiber product is taken on $([0,1] \times L')^k$. The space $\mathcal{M}_{k+1}^{\mathrm{main}}(M', L', \{J_{1,s}\}_s : \beta; \mathrm{twp}(s); \vec{\mathcal{P}})$ has a Kuranishi structure. If we take a multisection $\mathfrak{s}^{\mathrm{twp}(s)}$ transversal to 0, we obtain

$$
\mathcal{M}_{k+1}^{\mathrm{main}}(M', L', \{J_{1,s}\}_s : \beta; \mathrm{twp}(s); \vec{\mathcal{P}})^{\mathfrak{s}} = ((\mathfrak{s}^{\mathrm{twp}(s)})^{-1}(0), ev_0^+).
$$

We can take a simplicial decomposition of $(\mathfrak{s}^{\mathrm{twp}(s)})^{-1}(0)$ so that

$$
((\mathfrak{s}^{\mathrm{twp}(s)})^{-1}(0), ev_0^+)
$$

can be regarded as a singular chain in $[0,1] \times L'$. Moreover we may choose our simplicial decomposition so that each singular simplex of $(\mathfrak{s}^{\mathrm{twp}(s)})^{-1}(0)$ is adapted. (See Subsection 7.2.10.)

We can easily prove the following:

(4.6.36.1) $\deg \mathcal{M}_{k+1}^{\mathrm{main}}(M', L', \{J_{1,s}\}_s; \beta; \mathrm{twp}(s); \vec{\mathcal{P}})^{\mathfrak{s}} = 2 - k + \sum \deg \mathcal{P}_i - \mu(\beta),$

where deg is the codimension (of the chain), which is equal to the cohomology degree. We also remark that the boundary of the moduli space

$$\mathcal{M}_{k+1}^{\mathrm{main}}(M', L', \{J_{1,s}\}_s; \beta; \mathrm{twp}(s); \vec{\mathcal{P}})^{\mathfrak{s}}$$

can be described as a fiber product of similar moduli spaces.

On the other hand, if we take a multisection $\mathfrak{s}^{\mathrm{top}(\rho),\mathrm{twp}(s)}$ on the space

$$\mathcal{M}_{k+1}^{\mathrm{main}}(M', L', \{J_{\rho,s}\}_{\rho,s} : \beta; \mathrm{top}(\rho), \mathrm{twp}(s); \vec{P})$$

transversal 0, we obtain

$$\mathcal{M}_{k+1}^{\mathrm{main}}(M', L', \{J_{\rho,s}\}_{\rho,s} : \beta; \mathrm{top}(\rho), \mathrm{twp}(s); \vec{P})^{\mathfrak{s}} = ((\mathfrak{s}^{\mathrm{top}(\rho),\mathrm{twp}(s)})^{-1}(0), ev_0^+).$$

We can take a simplicial decomposition of $(\mathfrak{s}^{\mathrm{top}(\rho),\mathrm{twp}(s)})^{-1}(0)$ so that the pair $((\mathfrak{s}^{\mathrm{top}(\rho),\mathrm{twp}(s)})^{-1}(0), ev_0^+)$ can be regarded as a singular chain in $[0,1] \times L'$. Moreover we may choose our simplicial decomposition such that each singular simplex of $(\mathfrak{s}^{\mathrm{twp}(s)})^{-1}(0)$ satisfies Condition 4.6.30. (See Subsection 7.2.10.) We can easily calculate its degree as:

(4.6.36.2)
$$\begin{aligned} &\deg \mathcal{M}_{k+1}^{\mathrm{main}}(M', L', \{J_{\rho,s}\}_{\rho,s} : \beta; \mathrm{top}(\rho), \mathrm{twp}(s); \vec{P})^{\mathfrak{s}} \\ &= 3 - k + \sum \deg P_i - \mu(\beta). \end{aligned}$$

Now the main result we need to construct a filtered A_∞ structure on a countably generated subcomplex of $S([0,1] \times L'; \partial)$ is the following. The proof will be given in Subsection 7.2.10. Strictly speaking we prove the $A_{n,K}$ version of Proposition 4.6.37 (that is Propositions 7.2.160 and 7.2.162) in Subsection 7.2.10 and use it to prove the A_∞ version in Subsections 7.2.11-7.2.13.

PROPOSITION 4.6.37. *There exist a countable set $\mathcal{X}([0,1] \times L')$ of singular simplices which generates a subcomplex $C([0,1] \times L')$ of $S([0,1] \times L')$ and a system of multisections $\mathfrak{s}^{\mathrm{twp}(s)}$, $\mathfrak{s}^{\mathrm{top}(\rho),\mathrm{twp}(s)}$ transversal to 0 with the following properties:*

(4.6.38.1)   *Every element of $\mathcal{X}([0,1] \times L')$ is adapted and satisfies Condition 4.6.33. Elements of $\mathcal{X}([0,1] \times L')$ are not contained in $S(\{0,1\} \times L')$.*
(4.6.38.2)   *If $\mathcal{P}_i \in \mathcal{X}([0,1] \times L')$, then*

$$\mathcal{M}_{k+1}^{\mathrm{main}}(M', L', \{J_{1,s}\}_s : \beta; \mathrm{twp}(s); \vec{\mathcal{P}})^{\mathfrak{s}} \in C([0,1] \times L').$$

(4.6.38.3)   *The system of multisections $\mathfrak{s}^{\mathrm{twp}(s)}$, $\mathfrak{s}^{\mathrm{top}(\rho),\mathrm{twp}(s)}$ are compatible at the boundaries of $\mathcal{M}_{k+1}^{\mathrm{main}}(M', L', \{J_{1,s}\}_s : \beta; \mathrm{twp}(s); \vec{\mathcal{P}})$ and $\mathcal{M}_{k+1}^{\mathrm{main}}(M', L', \{J_{\rho,s}\}_{\rho,s} : \beta; \mathrm{top}(\rho), \mathrm{twp}(s); \vec{P})^{\mathfrak{s}}$.*
(4.6.38.4)   *If $P \in \mathcal{X}_2(L')$, then $\mathrm{Incl}_{1,\beta_0}(P) \in C([0,1] \times L')$.*
(4.6.38.5)   *The inclusion $C([0,1] \times L') \to S([0,1] \times L')$ induces an isomorphism on the cohomology groups.*
(4.6.38.6)   *Let $\mathcal{P}_i \in C([0,1] \times L')$ and denote $\vec{\mathcal{P}} = (\mathcal{P}_1, \cdots, \mathcal{P}_k)$. We put $\mathcal{P}_i|_{s=0} = \mathrm{Eval}_{s=0}(\mathcal{P}_i)$ and $\vec{\mathcal{P}}|_{s=0} = (\mathcal{P}_1|_{s=0}, \cdots, \mathcal{P}_k|_{s=0})$. We then have*

$$\mathrm{Eval}_{s=0}(\mathcal{M}_{k+1}^{\mathrm{main}}(M', L', \{J_{1,s}\}_s : \beta; \mathrm{twp}(s); \vec{\mathcal{P}})^{\mathfrak{s}}) = \mathcal{M}_{k+1}^{\mathrm{main}}((M', L'), J' : \beta; \vec{\mathcal{P}}|_{s=0})^{\mathfrak{s}}.$$

If we put $\mathcal{P}_i|_{s=1} = \mathrm{Eval}_{s=1}(\mathcal{P}_i)$ and $\vec{\mathcal{P}}|_{s=1} = (\mathcal{P}_1|_{s=1}, \cdots, \mathcal{P}_k|_{s=1})$, then we have

$$\mathrm{Eval}_{s=1}(\mathcal{M}_{k+1}^{\mathrm{main}}(M', L', \{J_{1,s}\}_s : \beta; \mathrm{twp}(s); \vec{\mathcal{P}})^{\mathfrak{s}}) = \mathcal{M}_{k+1}^{\mathrm{main}}((M', L'), J' : \beta; \vec{\mathcal{P}}|_{s=1})^{\mathfrak{s}'}.$$

(In the above equalities, we recall that $J_{1,0} = J_{1,1} = J'$ from (4.6.26.4)).

(4.6.38.7)   *For $P_i \in C(L)$, we have*

$$\mathcal{M}_{k+1}^{\mathrm{main}}(M', L', \{J_{\rho,s}\}_{\rho,s} : \beta; \mathrm{top}(\rho), \mathrm{twp}(s); \vec{P})^{\mathfrak{s}} \in C([0,1] \times L').$$

(4.6.38.8)   *We can define*

$$\mathrm{Incl}_{k,\beta} : B_k(C(L')[1]) \to C([0,1] \times L')$$

such that $\mathrm{Incl}_{1,\beta_0}$ *and* $\mathrm{Incl}_{k,\beta}$ *define a filtered A_∞ homomorphism* $\mathrm{Incl} : C(L')[1] \to C([0,1] \times L')$ *satisfying*

$$\mathrm{Eval}_{s=s_0} \circ \mathrm{Incl} = id.$$

We will use Proposition 4.6.37 to construct the following Diagram 4.6.1.

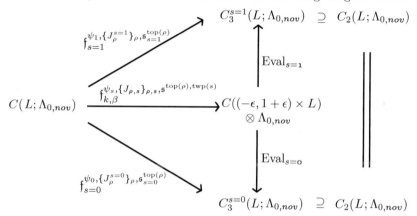

Diagram 4.6.1

Proposition 4.6.37 will be proved in Subsection 7.2.10. We remark that Incl in Proposition 4.6.37 does *not* satisfy (4.2.3.1). (See Remark 7.2.172.)

By using this proposition, we define a structure of filtered A_∞ algebra on $C([0,1] \times L', \Lambda_{0,nov})$. Here $C([0,1] \times L', \Lambda_{0,nov})$ is a completion of $C([0,1] \times L') \otimes \Lambda_{0,nov}$. Let $\mathcal{P}_i \in C([0,1] \times L')$. We define

$$\mathfrak{m}_{k,\beta}(\mathcal{P}_1, \cdots, \mathcal{P}_k) = \mathcal{M}_{k+1}^{\mathrm{main}}(M', L', \{J_{1,s}\}_s : \beta; \mathrm{twp}(s); \vec{\mathcal{P}})^{\mathfrak{s}} \in C([0,1] \times L')$$

for $(k, \beta) \neq (1, \beta_0)(= (1, 0))$ and $\mathfrak{m}_{1,\beta_0}(\mathcal{P}) = (-1)^{n+1}\partial\mathcal{P}$, where $n = \dim L$. (Note $\mathcal{P}$ is a singular simplex of the $(n+1)$-dimensional space $[0,1] \times L'$.) We then put:

$$\mathfrak{m}_k = \sum_\beta \mathfrak{m}_{k,\beta} \otimes T^{\omega(\beta)} e^{\frac{\mu(\beta)}{2}}.$$

LEMMA 4.6.39. $(C([0,1] \times L', \Lambda_{0,nov}), \mathfrak{m})$ *is a filtered A_∞ algebra.*

The proof is similar to the proof of Theorem 3.5.11, using Proposition 4.6.37. We omit it. We next use (4.6.38.4), (4.6.38.6) and (4.6.38.7) to construct several A_∞ homomorphisms. We first define

$$\mathrm{Eval}_{s=0} : (C([0,1] \times L', \Lambda_{0,nov}), \mathfrak{m}) \to (C_3^{s=0}(L'; \Lambda_{0,nov}), \mathfrak{m}_k^{J', \mathfrak{s}''_{s=0}}),$$

$$\mathrm{Eval}_{s=1} : (C([0,1] \times L', \Lambda_{0,nov}), \mathfrak{m}) \to (C_3^{s=1}(L'; \Lambda_{0,nov}), \mathfrak{m}_k^{J', \mathfrak{s}''_{s=1}})$$

as follows: $(\mathrm{Eval}_{s=s_0})_1$ is defined by (4.6.32). We put $(\mathrm{Eval}_{s=s_0})_k = 0$ for $k \neq 1$. Then (4.6.38.6) implies that $\mathrm{Eval}_{s=s_0}$ is a filtered A_∞ homomorphism.

We define a filtered A_∞ homomorphism

$$\text{Incl} : (C_2(L'; \Lambda_{0,nov}), \mathfrak{m}_k^{J',\mathfrak{s}'}) \to (C([0,1] \times L', \Lambda_{0,nov}), \mathfrak{m})$$

by (4.6.38.8).

We remark that we can take $\mathcal{X}(([0,1] \times L')$ so that $(\text{Eval}_{s=0})_1 \oplus (\text{Eval}_{s=1})_1$ given above is surjective. (This fact will be used in Subsection 7.2.13.) Then $(C([0,1] \times L', \Lambda_{0,nov}), \mathfrak{m})$ is a model of $[0,1] \times (C(L'; \Lambda_{0,nov}), \mathfrak{m}_k)$ in some generalized sense. (See Definition 7.2.174.)

Furthermore, we define

$$\mathfrak{f}^{\psi,\{J_{\rho,s}\}_{\rho,s},\mathfrak{s}^{\text{top}(\rho),\text{twp}(s)}} : (C_1(L; \Lambda_{0,nov}), \mathfrak{m}_k^{J,\mathfrak{s}}) \to (C([0,1] \times L') \otimes \Lambda_{0,nov}, \mathfrak{m})$$

by

$$\mathfrak{f}_k^{\psi,\{J_{\rho,s}\}_{\rho,s},\mathfrak{s}^{\text{top}(\rho),\text{twp}(s)}} = \sum_\beta \mathfrak{f}_{k,\beta}^{\psi,\{J_{\rho,s}\}_{\rho,s},\mathfrak{s}^{\text{top}(\rho),\text{twp}(s)}} T^{\omega(\beta)} e^{\mu_L(\beta)/2},$$

where

$$\mathfrak{f}_{k,\beta}^{\psi,\{J_{\rho,s}\}_{\rho,s},\mathfrak{s}^{\text{top}(\rho),\text{twp}(s)}} (P_1, \cdots, P_k)$$
$$= \mathcal{M}_{k+1}^{\text{main}}(M', L', \{J_{\rho,s}\}_{\rho,s} : \beta; \text{top}(\rho), \text{twp}(s); \vec{P})^{\mathfrak{s}}.$$

(See Diagram 4.6.1.) Here we recall that the right hand side is defined by using (4.6.29) and the multisection $\mathfrak{s}^{\text{top}(\rho),\text{twp}(s)}$. We remark that the right hand side is contained in $C([0,1] \times L')$ by (4.6.38.7).

We can prove that $\mathfrak{f}^{\psi,\{J_{\rho,s}\}_{\rho,s},\mathfrak{s}^{\text{top}(\rho),\text{twp}(s)}}$ is a filtered A_∞ homomorphism in a way similar to the proof of Theorem 4.6.1. The following lemma is immediate from definitions.

LEMMA 4.6.40. *We have*

(4.6.41.1) $\text{Eval}_{s=0} \circ \mathfrak{f}^{\psi,\{J_{\rho,s}\}_{\rho,s},\mathfrak{s}^{\text{top}(\rho),\text{twp}(s)}} = \mathfrak{f}_{s=0}^{\psi_0,\{J_\rho^{s=0}\}_\rho,\mathfrak{s}_{s=0}^{\text{top}(\rho)}}$,

(4.6.41.2) $\text{Eval}_{s=1} \circ \mathfrak{f}^{\psi,\{J_{\rho,s}\}_{\rho,s},\mathfrak{s}^{\text{top}(\rho),\text{twp}(s)}} = \mathfrak{f}_{s=1}^{\psi_1,\{J_\rho^{s=1}\}_\rho,\mathfrak{s}_{s=1}^{\text{top}(\rho)}}$.

Now let

$$I_0 : (C_2(L'; \Lambda_{0,nov}), \mathfrak{m}_k^{J',\mathfrak{s}'}) \to (C_3^{s=0}(L'; \Lambda_{0,nov}), \mathfrak{m}_k^{J',\mathfrak{s}''_{s=0}})$$
$$I_1 : (C_2(L'; \Lambda_{0,nov}), \mathfrak{m}_k^{J',\mathfrak{s}'}) \to (C_3^{s=1}(L'; \Lambda_{0,nov}), \mathfrak{m}_k^{J',\mathfrak{s}''_{s=1}})$$

be inclusions and let K_0, K_1 be their homotopy inverses respectively. Then the following lemma also follows from (4.6.38.8).

LEMMA 4.6.42. $\text{Eval}_{s=0} \circ \text{Incl} = I_0$. $\text{Eval}_{s=1} \circ \text{Incl} = I_1$.

Finally we show

LEMMA 4.6.43. $K_0 \circ \text{Eval}_{s=0}$ *is homotopic to* $K_1 \circ \text{Eval}_{s=1}$.

PROOF. We have

$$K_0 \circ \text{Eval}_{s=0} \circ \text{Incl} = K_0 \circ I_0 \sim id \sim K_1 \circ I_1 = K_1 \circ \text{Eval}_{s=1} \circ \text{Incl}.$$

By (4.6.38) and Theorem 4.2.45, the filtered A_∞ homomorphism Incl is a homotopy equivalence. The lemma follows.   □

$$
\begin{array}{ccccc}
C_1 & \xrightarrow{\ \mathfrak{f}_{s=0}^{\ \psi_0, \{J_\rho^{s=0}\}_\rho, \mathfrak{s}_{s=0}^{\text{top}(\rho)}}\ } & C_3^{s=0} & \xleftarrow{\ I_0\ } & C_2 \\[2mm]
\Big\| & & \Big\uparrow {\scriptstyle \mathrm{Eval}_{s=0}} & & \Big\| \\[2mm]
C_1 & \xrightarrow{\ \mathfrak{f}^{\ \psi, \{J_{\rho,s}\}_{\rho,s}, \mathfrak{s}^{\text{top}(\rho),\text{twp}(s)}}\ } & C([0,1] \times L') & \xleftarrow{\ \text{Incl}\ } & C_2 \\[2mm]
\Big\| & & \Big\downarrow {\scriptstyle \mathrm{Eval}_{s=1}} & & \Big\| \\[2mm]
C_1 & \xrightarrow{\ \mathfrak{f}_{s=1}^{\ \psi_1, \{J_\rho^{s=1}\}_\rho, \mathfrak{s}_{s=1}^{\text{top}(\rho)}}\ } & C_3^{s=1} & \xleftarrow{\ I_1\ } & C_2
\end{array}
$$

Diagram 4.6.2

Then Theorem 4.6.25 now follows from Lemmas 4.6.40 and 4.6.43. $\qquad\qquad\square$

We have thus completed the proof of Theorem 4.1.2.

We can prove the homotopy-unital versions of Theorems 4.1.1 and 4.1.2 as well. Namely the homotopy equivalence $\mathfrak{g}^{\psi,\{J_\rho\}_\rho,\mathfrak{s}^{\text{top}(\rho)}}$ is unital and the "homotopic" in the statement of Theorem 4.6.25 can be replaced by "u-homotopic". This version can be proved by a combination of the arguments of this section and Sections 7.2,7.3.

4.6.3. Compositions. Let $L \subset M$ be a relatively spin Lagrangian submanifold and $\psi : M \to M'$ a symplectic diffeomorphism. In Subsection 4.6.1 we constructed a filtered A_∞ homomorphism associated to ψ from the filtered A_∞ algebra associated to L to one associated to $L' = \psi(L)$. For another symplectic diffeomorphism $\psi' : M' \to M''$, we defined a filtered A_∞ homomorphism from the filtered A_∞ algebra associated to L' to one associated to $L'' = (\psi' \circ \psi)(L)$. In this subsection, we show the composition of these A_∞ homomorphisms coincides up to homotopy to the A_∞ homomorphism associated to $\psi'' = \psi' \circ \psi$. (Theorem 4.6.44).

We fix compatible almost complex structures J, J', J''. We also take countable sets of smooth singular simplices $\mathcal{X}_a(L)$, $\mathcal{X}_b(L')$, $\mathcal{X}_c(L'')$ which generate complexes $C_a(L;\Lambda_{0,nov})$, $C_b(L';\Lambda_{0,nov})$, $C_c(L'';\Lambda_{0,nov})$, respectively. By using multisections $\mathfrak{s}, \mathfrak{s}', \mathfrak{s}''$ of appropriate moduli spaces we obtain filtered A_∞ algebras

$$
(C_a(L;\Lambda_{0,nov}), \mathfrak{m}_k^{J,\mathfrak{s}}), \quad (C_b(L';\Lambda_{0,nov}), \mathfrak{m}_k^{J',\mathfrak{s}'}), \quad (C_c(L'';\Lambda_{0,nov}), \mathfrak{m}_k^{J'',\mathfrak{s}''})
$$

respectively.

By Theorem 4.6.1 and Corollary 4.6.2 we can find A_∞ homomorphisms

$$
\mathfrak{g}^{\psi,\{J_\rho\}_\rho,\mathfrak{s}^{\text{top}(\rho)}} : (C_a(L;\Lambda_{0,nov}), \mathfrak{m}_k^{J,\mathfrak{s}}) \to (C_b(L';\Lambda_{0,nov}), \mathfrak{m}_k^{J',\mathfrak{s}'})
$$
$$
\mathfrak{g}^{\psi',\{J'_\rho\}_\rho,\mathfrak{s}^{\text{top}(\rho)'}} : (C_b(L';\Lambda_{0,nov}), \mathfrak{m}_k^{J',\mathfrak{s}'}) \to (C_c(L'';\Lambda_{0,nov}), \mathfrak{m}_k^{J'',\mathfrak{s}''})
$$
$$
\mathfrak{g}^{\psi'',\{J''_\rho\}_\rho,\mathfrak{s}^{\text{top}(\rho)''}} : (C_a(L;\Lambda_{0,nov}), \mathfrak{m}_k^{J,\mathfrak{s}}) \to (C_c(L'';\Lambda_{0,nov}), \mathfrak{m}_k^{J'',\mathfrak{s}''}),
$$

where $\{J_\rho\}_\rho$, $\{J'_\rho\}_\rho$, $\{J''_\rho\}_\rho$ are homotopies from J^ψ to J', from $J'^{\psi'}$ to J'', from $J^{\psi'\circ\psi}$ to J'' respectively.

We remark that the notations $C_1(L;\Lambda_{0,nov})$, $C_2(L';\Lambda_{0,nov})$, and $C_3(L';\Lambda_{0,nov})$ are used in Subsection 4.6.2. In this subsection, we use suffix a, b, c in place of $1, 2, 3$. This is because when we consider $\mathfrak{g}^{\psi,\{J_\rho\}_\rho,\mathfrak{s}^{\text{top}(\rho)}}$, the module $C_b(L';\Lambda_{0,nov})$ plays the role of $C_2(L'; \Lambda_{0,nov})$, on the other hand, when we consider $\mathfrak{g}^{\psi', \{J'_\rho\}_\rho, \mathfrak{s}^{top(\rho)'}}$ the module $C_b(L'; \Lambda_{0,nov})$ plays the role of $C_1(L'; \Lambda_{0,nov})$.

THEOREM 4.6.44. *The composition* $\mathfrak{g}^{\psi', \{J'_\rho\}_\rho, \mathfrak{s}^{top(\rho)'}} \circ \mathfrak{g}^{\psi, \{J_\rho\}_\rho, \mathfrak{s}^{top(\rho)}}$ *is homotopic to* $\mathfrak{g}^{\psi'', \{J''_\rho\}_\rho, \mathfrak{s}^{top(\rho)''}}$.

PROOF. We have already proved that $\mathfrak{g}$ does not depend on $\psi, \{J_\rho\}_\rho, \mathfrak{s}^{top(\rho)}$ etc. in the last subsection. So we may assume that $\{J''_\rho\}_\rho$ is given by

$$J''_\rho = \begin{cases} (J'_{2\rho})^{\psi'} & \rho \le 1/2, \\ J''_{2\rho-1} & \rho > 1/2. \end{cases}$$

We recall that $\mathfrak{g}^{\psi'', \{J''_\rho\}_\rho, \mathfrak{s}^{top(\rho)''}}$ is defined by using $\mathcal{M}^{main}_{k+1}(M, L'', \{J''_\rho\}_\rho : \beta; top(\rho))$. Then we show the following lemma.

LEMMA 4.6.45. $\mathcal{M}^{main}_{k+1}(M'', L'', \{J''_\rho\}_\rho : \beta; top(\rho))$ *is isomorphic to the union of the fiber products*

$$\bigcup_{\ell_1, \cdots, \ell_m} \bigcup_{\sum_{i=1}^m \ell_i = k} \bigcup_{\beta_{last} + \sum_i \beta_i = \beta} \mathcal{M}^{main}_{m+1}(M'', L'', \{J'_\rho\}_\rho : \beta_{last}; top(\rho))$$

$$\times \left(\prod_{i=1}^m \mathcal{M}^{main}_{\ell_i+1}(M', L', \{J_\rho\}_\rho : \beta_i; top(\rho)) \right).$$

Here fiber products are taken over L'.

PROOF. Let $((\Sigma, \vec{z}), (u_\alpha), (\rho_\alpha)) \in \mathcal{M}^{main}_{k+1}(M'', L'', \{J''_\rho\}_\rho : \beta; top(\rho))$. We consider the component Σ_α such that $\rho_\alpha > 1/2$ and denotes by Σ_0 the union of such components. By (4.6.7.2) Σ_0 is connected. We restrict u and ρ to D_0. It is easy to see that this restriction defines an element of $\mathcal{M}^{main}_{m+1}(M'', L'', \{J'_\rho\}_\rho : \beta_{last}; top(\rho))$, here m is the number of the connected components of $\Sigma \setminus \Sigma_0$. We thus find the first factor of the fiber produce. Let Σ_i $(i = 1, \cdots, m)$ be the connected component of $\Sigma \setminus \Sigma_0$. Restriction of u and τ to Σ_i defines an element of $\mathcal{M}^{main}_{\ell_i+1}(M', L', \{J_\rho\}_\rho : \beta_i; top(\rho))$. The lemma follows. $\square$

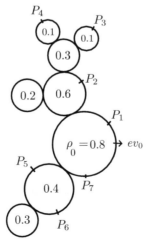

Figure 4.6.6 $\mathfrak{f}^{\psi'}_6 \left(\psi(P_1), \psi(P_2), \mathfrak{f}^{\psi}_2(P_3, P_4), \mathfrak{f}^{\psi}_0(1), \mathfrak{f}^{\psi}_2(P_5, P_6), \psi(P_7) \right)$

We can choose multisection $\mathfrak{s}^{\mathrm{top}(\rho)\prime\prime}$ so that it is compatible with the isomorphism in Lemma 4.6.45. Then we have

$$(4.6.46) \qquad \mathfrak{f}^{\psi',\{J'_\rho\}_\rho,\mathfrak{s}^{\mathrm{top}(\rho)\prime}} \circ \mathfrak{f}^{\psi,\{J_\rho\}_\rho,\mathfrak{s}^{\mathrm{top}(\rho)}} = \mathfrak{f}^{\psi'',\{J''_\rho\}_\rho,\mathfrak{s}^{\mathrm{top}(\rho)\prime\prime}}.$$

More precisely we have the following commutative Diagram 4.6.3.

In Diagram 4.6.3, the subcomplex $C_{a,b}(L',\Lambda_{0,nov})$ is $C_3(L',\Lambda_{0,nov})$ if we use the notation of Subsection 4.6.2.

$$C_{a,c}(L'',\Lambda_{0,nov}) \qquad\qquad \longleftarrow \qquad\qquad C_c(L'',\Lambda_{0,nov})$$

$$\searrow \qquad\qquad\qquad\qquad \downarrow$$

$$\uparrow \mathfrak{f}^{\psi'',\{J''_\rho\}_\rho,\mathfrak{s}^{\mathrm{top}(\rho)\prime\prime}} \qquad C_{(a,b),c}(L'_1,\Lambda_{0,nov}) \longleftarrow C_{b,c}(L'',\Lambda_{0,nov})$$

$$\mathfrak{f}^{\psi',\{J'_\rho\}_\rho,\mathfrak{s}^{\mathrm{top}(\rho)\prime}}_{\mathrm{ext}}\uparrow \qquad\qquad \mathfrak{f}^{\psi',\{J'_\rho\}_\rho,\mathfrak{s}^{\mathrm{top}(\rho)\prime}}\uparrow$$

$$C_a(L,\Lambda_{0,nov}) \xrightarrow[\ \mathfrak{f}^{\psi,\{J_\rho\}_\rho,\mathfrak{s}^{\mathrm{top}(\rho)}}\ ]{} C_{a,b}(L',\Lambda_{0,nov}) \longleftarrow C_b(L',\Lambda_{0,nov})$$

Diagram 4.6.3

By definition, the composition

$$C_a(L,\Lambda_{0,nov}) \xrightarrow{\ \mathfrak{f}^{\psi,\{J_\rho\}_\rho,\mathfrak{s}^{\mathrm{top}(\rho)}}\ } C_{a,b}(L',\Lambda_{0,nov}) \longrightarrow C_b(L',\Lambda_{0,nov})$$

is $\mathfrak{g}^{\psi,\{J_\rho\}_\rho,\mathfrak{s}^{\mathrm{top}(\rho)}}$. (Here $C_{a,b}(L',\Lambda_{0,nov}) \to C_b(L',\Lambda_{0,nov})$ is the homotopy inverse of the inclusion.)

In the same way the composition of the two arrows in the third column is $\mathfrak{g}^{\psi',\{J'_\rho\}_\rho,\mathfrak{s}^{\mathrm{top}(\rho)\prime}}$. (Here we invert the direction of one of the arrows.) Also the composition of the arrow in the first column and the homotopy inverse of the first line, namely the composition:

$$C_a(L,\Lambda_{0,nov}) \xrightarrow{\ \mathfrak{f}^{\psi'',\{J''_\rho\}_\rho,\mathfrak{s}^{\mathrm{top}(\rho)\prime\prime}}\ } C_{a,c}(L'',\Lambda_{0,nov}) \longrightarrow C_c(L'',\Lambda_{0,nov})$$

is $\mathfrak{g}^{\psi'',\{J''_\rho\}_\rho,\mathfrak{s}^{\mathrm{top}(\rho)\prime\prime}}$.

(4.6.46) implies that we can find

$$C_{(a,b),c}(L'_1,\Lambda_{0,nov}) \supset C_{a,c}(L'_1,\Lambda_{0,nov}) \cup C_{b,c}(L'_1,\Lambda_{0,nov})$$

and $\mathfrak{f}^{\psi',\{J'_\rho\}_\rho,\mathfrak{s}^{\mathrm{top}(\rho)\prime}}_{\mathrm{ext}}$ such that Diagram 4.6.3 commutes. (Compare Lemma 7.2.299.) Theorem 4.6.44 follows. $\qquad\square$

We can also prove that we may replace 'homotopic' by 'hu-homotopic' in Theorem 4.6.44. This point will follow from a combination of the argument above and one in Section 7.3.

4.6.4. Homotopy equivalence and the operator $\mathfrak{q}$ I: changing the cycle in the interior.
In the remaining subsections of Section 4.6, we will discuss deformation of our filtered A_∞ algebra $(C(L;\Lambda_{0,nov}),\mathfrak{m})$ by a cocycle $\mathfrak{b}$ in $C^2(M;\Lambda^+_{0,nov}) = C(M;\Lambda^+_{0,nov})[2]^0$ using the operator $\mathfrak{q}$ we introduced in Section 3.8. We defined the filtered A_∞ algebra $(C(L;\Lambda_{0,nov}),\mathfrak{m}^{(\mathfrak{b},0)})$ deformed by $\mathfrak{b}$ in Subsection 3.8.5. Hereafter we simply write $\mathfrak{m}^\mathfrak{b}$ in place of $\mathfrak{m}^{(\mathfrak{b},0)}$. In this subsection, we show that $(C(L;\Lambda_{0,nov}),\mathfrak{m}^\mathfrak{b})$ depends only on the cohomology class of $\mathfrak{b}$ up to the

strict homotopy equivalence (Theorem 4.6.47). We remark that for each cochain $b \in C^1(L; \Lambda_{0,nov}^+)$, we defined the deformed filtered A_∞ algebra $(C(L; \Lambda_{0,nov}), \mathfrak{m}^b)$ in Subsection 3.6.1. (See Proposition 3.6.10). It is independent of b up to the (non-strict) homotopy equivalence. Namely it does *not* even depend on the gauge equivalence class of b, (Remark 4.3.17).

This subsection is of purely algebraic nature. The results hold for any filtered A_∞ algebra C that has an operator $\mathfrak{q}$ satisfying the conclusion of Theorem 3.8.32. (However we state the results only for the case of our geometric example.) In the following three subsections (Subsections 4.6.4-4.6.6), we assume $R \supseteq \mathbb{Q}$ and use the notations of Section 3.8.

THEOREM 4.6.47. *Let $\mathfrak{b}_0, \mathfrak{b}_1 \in C^2(M; \Lambda_{0,nov}^+)$ be cycles representing the same cohomology class in $H^2(M; \Lambda_{0,nov})$. Then, the filtered A_∞ algebra $(C, \mathfrak{m}^{\mathfrak{b}_0})$ is strictly homotopy equivalent to $(C, \mathfrak{m}^{\mathfrak{b}_1})$.*

Theorem 4.6.47 is proved in Subsection 7.4.6. See Theorem 7.4.118 there. We also need the following proposition which we use in Definition 4.6.50.

Let $\mathfrak{b}_i \in C(M; \Lambda_{0,nov}^+)$ $i = 0, 1, 2$ be cycles representing the same homology class. Let

(4.6.48) $$\mathfrak{f}_{ij} : (C, \mathfrak{m}^{\mathfrak{b}_i}) \to (C, \mathfrak{m}^{\mathfrak{b}_j})$$

be the homotopy equivalence given by Theorem 4.6.47.

PROPOSITION 4.6.49. *$\mathfrak{f}_{12} \circ \mathfrak{f}_{01}$ is shu-homotopic to $\mathfrak{f}_{02}$.*

Proposition 4.6.49 is also proved in Subsection 7.4.6. See Theorem 7.4.134. Using Proposition 4.6.49 we can generalize Definition 4.3.26 as follows.

DEFINITION-COROLLARY 4.6.50. *Let $(\mathfrak{b}_0, b_0), (\mathfrak{b}_1, b_1) \in \widehat{\mathcal{M}}_{def}(L)$. We say that they are gauge equivalent to each other and write $(\mathfrak{b}_0, b_0) \sim (\mathfrak{b}_1, b_1)$ if $[\mathfrak{b}_0] = [\mathfrak{b}_1] \in H^1(L; \Lambda_{0,nov})$ and $\mathfrak{f}_*(b_0) \sim b_1$ where*

$$\mathfrak{f} : (C(L; \Lambda_{0,nov}), \mathfrak{m}^{\mathfrak{b}_0}) \to (C(L; \Lambda_{0,nov}), \mathfrak{m}^{\mathfrak{b}_1})$$

is as in Theorem 4.6.47.

Proposition 4.6.49 *implies that gauge equivalence is an equivalence relation. We can define an equivalence relation $\sim$ on $\widehat{\mathcal{M}}_{weak,def}(L)$ in the same way.*

The set of $\sim$ equivalence classes of $\widehat{\mathcal{M}}_{def}(L)$ and of $\widehat{\mathcal{M}}_{weak,def}(L)$ coincides with $\mathcal{M}_{def}(L)$ and $\mathcal{M}_{weak,def}(L)$ in Definition 4.3.26, respectively.

LEMMA 4.6.51. *If $(\mathfrak{b}_i, b_i) \in \widehat{\mathcal{M}}_{weak,def}(L)$ and $(\mathfrak{b}_0, b_0) \sim (\mathfrak{b}_1, b_1)$, then*

$$\mathfrak{PD}(\mathfrak{b}_0, b_0) = \mathfrak{PD}(\mathfrak{b}_1, b_1).$$

See Subsection 7.4.6 for its proof.

There is a natural projection $\pi_{amb} : \mathcal{M}_{def}(L) \to H^2(M; \Lambda_{0,nov}^+)$. Lemma 4.6.51 implies that we have the potential function

$$\mathfrak{PD}_i : \mathcal{M}_{weak,def}(L^{(i)}) \to \Lambda_{0,nov}^{(0)}.$$

together with $\pi_{amb,i} : \mathcal{M}_{weak,def}(L^{(i)}) \to H^2(M; \Lambda_{0,nov}^+)$. See Subsection 4.3.3. Here

$$\mathcal{M}_{weak,def}(L^{(i)}) = \{(\mathfrak{b}, b) \mid \mathfrak{b} \in H^2(M; \Lambda_{0,nov}^+),$$
$$b \in \mathcal{M}_{weak}(C(L^{(i)}; \Lambda_{0,nov}), \mathfrak{m}^{\mathfrak{b}})\}.$$

In Subsection 5.2.4 Propositions 5.2.37 (3) and 5.2.38 (2), we will prove that the
Floer cohomology defined in Subsection 3.8.7 does not change when we change the
bounding cochains in a given gauge equivalence class. It follows that, the Floer
cohomology group $HF((L^{(1)}, (\mathfrak{b}_1, b_1)), (L^{(0)}, (\mathfrak{b}_0, b_0)); \Lambda_{0,nov})$ is parametrized by

$$([\mathfrak{b}_1, b_1], [\mathfrak{b}_0, b_0])$$
$$\in \mathcal{M}_{\text{weak,def}}(L^{(1)}) \times_{H^2(M;\Lambda_{0,nov}^+) \times \Lambda_{0,nov}^{(0)}} \mathcal{M}_{\text{weak,def}}(L^{(0)})$$
$$= \{([\mathfrak{b}_1, b_1], [\mathfrak{b}_0, b_0]) \mid \pi_{\text{amb},1}[\mathfrak{b}_1, b_1] = \pi_{\text{amb},0}[\mathfrak{b}_0, b_0],$$
$$\mathfrak{PO}_1[\mathfrak{b}_1, b_1] = \mathfrak{PO}_0[\mathfrak{b}_0, b_0]\}.$$

Hereafter we also denote by the same symbol the gauge equivalence class of $(\mathfrak{b}_i, b_i)$
in the sense of Definition 4.6.50.

**4.6.5. Homotopy equivalence and the operator q II: invariance of
symplectic diffeomorphisms 1.** In this subsection and the next, we will prove
the following Theorem 4.6.52.

Let (M, ω), (M', ω') be symplectic manifolds and $\psi : M \to M'$ a symplectic
diffeomorphism. Let $L \subset M$ be relatively spin Lagrangian submanifold and $L' = \psi(L)$. We fix various choices (compatible almost complex structures, perturbations,
and countable sets of smooth singular simplices), for M, L and M', L' to define
$(C(L; \Lambda_{0,nov}), \mathfrak{m})$ and $(C(L'; \Lambda_{0,nov}), \mathfrak{m})$. For each $[\mathfrak{b}] \in H^2(M; \Lambda_{0,nov}^+)$ and $[\mathfrak{b}'] \in H^2(M'; \Lambda_{0,nov}^+)$, we have obtained the filtered A_∞ algebras $(C(L; \Lambda_{0,nov}), \mathfrak{m}^{\mathfrak{b}})$ and
$(C(L'; \Lambda_{0,nov}), \mathfrak{m}^{\mathfrak{b}'})$ whose homotopy types depend only on the cohomology classes
of $\mathfrak{b}$ and $\mathfrak{b}'$ respectively.

THEOREM 4.6.52. *For each* $[\mathfrak{b}] \in H^2(M; \Lambda_{0,nov}^+)$, *there exists a homotopy
equivalence of filtered A_∞ algebras*

$$\psi_*^{\mathfrak{b}} : (C(L; \Lambda_{0,nov}), \mathfrak{m}^{\mathfrak{b}}) \longrightarrow (C(L'; \Lambda_{0,nov}), \mathfrak{m}^{\psi_* \mathfrak{b}}).$$

*It is independent of the choice of symplectic isotopy in the same sense as in Theorem
4.1.2.*

Before proving Theorem 4.6.52, we derive several consequence of it. We begin
with the following corollary which is nothing but Theorem B (B.3) in Introduction.

COROLLARY 4.6.53. *Any symplectic diffeomorphism* $\psi : M \to M'$ *with* $L' = \psi(L)$ *as above induces a map* ψ_* *with the following commutative diagrams:*

$$
\begin{array}{ccc}
\mathcal{M}_{\text{weak,def}}(L) & \xrightarrow{\psi_*} & \mathcal{M}_{\text{weak,def}}(L') \\
\pi_{\text{amb}} \downarrow & & \downarrow \pi_{\text{amb}} \\
H^2(M; \Lambda_{0,nov}^+) & \xrightarrow{\psi_*} & H^2(M'; \Lambda_{0,nov}^+)
\end{array}
\qquad
\begin{array}{ccc}
\mathcal{M}_{\text{weak,def}}(L) & \xrightarrow{\psi_*} & \mathcal{M}_{\text{weak,def}}(L') \\
\mathfrak{PO} \downarrow & & \downarrow \mathfrak{PO} \\
\Lambda_{0,nov}^{(0)} & =\!=\!= & \Lambda_{0,nov}^{(0)}
\end{array}
$$

Diagram 4.6.4

*In these diagrams, the horizontal arrows are isomorphisms. The bottom arrow
in Diagram 4.6.4 is just given by* ψ^{-1*}, *the pull back by* ψ^{-1}.

PROOF OF COROLLARY 4.6.53. We can write

$$\mathcal{M}_{\text{weak,def}}(L) = \{(\mathfrak{b}, b) \mid \mathfrak{b} \in H^2(M; \Lambda^+_{0,nov}),$$
$$b \in \mathcal{M}_{\text{weak}}(C(L; \Lambda_{0,nov}), \mathfrak{m}^{\mathfrak{b}})\}/ \sim .$$

From Theorem 4.6.52, we have a homotopy equivalence

$$\psi^{\mathfrak{b}}_* : (C(L; \Lambda_{0,nov}), \mathfrak{m}^{\mathfrak{b}}) \longrightarrow (C(L'; \Lambda_{0,nov}), \mathfrak{m}^{\psi_* \mathfrak{b}})$$

for $[\mathfrak{b}] \in H^2(M; \Lambda^+_{0,nov})$. By Theorem 4.3.22, the functor $\mathcal{M}_{\text{weak}}$ is homotopy invariant and the homotopy equivalence map $\psi^{\mathfrak{b}}_*$ induces the bijection

$$(\psi^{\mathfrak{b}}_*)_* : \mathcal{M}_{\text{weak}}(C(L; \Lambda_{0,nov}), \mathfrak{m}^{\mathfrak{b}}) \to \mathcal{M}_{\text{weak}}(C(L'; \Lambda_{0,nov}), \mathfrak{m}^{\psi_* \mathfrak{b}})$$

defined by $(\psi^{\mathfrak{b}}_*)_*(b) = \psi^{\mathfrak{b}}_*(e^b)$. See also Lemma 3.6.36. We now put

$$\psi_*(\mathfrak{b}, b) = (\psi_* \mathfrak{b}, (\psi^{\mathfrak{b}}_*)_*(b)),$$

where $\psi_* \mathfrak{b}$ is the pull back of $\mathfrak{b}$ by ψ^{-1}. Then by using Lemma 4.3.23, we can find that this map ψ_* has the required properties. $\square$

PROOF OF THEOREM B (B.4). We use the notation of Theorem B. Let $\mathbf{b}_i = (\mathfrak{b}, b_i)$, $(i = 0, 1)$. By Theorem 4.6.52 we have a homotopy equivalence

$$\psi^{\mathfrak{b}}_* : (C(L; \Lambda_{0,nov}), \mathfrak{m}^{\mathfrak{b}}) \to (C(L'; \Lambda_{0,nov}), \mathfrak{m}^{\psi_* \mathfrak{b}}).$$

Hence we have

$$(\psi^{\mathfrak{b}}_*)_* : \mathcal{M}(C(L; \Lambda_{0,nov}), \mathfrak{m}^{\mathfrak{b}}) \to \mathcal{M}(C(L'; \Lambda_{0,nov}), \mathfrak{m}^{\psi_* \mathfrak{b}}).$$

We define

$$\psi_*(b_i) = (\psi^{\mathfrak{b}}_*)_*(b_i).$$

We put

$$\delta_{\mathbf{b}_1, \mathbf{b}_0}(x) = \mathfrak{m}^{\mathfrak{b}}(e^{b_1} x e^{b_0}), \qquad \delta_{\psi_* \mathbf{b}_1, \psi_* \mathbf{b}_0}(y) = \mathfrak{m}^{\psi_* \mathfrak{b}}(e^{\psi_* b_1} y e^{\psi_* b_0}).$$

We define

$$\psi^{\mathbf{b}_1, \mathbf{b}_0}_* : (C(L; \Lambda_{0,nov}), \delta_{\mathbf{b}_1, \mathbf{b}_0}) \to (C(L'; \Lambda_{0,nov}), \delta_{\psi_* \mathbf{b}_1, \psi_* \mathbf{b}_0})$$

by

$$\psi^{\mathbf{b}_1, \mathbf{b}_0}_*(x) = \psi^{\mathfrak{b}}_*(e^{b_1} x e^{b_0}).$$

It is easy to see that $\psi^{\mathbf{b}_1, \mathbf{b}_0}_*$ is a chain map. Hence we obtain

$$(4.6.54) \qquad \begin{aligned} (\psi^{\mathbf{b}_1, \mathbf{b}_0}_*)_* : HF((L, \mathbf{b}_1), (L, \mathbf{b}_0); \Lambda_{0,nov}) \\ \to HF((L', \psi_* \mathbf{b}_1), (L', \psi_* \mathbf{b}_0); \Lambda_{0,nov}). \end{aligned}$$

We remark that $\psi^{\mathbf{b}_1, \mathbf{b}_0}_* \equiv \psi_*$ mod $\Lambda^+_{0,nov}$ induce an isomorphism on $\overline{\mathfrak{m}}_1$ cohomology. Proposition 5.2.38 (2) (which is proved in Section 5.2) implies that (4.6.54) is an isomorphism. (Alternatively we can use the spectral sequence which will be established in Chapter 6 to prove that (4.6.54) is an isomorphism.) Theorem B (B.4) is now proved. $\square$

To prove Theorem 4.6.52 we need to combine the construction in the proof of Theorem 4.6.1 with the construction in Subsection 3.8.6. For this purpose we first state the result carefully specifying the choice of countably generated subcomplex etc. Let us first take, as in Theorem 3.8.32, countable sets of smooth singular simplices $\mathcal{X}_{1+}(L) \supset \mathcal{X}_1(L)$ of L and $\mathcal{X}(M)$ of M such that for any $Q \in \mathcal{X}(M)$ is transversal to L and that $Q \cap L \in \mathcal{X}_1(L) \subset \mathcal{X}_{2+}(L)$, by taking appropriate triangulation of $Q \cap L$. Moreover we can define the operator

$$\mathfrak{q}_{\ell,k} : E_\ell C(M; \Lambda_{0,nov})[2] \otimes B_k C_{1+}(L; \Lambda_{0,nov})[1] \longrightarrow C_{1+}(L; \Lambda_{0,nov})[1],$$

where $C(M; \Lambda_{0,nov})$, $C_{1+}(L; \Lambda_{0,nov})$ are generated by $\mathcal{X}(M)$, $\mathcal{X}_{1+}(L)$ respectively. We can also choose $\mathcal{X}(M')$, $\mathcal{X}_{2+}(L')$ so that

$$\mathfrak{q}_{\ell,k} : E_\ell C(M'; \Lambda_{0,nov})[2] \otimes B_k C_{2+}(L'; \Lambda_{0,nov})[1] \longrightarrow C_{2+}(L'; \Lambda_{0,nov})[1]$$

is well defined, where $C(M'; \Lambda_{0,nov})$, $C_{2+}(L'; \Lambda_{0,nov})$ are generated by the sets $\mathcal{X}(M')$, $\mathcal{X}_{1+}(L')$ respectively.

We may choose $\mathcal{X}'(M')$ which contains $\psi(\mathcal{X}(M))$ and $\mathcal{X}(M')$ such that

$$H^*(C'(M'; \Lambda_{0,nov})) \cong H^*(M; \Lambda_{0,nov}),$$

where $C'(M'; \Lambda_{0,nov})$ is generated by $\mathcal{X}'(M')$. Under the situation above, we can show the following.

PROPOSITION 4.6.55. *There exists a countable set of smooth singular simplices* $\mathcal{X}_{3+}(L')$ *(which generates* $C_{3+}(L'; \Lambda_{0,nov})$*) containing* $\mathcal{X}_3(L')$ *in Theorem 4.6.1 and* $\mathcal{X}_{2+}(L')$*, and a sequence of operators*

$$\mathfrak{f}_{\ell,k} : E_\ell C(M; \Lambda_{0,nov})[2] \otimes B_k C_{1+}(L; \Lambda_{0,nov})[1] \longrightarrow C_{3+}(L'; \Lambda_{0,nov})[1]$$

of degree 0 with the following properties.

(4.6.56.1) $\mathfrak{f}_{0,k} = \mathfrak{f}_k$, *where* $\mathfrak{f}_k$ $(k = 0, 1, 2, \cdots)$ *is the filtered* A_∞ *homomorphism as in Definition 4.6.12.*
(4.6.56.2)

$$\mathfrak{q}_{\ell,k} : E_\ell C(M'; \Lambda_{0,nov})[2] \otimes B_k C_{2+}(L'; \Lambda_{0,nov})[1] \longrightarrow BC_{2+}(L'; \Lambda_{0,nov})[1]$$

is extended to

$$\mathfrak{q}_{\ell,k} : E_\ell C'(M'; \Lambda_{0,nov})[2] \otimes B_k C_{3+}(L'; \Lambda_{0,nov})[1] \longrightarrow BC_{3+}(L'; \Lambda_{0,nov})[1]$$

which satisfy (3.8.33).
(4.6.56.3) *We define*

$$\widehat{\widehat{\mathfrak{f}}} : EC(M; \Lambda_{0,nov})[2] \otimes BC_{1+}(L; \Lambda_{0,nov})[1] \longrightarrow BC_{3+}(L'; \Lambda_{0,nov})[1]$$

so that its $B_m C_{3+}(L'; \Lambda_{0,nov})[1]$ *component is given by*

$$(\pi_m \circ \widehat{\widehat{\mathfrak{f}}})(\mathbf{y} \otimes \mathbf{x}) = \sum_{c_1, c_2} (-1)^{\epsilon(c_1, c_2)} \mathfrak{f}(\mathbf{y}_{c_1}^{(m;1)} \otimes \mathbf{x}_{c_2}^{(m;1)}) \otimes \cdots \otimes \mathfrak{f}(\mathbf{y}_{c_1}^{(m;m)} \otimes \mathbf{x}_{c_2}^{(m;m)}),$$

where $\epsilon(c_1, c_2) = \sum_{1 \le j < i \le m} \deg \mathbf{y}_{c_1}^{(m;i)} \deg' \mathbf{x}_{c_1}^{(m;j)}$. *Then we have*

$$\mathfrak{f}(\widehat{\delta}_M(\mathbf{y}) \otimes \mathbf{x}) + \sum_c \mathfrak{q}(\psi_*^\otimes(\mathbf{y}_{c_1}^{(2;1)}) \otimes \widehat{\widehat{\mathfrak{f}}}(\mathbf{y}_c^{(2;2)} \otimes \mathbf{x}))$$

(4.6.57)
$$- \sum_{c_1, c_2} (-1)^{\deg \mathbf{y}_{c_1}^{(2;2)} \deg' \mathbf{x}_{c_2}^{(3;1)} + \deg' \mathbf{x}_{c_2}^{(3;1)} + \deg \mathbf{y}_{c_1}^{(2;1)}}$$

$$\mathfrak{f}(\mathbf{y}_{c_1}^{(2;1)} \otimes (\mathbf{x}_{c_2}^{(3;1)} \otimes \mathfrak{q}(\mathbf{y}_{c_1}^{(2;2)} \otimes \mathbf{x}_{c_2}^{(3;2)}) \otimes \mathbf{x}_{c_2}^{(3;3)})) = 0.$$

Here $\psi_*^\otimes : EC(M; \Lambda_{0,nov})[1] \to EC'(M'; \Lambda_{0,nov})[1]$ *is induced by*

$$\psi_* : C(M; \Lambda_{0,nov})[1] \to C'(M'; \Lambda_{0,nov})[1].$$

We prove Proposition 4.6.55 in the next subsection. In this subsection we show that Proposition 4.6.55 implies Theorem 4.6.52. We define

$$\psi_*^\flat : BC_{1+}(L; \Lambda_{0,nov})[1] \longrightarrow C_{3+}(L'; \Lambda_{0,nov})[1]$$

by

$$\psi_*^\flat(\mathbf{x}) = \mathfrak{f}(e^\flat \otimes \mathbf{x}).$$

Then, since $\Delta(e^\flat) = e^\flat \otimes e^\flat$, we find

$$\widehat{\psi}_*^\flat(\mathbf{x}) = \widehat{\widehat{\mathfrak{f}}}(e^\flat \otimes \mathbf{x}).$$

Here $\widehat{\psi}_*^\flat : BC_{1+}(L; \Lambda_{0,nov})[1] \to BC_{3+}(L'; \Lambda_{0,nov})[1]$ is the coalgebra homomorphism induced by $\psi_*^\flat : BC_{1+}(L; \Lambda_{0,nov})[1] \to C_{3+}(L'; \Lambda_{0,nov})[1]$ and $\widehat{\widehat{\mathfrak{f}}}$ is as in (4.6.56.3).

Therefore (4.6.57) implies

$$\mathfrak{q}(e^{\psi_*(\mathfrak{b})} \otimes \widehat{\psi}_*^\flat(\mathbf{x})) = \sum_c (-1)^{\deg' \mathbf{x}_c^{(3;1)}} \mathfrak{f}(e^\flat \otimes (\mathbf{x}_c^{(3;1)} \otimes \mathfrak{q}(e^\flat \otimes \mathbf{x}_c^{(3;2)}) \otimes \mathbf{x}_c^{(3;3)})).$$

The left hand side is $\mathfrak{m}^{\psi_*(\mathfrak{b})}(\widehat{\psi}_*^\flat(\mathbf{x}))$. The right hand side is $\psi_*^\flat(\widehat{d}^\flat(\mathbf{x}))$. Hence $\psi_*^\flat$ defines an A_∞ homomorphism:

$$(C_{1+}(L; \Lambda_{0,nov}), \mathfrak{m}^\flat) \to (C_{3+}(L'; \Lambda_{0,nov}), \mathfrak{m}^{\psi_*\,\flat}).$$

If we reduce the coefficients to R, it induces an isomorphism on $\overline{\mathfrak{m}}_1$-cohomology, since the map is induced by ψ. Hence $\widehat{\psi}_*^\flat$ is a homotopy equivalence by Theorem 4.2.45.

We next find $\mathfrak{b}' \in C'(M'; \Lambda_{0,nov}^+)$ cohomologous to $\psi_*\mathfrak{b}$. Then it follows that the filtered A_∞ algebra $(C_{3+}(L'; \Lambda_{0,nov}), \mathfrak{m}^{\psi_*(\mathfrak{b})})$ is homotopy equivalent to $(C_{3+}(L'; \Lambda_{0,nov}), \mathfrak{m}^{\mathfrak{b}'})$ by Theorem 4.6.47.

Finally the inclusion $(C_{2+}(L'; \Lambda_{0,nov}), \mathfrak{m}^\flat) \to (C_{3+}(L'; \Lambda_{0,nov}), \mathfrak{m}^\flat)$ is a homotopy equivalence by Theorem 4.2.45. Thus we have constructed the homotopy equivalence in Theorem 4.6.52. We can prove that the homotopy equivalence is independent of the various choices we made, up to homotopy in the same way as in Subsection 4.6.2 using the 'twp' version of the construction. Hence the proof of Theorem 4.6.52 assuming Proposition 4.6.55 is now complete. $\square$

We can also prove a result similar to Theorem 4.6.44 for the homotopy equivalence in Theorem 4.6.52. It implies Theorem B (B.5). The homotopy-unital version of Theorem 4.6.52 can also be proved. Namely the homotopy equivalence in Theorem 4.6.52 is hu-homotopy equivalence. The proof is a straightforward combination of the techniques we have already been discussed.

4.6.6. Homotopy equivalence and the operator $\mathfrak{q}$ III: invariance of symplectic diffeomorphisms 2. In this subsection, we prove Proposition 4.6.55. The argument on the choices of $\mathcal{X}_{3+}(L')$ and $\mathcal{X}'(M')$ in Subsection 4.6.5 is similar to one in Section 7.2.

The construction of the operator $\mathfrak{f}_{\ell,k}$ is a combination of the constructions in Subsections 4.6.1 and 3.8.6. We use notations of Subsections 4.6.1 and 4.6.5. We consider $(\Sigma, \vec{z}, \vec{z}^+) \in \mathcal{M}_{k+1,\ell}^{\mathrm{main}}$ and define an order on its component as in Definition 4.6.6. (We recall that we include tree of bubbled spheres to the component where it is rooted.)

DEFINITION 4.6.58. We define $\mathcal{M}_{k+1,\ell}^{\mathrm{main}}(M', L', \{J_\rho\}_\rho; \beta; \mathrm{top}(\rho))$ to be the set of all equivalence classes $((\Sigma, \vec{z}, \vec{z}^+), (u_\alpha), (\rho_\alpha))$ satisfying (4.6.7.1), (4.6.7.2), (4.6.7.4), (4.6.7.5) and

$(4.6.7.3')$ $((\Sigma, \vec{z}, \vec{z}^+), (u_\alpha))$ is stable in the sense of Definition 2.1.24.

We define an evaluation map

$$ev = (ev^{\mathrm{int}}, ev_+^b, ev_0^b) = (ev_1^{\mathrm{int}}, \cdots, ev_\ell^{\mathrm{int}}, ev_1^b, \cdots, ev_k^b, ev_0^b)$$
$$: \mathcal{M}_{k+1,\ell}^{\mathrm{main}}(M', L', \{J_\rho\}_\rho : \beta; \mathrm{top}(\rho)) \to M^\ell \times L^k \times L'$$

in a similar way in Subsection 4.6.1. (Here 'b' stands for 'boundary' and 'int' stands for interior.) For $P_i \in \mathcal{X}_1(L)$ and $Q_i \in \mathcal{X}(M)$, we put

$$\mathcal{M}_{k+1,\ell}^{\mathrm{main}}(M', L', \{J_\rho\}_\rho : \beta; \mathrm{top}, \rho; \vec{Q}, \vec{P})$$
$$= \mathcal{M}_{k+1,\ell}^{\mathrm{main}}(M', L', \{J_\rho\}_\rho : \beta; \mathrm{top}, \rho)_{(ev_{\mathrm{int}}, ev_+^b)}$$
$$\times \left(Q_1 \times \cdots \times Q_\ell \times P_1 \times \cdots \times P_k \right).$$

We take an appropriate Kuranishi structure and multisection $\mathfrak{s}$ and put

$$\mathcal{M}_{k+1,\ell}^{\mathrm{main}}(M', L', \{J_\rho\}_\rho : \beta; \mathrm{top}(\rho); \vec{Q}, \vec{P})^{\mathfrak{s}} = (\mathfrak{s}^{-1}(0), ev_0).$$

(We take a triangulation and order on the set of vertices to define the right hand side as a singular chain.) Then we define the following.

DEFINITION 4.6.59. We put

$$\mathfrak{f}_{\ell,k;\beta}((Q_1 \otimes \cdots \otimes Q_\ell) \otimes (P_1 \otimes \cdots \otimes P_k))$$
$$= \frac{1}{\ell!} \mathcal{M}_{k+1,\ell}^{\mathrm{main}}(M', L', \{J_\rho\}_\rho : \beta; \mathrm{top}, \rho; \vec{Q}, \vec{P})^{\mathfrak{s}}$$

and $\mathfrak{f}_{\ell,k} = \sum_\beta T^{\omega(\beta)} e^{\mu(\beta)/2} \mathfrak{f}_{\ell,k;\beta}$.

Then the proof of (4.6.57) is now a straightforward analog of the proofs of Proposition 4.6.1 and Theorem 3.8.32 and is left to the reader. The proof of Proposition 4.6.55 is now complete. $\square$

CHAPTER 5

Homotopy equivalence of A_∞ bimodules

5.1. Novikov rings

5.1.1. Reduction to universal Novikov ring. In this book we use the universal Novikov ring Λ_{nov} and its sub-ring $\Lambda_{0,nov}$ as the coefficient ring of Floer cohomology. We denote by R the ground ring of the universal Novikov ring. In Chapter 2 and several other references, different types of the Novikov rings are used to study Floer cohomology. In this section we clarify the relationship between them but the results on the other types of Novikov rings will not be used in this book.

We first consider the case of *one* Lagrangian submanifold L. Recall from Definition 2.4.17 that we define the equivalence relation $\beta \sim \beta'$ in $\pi_2(M, L)$ by $E(\beta) = E(\beta')$ and $\mu_L(\beta) = \mu_L(\beta')$, where μ_L is the Maslov index homomorphism and $E(\beta)$ the symplectic area $E(\beta) = \int_\beta \omega$ and denote the set of the corresponding equivalence classes by $\Pi(L) = \pi_2(M, L)/\sim$. We put

$$\Lambda(L) = \left\{ \sum_{\beta \in \Pi(L)} a_\beta [\beta] \ \middle| \ \#\{\beta \mid a_\beta \neq 0, E(\beta) < C\} \text{ is finite for each } C \right\}.$$

Floer's cochain complex $CF(L, L)$ we described in Chapter 2 is a module over $\Lambda(L)$. We define a homomorphism $I_L : \Lambda(L) \to \Lambda_{nov}$ by

$$I_L \left(\sum_{\beta \in \Pi(L)} a_\beta [\beta] \right) = \sum_\beta a_\beta T^{E(\beta)} e^{\frac{\mu_L(\beta)}{2}}.$$

The following lemma is an immediate consequence of the definitions.

LEMMA 5.1.1. *Let $\psi : M \to M'$ be a symplectic diffeomorphism such that $\psi(L) = L'$. Then the map $\psi_* : \pi_2(M, L) \to \pi_2(M', L')$ canonically induces homomorphisms*

$$\psi_* : \Pi(L) \to \Pi(L'), \quad \psi_* : \Lambda(L) \to \Lambda(L').$$

Moreover we have the identity $I_{L'} \circ \psi_* = I_L$.

Now we recall the definition of the Novikov ring $\Lambda(L^{(0)}, L^{(1)}; \ell_0)$ for a *pair* of Lagrangian submanifolds $(L^{(0)}, L^{(1)})$: In Section 2.2 we introduced the space $\Omega(L^{(0)}, L^{(1)})$ of the paths joining $L^{(0)}$ to $L^{(1)}$. Choosing a base point ℓ_0 and considering its associated connected component, $\Omega(L^{(0)}, L^{(1)}; \ell_0)$ of $\Omega(L^{(0)}, L^{(1)})$, we defined a covering space $\widetilde{\Omega}(L^{(0)}, L^{(1)}; \ell_0)$ of $\Omega(L^{(0)}, L^{(1)}; \ell_0)$ in Definition 2.2.4 and denoted by $\Pi(L^{(0)}, L^{(1)}; \ell_0)$ the group of deck transformations of the covering.

We recall the homomorphisms

$$E_{\ell_0} : \Pi(L^{(0)}, L^{(1)}; \ell_0) \to \mathbb{R} \quad \text{and} \quad \mu_{\ell_0} : \Pi(L^{(0)}, L^{(1)}; \ell_0) \to \mathbb{Z}$$

constructed by measuring the symplectic areas and the Maslov indices respectively in Subsection 2.2.1. (See the paragraph right before Corollary 2.2.5 where we just denoted them by E and μ.) Here we write E_{ℓ_0}, μ_{ℓ_0} to specify their dependence on the choices of ℓ_0 respectively. We note that when both $L^{(0)}$ and $L^{(1)}$ are orientable, we have $\text{Image}(\mu_{\ell_0}) \subset 2\mathbb{Z}$. Then we defined $\Lambda^k(L^{(0)}, L^{(1)}; \ell_0)$ as the set of formal sums

$$\sum_{\substack{\beta \in \Pi(L^{(0)}, L^{(1)}; \ell_0) \\ \mu_{\ell_0}(\beta) = k}} a_\beta [\beta]$$

with $a_\beta \in R$ such that for each constant $C \in \mathbb{R}$, the set

$$\{\beta \in \Pi(L^{(0)}, L^{(1)}; \ell_0) \mid E_{\ell_0}(\beta) \leq C, \ a_\beta \neq 0\}$$

is of finite order. Then $\Lambda(L^{(0)}, L^{(1)}; \ell_0)$ is the direct sum

$$\Lambda(L^{(0)}, L^{(1)}; \ell_0) = \bigoplus_k \Lambda^k(L^{(0)}, L^{(1)}; \ell_0).$$

See Definition 2.2.6. Floer's cochain complex $CF(L^{(1)}, L^{(0)}; \ell_0)$ we defined in Sections 2.3 and 2.4 is a module over this ring $\Lambda(L^{(0)}, L^{(1)}; \ell_0)$. In fact, as a graded module, $CF(L^{(1)}, L^{(0)}; \ell_0)$ depends also on the choice of λ^0. (See Subsection 2.2.2 for the definition of λ^0.) To highlight this dependence, we will write

$$CF(L^{(1)}, L^{(0)}; \ell_0) = CF(L^{(1)}, L^{(0)}; \ell_0, \lambda^0).$$

But the Novikov ring $\Lambda(L^{(0)}, L^{(1)}; \ell_0)$ does not depend on the choice of λ^0. (See Subsection 2.2.2).

We now study how $\Lambda(L^{(0)}, L^{(1)}; \ell_0)$ depends on the choice of ℓ_0. By definition, it is a completion of the group ring $G(\Pi(L^{(1)}, L^{(0)}; \ell_0))$ with respect to the energy filtration, and so it is enough to study the dependence of $\Pi(L^{(1)}, L^{(0)}; \ell_0)$ on ℓ_0.

First of all, we note from the definition of $\Pi(L^{(0)}, L^{(1)}; \ell_0)$ that we have

$$\Pi(L^{(0)}, L^{(1)}; \ell_0) = \frac{\pi_1(\Omega(L^{(1)}, L^{(0)}); \ell_0)}{\text{Ker}\, E_{\ell_0} \cap \text{Ker}\, \mu_{\ell_0}}.$$

Consider a path $\gamma : [0, 1] \to \Omega(L^{(0)}, L^{(1)})$ joining ℓ_0 to ℓ_0'. The conjugate concatenation map by γ on $\mathcal{L}(\Omega(L^{(0)}, L^{(1)}); \ell_0)$ to $\mathcal{L}(\Omega(L^{(0)}, L^{(1)}); \ell_0')$

$$w \to \gamma \# w \# \gamma^{-1}$$

induces a homeomorphism

$$\gamma_* : \mathcal{L}(\Omega(L^{(0)}, L^{(1)}); \ell_0) \to \mathcal{L}(\Omega(L^{(0)}, L^{(1)}); \ell_0')$$

where $\mathcal{L}(\Omega(L^{(0)}, L^{(1)}); \ell_0)$ denotes the space of loops based at ℓ_0. Here we denote by γ^{-1} the time-reversal path of γ, i.e., $\gamma^{-1}(t) = \gamma(1-t)$. It is immediate to check γ_* induces an isomorphism

(5.1.2) $$\gamma_* : \pi_1(\Omega(L^{(0)}, L^{(1)}); \ell_0) \to \pi_1(\Omega(L^{(0)}, L^{(1)}); \ell_0')$$

that respects the energy and the Maslov index in that it satisfies

$$E_{\ell_0'} \circ \gamma_* = E_{\ell_0}, \quad \mu_{\ell_0'} \circ \gamma_* = \mu_{\ell_0}.$$

Therefore (5.1.2) induces an isomorphism

$$\gamma_* : \Pi(L^{(0)}, L^{(1)}; \ell_0) \to \Pi(L^{(0)}, L^{(1)}; \ell_0').$$

We summarize this discussion into

PROPOSITION 5.1.3. *Let ℓ_0' be an element of $\Omega(L^{(0)}, L^{(1)})$ contained in the same component as ℓ_0. Then each choice of the path $\gamma : [0,1] \to \Omega(L^{(0)}, L^{(1)})$ joining ℓ_0 to ℓ_0', determines an isomorphism*

$$\gamma_* : \Pi(L^{(0)}, L^{(1)}; \ell_0) \to \Pi(L^{(0)}, L^{(1)}; \ell_0')$$

depending only on the homotopy class of the path γ, and satisfies

$$E_{\ell_0} = E_{\ell_0'} \circ \gamma_*, \quad \mu_{\ell_0} = \mu_{\ell_0'} \circ \gamma_*.$$

In particular, γ_* induces an isomorphism of the Novikov rings

$$\gamma_* : \Lambda(L^{(0)}, L^{(1)}; \ell_0) \to \Lambda(L^{(0)}, L^{(1)}; \ell_0')$$

which respects both the filtration and the grading, and which does not depend on the choice of path γ between ℓ_0 and ℓ_0'.

Therefore we have a canonical isomorphism between two rings $\Lambda(L^{(0)}, L^{(1)}; \ell_0)$ and $\Lambda(L^{(0)}, L^{(1)}; \ell_0')$ as long as ℓ_0' lies in the same component of ℓ_0.

Now we define the embedding of $\Lambda(L^{(0)}, L^{(1)}; \ell_0)$ into Λ_{nov} as follows.

DEFINITION 5.1.4. We define the

$$I_{L^{(0)}, L^{(1)}; \ell_0} : \Lambda(L^{(0)}, L^{(1)}; \ell_0) \to \Lambda_{nov}$$

by

$$I_{L^{(0)}, L^{(1)}; \ell_0} \left(\sum_{\beta \in \Pi(L^{(0)}, L^{(1)}; \ell_0)} a_\beta [\beta] \right) = \sum_{\beta \in \Pi(L^{(0)}, L^{(1)}; \ell_0)} a_\beta T^{E_{\ell_0}(\beta)} e^{\frac{\mu_{\ell_0}(\beta)}{2}}.$$

We would like to recall that $\mu_{\ell_0}(\beta)$ is always even when L_0 and L_1 are orientable and so the image of $I_{L^{(0)}, L^{(1)}; \ell_0}$ really lies in Λ_{nov}. In general we need to extend the universal Novikov ring Λ_{nov} to $\Lambda_{nov}[e^{1/2}]$ to define the map $I_{L^{(0)}, L^{(1)}; \ell_0}$.

Now it is immediate to check the following lemmas which are the counterparts of Lemma 5.1.1 for the *pairs* of Lagrangian submanifolds.

LEMMA 5.1.5. *Under the above mentioned canonical isomorphism between two Novikov rings $\Lambda(L^{(0)}, L^{(1)}; \ell_0)$ and $\Lambda(L^{(0)}, L^{(1)}; \ell_0')$, we have*

$$I_{L^{(0)}, L^{(1)}; \ell_0} = I_{L^{(0)}, L^{(1)}; \ell_0'}.$$

LEMMA 5.1.6. *Let $\psi : M \to M'$ be a symplectic diffeomorphism such that $\psi(L^{(i)}) = L^{(i)\prime}$ are satisfied for $i = 0, 1$. Then we have an isomorphism*

$$\psi_* : \Pi(L^{(0)}, L^{(1)}; \ell_0) \to \Pi(L_0', L_1'; \psi(\ell_0))$$

and then

$$\psi_* : \Lambda(L^{(0)}, L^{(1)}; \ell_0) \to \Lambda(L^{(0)\prime}, L^{(1)\prime}; \psi(\ell_0)).$$

Moreover it satisfies

$$I_{\Lambda(L^{(0)\prime}, L^{(1)\prime}; \ell_0'} \circ \psi_* = I_{L^{(0)}, L^{(1)}; \ell_0}.$$

5.1.2. Hamiltonian independence of the Novikov ring. Let $\{\psi_t^{(0)}\}_{0 \leq t \leq 1}$ and $\{\psi_t^{(1)}\}_{0 \leq t \leq 1}$ be two Hamiltonian isotopies, which we use to move $L^{(0)}$ and $L^{(1)}$ respectively. We put $\vec{\psi} = (\{\psi_t^{(0)}\}_t, \{\psi_t^{(1)}\}_t)$. For a path $\ell : [0,1] \to M$ with $\ell(i) \in L^{(i)}$, we define $\ell^{\vec{\psi}} : [0,1] \to M$ by

$$\ell^{\vec{\psi}}(t) = (\psi_t^{(1)} \circ \psi_{1-t}^{(0)})(\ell(t)).$$

It induces a map

$$I_{\vec{\psi}} = I_{\psi^{(0)}, \psi^{(1)}} : \Omega(L^{(0)}, L^{(1)}) \to \Omega(\psi_1^{(0)}(L^{(0)}), \psi_1^{(1)}(L^{(1)})).$$

We consider the connected component $\Omega(\psi_1^{(0)}(L^{(0)}), \psi_1^{(1)}(L^{(1)}); \ell_0^{\vec{\psi}})$ of the space $\Omega(\psi_1^{(0)}(L^{(0)}), \psi_1^{(1)}(L^{(1)}))$ of paths containing $\ell_0^{\vec{\psi}} = I_{\vec{\psi}}(\ell_0)$. Denote by

$$\Pi(\psi_1^{(0)}(L^{(0)}), \psi_1^{(1)}(L^{(1)}); \ell_0^{\vec{\psi}})$$

the corresponding covering group.

When we fix a section λ^0 of $\ell_0^* \Lambda M$, we consider the induced section $\lambda_{\vec{\psi}}^0(t) = (\psi_t^{(1)} \circ \psi_{1-t}^{(0)})_*(\lambda^0(t))$ over $(\ell_0^{\vec{\psi}})^* \Lambda M$.

PROPOSITION 5.1.7. *The map $I_{\vec{\psi}} : \ell \mapsto \ell^{\vec{\psi}}$ induces an isomorphism*

$$I_{\vec{\psi}*} : \Pi(L^{(0)}, L^{(1)}; \ell_0) \cong \Pi(\psi_1^{(0)}(L^{(0)}), \psi_1^{(1)}(L^{(1)}); \ell_0^{\vec{\psi}})$$

such that

$$E_{\ell_0^{\vec{\psi}}} \circ I_{\vec{\psi}} = E_{\ell_0}, \quad \mu_{\lambda^0} \circ I_{\vec{\psi}} = \mu_{\lambda_{\vec{\psi}}^0}.$$

PROOF. Without loss of any generality, we will assume $\psi_\rho^{(0)} \equiv id$. So, in place of $\vec{\psi} = (id, \psi)$, we write ψ. The following lemma is immediate from the definition of $\Omega(L^{(0)}, L^{(1)}; \ell_0)$.

LEMMA 5.1.8. *Let $\gamma : S^1 \to \Omega(L^{(0)}, L^{(1)}; \ell_0)$ be a loop, and let $\nu : S^1 \times [0,1] \to M$ be the corresponding map induced by γ. Then the followings are equivalent:*

(5.1.9.1) *γ is lifted to a loop $\tilde{\gamma} : S^1 \to \widetilde{\Omega}(L^{(0)}, L^{(1)}; \ell_0)$.*
(5.1.9.2) *$\int_{S^1 \times [0,1]} \nu^* \omega = 0$ and $\mu([\gamma]) = 0$ where the homomorphism*

$$\mu : \pi_1(\Omega(L^{(0)}, L^{(1)}), \ell_0) \to \mathbb{Z}$$

is the Maslov index as defined in Subsection 2.2.1.

For a given Hamiltonian isotopy $\{\psi_\rho\}_{0 \leq \rho \leq 1}$, we consider the map

$$I_\psi : \Omega(L^{(0)}, L^{(1)}) \to \Omega(L^{(0)}, \psi_1(L^{(1)}))$$

defined as above. To prove Proposition 5.1.7, it will be enough to prove

LEMMA 5.1.10. *For a given loop $\gamma : S^1 \to \Omega(L^{(0)}, L^{(1)})$, the following two conditions are equivalent:*

(5.1.11.1) *γ can be lifted to $\tilde{\gamma} : S^1 \to \tilde{\Omega}(L^{(0)}, L^{(1)})$.*
(5.1.11.2) *$I_\psi(\gamma) : S^1 \to \Omega(L^{(0)}, \psi_1(L^{(0)}))$ can be lifted to a loop $\widetilde{I_\psi \circ \gamma} : S^1 \to \tilde{\Omega}(L^{(0)}, \psi_1(L^{(1)}))$.*

PROOF. Suppose (5.1.11.1) holds and let $\nu : S^1 \times [0,1] \to M$ be the natural map associated to γ which is defined by $\nu(\sigma, \rho) = \gamma(\sigma)(\rho)$. Obviously the natural map $\nu_\psi : S^1 \times [0,1] \to M$ associated to the loop $I_\psi(\gamma) : S^1 \to \Omega(L^{(0)}, \psi_1(L^{(1)}))$ is given by

$$(5.1.12) \qquad \nu_\psi(\sigma, \rho) = \psi_\rho(\nu(\sigma, \rho)) = \psi_\rho(\gamma(\sigma)(\rho)).$$

By Lemma 5.1.8, it is enough to prove the following two equalities:

$$(5.1.13.1) \qquad \int \nu_\psi^* \omega = \int \nu^* \omega$$

$$(5.1.13.2) \qquad \mu_{\lambda^0}([\gamma]) = \mu_{\lambda^0_{\{id,\psi\}}}([I_\psi(\gamma)]).$$

Let $H : [0,1] \times M \to \mathbb{R}$ be the Hamiltonian generating the isotopy ψ. We compute

$$\int \nu_\psi^* \omega = \int_{S^1 \times [0,1]} \omega \left(\frac{\partial \nu_\psi}{\partial \sigma}, \frac{\partial \nu_\psi}{\partial \rho} \right) d\sigma d\rho.$$

Then by (5.1.12), we have

$$\frac{\partial \nu_\psi}{\partial \sigma} = d\psi_\rho \left(\frac{\partial \nu}{\partial \sigma} \right), \qquad \frac{\partial \nu_\psi}{\partial \rho} = X_H(\nu) + d\psi_\rho \left(\frac{\partial \nu}{\partial \rho} \right)$$

(where $d\psi_\rho$ denotes the differential of ψ_ρ) and so

$$\int \nu_\psi^* \omega = \int_{S^1 \times [0,1]} \omega \left(d\psi_\rho \left(\frac{\partial \nu}{\partial \sigma} \right), X_H(\nu) + d\psi_\rho \left(\frac{\partial \nu}{\partial \rho} \right) \right) d\sigma d\rho$$

$$= \int_{S^1 \times [0,1]} \frac{\partial}{\partial \sigma} H(\psi_\rho(\nu(\sigma, \rho))) \, d\sigma d\rho + \int \nu^* \omega = \int \nu^* \omega.$$

This proves (5.1.13.1).

For the proof of (5.1.13.2), we consider the bundle pairs $(\nu^* TM, \nu_0^* TL^{(0)} \sqcup \nu_1^* TL^{(1)})$ and $(\nu_\psi^* TM, \nu_0^* TL^{(0)} \sqcup (\psi_1 \circ \nu_1)^* TL^{(1)})$. One can immediately check that the two bundle pairs are homotopic as a symplectic bundle pair via the family of maps $\nu_\psi^s : S^1 \times [0,1] \to M$ defined by the reparametrized maps

$$\nu_\psi^s(\sigma, \rho) = \psi_{s\rho}(\nu(\sigma, \rho)); \quad s \in [0,1].$$

Therefore by the homotopy invariance of the index of symplectic bundle pairs, we obtain $\mu(E_\nu, L_\nu) = \mu(E_{\nu_\psi}, L_{\nu_\psi})$. This finishes the proof of Lemma 5.1.10. $\qquad \square$

Now, we go back to the proof of Proposition 5.1.7. It immediately follows from Lemma 5.1.8 that the map I_ψ defined as above induces a natural map of the covering groups, i.e.,

$$I_\psi : \Pi(L^{(0)}, L^{(1)}; \ell_0) \to \Pi(L^{(0)}, \psi_1(L^{(1)}); \ell_0^{\vec{\psi}}).$$

The compatibility

$$E_{\ell_0^{\vec{\psi}}} \circ I_\psi = E_{\ell_0}$$

also follows from (5.1.13.1). Hence we have proved Proposition 5.1.7. $\qquad \square$

Proposition 5.1.7 implies the following:

COROLLARY 5.1.14. *There exists an isomorphism*

$$I_{\vec{\psi},*} : \Lambda(L^{(0)}, L^{(1)}; \ell_0) \to \Lambda(\psi_1^{(0)}(L^{(0)}), \psi_1^{(1)}(L^{(1)}); \ell_0^{\vec{\psi}})$$

such that

$$I_{\phi_1^{(0)}(L^{(0)}), \phi_1^{(1)}(L^{(1)})); \ell_0^{\vec{\phi}}} \circ I_{\vec{\phi},*} = I_{L^{(0)}, L^{(1)}; \ell_0}.$$

5.1.3. Floer cohomologies over $\Lambda(L^{(0)}, L^{(1)}; \ell_0)$ and Λ_{nov}. In Chapter 2, we discussed the construction of Floer cohomology for a pair of Lagrangian submanifolds with coefficients in $\Lambda(L^{(0)}, L^{(1)}; \ell_0)$ with some restriction on the Lagrangian submanifolds. On the other hand, in Chapter 3, we constructed the filtered A_∞ bimodule for a general relatively spin pair of Lagrangian submanifolds, which uses $\Lambda_{0,nov}$ or its localization Λ_{nov} as its coefficients. If all the obstructions vanish, or if the Maurer-Cartan moduli spaces $\mathcal{M}(L^{(i)})$ is non-empty for both $i = 0, 1$, we obtain the Floer cohomology of the pair $(L^{(0)}, L^{(1)})$ after we deform the Floer coboundary map.

In this subsection, we explain the relationship between the earlier construction of the Floer cohomology described in Chapter 2 and our construction in Chapter 3 which uses the A_∞ bimodule.

Let $(L^{(0)}, L^{(1)})$ be a transversal pair of Lagrangian submanifolds. In the beginning, we assume that it is a relatively spin pair. Note that since both $L^{(i)}$, $i = 0, 1$ are oriented in this case, the parity of the Maslov-Morse index of each intersection point is well-defined, i.e., the parity of $\mu([\ell_p, w])$ does not depend on the bounding path w.

Then the module $C(L^{(1)}, L^{(0)}; \Lambda_{0,nov})$, (resp. $C(L^{(1)}, L^{(0)}; \Lambda_{nov})$), which we defined in Definition 3.7.20, is a free module generated by $\langle p \rangle$ over $\Lambda_{0,nov}$, (resp. Λ_{nov}). Here, we write

$$\langle p \rangle = T^{-\mathcal{A}_{\ell_0}([\ell_p, w])} e^{-\mu_{\ell_0}([\ell_p, w])/2}[\ell_p, w], \qquad \text{if } \mu_{\ell_0}([\ell_p, w]) \text{ is even,}$$

and

$$\langle p \rangle = T^{-\mathcal{A}_{\ell_0}([\ell_p, w])} e^{-(\mu_{\ell_0}([\ell_p, w])-1)/2}[\ell_p, w], \qquad \text{if } \mu_{\ell_0}([\ell_p, w]) \text{ is odd.}$$

Thus the action of $\langle p \rangle$ is 0, and the degree of $\langle p \rangle$ is either 0 or 1 depending on the parity of the Maslov-Morse index of p respectively. If we write

$$\overline{V} = \bigoplus_k \bigoplus_{p \in L^{(0)} \cap L^{(1)}} \mathbb{Q} e^k \langle p \rangle,$$

$C(L^{(1)}, L^{(0)}; \Lambda_{0,nov})$ is generated by $\overline{V}$ as a $\Lambda_{0,nov}^{(0)}$-module (cf. Section 6.3), which spans the energy-zero subspace. In other words, we regard $\langle p \rangle$ as the generator with energy zero. By Remark 3.7.46, we have

$$C(L^{(1)}, L^{(0)}; \Lambda_{0,nov}) = \widehat{\bigoplus_{[\ell_0] \in \pi_0(\Omega(L^{(0)}, L^{(1)}))}} C(L^{(1)}, L^{(0)}; \Lambda_{0,nov}; \ell_0).$$

Here $\widehat{\bigoplus}$ is a completion of the direct sum.

Recall the definition (Definition 2.4.2) of the Floer cochain module. By definition, we have an inclusion

(5.1.15.1) $CF^*(L^{(1)}, L^{(0)}; \ell_0) \to C^*(L^{(1)}, L^{(0)}; \Lambda_{nov}; \ell_0)$

defined by

$$(5.1.15.2) \qquad [\ell_p, w] \mapsto e^{(\mu([\ell_p,w])-\mu(\langle p \rangle))/2} T^{\mathcal{A}_{\ell_0}([\ell_p,w])} \langle p \rangle.$$

It is compatible with the inclusion $I_{L^{(0)},L^{(1)};\ell_0} : \Lambda(L^{(0)}, L^{(1)}; \ell_0) \to \Lambda_{nov}$ in Definition 5.1.4.

The degree 0-part of the Novikov ring $\Lambda(L^{(0)}, L^{(1)}; \ell_0)$ is a field, i.e., all nonzero elements are invertible, if the ground ring of the Novikov ring is a field. (See [HoSa95].). The degree 0-part of the universal Novikov ring $\Lambda_{nov}^{(0)}$ is also a field. By $I_{L^{(0)},L^{(1)};\ell_0}$ in Definition 5.1.4, $\Lambda^{(0)}(L^{(0)}, L^{(1)}; \ell_0)$ is embedded in $\Lambda_{nov}^{(0)}$ and $\Lambda_{nov}^{(0)}$ is a field extension of $\Lambda^{(0)}(L^{(0)}, L^{(1)}; \ell_0)$. In particular, $\Lambda_{nov}^{(0)}$ is flat over $\Lambda^{(0)}(L^{(0)}, L^{(1)}; \ell_0)$ and the process of taking the cohomology commutes with the extension of coefficients. Note also that $\Lambda(L^{(0)}, L^{(1)}; \ell_0)$ is the completion of the ring $\bigoplus_k \Lambda^{(0)}(L^{(0)}, L^{(1)}; \ell_0)e^k$ with respect to the energy filtration. (Here e does not effect the energy but shift the degree by 2.)

Now we consider the case when $L^{(i)}$ are monotone Lagrangian submanifolds with the minimal Maslov number at least 3 (as in Theorem 2.4.42). In case we assume $L^{(i)}$ are oriented and relatively spin we put $R = \mathbb{Z}$. In general (where we do not assume that $L^{(i)}$ are oriented either) we take $R = \mathbb{Z}_2$.

We consider the module $CF^*(L^{(1)}, L^{(0)}; \ell_0)$ and the coboundary operator

$$\delta_0 : CF^*(L^{(1)}, L^{(0)}; \ell_0) \to CF^{*+1}(L^{(1)}, L^{(0)}; \ell_0)$$

defined as in Subsections 2.3.3 and 2.4.1. By Theorem 2.4.42, we have: $\delta_0 \circ \delta_0 = 0$ in our situation. Hence Floer cohomology

$$HF(L^{(1)}, L^{(0)}; \ell_0) = \operatorname{Ker} \delta_0 / \operatorname{Im} \delta_0$$

is defined and is a $\Lambda(L^{(0)}, L^{(1)}; \ell_0)$ module.

If $L^{(i)}$ are not orientable, the parity of the intersection point is not necessarily well-defined: the parity of the Maslov-Morse index $\mu_{\ell_0}([\ell_p, w])$ may depend on the choice of the bounding path w connecting ℓ_0 and ℓ_p. In this case, we slightly modify the set-up. We define $\langle p \rangle$ to be the formal generator with energy 0 and the degree 0. Then we extend the universal Novikov ring by allowing the half-integer power of e. Then we have the inclusion

$$(5.1.16.1) \qquad CF^*(L^{(1)}, L^{(0)}; \ell_0) \to C^*(L^{(1)}, L^{(0)}; \Lambda_{nov}[e^{1/2}]; \ell_0)$$

by

$$(5.1.16.2) \qquad [\ell_p, w] \mapsto e^{\mu([\ell_p,w])/2} T^{\mathcal{A}_{\ell_0}([\ell_p,w])} \langle p \rangle.$$

We remark that in the monotone case the construction in Chapter 3 can be performed over $R = \mathbb{Z}$ or $\mathbb{Z}_2$ and hence Floer cohomology is defined over $R = \mathbb{Z}$ or $\mathbb{Z}_2$.

PROPOSITION 5.1.17. (1) *If the minimal Maslov numbers of $L^{(i)}$ are at least 3, then there exists a bounding cochain $b^{(i)} \in C^1(L^{(i)}; \Lambda_{0,nov})$ such that $b^{(i)} =*

$\sum_k T^{\lambda_k} e^{n_k} b_k^{(i)}$ with $\deg b_k^{(i)} < 0$. *Moreover the homomorphism (5.1.16.2) induces an isomorphism*

$$\bigoplus_{[\ell_0] \in \pi_0(\Omega(L^{(0)}, L^{(1)}))} HF(L^{(1)}, L^{(0)}; \ell_0) \otimes_{\Lambda(L^{(0)}, L^{(1)})} \Lambda_{nov}^{\mathbb{Z}_2}[e^{1/2}]$$

$$\cong HF((L^{(1)}, b^{(1)}), (L^{(0)}, b^{(0)}); \Lambda_{nov}^{\mathbb{Z}_2})[e^{1/2}].$$

If $(L^{(1)}, L^{(0)})$ is a relatively spin pair in addition, then we have

$$\bigoplus_{[\ell_0] \in \pi_0(\Omega(L^{(0)}, L^{(1)}))} HF(L^{(1)}, L^{(0)}; \ell_0) \otimes_{\Lambda(L^{(0)}, L^{(1)})} \Lambda_{nov}^{\mathbb{Z}}$$

$$\cong HF((L^{(1)}, b^{(1)}), (L^{(0)}, b^{(0)}); \Lambda_{nov}^{\mathbb{Z}}).$$

(2) *We assume that $L^{(1)} = \psi(L^{(0)})$ for a Hamiltonian diffeomorphism ψ and that the minimal Maslov number of $L^{(0)}$ is at least 2. Then the same conclusion holds.*

PROOF. Since minimal Maslov number is at least 3 it follows that

$$\dim \mathcal{M}_1(L^{(i)}; \beta) \geq \dim L^{(i)} + 1$$

whenever $\mathcal{M}_1(L^{(i)}; \beta) \neq \emptyset$ and $\beta \neq 0$. Hence

$$\mathfrak{m}_0^{L^{(i)}}(1) = \sum_k T^{\lambda_k} e^{n_k} \mathfrak{m}_{0,k}^{L^{(i)}}(1)$$

with

$$\mathfrak{m}_{0,k}^{L^{(i)}}(1) \in C^{\dim L^{(i)} - \dim \mathcal{M}_1(L^{(i)}; \beta)}(L^{(i)}; \mathbb{Q}) \subset \bigoplus_{j < 0} C^j(L^{(i)}; \mathbb{Q}).$$

Therefore we can show by induction that obstruction vanishes. We can also prove that there exists $b^{(i)} \in C^1(L^{(i)}; \Lambda_{0,nov})$ such that

$$b^{(i)} = \sum_k T^{\lambda_k} e^{n_k} b_k^{(i)}$$

with $\deg b_k^{(i)} < 0$.

Using the fact that the cohomology degree of $b_k^{(i)}$ is negative (that is homology dimension of $b_k^{(i)}$ is bigger than $\dim L^{(i)}$), we can prove that

$$\delta_{b^{(1)}, b^{(0)}} = \delta_{0,0},$$

by dimension counting. (Here $\delta_{b^{(1)}, b^{(0)}}$ is as in (3.7.16).)

It is then immediate from definition that (5.1.16) is a chain map. It follows from the definition that (5.1.16) induces an isomorphism

$$CF^*(L^{(1)}, L^{(0)}; \ell_0) \otimes_{\Lambda(L^{(0)}, L^{(1)}; \ell_0)} \Lambda_{nov}[e^{1/2}] \to C^*(L^{(1)}, L^{(0)}; \Lambda_{nov}[e^{1/2}]; \ell_0).$$

Therefore the flatness mentioned before finishes the proof of the proposition.

The proof of (2) is similar.   □

REMARK 5.1.18. If the Maslov classes of $L^{(0)}$ and $L^{(1)}$ vanish, we can equip them with a grading in the sense of [**Sei00**] which provides each intersection point of $L^{(0)}$ and $L^{(1)}$ with a canonical grading. Therefore the Floer graded cochain complex $C^*(L^{(1)}, L^{(0)}; \Lambda_{nov}^{(0)})$ is defined, whenever the obstructions vanish. Similarly, if we denote the greatest common divisor of the minimal Maslov numbers of $L^{(0)}$ and $L^{(1)}$ by $2N$, we can define the Floer cochain complex over the subring $\Lambda_{nov,N}$ of the universal Novikov ring Λ_{nov}, where the ring $\Lambda_{nov,N}$ is defined as

$$\Lambda_{nov,N} = \left\{ \sum_i a_i e^{\mu_i} T^{\lambda_i} \in \Lambda_{nov} \ \middle| \ \mu_i \text{ is an integral multiple of } N \right\}.$$

By the similar arguments as above in the monotone case, we establish the isomorphism

$$\bigoplus_{[\ell_0] \in \pi_0(\Omega(L^{(0)}, L^{(1)}))} HF(L^{(1)}, L^{(0)}; \ell_0) \otimes_{\Lambda(L^{(0)}, L^{(1)}; \ell_0)} \Lambda_{nov,N}^{\mathbb{Z}}$$

$$\cong HF((L^{(1)}, 0), (L^{(0)}, 0); \Lambda_{nov,N}^{\mathbb{Z}})$$

for the general unobstructed cases. We will discuss this point more in Subsection 5.4.6.

5.2. Homotopy equivalences of A_∞ bimodules: the algebraic framework

5.2.1. Weakly filtered A_∞ bimodule homomorphisms. In Subsections 3.7.1 and 3.7.2, we defined the basic notions on the filtered A_∞ bimodule and the filtered A_∞ bimodule homomorphisms over $\Lambda_{0,nov}$. For the later applications, we need to consider both $\Lambda_{0,nov}$ and Λ_{nov} as the coefficients. So we begin with discussing A_∞ bimodule homomorphisms over Λ_{nov}.

Let $(C_i, \mathfrak{m})$ and $(C_i', \mathfrak{m}')$ $(i = 0, 1)$ be filtered A_∞ algebras over $\Lambda_{0,nov}$ and $\mathfrak{f}^{(i)} : C_i \to C_i'$ be filtered A_∞ homomorphisms between them. Consider a filtered (C_1, C_0) A_∞ bimodule $(D, \mathfrak{n})$ and a filtered (C_1', C_0') A_∞ bimodule $(D', \mathfrak{n}')$, which are defined over $\Lambda_{0,nov}$. We denote

$$\widetilde{D} = D \otimes_{\Lambda_{0,nov}} \Lambda_{nov},$$

which is a filtered A_∞ bimodule over Λ_{nov}. We note that $\widetilde{D}$ has the filtration $F^\lambda \widetilde{D}$ over $\lambda \in \mathbb{R}$, while D has the filtration $F^\lambda D$ over $\lambda \geq 0$. We define $\widetilde{D}'$ in the same way.

DEFINITION 5.2.1. Let $\widetilde{D}, \widetilde{D}'$ be the filtered A_∞ bimodules over Λ_{nov} defined as above. A *weakly filtered A_∞ bimodule homomorphism* $\widetilde{D} \to \widetilde{D}'$ *over* $(\mathfrak{f}^{(1)}, \mathfrak{f}^{(0)})$ is a family of Λ_{nov}-module homomorphisms

$$\varphi_{k_1,k_0} : B_{k_1} C_1[1] \ \widehat{\otimes} \ \widetilde{D}[1] \ \widehat{\otimes} \ B_{k_0} C_0[1] \longrightarrow \widetilde{D}'[1]$$

(where the tensor products are taken over $\Lambda_{0,nov}$) with the following properties:

(5.2.2.1) There exists $c \geq 0$ independent of k_1, k_0 such that

$$\varphi_{k_1,k_0} \left(F^{\lambda_1} B_{k_1} C_1[1] \ \widehat{\otimes} \ F^\lambda \widetilde{D}[1] \ \widehat{\otimes} \ F^{\lambda_0} B_{k_0} C_0[1] \right) \subseteq F^{\lambda_1 + \lambda + \lambda_0 - c} \widetilde{D}'[1].$$

(5.2.2.2)   The co-module homomorphism

$$\widehat{\varphi} = \sum_{k_1,k_0} \widehat{\varphi}_{k_1,k_0} : BC_1[1] \,\widehat{\otimes}\, \widetilde{D}[1] \,\widehat{\otimes}\, BC_0[1] \to BC_1'[1] \,\widehat{\otimes}\, \widetilde{D}'[1] \,\widehat{\otimes}\, BC_0'[1]$$

induced by φ_{k_1,k_0} and $\mathfrak{f}^{(i)}$ (see Definition 3.7.7) is a cochain map. Namely $\widehat{\varphi} \circ \widehat{d} = \widehat{d'} \circ \widehat{\varphi}$, where $\widehat{d}$ and $\widehat{d'}$ are defined as in (3.7.2). We simply write this bimodule homomorphism as $\varphi : \widetilde{D} \to \widetilde{D}'$.

When we need to specify the constant c in (5.2.2.1), we call $\varphi = \{\varphi_{k_1,k_0}\}$ a *c-weakly filtered A_∞ bimodule homomorphism* and c the *energy loss*.

Suppose that $(C_i, \mathfrak{m})$, $(C_i', \mathfrak{m}')$ have units and $\mathfrak{f}^{(i)}$, $(D, \mathfrak{n})$, $(D', \mathfrak{n}')$ are unital. (See Definitions 3.7.5.) As we defined in Subsection 3.7.2, we say that a weakly filtered A_∞ bimodule homomorphism $\varphi : \widetilde{D} \to \widetilde{D}'$ is *unital* if it satisfies (3.7.11). Furthermore, when $(C_i, \mathfrak{m})$, $(C_i', \mathfrak{m}')$ have homotopy units and $\mathfrak{f}^{(i)}$, $(D, \mathfrak{n})$, $(D', \mathfrak{n}')$ are homotopy-unital (see Definitions 3.7.5), we say a weakly filtered A_∞ bimodule homomorphism is *homotopy-unital* if it extends to a unital weakly filtered A_∞ bimodule homomorphism over $(\mathfrak{f}^{(1),+}, \mathfrak{f}^{(0),+})$. See Definition 3.7.12.

To define a gapped condition for the weakly filtered A_∞ bimodule homomorphisms, we first need to define an analogue of the monoid $G \subseteq \mathbb{R}_{\geq 0} \times 2\mathbb{Z}$ introduced in Condition 3.1.6.

DEFINITION 5.2.3. (*G-set G'*) Let $G \subset \mathbb{R}_{\geq 0} \times 2\mathbb{Z}$ be a monoid satisfying Condition 3.1.6. For $G \subset \mathbb{R} \times 2\mathbb{Z}$, we call a set G' a *G-set* if it holds that whenever $g \in G$ and $g' \in G'$, $g + g' \in G'$.

We will consider a G-set G' that satisfies the conditions:

(5.2.4.1)   There exists $c \geq 0$ such that $-c \leq \lambda$ for any $(\lambda, \mu) \in G'$.
(5.2.4.2)   Let $\pi : \mathbb{R} \times 2\mathbb{Z} \to \mathbb{R}$ be the projection. Then $\pi(G') \subset \mathbb{R}$ is discrete.
(5.2.4.3) $G' \cap (\{\lambda\} \times 2\mathbb{Z})$ is a finite set for any $\lambda \in \mathbb{R}$.

DEFINITION 5.2.5. Let $\varphi : \widetilde{D} \to \widetilde{D}'$ be a weakly filtered A_∞ bimodule homomorphism over $\mathfrak{f}^{(i)} : C_i \to C_i'$ ($i = 0, 1$). We assume $\mathfrak{f}^{(i)}$ are G-gapped. Let G' be a G-set satisfying (5.2.4). We can enumerate the elements of G' as $G' = \{(\lambda_i', \mu_i') \,|\, i = 0, 1, 2, \cdots\}$ where $\lambda_i' \uparrow \infty$. We say that φ is *G'-gapped* if the homomorphism φ_{k_1,k_0} given in (5.2.2.1) is decomposed to

$$\varphi_{k_1,k_0} = \sum_i T^{\lambda_i'} e^{\mu_i'/2} \varphi_{k_1,k_0,i},$$

where

$$\varphi_{k_1,k_0,i} : B_{k_1}\overline{C}_1[1] \otimes \overline{D}[1] \otimes B_{k_0}\overline{C}_0[1] \to \overline{D}'[1]$$

are R-module homomorphisms. Here we identify $\widetilde{D} = \overline{D} \otimes_R \Lambda_{nov}$.

To define gapped condition for *weakly filtered A_∞ bimodule* we use G-set. In all other cases we use monoid G, to define gapped conditions.

5.2.2. Deformations of A_∞ bimodule homomorphisms. We defined the deformations of the filtered A_∞ algebras and the filtered A_∞ bimodules in Subsections 3.6.1 and 3.7.3 respectively. In this subsection, we will define the deformations of the filtered A_∞ algebra homomorphisms and the filtered A_∞ bimodule homomorphisms.

For this purpose, we first introduce the notion of the pull-back of the filtered A_∞ bimodule structures. Let $(D, \mathfrak{n})$, $(D', \mathfrak{n})$ be filtered A_∞ bimodules defined over $\Lambda_{0,nov}$ as in the previous subsection.

LEMMA 5.2.6. *Let $(D, \mathfrak{n})$ be a filtered (C_1', C_0') A_∞ bimodule, and let $\mathfrak{f}^{(i)} : C_i \to C_i'$ $(i = 0, 1)$ be filtered A_∞ homomorphisms. Then there exists a structure of a (C_1, C_0) filtered A_∞ bimodule on D, which we denote by $((\mathfrak{f}^{(1)}, \mathfrak{f}^{(0)})^*D, (\mathfrak{f}^{(1)}, \mathfrak{f}^{(0)})^*\mathfrak{n})$. Moreover there exists a filtered A_∞ bimodule homomorphism $\varphi : (\mathfrak{f}^{(1)}, \mathfrak{f}^{(2)})^*D \to D$ over $(\mathfrak{f}^{(1)}, \mathfrak{f}^{(0)})$ such that $\varphi_{0,0}$ is identity.*

The (unfiltered or weakly filtered) or/and (unital or homotopy-unital) versions also hold.

REMARK 5.2.7. Here and hereafter, we mean by "the (unfiltered or weakly filtered) or/and (unital or homotopy-unital) versions" all of the following 9 versions. Namely, unfiltered unital, weakly filtered unital, filtered unital, unfiltered homotopy-unital, weakly filtered homotopy-unital, filtered homotopy-unital, unfiltered non-unital, weakly filtered non-unital, and filtered non-unital versions.

DEFINITION 5.2.8. We call $(\mathfrak{f}^{(1)}, \mathfrak{f}^{(0)})^*D$ the *pull-back* of the bimodule D by $(\mathfrak{f}^{(1)}, \mathfrak{f}^{(0)})$.

PROOF OF LEMMA 5.2.6. We define

$$(\mathfrak{f}^{(1)}, \mathfrak{f}^{(0)})^*\mathfrak{n} : \widehat{B}C_1[1] \,\widehat{\otimes}\, D[1] \,\widehat{\otimes}\, \widehat{B}C_0[1] \to D[1]$$

by

$$(\widehat{\mathfrak{f}}^{(1)}, \mathfrak{f}^{(0)})^*\mathfrak{n}(\mathbf{x}, y, \mathbf{z}) = \mathfrak{n}(\widehat{\mathfrak{f}}^{(1)}(\mathbf{x}), y, \widehat{\mathfrak{f}}^{(0)}(\mathbf{z})),$$

where $\mathfrak{n}$ in the right hand side is the given (C_1', C_0') A_∞ bimodule structure on D. It is easy to see that this defines a filtered (C_1, C_0) A_∞ bimodule structure. We put $\varphi_{k_1,k_0} = 0$ for $(k_1, k_0) \neq (0, 0)$ and $\varphi_{0,0} = id$. It is easy to see that φ is a filtered A_∞ bimodule homomorphism over $(\mathfrak{f}^{(1)}, \mathfrak{f}^{(0)})$. $\square$

The pull-back operation is functorial. Namely we have the following lemma. In the situation of Lemma 5.2.6, let $\mathfrak{g}^{(i)} : C_i' \to C_i''$ $(i = 0, 1)$ be filtered A_∞ homomorphisms and D' a filtered (C_1'', C_0'') A_∞ bimodule.

LEMMA 5.2.9. *A filtered A_∞ bimodule homomorphism $\varphi : D \to D'$ over a pair of filtered A_∞ homomorphisms $(\mathfrak{g}^{(1)}, \mathfrak{g}^{(0)})$ induces a filtered A_∞ bimodule homomorphism*

$$(\mathfrak{f}^{(1)}, \mathfrak{f}^{(0)})^*\varphi : (\mathfrak{f}^{(1)}, \mathfrak{f}^{(0)})^*D \to (\mathfrak{g}^{(1)} \circ \mathfrak{f}^{(1)}, \mathfrak{g}^{(0)} \circ \mathfrak{f}^{(0)})^*D'$$

over identity.

(The unfiltered or weakly filtered) or/and (unital or homotopy-unital) versions also hold.

PROOF. The proof follows just by defining $(\mathfrak{f}^{(1)}, \mathfrak{f}^{(0)})^*\varphi$ to be

$$((\mathfrak{f}^{(1)}, \mathfrak{f}^{(0)})^*\varphi)(\mathbf{x}, y, \mathbf{z}) = \varphi(\widehat{\mathfrak{f}}^{(1)}(\mathbf{x}), y, \widehat{\mathfrak{f}}^{(0)}(\mathbf{z})).$$

$\square$

DEFINITION 5.2.10. We call $(\mathfrak{f}^{(1)}, \mathfrak{f}^{(0)})^*\varphi$ the *pull back* of φ by $(\mathfrak{f}^{(1)}, \mathfrak{f}^{(0)})$.

5.2.2.1. Definition of coalgebra isomorphisms. Now we define the deformations of the filtered A_∞ algebra homomorphisms. As we saw in Subsection 3.6.2, a filtered A_∞ algebra $(C, \mathfrak{m})$ can be deformed by any $b \in C[1]^0$ with $b \equiv 0 \mod \Lambda_{0,nov}^+$ so that

$$\mathfrak{m}_k^b(x_1, \cdots, x_k) = \mathfrak{m}(e^b x_1 e^b x_2 \cdots e^b x_k e^b).$$

See Definition 3.6.9 and Proposition 3.6.10. Corresponding to this, we will deform a filtered A_∞ algebra homomorphism. For this purpose, we introduce a coalgebra isomorphism on the bar complex $\widehat{B}C[1]$ as follows.

For $b \in C[1]^0$ with $b \equiv 0 \mod \Lambda_{0,nov}^+$, we define $\mathfrak{t}_{b,k} : B_k C[1] \to C[1]$ by $\mathfrak{t}_{b,0}(1) = b$, and $\mathfrak{t}_{b,k} = 0$ if $k \neq 0$. It induces a coalgebra homomorphism

$$\hat{\mathfrak{t}}_b : \widehat{B}C[1] \to \widehat{B}C[1].$$

Its restriction $\hat{\mathfrak{t}}_{b,k}$ to $B_k C[1]$ is

$$(5.2.11) \qquad \hat{\mathfrak{t}}_{b,k}(x_1, \cdots, x_k) = e^b \otimes x_1 \otimes e^b \otimes \cdots \otimes e^b \otimes x_k \otimes e^b.$$

Since $b \equiv 0 \mod \Lambda_{0,nov}^+$, we have $\hat{\mathfrak{t}}_b \equiv id \mod \Lambda_{0,nov}^+$ and by $\hat{\mathfrak{t}}_b$ the energy of each terms does not decrease. Hence it preserves the energy filtration and converges in the completion $\widehat{B}C[1]$ with respect to the energy filtration.

LEMMA 5.2.12. (1) $\hat{\mathfrak{t}}_b$ *is a coalgebra isomorphism on* $\widehat{B}C[1]$.

(2) *Moreover* $\hat{d} \circ \hat{\mathfrak{t}}_b = \hat{\mathfrak{t}}_b \circ \hat{d}^b$. *Thus it defines a filtered A_∞ homomorphism which we denote by* $\mathfrak{t}_b : (C, \mathfrak{m}^b) \to (C, \mathfrak{m})$.

PROOF. (1) The injectivity is obvious. To prove the surjectivity, we will inductively solve the equation

$$(5.2.13) \qquad\qquad \hat{\mathfrak{t}}_b(\mathbf{x}) = \mathbf{y}$$

for any $\mathbf{y} = y_1 \otimes \cdots \otimes y_\ell \in B_\ell C[1]$. For a non negative integer K, we say that $\mathbf{x} \in \widehat{B}C[1]$ is a *K-approximate solution* of (5.2.13) if it satisfies

$$\hat{\mathfrak{t}}_b(\mathbf{x})|_{B_{12\cdots(\ell+K)}C[1]} = \mathbf{y},$$

where $B_{12\cdots(\ell+K)}C[1] = \bigoplus_{k=1}^{\ell+K} B_k C[1]$ as in (4.4.5). We also denote

$$B_{\ell\cdots(\ell+K)}C[1] = \bigoplus_{k=\ell}^{\ell+K} B_k C[1].$$

SUBLEMMA 5.2.14. *Take any* $\mathbf{y} = y_1 \otimes \cdots \otimes y_\ell \in B_\ell C[1]$. *Then there exists a sequence* $\{a_{i_0,\cdots,i_\ell}\}_{i_j \geq 0, \ell > 0}$ *of integers such that the sum*

$$\mathbf{x}_{(\ell+K)} = \sum_{i_0+\cdots+i_\ell \leq K} a_{i_0,\cdots,i_\ell} b^{\otimes i_0} \otimes y_1 \otimes \cdots \otimes y_\ell \otimes b^{\otimes i_\ell} \in B_{\ell\cdots(\ell+K)}C[1]$$

is a K-approximate solution of (5.2.13) for any $K = 0, 1, 2, \cdots$.

PROOF OF SUBLEMMA 5.2.14. We prove the sublemma by induction on K. First we note that

$$\hat{t}_{b,k} \;:\; B_k C[1] \to \widehat{\bigoplus}_{\ell \geq k} B_\ell C[1]$$

and $\pi_k \circ \hat{t}_{b,k} = id$, where $\pi_k : \widehat{\bigoplus}_{\ell \geq k} B_\ell C[1] \to B_k C[1]$ is the projection. For $K = 0$, we put $a_0 = 1$. Then it is easy to see that

$$\mathbf{x}_{(\ell)} = y_1 \otimes \cdots \otimes y_\ell \in B_\ell C[1]$$

is a 0-approximate solution. Suppose that

$$\mathbf{x}_{(\ell+K)} = \sum_{i_0 + \cdots + i_\ell \leq K} a_{i_0, \cdots, i_\ell} b^{\otimes i_0} \otimes y_1 \otimes \cdots \otimes y_\ell \otimes b^{\otimes i_\ell}$$

is a K-approximate solution. Since we have

$$\hat{t}_b(\mathbf{x}_{(\ell+K)})\big|_{B_{1\cdots(\ell+K)}C[1]} = y_1 \otimes \cdots \otimes y_\ell,$$

by the induction hypothesis, we can put

$$\hat{t}_b(\mathbf{x}_{(\ell+K)}) = y_1 \otimes \cdots \otimes y_\ell + \sum_{i_0 + \cdots + i_\ell > K} a'_{i_0, \cdots, i_\ell} b^{\otimes i_0} \otimes y_1 \otimes \cdots \otimes y_\ell \otimes b^{\otimes i_\ell}$$

for some integers $a'_{i_0, \cdots, i_\ell}$. We define $\mathbf{x}_{(\ell+K+1)}$ by

$$\mathbf{x}_{(\ell+K+1)} = \mathbf{x}_{(\ell+K)} - \sum_{i_0 + \cdots + i_\ell = K+1} a'_{i_0, \cdots, i_\ell} \hat{t}_b(b^{\otimes i_0} \otimes y_1 \otimes \cdots \otimes y_\ell \otimes b^{\otimes i_\ell}).$$

Then we can easily see that $\mathbf{x}_{(\ell+K+1)}$ is a $(K+1)$-approximate solution that satisfies

$$\mathbf{x}_{\ell+K+1} \equiv \mathbf{x}_{\ell+K} \quad \mathrm{mod} \; \widehat{\bigoplus}_{k \geq \ell+K+1} B_k C[1].$$

This proves the sublemma. $\square$

Now the last formula in the above proof implies that the direct limit

$$\mathbf{x} := \lim_{K \to \infty} \mathbf{x}_{(\ell+K)}$$

exists. Furthermore, since we assume $b \equiv 0 \mod \Lambda^+_{0,nov}$, this limit also converges in the completion $\widehat{B}C[1]$ with respect to the energy filtration, which then provides a solution of (5.2.13). Thus we have finished the proof of the assertion (1) in Lemma 5.2.12.

(2) It is a direct calculation to show $\hat{d} \circ \hat{t}_b = \hat{t}_b \circ \hat{d}^b$. Moreover as we noted just before Lemma 5.2.12, $\hat{t}_b$ preserves the energy filtration so it satisfies (3.2.25.1). $\square$

5.2.2.2. Deformation of the A_∞ algebra homomorphisms. Next we consider a filtered A_∞ algebra homomorphism $\mathfrak{f} : C \to C'$ between the filtered A_∞ algebras $(C, \mathfrak{m})$ and $(C', \mathfrak{m}')$. We denote by $\hat{\mathfrak{f}} : \widehat{B}C[1] \to \widehat{B}C'[1]$ the induced coalgebra homomorphism (see (3.2.28)). We recall from Lemma 3.6.37 (1) that for any $b \in C[1]^0$ with $b \equiv 0 \mod \Lambda^+_{0,nov}$, we defined $\mathfrak{f}_*(b)$ by

$$\mathfrak{f}_*(b) = \mathfrak{f}(e^b) = \mathfrak{f}_0(1) + \mathfrak{f}_1(b) + \mathfrak{f}_2(b,b) + \cdots \in C[1]^0,$$

where $\mathfrak{f} = \sum_{k=0}^{\infty} \mathfrak{f}_k$. Note that we have $\mathfrak{f}_*(b) \equiv 0 \mod \Lambda^+_{0,nov}$ as well. Hence we can also consider the coalgebra isomorphism $\hat{t}_{\mathfrak{f}_*(b)}$ on $\widehat{B}C'[1]$.

DEFINITION-LEMMA 5.2.15. *For any* $b \in C[1]^0$ *with* $b \equiv 0 \mod \Lambda^+_{0,nov}$, *we define* $\widehat{\mathfrak{f}}^b = \hat{\mathfrak{t}}^{-1}_{\mathfrak{f}_*(b)} \circ \widehat{\mathfrak{f}} \circ \hat{\mathfrak{t}}_b : \widehat{B}C[1] \to \widehat{B}C'[1]$.

See the following commutative diagram.

$$
\begin{array}{ccc}
(\widehat{B}C[1], \widehat{d}) & \xrightarrow{\ \widehat{\mathfrak{f}}\ } & (\widehat{B}C'[1], \widehat{d}') \\[4pt]
\hat{\mathfrak{t}}_b \big\uparrow & & \big\downarrow \hat{\mathfrak{t}}^{-1}_{\mathfrak{f}_*(b)} \\[4pt]
(\widehat{B}C[1], \widehat{d}^b) & \xrightarrow{\ \widehat{\mathfrak{f}}^b\ } & (\widehat{B}C'[1], \widehat{d'}^{\mathfrak{f}_*(b)}).
\end{array}
$$

Diagram 5.2.1

Obviously $\widehat{\mathfrak{f}}^b$ is a coalgebra homomorphism. By Lemma 5.2.12 (2), we have $\widehat{\mathfrak{f}}^b \circ \widehat{d}^b = \widehat{d'}^{\mathfrak{f}_*(b)} \circ \widehat{\mathfrak{f}}^b$. Moreover we note that $\hat{\mathfrak{t}}^{-1}_{\mathfrak{f}_*(b)}$ also satisfies $\hat{\mathfrak{t}}^{-1}_{\mathfrak{f}_*(b)} \equiv id \mod \Lambda^+_{0,nov}$ and the energy of the positive energy part is increased, because by the construction in Sublemma 5.2.14 $\hat{\mathfrak{t}}^{-1}_{\mathfrak{f}_*(b)}$ is given by the positive power series of $\mathfrak{f}_*(b)$. Thus $\mathfrak{f}^b$ satisfies (3.2.27.1). Therefore $\widehat{\mathfrak{f}}^b$ defines a filtered A_∞ homomorphism denoted by $\mathfrak{f}^b : (C, \mathfrak{m}^b) \to (C', \mathfrak{m}'^{\mathfrak{f}_*(b)})$.

We call $\mathfrak{f}^b$ the *deformation of the filtered A_∞ algebra homomorphism* $\mathfrak{f} : C \to C'$ *by* b. The next lemma plays a fundamental role in our argument.

LEMMA 5.2.16. *The filtered A_∞ algebra homomorphism* $\mathfrak{f}^b$ *is always strict. Namely we have* $\mathfrak{f}^b_0 = 0$.

PROOF. It suffices to show that $\mathfrak{f}^b_0(1) = 0$. We note that

$$
\widehat{\mathfrak{f}}(e^b) = e^{\mathfrak{f}_*(b)}, \quad \widehat{\mathfrak{f}}^b(1) = 1 + \mathfrak{f}^b_0(1) + \mathfrak{f}^b_0(1) \otimes \mathfrak{f}^b_0(1) + \cdots = e^{\mathfrak{f}^b_0(1)}.
$$

Then by definition of $\mathfrak{t}_b$ we have

$$
e^{\mathfrak{f}^b_0(1)} = \widehat{\mathfrak{f}}^b(1) = \hat{\mathfrak{t}}^{-1}_{\mathfrak{f}_*(b)} \circ \widehat{\mathfrak{f}}(e^b) = \hat{\mathfrak{t}}^{-1}_{\mathfrak{f}_*(b)}(e^{\mathfrak{f}_*(b)}) = 1.
$$

This implies that $\mathfrak{f}^b_0(1) = 0$ as required. $\square$

The unital and homotopy-unital versions also hold as follows.

LEMMA 5.2.17. *Let* $(C, \mathfrak{m}), (C', \mathfrak{m}')$ *be unital (resp. homotopy-unital) filtered A_∞ algebras and* $\mathfrak{f} : (C, \mathfrak{m}) \to (C', \mathfrak{m}')$ *a unital (resp. homotopy-unital) filtered A_∞ homomorphism. Then for any* $b \in C[1]^0$ *with* $b \equiv 0 \mod \Lambda^+_{0,nov}$ *the deformed filtered A_∞ homomorphism* $\mathfrak{f}^b : (C, \mathfrak{m}^b) \to (C', \mathfrak{m}'^{\mathfrak{f}_*(b)})$ *is unital (resp. homotopy-unital). Moreover it is strict for both cases.*

5.2.2.3. Deformation of the A_∞ bimodule homomorphisms. Next we define the deformations of the filtered A_∞ bimodule homomorphism. The definition can be formulated in a way similar to the case of the filtered A_∞ algebra homomorphisms we have just discussed.

Let $\mathfrak{f}^{(i)} : C_i \to C'_i$ $(i = 0, 1)$ be filtered A_∞ algebra homomorphisms and $(D, \mathfrak{n})$ (resp. $(D', \mathfrak{n}')$) a filtered (C_1, C_0) (resp. (C'_1, C'_0)) A_∞ bimodule. Consider a filtered A_∞ bimodule homomorphism over $(\mathfrak{f}^{(1)}, \mathfrak{f}^{(0)})$ $\varphi : (D, \mathfrak{n}) \to (D', \mathfrak{n}')$ and let $\widehat{\varphi} : \widehat{B}C_1[1] \widehat{\otimes} D[1] \widehat{\otimes} \widehat{B}C_0[1] \to \widehat{B}C'_1[1] \widehat{\otimes} D'[1] \widehat{\otimes} \widehat{B}C'_0[1]$ be the induced homomorphism given as in Definition 3.7.7. We denote by $\widehat{d}, \widehat{d}'$ the coderivations induced by $\mathfrak{n}, \mathfrak{n}'$ as in (3.7.3) respectively. For $b_i \in C_i[1]^0$ with $b_i \equiv 0 \mod \Lambda^+_{0,nov}$, we defined the deformed filtered A_∞ bimodule $(D, {}^{b_1}\widehat{d}{}^{b_0})$ in Definition-Lemma 3.7.13. Also $(D', \widehat{d'})$ is deformed by $\mathfrak{f}_*^{(i)}(b_i) \in C_i'[1]^0$ to $(D', {}^{\mathfrak{f}_*^{(1)}(b_1)}\widehat{d'}{}^{\mathfrak{f}_*^{(0)}(b_0)})$ on which $(C_1', \mathfrak{m}'^{\mathfrak{f}_*^{(1)}(b_1)})$ and $(C_0', \mathfrak{m}'^{\mathfrak{f}_*^{(0)}(b_0)})$ act. On the other hand, from Definition-Lemma 5.2.15, $\mathfrak{f}^{(i)}$ are also deformed by b_i to obtain $\mathfrak{f}^{(i)b_i} : (C_i, \mathfrak{m}^{b_i}) \to (C_i', \mathfrak{m}'^{\mathfrak{f}_*(b_i)})$ which are strict by Lemma 5.2.16.

DEFINITION-LEMMA 5.2.18. *For $b_i \in C_i[1]^0$ with $b_i \equiv 0 \mod \Lambda_{0,nov}^+$, we define*

$$ {}^{b_1}\widehat{\varphi}{}^{b_0} = \left(\hat{\mathfrak{t}}_{\mathfrak{f}_*^{(1)}(b_1)}^{-1} \otimes id \otimes \hat{\mathfrak{t}}_{\mathfrak{f}_*^{(0)}(b_0)}^{-1}\right) \circ \widehat{\varphi} \circ \left(\hat{\mathfrak{t}}_{b_1} \otimes id \otimes \hat{\mathfrak{t}}_{b_0}\right). $$

See the following commutative diagram.

$$
\begin{array}{ccc}
(\widehat{B}C_1[1]\widehat{\otimes}\widehat{D}[1]\widehat{\otimes}\widehat{B}C_0[1], \widehat{d}) & \xrightarrow{\;\;\widehat{\varphi}\;\;} & (\widehat{B}C_1'[1]\widehat{\otimes}\widehat{D'}[1]\widehat{\otimes}\widehat{B}C_0'[1], \widehat{d'}) \\[4pt]
{}^{\hat{\mathfrak{t}}_{b_1}\otimes id\otimes \hat{\mathfrak{t}}_{b_0}}\big\uparrow & & \Big\downarrow {}^{\hat{\mathfrak{t}}_{\mathfrak{f}_*^{(1)}(b_1)}^{-1}\otimes id\otimes \hat{\mathfrak{t}}_{\mathfrak{f}_*^{(0)}(b_0)}^{-1}} \\[4pt]
(\widehat{B}C_1[1]\widehat{\otimes}\widehat{D}[1]\widehat{\otimes}\widehat{B}C_0[1], {}^{b_1}\widehat{d}{}^{b_0}) & \xrightarrow{\;\;{}^{b_1}\widehat{\varphi}{}^{b_0}\;\;} & (\widehat{B}C_1'[1]\widehat{\otimes}\widehat{D'}[1]\widehat{\otimes}\widehat{B}C_0'[1], {}^{\mathfrak{f}_*^{(1)}(b_1)}\widehat{d'}{}^{\mathfrak{f}_*^{(0)}(b_0)})
\end{array}
$$

Diagram 5.2.2

Then ${}^{b_1}\widehat{\varphi}{}^{b_0}$ defines a filtered A_∞ bimodule homomorphism over the strict A_∞ homomorphisms $(\mathfrak{f}^{(1)b_1}, \mathfrak{f}^{(0)b_0})$:

$$ {}^{b_1}\varphi^{b_0} \;:\; (D, {}^{b_1}\widehat{d}{}^{b_0}) \to (D', {}^{\mathfrak{f}_*^{(1)}(b_1)}\widehat{d'}{}^{\mathfrak{f}_*^{(0)}(b_0)}). $$

The unital and homotopy-unital versions holds. Moreover the weakly filtered and/or (unital, homotopy-unital) versions also hold. We call ${}^{b_1}\varphi^{b_0}$ the deformation of the filtered A_∞ bimodule homomorphism φ by b_1, b_0.

PROOF. The proofs are straightforward. So we omit them. $\square$

5.2.2.4. The unobstructed cases. Now we assume that C_i $(i = 0, 1)$ are unobstructed. Take a bounding cochain $b_i \in \mathcal{M}(C_i)$. If $\mathfrak{f} : C_i \to C_i'$ is an A_∞ algebra homomorphism, then Lemma 3.6.36 shows that $\mathfrak{f}_*(b_i)$ defines a bounding cochain. Therefore $\mathfrak{f}_*(b_i) \in \mathcal{M}(C_i') \neq \emptyset$ and so $(C_i', \mathfrak{m}^{\mathfrak{f}_*(b_i)})$ are unobstructed. Moreover by Lemma 3.7.14, we have the complexes (D, δ_{b_1, b_0}) and $(D', \delta_{\mathfrak{f}_*^{(1)}(b_1), \mathfrak{f}_*^{(0)}(b_0)})$. Then we can show the following.

LEMMA 5.2.19. *We consider the situation of Definition-Lemma 5.2.18. Then for any bounding cochains $b_i \in \mathcal{M}(C_i)$, the deformed A_∞ bimodule homomorphism ${}^{b_1}\varphi^{b_0}$ over $(\mathfrak{f}^{(1)b_1}, \mathfrak{f}^{(0)b_0})$ induces a cochain map*

$$ {}^{b_1}\varphi^{b_0} \;:\; (D, \delta_{b_1, b_0}) \to (D', \delta_{\mathfrak{f}_*^{(1)}(b_1), \mathfrak{f}_*^{(0)}(b_0)}). $$

Here $\delta_{b_1, b_0}(y) = {}^{b_1}\mathfrak{n}^{b_0}(y) = \mathfrak{n}(e^{b_1} y e^{b_0})$ for $y \in D$. See Definition-Lemma 3.7.13(2). If C_i are unital and weakly unobstructed, then for any $b_i \in \mathcal{M}_{weak}(C_i)$ satisfying $\mathfrak{PO}(b_1) = \mathfrak{PO}(b_0)$ the induced map ${}^{b_1}\varphi^{b_0}$ is also a cochain map. The weakly filtered or/and homotopy-unital versions also hold.

PROOF. Since $\mathfrak{m}_0^{b_i} = \mathfrak{m}_0'^{\mathfrak{f}_*^{(i)}(b_i)} = 0$ and $\mathfrak{f}^{(i)b_i}$ are strict by Lemma 5.2.16, it is enough to show the following general facts.

SUBLEMMA 5.2.20. (1) *Let $(D, \mathfrak{n})$ be a $((C_1, \mathfrak{m}^{(1)}), (C_0, \mathfrak{m}^{(0)}))$ filtered A_∞ bimodule. If $\mathfrak{m}_0^{(i)} = 0$ for $i = 0, 1$, then $\mathfrak{n}_{0,0} \circ \mathfrak{n}_{0,0} = 0$.*

(2) *In addition, let $(C_i', \mathfrak{m}'^{(i)})$ be filtered A_∞ algebras with $\mathfrak{m}_0'^{(i)} = 0$ and $(D', \mathfrak{n}')$ a $((C_1', \mathfrak{m}'^{(1)}), (C_0', \mathfrak{m}'^{(0)}))$ filtered A_∞ bimodule. Then a filtered A_∞ bimodule homomorphism $\varphi : D \to D'$ over $(\mathfrak{f}^{(1)}, \mathfrak{f}^{(0)})$ induces a cochain map*

$$\varphi_{0,0} \ : \ (D, \mathfrak{n}_{0,0}) \to (D', \mathfrak{n}_{0,0}'),$$

if $\mathfrak{f}^{(i)} : C_i \to C_i'$ are strict for $i = 0, 1$.

We like to emphasize that the assumption that $\mathfrak{f}^{(i)}$ are *strict* is essential in (2).

PROOF OF SUBLEMMA 5.2.20. We denote by $\hat{d}, \hat{d}'$ the coderivations induced by $\mathfrak{n}, \mathfrak{n}'$ respectively and by $\hat{d}^{(i)}, \hat{d}'^{(i)}$ the induced ones from $\mathfrak{m}^{(i)}, \mathfrak{m}'^{(i)}$ respectively. Then $\hat{d}^{(i)}(1) = \hat{d}'^{(i)}(1) = 0$ if $\mathfrak{m}_0^{(i)} = \mathfrak{m}_0'^{(i)} = 0$.

(1) Since

$$\hat{d}(y) = \mathfrak{n}_{0,0}(y) + \hat{d}^{(1)}(1) \otimes y + (-1)^{\deg' y} y \otimes \hat{d}^{(0)}(1)$$

for $y \in D$, we have $\hat{d}(y) = \mathfrak{n}_{0,0}(y)$ by the assumption. Then (1) follows from the definition of the A_∞ bimodule.

(2) Since $\hat{\mathfrak{f}}^{(i)}(1) = e^{\mathfrak{f}_0^{(i)}(1)}$, we have $\hat{\mathfrak{f}}^{(i)}(1) = 1$ by assumption. Then from Definition 3.7.7 and (3.7.2) we have

$$\hat{d}' \circ \hat{\varphi}(y) = \hat{d}' \left(\hat{\mathfrak{f}}^{(1)}(1) \otimes \varphi_{0,0}(y) \otimes \hat{\mathfrak{f}}^{(0)}(1) \right) = \hat{d}'(\varphi_{0,0}(y))$$

$$= \mathfrak{n}_{0,0}' \circ \varphi_{0,0}(y) + \hat{d}'^{(1)}(1) \otimes \varphi_{0,0}(y) + (-1)^{\deg' y} \varphi_{0,0}(y) \otimes \hat{d}'^{(0)}(1)$$

$$= \mathfrak{n}_{0,0}' \circ \varphi_{0,0}(y),$$

because of the assumption $\mathfrak{m}_0'^{(i)} = 0$. On the other hand, we have

$$\hat{\varphi} \circ \hat{d}(y) = \hat{\varphi} \left(\mathfrak{n}_{0,0}(y) + \hat{d}^{(1)}(1) \otimes y + (-1)^{\deg' y} y \otimes \hat{d}^{(0)}(1) \right) = \hat{\varphi}(\mathfrak{n}_{0,0}(y))$$

$$= \hat{\mathfrak{f}}^{(1)}(1) \otimes \varphi_{0,0}(\mathfrak{n}_{0,0}(y)) \otimes \hat{\mathfrak{f}}^{(0)}(1)$$

$$= \varphi_{0,0} \circ \mathfrak{n}_{0,0}(y).$$

Therefore we obtain $\mathfrak{n}_{0,0}' \circ \varphi_{0,0} = \varphi_{0,0} \circ \mathfrak{n}_{0,0}$ as required. Thus we have finished the proof of Sublemma 5.2.20. $\square$

We can prove the homotopy-unital and weakly unobstructed version of Sublemma 5.2.20 in a similar way. Hence the proof of Lemma 5.2.19 is now complete.$\square$

5.2.3. Homotopy between A_∞ bimodule homomorphisms. In this subsection, we give the definition of the homotopy between the A_∞ bimodule homomorphisms and state the main theorem, Theorem 5.2.35, of this section. We will proceed in the same way as for the case of the filtered A_∞ algebras provided in Chapter 4. Let D be a filtered (C_1, C_0) A_∞ bimodule and $\mathfrak{C}_i$ a model of $[0, 1] \times C_i$.

DEFINITION 5.2.21. A model of $[0, 1] \times D$ is a filtered $(\mathfrak{C}_1, \mathfrak{C}_0)$ A_∞ bimodule $\mathfrak{D}$ equipped with A_∞ bimodule homomorphisms $\mathrm{Eval}_{s=s_0} : \mathfrak{D} \to D$ over $\mathrm{Eval}_{s=s_0} : \mathfrak{C}_i \to C_i$ (for $s_0 = 0, 1$) and $\mathrm{Incl} : D \to \mathfrak{D}$ over $\mathrm{Incl} : C_i \to \mathfrak{C}_i$ with the following properties.

(5.2.22.1) $\mathrm{Eval}_{s=s_0} \circ \mathrm{Incl}$ is equal to the identity.

(5.2.22.2) $(\mathrm{Eval}_{s=s_0})_{k_1,k_0} = (\mathrm{Incl})_{k_1,k_0} = 0$ for $(k_1, k_0) \neq (0, 0)$.

(5.2.22.3) $(\mathrm{Eval}_{s=0})_{0,0} \oplus (\mathrm{Eval}_{s=1})_{0,0} : \mathfrak{D} \to D \oplus D$ is split surjective.

(5.2.22.4) $(\mathrm{Incl})_{0,0} : D \to \mathfrak{D}$ induces a cochain homotopy equivalence between $\bar{\mathfrak{n}}_{0,0}$ complexes.

When everything $(C_i, \mathfrak{C}_i, \mathrm{Eval}_{s=s_0}, \mathrm{Incl})$ in the definition above is unital (resp. homotopy-unital), we call $\mathfrak{D}$ a *unital model* (resp. *homotopy-unital model*) of $[0,1] \times D$. The unfiltered versions can be defined in the same way.

For a filtered A_∞ bimodule $\widetilde{D}$ over Λ_{nov}, we simply take $\widetilde{\mathfrak{D}} = \mathfrak{D} \otimes_{\Lambda_{0,nov}} \Lambda_{nov}$ as a model of $[0,1] \times \widetilde{D}$.

We remark that (5.2.22.4) does not make sense for filtered A_∞ bimodule over Λ_{nov}.

THEOREM 5.2.23. *For any filtered $(C_1\ C_0)$ A_∞ bimodule D and any choices of models $\mathfrak{C}_i$ of $[0,1] \times C_i$, there exists a model of $[0,1] \times D$. If C_i and D are unital, there exists a unital model of $[0,1] \times D$. The unfiltered versions also hold. If C_1, C_0 and D are gapped, then we can take a gapped model of D.*

For the proof we use the following:

LEMMA 5.2.24. *The existence of a model of $[0,1] \times D$ is independent of the choices of the models of $[0,1] \times C_i$ $(i = 0, 1)$.*

PROOF. Suppose that for some models $\mathfrak{C}_i$ of $[0,1] \times C_i$ there exists a model $\mathfrak{D}$ of $[0,1] \times D$ which is a filtered $(\mathfrak{C}_1\ \mathfrak{C}_0)$ A_∞ bimodule. Let $\mathfrak{C}'_i$ be another models of $[0,1] \times C_i$. We apply Theorem 4.2.34 to the identity and obtain $\mathfrak{ID}_i : \mathfrak{C}'_i \to \mathfrak{C}_i$ which commute Eval and Incl. Then by Lemma 5.2.9, the filtered $(\mathfrak{C}'_1, \mathfrak{C}'_0)$ A_∞ bimodule $(\mathfrak{ID}_1, \mathfrak{ID}_0)^* \mathfrak{D}$ gives a model of $[0,1] \times D$. $\square$

PROOF OF THEOREM 5.2.23. By Lemma 5.2.24, it suffices to construct a model of $[0,1] \times D$ for some specific choices of $\mathfrak{C}_i$. Below we consider the cases of $\mathfrak{C}_i = Poly([0,1], C_i)$ and $\mathfrak{C}_i = C_i^{[0,1]}$. (See Subsection 4.2.1.) For the proof of Theorem 5.2.23 itself, it suffices to consider the case $\mathfrak{C}_i = C_i^{[0,1]}$. But it might be also useful to describe the case $\mathfrak{C}_i = Poly([0,1], C_i)$ explicitly. In this proof of Theorem 5.2.23 we will denote the filtered A_∞ bimodule structure on $\mathfrak{D}$ by $\mathfrak{N}_{k_1,k_0}$ and the filtered A_∞ bimodule structure on D by $\mathfrak{n}_{k_1,k_0}$.

First we consider the case $\mathfrak{C}_i = Poly([0,1], C_i)$. We consider the set of

$$y(s) = \sum_i y_i(s) T^{\lambda_i}, \qquad y'(s) = \sum_i y'_i(s) T^{\lambda_i},$$

such that $y_i : [0,1] \to D^k[1] = D^{k+1}$ and $y'_i : [0,1] \to D^{k-1}[1] = D^k$ are polynomials of the variable s and $\lambda_i \geq 0$, $\lim_{i \to \infty} \lambda_i = +\infty$. We define $Poly([0,1], D)^k$ to be the set of all such $\mathbf{y} = (y, y')$.

We define a $(Poly([0,1], C_1), Poly([0,1], C_0))$ filtered A_∞ bimodule structure on $Poly([0,1], D)$ by

$$\mathfrak{N}_{k_1,k_0}(\mathbf{x}_1^{(1)}, \cdots, \mathbf{x}_{k_1}^{(1)}, \mathbf{y}, \mathbf{x}_1^{(0)}, \cdots, \mathbf{x}_{k_0}^{(0)}) = (\widetilde{u}, \widetilde{v})$$

for $\mathbf{x}_j^{(i)} = (x_j^{(i)}, x_j'^{(i)}) \in Poly([0,1], C_i)$, $(i = 0, 1)$ and $y \in Poly([0,1], D)$. Here $\widetilde{u}$ and $\widetilde{v}$ are defined as follows: If we write $\mathbf{x}_j^{(i)}(s) = (x_j^{(i)}(s), x_j'^{(i)}(s))$ and $\mathbf{y}(s) =$

$(y(s), y'(s))$, then we define

$$\widetilde{u}(s) = \mathfrak{n}_{k_1,k_0}(x_1^{(1)}(s), \cdots, x_{k_1}^{(1)}(s), y(s), x_1^{(0)}(s), \cdots, x_{k_0}^{(0)}(s))$$

and

$$\widetilde{v}(s) = \sum_{j=1}^{k_1}(-1)^{\epsilon_j}\mathfrak{n}_{k_1,k_0}(x_1^{(1)}(s), \cdots, x_j'^{(1)}(s), \cdots, x_{k_1}^{(1)}(s), y(s), x_1^{(0)}(s), \cdots, x_{k_0}^{(0)}(s))$$

$$+ (-1)^{\epsilon}\mathfrak{n}_{k_1,k_0}(x_1^{(1)}(s), \cdots, x_{k_1}^{(1)}(s), y'(s), x_1^{(0)}(s), \cdots, x_{k_1}^{(0)}(s))$$

$$+ \sum_{j=1}^{k_0}(-1)^{\epsilon_j'}\mathfrak{n}_{k_1,k_0}(x_1^{(1)}(s), \cdots, x_{k_1}^{(1)}(s), y(s), x_1^{(0)}(s), \cdots, x_j'^{(0)}(s), \cdots, x_{k_0}^{(0)}(s))$$

for $(k_1, k_0) \neq (0,0)$, and

$$\widetilde{v}(s) = \frac{\partial y'(s)}{\partial s} - \mathfrak{n}_{0,0}(y'(s))$$

for $(k_1, k_0) = (0, 0)$. Here $\epsilon_j, \epsilon, \epsilon_j'$ are given by

$$\epsilon_j = \left(\sum_{i=1}^{j-1} \deg' x_i^{(1)}(s)\right) + 1, \quad \epsilon = \left(\sum_{i=1}^{k_1} \deg' x_i^{(1)}(s)\right) + 1$$

$$\epsilon_j' = \left(\sum_{i=1}^{k_1} \deg' x_i^{(1)}(s) + \deg' y(s) + \sum_{i=1}^{j-1} \deg' x_i^{(0)}(s)\right) + 1.$$

We define a filtered A_∞ bimodule homomorphism

$$\mathrm{Eval}_{s=s_0} : Poly([0,1], D) \to D$$

over $(\mathrm{Eval}_{s=s_0}, \mathrm{Eval}_{s=s_0})$ by

$$(\mathrm{Eval}_{s=s_0})_{0,0}(y, y') = y(s_0), \quad (\mathrm{Eval}_{s=s_0})_{k_1,k_0} = 0, \quad \text{for } (k_1, k_0) \neq (0, 0)$$

and $\mathrm{Incl}_{s=s_0} : D \to Poly([0,1], D)$ by

$$(\mathrm{Incl}_{s=s_0})_{0,0}(v) = (v, 0), \quad (\mathrm{Incl}_{s=s_0})_{k_1,k_0} = 0, \quad \text{for } (k_1, k_0) \neq (0, 0).$$

The proof that $Poly([0, 1], D)$ is a model of $[0, 1] \times D$ is straightforward and is omitted.

We next consider the case $\mathfrak{C}_i = C_i^{[0,1]}$. We recall that $C_i^{[0,1]} = C_i \oplus C_i[-1] \oplus C_i$. See Subsection 4.2.1. Similarly we put

$$\mathfrak{D} = D \oplus D[-1] \oplus D.$$

We define $\mathfrak{I}_0, \mathfrak{I}_1 : D \to \mathfrak{D}$ and $\mathfrak{J} : D \to \mathfrak{D}$ by

$$\mathfrak{I}_0(u) = (u, 0, 0), \quad \mathfrak{I}_1(w) = (0, 0, w), \quad \mathfrak{J}(v) = (0, v, 0).$$

Note $\mathfrak{I}_0$ and $\mathfrak{I}_1$ preserve the degree and $\mathfrak{J}$ has degree $+1$. We are ready to define a filtered A_∞ bimodule structure on $\mathfrak{D}$ which we denote by $\mathfrak{N}$. For $u, v, w \in D$ we set

$$\mathfrak{N}_{0,0}(\mathfrak{I}_0(u)) = \mathfrak{I}_0(\mathfrak{n}_{0,0}u) + (-1)^{\deg' v}\mathfrak{J}(u),$$

(5.2.25) $\qquad \mathfrak{N}_{0,0}(\mathfrak{I}_1(w)) = \mathfrak{I}_1(\mathfrak{n}_{0,0}w) - (-1)^{\deg' v}\mathfrak{J}(w),$

$$\mathfrak{N}_{0,0}(\mathfrak{J}(v)) = \mathfrak{J}(\mathfrak{n}_{0,0}v).$$

$$(5.2.26) \qquad \begin{aligned} (\mathrm{Eval}_{s=0})_1(u,v,w) = u, \quad & (\mathrm{Eval}_{s=1})_1(u,v,w) = w. \\ (\mathrm{Incl})_1(v) = \mathfrak{I}_0(v) + \mathfrak{I}_1(v) &= (v,0,v). \end{aligned}$$

We define the filtered A_∞ bimodule structure on $\mathfrak{D}$ as follows. We take $\mathbf{x}^{(i)}, \mathbf{z}^{(i)} \in BC_i[1]$ and $y^{(i)} \in C_i[1]$. For $u,v,w \in D$ we set

$$\mathfrak{N}(\mathfrak{I}_0(\mathbf{x}^{(1)}), \mathfrak{I}_0(u), \mathfrak{I}_0(\mathbf{x}^{(0)})) = \mathfrak{I}_0(\mathfrak{n}(\mathbf{x}^{(1)}, u, \mathbf{x}^{(0)}))$$

$$\mathfrak{N}(\mathfrak{I}_1(\mathbf{z}^{(1)}), \mathfrak{I}_1(w), \mathfrak{I}_1(\mathbf{z}^{(0)})) = \mathfrak{I}_1(\mathfrak{n}(\mathbf{z}^{(1)}, w, \mathbf{z}^{(0)}))$$

$$\mathfrak{N}(\mathfrak{I}_0(\mathbf{x}^{(1)}), \mathfrak{I}_0(u), \mathfrak{I}_0(\mathbf{x}^{(0)}), \mathfrak{J}(y^{(0)}), \mathfrak{I}_1(\mathbf{z}^{(0)}))$$
$$= (-1)^{\deg' \mathbf{z}^{(0)}} \mathfrak{J}(\mathfrak{n}(\mathbf{x}^{(1)}, u, \mathbf{x}^{(0)}, y^{(0)}, \mathbf{z}^{(0)}))$$

$$\mathfrak{N}(\mathfrak{I}_0(\mathbf{x}^{(1)}), \mathfrak{J}(v), \mathfrak{I}_1(\mathbf{z}^{(0)})) = (-1)^{\deg' \mathbf{z}^{(0)}} \mathfrak{J}(\mathfrak{n}(\mathbf{x}^{(1)}, v, \mathbf{z}^{(0)}))$$

$$\mathfrak{N}(\mathfrak{I}_0(\mathbf{x}^{(1)}), \mathfrak{J}(y^{(1)}), \mathfrak{I}_1(\mathbf{z}^{(1)}), \mathfrak{I}_1(w), \mathfrak{I}_1(\mathbf{z}^{(0)}))$$
$$= (-1)^{\deg' \mathbf{z}^{(1)} + \deg' w + \deg' \mathbf{z}^{(0)}} \mathfrak{J}(\mathfrak{n}(\mathbf{x}^{(1)}, y^{(1)}, \mathbf{z}^{(1)}, w, \mathbf{z}^{(0)})).$$

For the other cases, we put $\mathfrak{N} = 0$. We can prove that this defines a filtered A_∞ bimodule structure in the same way as in the proof of Lemma 4.2.25. The unfiltered or/and (unital or homotopy-unital) versions are similar. We have finished the proof of Theorem 5.2.23. $\qquad\square$

The following Theorem 5.2.27, which is an analog to Theorem 4.2.34, is fundamental to the study of homotopy between the A_∞ bimodule homomorphisms.

Let D (resp. D') be a filtered (C_1, C_0) A_∞ bimodule (resp. filtered (C_1', C_0') A_∞ bimodule). Let $\mathfrak{D}$ (resp. $\mathfrak{D}'$) be a filtered $(\mathfrak{C}_1, \mathfrak{C}_0)$ A_∞ bimodule (resp. filtered $(\mathfrak{C}_1', \mathfrak{C}_0')$ A_∞ bimodule) and a model of $[0,1] \times D$ (resp. $[0,1] \times D'$). Let $\mathfrak{f}^{(i)} : C_i \to C_i'$ and $\mathfrak{F}^{(i)} : \mathfrak{C}_i \to \mathfrak{C}_i'$ be filtered A_∞ homomorphisms such that $\mathrm{Eval}_{s=s_0} \circ \mathfrak{F}^{(i)} = \mathfrak{f}^{(i)} \circ \mathrm{Eval}_{s=s_0}$ and $\mathrm{Incl} \circ \mathfrak{f}^{(i)} = \mathfrak{F}^{(i)} \circ \mathrm{Incl}$. Let $\varphi : D \to D'$ be a filtered A_∞ bimodule homomorphism over $(\mathfrak{f}^{(1)}, \mathfrak{f}^{(0)})$. We assume that everything is G-gapped.

THEOREM 5.2.27. *There exists a filtered A_∞ bimodule homomorphism $\varphi^{\times[0,1]} : \mathfrak{D} \to \mathfrak{D}'$ over $(\mathfrak{F}^{(1)}, \mathfrak{F}^{(0)})$ such that*

$$\mathrm{Eval}_{s=s_0} \circ \varphi^{\times[0,1]} = \varphi \circ \mathrm{Eval}_{s=s_0} \qquad (\text{for } s_0 = 0, 1),$$
$$\mathrm{Incl} \circ \varphi = \varphi^{\times[0,1]} \circ \mathrm{Incl}.$$

The (unfiltered or weakly filtered) or/and (unital or homotopy-unital) versions also hold.

The proof of Theorem 5.2.27 is parallel to that of Theorem 4.2.34. It is also similar to the proof of Theorem 5.2.35, a bimodule version of Whitehead theorem, which we will prove in Subsections 5.2.5, 5.2.6 and 5.2.7. Therefore we omit the proof of Theorem 5.2.27, except that we need to prove the following lemma here for the case of the weakly filtered A_∞ bimodule homomorphism, since Theorem 5.2.35 does not handle this case whose correct formulation we do not know.

LEMMA 5.2.28. *The filtered version of Theorem 5.2.27 implies the corresponding weakly filtered version thereof. Namely, if φ is weakly filtered, then we can take $\varphi^{\times[0,1]}$ as a weakly filtered A_∞ bimodule homomorphism. If the energy loss of φ is c, then the energy loss of $\varphi^{\times[0,1]}$ is c.*

PROOF. We assumed that $\mathfrak{f}^{(i)}$, $\mathfrak{F}^{(i)}$ etc. are G-gapped. Moreover we assume that $\tilde{\varphi} : \tilde{D} \to \tilde{D}'$ is G'-gapped for some G-set G' satisfying (5.2.4). We put $c = \max\{-\lambda_0, 0\}$, where $\lambda_0 = \min\{\lambda'_i \mid (\lambda'_i, \mu'_i) \in G'\}$. Define

$$G' + c = \{(\lambda'_i + c, \mu'_i) \mid (\lambda'_i, \mu'_i) \in G'\}.$$

Then $G' + c$ is a G-set that satisfies (5.2.4) and $G' + c \subseteq \mathbb{R}_{\geq 0} \times 2\mathbb{Z}$. Now let

$$\widetilde{\varphi}_{k_1, k_0} = \sum_i T^{\lambda'_i} e^{\mu'_i/2} \varphi_{k_1, k_0, i}.$$

We then define

$$T^c \widetilde{\varphi}_{k_1, k_0} = \sum_i T^{c + \lambda'_i} e^{\mu'_i/2} \varphi_{k_1, k_0, i}.$$

We may regard $T^c \widetilde{\varphi}_{k_1, k_0}$ as a $(G' + c)$-gapped filtered A_∞ bimodule homomorphism $D \to D'$ over $(\mathfrak{f}^{(1)}, \mathfrak{f}^{(0)})$. Hence we apply the filtered version of Theorem 5.2.27 to $T^c \widetilde{\varphi}$ and obtain $T^c \widetilde{\varphi}^{\times[0,1]}$. Let $\langle G' + c \rangle$ be the monoid generated by $G' + c$. It satisfies Condition 3.1.6.

Now by multiplying T^{-c} in the same way, we obtain a $\langle G' + c \rangle - c$-gapped weakly filtered A_∞ bimodule homomorphism $\widetilde{\varphi}^{\times[0,1]} : \widetilde{\mathfrak{D}} \to \widetilde{\mathfrak{D}}'$ which has the required properties. Here $\langle G' + c \rangle - c = \{(\lambda'_i - c, \mu'_i) \mid (\lambda'_i, \mu'_i) \in \langle G' + c \rangle\}$. It is a $\langle G' + c \rangle$-set. $\square$

Once we extend G' to $G'' = \langle G' + c \rangle - c$, we do not need to extend it any further since $G'' = \langle G'' + c \rangle - c$.

DEFINITION 5.2.29. Let $\varphi, \psi : D \to D'$ be filtered A_∞ bimodule homomorphisms over $(\mathfrak{f}^{(1)}, \mathfrak{f}^{(0)})$ and $(\mathfrak{g}^{(1)}, \mathfrak{g}^{(0)})$ respectively. Here $\mathfrak{f}^{(i)} : C_i \to C'_i$, $\mathfrak{g}^{(i)} : C_i \to C'_i$ are filtered A_∞ homomorphisms. We say that φ is *homotopic* to ψ and write $\varphi \sim \psi$ if the following condition (5.2.30) holds.

(5.2.30)   There exist models $\mathfrak{D}', \mathfrak{C}'_i$ of $[0,1] \times D'$, $[0,1] \times C'_i$ respectively and homotopies $\mathfrak{F}^{(i)} : C_i \to \mathfrak{C}'_i$ between $\mathfrak{f}^{(i)}$ and $\mathfrak{g}^{(i)}$. Moreover there exists a filtered A_∞ bimodule homomorphism $\Phi : D \to \mathfrak{D}'$ over $(\mathfrak{F}^{(1)}, \mathfrak{F}^{(0)})$ such that

$$\text{Eval}_{s=0} \circ \Phi = \varphi, \quad \text{Eval}_{s=1} \circ \Phi = \psi.$$

We call Φ a *homotopy* from φ to ψ.

If Φ as in (5.2.30) exists for the given models $\mathfrak{C}'_i$, $\mathfrak{D}'$, $\mathfrak{F}^{(i)}$, we write $\varphi \sim_{(\mathfrak{C}'_i, \mathfrak{D}', \mathfrak{F}^{(i)})} \psi$. We define $\sim_{(\mathfrak{C}'_i, \mathfrak{F}^{(i)})}$, $\sim_{(\mathfrak{C}'_i, \mathfrak{D}')}$, $\sim_{(\mathfrak{C}'_i)}$ in a similar way.

We write $\varphi \sim_s \psi$, in case $\varphi \sim_{\mathfrak{F}^{(i)}} \psi$ for a strict $\mathfrak{F}^{(i)}$.

We define the (unfiltered or weakly filtered) and/or (unital or homotopy-unital) versions in a similar way. The homotopy-unital version is defined as the unital version of φ^+, ψ^+. (See Definition 3.7.12 as for this notation.)

We use the notations $\sim_u$, $\sim_{hu}$, $\sim_{su}$ etc. as in the case of the filtered A_∞ algebra homomorphisms in Subsection 4.2.3.

LEMMA 5.2.31. *The relation* $\sim_{(\mathfrak{C}'_i, \mathfrak{D}')}$ *is independent of the choices of* $\mathfrak{C}'_i$ *and* $\mathfrak{D}'$. $\sim_{(\mathfrak{C}'_i)}$ *is independent of the choices of* $\mathfrak{C}'_i$. $\sim_{(\mathfrak{C}'_i, \mathfrak{D}', \mathfrak{F}^{(i)})}$ *is independent of the choice of* $\mathfrak{D}'$.

PROOF. We assume $\varphi \sim_{(\mathfrak{C}'_i, \mathfrak{D}')} \psi$ and let Φ be a homotopy, which is defined over $(\mathfrak{F}^{(1)}, \mathfrak{F}^{(0)})$. We take an alternative choice $\mathfrak{C}''_i, \mathfrak{D}''$. Then by Theorems 4.2.34 and 5.2.27 there exist $\mathfrak{ID}_i : \mathfrak{C}'_i \to \mathfrak{C}''_i$ and $\mathfrak{ID} : \mathfrak{D}' \to \mathfrak{D}''$ such that $\mathfrak{ID}_i$ is a filtered A_∞ homomorphism satisfying $\mathrm{Eval}_{s=s_0} \circ \mathfrak{ID}_i =$ identity, and $\mathfrak{ID}$ is a filtered A_∞ bimodule homomorphism over $(\mathfrak{ID}_1, \mathfrak{ID}_0)$ satisfying $\mathrm{Eval}_{s=s_0} \circ \mathfrak{ID} =$ identity. Then $\mathfrak{ID} \circ \Phi : D \to \mathfrak{D}''$ is a homotopy between φ and ψ. Thus we have proved the first part of the lemma. The proofs of the second and the third part are similar. $\square$

REMARK 5.2.32. It seems that the relation $\sim_{(\mathfrak{C}'_i, \mathfrak{D}', \mathfrak{F}^{(i)})}$ depends on the choice of $\mathfrak{F}^{(i)}$ in general. However it is invariant under the change of $\mathfrak{F}^{(i)}$ under the "homotopy relative to boundary". We will not prove this statement because we do not use it. It appears that the correct language to describe this situation (as well as the situation of Proposition 5.2.43) is that of the fibered category (see [**Grot71**]).

Hereafter we do not write $\sim_{(\mathfrak{C}'_i, \mathfrak{D}')}$, $\sim_{(\mathfrak{C}'_i)}$ and write them simply by $\sim$. We also write $\sim_{\mathfrak{F}^{(i)}}$ in place of $\sim_{(\mathfrak{C}'_i, \mathfrak{F}^{(i)})}$, $\sim_{(\mathfrak{C}'_i, \mathfrak{D}', \mathfrak{F}^{(i)})}$.

LEMMA 5.2.33. *The relation $\sim$ between filtered A_∞ bimodule homomorphisms is an equivalence relation and is compatible with composition.*

The proof is similar to that of Proposition 4.2.37 and Lemma 4.2.43 and omitted.

We remark that the (unfiltered or weakly filtered) and/or (unital or homotopy-unital) versions of Lemmas 5.2.31 and 5.2.33 also hold.

DEFINITION 5.2.34. Let $\varphi : D \to D'$ be a filtered A_∞ bimodule homomorphism over $(\mathfrak{f}^{(1)}, \mathfrak{f}^{(0)})$, where $\mathfrak{f}^{(i)} : C_i \to C'_i$, are filtered A_∞ homomorphisms. We say that φ is a *homotopy equivalence* if there exists $\psi : D' \to D$ such that $\psi \circ \phi$ is homotopic to the identity. We say that D *is homotopy equivalent to* D' if there exists a homotopy equivalence $\varphi : D \to D'$. We define the (unfiltered or weakly filtered) and/or (unital or homotopy-unital) versions in the same way.

When $\mathfrak{f}^{(i)}$ are strict and the homotopies involved are also over the strict filtered A_∞ homomorphisms, we say φ is a *strict homotopy equivalence*.

We remark that if $\varphi : D \to D'$ over $(\mathfrak{f}^{(1)}, \mathfrak{f}^{(0)})$ is a homotopy equivalence then $\mathfrak{f}^{(i)}$ are necessarily homotopy equivalences.

Now we are ready to state our main theorem in this section. This is a version of the Whitehead theorem for the filtered A_∞ bimodule homomorphisms.

THEOREM 5.2.35. *Let $\varphi : D \to D'$ be a gapped filtered A_∞ bimodule homomorphism over $(\mathfrak{f}^{(1)}, \mathfrak{f}^{(0)})$, where $\mathfrak{f}^{(i)} : C_i \to C'_i$ are homotopy equivalences with $(\mathfrak{f}^{(i)})^{-1}$ being their homotopy inverses. Suppose that $\overline{\varphi} : \overline{D} \to \overline{D}'$ induces an isomorphism on $\overline{\mathfrak{n}}_{0,0}$ cohomology. Then φ is a homotopy equivalence. The homotopy inverse φ^{-1} of φ is taken over $((\mathfrak{f}^{(1)})^{-1}, (\mathfrak{f}^{(0)})^{-1})$. Moreover the homotopy from identity to $\varphi^{-1} \circ \varphi$ can be taken over any homotopies from identity to $(\mathfrak{f}^{(i)})^{-1} \circ \mathfrak{f}^{(i)}$.*

The unfiltered and/or (unital or homotopy-unital) and/or strict versions also hold.

The proof again proceeds in the same way as those of Theorems 4.2.34 and 4.2.45 using induction twice (on the number and the energy filtrations). We will give the proof of Theorem 5.2.35 in Subsections 5.2.5, 5.2.6 and 5.2.7.

REMARK 5.2.36. We do not know the corresponding statement for the *weakly filtered* A_∞ bimodule homomorphisms over Λ_{nov} (Definition 5.2.1), since we do not know how to handle the energy filtration. In addition we note that the hypothesis that $\overline{\varphi} : \overline{D} \to \overline{D}'$ *induces isomorphism on* $\overline{\mathfrak{n}}_{0,0}$ *cohomology* does not make sense for the weakly filtered case since φ does not induce $\overline{\varphi}$ in that case.

On the other hand if $\mathfrak{f}^{(1)}, \mathfrak{f}^{(0)}$ are strict, one might try to use the number filtration directly without using the energy filtration. (See Sublemma 5.2.20.) However we are not sure if the resulting "homotopy inverse" is weakly filtered or not.

The trick we used to handle the weakly filtered version of Theorem 5.2.27 (Lemma 5.2.28) does not work for the case of Theorem 5.2.35. This trouble associated to the weakly filtered version of Theorem 5.2.35 may be related to Theorem J which we will prove in Chapter 6.

5.2.4. Gauge invariance and the category $\mathfrak{H}\mathfrak{A}_\infty(C_1, C_0)$. Before we prove Theorem 5.2.35, we apply this theorem to show that the homotopy class of the filtered A_∞ bimodules $(D, {}^{b_1}\mathfrak{n}^{b_0})$ deformed by b_1, b_0 is independent of the choices of the representatives b_i in the gauge equivalence classes. In particular, this will imply that the Floer cohomology is invariant under the gauge equivalence of b_i. See Section 4.3 for the definition of the gauge equivalence relation on $\widehat{\mathcal{M}}(C)$.

PROPOSITION 5.2.37. (1) *Let $(D, \mathfrak{n})$ be a filtered (C_1, C_0) A_∞ bimodule and $b_1, b_1' \in \widehat{\mathcal{M}}(C_1)$, $b_0, b_0' \in \widehat{\mathcal{M}}(C_0)$. If $b_1 \sim b_1'$ and $b_0 \sim b_0'$, then $(D, {}^{b_1}\mathfrak{n}^{b_0})$ is strictly homotopy equivalent to $(D, {}^{b_1'}\mathfrak{n}^{b_0'})$.*

(2) *Assume that C_i, C_i' and D are unital and $b_1, b_1' \in \widehat{\mathcal{M}}_{\mathrm{weak}}(C_1)$, $b_0, b_0' \in \widehat{\mathcal{M}}_{\mathrm{weak}}(C_0)$. If $b_1 \sim b_1'$, $b_0 \sim b_0'$ and $\mathfrak{PO}(b_1) = \mathfrak{PO}(b_0)$, then $(D, {}^{b_1}\mathfrak{n}^{b_0})$ is su-homotopy equivalent to $(D, {}^{b_1'}\mathfrak{n}^{b_0'})$. (See Definitions 5.2.34 and also 4.2.42). The homotopy-unital version also holds.*

(3) *Let $(L^{(0)}, L^{(1)})$ be a relatively spin pair of Lagrangian submanifolds and $(\mathfrak{b}, b_i)$ and $(\mathfrak{b}', b_i') \in \mathcal{M}_{\mathrm{weak,def}}(L^{(i)})$. We assume that $\mathfrak{PO}((\mathfrak{b}, b_0)) = \mathfrak{PO}((\mathfrak{b}, b_1))$. If $(\mathfrak{b}, b_i) \sim (\mathfrak{b}', b_i')$ $(i = 0, 1)$, then the unital fibered A_∞ bimodule*

$$(C(L^{(1)}, L^{(0)}; \Lambda_{0,nov}), {}^{(\mathfrak{b},b_1)}\mathfrak{n}^{+(\mathfrak{b},b_0)})$$

is shu-homotopy equivalent to $(C(L^{(1)}, L^{(0)}; \Lambda_{0,nov}), {}^{(\mathfrak{b}',b_1')}\mathfrak{n}^{+(\mathfrak{b}',b_0')})$. See Lemma-Definition 3.8.75.

In each of the cases (1),(2),(3), *we may choose the homotopy equivalence so that it is congruent to the identity module $\Lambda_{0,nov}^+$.*

PROOF. Let $\widetilde{b}_i \in \widehat{\mathcal{M}}(\mathfrak{C}_i)$ be a homotopy from b_i to b_i'. We take a model $\mathfrak{D}$ of $[0, 1] \times D$ which is a $(\mathfrak{C}_1, \mathfrak{C}_0)$ bimodule. Since $\mathrm{Eval}_{s=0}\widetilde{b}_1 = b_1$, $\mathrm{Eval}_{s=1}\widetilde{b}_1 = b_1'$ and $\mathrm{Eval}_{s=0}\widetilde{b}_0 = b_0$, $\mathrm{Eval}_{s=1}\widetilde{b}_0 = b_0'$, it follows from Definition-Lemma 5.2.18 that $\mathrm{Eval}_{s=0}$ induces an A_∞ bimodule homomorphism $(\mathfrak{D}, {}^{\widetilde{b}_1}\mathfrak{n}^{\widetilde{b}_0}) \to (D, {}^{b_1}\mathfrak{n}^{b_0})$ and $\mathrm{Eval}_{s=1}$ induces $(\mathfrak{D}, {}^{\widetilde{b}_1}\mathfrak{n}^{\widetilde{b}_0}) \to (D, {}^{b_1'}\mathfrak{n}^{b_0'})$. They are strict homotopy equivalences by Theorem 5.2.35. Proposition 5.2.37 (1) now follows. Proposition 5.2.37 (2) can be proved in the same way using Lemma 4.3.23.

To prove Proposition 5.2.37 (3), we first take $\mathfrak{f}_i : (C_i, \mathfrak{m}^{\mathfrak{b}}) \to (C_i', \mathfrak{m}^{\mathfrak{b}'})$ in Theorem 4.6.47. By Lemmas 5.2.16, 5.2.17, we have a strict homotopy equivalence $\mathfrak{f}_i^{b_i} : (C_i, \mathfrak{m}^{(\mathfrak{b},b_i)}) \to (C_i', \mathfrak{m}^{(\mathfrak{b}',\mathfrak{f}_{i*}b_i)})$. Hence, by Lemma 5.2.19, we have a strict homotopy equivalence

$$(D, {}^{(\mathfrak{b},b_1)}\mathfrak{n}^{(\mathfrak{b},b_0)}) \sim (D, {}^{(\mathfrak{b}',\mathfrak{f}_{1*}b_1)}\mathfrak{n}^{(\mathfrak{b}',\mathfrak{f}_{0*}b_0)})$$

over $(\mathfrak{f}_1^{b_1}, \mathfrak{f}_0^{b_0})$.

On the other hand, by Definition 4.6.50, $(\mathfrak{b}, b_i) \sim (\mathfrak{b}', b_i')$ implies $\mathfrak{f}_{i*}b_i \sim b_i'$ in $\widehat{\mathcal{M}}_{\mathrm{weak}}(C_i, \mathfrak{m}^{\mathfrak{b}'})$. Therefore a similar argument as above implies

$$(D, {}^{(\mathfrak{b}',\mathfrak{f}_{1*}b_1)}\mathfrak{n}^{(\mathfrak{b}',\mathfrak{f}_{0*}b_0)}) \sim (D, {}^{(\mathfrak{b}',b_1')}\mathfrak{n}^{(\mathfrak{b}',b_0')}).$$

Proposition 5.2.37 (3) follows.

The last statement of the proposition is obvious from construction. $\qquad\square$

PROPOSITION 5.2.38. (1) *Let* $\varphi, \psi : D \to D'$ *be filtered* A_∞ *bimodule homomorphisms over the strict filtered* A_∞ *homomorphisms. Assume* $\varphi \sim_s \psi$. *Then we have*

$$\varphi_* = \psi_* : H^*(D, \mathfrak{n}_{0,0}) \to H^*(D', \mathfrak{n}_{0,0}').$$

(2) *A homotopy equivalence of filtered* A_∞ *bimodules over a strict homotopy equivalence of strict filtered* A_∞ *algebras induces an isomorphism of the* $\mathfrak{n}_{0,0}$ *cohomology.*

PROOF. We take $D'^{[0,1]}$ as a model of $[0,1] \times D'$. Then by Lemma 5.2.31, we have a homotopy $\Phi = \{\Phi_{i,j}\}_{i,j=0,1,\cdots} : D \to D'^{[0,1]}$ from φ to ψ. Since $D'^{[0,1]} = D \oplus D[-1] \oplus D$, we may write $\Phi_{0,0} = \varphi_{0,0} \oplus \Phi_{0,0}' \oplus \psi_{0,0}$. Since $\varphi \sim_s \psi$ implies that $\Phi_{0,0}$ is an A_∞ bimodule homomorphism over strict A_∞ algebra homomorphisms, we find that

$$\psi_{0,0} - \phi_{0,0} = \pm\mathfrak{n}_{0,0}' \circ \Phi_{0,0}' \pm \Phi_{0,0}' \circ \mathfrak{n}_{0,0}.$$

(1) of the proposition follows. (2) is an immediate consequence of (1). $\qquad\square$

REMARK 5.2.39. We can find a formula similar to (4.2.39). We leave it to the readers.

By applying Propositions 5.2.37 and 5.2.38 to the associated filtered A_∞ bimodule $C(L^{(1)}, L^{(0)}, \Lambda_{0,nov})$ to a relatively spin pair of Lagrangian submanifolds $(L^{(1)}, L^{(0)})$ constructed in Subsections 3.7.4 and 3.7.5, we immediately obtain the following.

COROLLARY 5.2.40. (1) *If* $b_i \sim b_i' \in \widehat{\mathcal{M}}(L^{(i)})$, *then*

$$HF((L^{(1)}, b_1); (L^{(0)}, b_0); \Lambda_{0,nov}) \cong HF((L^{(1)}, b_1'); (L^{(0)}, b_0'); \Lambda_{0,nov}).$$

(2) *If* $b_i \sim b_i' \in \widehat{\mathcal{M}}_{\mathrm{weak}}(L^{(i)})$ *and* $\mathfrak{PO}_{L^{(1)}}(b_1) = \mathfrak{PO}_{L^{(0)}}(b_0)$, *then*

$$HF((L^{(1)}, b_1); (L^{(0)}, b_0); \Lambda_{0,nov}) \cong HF((L^{(1)}, b_1'); (L^{(0)}, b_0'); \Lambda_{0,nov}).$$

(3) *If* $(\mathfrak{b}, b_i) \sim (\mathfrak{b}', b_i') \in \widehat{\mathcal{M}}_{\mathrm{weak,def}}(L^{(i)})$ *and* $\mathfrak{PO}_{L^{(0)}}(\mathfrak{b}, b_0) = \mathfrak{PO}_{L^{(1)}}(\mathfrak{b}, b_1)$, *then*

$$HF((L^{(1)}, (\mathfrak{b}, b_1)), (L^{(0)}, (\mathfrak{b}, b_0)); \Lambda_{0,nov})$$
$$\cong HF((L^{(1)}, (\mathfrak{b}', b_1')), (L^{(0)}, (\mathfrak{b}', b_0')); \Lambda_{0,nov}).$$

The isomorphisms above are canonical.

In Subsection 5.2.2, we defined the pull-back of the filtered A_∞ bimodule structures. The pull back operation is compatible with the homotopy equivalence in the following sense.

LEMMA 5.2.41. *If* $\mathfrak{f}^{(i)} : C_i \to C_i'$ *are homotopic to* $\mathfrak{f}^{(i)\prime} : C_i \to C_i'$ *respectively and* D *is a* (C_1', C_0') *filtered* A_∞ *bimodule, then the pull-back* $(\mathfrak{f}^{(1)}, \mathfrak{f}^{(0)})^* D$ *is homotopy equivalent to* $(\mathfrak{f}^{(1)\prime}, \mathfrak{f}^{(0)\prime})^* D$.

The (unfiltered or weakly filtered) or/and (unital or homotopy-unital) versions also hold.

PROOF. Let $\mathfrak{h}^{(i)} : C_i \to \mathfrak{C}_i'$ be a homotopy from $\mathfrak{f}^{(i)}$ to $\mathfrak{f}^{(i)\prime}$. Take a $(\mathfrak{C}_1', \mathfrak{C}_0')$ filtered A_∞ bimodule $\mathfrak{D}$ which is a model of $[0,1] \times D$. Then by Lemma 5.2.9 there exist filtered A_∞ bimodule homomorphisms

$$\mathrm{Eval}_{s=0} : (\mathfrak{h}^{(1)}, \mathfrak{h}^{(0)})^* \mathfrak{D} \to (\mathfrak{f}^{(1)}, \mathfrak{f}^{(0)})^* D,$$
$$\mathrm{Eval}_{s=1} : (\mathfrak{h}^{(1)}, \mathfrak{h}^{(0)})^* \mathfrak{D} \to (\mathfrak{f}^{(1)\prime}, \mathfrak{f}^{(0)\prime})^* D.$$

They are homotopy equivalences by Theorem 5.2.35. The lemma follows.

(Note that the above argument dose not directly apply to the weakly filtered version. However it is easy to see that the filtered version implies the weakly filtered version.) $\square$

In the various circumstances, especially in Sections 5.3 and 5.4, we need to replace the given filtered A_∞ algebras by other homotopy equivalent ones. We then also need to replace a filtered (C_1, C_0) A_∞ bimodule by a filtered (C_1', C_0') A_∞ bimodule when C_i is homotopy equivalent to C_i'. Here we would like to verify that these replacements are possible. To make the relevant statements transparent, introducing the concept of the category of filtered (C_1, C_0) A_∞ bimodules seems to be useful.

DEFINITION 5.2.42. (1) The object of the category $\mathfrak{A}_\infty(C_1, C_0)$ is a (C_1, C_0) filtered A_∞ bimodule D. A morphism from D to D' is a filtered A_∞ bimodule homomorphism from D to D' over the identity.

(2) Let $\varphi, \psi : D \to D'$ be two morphisms. We say that $\varphi \sim \psi$ if $\varphi \sim_{\mathrm{Incl}} \psi$. Namely $\varphi \sim \psi$ if there exists a filtered A_∞ bimodule homomorphism $\Psi : D \to \mathfrak{D}'$ over Incl : $C_i \to \mathfrak{C}_i$ such that $\mathrm{Eval}_{s=0} \circ \Psi = \varphi$ and $\mathrm{Eval}_{s=1} \circ \Psi = \psi$. It is easy to see that $\sim$ is an equivalence relation.

(3) We define the category $\mathfrak{H}\mathfrak{A}_\infty(C_1, C_0)$ so that it has the same objects as $\mathfrak{A}_\infty(C_1, C_0)$ and its morphism is the $\sim$ equivalence class of morphisms of $\mathfrak{A}_\infty(C_1, C_0)$.

(4) We can define the (unfiltered or weakly filtered) and/or (unital or homotopy unital) versions in a similar way. We denote them by $\mathfrak{H}\mathfrak{A}_\infty(\overline{C}_1, \overline{C}_0)$, $\mathfrak{H}\mathfrak{A}_{\infty u}(C_1, C_0)$, $\mathfrak{H}\mathfrak{A}_{\infty hu}(\overline{C}_1, \overline{C}_0)$ etc.

PROPOSITION 5.2.43. *If* $\mathfrak{f}^{(i)} : C_i \to C_i'$, $(i = 0, 1)$ *are homotopy equivalences, then the pull-back operation* $D \mapsto (\mathfrak{f}^{(1)}, \mathfrak{f}^{(0)})^* D$ *induces an equivalence of categories*

$$\mathfrak{H}\mathfrak{A}_\infty(C_1', C_0') \longrightarrow \mathfrak{H}\mathfrak{A}_\infty(C_1, C_0).$$

The (unfiltered or weakly filtered) and/or (unital or homotopy-unital) versions hold.

PROOF. Let $\varphi : D \to D'$ be a morphism of $\mathfrak{A}_\infty(C_1', C_0')$. By Lemma 5.2.9 it induces a morphism

$$(\mathfrak{f}^{(1)}, \mathfrak{f}^{(0)})^* \varphi : (\mathfrak{f}^{(1)}, \mathfrak{f}^{(0)})^* D \to (\mathfrak{f}^{(1)}, \mathfrak{f}^{(0)})^* D'$$

of $\mathfrak{A}_\infty(C_1, C_0)$.

Suppose that $\varphi \sim \psi$. Let $\mathfrak{h} : D \to \mathfrak{D}'$ be a homotopy from φ to ψ. Then we have $(\mathfrak{f}^{(1)}, \mathfrak{f}^{(0)})^* \mathfrak{h} : (\mathfrak{f}^{(1)}, \mathfrak{f}^{(0)})^* D \to (\mathfrak{f}^{(1)}, \mathfrak{f}^{(0)})^* \mathfrak{D}'$. It is easy to see that $(\mathfrak{f}^{(1)}, \mathfrak{f}^{(0)})^* \mathfrak{D}'$ is a model of $[0,1] \times (\mathfrak{f}^{(1)}, \mathfrak{f}^{(0)})^* D'$. Hence $(\mathfrak{f}^{(1)}, \mathfrak{f}^{(0)})^* \mathfrak{h}$ is a homotopy from $(\mathfrak{f}^{(1)}, \mathfrak{f}^{(0)})^* \varphi$ to $(\mathfrak{f}^{(1)}, \mathfrak{f}^{(0)})^* \psi$. Thus we obtain a functor $\mathfrak{H}\mathfrak{A}_\infty(C_1', C_0') \to \mathfrak{H}\mathfrak{A}_\infty(C_1, C_0)$.

If $(\mathfrak{f}^{(i)})^{-1}$ is a homotopy inverse to $\mathfrak{f}^{(i)}$, then by Lemma 5.2.41 the homomorphism $((\mathfrak{f}^{(1)})^{-1}, (\mathfrak{f}^{(0)})^{-1})^*$ is an inverse to $(\mathfrak{f}^{(1)}, \mathfrak{f}^{(0)})^*$. $\qquad\square$

5.2.5. Obstructions to defining A_∞ bimodule homomorphisms I. The subsections Subsections 5.2.5, 5.2.6 and 5.2.7 of the rest of this section will be occupied with the proof of Theorem 5.2.35. For this purpose, we need to develop some obstruction theory of the A_∞ bimodule homomorphisms, which we explain in this subsection.

We begin with the unfiltered case. We first define the notions of $A_{K,L}$ bimodules and $A_{K,L}$ bimodule homomorphisms for two given integers $K, L \in \mathbb{Z}_+$. Let $\overline{C}_1$ be an A_K algebra and $\overline{C}_0$ an A_L algebra. Then we have the coalgebra homomorphisms

$$\widehat{d}_{1\cdots K}^{(1)} : B_{1\cdots K}\overline{C}_1[1] \to B_{1\cdots K}\overline{C}_1[1]$$
$$\widehat{d}_{1\cdots L}^{(0)} : B_{1\cdots L}\overline{C}_0[1] \to B_{1\cdots L}\overline{C}_0[1]$$

as in Definition 4.4.6. For a graded R module $\overline{D}$ we consider a family of operations

$$\overline{\mathfrak{n}}_{k_1,k_0} : B_{k_1}\overline{C}_1[1] \otimes \overline{D}[1] \otimes B_{k_0}\overline{C}_0[1] \longrightarrow \overline{D}[1]$$

of degree $+1$ for $k_1 \leq K, k_0 \leq L$. We extend $\overline{\mathfrak{n}}_{k_1,k_0}$ to a bi-coderivation:

$$\widehat{\overline{d}}_{1\cdots K, 1\cdots L} : B_{1\cdots K}\overline{C}_1[1] \otimes \overline{D}[1] \otimes B_{1\cdots L}\overline{C}_0[1] \to B_{1\cdots K}\overline{C}_1[1] \otimes \overline{D}[1] \otimes B_{1\cdots L}\overline{C}_0[1]$$

defined by

$$\widehat{\overline{d}}_{1\cdots K, 1\cdots L}(\mathbf{x}_1 \otimes y \otimes \mathbf{x}_0)$$
$$= \sum_{a,b} (-1)^{\deg' \mathbf{x}_{1,a}'} \mathbf{x}_{1,a}' \otimes \overline{\mathfrak{n}}(\mathbf{x}_{1,a}'' \otimes y \otimes \mathbf{x}_{0,b}') \otimes \mathbf{x}_{0,b}''$$
$$+ \widehat{\overline{d}}_{1\cdots K}^{(1)} \mathbf{x}_1 \otimes y \otimes \mathbf{x}_0 + (-1)^{\deg' \mathbf{x}_1 + \deg' y} \mathbf{x}_1 \otimes y \otimes \widehat{\overline{d}}_{1\cdots L}^{(0)} \mathbf{x}_0.$$

Here we use (Conv. 3) (1.36).

DEFINITION 5.2.44. (1) We say that $(\overline{D}, \overline{\mathfrak{n}})$ is a $(\overline{C}_1, \overline{C}_0)$ $A_{K,L}$ *bimodule*, if

$$\widehat{\overline{d}}_{1\cdots K, 1\cdots L} \circ \widehat{\overline{d}}_{1\cdots K, 1\cdots L} = 0.$$

Moreover let $\overline{C}_1'$ (resp. $\overline{C}_0'$) be an A_K algebra (resp. A_L algebra) and $\overline{D}'$ a $(\overline{C}_1', \overline{C}_0')$ $A_{K,L}$ bimodule. Let $\overline{\mathfrak{f}}^{(1)} : \overline{C}_1 \to \overline{C}_1'$ (resp. $\overline{\mathfrak{f}}^{(0)} : \overline{C}_0 \to \overline{C}_0'$) be an A_K (resp. A_L) homomorphism. We consider

$$\overline{\varphi}_{k_1,k_0} : B_{k_1}\overline{C}_1[1] \otimes \overline{D}[1] \otimes B_{k_0}\overline{C}_0[1] \to \overline{D}'[1],$$

for $k_1 \leq K, k_0 \leq L$. It (together with $\overline{\mathfrak{f}}^{(i)}$) induces

$$\widehat{\overline{\varphi}}_{k_1,k_0} : B_{1\cdots k_1}\overline{C}_1[1] \otimes \overline{D}[1] \otimes B_{1\cdots k_0}\overline{C}_0[1] \to B_{1\cdots k_1}\overline{C}_1'[1] \otimes \overline{D}'[1] \otimes B_{1\cdots k_0}\overline{C}_0'[1].$$

DEFINITION 5.2.44. (2) We say that $\overline{\varphi}_{k_1,k_0}$, $k_1 \leq K$, $k_0 \leq L$, is an $A_{K,L}$ *bimodule homomorphism over* $(\vec{\mathfrak{f}}^{(1)}, \vec{\mathfrak{f}}^{(0)})$ if $\widehat{\overline{\varphi}}_{k_1,k_0}$ $(k_1 \leq K, \ k_0 \leq L)$ is a cochain homomorphism.

We remark that an $A_{K',L'}$ structure induces an $A_{K,L}$ structure for $K \leq K', L \leq L'$. We describe an obstruction to extend $A_{K,L}$ bimodule homomorphisms to $A_{K+1,L}$ or $A_{K,L+1}$ bimodule homomorphisms. Consider an R module

$$Hom(B_{K+1}\overline{C}_1[1] \otimes \overline{D}[1] \otimes B_L\overline{C}_0[1], \overline{D}'[1])$$

and define a coboundary operator

$$\delta_1 : Hom(B_{K+1}\overline{C}_1[1] \otimes \overline{D}[1] \otimes B_L\overline{C}_0[1], \overline{D}'[1])$$
$$\to Hom(B_{K+1}\overline{C}_1[1] \otimes \overline{D}[1] \otimes B_L\overline{C}_0[1], \overline{D}'[1])$$

by

$$(5.2.45) \qquad \delta_1(\mathfrak{T}) = \overline{\mathfrak{n}}_{0,0} \circ \mathfrak{T} - (-1)^{\deg \mathfrak{T}}\mathfrak{T} \circ (\widehat{\overline{\mathfrak{m}}}_1 \hat{\otimes} 1 \hat{\otimes} 1 + 1 \hat{\otimes} \overline{\mathfrak{n}}_{0,0} \hat{\otimes} 1 + 1 \hat{\otimes} 1 \hat{\otimes} \widehat{\overline{\mathfrak{m}}}_1),$$

where $\widehat{\overline{\mathfrak{m}}}_1 : \overline{B}C_i[1] \to \overline{B}C_i[1]$ is a coderivation induced by $\overline{\mathfrak{m}}_1$ on $\overline{C}_i$. (See (7.1).) We use the same symbols $\widehat{\overline{\mathfrak{m}}}_1$ and $\overline{\mathfrak{m}}$ for both $\overline{C}_i$ $(i = 0, 1)$ to simplify the notations, when no confusion occurs.

LEMMA 5.2.46. *If* $\overline{\varphi} : \overline{D} \to \overline{D}'$ *is an* $A_{K,L}$ *bimodule homomorphism, then there exists* $o_{K+1,L}(\overline{\varphi}) \in Hom(B_{K+1}\overline{C}_1[1] \otimes \overline{D}[1] \otimes B_L\overline{C}_0[1], \overline{D}'[1])$ *of degree 1, such that the following holds.*

$(5.2.47.1)$ $\delta_1(o_{K+1,L}(\overline{\varphi})) = 0$.
$(5.2.47.2)$ $[o_{K+1,L}(\overline{\varphi})] = 0$ *as* δ_1 *cohomology class, if and only if there exists an* $A_{K+1,L}$ *bimodule homomorphism extending* $\overline{\varphi}$.
$(5.2.47.3)$ *If* $\overline{\varphi}'$ *is* $A_{K,L}$ *homotopic to* $\overline{\varphi}$ *then* $[o_{K+1,L}(\overline{\varphi})] = [o_{K+1,L}(\overline{\varphi}')]$ *as* δ_1 *cohomology class. (We can define a notion of* $A_{K,L}$ *homotopy in an obvious way.)*
$(5.2.47.4)$ *We assume that* $\overline{\mathfrak{g}}_{(i)} : \overline{C}'_i \to \overline{C}''_i$, $\overline{\mathfrak{g}}'_{(i)} : \overline{C}''_i \to \overline{C}_{i+1}$ *are* A_∞ *homomorphisms and* $\overline{\varphi}' : \overline{D}' \to \overline{D}''$ *and* $\overline{\varphi}'' : \overline{D}''' \to \overline{D}$ *are* $A_{K+1,L}$ *bimodule homomorphisms over* $(\overline{\mathfrak{g}}_{(1)}, \overline{\mathfrak{g}}_{(0)})$ *and over* $(\overline{\mathfrak{g}}'_{(1)}, \overline{\mathfrak{g}}'_{(0)})$ *respectively, Then we have*

$$[o_{K+1,L}(\overline{\varphi}' \circ \overline{\varphi} \circ \overline{\varphi}'')] = (\overline{\varphi}'_1)_* \circ [o_{K+1,L}(\overline{\varphi})] \circ (\overline{\varphi}''_1 \otimes \cdots \otimes \overline{\varphi}''_1)_*.$$

$(5.2.47.5)$ *Similarly we can define* $o_{K,L+1}(\overline{\varphi})$ *and the corresponding statements above also hold for* $o_{K,L+1}(\overline{\varphi})$.

PROOF. The proof is similar to the proof of Theorem 4.5.1. Namely we put

$$o_{K+1,L}(\overline{\varphi})(\mathbf{x} \otimes y \otimes \mathbf{z}) = (\widehat{d} \circ \widehat{\overline{\varphi}}_{K+1,L} - \widehat{\overline{\varphi}}_{K+1,L} \circ \widehat{d})(\mathbf{x} \otimes y \otimes \mathbf{z}).$$

We omit the detail.   □

5.2.6. Whitehead theorem for A_∞ bimodule homomorphisms. The purpose of this subsection is to prove the unfiltered version of Theorem 5.2.35 using the number filtration.

Let $\overline{C}_i$, $\overline{C}'_i$ be A_∞ algebras and $\overline{D}$ (resp. $\overline{D}'$) be a $(\overline{C}_1, \overline{C}_0)$ bimodule (resp. $(\overline{C}'_1, \overline{C}'_0)$ bimodule). Let $\vec{\mathfrak{f}}^{(i)} : \overline{C}_i \to \overline{C}'_i$ be homotopy equivalences with $(\vec{\mathfrak{f}}^{(i)})^{-1}$ being their homotopy inverses. $(i = 0, 1)$. We assume that $\overline{\varphi} : \overline{D} \to \overline{D}'$ is an

A_∞ bimodule homomorphism over $(\bar{\mathfrak{f}}^{(1)}, \bar{\mathfrak{f}}^{(0)})$ which induces an isomorphism on $\bar{\mathfrak{n}}_{0,0}$ cohomology. We are going to show that there exists a homotopy inverse $\bar\varphi' : \overline{D}' \to \overline{D}$ over $((\bar{\mathfrak{f}}^{(1)})^{-1}, (\bar{\mathfrak{f}}^{(0)})^{-1})$.

For this purpose, we will prove the following by induction on K and L. Let $\bar{\mathfrak{h}}^{(i)} : \overline{C}_i \to \overline{\mathfrak{C}}_i$ be homotopies from identity to $(\bar{\mathfrak{f}}^{(i)})^{-1} \circ \bar{\mathfrak{f}}^{(i)}$. Let $\overline{\mathfrak{D}}$ be a model of $[0,1] \times \overline{D}$. (We remark that we can take any choices of $\overline{\mathfrak{D}}$ and $\bar{\mathfrak{h}}^{(i)}$. This is important to prove the last part of the Theorem 5.2.35.)

PROPOSITION 5.2.48. *For any $K, L = 1, 2, \cdots$, there exist an $A_{K,L}$ bimodule homomorphism $\bar\varphi'_{(K,L)} : \overline{D}' \to \overline{D}$ over $((\bar{\mathfrak{f}}^{(1)})^{-1}, (\bar{\mathfrak{f}}^{(0)})^{-1})$ and an $A_{K,L}$ bimodule homomorphism $\overline{\mathfrak{H}}_{(K,L)} : \overline{D} \to \overline{\mathfrak{D}}$ over $(\bar{\mathfrak{h}}^{(1)}, \bar{\mathfrak{h}}^{(0)})$ such that*

(5.2.49.1) *If $K' \leq K$ and $L' \leq L$, $\widehat{\bar\varphi}'_{(K,L)}$ coincides with $\widehat{\bar\varphi}'_{(K',L')}$ on $B_{1 \cdots K'} \overline{C}'_1[1] \otimes \overline{D}'[1] \otimes B_{1 \cdots L'} \overline{C}'_0[1]$. Also $\widehat{\overline{\mathfrak{H}}}_{(K,L)}$ coincides with $\widehat{\overline{\mathfrak{H}}}_{(K',L')}$ on $B_{1 \cdots K'} \overline{C}_1[1] \otimes \overline{D}[1] \otimes B_{1 \cdots L'} \overline{C}_0[1]$.*

(5.2.49.2) $\mathrm{Eval}_{s=0} \circ \overline{\mathfrak{H}} = id$, $\mathrm{Eval}_{s=1} \circ \overline{\mathfrak{H}} = \widehat{\bar\varphi}'_{(K,L)} \circ \widehat{\bar\varphi}$.

PROOF. The proof is by induction on K and L. Namely we assume the proposition for K, L and will prove the case of $K+1$, L and of K, $L+1$. We prove the case of $K+1$, L only.

We consider $\overline{\mathfrak{H}}_{(K,L)} : \overline{D} \to \overline{\mathfrak{D}}$. Since $\mathrm{Eval}_{s=0} \circ \overline{\mathfrak{H}}_{(K,L)}$ is identity and $\mathrm{Eval}_{s=0}$ induces an isomorphism on cohomology, it follows from Lemma 5.2.46 that we find $\overline{\mathfrak{H}}^0_{K+1,L}$ and extends $\overline{\mathfrak{H}}_{(K,L)}$ to $\overline{\mathfrak{H}}^0_{(K+1,L)}$. Moreover we may assume that

$$\mathrm{Eval}_{s=0} \circ \overline{\mathfrak{H}}^0_{(K+1,L)} = id.$$

(We can prove this fact by using an argument similar to the beginning of the proof of Proposition 4.5.6.)

On the other hand, since $\widehat{\bar\varphi}'_{(K,L)} \circ \widehat{\bar\varphi}$ is homotopic to identity and $\widehat{\bar\varphi}$ induces an isomorphism on cohomology, it follows from Lemma 5.2.46 that there exists $\widehat{\bar\varphi}'_{K+1,L}$ which extends $\widehat{\bar\varphi}'_{(K,L)}$ to $\widehat{\bar\varphi}'_{(K+1,L)}$.

We consider the difference

$$\Xi = -\mathrm{Eval}_{s=1} \circ \overline{\mathfrak{H}}^0_{(K+1,L)} + \widehat{\bar\varphi}'_{(K+1,L)} \circ (\bar\varphi_1 \otimes \cdots \otimes \bar\varphi_1).$$

Ξ is an element of $Hom(B_{K+1}\overline{C}_1[1] \otimes \overline{D}[1] \otimes B_L\overline{C}_0[1], \overline{D}[1])$ and is a δ_1 cocycle. Then since $\bar{\mathfrak{f}}_1^{(1)\otimes(K+1)} \otimes \bar\varphi_1 \otimes \bar{\mathfrak{f}}_1^{(0)\otimes L}$ is a cochain homotopy equivalence, there exists a δ_1 cocycle $\Delta\bar\varphi'_{(K+1,L)} \in Hom(B_{K+1}\overline{C}'_1[1] \otimes \overline{D}'[1] \otimes B_L\overline{C}'_0[1], \overline{D}[1])$ such that $[\Xi + \Delta\bar\varphi'_{(K+1,L)} \circ (\bar{\mathfrak{f}}_1^{(1)\otimes(K+1)} \otimes \bar\varphi_1 \otimes \bar{\mathfrak{f}}_1^{(0)\otimes L})] = 0$. Replacing $\bar\varphi'_{(K+1,L)}$ by $\bar\varphi'_{(K+1,L)} + \Delta\bar\varphi'_{(K+1,L)}$, we may assume $[\Xi] = 0$. Namely there exists $\Delta_1\overline{\mathfrak{H}}_{(K+1,L)} \in Hom(B_{K+1}\overline{C}_1[1] \otimes \overline{D}[1] \otimes B_L\overline{C}_0[1], \overline{D}[1])$ such that

$$\delta_1(\Delta_1\overline{\mathfrak{H}}_{(K+1,L)})$$
$$= \bar\varphi'_{(K+1,L)} \circ (\bar{\mathfrak{f}}_1^{(1)\otimes(K+1)} \otimes \bar\varphi_1 \otimes \bar{\mathfrak{f}}_1^{(0)\otimes L}) - (\mathrm{Eval}_{s=1})_1 \circ \overline{\mathfrak{H}}^0_{(K+1,L)}.$$

From (5.2.22.3), we find

$$\Delta\overline{\mathfrak{H}}_{(K+1,L)} \in Hom(B_{K+1}\overline{C}_1[1] \otimes \overline{D}[1] \otimes B_L\overline{C}_0[1], \overline{\mathfrak{D}}[1])$$

such that

$$(\overline{\mathrm{Eval}}_{s=0})_1 \circ \Delta\overline{\mathfrak{H}}_{(K+1,L)} = 0, \quad (\overline{\mathrm{Eval}}_{s=1})_1 \circ \Delta\overline{\mathfrak{H}}_{(K+1,L)} = \Delta_1\overline{\mathfrak{H}}_{(K+1,L)}.$$

Now it is straightforward to check that

$$\overline{\mathfrak{H}}_{(K+1,L)} = \overline{\mathfrak{H}}^0_{(K+1,L)} + \delta_1(\Delta\overline{\mathfrak{H}}_{(K+1,L)})$$

has required properties.   □

Using Proposition 5.2.48 we can prove the unfiltered version of Theorem 5.2.35 as in the case of the A_∞ algebras.   □

Before going to the filtered version, we mention the way to prove the unital unfiltered version of Theorem 5.2.35. The main difference is to use

$$\overline{C}_1[1] \otimes B_{K-1}\overline{C}_{1\mathrm{red}}[1] \otimes \overline{D}[1] \otimes B_{L-1}\overline{C}_{0\mathrm{red}}[1] \otimes \overline{C}_0[1].$$

Here $\overline{C}_{\mathrm{red}} = \overline{C}/R[\mathbf{e}]$ for unit $\mathbf{e}$. We then can modify the proof of Theorem 5.2.35 in a way similar to the argument of Subsection 4.4.4. The detail is left for the readers.

5.2.7. Obstructions to defining A_∞ bimodule homomorphisms II. To complete the proof of Theorem 5.2.35, we use the energy filtration. So we need the argument similar to one in Subsections 4.5.4 and 4.5.5. The obstruction is formulated by using a version of Hochschild cohomology, which we define below. Let $\overline{C}_i, \overline{C}'_i$ $i = 0,1$ be A_∞ algebras and $\overline{\mathfrak{f}}^{(i)} : \overline{C}_i \to \overline{C}'_i$ be A_∞ homomorphisms. Let $\overline{D}, \overline{D}'$ be graded R modules. We put:

$$(5.2.50) \quad \begin{aligned} B\overline{D}B &= B\overline{C}_1[1] \otimes \overline{D}[1] \otimes B\overline{C}_0[1], \\ B\overline{D}'B &= B\overline{C}'_1[1] \otimes \overline{D}'[1] \otimes B\overline{C}'_0[1]. \end{aligned}$$

Then $B\overline{D}B$ becomes a $(B\overline{C}_1[1], B\overline{C}_0[1])$ bi-comodule by putting

$$\Delta_{\mathrm{Left}}(\mathbf{x} \otimes y \otimes \mathbf{z}) = \sum_a (\mathbf{x}_a^1) \otimes (\mathbf{x}_a^2 \otimes y \otimes \mathbf{z}),$$

$$\Delta_{\mathrm{Right}}(\mathbf{x} \otimes y \otimes \mathbf{z}) = \sum_b (\mathbf{x} \otimes y \otimes \mathbf{z}_b^1) \otimes \mathbf{z}_b^2,$$

where

$$(5.2.51) \quad \Delta(\mathbf{x}) = \sum_a \mathbf{x}_a^1 \otimes \mathbf{x}_a^2, \quad \Delta(\mathbf{z}) = \sum_b \mathbf{z}_b^1 \otimes \mathbf{z}_b^2.$$

DEFINITION 5.2.52. We put

$$CH(\overline{C}_1, \overline{D}, \overline{C}_0; \overline{C}'_1, \overline{D}', \overline{C}'_0)$$

$$= \prod_{k_1=0}^{\infty} \prod_{k_0=0}^{\infty} Hom(B_{k_1}\overline{C}_1[1] \otimes \overline{D}[1] \otimes B_{k_0}\overline{C}_0[1], \overline{D}'[1]).$$

Every element

$$\mathcal{T} = (\mathcal{T}_{0,0}, \cdots, \mathcal{T}_{k_1,k_0}, \cdots) \in CH(\overline{C}_1, \overline{D}, \overline{C}_0; \overline{C}'_1, \overline{D}', \overline{C}'_0)$$

uniquely extends to a bicoderivation: $\widehat{\mathcal{T}} : B\overline{D}B \to B\overline{D}'B$ by putting

$$\widehat{\mathcal{T}}(\mathbf{x}, y, \mathbf{z}) = \sum_{a,b,k_1,k_0} \widehat{\mathsf{f}}(\mathbf{x}_a^1) \otimes \mathcal{T}_{k_1,k_0}(\mathbf{x}_a^2, y, \mathbf{z}_b^1) \otimes \widehat{\mathsf{f}}'(\mathbf{z}_b^2),$$

where we use the convention (5.2.51). Namely we have

$$\Delta_{\text{Left}} \circ \widehat{\mathcal{T}} = (\widehat{\mathsf{f}} \widehat{\otimes} \widehat{\mathcal{T}}) \circ \Delta_{\text{Left}}, \qquad \Delta_{\text{Right}} \circ \widehat{\mathcal{T}} = (\widehat{\mathcal{T}} \widehat{\otimes} \widehat{\mathsf{f}}') \circ \Delta_{\text{Right}}.$$

We can define a coboundary operator δ on $CH(\overline{C}_1, \overline{D}, \overline{C}_0; \overline{C}_1', \overline{D}', \overline{C}_0')$ by

$$\widehat{\delta}_{\overline{\mathsf{f}}^{(1)}, \overline{\mathsf{f}}^{(0)}} \mathcal{T} = \widehat{d} \circ \widehat{\mathcal{T}} - (-1)^{\deg \mathcal{T}} \widehat{\mathcal{T}} \circ \widehat{d}.$$

DEFINITION 5.2.53. We call the complex

$$(CH(\overline{C}_1, \overline{D}, \overline{C}_0; \overline{C}_1, \overline{D}', \overline{C}_0'), \delta_{\overline{\mathsf{f}}^{(1)}, \overline{\mathsf{f}}^{(0)}})$$

the *Hochschild complex* and we note by $HH(\overline{C}_1, \overline{D}, \overline{C}_0; \overline{C}_1', \overline{D}', \overline{C}_0'; \overline{\mathsf{f}}^{(1)}, \overline{\mathsf{f}}^{(0)})$ its cohomology, and call it *Hochschild cohomology*.

We can generalize Proposition 4.4.48 in an obvious way.

DEFINITION 5.2.54. We say $\varphi = \{\varphi_{k_1,k_0}\}$ is a *filtered A_∞ bimodule homomorphism modulo T^λ (over $(\overline{\mathsf{f}}^{(1)}, \overline{\mathsf{f}}^{(0)})$)*, if it satisfies the condition in Definition 3.7.7 (2) and

$$\widehat{d} \circ \widehat{\varphi}_{k_1,k_0} - \widehat{\varphi}_{k_1,k_0} \circ \widehat{d} \equiv 0 \mod T^\lambda.$$

We still use the notation of Definition 5.2.1. We take G so that all the filtered A_∞ algebras, filtered A_∞ homomorphisms and filtered A_∞ bimodules we discuss are G-gapped. We can enumerate the elements of G such that $G = \{(\lambda_i, \mu_i) \mid i = 0, 1, 2, \cdots\}$ with $\lambda_0 = 0$, $\lambda_i \uparrow \infty$. Let $\varphi = \{\varphi_{k_1,k_0}\}$ is a filtered A_∞ bimodule homomorphism modulo T^{λ_i} over $(\overline{\mathsf{f}}^{(1)}, \overline{\mathsf{f}}^{(0)})$. In particular $\overline{\varphi} = \{\overline{\varphi}_{k_1,k_0}\}$ is an A_∞ bimodule homomorphism over $(\overline{\mathsf{f}}^{(1)}, \overline{\mathsf{f}}^{(0)})$.

PROPOSITION 5.2.55. *There exists* $o_{\lambda_{i+1}}(\varphi) \in CH(\overline{C}_1, \overline{D}, \overline{C}_0; \overline{C}_1', \overline{D}', \overline{C}_0')$ *such that*

(5.2.56.1) $\quad \delta_{\overline{\mathsf{f}}^{(1)}, \overline{\mathsf{f}}^{(0)}}(o_{\lambda_{i+1}}(\varphi)) = 0.$

(5.2.56.2) $\quad \varphi$ *extends to an A_∞ bimodule homomorphism modulo $T^{\lambda_{i+1}}$ if and only if* $[o_{\lambda_{i+1}}(\varphi)] = 0 \in HH(\overline{C}_1, \overline{D}, \overline{C}_0; \overline{C}_1', \overline{D}', \overline{C}_0'; \overline{\mathsf{f}}^{(1)}, \overline{\mathsf{f}}^{(0)}).$

(5.2.56.3) *The cohomology class $[o_{\lambda_{i+1}}(\varphi)]$ is invariant of the homotopy class of φ. (We can make this statement precise in the same way as Remark 4.5.18.)*

(5.2.56.4) *We assume that $\overline{\mathsf{g}}_{(i)} : \overline{C}_i' \to \overline{C}_i''$, $\overline{\mathsf{g}}_{(i)}' : \overline{C}_i''' \to \overline{C}_i$ are A_∞ homomorphisms and $\overline{\varphi}' : \overline{D}' \to \overline{D}''$ and $\overline{\varphi}'' : \overline{D}''' \to \overline{D}$ are A_∞ bimodule homomorphism over $(\overline{\mathsf{g}}_{(1)}, \overline{\mathsf{g}}_{(0)})$ and over $(\overline{\mathsf{g}}_{(1)}', \overline{\mathsf{g}}_{(0)}')$ respectively. Then we have*

$$[o_{\lambda_{i+1}}(\overline{\varphi}' \circ \overline{\varphi} \circ \overline{\varphi}'')] = (\overline{\varphi}', \overline{\varphi}'')_* [o_{\lambda_{i+1}}(\overline{\varphi})].$$

The proof of Proposition 5.2.55 is similar to that of Definition-Proposition 4.5.16 and is omitted.

Now we use Proposition 5.2.55 to complete the proof of the filtered version of Theorem 5.2.35. We can prove the following proposition by induction on i. We consider the situation of Theorem 5.2.35.

PROPOSITION 5.2.57. *For any $i = 1, 2, \cdots$, there exists $\varphi' : D' \to D$ a filtered A_∞ bimodule homomorphism modulo T^{λ_i} over $(\mathfrak{f}^{(1)})^{-1}, (\mathfrak{f}^{(0)})^{-1}$. Also there exists $\mathfrak{H} : D \to \mathfrak{D}$ a filtered A_∞ bimodule homomorphism module T^{λ_i} over $\mathfrak{F}^{(i)}$ (a homotopy from identity to $(\mathfrak{f}^{(i)})^{-1} \circ \mathfrak{f}^{(i)}$), such that*

$$\mathrm{Eval}_{s=0} \circ \mathfrak{H} = id, \qquad \mathrm{Eval}_{s=1} \circ \mathfrak{H} = \varphi' \circ \varphi.$$

Using Proposition 5.2.55, the proof goes in the same way as the argument of Subsection 4.5.5. We omit it.

Thus we have finished the proof of Theorem 5.2.35. $\qquad\square$

5.3. Homotopy equivalences of A_∞ bimodules: the geometric realization

5.3.1. Construction of filtered A_∞ bimodule homomorphisms.
The goal of this subsection is to prove that the homotopy type of the filtered A_∞ bimodule constructed from a relatively spin pair of Lagrangian submanifolds is independent of the various choices we made to define it. Theorem 5.3.1 is our main result of this subsection.

Let $(L^{(0)}, L^{(1)})$ be a relatively spin pair of Lagrangian submanifolds of M and ψ a symplectic diffeomorphism $\psi : M \to M'$. Let $\{J_t\}_t$, $\{J'_t\}_t$ $(t \in [0, 1])$ be families of compatible almost complex structures on M and M' respectively. For $t = i = 0, 1$, we take homotopies of almost complex structures $\{J^{(i)}_\rho\}_\rho$ from $J^\psi_i = \psi_*(J_i)$ to J'_i on M':

$$
\begin{array}{ccc}
J^\psi_1 = J^{(1)}_0 & \overset{J^{(1)}_\rho}{\sim} & J^{(1)}_1 = J'_1 \\
J^\psi_t \wr & & \wr J'_t \\
J^\psi_0 = J^{(0)}_0 & \overset{J^{(0)}_\rho}{\sim} & J^{(0)}_1 = J'_0.
\end{array}
$$

Diagram 5.3.1

We choose multisections $\mathfrak{s}_i^{\mathrm{top}(\rho)}$ $(i = 0, 1)$ and define

$$\mathfrak{f}^{i,\psi,\{J^{(i)}_\rho\}_\rho,\mathfrak{s}_i^{\mathrm{top}(\rho)}} : (C_1(L^{(i)}; \Lambda_{0,nov}), \mathfrak{m}_k^{J_i,\mathfrak{s}_i}) \to (C_3(L^{(i)\prime}; \Lambda_{0,nov}), \mathfrak{m}_k^{J'_i,\mathfrak{s}'_i})$$

$$\mathfrak{g}^{i,\psi,\{J^{(i)}_\rho\}_\rho,\mathfrak{s}_i^{\mathrm{top}(\rho)}} : (C_1(L^{(i)}; \Lambda_{0,nov}), \mathfrak{m}_k^{J_i,\mathfrak{s}_i}) \to (C_2(L^{(i)\prime}; \Lambda_{0,nov}), \mathfrak{m}_k^{J'_i,\mathfrak{s}'_i})$$

in Section 4.6. Here we denote $L^{(i)\prime} = \psi(L^{(i)})$ and C_1, C_2 are determined by the choices of the countable sets $\mathcal{X}_1(L^{(i)})$, $\mathcal{X}_2(L^{(i)\prime})$ of smooth singular simplices in $L^{(i)}$, $L^{(i)\prime}$ which are chosen in Section 3.5 (and 7.2) to construct the structures of the filtered A_∞ algebras for $L^{(i)}$ and $L^{(i)\prime}$ respectively. C_3 is determined by another choice of the countable set $\mathcal{X}_3(L^{(i)\prime}) \supset \mathcal{X}_2(L^{(i)\prime})$ of chains in $L^{(i)\prime}$ we made in Theorem 4.6.1 to construct the filtered A_∞ homomorphism $\mathfrak{f}^{i,\psi,\{J^{(i)}_\rho\}_\rho,\mathfrak{s}_i^{\mathrm{top}(\rho)}}$. The filtered A_∞ homomorphism $\mathfrak{g}^{i,\psi,\{J^{(i)}_\rho\}_\rho,\mathfrak{s}_i^{\mathrm{top}(\rho)}}$ is defined by composing $\mathfrak{f}^{i,\psi,\{J^{(i)}_\rho\}_\rho,\mathfrak{s}_i^{\mathrm{top}(\rho)}}$ with the homotopy inverse of

$$(C_2(L^{(i)\prime}; \Lambda_{0,nov}), \mathfrak{m}_k^{J'_i,\mathfrak{s}'_i}) \to (C_3(L^{(i)\prime}; \Lambda_{0,nov}), \mathfrak{m}_k^{J'_i,\mathfrak{s}'_i})$$

induced by the natural inclusion $\mathcal{X}_2(L^{(i)\prime}) \subset \mathcal{X}_3(L^{(i)\prime})$. See the beginning of Subsection 4.6.1 (Theorem 4.6.1).

We consider the case where $L^{(0)} \cap L^{(1)}$ and $L^{(0)\prime} \cap L^{(1)\prime}$ are transversal and study $C(L^{(1)}, L^{(0)}; \Lambda_{0,nov})$, $C(L^{(1)\prime}, L^{(0)\prime}; \Lambda_{0,nov})$ defined in Subsection 3.7.4. We can generalize this to the case when $L^{(0)}$ and $L^{(1)}$ have clean intersection (the Bott-Morse case). We will discuss the Bott-Morse case when we study another situation, where we move two Lagrangian submanifolds by two different Hamiltonian isotopies. It is a modification to adapt the argument there to our situation.

The following is the main result of this subsection:

THEOREM 5.3.1. *There exists a filtered A_∞ bimodule homomorphism*

$$\varphi : C(L^{(1)}, L^{(0)}; \Lambda_{0,nov}) \to C(L^{(1)\prime}, L^{(0)\prime}; \Lambda_{0,nov})$$

over $(\mathfrak{g}^{1,\psi,\{J_\rho^{(1)}\}_\rho, \mathfrak{s}_1^{\mathrm{top}(\rho)}}, \mathfrak{g}^{0,\psi,\{J_\rho^{(0)}\}_\rho \mathfrak{s}_0^{\mathrm{top}(\rho)}})$ *which is a homotopy equivalence.*

We remark that in Theorem 5.3.1 we are moving two Lagrangian submanifolds at the same time by the *same* symplectic diffeomorphism ψ. In this case, Floer cohomology over $\Lambda_{0,nov}$ is well defined. In Subsections 5.3.2, 5.3.3 and 5.3.4, we will study more delicate case where we move two Lagrangian submanifolds by *different Hamiltonian* isotopies. In that case we can still construct a homotopy equivalence. However we need to take Λ_{nov} as the coefficient ring and obtain (only) a *weakly filtered A_∞ bimodule homomorphism*, which is introduced in Subsection 5.2.1.

PROOF. The proof is similar to that of Theorem 4.6.1 but we need to use a two-parameter family of compatible almost complex structures. We first remark that we may take $J_\rho^{(i)}$ such that $J_\rho^{(i)} = J_0^{(i)}$ for $\rho < \epsilon$ and $J_\rho^{(i)} = J_1^{(i)}$ for $1 - \epsilon < \rho$. Here ϵ is a sufficiently small positive number.

Then we can find a diffeomorphism $\chi : \mathbb{R} \to (0, 1)$ such that

(5.3.2.1) $\chi(\tau_1) < \chi(\tau_2)$ for $-A \le \tau_1 < \tau_2 \le A$.

(5.3.2.2) $J_{\chi(\tau)}^\psi = J_0^\psi$ for $\tau < -A$ and $J_{\chi(\tau)}^\psi = J_1^\psi$ for $\tau > A$.

We take a two-parameter family $\{J_{\tau,t}\}_{\tau,t}$, $\tau \in \mathbb{R}$, $t \in [0,1]$ of compatible almost structures on M' such that

(5.3.3.1) $J_{\tau,0} = J_{\chi(\tau)}^{(0)}$, $J_{\tau,1} = J_{\chi(\tau)}^{(1)}$.

(5.3.3.2) $J_{\tau,t} = J_t^\psi$ if $\tau < -A$. $J_{\tau,t} = J_t'$ if $\tau > A$.

(Recall $J_0^{(i)} = J_i^\psi$.) The existence of such a family follows from the contractibility of the set of all compatible almost complex structures.

Let $[\ell_p, w] \in Cr(L^{(0)}, L^{(1)})$ and $[\ell_q, w'] \in Cr(L^{(0)\prime}, L^{(1)\prime})$. We also consider $\psi([\ell_p, w]) = [\psi \circ \ell_p, \psi \circ w] \in Cr(L^{(0)\prime}, L^{(1)\prime})$. We define a moduli space

$$\overset{\circ}{\mathcal{M}}_{k_1,k_0}(L^{(1)\prime}, L^{(0)\prime}, \{J_{\tau,t}\}_{\tau,t}; [\ell_p, w], [\ell_q, w']; \mathrm{top}(\tau))$$

as follows. Let $\Sigma = \mathbb{R} \times [0, 1]$ plus possibly sphere bubbles, as before. We consider $(\Sigma; u; \vec{\tau}^{(1)}, \vec{\tau}^{(0)})$ with the following properties.

(5.3.4.1) $u : \Sigma \to M'$ satisfies

$$\frac{\partial u}{\partial \tau} + J_{\tau,t} \frac{\partial u}{\partial t} = 0$$

on $\mathbb{R} \times [0, 1]$. If a bubble tree of spheres is attached at (τ, t) then all the spheres in the tree are $J_{\tau,t}$-holomorphic. We also assume the stability condition.

(5.3.4.2) $u(\tau,0) \subset L^{(0)'}$, $u(\tau,1) \subset L^{(1)'}$.

(5.3.4.3) $\lim_{\tau \to -\infty} u = \psi(p)$, $\lim_{\tau \to +\infty} u = q$.

(5.3.4.4) $\vec{\tau}^{(0)} = (\tau_1^{(0)}, \cdots, \tau_{k_0}^{(0)})$ with $-\infty < \tau_1^{(0)} < \cdots < \tau_{k_0}^{(0)} < +\infty$. $\vec{\tau}^{(1)} =$
$(\tau_1^{(1)}, \cdots, \tau_{k_1}^{(1)})$ with $-\infty < \tau_{k_1}^{(1)} < \cdots < \tau_1^{(1)} < +\infty$.

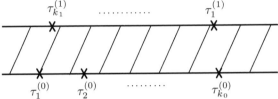

Figure 5.3.1

Then $\overset{\circ}{\mathcal{M}}_{k_1,k_0}(L^{(1)'}, L^{(0)'}, \{J_{\tau,t}\}_{\tau,t}; [\ell_p, w], [\ell_q, w']; \mathrm{top}(\tau))$ is defined as the set of all $\sim$ equivalence classes of such $(\Sigma; u; \vec{\tau}^{(0)}, \vec{\tau}^{(1)})$, where the equivalence relation $\sim$ is defined in a similar way as Definition 2.1.24.

We define the evaluation map

$$ev = (ev_1^{(1)}, \dots, ev_{k_1}^{(1)}; ev_1^{(0)}, \dots, ev_{k_0}^{(0)})$$
$$: \overset{\circ}{\mathcal{M}}_{k_1,k_0}(L^{(1)'}, L^{(0)'}, \{J_{\tau,t}\}_{\tau,t}; \psi([\ell_p, w]), [\ell_q, w']; \mathrm{top}(\tau))$$
$$\to (L^{(1)})^{k_1} \times (L^{(0)})^{k_0}$$

by

$$ev((\Sigma; u; \vec{\tau}^{(1)}, \vec{\tau}^{(0)})) = \Big(\psi^{-1}(u(\tau_1^{(1)}, 1)), \cdots, \psi^{-1}(u(\tau_{k_1}^{(1)}, 1)),$$
$$\psi^{-1}(u(\tau_1^{(0)}, 0)), \cdots, \psi^{-1}(u(\tau_{k_0}^{(0)}, 0)) \Big).$$

We also define

$$ev_{\mathrm{time},(0)} = (ev_{\mathrm{time},(0),1}, \cdots, ev_{\mathrm{time},(0),k_0})$$
$$: \overset{\circ}{\mathcal{M}}_{k_1,k_0}(L^{(1)'}, L^{(0)'}, \{J_{\tau,t}\}_{\tau,t}; [\ell_p, w], [\ell_q, w']; \mathrm{top}(\tau)) \to \mathbb{R}^{k_0}$$

by $ev_{\mathrm{time},(0),j}((\Sigma; u; \vec{\tau}^{(1)}, \vec{\tau}^{(0)})) = \tau_j^{(0)}$. We define

$$ev_{\mathrm{time},(1)} = (ev_{\mathrm{time},(1),1}, \cdots, ev_{\mathrm{time},(1),k_1})$$
$$: \overset{\circ}{\mathcal{M}}_{k_1,k_0}(L^{(1)'}, L^{(0)'}; \{J_{\tau,t}\}_{\tau,t}; [\ell_p, w], [\ell_q, w']; \mathrm{top}(\tau)) \to \mathbb{R}^{k_1}$$

in the same way.

To define the filtered A_∞ bimodule homomorphism, we need to combine the moduli space $\overset{\circ}{\mathcal{M}}_{k_1,k_0}(L^{(1)'}, L^{(0)'}, \{J_{\tau,t}\}_{\tau,t}; [\ell_p, w], [\ell_q, w']; \mathrm{top}(\tau))$ with

$$\mathcal{M}_{k+1}^{\mathrm{main}}(M', L^{(i)'}, \{J_\rho^{(i)}\}_\rho; \mathrm{top}(\rho))$$

we used in Section 4.6 as follows. Here we remark that the parameters ρ and τ are related by the following coordinate change:

$$\rho = \chi(\tau), \quad \tau \in \mathbb{R}, \quad \rho \in [0,1].$$

Strictly speaking, we take $\chi : \mathbb{R} \to (0,1)$ as a diffeomorphism satisfying (5.3.2) but the almost complex structures parametrized by $\chi(\tau)$ for $\tau < -A, \tau > A$ are constant.

Let $l_1^{(0)}, \cdots, l_a^{(0)}, l_1^{(1)}, \cdots, l_b^{(1)}$ be nonnegative integers such that $\sum_{i=1}^{a} l_i^{(0)} = k_0$, $\sum_{i'=1}^{b} l_{i'}^{(1)} = k_1$. We consider the system

$$\mathfrak{D} = \Big((\Sigma; u; \vec{\tau}^{(1)}, \vec{\tau}^{(0)}); ((\Sigma_{(1),i'}, \vec{z}_{(1),i'}), (u_{(1),i',\alpha}), (\rho_{(1),i',\alpha}))$$

$$; ((\Sigma_{(0),i}, \vec{z}_{(0),i}), (u_{(0),i,\alpha}), (\rho_{(0),i,\alpha})) \Big)$$

$i = 1, \cdots, a$, $i' = 1, \cdots, b$ with the following properties:

(5.3.5.1) $(\Sigma; u; \vec{\tau}^{(1)}, \vec{\tau}^{(0)}) \in \mathring{\mathcal{M}}_{b,a}(L^{(1)\prime}, L^{(0)\prime}; \{J_{\tau,t}\}_{\tau,t}; [\ell_p, w], [\ell_q, w']; \mathrm{top}(\tau)).$

(5.3.5.2)
$$((\Sigma_{(0),i}, \vec{z}_{(0),i}), (u_{(0),i,\alpha}), (\rho_{(0),i,\alpha}))$$
$$\in \mathcal{M}_{l_i^{(0)}+1}^{\mathrm{main}}(M'; L^{(0)\prime}, \{J_\rho^{(0)}\}_\rho : \beta_i^{(0)}; \mathrm{top}(\rho)).$$

(5.3.5.3)
$$((\Sigma_{(1),i'}, \vec{z}_{(1),i'}), (u_{(1),i',\alpha}), (\rho_{(1),i',\alpha}))$$
$$\in \mathcal{M}_{l_{i'}^{(1)}+1}^{\mathrm{main}}(M'; L^{(1)\prime}, \{J_\rho^{(1)}\}_\rho : \beta_{i'}^{(1)}; \mathrm{top}(\rho)).$$

(5.3.5.4) $ev_0((\Sigma_{(0),i}, \vec{z}_{(0),i}), (u_{(0),i,\alpha}), (\rho_{(0),i,\alpha})) = u(\chi(\tau_i^{(0)}), 0).$

(5.3.5.5) $ev_0((\Sigma_{(1),i'}, \vec{z}_{(1),i'}), (u_{(1),i',\alpha}), (\rho_{(1),i',\alpha})) = u(\chi(\tau_{i'}^{(1)}), 1).$

(5.3.5.6) $\rho_{(0),i,0} \le \chi(\tau_i^{(0)})$. $\rho_{(1),i',0} \le \chi(\tau_{i'}^{(1)})$.

(5.3.5.7) $(\sum_i \beta_i^{(0)} + \sum_{i'} \beta_{i'}^{(1)}) \# w \sim w'$.

Here we recall that $\rho_{(0),i,0}$ is the "time" associated to the last component of $D_{(0),i}$. In other words, $u_{(0),i,0}$ is $J_{\rho_{(0),i,0}}^{(0)}$ holomorphic. We also recall that $\chi : \mathbb{R} \to (0,1)$ is given in (5.3.2).

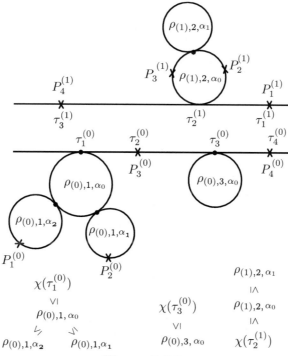

Figure 5.3.2

By an abuse of notations we allow the case $l_j^{(i)} = 1$, $\beta_j^{(i)} = 0$ ($i = 0$ or 1.) (In such a case $\mathcal{M}_2^{\mathrm{main}}(M'; L^{(i)}, \{J_\rho^{(i)}\}_\rho : 0; \mathrm{top}(\rho))$ was not defined.) We *define* $\mathcal{M}_2^{\mathrm{main}}(M'; L^{(i)\prime}, \{J_\rho^{(i)}\}_\rho : 0; \mathrm{top}(\rho)) = \{\text{one point}\}$ and Conditions (5.3.5.4), (5.3.5.5) and (5.3.5.6) are void. See Figure 5.3.2.

Let
$$\mathcal{M}_{k_1,k_0}^{\mathrm{unbr}}(L^{(1)\prime}, L^{(0)\prime}, \{J_{\tau,t}\}_{\tau,t}; [\ell_p, w], [\ell_q, w']; \mathrm{top}(\tau))$$
be the set of all such systems $\mathfrak{D}$. (It can be defined as a union of the fiber products of moduli spaces.) Here 'unbr' stands for unbroken.

There exists an evaluation map
$$ev = (ev_1^{(1)}, \dots, ev_{k_1}^{(1)}; ev_1^{(0)}, \dots, ev_{k_0}^{(0)})$$
$$: \mathcal{M}_{k_1,k_0}^{\mathrm{unbr}}(L^{(1)\prime}, L^{(0)\prime}; \{J_{\tau,t}\}_{\tau,t}; [\ell_p, w], [\ell_q, w']; \mathrm{top}(\tau)) \to (L^{(1)})^{k_1} \times (L^{(0)})^{k_0},$$

where $ev_m^{(0)}$ is defined as follows. We take i, j such that $m = l_1^{(0)} + \cdots + l_{i-1}^{(0)} + j$. Then
$$ev_m^{(0)}(\mathfrak{D}) = ev_j((\Sigma_{(0),i}, \vec{z}_{(0),i}), (u_{(0),i,\alpha}), (\rho_{(0),i,\alpha}))),$$

where ev_j on the right hand side is defined in a way similar to Subsection 4.6.1. (This is the case when m-th evaluation map is taken at the j-th marked point on the i-th bubble.) We remark that in the case when $l_i^{(0)} = 1$ and $\beta_i^{(0)} = 0$, we put
$$ev_m^{(0)} = ev_j((\Sigma; u; \vec{\tau}^{(1)}, \vec{\tau}^{(0)})),$$

where $l_1^{(0)} + \cdots + l_{i-1}^{(0)} + 1 = j$. (This is the case when the m-th evaluation map is taken at a marked point on $\mathbb{R} \times \{0\}$.)

We can compactify $\mathcal{M}_{k_1,k_0}^{\mathrm{unbr}}(L^{(1)\prime}, L^{(0)\prime}, \{J_{\tau,t}\}_{\tau,t}; [\ell_p, w], [\ell_q, w']; \mathrm{top}(\tau))$ to
$$\mathcal{M}_{k_1,k_0}(L^{(1)\prime}, L^{(0)\prime}; \{J_{\tau,t}\}_{\tau,t}; [\ell_p, w], [\ell_q, w']; \mathrm{top}(\tau)).$$

Here we put
$$\mathcal{M}_{k_1,k_0}(L^{(1)\prime}, L^{(0)\prime}; \{J_{\tau,t}\}_{\tau,t}; [\ell_p, w], [\ell_q, w']; \mathrm{top}(\tau))$$
$$= \coprod_{l_0,l_1} \coprod_{m_1,m_0} \coprod_{p',w''} \coprod_{q',w'''} \mathcal{M}_{l_1,l_0}(L^{(1)\prime}, L^{(0)\prime}; \{J_{0,t}\}_t; [\ell_p, w], [\ell_{p'}, w''])$$
$$\times \mathcal{M}_{k_1-l_1-m_1,k_0-l_0-m_0}^{\mathrm{unbr}}(L^{(1)\prime}, L^{(0)\prime}; \{J_{\tau,t}\}_{\tau,t}; [\ell_{p'}, w''], [\ell_{q'}, w''']; \mathrm{top}(\tau))$$
$$\times \mathcal{M}_{m_1,m_0}(L^{(1)\prime}, L^{(0)\prime}; \{J_{1,t}\}_t; [\ell_{q'}, w'''], [\ell_q, w']),$$

where
$$\mathcal{M}_{l_1,l_0}(L^{(1)\prime}, L^{(0)\prime}; \{J_{0,t}\}_t; [\ell_p, w], [\ell_{p'}, w''])$$
and
$$\mathcal{M}_{m_1,m_0}(L^{(1)\prime}, L^{(0)\prime}; \{J_{1,t}\}_t; [\ell_{q'}, w'''], [\ell_q, w'])$$
are defined as in (3.7.31). (We put $\{J_{i,t}\}_t$ in the notation to specify the one parameter family of almost complex structures we use.)

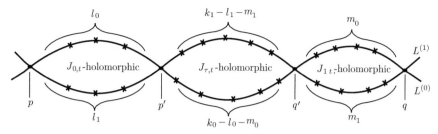

Figure 5.3.3

We extend ev to this compactification in a way similar to (3.7.30), (3.7.33). Now for $\vec{P}^{(i)} = (P_1^{(i)}, \cdots, P_{k_i}^{(i)})$ with $P_j^{(i)} \in C_1(L^{(i)}; \mathbb{Q})$ $(i = 0, 1)$, we define

$$\mathcal{M}_{k_1, k_0}(L^{(1)\prime}, L^{(0)\prime}; \{J_{\tau,t}\}_{\tau,t}; [\ell_p, w], [\ell_q, w']; \mathrm{top}(\tau); \vec{P}^{(1)}; \vec{P}^{(0)})$$

as the fiber product

$$\mathcal{M}_{k_1, k_0}(L^{(1)\prime}, L^{(0)\prime}; \{J_{\tau,t}\}_{\tau,t}; [\ell_p, w], [\ell_q, w']; \mathrm{top}(\tau)) \times \left(\prod_j P_j^{(1)} \times \prod_i P_j^{(0)} \right)$$

over $(L^{(1)})^{k_1} \times (L^{(0)})^{k_0}$.

PROPOSITION 5.3.6.
(1) $\mathcal{M}_{k_1, k_0}(L^{(1)\prime}, L^{(0)\prime}; \{J_{\tau,t}\}; [\ell_p, w], [\ell_q, w']; \vec{P}^{(1)}; \vec{P}^{(0)})$ *is a space with oriented Kuranishi structure of dimension*

$$(5.3.7) \qquad \mu([\ell_q, w']) - \mu([\ell_p, w]) + k_0 + k_1 - \sum \deg P_i^{(0)} - \sum \deg P_i^{(1)}.$$

(2) *There exists a multisection $\mathfrak{s}$ on our moduli space*

$$\mathcal{M}_{k_1, k_0}(L^{(1)\prime}, L^{(0)\prime}, \{J_{\tau,t}\}_{\tau,t}; [\ell_p, w], [\ell_q, w']; \mathrm{top}(\tau); \vec{P}^{(1)}; \vec{P}^{(0)})$$

compatible at infinity with various other multisections we already chosen. We put

$$\mathcal{M}_{k_1, k_0}(L^{(1)\prime}, L^{(0)\prime}; \{J_{\tau,t}\}_{\tau,t}; [\ell_p, w], [\ell_q, w']; \mathrm{top}(\tau); \vec{P}^{(1)}; \vec{P}^{(0)})^{\mathfrak{s}} = \mathfrak{s}^{-1}(0).$$

It is a $\mathbb{Q}$ chain whose dimension is given by (5.3.7). (We regard it as a singular chain by taking appropriate triangulation.)

The proof is the same as other statement deferred to Chapter 7.

Let

$$T^{\lambda_j^{(i)}} e^{\mu_j^{(i)}} P_j^{(i)} \in C_1(L^{(i)}, \Lambda_{0,nov}), \quad (i = 0, 1 \text{ and } j = 1, \cdots, k_i)$$

and

$$T^{\lambda} e^{\mu}[\ell_p, w] \in C(L^{(1)}, L^{(0)}; \Lambda_{0,nov}).$$

Now we define

$$\phi_{k_1,k_0}\left(T^{\lambda_1^{(1)}}e^{\mu_1^{(1)}}P_1^{(1)},\cdots,T^{\lambda_{k_1}^{(1)}}e^{\mu_{k_1}^{(1)}}P_{k_1}^{(1)}, T^\lambda e^\mu[\ell_p,w],\right.$$

$$\left. T^{\lambda_1^{(0)}}e^{\mu_1^{(0)}}P_1^{(0)},\cdots,T^{\lambda_{k_0}^{(0)}}e^{\mu_{k_0}^{(0)}}P_{k_0}^{(0)}\right)$$

$$=\sum \#\left(\mathcal{M}_{k_1,k_0}(L^{(1)\prime},L^{(0)\prime},\{J_{\tau,t}\}_{\tau,t};[\ell_p,w],[\ell_q,w'];\mathrm{top}(\tau);\right.$$

$$\left. \vec{P}^{(1)};\vec{P}^{(0)})^{\mathfrak{s}}\right)T^{\lambda'}e^{\mu'}[\ell_q,w'],$$

where the sum is taken over the choices of $[\ell_q,w']$ such that the moduli space appears are of 0 dimensional and

$$\lambda'=\sum_{i=1}^{k_0}\lambda_i^{(0)}+\lambda+\sum_{i=1}^{k_1}\lambda_i^{(1)},\quad \mu'=\sum_{i=1}^{k_0}\mu_i^{(0)}+\mu+\sum_{i=1}^{k_1}\mu_i^{(1)}.$$

LEMMA 5.3.8. $\phi=\{\phi_{k_1,k_0}\}_{k_1,k_0}$ is a filtered A_∞ bimodule homomorphism over the pair of the filtered A_∞ homomorphisms

$$(\mathfrak{f}^{1,\psi,\{J_\rho^{(1)}\}_\rho,\mathfrak{s}_1^{\mathrm{top}(\rho)}},\mathfrak{f}^{0,\psi,\{J_\rho^{(0)}\}_\rho,\mathfrak{s}_0^{\mathrm{top}(\rho)}}).$$

Here $\mathfrak{f}^{0,\psi,\{J_\rho^{(0)}\}_\rho,\mathfrak{s}_0^{\mathrm{top}(\rho)}}$, $\mathfrak{f}^{1,\psi,\{J_\rho^{(1)}\}_\rho,\mathfrak{s}_1^{\mathrm{top}(\rho)}}$ are defined in Section 4.6.

PROOF. To prove Lemma 5.3.8 we need to study the boundary of the moduli space $\mathcal{M}_{k_1,k_0}(L^{(1)\prime},L^{(0)\prime},\{J_{\tau,t}\}_{\tau,t};[\ell_p,w],[\ell_q,w'];\mathrm{top}(\tau);\vec{P}^{(1)};\vec{P}^{(0)})$ when its virtual dimension is 1. Let $\mathfrak{D}_j$, $j=1,2,\cdots$ be a sequence of elements of the moduli space $\mathcal{M}_{k_1,k_0}(L^{(1)\prime},L^{(0)\prime},\{J_{\tau,t}\}_{\tau,t};[\ell_p,w],[\ell_q,w'];\mathrm{top}(\tau);\vec{P}^{(1)};\vec{P}^{(0)})$ converging to a boundary point in the compactification. We may assume that the combinatorial type of $\mathfrak{D}_j$ does not depend on j. We put

$$\mathfrak{D}_j=\left((\Sigma_j;u_j;\vec{\tau}^{(1),(j)},\vec{\tau}^{(0),(j)});((\Sigma_{(1),i',(j)},\vec{z}_{(1),i',(j)}),(u_{(1),i',(j),\alpha}),\right.$$

$$\left.(\rho_{(1),i',(j),\alpha}));((\Sigma_{(0),i,(j)},\vec{z}_{(0),i',(j)}),(u_{(0),i,(j),\alpha}),(\rho_{(0),i,(j),\alpha}))\right).$$

(See (5.3.5).) Then as $j\to\infty$ one of the following occurs.

(5.3.9.1) u_j splits into two. One of them slides to the part $\tau\to-\infty$.
(5.3.9.2) u_j splits into two. One of them slides to the part $\tau\to+\infty$.
(5.3.9.3) u_j bubbles at $t=0$.
(5.3.9.4) u_j bubbles at $t=1$.
(5.3.9.5.p) One of the components $\Sigma_{(p),i,(j),\alpha}$ $(p=0,1)$ of $\Sigma_{(p),i,(j)}$ splits into two.
(5.3.9.6.p)

$$\lim_{j\to\infty}\rho_{(p),i,(j),\alpha}=\lim_{j\to\infty}\rho_{(p),i,(j),\alpha'}$$

where the intersection $\Sigma_{(p),i,\alpha,(j)}\cap\Sigma_{(p),i,(j),\alpha'}$ is not empty.
(5.3.9.7.p) $\lim_{j\to\infty}\rho_{(p),i,(j),\alpha}=0$.
(5.3.9.8.p) $\lim_{j\to\infty}\rho_{(p),i,(j),0}=\lim_{j\to\infty}\chi(\tau_i^{(p),(j)})$. Here $\alpha=0$ is the index of the component containing the 0-th marked point.

(5.3.9.8.p) corresponds to the case where the equality holds in (5.3.5.6).

See the following Figures 5.3.4 – 5.3.10.

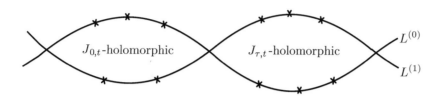

Figure 5.3.4 (5.3.9.1)

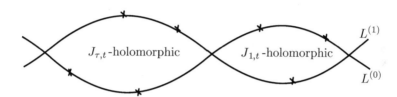

Figure 5.3.5 (5.3.9.2)

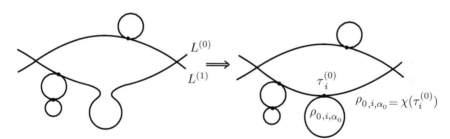

Figure 5.3.6 (5.3.9.3)

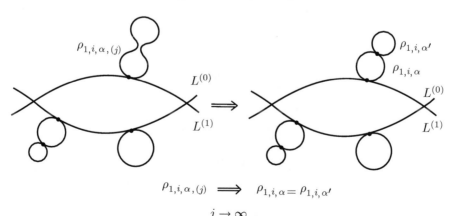

$$\rho_{1,i,\alpha,(j)} \implies \rho_{1,i,\alpha} = \rho_{1,i,\alpha'}$$

$$j \to \infty$$

Figure 5.3.7 (5.3.9.5.1)

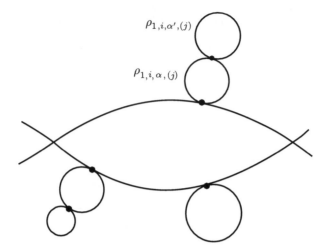

$$\lim_{j\to\infty} \rho_{1,i,\alpha,(j)} = \lim_{j\to\infty} \rho_{1,i,\alpha',(j)}$$

Figure 5.3.8 (5.3.9.6.1)

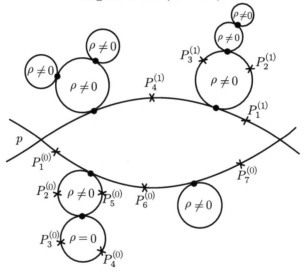

Figure 5.3.9 (5.3.9.7.0)

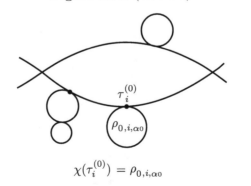

$$\chi(\tau_i^{(0)}) = \rho_{0,i,\alpha_0}$$

Figure 5.3.10 (5.3.9.8.0)

As in Section 4.6, we find that $(5.3.9.5.p)$ cancels with $(5.3.9.6.p)$. (See Figures 5.3.7 and 5.3.8.) We also can see easily that $(5.3.9.3)$ cancels with $(5.3.9.8.0)$ and $(5.3.9.4)$ cancels with $(5.3.9.8.1)$. (See Figures 5.3.6 an 5.3.10.)

We can also find that the end corresponding to $(5.3.9.1)$ (after taking fiber product) will become (See Figure 5.3.4.)

$$\phi\Big(P_1^{(1)}, \cdots, P_{m'}^{(1)}, \mathfrak{n}\Big(P_{m'+1}^{(1)}, \cdots, P_{k_1}^{(1)}, [\ell_p, w],$$
$$P_1^{(0)}, \cdots, P_m^{(0)}\Big), P_{m+1}^{(0)}, \cdots, P_{k_0}^{(0)}\Big).$$

$(5.3.9.2)$ will become (See Figure 5.3.5.)

$$\mathfrak{n}\Big(P_1^{(1)}, \cdots, P_{m'}^{(1)}, \phi\Big(P_{m'+1}^{(1)}, \cdots, P_{k_1}^{(1)}, [\ell_p, w],$$
$$P_1^{(0)}, \cdots, P_m^{(0)}\Big), P_{m+1}^{(0)}, \cdots, P_{k_0}^{(0)}\Big).$$

$(5.3.9.7.0)$ will become

$$\phi\left(P_1^{(1)}, \cdots, P_{k_1}^{(1)}, [\ell_p, w], \widehat{d}(P_1^{(0)}, \cdots, P_{k_0}^{(0)})\right).$$

For example, Figure 5.3.9 corresponds to

$$\phi_{4,6}(P_1^{(1)}, P_2^{(1)}, P_3^{(1)}, P_4^{(1)}, [p, w], P_1^{(0)}, P_2^{(0)}, \mathfrak{m}_2(P_3^{(0)}, P_4^{(0)}), P_5^{(0)}, P_6^{(0)}, P_7^{(0)}).$$

$(5.3.9.7.1)$ will become

$$\phi\left(\widehat{d}(P_q^{(1)}, \cdots, P_{k_1}^{(1)}), [\ell_p, w], P_1^{(0)}, \cdots, P_{k_0}^{(0)}\right).$$

Then Lemma 5.3.8 follows from these observations.   □

LEMMA 5.3.10. *The filtered A_∞ homomorphism in Lemma* 5.3.8 *is a homotopy equivalence.*

PROOF. We remark that after reducing the coefficient to $\mathbb{Q}$, the $\overline{\mathfrak{n}}_{0,0}$ cohomology of the filtered A_∞ bimodule $C(L^{(1)}, L^{(0)}; \Lambda_{0,nov})$ is nothing but the $\mathbb{Q}$ vector space whose basis correspond bijectively to the intersection points $L^{(1)} \cap L^{(0)}$. It is easy to see that $L^{(0)\prime} \cap L^{(1)\prime} = \psi(L^{(1)} \cap L^{(0)})$. It follows easily that ϕ induces an isomorphism of $\overline{\mathfrak{n}}_{0,0}$ cohomology after reducing the coefficient to $\mathbb{Q}$. The lemma now follows from Theorem 5.2.35.   □

Theorem 5.3.1 now follows from Lemma 5.3.10 and Proposition 5.2.43.   □

We can prove that the homotopy equivalence obtained in Theorem 5.3.1 up to homotopy, depends only on the symplectic isotopy class of ψ and independent of all other choices involved. Also we can show that the composition of the symplectic diffeomorphism ψ corresponds to the composition of the homotopy equivalence φ. Namely we have the following two Theorems 5.3.11 and 5.3.12.

For a symplectic diffeomorphism $\psi : M \to M'$, we denote by φ^ψ the homotopy equivalence

$$\varphi^\psi : C(L^{(1)}, L^{(0)}; \Lambda_{0,nov}) \to C(\psi(L^{(1)}), \psi(L^{(0)}); \Lambda_{0,nov})$$

over $(\mathfrak{g}^{1,\psi,\{J_\rho^{(1)}\}_\rho,\mathfrak{s}_1^{\text{top}(\rho)}}, \mathfrak{g}^{0,\psi,\{J_\rho^{(0)}\}_\rho,\mathfrak{s}_0^{\text{top}(\rho)}})$ constructed in Theorem 5.3.1. We denote by ϕ^ψ the homotopy equivalence

$$\phi^\psi : C(L^{(1)}, L^{(0)}; \Lambda_{0,nov}) \to C(\psi(L^{(1)}), \psi(L^{(0)}); \Lambda_{0,nov})$$

over $(\mathfrak{f}^{1,\psi,\{J_\rho^{(1)}\}_\rho,\mathfrak{s}_1^{\text{top}(\rho)}}, \mathfrak{f}^{0,\psi,\{J_\rho^{(0)}\}_\rho,\mathfrak{s}_0^{\text{top}(\rho)}})$ constructed in Lemma 5.3.10.

Strictly speaking, to define φ^ψ, ϕ^ψ we need to fix various other choices. Especially we fix the choice of multisection $\mathfrak{s}$. So we write $\varphi^{\psi,\mathfrak{s}}$, $\phi^{\psi,\mathfrak{s}}$.

Let $\{\psi_s\}_s$, $s \in [0,1]$ be a smooth family of symplectic diffeomorphisms such that

$$L^{(0)\prime} = \psi_s(L^{(0)}), \qquad L^{(1)\prime} = \psi_s(L^{(1)})$$

are independent of s.

THEOREM 5.3.11. φ in Theorem 5.3.1 is independent of the choices of the family of almost complex structures $\{J_{\tau,t}\}_{\tau,t}$, multisection etc, and depends only on the symplectic isotopy class of ψ up to homotopy. Namely $\varphi^{\psi_0,\mathfrak{s}_0}$ is homotopic to $\varphi^{\psi_1,\mathfrak{s}_1}$.

Let $\psi' : M' \to M''$ be another symplectic diffeomorphism. Using it we define $\varphi^{\psi'}$, $\phi^{\psi'}$ and $\varphi^{\psi'\circ\psi}$, $\phi^{\psi'\circ\psi}$.

THEOREM 5.3.12. $\varphi^{\psi'\circ\psi}$ is homotopic to the composition $\varphi^{\psi'} \circ \varphi^\psi$.

The proofs of Theorems 5.3.11 and 5.3.12 are similar to and easier than the proofs of Theorems 5.3.27 and 5.3.39 which will be given in Subsections 5.3.3 and 5.3.4 respectively, and hence omitted.

5.3.2. Moving Lagrangian submanifolds by Hamiltonian isotopies.
In this section, we consider the case where we move two Lagrangian submanifolds *separately* by two different Hamiltonian isotopies.

Let $\psi^{(i)} = \{\psi_\rho^{(i)}\}_\rho$, $\rho \in [0,1]$, $i = 0,1$ be Hamiltonian isotopies such that $\psi_0^{(i)} = id$. Let $(L^{(0)}, L^{(1)})$ be a relatively spin pair of Lagrangian submanifolds. We put

$$(5.3.13) \qquad L^{(i)\prime} = \psi_1^{(i)}(L^{(i)}).$$

We remark here that in (5.3.13), we are moving $L^{(0)}$ and $L^{(1)}$ by different symplectic diffeomorphisms $\psi_1^{(0)}, \psi_1^{(1)}$. This is the point that the argument of this subsection is different from one of the last subsection.

We consider the case when a pair of Lagrangian submanifolds are not necessarily transversal but of clean intersection. Namely we assume $L^{(0)} \cap L^{(1)}$ and $L^{(0)\prime} \cap L^{(1)\prime}$ are of clean intersection. We put

$$L^{(0)} \cap L^{(1)} = \bigcup_{h\in\pi_0(L^{(0)}\cap L^{(1)})} R_h, \quad L^{(0)\prime} \cap L^{(1)\prime} = \bigcup_{h'\in\pi_0(L^{(0)\prime}\cap L^{(1)\prime})} R'_{h'}.$$

Let $\Theta_{R_h}^-$, $\Theta_{R'_{h'}}^-$ be the real line bundles introduced in Subsection 3.7.5.

Let J_t, J'_t, $t \in [0,1]$ be families of compatible almost complex structures. Using J_0, J'_0, J_1, J'_1 and $\mathcal{X}_1(L^{(i)})$, $\mathcal{X}_2(L^{(i)\prime})$ (choices of countable sets of chains on $L^{(i)}, L^{(i)\prime}$) and the choices of multisections $\mathfrak{s}_i, \mathfrak{s}'_i$ of appropriate moduli spaces, we obtain the filtered A_∞ algebras $(C_1(L^{(i)}; \Lambda_{0,nov}), \mathfrak{m}_k^{J_i,\mathfrak{s}_i})$, $(C_2(L^{(i)\prime}; \Lambda_{0,nov}), \mathfrak{m}_k^{J'_i,\mathfrak{s}'_i})$.

We choose $\mathcal{X}_1(R_h)$ and $\mathcal{X}_2(R'_{h'})$, countable sets of smooth singular simplices (with $\Theta^-_{R_h}, \Theta^-_{R'_{h'}}$ coefficients) as in Subsection 3.7.5. Then, by Theorem 3.7.72, we obtain the filtered A_∞ bimodules

$$(C_1(L^{(1)}, L^{(0)}; \Lambda_{0,nov}), \mathfrak{n}^{J,\mathfrak{s}}_{k_1,k_0}), \quad (C_2(L^{(1)\prime}, L^{(0)\prime}; \Lambda_{0,nov}), \mathfrak{n}^{J',\mathfrak{s}'}_{k_1,k_0}).$$

Later we will take suitable countable sets $\mathcal{X}_3(R'_{h'}) \supset \mathcal{X}_2(R'_{h'})$. In such a case, we will denote by $(C_3(L^{(1)\prime}, L^{(0)\prime}; \Lambda_{0,nov}), \mathfrak{n}^{J',\mathfrak{s}'}_{k_1,k_0})$ the filtered A_∞ bimodule obtained by using the countable set $\mathcal{X}_3(R'_{h'})$.

We take two homotopies $\{J^{(i)}_\rho\}_\rho$ of compatible almost complex structures joining $J^{\psi^{(i)}_1}_i$ to J'_i, $(i = 0, 1)$:

$$
\begin{array}{ccc}
J^{\psi^{(1)}_1}_1 = J^{(1)}_0 & \overset{J^{(1)}_\rho}{\sim} & J^{(1)}_1 = J'_1 \\
\wr & & \wr \\
J^{\psi^{(0)}_1}_0 = J^{(0)}_0 & \overset{J^{(0)}_\rho}{\sim} & J^{(0)}_1 = J'_0.
\end{array}
$$

Diagram 5.3.2

Together with the choices of multisections, which we write $\mathfrak{s}^{\text{top}(\rho)}_i$, we obtain the filtered A_∞ homomorphisms

$$\mathfrak{g}^{i,\psi^{(i)}_1,\{J^{(i)}_\rho\}_\rho,\mathfrak{s}^{\text{top}(\rho)}_i} : (C_1(L^{(i)}; \Lambda_{0,nov}), \mathfrak{m}^{J_i,\mathfrak{s}_i}_k) \to (C_2(L^{(i)\prime}; \Lambda_{0,nov}), \mathfrak{m}^{J'_i,\mathfrak{s}'_i}_k)$$

as in Subsection 4.2.2. We recall that there exists $\mathcal{X}_3(L^{(i)\prime}) \supset \mathcal{X}_2(L^{(i)\prime})$ and

$$\mathfrak{f}^{i,\psi^{(i)}_1,\{J^{(i)}_\rho\}_\rho,\mathfrak{s}^{\text{top}(\rho)}_i} : (C_1(L^{(i)}; \Lambda_{0,nov}), \mathfrak{m}^{J_i,\mathfrak{s}_i}_k) \to (C_3(L^{(i)}; \Lambda_{0,nov}), \mathfrak{m}^{J'_i,\mathfrak{s}'_i}_k)$$

such that $\mathfrak{g}^{i,\psi^{(i)}_1,\{J^{(i)}_\rho\}_\rho,\mathfrak{s}^{\text{top}(\rho)}_i}$ is a composition of $\mathfrak{f}^{i,\psi^{(i)}_1,\{J^{(i)}_\rho\}_\rho,\mathfrak{s}^{\text{top}(\rho)}_i}$ and the homotopy inverse to the filtered A_∞ homomorphism induced by the inclusion $\mathcal{X}_2(L^{(i)\prime}) \subset \mathcal{X}_3(L^{(i)\prime})$.

Let $\|\{\psi^{(i)}_\rho\}_\rho\|$ be the Hofer length of the Hamiltonian isotopy $\{\psi^{(i)}_\rho\}_\rho$ from identity. (We will review its definition in Subsection 5.3.5.) Let $\mathfrak{E}$ be any number such that

$$\mathfrak{E} \geq \|\{\psi^{(1)}_\rho\}_\rho\| + \|\{\psi^{(0)}_\rho\}_\rho\|.$$

The following is the main result of Subsections 5.3.2-5.3.5.

THEOREM 5.3.14. *There exists an $\mathfrak{E}$-weakly filtered A_∞ bimodule homomorphism*

$$(5.3.15) \qquad \varphi : (C_1(L^{(1)}, L^{(0)}; \Lambda_{nov}), \mathfrak{n}^{J_t,\mathfrak{s}}_{k_1,k_0}) \to (C_2(L^{(1)\prime}, L^{(0)\prime}; \Lambda_{nov}), \mathfrak{n}^{J'_t,\mathfrak{s}'}_{k_1,k_0})$$

over $\mathfrak{g}^{1,\psi^{(1)}_1,\{J^{(1)}_\rho\}_\rho,\mathfrak{s}^{\text{top}(\rho)}_1}$, $\mathfrak{g}^{0,\psi^{(0)}_1,\{J^{(0)}_\rho\}_\rho,\mathfrak{s}^{\text{top}(\rho)}_0}$. *Furthermore* (5.3.15) *is a homotopy equivalence.*

REMARK 5.3.16. We again emphasize that we are taking Λ_{nov} as the coefficient. In case we move two Lagrangian submanifolds by different Hamiltonian isotopies, Floer cohomology over $\Lambda_{0,nov}$ is *not* preserved. See the example in Subsection 3.7.6.

PROOF. In this subsection, we give the construction of the A_∞ bimodule homomorphism φ in Theorem 5.3.14. In the next two Subsections 5.3.3, 5.3.4, we will prove that it is indeed a homotopy equivalence.

Using the homotopies $\{J_\rho^{(i)}\}_\rho$ above, we take a two-parameter family $\{J_{\tau,t}\}_{\tau,t}$ of compatible almost complex structures such that

$$(5.3.17.1) \quad J_{\tau,0} = \left(J_{\chi(\tau)}^{(0)}\right)^{\psi_{\chi(\tau)}^{(0)} \circ (\psi_1^{(0)})^{-1}}, \quad J_{\tau,1} = \left(J_{\chi(\tau)}^{(1)}\right)^{\psi_{\chi(\tau)}^{(1)} \circ (\psi_1^{(1)})^{-1}}. \quad \text{(Here the}$$

almost complex structure $(J_\rho^{(0)})^{\psi_\rho^{(0)} \circ (\psi_1^{(0)})^{-1}}$ is obtained from $J_\rho^{(0)}$ by the diffeomorphism $\psi_\rho^{(0)} \circ (\psi_1^{(0)})^{-1}$, and the diffeomorphism $\chi : \mathbb{R} \ni \tau \mapsto \rho = \chi(\tau) \in (0,1)$ is as in (5.3.2).)

$(5.3.17.2) \quad J_{\tau,t} = J_t$ if $\tau < -A$, $J_{\tau,t} = J_t'$ if $\tau > A$.

$$
\begin{array}{ccc}
 & J_1 & \overset{J_{\tau,1}}{\sim} & J_1' \\
J_t \wr & & & \wr J_t' \\
 & J_0 & \overset{J_{\tau,0}}{\sim} & J_0'
\end{array}
$$

$$(\tau < -A) \qquad\qquad (A < \tau).$$

Recall that $\widetilde{\pi}_0(L^{(0)} \cap L^{(1)})$ is the set of all equivalence classes satisfying (3.7.49). See Definition 3.7.50. Let $[h,w] \in \widetilde{\pi}_0(L^{(0)} \cap L^{(1)})$, $[h',w'] \in \widetilde{\pi}_0(L^{(0)\prime} \cap L^{(1)\prime})$. Let Σ be $\mathbb{R} \times [0,1]$ with possibly sphere bubbles as before. We consider $(\Sigma; u; \vec{\tau}^{(1)}, \vec{\tau}^{(0)})$ with the following properties.

$(5.3.18.1) \quad u : \Sigma \to M$ satisfies

$$\frac{\partial u}{\partial \tau} + J_{\tau,t} \frac{\partial u}{\partial t} = 0$$

on $\mathbb{R} \times [0,1]$. If a bubble tree of spheres is attached at (τ,t), then all the spheres in the tree are $J_{\tau,t}$-holomorphic. We also assume the stability condition.

$(5.3.18.2) \quad u(\tau,0) \in \psi_{\chi(\tau)}^{(0)}(L^{(0)})$, $u(\tau,1) \in \psi_{\chi(\tau)}^{(1)}(L^{(1)})$.

$(5.3.18.3) \quad \lim_{\tau \to -\infty} u(\tau) \in R_h$, $\lim_{\tau \to +\infty} u(\tau) \in R_{h'}'$.

$(5.3.18.4) \quad w \# ((I_{\psi^{(0)},\psi^{(1)}}^\chi)^{-1} u) \sim (I_{\psi^{(0)},\psi^{(1)}}^\chi)^{-1} w'$. We explain the notation below.

$(5.3.18.5) \quad \vec{\tau}^{(0)} = (\tau_1^{(0)}, \cdots, \tau_{k_0}^{(0)})$ with $-\infty < \tau_1^{(0)} < \cdots < \tau_{k_0}^{(0)} < +\infty$. $\vec{\tau}^{(1)} = (\tau_1^{(1)}, \cdots, \tau_{k_1}^{(1)})$ with $-\infty < \tau_1^{(1)} < \cdots < \tau_{k_1}^{(1)} < +\infty$.

We now explain the Condition (5.3.18.4). We should first note that u satisfies a *moving* boundary condition unlike the case of the boundary map where *fixed* Lagrangians are used. Furthermore w and w' satisfy different boundary conditions, which are connected by $\psi^{(0)}$ and $\psi^{(1)}$. The map

$$I_{\vec{\psi}} = I_{\psi^{(0)},\psi^{(1)}} : \Omega(L^{(0)}, L^{(1)}) \to \Omega(\psi_1^{(0)}(L^{(0)}), \psi_1^{(1)}(L^{(1)}))$$

was defined by

$$(I_{\psi^{(0)},\psi^{(1)}}(\ell))(t) = (\psi_t^{(1)} \circ \psi_{1-t}^{(0)})(\ell(t))$$

in Subsection 5.1.2. We define the map $I_{\psi^{(0)},\psi^{(1)}}^\chi$ by

$$(I_{\psi^{(0)},\psi^{(1)}}^\chi(u))(\tau,t) = (\psi_{\chi(\tau)t}^{(1)} \circ \psi_{\chi(\tau)(1-t)}^{(0)})(u(\tau,t))$$

which transforms u satisfying the boundary condition with $(L^{(0)}, L^{(1)})$ to the one satisfying the moving boundary condition (5.3.18.2). Therefore both terms in the equivalence (5.3.18.4) satisfy the boundary conditions on $L^{(0)}$ at $t = 0$ and on $L^{(1)}$ at $t = 1$. And it is easy to see that

$$((I^X_{\psi^{(0)}, \psi^{(1)}})^{-1}(w'))(0, t) = \ell_0(t)$$

since $w'(0, t) = \ell_0^{\psi^{(0)}\psi^{(1)}}(t) = (I_{\psi^{(0)}, \psi^{(1)}}(\ell_0))(t)$ by definition (cf. Section 2.2), and

$$((I^X_{\psi^{(0)}, \psi^{(1)}})^{-1}(w'))(1, t) = ((I_{\psi^{(0)}, \psi^{(1)}})^{-1}(\ell_q))(t)$$
$$= ((I_{\psi^{(0)}, \psi^{(1)}})^{-1}(u(\infty, \cdot)))(t)$$

by the asymptotic condition of u at $\tau = \infty$. Therefore the equivalence relation asked in (5.3.18.4) makes sense.

Now we denote by

(5.3.19) $\overset{\circ}{\mathcal{M}}_{k_1, k_0}((L^{(1)}, \psi^{(1)}), (L^{(0)}, \psi^{(0)}); \{J_{\tau, t}\}_{\tau, t}; [h, w], [h', w']; \text{top}(\tau))$

the moduli space of solutions of (5.3.18).

In order to obtain the weakly filtered A_∞ bimodule homomorphism from the moduli space (5.3.19), we need an inequality (5.3.21) below. This is not automatic unlike the case where the boundary Lagrangian submanifolds are fixed. A similar estimate was carried out by the second named author in [Oh93] but not in an optimal way.

PROPOSITION 5.3.20. *If the moduli space (5.3.19) is non-empty, then*

(5.3.21.1) $0 \le \mathcal{A}_{\ell^{(0)}\psi^{(0)}\psi^{(1)}}([\ell_q, w']) - \mathcal{A}_{\ell_0}([\ell_p, w]) + \mathfrak{E},$

where $p \in R_h, q \in R'_{h'}$. In particular we have

(5.3.21.2) $\mathcal{A}_{\ell^{(0)}\psi^{(0)}\psi^{(1)}}([\ell_q, w']) - \mathcal{A}_{\ell_0}([\ell_p, w]) \ge -\mathfrak{E}.$

Here $\mathfrak{E} = \|\psi^{(0)}\| + \|\psi^{(1)}\|$.

The proof of Proposition 5.3.20 will be given in Subsection 5.3.5.

REMARK 5.3.22. In the cases of the earlier subsections where we considered the Cauchy-Riemann equation with *fixed* Lagrangian boundary condition, a similar statement with $\mathfrak{E} = 0$ is rather obvious. And it was used to show that the map φ obtained is not only weakly filtered but also filtered.

We next take a fiber product of the moduli space (5.3.19) and the moduli spaces that we used in Section 4.6 to define $\mathfrak{f}^{i, \psi^{(i)}, \{J^{(i)}_\rho\}_\rho, \mathfrak{s}_i^{\text{top}(\rho)}}$, in a way similar to the previous subsection. We first define the evaluation maps

$$ev = (ev_1^{(1)}, \ldots, ev_{k_1}^{(1)}; ev_{-\infty}, ev_1^{(0)}, \ldots, ev_{k_0}^{(0)}; ev_{+\infty})$$
$$: \overset{\circ}{\mathcal{M}}_{k_1, k_0}((L^{(1)}, \psi^{(1)}), (L^{(0)}, \psi^{(0)}); \{J_{\tau, t}\}_{\tau, t}; [h, w], [h', w']; \text{top}(\tau))$$
$$\to (L^{(1)})^{k_1} \times R_h \times (L^{(0)})^{k_0} \times R'_{h'}$$

by

$$ev((\Sigma; u; \vec{\tau}^{(0)}, \vec{\tau}^{(1)}))$$

$$= \left(\left(\psi^{(1)}_{\chi(\tau_1^{(1)})} \right)^{-1} u(\tau_1^{(1)}, 1), \cdots, \left(\psi^{(1)}_{\chi(\tau_{k_1}^{(1)})} \right)^{-1} u(\tau_{k_1}^{(1)}, 1), \lim_{\tau \to -\infty} u(\tau), \right.$$

$$\left. \left(\psi^{(0)}_{\chi(\tau_1^{(0)})} \right)^{-1} u(\tau_1^{(0)}, 0), \cdots, \left(\psi^{(0)}_{\chi(\tau_{k_0}^{(0)})} \right)^{-1} u(\tau_{k_0}^{(0)}, 0), \lim_{\tau \to +\infty} u(\tau) \right).$$

We also define

$$ev_{\text{time},(0)} = (ev_{\text{time},(0),1}, \cdots, ev_{\text{time},(0),k})$$

$$: \overset{\circ}{\mathcal{M}}_{k_1,k_0}((L^{(1)}, \psi^{(1)}), (L^{(0)}, \psi^{(0)}); \{J_{\tau,t}\}_{\tau,t}; [h, w], [h', w']; \text{top}(\tau)) \to \mathbb{R}^{k_0}$$

by $ev_{\text{time},(0),j}((\Sigma; u; \vec{\tau}^{(0)}, \vec{\tau}^{(1)})) = \tau_j^{(0)}$ and

$$ev_{\text{time},(1)} = (ev_{\text{time},(1),1}, \cdots, ev_{\text{time},(1),\ell})$$

$$: \overset{\circ}{\mathcal{M}}_{k_1,k_0}((L^{(1)}, \psi^{(1)}), (L^{(0)}, \psi^{(0)}); \{J_{\tau,t}\}_{\tau,t}; [h, w], [h', w']; \text{top}(\tau)) \to \mathbb{R}^{k_1}$$

in the same way.

Let $l_1^{(0)}, \cdots, l_a^{(0)}, l_1^{(1)}, \cdots, l_b^{(1)}$ be nonnegative integers such that $\sum l_i^{(0)} = k_0$, $\sum l_i^{(1)} = k_1$. We consider the system

$$\mathfrak{D} = \left((\Sigma; u; \vec{\tau}^{(1)}, \vec{\tau}^{(0)}); (\Sigma_{(1),i}, \vec{z}_{(1),i}), (u_{(1),i,\alpha}), (\rho_{(1),i,\alpha}); i = 1, \cdots, b : \right.$$

$$\left. (\Sigma_{(0),i}, \vec{z}_{(0),i}), (u_{(0),i,\alpha}), (\rho_{(0),i,\alpha})); i = 1, \cdots, a \right)$$

with the following properties. The properties stated in (5.3.23) below is similar to those in (5.3.5):

(5.3.23.1)
$$(\Sigma; u; \vec{\tau}^{(1)}, \vec{\tau}^{(0)})$$
$$\in \overset{\circ}{\mathcal{M}}_{b,a}((L^{(1)}, \psi^{(1)}), (L^{(0)}, \psi^{(0)}); \{J_{\tau,t}\}_{\tau,t}; [h, w], [h', w']; \text{top}(\tau)).$$

(5.3.23.2)
$$((\Sigma_{(0),i}, \vec{z}_{(0),i}), (u_{(0),i,\alpha}), (\rho_{(0),i,\alpha}))$$
$$\in \mathcal{M}^{\text{main}}_{l_i^{(0)}+1}(M, L^{(0)}, \{J_\rho^{(0)}\}_\rho : \beta_i^{(0)}; \text{top}(\rho)).$$

(5.3.23.3)
$$((\Sigma_{(1),i}, \vec{z}_{(1),i}), (u_{(1),i,\alpha}), (\rho_{(1),i,\alpha}))$$
$$\in \mathcal{M}^{\text{main}}_{l_i^{(1)}+1}(M, L^{(1)}, \{J_\rho^{(1)}\}_{\rho:\beta_i^{(1)}}; \text{top}(\rho)).$$

(5.3.23.4)
$$ev_0((\Sigma_{(0),i}, \vec{z}_{(0),i}), (u_{(0),i,\alpha}), (\rho_{(0),i,\alpha}))$$
$$= \left(\psi_1^{(0)} \circ \left(\psi^{(0)}_{\chi(\tau_i^{(0)})} \right)^{-1} \circ u \right) (\tau_i^{(0)}, 0).$$

(5.3.23.5)
$$ev_0((\Sigma_{(1),i}, \vec{z}_{(1),i}), (u_{(1),i,\alpha}), (\rho_{(1),i,\alpha}))$$
$$= \left(\psi_1^{(1)} \circ \left(\psi^{(1)}_{\chi(\tau_i^{(1)})} \right)^{-1} \circ u \right) (\tau_i^{(1)}, 1).$$

(5.3.23.6) $\rho_{(0),i,0} \leq \chi(\tau_i^{(0)})$. $\rho_{(1),i,0} \leq \chi(\tau_i^{(1)})$.

(5.3.23.7) $(\sum_i \beta_i^{(0)} + \sum_i \beta_i^{(1)}) \# w \# ((I_{\psi^{(0)},\psi^{(1)}}^\chi)^{-1} u) \sim (I_{\psi^{(0)},\psi^{(1)}}^\chi)^{-1} w'$.

Here we recall that $\tau_{(1),i,0}$ is the "time" associated to the last component of $D_{(0),i}$. In particular, $u_{(0),i,0}$ is $J_{\tau_{(0),i,0}}^{(0)}$ holomorphic.

By an abuse of notations as before, we allow the case

$$ l_j^{(i)} = 1, \quad \beta_j^{(i)} = 0 \quad i = 0 \text{ or } 1 $$

for which the moduli space $\mathcal{M}_2^{\text{main}}(M, L^{(i)}, \{J_\rho^{(i)}\}_\rho : 0; \text{top}(\tau))$ was not defined. Here we just *define* it to be

$$ \mathcal{M}_2^{\text{main}}(M, L^{(i)}, \{J_\rho^{(i)}\}_\rho : 0; \text{top}(\tau)) = \{\text{one point}\} $$

with Conditions (5.3.23.4), (5.3.23.5) and (5.3.23.6) being void.

We note that most of the conditions here are the same as those in (5.3.5) except that (5.3.23.4), (5.3.23.5) and (5.3.23.7) are suitably modified.

Let $\mathcal{M}_{k_1,k_0}^{\text{unbr}}((L^{(1)}, \psi^{(1)}), (L^{(0)}, \psi^{(0)}); \{J_{\tau,t}\}_{\tau,t}; [h, w], [h', w']; \text{top}(\tau))$ be the set of all such systems $\mathfrak{D}$. (It can be defined as the union of the fiber products of several moduli spaces.) We define its compactification by

$$ \mathcal{M}_{k_1,k_0}((L^{(1)}, \psi^{(1)}), (L^{(0)}, \psi^{(0)}); \{J_{\tau,t}\}_{\tau,t}; [h, w], [h', w']; \text{top}(\tau)) $$

$$ = \coprod_{\substack{l_0,l_1 \\ m_1,m_0}} \coprod_{\substack{h'',w'' \\ h''',w'''}} \mathcal{M}_{l_1,l_0}(\psi_0^{(1)}(L^{(1)}), \psi_0^{(0)}(L^{(0)}); \{J_{0,t}\}_t; [h, w], [h'', w'']) $$

$$ \times_{R_{h''}} \mathcal{M}_{k_1-l_1-m_1,k_0-l_0-m_0}^{\text{unbr}}((L^{(1)}, \psi^{(1)}), (L^{(0)}, \psi^{(0)}); \{J_{\tau,t}\}_{\tau,t}; $$

$$ [h'', w''], [h''', w''']; \text{top}(\tau)) $$

$$ \times_{R_{h'''}} \mathcal{M}_{m_1,m_0}(\psi_1^{(1)}(L^{(1)}), \psi_1^{(0)}(L^{(0)}); \{J_{1,t}\}_t; [h''', w'''], [h', w']). $$

Here, the moduli spaces $\mathcal{M}_{l_1,l_0}(\psi_0^{(1)}(L^{(1)}), \psi_0^{(0)}(L^{(0)}); \{J_{0,t}\}_t; [h, w], [h'', w''])$ and $\mathcal{M}_{m_1,m_0}(\psi_1^{(1)}(L^{(1)}), \psi_1^{(0)}(L^{(0)}); \{J_{1,t}\}_t; [h''', w'''], [h', w'])$, in the above formula, are the moduli spaces defined as in (3.7.56).

We can extend the above evaluation map ev to this compactification

$$ ev = (ev_1^{(1)}, \dots, ev_{k_1}^{(1)}; ev_{-\infty}; ev_1^{(0)}, \dots, ev_{k_0}^{(0)}, ev_{+\infty}) $$

$$: \mathcal{M}_{k_1,k_0}((L^{(1)}, \psi^{(1)}), (L^{(0)}, \psi^{(0)}); \{J_{\tau,t}\}_{\tau,t}; [h, w], [h', w']; \text{top}(\tau)) $$

$$ \longrightarrow (L^{(1)})^{k_1} \times R_h \times (L^{(0)})^{k_0} \times R'_{h'} $$

in the same way as in (5.3.5). Now we define the moduli space

(5.3.24)
$$ \mathcal{M}_{k_1,k_0}((L^{(1)}, \psi^{(1)}), (L^{(0)}, \psi^{(0)}); \{J_{\tau,t}\}_{\tau,t}; [h, w], [h', w']; \text{top}(\tau); \vec{P}^{(1)}, S, \vec{P}^{(0)}) $$

as the fiber product

$$ \mathcal{M}_{k_1,k_0}((L^{(1)}, \psi^{(1)}), (L^{(0)}, \psi^{(0)}); \{J_{\tau,t}\}_{\tau,t}; [h, w], [h', w']; \text{top}(\tau)) $$

$$ ev \times \left(\prod_i P_i^{(1)} \times S \times \prod_i P_i^{(0)} \right). $$

Via the evaluation map $ev_{+\infty}$ we may regard this as a chain on $R'_{h'}$.

In a way similar to Proposition 5.3.6, the moduli space (5.3.24) has a Kuranishi structure, and we can define a multisection $\mathfrak{s}$ on it that is compatible with other multisections we have already determined. We put

$$\mathcal{M}_{k_1,k_0}((L^{(1)}, \psi^{(1)}), (L^{(0)}, \psi^{(0)})$$
$$; \{J_{\tau,t}\}_{\tau,t}; [h, w], [h', w']; \mathrm{top}(\tau); \vec{P}^{(1)}, S, \vec{P}^{(0)})^{\mathfrak{s}} = \mathfrak{s}^{-1}(0),$$

which defines a $\mathbb{Q}$-chain by taking appropriate triangulation. (We can handle orientation problem in the same was as Subsection 3.7.5.) Then as in the previous subsection, we define ϕ_{k_1,k_0} by

$$\phi_{k_1,k_0}\Big(T^{\lambda_1^{(1)}} e^{\mu_1^{(1)}} P_1^{(1)}, \cdots, T^{\lambda_{k_1}^{(1)}} e^{\mu_{k_1}^{(1)}} P_{k_1}^{(1)}, T^\lambda e^\mu S,$$
$$T^{\lambda_1^{(0)}} e^{\mu_1^{(0)}} P_1^{(0)}, \cdots, T^{\lambda_{k_0}^{(0)}} e^{\mu_{k_0}^{(0)}} P_{k_0}^{(0)}\Big)$$
$$= \sum_{[h', w'] \in \tilde{\pi}_0(L^{(0)'} \cap L^{(1)'})} T^{\lambda'} e^{\mu'} \Big[\mathcal{M}_{k_1,k_0}((L^{(1)}, \psi^{(1)}), (L^{(0)}, \psi^{(0)});$$
$$\{J_{\tau,t}\}_{\tau,t}; [h, w], [h', w']; \mathrm{top}(\tau); \vec{P}^{(1)}, S, \vec{P}^{(0)})^{\mathfrak{s}}, ev_+\Big]$$

where

$$\lambda' = \sum_{i=1}^{k_0} \lambda_i^{(0)} + \lambda + \sum_{i=1}^{k_1} \lambda_i^{(1)}, \qquad \mu' = \sum_{i=1}^{k_0} \mu_i^{(0)} + \mu + \sum_{i=1}^{k_1} \mu_i^{(1)}.$$

LEMMA 5.3.25. *Let ϕ_{k_1,k_0} be the maps defined as above.*
(5.3.26.1)   *We can choose a countable set of smooth singular simplices $\mathcal{X}_3(R'_{h'})$ such that the image of ϕ_{k_1,k_0} is contained in $C_3(L^{(1)'}, L^{(0)'}; \Lambda_{0,nov})$.*
(5.3.26.2)   *The natural inclusion induces a chain homotopy equivalence*

$$C_2(L^{(1)'}, L^{(0)'}; \mathbb{Q}) \to C_3(L^{(1)'}, L^{(0)'}; \mathbb{Q}).$$

(5.3.26.3) $\phi = \{\phi_{k_1,k_0}\}_{k_1,k_0}$ *is a $\mathfrak{E}$-weakly filtered A_∞ bimodule homomorphism over* $(\mathfrak{f}^{1,\psi_1^{(1)}}, \{J_\rho^{(1)}\}_\rho, \mathfrak{s}_1^{\mathrm{top}(\rho)}, \mathfrak{f}^{0,\psi_1^{(0)}}, \{J_\rho^{(0)}\}_\rho, \mathfrak{s}_0^{\mathrm{top}(\rho)})$:

$$\phi = \{\phi_{k_1,k_0}\}_{k_1,k_0} : C_1(L^{(1)}, L^{(0)}; \Lambda_{nov}) \to C_3(L^{(1)'}, L^{(0)'}; \Lambda_{nov}).$$

The proof is the same as that of Lemma 5.3.8. Note that the inequality (5.3.21.2) implies that ϕ_{k_1,k_0} is a weakly $\mathfrak{E}$-filtered A_∞ bimodule homomorphism.□

By (5.3.26.2) and Theorem 5.2.35, we derive that the natural inclusion

$$C_2(L^{(1)'}, L^{(0)'}; \Lambda_{0,nov}) \to C_3(L^{(1)'}, L^{(0)'}; \Lambda_{0,nov})$$

is a homotopy equivalence (over inclusion $C_2(L^{(i)'}) \to C_3(L^{(i)'})$). Here we note that we are working over $\Lambda_{0,nov}$ coefficients, not Λ_{nov} coefficients. Hence we can apply Theorem 5.2.35 and obtain the homotopy inverse. Then by composing ϕ and the homotopy inverse, we have constructed a weakly filtered A_∞ bimodule homomorphism denoted by φ

$$\varphi : C_1(L^{(1)}, L^{(0)}; \Lambda_{nov}) \to C_2(L^{(1)'}, L^{(0)'}; \Lambda_{nov})$$

wanted in Theorem 5.3.14. In the next two subsections, we will prove that this homomorphism is indeed a homotopy equivalence.

We would like to note that in Subsection 5.3.1 once a *filtered* A_∞ bimodule homomorphism were constructed, Theorem 5.2.35 would immediately imply that it is a homotopy equivalence. However since the homomorphism ϕ constructed in Lemma 5.3.25 is only *weakly filtered*, we can not apply Theorem 5.2.35 to ϕ. This forces us to directly construct a homotopy inverse using the geometry to prove that ϕ is a homotopy equivalence. We will carry out this geometric construction in Subsections 5.3.3 and 5.3.4.

5.3.3. Homotopies between bimodule homomorphisms. In this subsection we will prove the following.

THEOREM 5.3.27. *The $\mathfrak{E}$-weakly filtered A_∞ bimodule homomorphism ϕ in Theorem 5.3.14 is independent of the various choices we made but depends only on the homotopy classes of $\{\psi_\rho^{(0)}\}_\rho, \{\psi_\rho^{(1)}\}_\rho$ (relative to the boundary) up to the homotopy of bimodule homomorphisms.*

PROOF. To prove Theorem 5.3.27, it suffices to show that the $\mathfrak{E}$-weakly filtered A_∞ bimodule homomorphism ϕ constructed in the last subsection is invariant of various choices up to homotopy.

We remark that to define ϕ, we made the following choices:

- $\psi^{(0)} = \{\psi_\rho^{(0)}\}_\rho$, $\psi^{(1)} = \{\psi_\rho^{(1)}\}_\rho$, Hamiltonian isotopies.
- $\{J_{\tau,t}\}_{\tau,t}$, two parameter family of compatible almost complex structures.
- $\mathfrak{s}$, the multisections.
- A countable set of smooth singular simplices $\mathcal{X}_3(R'_{h'})$ on $R'_{h'}$.

We write
$$\phi_{s=0}^{\psi^{(0)s=0},\psi^{(1)s=0},\{J_{\tau,t,s=0}\}_{\tau,t},\mathfrak{s}_{s=0}}$$
to specify these choices. It is a weakly filtered A_∞ bimodule homomorphism over a pair of filtered A_∞ algebra homomorphisms
$$(\mathfrak{f}_{s=0}^{0,\psi^{(0)s=0},\{J_\rho^{(0)}\}_\rho,\mathfrak{s}_{s=0}^{\text{top}(\rho)}}, \mathfrak{f}_{s=0}^{1,\psi^{(1)s=0},\{J_\rho^{(1)}\}_\rho,\mathfrak{s}_{s=0}^{\text{top}(\rho)}}).$$
(See the notation in Subsection 4.6.2.)

We take the second choices $\psi^{(0)s=1}, \psi^{(1)s=1}, \{J_{\tau,t,s=1}\}_{\tau,t}, \mathfrak{s}_{s=1}$ and then obtain a weakly filtered A_∞ bimodule homomorphism
$$\phi_{s=1}^{\psi^{(0)s=1},\psi^{(1)s=1},\{J_{\tau,t,s=1}\}_{\tau,t},\mathfrak{s}_{s=1}}$$
over
$$(\mathfrak{f}_{s=1}^{0,\psi^{(0)s=1},\{J_\rho^{(0)}\}_\rho,\mathfrak{s}_{s=1}^{\text{top}(\rho)}}, \mathfrak{f}_{s=1}^{1,\psi^{(1)s=1},\{J_\rho^{(1)}\}_\rho,\mathfrak{s}_{s=1}^{\text{top}(\rho)}}).$$

We assume that the families $\psi^{(0)s=1}, \psi^{(1)s=1}$ are homotopic to the families $\psi^{(0)s=0}, \psi^{(1)s=0}$, respectively. Namely we assume that there exists a two-parameter family $\{\psi_{\rho,s}^{(i)}\}_{\rho,s}$ such that
$$\begin{cases} \psi_{\rho,0}^{(i)} = \psi_\rho^{(i)s=0}, \qquad \psi_{\rho,1}^{(i)} = \psi_\rho^{(i)s=1}, \qquad \psi_{0,s}^{(i)} = id, \\ \psi_{1,s}^{(i)}(L^{(i)}) = \psi_1^{(i)s=0}(L^{(i)}) = \psi_1^{(i)s=1}(L^{(i)}). \end{cases}$$

We put
$$\psi_{1,s}^{(i)}(L^{(i)}) = L^{(i)\prime}, \qquad (i = 0, 1).$$
We also define an isotopy $\psi_{\rho,t,i} : M \to M$, $(i = 1, 0)$ with $0 \le \rho \le 1$ by
$$\psi_{\rho,t,i} = \psi_{\rho t,i}^{(1)} \circ \psi_{\rho(1-t),i}^{(0)}.$$

In Subsection 4.6.2, we constructed homotopies from the filtered A_∞ homomorphism

$$\mathfrak{f}_{s=0}^{i,\psi_1^{(i)s=0},\{J_\rho^{(i)}\}_\rho,\mathfrak{s}_{s=0}^{\mathrm{top}(\rho)}} \quad \text{to} \quad \mathfrak{f}_{s=1}^{i,\psi_1^{(i)s=1},\{J_\rho^{(i)}\}_\rho,\mathfrak{s}_{s=1}^{\mathrm{top}(\rho)}}.$$

The homotopies we constructed there, depend on the following data $(i = 0, 1)$:

- Hamiltonian isotopies $\{\psi_{1,s}^{(i)}\}_s$ such that $\psi_{1,0}^{(i)} = \psi^{(i)s=0}$, $\psi_{1,1}^{(i)} = \psi^{(i)s=1}$.
- Two-parameter families of almost complex structures $\{J_{\rho,s}^{(i)}\}_{\rho,s}$ satisfying Condition (4.6.26) (where we need to replace $\{J_\rho^{s=j}\}_\rho$ etc. by $\{J_\rho^{(i)s=j}\}_\rho$ $(j = 0, 1)$).
- Multisections $\mathfrak{s}_i^{\mathrm{twp}(s)}$, $\mathfrak{s}_i^{\mathrm{top}(\rho),\mathrm{twp}(s)}$.
- A countable set of smooth singular simplices on $[0, 1] \times L^{(i)}$ as in Condition 4.6.30.

We denote the homotopies by

(5.3.28)
$$\mathfrak{f}^{\psi_{1,s}^{(i)},J_{\rho,s}^{(i)},\mathfrak{s}_i^{\mathrm{top}(\rho),\mathrm{twp}(s)}}$$
$$: (C_1(L^{(i)}; \Lambda_{0,nov}), \mathfrak{m}_k^{J,\mathfrak{s}}) \to (C([0, 1] \times L^{(i)\prime}) \otimes \Lambda_{0,nov}, \mathfrak{m}^{(i)}).$$

Here $C([0, 1] \times L^{(i)\prime})$, $(i = 0, 1)$ are complex generated by the countable sets of smooth singular simplices as above on $[0, 1] \times L^{(i)\prime}$, and $\mathfrak{m}^{(i)}$ is an A_∞ structure on it obtained by using family of the almost structures $\{J_{1,s}^{(i)}\}_s$ etc. (See Proposition 4.6.37.)

Under the situation above, we will construct a homotopy between two filtered A_∞ bimodule homomorphisms

$$\phi_{s=0}^{\psi^{(0)s=0},\psi^{(1)s=0},\{J_{\tau,t,s=0}\}_{\tau,t},\mathfrak{s}_{s=0}} \quad \text{and} \quad \phi_{s=1}^{\psi^{(0)s=1},\psi^{(1)s=1},\{J_{\tau,t,s=1}\}_{\tau,t},\mathfrak{s}_{s=1}}.$$

For this purpose, we use a three-parameter family $\{J_{\tau,t,s}\}_{\tau,t,s}$ of compatible almost complex structures with the following properties (5.3.29). (We recall that $\{J_{\tau,s}^{(0)}\}_{\tau,s}$, $\{J_{\tau,s}^{(1)}\}_{\tau,s}$ are the two-parameter families of almost complex structures we used to construct (5.3.28) and $\{J_{\tau,t,s=0}\}_{\tau,t}$, $\{J_{\tau,t,s=1}\}_{\tau,t}$ are two parameter families of almost complex structures we used to construct the A_∞ bimodule homomorphisms $\phi_{s=0}^{\psi^{(0)s=0},\psi^{(1)s=0},\{J_{\tau,t,s=0}\}_{\tau,t},\mathfrak{s}_{s=0}}$ and $\phi_{s=1}^{\psi^{(0)s=1},\psi^{(1)s=1},\{J_{\tau,t,s=1}\}_{\tau,t},\mathfrak{s}_{s=1}}$.)

(5.3.29)
$$\begin{cases} J_{\tau,0,s} = J_{\tau,s}^{(0)} \\ J_{\tau,1,s} = J_{\tau,s}^{(1)} \\ J_{\tau,t,0} = (J_{\tau,t,s=0})^{\psi_{\chi^{-1}(\tau),t,0} \circ (\psi_{1,t,0})^{-1}} \\ J_{\tau,t,1} = (J_{\tau,t,s=1})^{\psi_{\chi^{-1}(\tau),t,1} \circ (\psi_{1,t,1})^{-1}} \\ J_{\tau,t,s} = J_t, \quad \text{if } \tau < -A \\ J_{\tau,t,s} = J_{\infty,t,s} \quad \text{is independent of } \tau \text{ for } \tau > A, \end{cases}$$

where A is a sufficiently large number and $(J_{\tau,t,s=i})^{\psi_{\chi^{-1}(\tau),t,i} \circ (\psi_{1,t,i})^{-1}}$ $(i = 0, 1)$ is the almost complex structure induced by $\psi_{\chi^{-1}(\tau),t,i} \circ (\psi_{1,t,i})^{-1}$ from the almost complex structure $J_{\tau,t,s=i}$.

For each fixed s, we have a one-parameter family of almost complex structures $\{J_{\infty,t,s}\}_t$. We will use this to construct a left $(C([0, 1] \times L^{(1)\prime}) \otimes \Lambda_{0,nov}, \mathfrak{m}^{(1)})$ right $(C([0, 1] \times L^{(0)\prime}) \otimes \Lambda_{0,nov}, \mathfrak{m}^{(0)})$ filtered A_∞ bimodule.

We first define a module where the filtered A_∞ bimodule structure will be defined. We recall that we take $\mathcal{X}_3(R'_{h'})$ for each $h' \in \pi_0(L^{(0)'} \cap L^{(1)'})$. We need to prove independence of this choice also. So let us assume that we use

$$\mathcal{X}_3^{s=0}(R'_{h'}) \quad \text{to define} \quad \phi_{s=0}^{\psi^{(0)s=0}, \psi^{(1)s=0}, \{J_{\tau,t,s=0}\}_{\tau,t}, \mathfrak{s}_{s=0}}$$

and

$$\mathcal{X}_3^{s=1}(R'_{h'}) \quad \text{to define} \quad \phi_{s=1}^{\psi^{(0)s=1}, \psi^{(1)s=1}, \{J_{\tau,t,s=1}\}_{\tau,t}, \mathfrak{s}_{s=1}}.$$

By Lemma 5.3.34 below, we can choose and fix a countable set $\mathcal{X}([0,1] \times R'_{h'})$ of smooth singular chains on $[0,1] \times R'_{h'}$ with $\pi^* \Theta^-_{R'_{h'}}$ coefficient satisfying (5.3.35). Here $\pi : [0,1] \times R'_{h'} \to R'_{h'}$ is the projection. (When no confusion occurs, we use the same notation $\Theta^-_{R'_{h'}}$ in place of $\pi^* \Theta^-_{R'_{h'}}$.) It generates a subcomplex $C([0,1] \times R'_{h'}; \pi^* \Theta^-_{R'_{h'}})$ of $S([0,1] \times R'_{h'}; \pi^* \Theta^-_{R'_{h'}})$ which is a complex of smooth singular chains with coefficients in $\pi^* \Theta^-_{R'_{h'}}$. As in Subsection 3.7.5, we define $\widehat{CF}_{BM,para}(L^{(1)'}, L^{(0)'}; \Lambda_{nov})$ to be a completion of

$$\left(C([0,1] \times R'_{h'}; \pi^* \Theta^-_{R'_{h'}}) \otimes_{\mathbb{Q}} \Lambda_{h'} \right) \otimes_{\mathbb{Q}} \Lambda_{nov},$$

where

$$\Lambda_{h'} = \operatorname{Span}_{\mathbb{Q}} \left\{ [h', w'_i] \mid [h', w'_i] \in \widetilde{\pi}_0(L^{(1)'} \cap L^{(0)'}), h' \in \pi_0(L^{(1)'} \cap L^{(0)'}) \right\}.$$

In a way similar to (3.7.19) in Subsection 3.7.4, we can also define an equivalence relation $\sim$ on $\widehat{CF}_{BM,para}(L^{(1)'}, L^{(0)'}; \Lambda_{nov})$. Then we put

$$C_{para}(L^{(1)'}, L^{(0)'}; \Lambda_{nov}) = \widehat{CF}_{BM,para}(L^{(1)'}, L^{(0)'}; \Lambda_{nov})/\sim,$$

(5.3.30) $C_{para}(L^{(1)'}, L^{(0)'}; \Lambda_{0,nov}) = $ the non-negative energy part of

$$C_{para}(L^{(1)'}, L^{(0)'}; \Lambda_{nov}).$$

Now we will define a filtered A_∞ bimodule structure on (5.3.30). Let

$$[h'_1, w'_1], [h'_2, w'_2] \in \widetilde{\pi}_0(L^{(0)'} \cap L^{(1)'}).$$

For each fixed s, we use $\{J_{\infty,t,s}\}_t$ to define the moduli space

$$\mathcal{M}_{k_1,k_0}(L^{(1)'}, L^{(0)'}; [h'_1, w'_1], [h'_2, w'_2]; \{J_{\infty,t,s}\}_t)$$

in the same way as (3.7.29) or (3.7.56). (Here we move the parameter t and consider the family $\{J_{\infty,t,s}\}_t$. We used the notation $\mathcal{M}_{k_1,k_0}([h,w],[h',w'])$ in (3.7.54) for this moduli space, in Subsection 3.7.5. Since we need to specify $L^{(i)}$, $\{J_{\infty,t,s}\}_t$ etc., we use a bit different notation in this subsection.) We put

(5.3.31)

$$\mathcal{M}_{k_1,k_0}(L^{(1)'}, L^{(0)'}; [h'_1, w'_1], [h'_2, w'_2]; \{J_{\infty,t,s}\}_{t,s}; \operatorname{twp}(s))$$
$$= \bigcup_{s \in [0,1]} \{s\} \times \mathcal{M}_{k_1,k_0}(L^{(1)'}, L^{(0)'}; [h'_1, w'_1], [h'_2, w'_2]; \{J_{\infty,t,s}\}_t).$$

We have an evaluation map

$$ev = (ev_1^{(1)}, \dots, ev_{k_1}^{(1)}; ev_{-\infty}; ev_1^{(0)}, \dots, ev_{k_0}^{(0)}; ev_{+\infty})$$

(5.3.32)

$$: \mathcal{M}_{k_1,k_0}(L^{(1)'}, L^{(0)'}; [h'_1, w'_1], [h'_2, w'_2]; \{J_{\infty,t,s}\}_{t,s}; \operatorname{twp}(s))$$
$$\longrightarrow (L^{(1)'})^{k_1} \times R'_{h'_1} \times (L^{(0)'})^{k_0} \times R'_{h'_2}$$

as in Subsections 3.7.4, 3.7.5.

Then $\mathcal{M}_{k_1,k_0}(L^{(1)\prime}, L^{(0)\prime}; [h'_1, w'_1], [h'_2, w'_2]; \{J_{\infty,t,s}\}_{t,s}; \mathrm{twp}(s))$ has a Kuranishi structure. Its orientation can be discussed in the same way as in Subsection 3.7.5.

For $(|\mathcal{P}_i^{(0)}|, f_i^{(0)}) \in C([0,1] \times L^{(0)\prime})$, $(|\mathcal{P}_i^{(1)}|, f_i^{(1)}) \in C([0,1] \times L^{(1)\prime})$ and $[\mathcal{S}, f] \in \mathcal{X}([0,1] \times R'_{h'_1})$, we put

$$f^{(0)}(x) = (f^{(0),s}(x), \overline{f}^{(0)}(x)) \in [0,1] \times L^{(0)\prime}$$

and decompose $f^{(1)}(x) = (f^{(1),s}(x), \overline{f}^{(1)}(x))$ and $f(x) = (f^s(x), \overline{f}(x))$ in the same way.

In the next definition we write $[\mathcal{P}_i^{(0)}]$ etc. in place of $[|\mathcal{P}_i^{(0)}|, f_i^{(0)}]$ for the simplicity. We write $\mathcal{P}_i^{(0)}\big|_{s_0} = (f_i^{(0),s})^{-1}(s_0)$ etc.

DEFINITION 5.3.33. For $[\mathcal{S}] \in \mathcal{X}([0,1] \times R'_{h'})$, we define

$$\mathfrak{n}_{k_1,k_0} = \sum_{[h'_2, w'_2]} \mathfrak{n}_{k_1,k_0;[h'_2,w'_2]},$$

where

$$\mathfrak{n}_{k_1,k_0;[h'_2,w'_2]}([\mathcal{P}_1^{(1)}], \cdots, [\mathcal{P}_{k_1}^{(1)}], [\mathcal{S}], [\mathcal{P}_1^{(0)}], \cdots, [\mathcal{P}_{k_0}^{(0)}])$$
$$= T^{E(w'_2)-E(w'_1)} e^{(\mu(w'_2)-\mu(w'_1))/2}[\mathcal{S}'].$$

Here $[\mathcal{S}']$ is defined as follows. We consider the fiber product

$$|\mathcal{S}'| = \bigcup_{s \in [0,1]} \Big(\{s\} \times \mathcal{M}_{k_1,k_0}(L^{(1)\prime}, L^{(0)\prime}; [h'_1, w'_1], [h'_2, w'_2]; \{J_{\infty,t,s}\}_t)$$
$$\times_{(L^{(1)\prime})^{k_1} \times R'_{h'_1} \times (L^{(0)\prime})^{k_0}} \Big(\prod \mathcal{P}_i^{(1)}\big|_s \times \mathcal{S}|_s \times \prod \mathcal{P}_i^{(0)}\big|_s \Big) \Big).$$

(Precisely, we use

$$\mathcal{M}_{k_1,k_0}(L^{(1)\prime}, L^{(0)\prime}; [h'_1, w'_1], [h'_2, w'_2]; \{J_{\infty,t,s}\}_{t,s}; \mathrm{twp}(s))$$

and the fiber product to define $|\mathcal{S}'|$ as follows:

$$|\mathcal{S}'| = \mathcal{M}_{k_1,k_0}(L^{(1)\prime}, L^{(0)\prime}; [h'_1, w'_1], [h'_2, w'_2]; \{J_{\infty,t,s}\}_{t,s}; \mathrm{twp}(s))$$
$$\times_{([0,1] \times L^{(1)\prime})^{k_1} \times ([0,1] \times R'_{h'_1}) \times ([0,1] \times L^{(0)\prime})^{k_0}} \Big(\prod \mathcal{P}_i^{(1)} \times \mathcal{S} \times \prod \mathcal{P}_i^{(0)} \Big).$$

To take the fiber product we use the following obvious map

$$\mathcal{M}_{k_1,k_0}(L^{(1)\prime}, L^{(0)\prime}; [h'_1, w'_1], [h'_2, w'_2]; \{J_{\infty,t,s}\}_{t,s}; \mathrm{twp}(s)) \ni (s, (\Sigma, \vec{\tau}, u))$$
$$\longmapsto s \in [0,1]$$

on each factor $[0,1]$ and the natural maps $[0,1] \times L^{(j)\prime} \to [0,1]$, $(j = 0,1)$ and $[0,1] \times R'_{h'} \to [0,1]$ together with the evaluation map ev.) $\mathcal{S}'$ is a space with Kuranishi structure. $[\mathcal{S}']$ is its fundamental chain (with $\Theta^-_{R'_{h'}}$ coefficients) defined by using a multisection and a triangulation of its zero set.

LEMMA 5.3.34. *We can choose a countable set* $\mathcal{X}([0,1] \times R'_{h'})$ *of smooth singular chains and multisections in Definition 5.3.33, with the following properties.*

(5.3.35.1) $[\mathcal{S}']$ *in Definition 5.3.33 can be decomposed into a sum of elements of* $\mathcal{X}([0,1] \times R'_{h'})$.

(5.3.35.2)   *Any elements of* $\mathcal{X}([0,1] \times R'_{h'})$ *satisfies Condition 4.6.30. (Here L' in Condition 4.6.30 should be replaced by $R'_{h'}$.)*

(5.3.35.3)   *For* $\mathcal{S} \in \mathcal{X}([0,1] \times R'_{h'})$, $\mathcal{S}|_{s=0} \in \mathcal{X}_3^{s=0}(R'_{h'})$ *and* $\mathcal{S}|_{s=1} \in \mathcal{X}_3^{s=1}(R'_{h'})$. *Here* $*|_{s=s_0} = \mathrm{Eval}_{s=s_0}(*)$ *is defined by* (4.6.32).

(5.3.35.4)   *The inclusion map from the chain complex generated by the countable set* $\mathcal{X}([0,1] \times R'_{h'})$ *to* $S([0,1] \times R'_{h'}; \pi^*\Theta_{R'_{h'}})$ *is a chain homotopy equivalence.*

The proof of Lemma 5.3.34 is similar to the proof of other statements we postponed until Section 7.2. By (5.3.35.1), $\mathfrak{n}_{k_1,k_0}$ defines a homomorphism

$$
(5.3.36) \quad
\begin{aligned}
B_{k_1}C([0,1] \times L^{(1)\prime}) &\otimes C_{para}(L^{(1)\prime}, L^{(0)\prime}; \Lambda_{0,nov}) \\
&\otimes B_{k_0}C([0,1] \times L^{(0)\prime}) \longrightarrow C_{para}(L^{(1)\prime}, L^{(0)\prime}; \Lambda_{0,nov}).
\end{aligned}
$$

It is straightforward to check that it defines a filtered A_∞ bimodule structure. Therefore we have defined a filtered A_∞ bimodule structure on the chain complex $C_{para}(L^{(1)\prime}, L^{(0)\prime}; \Lambda_{0,nov})$. Moreover by Formulae (5.3.35.2) and (5.3.35.3), we have a filtered A_∞ bimodule homomorphism

$$
\begin{aligned}
\mathrm{Eval}_{s=0} &: C_{para}(L^{(1)\prime}, L^{(0)\prime}; \Lambda_{0,nov}) \to C_3^{s=0}(L^{(1)\prime}, L^{(0)\prime}; \Lambda_{0,nov}), \\
\mathrm{Eval}_{s=1} &: C_{para}(L^{(1)\prime}, L^{(0)\prime}; \Lambda_{0,nov}) \to C_3^{s=1}(L^{(1)\prime}, L^{(0)\prime}; \Lambda_{0,nov})
\end{aligned}
$$

over $(\mathrm{Eval}_{s=s_0}, \mathrm{Eval}_{s=s_0})$. $(s_0 = 0, 1.)$ Here $C_3^{s=s_0}(L^{(1)\prime}, L^{(0)\prime}; \Lambda_{0,nov})$ $(s_0 = 0, 1)$ is a subcomplex generated by $\mathcal{X}_3^{s=s_0}(R'_{h'})$. We remark that we wrote them as $C_3(L^{(1)\prime}, L^{(0)\prime}; \Lambda_{0,nov})$ in Lemma 5.3.25. We here include $s = s_0$ in the notation to highlight its dependence on s_0. (The complex C_3 which we use to define $\phi_{s=0}$ is different from one which we use to define $\phi_{s=1}$.)

The homomorphisms $\mathrm{Eval}_{s=j}$ above is a homotopy equivalence by Theorem 5.2.35 and (5.3.35.4). (We remark that we are working over $\Lambda_{0,nov}$ coefficients here. Hence we can apply Theorem 5.2.35.)

We next construct a weakly filtered A_∞ bimodule homomorphism

$$
\phi_{\tau,s}^{\psi_{\tau,s}^{(*)}, J_{\tau,t,s}, \mathfrak{s}^{\mathrm{top}(\tau), \mathrm{twp}(s)}} : C(L^{(1)}, L^{(0)}; \Lambda_{nov}) \to C_{para}(L^{(1)\prime}, L^{(0)\prime}; \Lambda_{nov})
$$

over $(\mathfrak{f}^{\psi_{1,s}^{(1)}, J_{\rho,s}^{(1)}, \mathfrak{s}_1^{\mathrm{top}(\rho), \mathrm{twp}(s)}}, \mathfrak{f}^{\psi_{1,s}^{(0)}, J_{\rho,s}^{(0)}, \mathfrak{s}_0^{\mathrm{top}(\rho), \mathrm{twp}(s)}})$ such that

$$
(5.3.37) \quad
\begin{aligned}
&\mathrm{Eval}_{s=j} \circ \phi_{\rho,s}^{\psi_{\rho,s}^{(*)}, J_{\tau,t,s}, \mathfrak{s}^{\mathrm{top}(\tau), \mathrm{twp}(s)}} \\
&= \begin{cases}
\phi_{s=0}^{\psi^{(0)s=0}, \psi^{(1)s=0}, \{J_{\tau,t,s=0}\}_{\tau,t}, \mathfrak{s}_{s=0}} & \text{if } j = 0 \\
\phi_{s=1}^{\psi^{(0)s=1}, \psi^{(1)s=1}, \{J_{\tau,t,s=1}\}_{\tau,t}, \mathfrak{s}_{s=1}} & \text{if } j = 1.
\end{cases}
\end{aligned}
$$

(We recall that $\rho \in [0,1]$ and $\tau \in \mathbb{R}$ are related by the formula $\rho = \chi(\tau)$.) See the following commutative diagram.

$$
\begin{array}{ccc}
C(L^{(1)}, L^{(0)}; \Lambda_{nov}) & \xrightarrow{\phi_{s=0}} & C_3^{s=0}(L^{(1)\prime}, L^{(0)\prime}; \Lambda_{nov}) \\
\| & & \uparrow \text{Eval}_{s=0} \\
C(L^{(1)}, L^{(0)}; \Lambda_{nov}) & \longrightarrow & C_{para}(L^{(1)\prime}, L^{(0)\prime}; \Lambda_{nov}) \\
\| & & \downarrow \text{Eval}_{s=1} \\
C(L^{(1)}, L^{(0)}; \Lambda_{nov}) & \xrightarrow{\phi_{s=1}} & C_3^{s=1}(L^{(1)\prime}, L^{(0)\prime}; \Lambda_{nov}).
\end{array}
$$

Diagram 5.3.3

The construction is a family version of the construction of the last subsection. For each s we consider the two-parameter family $\{J_{\tau,t,s}\}_{\tau,t}$ of compatible almost complex structures, and a families $\{\psi_{\rho,s}^{(i)}\}_s$ of Hamiltonian isotopies. We use them in the same way as the last subsection and obtain

$$
\mathcal{M}_{k_1,k_0}(L^{(1)}, L^{(0)}; \{J_{\tau,s}\}_\tau; [h,w], [h',w']; \text{top}(\tau))
$$

for each s. We then put

$$
\mathcal{M}_{k_1,k_0}(L^{(1)}, L^{(0)}; \{J_{\tau,s}\}_{\tau,s}; [h,w], [h',w']; \text{top}(\tau), \text{twp}(s))
$$
$$
= \bigcup_{s \in [0,1]} \{s\} \times \mathcal{M}_{k_1,k_0}(L^{(1)}, L^{(0)}; \{J_{\tau,s}\}_\tau; [h,w], [h',w']; \text{top}(\tau)).
$$

Using this space, we define

$$
\phi^{\psi_{\tau,s}^{(*)}, J_{\tau,t,s}, \mathfrak{s}^{\text{top}(\tau), \text{twp}(s)}} = \{\phi_{k_1,k_0}^{\psi_{\tau,s}^{(*)}, J_{\tau,t,s}, \mathfrak{s}^{\text{top}(\tau), \text{twp}(s)}}\}_{k_1,k_0}
$$

as follows. We use the same notation as in Definition 5.3.33. We now put

$$
\phi_{k_1,k_0}^{\psi_{\rho,s}^{(*)}, J_{\tau,t,s}, \mathfrak{s}^{\text{top}(\tau), \text{twp}(s)}} = \sum_{[h',w']} \phi_{k_1,k_0;[h',w']}^{\psi_{\rho,s}^{(*)}, J_{\tau,t,s}, \mathfrak{s}^{\text{top}(\tau), \text{twp}(s)}}
$$

where the right hand side is defined as follows:

$$
\phi_{k_1,k_0;[h',w']}^{\psi_{\rho,s}^{(*)}, J_{\tau,t,s}, \mathfrak{s}^{\text{top}(\tau), \text{twp}(s)}}([P_1^{(1)}], \cdots, [P_{k_1}^{(1)}], [S], [P_1^{(0)}], \cdots, [P_{k_0}^{(0)}])
$$
$$
= T^{E(w')-E(w)} e^{(\mu(w')-\mu(w))/2}[\mathcal{S}'].
$$

The space $\mathcal{S}'$ is the following fiber product

$$
\bigcup_{s \in [0,1]} \{s\} \times \Big(\mathcal{M}_{k_1,k_0}(L^{(1)}, L^{(0)}; \{J_{\tau,s}\}_{\tau,s}; [h,w], [h',w']; \text{top}(\tau), \text{twp}(s))
$$
$$
\times_{(L^{(1)})^{k_1} \times R_{h'} \times (L^{(0)})^{k_0}} \Big(\prod P_i^{(1)} \times S \times \prod P_i^{(0)}\Big)\Big).
$$

$\mathcal{S}'$ is a space with Kuranishi structure and $[\mathcal{S}']$ is its fundamental chain defined by using a multisection and triangulation of its zero set.

We can choose multisections and $\mathcal{X}([0,1] \times R_{h'}')$ so that $[\mathcal{S}']$ is decomposed to elements of $\mathcal{X}([0,1] \times R_{h'}')$. Thus $\phi^{\psi_{\rho,s}^{(*)}, J_{\tau,t,s}, \mathfrak{s}^{\text{top}(\tau), \text{twp}(s)}}$ is defined.

In a way similar to the argument of the last subsection, we can prove that the map obtained is an A_∞ bimodule homomorphism. We remark that the moduli space $\mathcal{M}_{k_1,k_0}(L^{(1)}, L^{(0)}; \{J_{\tau,s}\}_{\tau,s}; [h,w], [h',w']; \mathrm{top}(\tau))$ for $s = 0, 1$ coincides with the moduli spaces we used to define a pair of filtered A_∞ bimodule homomorphisms $\phi^{\psi^{(0)s=0}, \psi^{(1)s=0}, \{J_{\tau,t,s=0}\}_{\tau,t}, \mathfrak{s}_{s=0}}_{s=0}$ and $\phi^{\psi^{(0)s=1}, \psi^{(1)s=1}, \{J_{\tau,t,s=1}\}_{\tau,t}, \mathfrak{s}_{s=1}}_{s=1}$, respectively. Therefore (5.3.37) follows.

LEMMA 5.3.38. *There exists a filtered A_∞ bimodule homomorphism*

$$\mathrm{Incl} : C_2(L^{(1)\prime}, L^{(0)\prime}; \Lambda_{0,nov})_{para} \longrightarrow C_{para}(L^{(1)\prime}, L^{(0)\prime}; \Lambda_{0,nov})$$

over $(\mathrm{Incl}^{L^{(1)}}, \mathrm{Incl}^{L^{(0)}})$ *where*

$$\mathrm{Incl}^{L^{(i)}} : (C_2(L^{(i)\prime}; \Lambda_{0,nov}), \mathfrak{m}^{J',\mathfrak{s}'}_k) \to (C_2([0,1] \times L^{(i)\prime}; \Lambda_{0,nov}), \mathfrak{m})$$

is as in (4.6.38.8). *The composition*

$$\mathrm{Eval}_{s=s_0} \circ \mathrm{Incl} : C_2(L^{(1)\prime}, L^{(0)\prime}; \Lambda_{0,nov}) \longrightarrow C_3^{s=s_0}(L^{(1)\prime}, L^{(0)\prime}; \Lambda_{0,nov})$$

is equal to the inclusion.

PROOF. We define

$$\mathrm{Incl}_{1,\beta_0} : C_2(L^{(i)\prime}; \mathbb{Q}) \to C_2([0,1] \times L^{(i)\prime}; \mathbb{Q})$$

using prism decomposition in the same way as the case of (4.6.38.8). We can then define $\mathrm{Incl}_{k,\beta}$ in the same way as the case of (4.6.38.8), Lemma 5.3.34 and Proposition 7.2.162. The detail is similar to the case of filtered A_∞ algebra and so is omitted. $\qquad\square$

We remark that Incl in Lemma 5.3.38 is defined over $\Lambda_{0,nov}$. Therefore we can use Theorem 5.2.35 to show that it is a homotopy equivalence.

We thus extend Diagram 5.3.3 to:

$$
\begin{array}{ccccc}
C(L^{(1)}, L^{(0)}) & \xrightarrow{\phi_{s=0}} & C_3^{s=0}(L^{(1)\prime}, L^{(0)\prime}) & \longleftarrow & C_2(L^{(1)\prime}, L^{(0)\prime}) \\
\| & & \uparrow{\scriptstyle \mathrm{Eval}_{s=0}} & & \| \\
C(L^{(1)}, L^{(0)}) & \longrightarrow & C_{para}(L^{(1)\prime}, L^{(0)\prime}) & \xleftarrow{\mathrm{Incl}} & C_2(L^{(1)\prime}, L^{(0)\prime}) \\
\| & & \downarrow{\scriptstyle \mathrm{Eval}_{s=1}} & & \| \\
C(L^{(1)}, L^{(0)}) & \xrightarrow{\phi_{s=1}} & C_3^{s=1}(L^{(1)\prime}, L^{(0)\prime}) & \longleftarrow & C_2(L^{(1)\prime}, L^{(0)\prime}),
\end{array}
$$

Diagram 5.3.4

where the 3 horizontal arrows of the right hand side are homotopy equivalences. We can now prove Theorem 5.3.27 in the same way as the proof of Lemma 4.6.43. $\square$

5.3.4. Compositions of Hamiltonian isotopies and of bimodule homomorphisms. In this subsection, we prove the following Theorem 5.3.39 and use it to complete the proof of Theorem 5.3.14. We write $\phi^{\psi^{(0)}, \psi^{(1)}}$ in place of $\phi^{\psi^{(0)}, \psi^{(1)}, \{J_{\tau,t}\}_{\tau,t}, \mathfrak{s}}$ since we have already checked in Theorem 5.3.27 that it is independent of the choices of $\{J_{\tau,t}\}_{\tau,t}$, $\mathfrak{s}$ and $\mathcal{X}_3(R'_{h'})$ up to homotopy.

Let $\{\psi_\rho^{(0),(j)}\}_{0\le\rho\le1}$ and $\{\psi_\rho^{(1),(j)}\}_{0\le\rho\le1}$ $(j = I, II)$ be Hamiltonian isotopies with $\psi_0^{(0),(j)} = \psi_0^{(1),(j)} = id$. We define the composition $\psi^{(i),(II)}\#\psi^{(i),(I)}$ by

$$(\psi^{(i),(II)}\#\psi^{(i),(I)})_\rho = \begin{cases} \psi_{2\rho}^{(i),(I)} & \text{if } \rho < 1/2, \\ \psi_{2\rho-1}^{(i),(II)} \circ \psi_1^{(i),(I)} & \text{if } \rho \ge 1/2. \end{cases}$$

THEOREM 5.3.39. $\phi^{\psi^{(0),(II)}\#\psi^{(0),(I)},\psi^{(1),(II)}\#\psi^{(1),(I)}}$ is homotopic to the composition $\phi^{\psi^{(0),(II)},\psi^{(1),(II)}} \circ \phi^{\psi^{(0),(I)},\psi^{(1),(I)}}$. The same holds if we replace ϕ by φ.

PROOF. We put for $i = 0, 1$

$$L^{(i)\prime} = \psi_1^{(i),I}(L^{(i)}), \qquad L^{(i)\prime\prime} = \psi_1^{(i),II}(L^{(i)\prime}) = \psi_1^{(i),II} \circ \psi_1^{(i),I}(L^{(i)}).$$

Let

$$\phi^{\psi^{(0),(I)},\psi^{(1),(I)}} : (C(L^{(1)}, L^{(0)};\Lambda_{nov}),\mathfrak{n}_{k_1,k_0}^{J_t,\mathfrak{s}}) \to (C(L^{(1)\prime}, L^{(0)\prime};\Lambda_{nov}),\mathfrak{n}_{k_1,k_0}^{J_t',\mathfrak{s}'}),$$

$$\phi^{\psi^{(0),(II)},\psi^{(1),(II)}} : (C(L^{(0)\prime}, L^{(1)\prime};\Lambda_{nov}),\mathfrak{n}_{k_1,k_0}^{J_t',\mathfrak{s}}) \to (C(L^{(0)\prime\prime}, L^{(1)\prime\prime};\Lambda_{nov}),\mathfrak{n}_{k_1,k_0}^{J_t'',\mathfrak{s}''}).$$

Let $J_{\tau,t}^j$, $(j = I, II)$ be the family of compatible almost complex structures used to construct $\phi^{\psi^{(0),(j)},\psi^{(1),(j)}}$. We have

$$\begin{cases} J_{\tau,t}^I = J_t & \tau < -A \\ J_{\tau,t}^I = J_t' & \tau > A \\ J_{\tau,t}^{II} = J_t' & \tau < -A \\ J_{\tau,t}^{II} = J_t'' & \tau > A. \end{cases}$$

For $B > 100A$, we define $J_{\tau,t}^B$ by

$$\begin{cases} J_{\tau,t}^B = J_{\tau+B,t}^I & \tau \le 0, \\ J_{\tau,t}^B = J_{\tau-B,t}^{II} & \tau \ge 0. \end{cases}$$

We can use $J_{\tau,t}^B$ (for any $B > 100A$) to define $\phi^{\psi^{(0),(II)}\#\psi^{(0),(I)},\psi^{(1),(II)}\#\psi^{(1),(I)}}$ and the resulting A_∞ bimodule homomorphism is independent of $J_{\tau,t}^B$ up to homotopy by Theorem 5.3.27. Then we have an isomorphism of moduli spaces

$$\overset{\circ}{\mathcal{M}}_{k_1,k_0}(L^{(1)}, L^{(0)}; \{J_{\tau,t}^B\}_{\tau,t}; [h, w], [h', w']; \text{top}(\tau))$$

$$\cong$$

$$\bigcup_{[h'',w'']} \bigcup_{\substack{k_1^I+k_1^{II}=k_1 \\ k_0^I+k_0^{II}=k_0}} \overset{\circ}{\mathcal{M}}_{k_1^{II},k_0^{II}}(L^{(1)\prime}, L^{(0)\prime}; \{J_{\tau,t}^{(II)}\}_{\tau,t}; [h'', w''], [h', w']; \text{top}(\tau)))$$

$$\times_{R_{h''}''} \overset{\circ}{\mathcal{M}}_{k_1^I,k_0^I}(L^{(1)}, L^{(0)}; \{J_{\tau,t}^{(I)}\}_{\tau,t}; [h, w], [h'', w'']; \text{top}(\tau)),$$

by a gluing argument which is now standard. We can extend the isomorphism above to the compactifications. Then we can take a multisection of the moduli space $\mathcal{M}_{k_1,k_0}(L^{(1)}, L^{(0)}; \{J_{\tau,t}^B\}_{\tau,t}; [h, w], [h', w'])$ compatible with this isomorphism.

See Figure 5.3.11 for its compactification. For example, Figure 5.3.11 corresponds
to the term:

$$\phi_{3,2}^{II}\left(\psi_{1*}^{(0)}(P_1^{(1)}),\,\psi_{1*}^{(0)}(P_2^{(1)}),\,\mathfrak{f}_1^{\psi^{(0)}}(P_3^{(1)}),\right.$$

$$\left.\phi_{2,2}^{I}(P_4^{(1)},P_5^{(1)},S,P_1^{(0)},P_2^{(0)}),\,\psi_{1*}^{(1)}(P_3^{(0)}),\,\mathfrak{f}_0^{\psi^{(1)}}(1)\right).$$

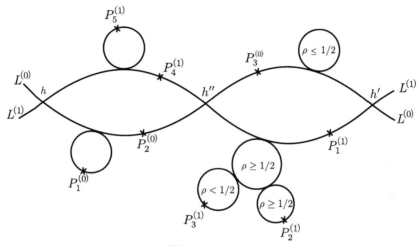

Figure 5.3.11

Then Theorem 5.3.39 follows.   □

We have now established Theorems 5.3.27 and 5.3.39. We can use them to
prove that $\phi^{\psi^{(0)},\psi^{(1)},\{J_{\tau,t}\}_{\tau,t},\mathfrak{s}}$ is a homotopy equivalence. Namely we take inverse
family $\psi^{(0)-1},\psi^{(1)-1}$ to $\psi^{(0)},\psi^{(1)}$, and $J_{\tau,t}^{-1},\mathfrak{s}_{\tau,t}^{-1}$ to $J_{\tau,t},\mathfrak{s}_{\tau,t}$ respectively. We then
use them to obtain $\phi^{\psi^{(0)-1},\psi^{(1)-1},\{J_{\tau,t}^{-1}\}_{\tau,t},\mathfrak{s}^{-1}}$. Theorems 5.3.27 and 5.3.39 imply
that $\phi^{\psi^{(0)-1},\psi^{(1)-1},\{J_{\tau,t}^{-1}\}_{\tau,t},\mathfrak{s}^{-1}}$ is a homotopy inverse to $\phi^{\psi^{(0)},\psi^{(1)},\{J_{\tau,t}\}_{\tau,t},\mathfrak{s}}$. (See
also Remark 7.2.128.) The proof of Theorem 5.3.14 is now complete.   □

5.3.5. An energy estimate. In this subsection we will prove Proposition
5.3.20. For this purpose, we need to recall some basic facts on Hofer's norm and
on the normalized Hamiltonians. We first recall the definition of Hofer's length
of the Hamiltonian isotopy $\{\psi_\rho\}_\rho$. In general, there is a one-one correspondence
between the isotopy $\{\psi_\rho\}_\rho$ and its generating Hamiltonian $K : [0,1] \times M \to \mathbb{R}$ *up
to the addition* of a ρ-dependent function $c : [0,1] \to \mathbb{R}$. To remove this ambiguity,
we consider only the normalized Hamiltonians. The standard normalization is the
following mean normalization on M when M is closed as in our case: we restrict
to the set of smooth functions $K : [0,1] \times M \to \mathbb{R}$ such that $\int_M K(\rho,x)\,d\mu(x) = 0$
for any ρ, where $d\mu$ is the Liouville measure of (M,ω). We will call such (time-
dependent) Hamiltonians $K : [0,1] \times M \to \mathbb{R}$ *normalized* Hamiltonians. Using these
normalized Hamiltonians, we define the Hofer length of the Hamiltonian isotopy
$\{\psi_\rho\}_\rho$ by

(5.3.40) $$\|\{\psi_\rho\}_\rho\| := \|K\| = \int_0^1 \left(\max_x K_\rho - \min_x K_\rho\right) d\rho.$$

The above definition of the Hofer length in fact does not depend on the normalization, but one important point of considering normalized Hamiltonians is in order. We will follow the exposition given in [**Oh05I**] here. Let $\psi_{\rho,t}$ be any two parameter family of Hamiltonian diffeomorphisms. Denote by $X_{\rho,t}$ and $Y_{\rho,t}$ the Hamiltonian vector fields

$$\frac{\partial \psi_{\rho,t}}{\partial \rho} \circ (\psi_{\rho,t})^{-1} = X_{\rho,t}, \qquad \frac{\partial \psi_{\rho,t}}{\partial t} \circ (\psi_{\rho,t})^{-1} = Y_{\rho,t}.$$

Then the following is a key identity (see [**Ban78**] for its derivation):

$$(5.3.41) \qquad \frac{\partial X_{\rho,t}}{\partial t} = \frac{\partial Y_{\rho,t}}{\partial \rho} + [X_{\rho,t}, Y_{\rho,t}].$$

Now we represent the vector fields $X_{\rho,t}$ and $Y_{\rho,t}$ by the corresponding normalized Hamiltonians $F(\rho,t,\cdot)$ and $K(\rho,t,\cdot)$ which are uniquely determined by $X_{\rho,t}$ and $Y_{\rho,t}$ respectively. (5.3.41) implies that the Hamiltonian F and K will satisfy

$$(5.3.42) \qquad \frac{\partial F}{\partial t}(\rho,t,x) = \frac{\partial K}{\partial \rho}(\rho,t,x) - \{F,K\}(\rho,t,x) + c(\rho,t)$$

for some function $c : [0,1]^2 \to \mathbb{R}$ which depends only on (ρ,t). Here $\{F,K\}$ is the Poisson bracket i.e. $\{F,K\} = dF(X_K)$ which satisfies the relation

$$[X_F, X_K] = -X_{\{F,K\}}.$$

Recall that the Poisson bracket $\{F,K\}$ is automatically normalized by Liouville's theorem. Integrating (5.3.42) over M proves $c \equiv 0$. Therefore F, K must satisfy

$$(5.3.43) \qquad \frac{\partial F}{\partial t} = \frac{\partial K}{\partial \rho} - \{F,K\}.$$

We summarize the above discussion in the following lemma.

LEMMA 5.3.44. *Let $\{\psi_{\rho,t}\}_{\rho,t}$ be a smooth two parameter family of Hamiltonian diffeomorphisms with $(\rho,t) \in [0,1]^2$, and F, K be the normalized Hamiltonians associated as above. Then (5.3.43) holds.*

We now restate of Proposition 5.3.20 as Proposition 5.3.45 below. (The action functional $\mathcal{A}$ is defined at the beginning of Subsection 2.2.2.)

PROPOSITION 5.3.45. *Let $\psi^{(0)} = \{\psi_\rho^{(0)}\}_\rho$ and $\psi^{(1)} = \{\psi_\rho^{(1)}\}_\rho$ be any Hamiltonian isotopies with the fixed $\psi_1^{(0)}$ and $\psi_1^{(1)}$ respectively. Let $[\ell_p, w] \in \widetilde{\Omega}_{\ell_0}(L, L')$ and $[\ell_q, w'] \in \Omega_{\ell^{(0)\prime}}(\psi_1^{(0)}(L), \psi^{(1)}(L'))$ such that the moduli space (5.3.19) is non-empty. Then we have*

$$(5.3.46.1) \qquad 0 \le \mathcal{A}_{\ell_0^{(\psi^{(0)}, \psi^{(1)})}}([\ell_q, w']) - \mathcal{A}_{\ell_0}([\ell_p, w]) + \mathfrak{E}.$$

In particular, we have

$$(5.3.46.2) \qquad \mathcal{A}_{\ell_0^{(\psi^{(0)}, \psi^{(1)})}}([\ell_q, w']) - \mathcal{A}_{\ell_0}([\ell_p, w]) \ge -\mathfrak{E} = -\mathfrak{E}(\psi^{(0)}, \psi^{(1)}).$$

In fact, we can choose

$$(5.3.47) \qquad \mathfrak{E} = \|\{\psi_\rho^{(0)}\}_\rho\| + \|\{\psi_\rho^{(1)}\}_\rho\|$$

where $\|\{\psi_\rho^{(0)}\}_\rho\|$, $\|\{\psi_\rho^{(1)}\}_\rho\|$ are the Hofer lengths given in (5.3.40).

PROOF. Let $(\Sigma; u; \vec{\tau}^{(0)}, \vec{\tau}^{(1)})$ be an element of the moduli space (5.3.19), which is nonempty by assumption. Since u satisfies (5.3.18.1) for the family $\{J_{\tau,t}\}_{\tau,t}$ of almost complex structures compatible to ω, we have $\int u^*\omega \geq 0$. This positivity is the only place where we use the fact that u is a solution of the Cauchy-Riemann equation (5.3.18.1). (In the physics saying, $\int u^*\omega \geq 0$ *on shell.*) The calculation following henceforth in this proof applies in the *off-shell* setting.

Let u be any smooth map $\mathbb{R} \times [0,1] \to M$ of finite energy that satisfies the given Lagrangian boundary condition and has the suitable decay property at infinity as described in the end of Section 4.1 so that the map can be compactified: Namely, the composition

$$\overline{u}(\rho, t) = u(\chi^{-1}(\rho), t) : (0,1) \times [0,1] \to M$$

continuously extends to $[0,1] \times [0,1]$. For example, any finite energy solution of (5.3.18.1) for the pairs of L, L' of clean intersection will satisfy this decay property.

First we recall Proposition 5.1.7 or its proof (see (5.1.13.1)) from which we derive

(5.3.48) $$\mathcal{A}_{\ell_0}([(I_{(\psi^{(0)}, \psi^{(1)})})^{-1}\ell_q, (I_{(\psi^{(0)}, \psi^{(1)})})^{-1}w']) = \mathcal{A}_{\ell_0^{(\psi^{(0)}, \psi^{(1)})}}([\ell_q, w']).$$

It follows from (5.3.18.4) and (5.3.48) that

(5.3.49)
$$\mathcal{A}_{\ell_0^{(\psi^{(0)}, \psi^{(1)})}}([\ell_q, w']) - \mathcal{A}_{\ell_0}([\ell_p, w])$$
$$= \mathcal{A}_{\ell_0}([(I_{(\psi^{(0)}, \psi^{(1)})})^{-1}\ell_q, (I_{(\psi^{(0)}, \psi^{(1)})})^{-1}w']) - \mathcal{A}_{\ell_0}([\ell_p, w])$$
$$= \mathcal{A}_{\ell_0}([(I_{(\psi^{(0)}, \psi^{(1)})})^{-1}\ell_q, \widetilde{u}]) = \int \widetilde{u}^*\omega$$

where $\widetilde{u}$ is defined by

$$\widetilde{u}(\rho, t) = (\psi^{(1)}_{\rho t} \circ \psi^{(0)}_{\rho(1-t)})^{-1}(\overline{u}(\rho, t)).$$

We define the diffeomorphisms $\psi_{\rho, t}$ by

(5.3.50) $$\psi_{\rho, t} = (\psi^{(1)}_{\rho t} \circ \psi^{(0)}_{\rho(1-t)})^{-1}.$$

Then $\widetilde{u}(\rho, t) = \psi_{\rho, t}(\overline{u}(\chi^{-1}(\rho), t))$.

We now compute

(5.3.51)
$$\int \widetilde{u}^*\omega = \int_0^1 \int_0^1 \omega\left(\frac{\partial \widetilde{u}}{\partial \rho}, \frac{\partial \widetilde{u}}{\partial t}\right) d\rho \, dt$$
$$= \int_0^1 \int_0^1 \omega\left(\frac{\partial}{\partial \rho}(\psi_{\rho, t}(\overline{u}(\rho, t))), \frac{\partial}{\partial t}(\psi_{\rho, t}(\overline{u}(\rho, t)))\right) d\rho \, dt$$

and

(5.3.52)
$$\frac{\partial \widetilde{u}}{\partial \rho} = \frac{\partial}{\partial \rho}\left(\psi_{\rho, t}(\overline{u}(\rho, t))\right) = X_{K_{\rho, t}}(\widetilde{u}) + d\psi_{\rho, t}\left(\frac{\partial \overline{u}}{\partial \rho}(\rho, t)\right)$$
$$\frac{\partial \widetilde{u}}{\partial t} = \frac{\partial}{\partial t}\left(\psi_{\rho, t}(u(\rho, t))\right) = X_{F_{\rho, t}}(\widetilde{u}) + d\psi_{\rho, t}\left(\frac{\partial \overline{u}}{\partial t}(\rho, t)\right),$$

where $K_{\rho, t}$ and $F_{\rho, t}$ are the Hamiltonians generating the vector fields $\frac{\partial \psi_{\rho, t}}{\partial \rho} \circ \psi^{-1}_{\rho, t}$, $\frac{\partial \psi_{\rho, t}}{\partial t} \circ \psi^{-1}_{\rho, t}$ respectively.

Now we have

$$
\begin{aligned}
\int \widetilde{u}^* \omega = \int_0^1 \int_0^1 &\omega\left(X_{K_{\rho,t}}(\widetilde{u}) + d\psi_{\rho,t}\left(\frac{\partial \widetilde{u}}{\partial \rho}(\rho, t)\right),\right. \\
&\left. X_{F_{\rho,t}}(\widetilde{u}) + d\psi_{\rho,t}\left(\frac{\partial \widetilde{u}}{\partial t}(\rho, t)\right)\right) d\rho dt
\end{aligned}
$$

(5.3.53)

$$
\begin{aligned}
= &\int \omega\left(\frac{\partial \widetilde{u}}{\partial \rho}, X_{F_{\rho,t}}(\widetilde{u})\right) + \int \omega\left(X_{K_{\rho,t}}(\widetilde{u}), \frac{\partial \widetilde{u}}{\partial t}\right) \\
&- \int \omega(X_{K_{\rho,t}}(\widetilde{u}), X_{F_{\rho,t}}(\widetilde{u})) + \int \widetilde{u}^* \omega.
\end{aligned}
$$

Here we used (5.3.48), (5.3.51), (5.3.52) and the identity

$$
(a+b)(c+d) = (a+b)d + b(c+d) - bd + ac
$$

and that $\psi_{\rho,t}$ are symplectic. We also mention that we have

$$
\int_{[0,1]^2} \overline{u}^* \omega = \int_{\mathbb{R} \times [0,1]} u^* \omega
$$

which converges by the finite energy condition. This term will be non-negative if u is a solution of the Cauchy-Riemann equation (5.3.18.1).

Now we compute the first three terms in the right hand side of (5.3.53). With the definition of Hamiltonian vector fields, a straight-forward computation yields

(5.3.54)

$$
\begin{aligned}
\int_0^1 \int_0^1 \omega\left(\frac{\partial \widetilde{u}}{\partial \rho}, X_{F_{\rho,t}}(\widetilde{u})\right) d\rho dt &= -\int_0^1 \int_0^1 dF_{\rho,t}\left(\frac{\partial \widetilde{u}}{\partial \rho}\right) d\rho dt \\
&= -\int_0^1 (F_{1,t}(\widetilde{u}(1,t)) - F_{0,t}(\widetilde{u}(0,t)))\, dt + \int_0^1 \int_0^1 \frac{\partial F_{\rho,t}}{\partial \rho}(\widetilde{u})\, d\rho dt.
\end{aligned}
$$

Similarly we have

(5.3.55)

$$
\begin{aligned}
\int_0^1 \int_0^1 &\omega\left(X_{K_{\rho,t}}(\widetilde{u}), \frac{\partial \widetilde{u}}{\partial t}\right) d\rho dt \\
&= \int_0^1 (K_{\rho,1}(\widetilde{u}(\rho,1)) - K_{\rho,0}(\widetilde{u}(\rho,0)))\, d\rho - \int_0^1 \int_0^1 \frac{\partial K_{\rho,t}}{\partial t}(\widetilde{u})\, d\rho dt.
\end{aligned}
$$

Finally we have

(5.3.56)

$$
-\int_0^1 \int_0^1 \omega(X_{K_{\rho,t}}(\widetilde{u}), X_{F_{\rho,t}}(\widetilde{u})) d\rho dt = \int_0^1 \int_0^1 \{F_{\rho,t}, K_{\rho,t}\}\, d\rho dt.
$$

Summing up (5.3.54), (5.3.55), (5.3.56) and applying the identity (5.3.43), we have obtained

(5.3.57)

$$
\begin{aligned}
\int \widetilde{u}^* \omega = &-\int_0^1 (F_{1,t}(\widetilde{u}(1,t)) - F_{0,t}(\widetilde{u}(0,t)))\, dt \\
&+ \int_0^1 (K_{\rho,1}(\widetilde{u}(\rho,1)) - K_{\rho,0}(\widetilde{u}(\rho,0)))\, d\rho + \int u^* \omega.
\end{aligned}
$$

It remains to relate the first two terms in (5.3.57) with the Hofer lengths $\|\psi^{(0)}\|$ and $\|\psi^{(1)}\|$. Let $H^{(0)}$, $H^{(1)}$ be normalized Hamiltonian generating $\|\psi^{(0)}\|$ and $\|\psi^{(1)}\|$.

We first note that $F_{1,t}$ is the Hamiltonian generating the isotopy $\psi_{1,t} = (\psi_t^{(1)})^{-1}$ and hence

$$(5.3.58) \qquad\qquad F_{1,t}(x) = -H_t^{(1)}(\psi_t^{(1)}(x)).$$

Similarly we have

$$\psi_{0,t} = (\psi_t^{(0)})^{-1}, \ \psi_{\rho,0} \equiv id, \ \psi_{\rho,1} = (\psi_\rho^{(1)} \circ \psi_{(1-\rho)}^{(0)})^{-1}.$$

By the calculus of Hamiltonians, we obtain

$$(5.3.59) \qquad \begin{aligned} F_{0,t}(x) &= -H_t^{(0)}(\psi_t^{(0)}(x)) \\ K_{\rho,0}(x) &= 0 \\ K_{\rho,1}(x) &= H_{1-\rho}^{(0)}(\psi_{1-\rho}^{(0)}(x)) - H_\rho^{(1)}(\psi_\rho^{(1)}(\psi_{1-\rho}^{(0)}(x))). \end{aligned}$$

Substituting (5.3.58), (5.3.59) into (5.3.57), we obtain

$$(5.3.60) \qquad -\int_0^1 (F_{1,t}(\tilde{u}(1,t)) - F_{0,t}(\tilde{u}(0,t)))\, dt \geq \int_0^1 (\min_x H_t^{(1)} - \max_x H^{(0)})\, dt$$

and

$$(5.3.61) \qquad \begin{aligned} &\int_0^1 (K_{\rho,1}(\tilde{u}(\rho,1)) - K_{\rho,0}(\tilde{u}(\rho,0)))\, d\rho \\ &\geq \int_0^1 (\min_x H_{1-\rho}^{(0)} - \max_x H_\rho^{(1)})\, d\rho = \int_0^1 (\min_x H_\rho^{(0)} - \max_x H_\rho^{(1)})\, d\rho. \end{aligned}$$

Now we assume u satisfies the Cauchy-Riemann equation (5.3.18.1) in addition. Substituting (5.3.60), (5.3.61) and the inequality $\int u^*\omega \geq 0$ into (5.3.57), we have obtained

$$(5.3.62) \qquad\qquad \int \tilde{u}^*\omega \geq -(\|\psi^{(0)}\| + \|\psi^{(1)}\|).$$

This finishes the proof. $\qquad\qquad\qquad\qquad\qquad\qquad\qquad\qquad\qquad\qquad\qquad\qquad$ $\square$

REMARK 5.3.63. With given fixed Hamiltonian diffeomorphisms $\psi_1^{(0)}$ and $\psi_1^{(1)}$, we can consider *all* possible isotopy $\psi^{(0)}$ and $\psi^{(1)}$ with given end points and take the infimum

$$\|\psi_1^{(1)}\| = \inf_{H^{(1)} \mapsto \psi^{(1)}} \|H^{(1)}\|, \qquad \|\psi_1^{(0)}\| = \inf_{H^{(0)} \mapsto \psi^{(0)}} \|H^{(0)}\|$$

which are the Hofer norms of $\psi_1^{(i)}$ respectively. In this way, we can make the constant $\mathfrak{E} = \mathfrak{E}(\psi^{(0)}, \psi^{(1)})$ as close to the sum $\|\psi_1^{(0)}\| + \|\psi_1^{(1)}\|$. However the moduli space (5.3.19) depends on the choice of isotopies $\psi^{(0)}, \psi^{(1)}$ and so the energy estimate cannot be given solely in terms of the final Hamiltonian diffeomorphisms. One can reformulate the Floer theory in terms of the holomorphic sections of the Hamiltonian fibration with Lagrangian boundary conditions over the strip $\mathbb{R} \times [0,1]$ as Seidel did [**Sei03I**] in which one may express the above kind of energy estimate in a more intrinsic way.

5.3.6. The operators $\mathfrak{q}, \mathfrak{r}$ and homotopy equivalence. In Section 3.8 we generalized our construction by inserting interior marked points and introduced another deformations $(C(L; \Lambda_{0,nov}), \mathfrak{m}^{(\mathfrak{b},0)})$ of $(C(L; \Lambda_{0,nov}), \mathfrak{m})$ (which is parametrized by cycles $\mathfrak{b} \in C^2(M; \Lambda_0^+)$ of the ambient symplectic manifold). We used this deformation to define Floer cohomology under a weaker assumption in Subsection 3.8.7. More specifically, we defined left $(C(L^{(1)}; \Lambda_{0,nov}), \mathfrak{m}^{(\mathfrak{b},0)})$ right $(C(L^{(0)}; \Lambda_{0,nov}), \mathfrak{m}^{(\mathfrak{b},0)}))$ filtered A_∞ bimodule

$$(C(L^{(1)}, L^{(0)}; \Lambda_{0,nov}), \mathfrak{n}^{\mathfrak{b}}_{k_1,k_0}),$$

when $L^{(1)} \cap L^{(0)}$ is of clean intersection. In Section 4.6, we proved that the homotopy class of the deformed filtered A_∞ algebra $(C(L; \Lambda_{0,nov}), \mathfrak{m}^{(\mathfrak{b},0)})$ is independent of the various choices involved and depends only on L and the cohomology class of $\mathfrak{b}$ (up to the A_∞ isomorphism). The purpose of this subsection is to show that the homotopy class of the filtered A_∞ bimodule $(C(L^{(1)}, L^{(0)}; \Lambda_{nov}), \mathfrak{n}^{\mathfrak{b}}_{k_1,k_0})$ over Λ_{nov} is independent of the various choices involved. (There are again two versions depending on whether we move two Lagrangian submanifolds by the same symplectic diffeomorphism or by two separate Hamiltonian isotopies.)

Let $(L^{(1)}, L^{(0)})$ be a relatively spin pair of Lagrangian submanifolds of M and let $\psi : M \to M'$ be a symplectic diffeomorphism. Suppose that $L^{(1)}$ and $L^{(0)}$ are of clean intersection. We put $L^{(i)\prime} = \psi(L^{(i)})$. Let $[\mathfrak{b}] \in H^2(M; \Lambda_{0,nov}^+)$ and

$$\psi^{\mathfrak{b}}_{*;(i)} : (C(L^{(i)}; \Lambda_{0,nov}), \mathfrak{m}^{\mathfrak{b}}) \to (C(L^{(i)\prime}; \Lambda_{0,nov}), \mathfrak{m}^{\psi_* \mathfrak{b}})$$

the homotopy equivalence in Theorem 4.6.52. The following theorem can be proved by the same way as Theorem 5.3.1 by considering the complex

$$(C(L^{(1)\prime}, L^{(0)\prime}; \Lambda_{0,nov}), \mathfrak{m}^{\psi_* \mathfrak{b}})$$

associated to the canonical push-forwards of

$$\mathcal{X}_1(L^{(i)}), \quad J = \{J_t\}, \quad \mathfrak{s}_i, \quad \mathfrak{b}$$

under $\psi : M \to M'$, and then proving the homotopy equivalence between the push-forward and a different realization of $(C(L^{(1)\prime}, L^{(0)\prime}); \Lambda_{0,nov}), \mathfrak{n}^{\psi_* \mathfrak{b}}_{k_1,k_0})$ using another choices

$$\mathcal{X}_2(L^{(i)\prime}), \quad J' = \{J'_t\}, \quad \mathfrak{s}'_i.$$

This last step is a special case of the one considered in Theorem 5.3.65 below and so its proof is omitted.

THEOREM 5.3.64. *There exists a homotopy equivalence of the filtered A_∞ bimodules*

$$\varphi^{\mathfrak{b}}_* : (C(L^{(1)}, L^{(0)}; \Lambda_{0,nov}), \mathfrak{n}^{\mathfrak{b}}_{k_1,k_0}) \to (C(L^{(1)\prime}, L^{(0)\prime}; \Lambda_{0,nov}), \mathfrak{n}^{\psi_* \mathfrak{b}}_{k_1,k_0})$$

over $(\psi^{\mathfrak{b}}_{*;(1)}, \psi^{\mathfrak{b}}_{*;(0)})$. *Up to homotopy it is independent of the choice of symplectic isotopy in the sense we explain below and is functorial in the sense as in Theorem 5.3.12.*

Invariance up to homotopy of $\varphi^{\mathfrak{b}}_*$ in Theorem 5.3.64 is stated as follows. If ψ' is another symplectic diffeomorphism $(M, L) \to (M', L')$ which is isotopic to ψ through a homotopy of symplectic diffeomorphisms $\{\psi^t\}_{t \in [0,1]}$ such that $\psi^t(L) = L'$. Let $\varphi'^{\mathfrak{b}}_*$ be the filtered A_∞ bimodule homomorphism associated to ψ'.

Since $\psi_*\mathfrak{b}$ is homologous to $\psi'_*\mathfrak{b}$. we have a homotopy equivalence

$$I^{(i)} : (C(L^{(i)\prime}; \Lambda_{0,nov}), \mathfrak{m}^{\psi_*\mathfrak{b}}) \to (C(L^{(i)\prime}; \Lambda_{0,nov}), \mathfrak{m}^{\psi'_*\mathfrak{b}})$$

such that $I \circ \psi^{\mathfrak{b}}_{*;(i)}$ is homotopic to $\psi'^{\mathfrak{b}}_{*;(i)}$. Moreover there is a canonical homotopy equivalence

$$I : (C(L^{(1)\prime}, L^{(0)\prime}; \Lambda_{0,nov}), \mathfrak{n}^{\psi_*\mathfrak{b}}_{k_1,k_0}) \to (C(L^{(1)\prime}, L^{(0)\prime}; \Lambda_{0,nov}), \mathfrak{n}^{\psi'_*\mathfrak{b}}_{k_1,k_0})$$

of filtered A_∞ bimodule over $(I^{(1)}, I^{(0)})$. We like to mention that I, $I^{(i)}$ are obtained in a purely algebraic way from the fact that $\psi_*\mathfrak{b}$ is homologous to $\psi'_*\mathfrak{b}$, and its homotopy class is independent of various choices involved.

Now invariance up to homotopy of $\varphi^{\mathfrak{b}}_*$ in Theorem 5.3.64, means that the composition

$$I \circ \varphi^{\mathfrak{b}}_* : (C(L^{(1)}, L^{(0)}; \Lambda_{0,nov}), \mathfrak{n}^{\mathfrak{b}}_{k_1,k_0}) \to (C(L^{(1)\prime}, L^{(0)\prime}; \Lambda_{0,nov}), \mathfrak{n}^{\psi'_*\mathfrak{b}}_{k_1,k_0})$$

is homotopic to $\varphi'^{\mathfrak{b}}_*$ over the homotopy from $(\psi'^{\mathfrak{b}}_{*;(1)}, \psi'^{\mathfrak{b}}_{*;(0)})$ to $(I^{(1)} \circ \psi^{\mathfrak{b}}_{*;(1)}, I^{(0)} \circ \psi^{\mathfrak{b}}_{*;(0)})$ mentioned above.

We next take two Hamiltonian isotopies $\{\psi^{(i)}_\rho\}_\rho$ from M to M ($i = 0, 1$) such that $\psi^{(i)}_0 = id$. We put

$$L^{(0)\prime} = \psi^{(0)}_1(L^{(0)}), \quad L^{(1)\prime} = \psi^{(1)}_1(L^{(1)}).$$

Let

$$\psi^{(i)\mathfrak{b}}_* : (C(L^{(i)}; \Lambda_{0,nov}), \mathfrak{m}^{\mathfrak{b}}) \to (C(L^{(i)\prime}; \Lambda_{0,nov}), \mathfrak{m}^{\psi^{(i)}_*\mathfrak{b}})$$

be the homotopy equivalence constructed in Theorem 4.6.52. Since $\psi^{(i)}_*\mathfrak{b}$ is homologous to $\mathfrak{b}$, it follows from Theorem 4.6.47 that there exists a homotopy equivalence

$$I_{(i)} : (C(L^{(i)\prime}; \Lambda_{0,nov}), \mathfrak{m}^{\psi^{(i)}_*\mathfrak{b}}) \to (C(L^{(i)\prime}; \Lambda_{0,nov}), \mathfrak{m}^{\mathfrak{b}}).$$

THEOREM 5.3.65. *There exists a weakly filtered A_∞ bimodule homomorphism which is a homotopy equivalence of the filtered A_∞ bimodules*

$$\varphi^{\mathfrak{b}}_* : (C(L^{(1)}, L^{(0)}; \Lambda_{nov}), \mathfrak{n}^{\mathfrak{b}}_{k_1,k_0}) \to (C(L^{(1)\prime}, L^{(0)\prime}; \Lambda_{nov}), \mathfrak{n}^{\mathfrak{b}}_{k_1,k_0})$$

over $(I_{(1)} \circ \psi^{\mathfrak{b}}_{*;(1)}, I_{(0)} \circ \psi^{\mathfrak{b}}_{*;(0)})$. It is independent of the choice of the Hamiltonian isotopy in a similar sense as above and is functorial in the sense as Theorem 5.3.39.

The proof of Theorems 5.3.64 and 5.3.65 are straightforward combination of the arguments we discussed in this section and Subsection 4.6.6. Namely we include interior marked points to the moduli spaces we used to construct A_∞ bimodule homomorphisms and its homotopies and cut the moduli space by requiring the interior marked points to be sent to a point in $\mathfrak{b}$. We omit the details. (See also Subsections 7.4.7-7.4.9.)

5.3.7. Wrap-up of the proof of invariance of Floer cohomologies. Now we bring together the results of this section and the last to complete the proof of Theorems 4.1.4 and 4.1.5.

PROOF OF THEOREM 4.1.4. We use the notation of Theorem 4.1.4. By Theorems 5.3.1 and Lemma 5.2.19, we have a *strict* filtered A_∞ bimodule homomorphism

(5.3.66)
$$
{}^{b^{(1)}}\varphi^{b^{(0)}} : (C_1(L^{(1)}, L^{(0)}; \Lambda_{0,nov}), {}^{b^{(1)}}\mathfrak{n}^{b^{(0)}})
$$
$$
\to (C_2(L^{(1)'}, L^{(0)'}; \Lambda_{0,nov}), {}^{\psi_* b^{(1)}}\mathfrak{n}^{\psi_* b^{(0)}}).
$$

It induces a cochain homomorphism

(5.3.67)
$$
{}^{b^{(1)}}\varphi^{b^{(0)}} : (C_1(L^{(1)}, L^{(0)}; \Lambda_{0,nov}), \delta_{b^{(1)}, b^{(0)}})
$$
$$
\to (C_2(L^{(1)'}, L^{(0)'}; \Lambda_{0,nov}), \delta_{\psi_* b^{(1)}, \psi_* b^{(0)}}),
$$

and hence

(5.3.68)
$$
(({}^{b^{(1)}}\varphi^{b^{(0)}})_{0,0})_* : HF((L^{(1)}, b^{(1)}), (L^{(0)}, b^{(0)}); \Lambda_{0,nov})
$$
$$
\to HF((L^{(1)'}, \psi_* b^{(1)}), (L^{(0)'}, \psi_* b^{(0)}); \Lambda_{0,nov}).
$$

We will prove (5.3.68) is an isomorphism. (We remark the equality
$$
\varphi_* \equiv (\psi|_{L^{(1)} \cap L^{(0)}})_* : C_1(L^{(1)}, L^{(0)}; \Lambda_{0,nov}) \quad \mathrm{mod}\ \Lambda_{0,nov}^+
$$
as the homomorphisms $C_2(L^{(1)'}, L^{(0)'}; \Lambda_{0,nov})$.) Let
$$
\varphi^{-1} : (C_2(L^{(1)'}, L^{(0)'}; \Lambda_{0,nov}), \mathfrak{n}) \to (C_1(L^{(1)}, L^{(0)}; \Lambda_{0,nov}), \mathfrak{n})
$$
be the homotopy inverse to φ. (φ^{-1} is not strict in general.) Let $(\mathfrak{D}, \mathfrak{n})$ be a model of $[0, 1] \times (C_1(L^{(1)}, L^{(0)}; \Lambda_{0,nov}), \mathfrak{n})$, which is a $(\mathfrak{C}^{(1)}, \mathfrak{m})$, $(\mathfrak{C}^{(0)}, \mathfrak{m})$ bimodule. (Here $(\mathfrak{C}^{(i)}, \mathfrak{m})$ is a model of $[0, 1] \times (C(L^{(i)'}), \mathfrak{m})$.) Then there exists
$$
\Phi : (C_2(L^{(1)'}, L^{(0)'}; \Lambda_{0,nov}); \mathfrak{n}) \to (\mathfrak{D}, \mathfrak{n})
$$
such that

(5.3.69)
$$
\mathrm{Eval}_{s=0} \circ \Phi = id, \qquad \mathrm{Eval}_{s=1} \circ \Phi = \varphi^{-1} \circ \varphi.
$$

Φ is a bimodule homomorphism over $\Psi^{(i)} : (C(L^{(i)}), \mathfrak{m}) \to (\mathfrak{C}^{(i)}, \mathfrak{m})$. Here $\Psi^{(i)}$ is a homotopy from identity to $(\psi^{-1})_* \circ \psi_* : (C(L^{(i)}), \mathfrak{m}) \to (C(L^{(i)}), \mathfrak{m})$. (We denote by $\psi^{-1} : (\mathfrak{C}^{(i)'}, \mathfrak{m}) \to (\mathfrak{C}^{(i)}, \mathfrak{m})$ a homotopy inverse to ψ.)

Therefore, by Lemma 5.2.18, we obtain a *strict* filtered A_∞ bimodule homomorphisms (here and hereafter a filtered A_∞ bimodule homomorphism over a strict filtered A_∞ algebra homomorphism is called strict)

(5.3.70)
$$
{}^{\psi_* b^{(1)}}(\varphi^{-1})^{\psi_* b^{(0)}} : (C_2(L^{(1)'}, L^{(0)'}; \Lambda_{0,nov}), {}^{\psi_* b^{(1)}}\mathfrak{n}^{\psi_* b^{(0)}})
$$
$$
\to (C_1(L^{(1)}, L^{(0)}; \Lambda_{0,nov}), {}^{(\psi^{-1})_* \psi_* b^{(1)}}\mathfrak{n}^{(\psi^{-1})_* \psi_* b^{(0)}}),
$$

(5.3.71)
$$
{}^{b^{(1)}}\Phi^{b^{(0)}} : (C_1(L^{(1)}, L^{(0)}; \Lambda_{0,nov}), {}^{b^{(1)}}\mathfrak{n}^{b^{(0)}}) \to (\mathfrak{D}, {}^{\Psi_*^{(1)} b^{(1)}}\mathfrak{n}^{\Psi_*^{(0)} b^{(0)}}).
$$

By (5.3.69), $\mathrm{Eval}_{s=s_0}$ induces strict filtered A_∞ bimodule homomorphisms:

(5.3.72)
$$
{}^{\Psi_*^{(1)} b^{(1)}}(\mathrm{Eval}_{s=0})^{\Psi_*^{(0)} b^{(0)}} : (\mathfrak{D}, {}^{\Psi_*^{(1)} b^{(1)}}\mathfrak{n}^{\Psi_*^{(0)} b^{(0)}})
$$
$$
\to (C_1(L^{(1)}, L^{(0)}; \Lambda_{0,nov}), {}^{b^{(1)}}\mathfrak{n}^{b^{(0)}}),
$$

(5.3.73)
$$
{}^{\Psi_*^{(1)} b^{(1)}}(\mathrm{Eval}_{s=1})^{\Psi_*^{(0)} b^{(0)}} : (\mathfrak{D}, {}^{\Psi_*^{(1)} b^{(1)}}\mathfrak{n}^{\Psi_*^{(0)} b^{(0)}})
$$
$$
\to (C_1(L^{(1)}, L^{(0)}; \Lambda_{0,nov}), {}^{(\psi^{-1})_* \psi_* b^{(1)}}\mathfrak{n}^{(\psi^{-1})_* \psi_* b^{(0)}}).
$$

Moreover

$$(5.3.74) \quad \begin{aligned} ({}^{\Psi_*^{(1)}b^{(1)}}(\mathrm{Eval}_{s=0})^{\Psi_*^{(0)}b^{(0)}}) \circ ({}^{b^{(1)}}\Phi^{b^{(0)}}) &= id, \\ ({}^{\Psi_*^{(1)}b^{(1)}}(\mathrm{Eval}_{s=1})^{\Psi_*^{(0)}b^{(0)}}) \circ ({}^{b^{(1)}}\Phi^{b^{(0)}}) &= {}^{\psi_*b^{(1)}}(\varphi^{-1})^{\psi_*b^{(0)}} \circ ({}^{b^{(1)}}\varphi^{b^{(0)}}). \end{aligned}$$

The homomorphism ${}^{\Psi_*^{(1)}b^{(1)}}(\mathrm{Eval}_{s=0})^{\Psi_*^{(0)}b^{(0)}}$ induces an isomorphism

$$H(\mathfrak{D}; \delta_{\Psi_*^{(1)}b^{(1)}, \Psi_*^{(0)}b^{(0)}}) \cong HF((L^{(1)}, b^{(1)}), (L^{(0)}, b^{(0)}); \Lambda_{0,nov})$$

by Proposition 5.2.38 (2). Therefore, by the first formula of (5.3.74), ${}^{b^{(1)}}\Phi^{b^{(0)}}$ induces an isomorphism

$$(5.3.75) \quad HF((L^{(1)}, b^{(1)}), (L^{(0)}, b^{(0)}); \Lambda_{0,nov}) \cong H(\mathfrak{D}; \delta_{\Psi_*^{(1)}b^{(1)}, \Psi_*^{(0)}b^{(0)}}).$$

We can also prove that ${}^{\Psi_*^{(1)}b^{(1)}}(\mathrm{Eval}_{s=1})^{\Psi_*^{(0)}b^{(0)}}$ induces an isomorphism

$$(5.3.76) \quad \begin{aligned} &H(\mathfrak{D}; \delta_{\Psi_*^{(1)}b^{(1)}, \Psi_*^{(0)}b^{(0)}}) \\ &\cong HF((L^{(1)}, (\psi^{-1})_*\psi_*b^{(1)}), (L^{(0)}, (\psi^{-1})_*\psi_*b^{(0)}); \Lambda_{0,nov}) \end{aligned}$$

by Proposition 5.2.38 (2).

(5.3.75), (5.3.76) and the second formula of (5.3.74) imply that (5.3.68) is injective.

We can use homotopy from identity to $\varphi \circ \varphi^{-1}$ in a similar way to show that (5.3.68) is surjective.

In a way similar to the argument above, we can also derive from Theorem 5.3.11 and Lemma 5.2.19 that the isomorphism (5.3.68) depends only on the isotopy class of ψ_s. $\qquad \square$

PROOF OF THEOREM 4.1.5. We use Theorem 5.3.14 and Lemma 5.2.19 in the same way as above to prove Theorem 4.1.5. $\qquad \square$

We next discuss 'weak' and/or 'def' version of Theorems 4.1.4 and 4.1.5.

THEOREM 4.1.4a. *Let* $\mathbf{b}^{(0)} \in \widehat{\mathcal{M}}_{\mathrm{weak,def}}(L^{(0)})$, $\mathbf{b}^{(1)} \in \widehat{\mathcal{M}}_{\mathrm{weak,def}}(L^{(1)})$, $\mathbf{b}^{(0)\prime} \in \widehat{\mathcal{M}}_{\mathrm{weak,def}}(L^{(0)\prime})$, *and* $\mathbf{b}^{(1)\prime} \in \widehat{\mathcal{M}}_{\mathrm{weak,def}}(L^{(1)\prime})$. *Suppose that* $\psi_*([\mathbf{b}^{(0)}]) = [\mathbf{b}^{(0)\prime}]$ *and* $\psi_*([\mathbf{b}^{(1)}]) = [\mathbf{b}^{(1)\prime}]$. *We assume*

$$\mathfrak{PO}(\mathbf{b}^{(0)}) = \mathfrak{PO}(\mathbf{b}^{(1)}), \quad \pi_{\mathrm{amb}}(\mathbf{b}^{(0)}) = \pi_{\mathrm{amb}}(\mathbf{b}^{(1)}).$$

Then

$$(5.3.77) \quad \mathfrak{PO}(\mathbf{b}^{(0)\prime}) = \mathfrak{PO}(\mathbf{b}^{(1)\prime}), \quad \pi_{\mathrm{amb}}(\mathbf{b}^{(0)\prime}) = \pi_{\mathrm{amb}}(\mathbf{b}^{(1)\prime})$$

and there exists a filtered isomorphism

$$\begin{aligned} \psi_* : &HF((L^{(1)}, \mathbf{b}^{(1)}), (L^{(0)}, \mathbf{b}^{(0)}); \Lambda_{0,nov}) \\ &\cong HF((L^{(1)\prime}, \mathbf{b}^{(1)\prime}), (L^{(0)\prime}, \mathbf{b}^{(0)\prime}); \Lambda_{0,nov}). \end{aligned}$$

Moreover, if $\{\psi_s\}_s$ $(0 \le s \le 1)$ *is an isotopy of symplectic diffeomorphisms such that* $\psi_s(L^{(0)}) = L^{(0)\prime}$, $\psi_s(L^{(1)}) = L^{(1)\prime}$ *for each* s, *then* ψ_{0*} *is equal to* ψ_{1*}.

THEOREM 4.1.5a. *Let* $\mathbf{b}^{(i)} \in \widehat{\mathcal{M}}_{\mathrm{weak,def}}(L^{(0)})$ *and* $\mathbf{b}^{(i)\prime} \in \widehat{\mathcal{M}}_{\mathrm{weak,def}}(L^{(1)\prime})$ *for* $i = 0, 1$, *such that*

$$\mathfrak{PO}(\mathbf{b}^{(0)}) = \mathfrak{PO}(\mathbf{b}^{(1)}), \quad \pi_{\mathrm{amb}}(\mathbf{b}^{(0)}) = \pi_{\mathrm{amb}}(\mathbf{b}^{(1)}).$$

Let $\{\psi_\rho^{(0)}\}_\rho$ *and* $\{\psi_\rho^{(1)}\}_\rho$ $(0 \le \rho \le 1)$ *be Hamiltonian isotopies such that* $\psi_0^{(0)} = \psi_0^{(1)} = id$, $\psi_1^{(0)}(L^{(0)}) = L^{(0)\prime}$ *and* $\psi_1^{(1)}(L^{(1)}) = L^{(1)\prime}$.
  We suppose that $\psi_{1*}^{(0)}([\mathbf{b}^{(0)}]) = [\mathbf{b}^{(0)\prime}]$ *and* $\psi_{1*}^{(1)}([\mathbf{b}^{(1)}]) = [\mathbf{b}^{(1)\prime}]$.
  Then

(5.3.78) $$\mathfrak{PO}(\mathbf{b}^{(0)\prime}) = \mathfrak{PO}(\mathbf{b}^{(1)\prime}), \quad \pi_{\mathrm{amb}}(\mathbf{b}^{(0)\prime}) = \pi_{\mathrm{amb}}(\mathbf{b}^{(1)\prime}).$$

And $\psi^{(1)}$ *induce a weakly-filtered isomorphism*

$$(\{\psi_\rho^{(1)}\}_\rho, \{\psi_\rho^{(0)}\}_\rho)_* : HF((L^{(1)}, \mathbf{b}^{(1)}), (L^{(0)}, \mathbf{b}^{(0)}); \Lambda_{nov})$$
$$\cong HF((L^{(1)\prime}, \mathbf{b}^{(1)\prime}), (L^{(0)\prime}, \mathbf{b}^{(0)\prime}); \Lambda_{nov}).$$

Moreover, if $\{\psi_{\rho,s}^{(i)}\}_{\rho,s}$ $(i = 0, 1)$ *be a two parameter family of hamiltonian isotopies such that* $\psi_{0,s}^{(i)} = id$ *and* $\psi_{1,s}^{(i)}(L^{(i)}) = L^{(i)\prime}$ *for each* s, *then we have*

$$(\{\psi_{\rho,0}^{(1)}\}_\rho, \{\psi_{\rho,0}^{(0)}\}_\rho)_* = (\{\psi_{\rho,1}^{(1)}\}_\rho, \{\psi_{\rho,1}^{(0)}\}_\rho)_*.$$

PROOF. (5.3.77), (5.3.78) are consequence of Corollary 4.6.53. Then the rest of the proof of Theorems 4.1.4a 4.1.5a are the same as the proof of Theorems 4.1.4 and 4.1.5. We use Theorems 5.3.64 and 5.3.65 in place of Theorems 5.3.1 and 5.3.14 to obtain 'def' version. The weak version follows from the fact that the homotopy equivalences of Theorems 5.3.1, 5.3.14, 5.3.64 and 5.3.65 are homotopy unital. □

PROOF OF THEOREM B (B.1), (B.3), (B.4), (B.5). (B.1) is a consequence of Corollary 5.2.40. (B.3) and (B.4) are consequences of Theorem 4.1.4a. (B.5) is a consequence of Theorem 4.1.4a and the fact that the functoriality of the homotopy equivalence in Theorem 5.3.64. □

We remark that (B.2) was proved in Subsection 3.8.10. Hence the proof of Theorem B is completed. □

PROOF OF THEOREM G (G.1), (G.3), (G.4), (G.5). (G.1) is a consequence of Proposition 3.7.75. (G.3) is a consequence of Theorem 4.1.4a. (G.4) is a consequence of Theorem 4.1.5a. The construction of bimodule structure in (G.5) is given in Subsection 3.8.10. It is easy to see from the construction of isomorphism in Theorem 4.1.4a that the isomorphism is a bimodule homomorphism. This completes the proof of (G.5). □

(G.2) will be proved in Subsection 5.4.6.

5.4. Canonical models, Formal super schemes and Kuranishi maps

5.4.1. Canonical models, Kuranishi maps and bounding cochains. In this section, we will complete the proof of Theorems A and F in introduction. Namely we prove that the structure of filtered A_∞ algebra and filtered A_∞ bimodule which we constructed on the chain complex, induce filtered A_∞ structures on the

cohomology groups. We also describe the set $\widehat{\mathcal{M}}(C)$ of bounding cochains as the zero set of a formal map (the Kuranishi map). In other words we prove Theorem M in introduction. We also prove Theorem N and Corollaries O,P in Subsection 5.4.6. Throughout Section 5.4, we assume that the filtered A_∞ algebras and filtered A_∞ bimodules are *gapped* and also assume that R is a *field*. We however use the assumption R being a field only in the proof Lemma 5.4.28 and Lemma 5.4.51.

We start with Theorem 5.4.1 below, which is not new and was proved in [**Kad82**] (see also [**Mer99, KoS01**]), (if we replace the homotopy equivalence by the weak homotopy equivalence). We like to note that those papers we quote above use different sign conventions from ours. See also [**Fuk03II**].

THEOREM 5.4.1. *Any unfiltered A_∞ algebra $(\overline{C}, \overline{\mathfrak{m}})$ is homotopy equivalent to an A_∞ algebra $(\overline{C}', \overline{\mathfrak{m}}')$ with $\overline{\mathfrak{m}}'_1 = 0$.*

Instead of giving the proof of Theorem 5.4.1, we will provide the proof of an analogous result, Theorem 5.4.2, for the filtered A_∞ algebra later in Subsection 5.4.4. This version of the theorem has not previously appeared in the literature.

THEOREM 5.4.2. *Any gapped filtered A_∞ algebra $(C, \mathfrak{m})$ is homotopy equivalent to a gapped filtered A_∞ algebra $(C', \mathfrak{m}')$ with $\overline{\mathfrak{m}}'_1 = 0$. Here $(\overline{C}', \overline{\mathfrak{m}}')$ is the R-reduction of $(C', \mathfrak{m}')$. Moreover the homotopy equivalence can be taken as a gapped A_∞ homomorphism.*

Theorem W immediately follows from Theorem 5.4.2.

DEFINITION 5.4.3. (1) An unfiltered A_∞ algebra is called *canonical* if $\overline{\mathfrak{m}}_1 = 0$. A filtered A_∞ algebra is called *canonical* if $\overline{\mathfrak{m}}_1 = 0$.

A *canonical model* of a filtered A_∞ algebra C is defined to be a canonical filtered A_∞ algebra homotopy equivalent to C.

(2) Let $(C, \mathfrak{m}), (C', \mathfrak{m}')$ be filtered A_∞ algebras and $\widehat{d}, \widehat{d}'$ the coderivations on the bar complexes $\widehat{B}C[1], \widehat{B}C'[1]$ induced by $\mathfrak{m}, \mathfrak{m}'$ respectively. We say that $(C, \mathfrak{m})$ is *isomorphic* to $(C', \mathfrak{m}')$ if there exists a filtered A_∞ homomorphism $\mathfrak{f} : C \to C'$ such that the induced coalgebra homomorphism $\widehat{\mathfrak{f}} : \widehat{B}C[1] \to \widehat{B}C'[1]$ satisfying $\widehat{\mathfrak{f}} \circ \widehat{d} = \widehat{d}' \circ \widehat{\mathfrak{f}}$ is bijective and the inverse $\widehat{\mathfrak{f}}^{-1} : \widehat{B}C'[1] \to \widehat{B}C[1]$ satisfies $\widehat{d} \circ \widehat{\mathfrak{f}}^{-1} = \widehat{\mathfrak{f}}^{-1} \circ \widehat{d}'$. In this case we call $\mathfrak{f}$ an *isomorphism* of the filtered A_∞ algebras. The unfiltered version can be also defined in the same way.

(3) Let $(D, \mathfrak{n})$ $(D', \mathfrak{n}')$ be (C_1, C_0) filtered A_∞ bimodules and $\widehat{d}, \widehat{d}'$ the induced bi-coderivations. We say that $(D, \mathfrak{n})$ is *isomorphic* to $(D', \mathfrak{n}')$ if there exists a filtered A_∞ bimodule homomorphism $\varphi : D \to D'$ over identities such that the induced comodule homomorphism $\widehat{\varphi} : \widehat{B}C_1[1] \widehat{\otimes} D[1] \widehat{\otimes} \widehat{B}C_0[1] \to \widehat{B}C_1[1] \widehat{\otimes} D'[1] \widehat{\otimes} \widehat{B}C_0[1]$ is bijective and the inverse $\widehat{\varphi}^{-1} : \widehat{B}C_1[1] \widehat{\otimes} D'[1] \widehat{\otimes} \widehat{B}C_0[1] \to \widehat{B}C_1[1] \widehat{\otimes} D[1] \widehat{\otimes} \widehat{B}C_0[1]$ satisfies $\widehat{d} \circ \widehat{\varphi}^{-1} = \widehat{\varphi}^{-1} \circ \widehat{d}'$. In this case we call φ an *isomorphism* of the filtered A_∞ bimodules. The unfiltered version can be also defined in the same way.

REMARK 5.4.4. In [**Kon03**], Kontsevich called a similar notion (in the setting of L_∞ algebra), minimal. However in the theory of commutative D.G.A., Sullivan [**Sul78**] used the term "minimal" for a different concept. In fact if we regard de Rham complex $(\Omega(M), d)$ as an A_∞ algebra, its canonical model is its cohomology group $H(M; \mathbb{R})$ as a vector space. On the other hand, its minimal model (in the sense of Sullivan) is different from $H(M; \mathbb{R})$ unless M is formal.

So, in order to avoid confusion, we propose to use the name "canonical" instead here. Note if C is a canonical A_∞ algebra the dual of its Bar complex $BC[1]^*$ is a D.G.A. which is minimal in the sense of Sullivan.

We remark that the order we prove various algebraic results on filtered A_∞ algebra is rather different from those in many of the literatures such as [**MSS02, Lef03**]. Namely in those papers in the literature, a result analogous to Theorem 5.4.1 is first proved and is used, for example, to *define* the notion of homotopy equivalence. It seems to the authors that this is an influence of the tradition of rational homotopy theory and of homotopy theory of D.G.A.

In the category of D.G.A., several basic results such as Theorem 4.2.45 and Proposition 4.2.37 hold only for minimal D.G.A. Hence the existence of minimal model must be established at the beginning of the theory. On the other hand, in the category of (filtered) A_∞ algebras, Theorem 4.2.45, Proposition 4.2.37 etc. hold for *any* A_∞ algebra.

In this sense, in the theory of (filtered) A_∞ algebra, canonical (filtered) A_∞ algebra does *not* play the same role as minimal D.G.A. plays in the homotopy theory of D.G.A.

The following proposition justifies the term "canonical".

PROPOSITION 5.4.5. *Any homotopy equivalence between two (filtered) canonical A_∞ algebras is an isomorphism.*

PROOF. Let $\mathfrak{f} : C_1 \to C_2$ be a homotopy equivalence between two canonical filtered A_∞ algebras C_1, C_2. It induces a homotopy equivalence $\bar{\mathfrak{f}} : \overline{C}_1 \to \overline{C}_2$. We remark that $\overline{C}_i$ are also canonical. Therefore $\overline{C}_i$ is isomorphic to its $\overline{\mathfrak{m}}_1$ cohomology for each $i = 1, 2$ and so $\bar{\mathfrak{f}}_1 : \overline{C}_1 \to \overline{C}_2$ is an isomorphism of R modules. Using the number filtration in a standard way by now, we prove that $\widehat{\bar{\mathfrak{f}}} : B\overline{C}_1[1] \to B\overline{C}_2[1]$ is an isomorphism of R modules. Then using energy filtrations in an obvious way, we can find the inverse of $\widehat{\mathfrak{f}} : BC_1[1] \to BC_2[1]$. The proof of Proposition 5.4.5 is complete. $\qquad\square$

Therefore we can restate Theorem 5.4.2 as follows.

THEOREM 5.4.2′. *Any gapped filtered A_∞ algebra $(C, \mathfrak{m})$ has a canonical model which is unique up to isomorphism. Moreover the homotopy equivalence can be taken as a gapped A_∞ homomorphism. If $(C, \mathfrak{m})$ is homotopy-unital, the canonical model is unital.*

Statement on unit in Theorem 5.4.2′ does not follow from Theorem 5.4.2, directly. We prove it in Subsection 5.4.4 right after the proof of Theorem 5.4.2.

Applying this to our geometric situation, we derive the following whose proof follows immediately from the above discussions.

COROLLARY 5.4.6. *To each relatively spin Lagrangian submanifold L of a symplectic manifold, we can associate a unital canonical filtered A_∞ algebra $(C_{can}(L; \Lambda_{0,nov}), \mathfrak{m}_{can})$, which is independent of the almost complex structure and any other choices involved, up to unital isomorphism.*

We remark that $C_{can}(L; \Lambda_{0,nov}) \cong H(L; \Lambda_{0,nov})$. Hence Corollary 5.4.6 implies Theorem A immediately.

Now by using the canonical model, we will define the Kuranishi map and study the relation between the Kuranishi map and the moduli space $\widehat{\mathcal{M}}(C)$ of bounding cochains. From now on we *assume* that $H_*(\overline{C}, \overline{\mathbf{m}}_1)$ is finitely generated R module. In case when $\overline{C}$ is canonical it implies that $\overline{C}$ itself is finitely generated. It implies that C is finitely generated $\Lambda_{0,nov}$ module. (Recall that we always assume that C is a free $\Lambda_{0,nov}$ module and $C = \overline{C} \otimes_R \Lambda_{0,nov}$.)

DEFINITION 5.4.7. Let $(C, \mathbf{m})$ be a filtered A_∞ algebra. We take m variables s_i $(i = 1, \cdots, m)$ of even degree and ℓ variables h_i $(i = 1, \cdots, \ell)$ of odd degree. The ring of *super formal power series* $\Lambda_{0,nov}[[s_1, \cdots, s_m; h_1, \cdots, h_\ell]]$ is the ring of formal power series

$$\Lambda_{0,nov}[[s_1, \cdots, s_m; h_1, \cdots, h_\ell]] = \left\{ \sum_{k_1=0}^{\infty} \cdots \sum_{k_m=0}^{\infty} a_{k_1, \cdots, k_m} s_1^{k_1} \cdots s_m^{k_m} \right\}$$

with $a_{k_1, \cdots, k_m} \in \Lambda_{0,nov} \otimes \Omega(h_1, \cdots, h_\ell)$. Here $\Omega(h_1, \cdots, h_\ell)$ denotes the exterior algebra over R generated by basis $h_1, \cdots, h_\ell$.

We define the ring $R[[s_1, \cdots, s_m; h_1, \cdots, h_\ell]]$ in a similar way.

Now let $(C, \mathbf{m})$ be a canonical filtered A_∞ algebra. We choose a basis $\mathbf{v}_1, \cdots, \mathbf{v}_m$ of $C^{odd} = C[1]^{even}$ and $\mathbf{w}_1, \cdots, \mathbf{w}_\ell$ of C^{even}. For $1 \leq i \leq \ell + m$, let $\pi_i : C \to \Lambda_{0,nov}$ be the projection of an element of C to its coordinate of $\mathbf{v}_i$ for $i \leq m$, and to its coordinate of $\mathbf{w}_{i-m}$ for $i > m$. In case C is unital, we put $\mathbf{w}_\ell = \mathbf{e}$ (the unit).

DEFINITION 5.4.8. For $i = 1, \cdots, \ell + m$, we define

(5.4.9)
$$P_i(s_1, \cdots, s_m; h_1, \cdots, h_\ell) =$$
$$(\pi_i \circ \mathbf{m})(\exp(s_1 \mathbf{v}_1 + \cdots + s_m \mathbf{v}_m + h_1 \mathbf{w}_1 + \cdots + h_\ell \mathbf{w}_\ell))$$
$$\in \Lambda_{0,nov}[[s_1, \cdots, s_m; h_1, \cdots, h_\ell]].$$

We need to explain the meaning of the right hand side of (5.4.9). By using the notation $\mathbf{u}_i^0 = \mathbf{v}_i$, $\mathbf{u}_i^1 = \mathbf{w}_i$, $u_i^0 = s_i$, $u_i^1 = h_i$, and formally expanding the exponential function, the right hand side of (5.4.9) is defined to be the formal power series

(5.4.10)
$$\sum_k \sum_{(a_1, \cdots, a_k) \in \{1, \cdots, \max\{m,\ell\}\}^k} \sum_{(\epsilon_1, \cdots, \epsilon_k) \in \{0,1\}^k} (-1)^{\sum_{i<j} \epsilon_i \epsilon_j + \sum \epsilon_i}$$
$$u_{a_1}^{\epsilon_1} \cdots u_{a_k}^{\epsilon_k} (\pi_i \circ \mathbf{m})(\mathbf{u}_{a_1}^{\epsilon_1}, \cdots, \mathbf{u}_{a_k}^{\epsilon_k}).$$

DEFINITION 5.4.11. We call $P_i(s_1, \cdots, s_\ell; h_1, \cdots, h_m)$ a *super Kuranishi map* of the canonical filtered A_∞ algebra $(C, \mathbf{m})$. We put $h_i = 0$ and get $P_i^{bos}(s_1, \cdots, s_\ell)$. We call P_i^{bos} a *Kuranishi map* of $(C, \mathbf{m})$.

We define

$$\mathfrak{M}(C, \mathbf{m}) = \Lambda_{0,nov}[[s_1, \cdots, s_m; h_1, \cdots, h_\ell]]/(P_1, \cdots, P_{m+\ell}),$$
$$\mathfrak{M}(C, \mathbf{m})^{bos} = \Lambda_{0,nov}[[s_1, \cdots, s_m]]/(P_{m+1}^{bos}, \cdots, P_{m+\ell}^{bos}).$$

Here $(P_1, \cdots, P_{m+\ell})$ is the ideal generated by $P_1, \cdots, P_{m+\ell}$.

In the unital case, we put

$$\mathfrak{M}_{\text{weak}}(C, \mathbf{m}) = \Lambda_{0,nov}[[s_1, \cdots, s_m; h_1, \cdots, h_\ell]]/(P_1, \cdots, P_{m+\ell-1}),$$
$$\mathfrak{M}_{\text{weak}}(C, \mathbf{m})^{bos} = \Lambda_{0,nov}[[s_1, \cdots, s_m]]/(P_{m+1}^{bos}, \cdots, P_{m+\ell-1}^{bos}).$$

(Note $P_{m+\ell}^{bos} = P_{m+\ell}$ pick up the coefficient of the unit $\mathbf{e}$.)

For a general filtered A_∞ algebra $(C, \mathbf{m})$ which is not necessarily canonical, we define its (super) Kuranishi map to be the (super) Kuranishi map of its canonical model.

We recall that the canonical model of $(C, \mathbf{m})$ is isomorphic to its $\overline{\mathbf{m}}_1$ cohomology as a $\Lambda_{0,nov}$ module and hence the Kuranishi map is a formal map on the $\overline{\mathbf{m}}_1$ cohomology group of C over $\Lambda_{0,nov}$.

We also remark that $\mathfrak{M}(C, \mathbf{m})^{bos}$ is a *commutative* $\Lambda_{0,nov}$ algebra and $\mathfrak{M}(C, \mathbf{m})$ is a *super commutative* $\Lambda_{0,nov}$ algebra.

THEOREM 5.4.12. *The isomorphism class of $\mathfrak{M}(C, \mathbf{m})$ (resp. $\mathfrak{M}(C, \mathbf{m})^{bos}$) as a super commutative $\Lambda_{0,nov}$ algebra (resp. as commutative $\Lambda_{0,nov}$ algebra) is an invariant of the homotopy equivalence class of the A_∞ algebra $(C, \mathbf{m})$.*
The same holds for $\mathfrak{M}_{\text{weak}}(C, \mathbf{m})$ (resp. $\mathfrak{M}_{\text{weak}}(C, \mathbf{m})^{bos}$).

PROOF. Let $\mathfrak{f} : C \to C'$ be an A_∞ isomorphism between two canonical filtered A_∞ algebras. We choose a basis $\mathbf{v}_1, \cdots, \mathbf{v}_m$ of C^{odd} and $\mathbf{w}_1, \cdots, \mathbf{w}_\ell$ of C^{even} and let $s_i, (i = 1, \cdots, m)$ and $h_j, (j = 1, \cdots, \ell)$ be the corresponding formal coordinates. Similarly for C', we choose a basis $\mathbf{v}'_1, \cdots, \mathbf{v}'_{m'}, \mathbf{w}'_1, \cdots, \mathbf{w}'_{\ell'}$ and let s'_i, h'_j be the corresponding formal coordinates. Let $\pi'_j : C' \to \Lambda_{0,nov}, (j = 1, \cdots, m + \ell)$ be the projections with respect to the basis as before. We define

$$(5.4.13) \qquad \begin{aligned} \mathfrak{F}_j = &(\pi'_j \circ \mathfrak{f}) \left(\exp(s_1 \mathbf{v}_1 + \cdots + s_m \mathbf{v}_m + h_1 \mathbf{w}_1 + \cdots + h_\ell \mathbf{w}_\ell) \right) \\ &\in \Lambda_{0,nov}[[s_1, \cdots, s_m; h_1, \cdots, h_\ell]] \end{aligned}$$

whose meaning is as in (5.4.10) above. We define a homomorphism

$$\mathfrak{F} : \Lambda_{0,nov}[[s'_1, \cdots, s'_m; h'_1, \cdots, h'_\ell]] \to \Lambda_{0,nov}[[s_1, \cdots, s_m; h_1, \cdots, h_\ell]]$$

by putting $\mathfrak{F}(s'_j) = \mathfrak{F}_j$, $\mathfrak{F}(h'_j) = \mathfrak{F}_{j+m}$ and extending it to a $\Lambda_{0,nov}$ algebra homomorphism. We remark that the super Kuranishi map of $(C, \mathbf{m})$ defines a homomorphism

$$\mathfrak{P} : \Lambda_{0,nov}[[s_1, \cdots, s_m; h_1, \cdots, h_\ell]] \to \Lambda_{0,nov}[[s_1, \cdots, s_m; h_1, \cdots, h_\ell]]$$

induced by the assignment $\mathfrak{P}(s_j) = P_j$, $\mathfrak{P}(h_j) = P_{j+m}$. The same applies to $(C', \mathbf{m}')$. Since $\mathfrak{f}$ is an A_∞ homomorphism, it follows that the following diagram commutes.

$$
\begin{array}{ccc}
\Lambda_{0,nov}[[s'_1, \cdots, s'_m; h'_1, \cdots, h'_\ell]] & \xrightarrow{\ \mathfrak{P}\ } & \Lambda_{0,nov}[[s'_1, \cdots, s'_m; h'_1, \cdots, h'_\ell]] \\
\mathfrak{F} \downarrow & & \mathfrak{F} \downarrow \\
\Lambda_{0,nov}[[s_1, \cdots, s_m; h_1, \cdots, h_\ell]] & \xrightarrow{\ \mathfrak{P}\ } & \Lambda_{0,nov}[[s_1, \cdots, s_m; h_1, \cdots, h_\ell]]
\end{array}
$$

Diagram 5.4.1

Therefore this induces a ring homomorphism $\mathfrak{F} : \mathfrak{M}(C', \mathbf{m}) \to \mathfrak{M}(C, \mathbf{m})$. Evidently, the correspondence $\mathfrak{f} \mapsto \mathfrak{F}$ is functorial. Theorem 5.4.12 follows. $\square$

REMARK 5.4.14. We remark that the super Kuranishi map is a formal power series and so we cannot substitute the formal coordinates s_i by rational numbers. Whether we can find a canonical model with a convergent Kuranishi map seems to be an important question. In this respect, there are two kinds of convergence questions. One is whether one can substitute s_i by (small) rational numbers and the other is whether one can substitute T by a (small) nonnegative real number. Both of them seem to have fundamental importance in the study of homological mirror symmetry. We remark that the former convergence problem is related to Conjecture 3.6.46.

We next explain the relation between $\mathfrak{M}(C, \mathfrak{m})^{bos}$ and $\mathcal{M}(C, \mathfrak{m})$ that is the moduli space of bounding cochains. Let us denote by

$$Hom(\mathfrak{M}(C, \mathfrak{m})^{bos}, \Lambda_{0,nov})$$

the set of all *continuous* $\Lambda_{0,nov}$ algebra homomorphisms $\mathfrak{M}(C, \mathfrak{m})^{bos} \to \Lambda_{0,nov}$. Here we define a topology on $\mathfrak{M}(C, \mathfrak{m})^{bos}$ as follows: The formal power series ring $\Lambda_{0,nov}[[s_1, \cdots, s_m]]$ has two filtrations. One of them comes from the filtration of $\Lambda_{0,nov}$. The other one is induced by the ideal generated by $s_1, \cdots, s_m$. Let us denote by F the first filtration and by G the second filtration. We define a topology on $\Lambda_{0,nov}[[s_1, \cdots, s_m]]$ so that the set of

$$F^\lambda \Lambda_{0,nov}[[s_1, \cdots, s_m]] \cap G^n \Lambda_{0,nov}[[s_1, \cdots, s_m]]$$

for $\lambda \in \mathbb{R}$ and $n \in \mathbb{Z}$ provides the system of fundamental neighborhoods. Then the topology on $\mathfrak{M}(C, \mathfrak{m})^{bos}$ is induced by this system.

PROPOSITION 5.4.15.

$$Hom(\mathfrak{M}(C, \mathfrak{m})^{bos}, \Lambda_{0,nov}) \cong \widehat{\mathcal{M}}(C_{can}, \mathfrak{m}_{can}).$$

Here $(C_{can}, \mathfrak{m}_{can})$ is a canonical model of $(C, \mathfrak{m})$.

PROOF. By definition, it is enough to consider the case of a canonical filtered A_∞ algebra $(C, \mathfrak{m})$ and its Kuranishi map P_i^{bos}. Let $\varphi : \mathfrak{M}(C, \mathfrak{m})^{bos} \to \Lambda_{0,nov}$ be a continuous $\Lambda_{0,nov}$ algebra homomorphism. We put $\varphi(s_i) = b_i$. Since $\lim_{n \to \infty} s_i^n = 0$, it follows that $\lim_{n \to \infty} b_i^n = 0$ by the continuity of φ. Therefore we must have $b_i \in \Lambda_{0,nov}^+$. Then $\varphi \mapsto (\varphi(s_1), \cdots, \varphi(s_m))$ defines a homomorphism

$$Hom(\Lambda_{0,nov}[[s_1, \cdots, s_m]], \Lambda_{0,nov}) \to (\Lambda_{0,nov}^+)^m.$$

It is easy to see that this is indeed an isomorphism. On the other hand, it follows from (5.4.9) and Definition 5.4.11 that

$$(5.4.16) \qquad P_i^{bos}(b_1, \cdots, b_m) = 0, \quad i = m+1, \cdots, m+\ell$$

for $b_i \in \Lambda_{0,nov}^+$, if and only if

$$b = b_1 \mathbf{v}_1 + \cdots + b_m \mathbf{v}_m \in \widehat{\mathcal{M}}(C, \mathfrak{m}).$$

This finishes the proof. □

Theorem M is a consequence of 'weak' and 'def' version of Theorem 5.4.12 and Proposition 5.4.15. (See Subsection 5.4.6.)

REMARK 5.4.17. Instead of considering continuous homomorphisms to the universal Novikov ring, one can consider $Hom(\mathfrak{M}(C, \mathfrak{m})^{bos}, \mathfrak{A}^+)$ over an arbitrary Artin ring $\mathfrak{A}$ of which $\mathfrak{A}^+$ is the maximal ideal, or a complete valuation ring $\mathfrak{A}$ with a continuous homomorphism $\Lambda_{0,nov} \to \mathfrak{A}$. With this, our discussion above would become more along the line of the famous story of deformation functors over the Artin ring [Schl68]. Compare [Fuk03II].

5.4.2. The canonical models of filtered A_∞ bimodules. We next discuss a (C_1, C_0) filtered A_∞ bimodule D. We assume that C_1, C_0 and D are gapped. We would like to mention that we consider the case of $\Lambda_{0,nov}$ coefficient. Let $\mathfrak{n}_{k_1,k_0} : B_{k_1} C_1[1] \otimes D[1] \otimes B_{k_0} C_0[1] \to D[1]$ be the filtered A_∞ bimodule structure of D.

We recall from Proposition 5.2.43 that the homotopy category of filtered A_∞ bimodules is an invariant of the homotopy type of the coefficient A_∞ algebras and from Theorem 5.4.2 that each A_∞ algebra carries a canonical model. Based on these we will assume that C_1 and C_0 are canonical for the following discussion. The next result is an analog of Theorem 5.4.2.

THEOREM 5.4.18. *There exists a gapped filtered A_∞ bimodule $(D', \mathfrak{n}')$ over (C_1, C_0) which is homotopy equivalent to D and which satisfies*

$$\mathfrak{n}'_{0,0} \equiv 0 \mod \Lambda^+_{0,nov}.$$

Moreover the homotopy equivalence can be taken as a gapped A_∞ bimodule homomorphism. If C_1, C_0, D are homotopy-unital, then D' is unital.

The proof is similar to that of Theorem 5.4.2 and will be given later in Subsection 5.4.4.

DEFINITION 5.4.19. We call a filtered A_∞ bimodule D over canonical filtered A_∞ algebras *canonical* if $\mathfrak{n}_{0,0} \equiv 0 \mod \Lambda^+_{0,nov}$.

PROPOSITION 5.4.20. *Any homotopy equivalence between two canonical filtered A_∞ bimodules is an isomorphism.*

The proof is the same as that of Proposition 5.4.5 and so omitted.

Applying the above discussion to our geometric situation, we obtain the following corollary. We will prove it in Subsection 5.4.6.

COROLLARY 5.4.21. *To each relatively spin pair $(L^{(0)}, L^{(1)})$ of Lagrangian manifolds of M, which are of clean intersection, we can associate a unital canonical filtered A_∞ bimodule*

$$(C_{can}(L^{(1)}, L^{(0)}; \Lambda_{0,nov}), \mathfrak{n}_{can})$$

over $(C_{can}(L^{(i)}; \Lambda_{0,nov}), \mathfrak{m}_{can})$ $(i = 0, 1)$. The canonical model is independent of the choice of the compatible almost complex structure and other choices involved in the definition, up to isomorphism.

More explicitly, $C_{can}(L^{(1)}, L^{(0)}; \Lambda_{0,nov})$ is given by

$$C_{can}(L^{(1)}, L^{(0)}; \Lambda_{0,nov}) = \bigoplus_{[h,w] \in \widetilde{\pi}_0(L^{(1)} \cap L^{(0)})} H^*(R_h; \Lambda_{0,nov}).$$

Here $L^{(1)} \cap L^{(0)} = \cup_{h \in \pi_0(L^{(1)} \cap L^{(0)})} R_h$ is the decomposition of the connected components. As for the degree, we have for

$$S \otimes [h, w] \otimes T^\lambda e^\mu \in C^k_{can}(L^{(1)}, L^{(0)}; \Lambda_{0,nov})$$

with $S \in C^\ell(R_h; \Theta^-_{R_h})$,

$$k = \deg(S \otimes [h, w] \otimes T^\lambda e^\mu) = \ell + \mu([h, w]) + 2\mu.$$

See Subsection 3.7.5.

However we note that $C_{can}(L^{(1)}, L^{(0)}; \Lambda_{0,nov})$ is *not* an invariant of Hamiltonian isotopy of Lagrangian submanifolds. As we remarked before in Subsection 3.7.6, Floer cohomology is isomorphic under the Hamiltonian isotopy only over Λ_{nov} coefficient, not over $\Lambda_{0,nov}$. We will discuss this point more in Subsection 6.5.3. We do not know appropriate notion of the canonical models for the filtered A_∞ bimodules of the Λ_{nov} coefficients.

Theorem F follows immediately from Corollary 5.4.21.

5.4.3. Filtered A_∞ bimodules and complex of coherent sheaves. We next explain how a filtered A_∞ bimodule defines an object of the derived category of coherent sheaves on our formal scheme $\widehat{\mathcal{M}}(C, \mathfrak{m}) \times_{\Lambda_{0,nov}} \widehat{\mathcal{M}}(C', \mathfrak{m})$.

We first fix some notations. Let D be a (C, C') filtered A_∞ bimodule over $\Lambda_{0,nov}$. We assume that C, C' and D are gapped as before. (To simplify the notations, we use a (C, C') filtered A_∞ bimodule D instead of (C_1, C_0) filtered A_∞ bimodule D in this subsection.) We choose bases $\{\mathbf{v}_1, \cdots, \mathbf{v}_\ell\}$ of C^{odd} and $\{\mathbf{w}_1, \cdots, \mathbf{w}_m\}$ of C^{even} and write the corresponding formal coordinates as $s_1, \cdots, s_\ell$ and $h_1, \cdots, h_m$. We denote the corresponding objects for C' by putting primes. Let $D = \Lambda_{0,nov}^{\oplus d}$ and fix a basis $\mathbf{p}_1, \cdots, \mathbf{p}_d$ of D. (In the geometric situation of Lagrangian intersection Floer cohomology, $\mathbf{p}_i$'s correspond to intersection points of the pair of Lagrangian submanifolds or a basis of the cohomology group of $L^{(1)} \cap L^{(0)}$.) Let $\pi_i : D \to \Lambda_{0,nov}$ be the projection that maps each element of D to its coordinate of $\mathbf{p}_i$.

DEFINITION 5.4.22. We define

$$
\begin{aligned}
(5.4.23) \quad & Q_{i;j}(s_1, \cdots, h_\ell; s_1', \cdots, h_{\ell'}') \\
& = (\pi_j \circ \mathfrak{n})(\exp(s_1\mathbf{v}_1 + \cdots + h_\ell\mathbf{w}_\ell), \mathbf{p}_i, \exp(s_1'\mathbf{v}_1' + \cdots + h_{\ell'}'\mathbf{w}_{\ell'}')) \\
& \in \Lambda_{0,nov}[[s_1, \cdots, h_\ell]] \, \hat{\otimes} \, \Lambda_{0,nov}[[s_1', \cdots, h_{\ell'}']].
\end{aligned}
$$

The right hand side of (5.4.23) is understood in the same way as in (5.4.10). The map

$$
\mathbf{p}_i \mapsto \sum_j Q_{i;j}(s_1, \cdots, h_\ell; s_1', \cdots, h_{\ell'}') \cdot \mathbf{p}_j
$$

defines a homomorphism

$$
\mathfrak{Q}_0 : D \to \Lambda_{0,nov}[[s_1, \cdots, s_m; h_1, \cdots, h_\ell]] \hat{\otimes} D \, \hat{\otimes} \, \Lambda_{0,nov}[[s_1', \cdots, s_{m'}'; h_1', \cdots, h_{\ell'}']].
$$

Moreover $\mathfrak{Q}_0$ induces a bimodule homomorphism

$$
\begin{aligned}
\mathfrak{Q}_1 : & \Lambda_{0,nov}[[s_1, \cdots, s_m; h_1, \cdots, h_\ell]] \hat{\otimes} D \hat{\otimes} \Lambda_{0,nov}[[s_1', \cdots, s_{m'}'; h_1', \cdots, h_{\ell'}']] \\
& \to \Lambda_{0,nov}[[s_1, \cdots, s_m; h_1, \cdots, h_\ell]] \hat{\otimes} D \hat{\otimes} \Lambda_{0,nov}[[s_1', \cdots, s_{m'}'; h_1', \cdots, h_{\ell'}']]
\end{aligned}
$$

by

$$
\mathfrak{Q}_1(\mathbf{x}, y, \mathbf{z}) = (-1)^{\deg' \mathbf{x}} \mathbf{x} \otimes \mathfrak{Q}_0(y) \otimes \mathbf{z}.
$$

We define

$$
\begin{aligned}
\mathfrak{M}(D, \mathfrak{n}) = & (P_1, \cdots, P_{m+\ell}) \backslash \Lambda_{0,nov}[[s_1, \cdots, s_m; h_1, \cdots, h_\ell]] \\
& \hat{\otimes} \, D \, \hat{\otimes} \, \Lambda_{0,nov}[[s_1', \cdots, s_{m'}'; h_1', \cdots, h_{\ell'}']]/(P_1', \cdots, P_{m'+\ell'}'), \\
\mathfrak{M}(D, \mathfrak{n})^{bos} = & (P_{m+1}^{bos}, \cdots, P_{m+\ell}^{bos}) \backslash \Lambda_{0,nov}[[s_1, \cdots, s_m]] \\
& \hat{\otimes} \, D \, \hat{\otimes} \, \Lambda_{0,nov}[[s_1', \cdots, s_{m'}']]/(P_{m'+1}'^{bos}, \cdots, P_{m'+\ell'}'^{bos}).
\end{aligned}
$$

Here P_i (resp. P_i') are the super Kuranishi maps of C (resp. C').

Obviously $\mathfrak{M}(D, \mathfrak{n})$ is a $(\mathfrak{M}(C, \mathfrak{m}), \mathfrak{M}(C', \mathfrak{m}))$ bimodule and $\mathfrak{Q}_1$ induces a bimodule homomorphism $\mathfrak{Q} : \mathfrak{M}(D, \mathfrak{n}) \to \mathfrak{M}(D, \mathfrak{n})$.

PROPOSITION 5.4.24. *We have* $\mathfrak{Q}^2 = 0$.

PROOF. We put

$$\vec{s}\,\vec{v} = s_1 \mathbf{v}_1 + \cdots + s_m \mathbf{v}_m + h_1 \mathbf{w}_1 + \cdots + h_\ell \mathbf{w}_\ell$$

and similarly $\vec{s}'\vec{v}'$. Using the fact that $\mathfrak{n}$ is an A_∞ bi-comodule structure, we have

$$
\begin{aligned}
0 =& \mathfrak{n}\Big(\exp(\rho\vec{s}\vec{v}), \mathfrak{n}\Big(\exp(\vec{s}\vec{v}), \mathbf{p}_i, \exp(\vec{s}'\vec{v}') \Big), \exp(\vec{s}'\vec{v}') \Big) \\
&+ \mathfrak{n}\Big(\widehat{d}(\exp(\vec{s}\vec{v})), \mathbf{p}_i, \exp(\vec{s}'\vec{v}') \Big) \\
&+ (-1)^{\deg \mathbf{p}_i} \mathfrak{n}\Big(\exp(\rho\vec{s}\vec{v}), \mathbf{p}_i, \widehat{d}(\exp(\vec{s}'\vec{v}')) \Big).
\end{aligned}
$$

Here ρ is defined by

$$\rho(\mathbf{v}_i) = \mathbf{v}_i, \qquad \rho(\mathbf{w}_i) = -\mathbf{w}_i.$$

By definition of the super Kuranishi map, we derive that the second and the third terms are zero modulo the ideal generated by the super Kuranishi maps. It is easy to see that the first term gives $\mathfrak{Q}^2(\vec{s}\vec{v})$. $\qquad\square$

We have thus obtained a differential bimodule $(\mathfrak{M}(D, \mathfrak{n}), \mathfrak{Q})$ over a pair of differential graded algebras $(\mathfrak{M}(C, \mathfrak{m}), \mathfrak{M}(C', \mathfrak{m}))$. In particular, it gives a

$$\mathfrak{M}^{bos}(C, \mathfrak{m}) \otimes_{\Lambda_{0,nov}} \mathfrak{M}^{bos}(C', \mathfrak{m})$$

module with differential. Hence it defines a complex of sheaves $\mathfrak{M}(D, \mathfrak{n})^\sim$ on our formal scheme

$$\mathrm{Spf}(\mathfrak{M}^{bos}(C, \mathfrak{m})) \times_{\Lambda_{0,nov}} \mathrm{Spf}(\mathfrak{M}^{bos}(C', \mathfrak{m})).$$

(See [GrDi60].) This complex is coherent if D is finitely generated.

Let $b \in \widehat{\mathcal{M}}(C, \mathfrak{m})$ and $b' \in \widehat{\mathcal{M}}(C', \mathfrak{m})$. By Proposition 5.4.15, we identify them with continuous homomorphisms

$$i_b : \mathfrak{M}(C, \mathfrak{m}) \to \Lambda_{0,nov}, \quad i_{b'} : \mathfrak{M}(C', \mathfrak{m}) \to \Lambda_{0,nov}.$$

They determine a structure of $(\mathfrak{M}(C, \mathfrak{m}), \mathfrak{M}(C', \mathfrak{m}))$ bimodules on $\Lambda_{0,nov}$. We write $(\Lambda_{0,nov})_b$ and $_{b'}(\Lambda_{0,nov})$ for the corresponding left and right modules. The stalk of the sheaf $\mathfrak{M}(D, \mathfrak{n})^\sim$ is by definition (see [GrDi60]) given by

$$\mathfrak{M}(D, \mathfrak{n})^\sim_{b,b'} = (\Lambda_{0,nov})_b \otimes_{\mathfrak{M}(C,\mathfrak{m})} \mathfrak{M}(D, \mathfrak{n}) \otimes_{\mathfrak{M}(C',\mathfrak{m})} {}_{b'}(\Lambda_{0,nov}).$$

As a $\Lambda_{0,nov}$ module we find $\mathfrak{M}(D, \mathfrak{n})^\sim_{b,b'} \cong D$. However the differential induced on it by $\mathfrak{Q}$ *depends* on b, b'. The following immediately follows from the definition.

LEMMA 5.4.25. *The differential induced by* $\mathfrak{Q}$ *on* $\mathfrak{M}(D, \mathfrak{n})^\sim_{b,b'}$ *is nothing but* $\delta_{b,b'}$ *which is given by*

$$\delta_{b,b'}(\mathbf{p}) = \mathfrak{n}(e^b, \mathbf{p}, e^{b'}).$$

We also have the following

LEMMA 5.4.26. *If two* (C, C') *filtered* A_∞ *bimodules* D *and* D' *are isomorphic in the sense of Definition 5.4.3(3), then* $\mathfrak{M}(D, \mathfrak{n})^\sim$ *is isomorphic to* $\mathfrak{M}(D', \mathfrak{n})^\sim$ *as a complex of sheaves.*

PROOF. Let $\varphi : D \to D'$, $\varphi^{-1} : D' \to D$ be two filtered A_∞ homomorphisms over $(\mathfrak{f}, \mathfrak{g})$ with filtered A_∞ homomorphisms $\mathfrak{f} : C \to C$ and $\mathfrak{g} : C' \to C'$. Suppose that φ is an isomorphism and its inverse is φ^{-1}. Then φ naturally induces an isomorphism $\mathfrak{M}(D, \mathfrak{n})_{b,b'}^\sim \to \mathfrak{M}(D, \mathfrak{n})_{\mathfrak{f}(b),\mathfrak{g}(b')}^\sim$ in the stalk level at each $(b, b') \in \widehat{\mathcal{M}}(C, \mathfrak{m}) \times \widehat{\mathcal{M}}(C', \mathfrak{m}')$. Naturality of this stalk level isomorphism provides an isomorphism of complexes of sheaves. $\qquad\square$

In our geometric situation, this implies

COROLLARY 5.4.27. *Let $(L^{(1)}, L^{(0)})$ be a relatively spin pair of unobstructed Lagrangian submanifolds. Then we have an object of derived category of coherent sheaves $(\mathfrak{M}(L^{(1)}, L^{(0)})^\sim, \mathfrak{Q})$ such that it gives Floer cohomology at each $\Lambda_{0,nov}^+$ valued (rigid) points.*
$(\mathfrak{M}(L^{(1)}, L^{(0)})^\sim, \mathfrak{Q})$ is independent of the choice of compatible almost complex structure and other choices involved in the definition.

5.4.4. Construction of the canonical model.
Now we will prove Theorem 5.4.2 and 5.4.18 which have been postponed. The proofs we give below are similar to that in [**KoSo01**] and also similar to the construction of the Kuranishi map carried out in the preprint version [**FOOO00**] of this book which appeared in 2000 December.

PROOF OF THEOREM 5.4.2. We first need to define combinatorial analogies of Green's operator and of the Hodge-Kodaira decomposition theorem. We fix a subspace

$$\mathcal{H}^k \subset \operatorname{Ker} \overline{\mathfrak{m}}_1 \cap \overline{C}^k$$

so that restriction of the projection $\operatorname{Ker} \overline{\mathfrak{m}}_1 \cap \overline{C}^k \to H^k(\overline{C}; \overline{\mathfrak{m}}_1)$ to $\mathcal{H}^k$ becomes an isomorphism. The existence of such $\mathcal{H}^k$ follows from our assumption that $H^k(\overline{C}; \overline{\mathfrak{m}}_1)$ is a free R module and R is a field. We fix a projection $\operatorname{Ker} \overline{\mathfrak{m}}_1 \cap \overline{C}^k \to \mathcal{H}^k$ whose kernel coincides with $\operatorname{Im} \overline{\mathfrak{m}}_1 \cap \overline{C}^k$ and extend it to a map $\overline{C}^k \to \mathcal{H}^k$ in an arbitrary way. We denote the corresponding projection map such that $\operatorname{Im}(\Pi_{H,k}) = \mathcal{H}^k$ by $\Pi_{H,k} : \overline{C}^k \to \overline{C}^k$ and put $\Pi_H = \sum_k \Pi_{H,k}$.

LEMMA 5.4.28. *There exists a sequence of R module homomorphisms $\mathfrak{G}_k : \overline{C}^k \to \overline{C}^{k-1}$ such that*

$$1 - \Pi_{H,k} = -\overline{\mathfrak{m}}_1 \circ \mathfrak{G}_k - \mathfrak{G}_{k+1} \circ \overline{\mathfrak{m}}_1, \qquad \mathfrak{G}_k \circ \mathfrak{G}_{k+1} = 0.$$

PROOF. We can find a subspace $F_k \subset \overline{C}^k$ such that $F_k \oplus \operatorname{Im} \overline{\mathfrak{m}}_1 = \operatorname{Ker} \Pi_{H,k}$. It is easy to see that $\overline{\mathfrak{m}}_1$ induces an isomorphism $: F_k \cong \operatorname{Im} \overline{\mathfrak{m}}_1 \cap \overline{C}^{k+1}$. Let $-\mathfrak{G}_{k+1}$ be the inverse of it on $\operatorname{Im} \overline{\mathfrak{m}}_1$. We put it zero on $F_k + \mathcal{H}^k$. The lemma easily follows from this. $\qquad\square$

REMARK 5.4.29. We use the assumption R is a field only in this lemma and Lemma 5.4.51 below.

Let $G \subset \mathbb{R}_{\geq 0} \times 2\mathbb{Z}$ be as in Condition 3.1.6. Let $\{\lambda_i \mid i \in 0, 1, 2, \cdots\}$ be the projection of G to $\mathbb{R}_{\geq 0}$ such that such that $\lambda_0 = 0$ and $i < j \Rightarrow \lambda_i < \lambda_j$. We assume that all filtered A_∞ algebras and modules are G gapped. Then we can put

$$(5.4.30.1) \qquad \mathfrak{m}_k = \sum_i \mathfrak{m}_{k,i} T^{\lambda_i},$$

where $\mathfrak{m}_{k,i}$ does not contain T. That is,

$$\mathfrak{m}_{k,i} \ : \ B_k \overline{C}[1] \otimes R[e, e^{-1}] \to \overline{C}[1] \otimes R[e, e^{-1}].$$

We write

$$(5.4.30.2) \qquad \mathfrak{m}_{k,i}^\circ = \mathfrak{m}_{k,i} T^{\lambda_i}.$$

We set

$$C_{can} = \mathcal{H} \otimes \Lambda_{0,nov}$$

and will define a filtered A_∞ structure $\mathfrak{m}'(= \mathfrak{m}_{can})$ on it. The idea is that the operation $\mathfrak{m}'_k$ is defined as a sum over "trees".

We first extend $\Pi_{H,k}$ and $\mathfrak{G}_k$ as

$$\Pi_{H,k} \ : \ \overline{C}^k \otimes R[e, e^{-1}] \to \overline{C}^k \otimes R[e, e^{-1}]$$
$$\mathfrak{G}_k \ : \ \overline{C}^k \otimes R[e, e^{-1}] \to \overline{C}^{k-1} \otimes R[e, e^{-1}]$$

in an obvious way and use the same symbols.

We define the set G_k^+ of trees as follows. G_k^+ is a small modification of the moduli space G_k of the ribbon trees introduced in Section 3.4. Namely an element of G_k^+ is the 5-tuple $(T, i, v_0, V_{\mathrm{tad}}, \eta)$ such that:

(5.4.31.1) (T, i, v_0) satisfies Condition (3.4.1.3). (But it does not necessarily satisfy (3.4.1.1), (3.4.1.2). Namely T may have a vertex with two edges and may have interior vertex with one edge.)

(5.4.31.2) V_{tad} is a, possibly empty, subset of the set of all vertices with one edges. The set of all vertices with one edge is a disjoint union of $C_{\mathrm{ext}}^0(T)$ and V_{tad}. $v_0 \in C_{\mathrm{ext}}^0(T)$. We put $C_{\mathrm{int}}^0(T) = C^0(T) \setminus C_{\mathrm{ext}}^0(T)$ and $k = \#C_{\mathrm{ext}}^0(T)$. $C_{\mathrm{ext}}^0(T) = T \cap i^{-1}(\partial D^2)$.

(5.4.31.3) $\eta : C_{\mathrm{int}}^0(T) \to \{0, 1, 2, \cdots\}$ is a map. We require that if v is a vertex with two or one edge(s) then $\eta(v) > 0$.

We call an element of V_{tad} a *tad pole*. We regard it as an interior vertex. In other words, by choosing V_{tad}, we can specify the sets $C_{\mathrm{ext}}^0(T)$ and $C_{\mathrm{int}}^0(T)$.

Now for each $\Gamma = (T, i, v_0, V_{\mathrm{tad}}, \eta) \in G_{k+1}^+$, we will associate two homomorphisms

(5.4.32.1) $\mathfrak{m}_\Gamma : B_k \mathcal{H}[1] \otimes R[e, e^{-1}] \to \mathcal{H}[1] \otimes R[e, e^{-1}]$ of degree $+1$,

and

(5.4.32.2) $\mathfrak{f}_\Gamma : B_k \mathcal{H}[1] \otimes R[e, e^{-1}] \to \overline{C}[1] \otimes R[e, e^{-1}]$ of degree 0.

The definition of the operators (5.4.32) will be given by induction on the order of Γ, which we define below.

For $\Gamma = (T, i, v_0, V_{\mathrm{tad}}, \eta) \in G_{k+1}^+$ we define its energy $E(\Gamma)$ by

$$E(\Gamma) = \sum_{v \in C_{\mathrm{int}}^0(T)} \lambda_{\eta(v)}.$$

Let $\Gamma' = (T', i', v_0', V_{\text{tad}}', \eta') \in G_{k'+1}^+$. We say that $\Gamma' > \Gamma$ if one of the following holds.

(5.4.33.1) $E(\Gamma') > E(\Gamma)$.
(5.4.33.2) $E(\Gamma') = E(\Gamma)$ and $k' > k$.

We first consider the case

$$\#(C_{\text{int}}^0(T)) = 0.$$

In this case, there is only one element Γ_0 which has no interior vertex. We then put

$$\mathfrak{m}_{\Gamma_0} = 0, \qquad \mathfrak{f}_{\Gamma_0} = \text{inclusion} : \overline{\mathcal{H}}[1] \to \overline{C}[1].$$

Now consider $\Gamma = (T, i, v_0, V_{\text{tad}}, \eta) \in G_k^+$ with $\#(C_{\text{int}}^0(T)) = 1$. We note that there exists a unique such element $\Gamma_{k,\eta} = (T_k, i, v_0, V_{\text{tad}}, \eta)$ for each k and η. Here $k = 1, 2, \cdots$ and $\eta = 0, 1, 2, \cdots, (k, \eta) \neq (1, 0), (2, 0)$. (Note that η in this case may be regarded as a number $\eta = \eta(v) \in \{0, 1, 2, \cdots\}$.) (See Figure 5.4.1). Let v be the unique inner vertex of T_k. (In case $k = 0$, the vertex v is a tad pole.) We remark that in the figure we put v_0 on the top and $\Gamma_1, \ldots, \Gamma_\ell$ in counter clockwise order.

We define

(5.4.34) $$\begin{cases} \mathfrak{m}_{\Gamma_{k+1,\eta}} = \Pi_H \circ \mathfrak{m}_{k,\eta(v)} : B_k\overline{C}[1] \otimes R[e, e^{-1}] \to \mathcal{H}[1] \otimes R[e, e^{-1}] \\ \mathfrak{f}_{\Gamma_{k+1,\eta}} = \mathfrak{G} \circ \mathfrak{m}_{k,\eta(v)} : B_k\mathcal{H}[1] \otimes R[e, e^{-1}] \to \overline{C}[1] \otimes R[e, e^{-1}]. \end{cases}$$

Here $\mathfrak{m}_{k,\eta(v)}$ in the right hand side is the one given by (5.4.30.1). We remark that in cases $k = 1$ and $k = 2$, $\eta(v) > 0$ by assumption (5.4.31.3). This leads to the properties that $\overline{\mathfrak{m}}_0' = \overline{\mathfrak{m}}_1' = 0$ in the canonical model.

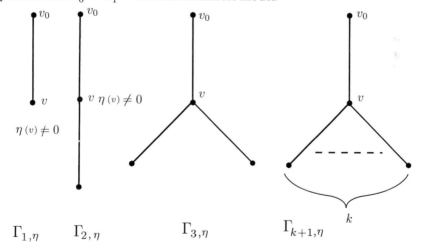

Figure 5.4.1

Next consider $\Gamma = (T, i, v_0, \eta) \in G_{k+1}^+$ with $\#(C_{\text{int}}^0(T)) > 1$. Let v_1 be the unique vertex connected with v_0 with one edge. Suppose that v_1 has $\ell + 1$ edges, labeled as $e_0, \cdots, e_\ell$. We enumerate them in the counter-clockwise order with respect to the embedding $i : T \to D^2$, starting from e_0 joining v_1 and v_0.

We cut the graph T at the mid point of the edges $e_1, \cdots, e_\ell$. Then we have ℓ elements $\Gamma_1 \in G_{k_1+1}^+, \cdots, \Gamma_\ell \in G_{k_\ell+1}^+$ such that $k = \sum_i k_i$. (See Figure 5.4.2.)

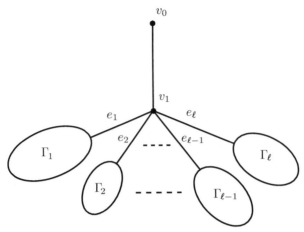

Figure 5.4.2

LEMMA 5.4.35. $\Gamma_i < \Gamma$ for all i.

PROOF. Since

$$\sum E(\Gamma_i) + \lambda_{\eta(v_1)} = E(\Gamma),$$

the lemma is obvious in case $\lambda_{\eta(v_1)} > 0$. Let us assume $\lambda_{\eta(v_1)} = 0$. Hence $\ell \geq 2$. If $E(\Gamma_i) < E(\Gamma)$ then $\Gamma_i < \Gamma$. If $E(\Gamma_i) = E(\Gamma)$, then there is no tad pole on $\Gamma \setminus \Gamma_i$. Therefore $\ell \geq 2$ implies that there exists an exterior vertex on $\Gamma \setminus \Gamma_i$. It follows that $k_i < k$. $\qquad\square$

Writing

$$\Delta^{\ell-1}\mathbf{x} = \sum_a \mathbf{x}_a^{(1)} \otimes \cdots \otimes \mathbf{x}_a^{(\ell)}$$

for $\mathbf{x} \in B_k\mathcal{H}[1] \otimes R[e, e^{-1}]$, we define

(5.4.36)
$$\begin{cases} \mathfrak{m}_\Gamma(\mathbf{x}) = \displaystyle\sum_a \Pi_H \circ \mathfrak{m}_{\ell,\lambda_{\eta(v_1)}}\big(\mathfrak{f}_{\Gamma_1}(\mathbf{x}_a^{(1)}) \otimes \cdots \otimes \mathfrak{f}_{\Gamma_\ell}(\mathbf{x}_a^{(\ell)})\big) \\[2mm] \mathfrak{f}_\Gamma(\mathbf{x}) = \displaystyle\sum_a \mathfrak{G} \circ \mathfrak{m}_{\ell,\lambda_{\eta(v_1)}}\big(\mathfrak{f}_{\Gamma_1}(\mathbf{x}_a^{(1)}) \otimes \cdots \otimes \mathfrak{f}_{\Gamma_\ell}(\mathbf{x}_a^{(\ell)})\big). \end{cases}$$

Here we put $\mathfrak{f}_{\Gamma_i}(\mathbf{x}_a^{(i)}) = 0$ unless $\mathbf{x}_a^{(i)} \in B_{k_i}\mathcal{H}[1] \otimes R[e, e^{-1}]$. (In view of Lemma 5.4.35, the right hand side is already defined.)

Now we define

DEFINITION 5.4.37.

$$\mathfrak{m}_k' = \sum_{\Gamma \in G_{k+1}^+} T^{E(\Gamma)}\mathfrak{m}_\Gamma, \qquad \mathfrak{f}_k = \sum_{\Gamma \in G_{k+1}^+} T^{E(\Gamma)}\mathfrak{f}_\Gamma.$$

We will prove that $\mathfrak{m}_k'$ defines a filtered A_∞ structure on C_{can} with $\overline{\mathfrak{m}}_1 = 0$ and that $\mathfrak{f}_k$ defines an A_∞ homomorphism from $(C_{can}, \mathfrak{m}')$ to $(C, \mathfrak{m})$.

Let $\widehat{\mathfrak{f}}$ be the coalgebra homomorphism induced by $\mathfrak{f}_k$, and $\widehat{\mathfrak{m}}_k'$ be the coderivation induced by $\mathfrak{m}_k'$. We put $\widehat{d}' = \sum \widehat{\mathfrak{m}}_k'$.

LEMMA 5.4.38. $\widehat{\mathfrak{f}} \circ \widehat{d}' = \widehat{d} \circ \widehat{\mathfrak{f}}$.

PROOF. We define an order on $\{(k,i) \mid k,i \in \mathbb{Z}_{\geq 0}\}$ by $(k',i') < (k,i)$ if and only if $i' < i$ or $i' = i, k' < k$. We will prove

$$(5.4.39.(k,i)) \qquad \widehat{\mathfrak{f}} \circ \widehat{d'} \equiv \widehat{d} \circ \widehat{\mathfrak{f}} \mod T^{\lambda_i} \qquad \text{on } B_k C_{can}[1]$$

by induction on this order. To start the induction we remark that the first step of the induction: $(5.4.39.(k,0))$ is trivial by definition $\mathfrak{m}_{\Gamma_0} = 0$, $\mathfrak{f}_{\Gamma_0} = $ inclusion.

Now we assume that $(5.4.39.(k',i'))$ for any (k',i') smaller than (k,i) and will prove $(5.4.39.(k,i))$. We note that the following identities hold:

$$(5.4.40) \qquad \begin{cases} \mathfrak{f}_k = \displaystyle\sum_{(\ell,j) \neq (1,0)} \mathfrak{G} \circ \mathfrak{m}_{\ell,j}^{\circ} \circ \widehat{\mathfrak{f}} & \text{on } B_k C_{can}[1], \\ \mathfrak{m}_k' = \displaystyle\sum_{(\ell,j) \neq (1,0)} \Pi_H \circ \mathfrak{m}_{\ell,j}^{\circ} \circ \widehat{\mathfrak{f}} & \text{on } B_k C_{can}[1]. \end{cases}$$

Here $\mathfrak{G}$ and Π_H are trivially extended over $\Lambda_{0,nov}$. We calculate $\widehat{d} \circ \widehat{\mathfrak{f}}$ on $B_k C_{can}[1]$

$$(5.4.41) \qquad \begin{aligned} \widehat{d} \circ \widehat{\mathfrak{f}} &= \mathfrak{m}_{1,0}^{\circ} \circ \widehat{\mathfrak{f}} + \sum_{(\ell,j) \neq (1,0)} \mathfrak{m}_{\ell,j}^{\circ} \circ \widehat{\mathfrak{f}} \\ &= \sum_{\Gamma \in G_{k+1}} T^{E(\Gamma)} \mathfrak{m}_{1,0}^{\circ} \circ \mathfrak{f}_\Gamma + \sum_{(\ell,j) \neq (1,0)} \mathfrak{m}_{\ell,j}^{\circ} \circ \widehat{\mathfrak{f}} \\ &= \sum_{(\ell,j) \neq (1,0)} \mathfrak{m}_{1,0}^{\circ} \circ \mathfrak{G} \circ \mathfrak{m}_{\ell,j}^{\circ} \circ \widehat{\mathfrak{f}} + \sum_{(\ell,j) \neq (1,0)} \mathfrak{m}_{\ell,j}^{\circ} \circ \widehat{\mathfrak{f}}. \end{aligned}$$

We apply Lemma 5.4.28 to the first term. Then one of the terms of Lemma 5.4.28 cancels with the second term of $(5.4.41)$ which leaves us

$$(5.4.42) \qquad \widehat{d} \circ \widehat{\mathfrak{f}} = - \sum_{(\ell,j) \neq (1,0)} \mathfrak{G} \circ \mathfrak{m}_{1,0}^{\circ} \circ \mathfrak{m}_{\ell,j}^{\circ} \circ \widehat{\mathfrak{f}} + \sum_{(\ell,j) \neq (1,0)} \Pi_H \circ \mathfrak{m}_{\ell,j}^{\circ} \circ \widehat{\mathfrak{f}}.$$

The second term here is nothing but $\mathfrak{m}_k' = \widehat{d'} = \mathfrak{f}_{\Gamma_0} \circ \widehat{d'}$ on $B_k C_{can}[1]$. On the other hand, it follows from the A_∞ formulae that the first term is equal to $\sum_{(\ell,j) \neq (1,0)} \mathfrak{G} \circ \mathfrak{m}_{\ell,j}^{\circ} \circ \widehat{d} \circ \widehat{\mathfrak{f}}$. Thus we have

$$(5.4.43) \qquad \widehat{d} \circ \widehat{\mathfrak{f}} = \sum_{(\ell,j) \neq (1,0)} \mathfrak{G} \circ \mathfrak{m}_{\ell,j}^{\circ} \circ \widehat{d} \circ \widehat{\mathfrak{f}} + \mathfrak{f}_{\Gamma_0} \circ \widehat{d'}.$$

We want to prove that the first term of $(5.4.43)$ is congruent to $\sum_{(\ell,j) \neq (1,0)} \mathfrak{G} \circ \mathfrak{m}_{\ell,j}^{\circ} \circ \widehat{\mathfrak{f}} \circ \widehat{d'}$ modulo T^{λ_i}.

We first consider the case when $\ell = 0, 1$. In this case (using $\mathfrak{m}_{0,0} = 0$) we find that $j > 0$. Namely $\mathfrak{m}_{\ell,j}^{\circ} \equiv 0 \mod T^{\lambda_1}$. By induction hypothesis, we have $\widehat{\mathfrak{f}} \circ \widehat{d'} \equiv \widehat{d} \circ \widehat{\mathfrak{f}} \mod T^{\lambda_{i-1}}$. Hence we obtain

$$(5.4.44) \qquad \mathfrak{G} \circ \mathfrak{m}_{\ell,j}^{\circ} \circ \widehat{d} \circ \widehat{\mathfrak{f}} \equiv \mathfrak{G} \circ \mathfrak{m}_{\ell,j}^{\circ} \circ \widehat{\mathfrak{f}} \circ \widehat{d'} \mod T^{\lambda_i},$$

if $\ell = 0, 1$ and $(\ell,j) \neq (1,0)$. We next consider the case when $\ell \geq 2$. Let $\mathbf{x} \in B_k C[1]$. We consider $B_\ell C[1]$ component of $(\widehat{\mathfrak{f}} \circ \widehat{d'})(\mathbf{x})$. We write it as $(\widehat{\mathfrak{f}} \circ \widehat{d'})_\ell(\mathbf{x})$. We then have

$$(\widehat{\mathfrak{f}} \circ \widehat{d'})_\ell(\mathbf{x}) = \sum_a \sum_j (-1)^{\deg' \mathbf{x}_{1;a} + \cdots + \deg' \mathbf{x}_{j-1;a}}$$

(5.4.45)

$$\mathfrak{f}(\mathbf{x}_{1;a}) \otimes \cdots \otimes (\mathfrak{f} \circ \widehat{d'})(\mathbf{x}_{j;a}) \otimes \cdots \otimes \mathfrak{f}(\mathbf{x}_{\ell;a}).$$

(Here we use (Conv.3) (1.35).) Let us define the integer $k_{j,a}$ by the one for which $\mathbf{x}_{j;a} \in B_{k_{j;a}} C[1]$. We have

(5.4.46)
$$\sum_j k_{j;a} = k.$$

Now we apply induction hypothesis to find

(5.4.47)
$$\mathfrak{f}(\mathbf{x}_{1;a}) \otimes \cdots \otimes (\mathfrak{f} \circ \widehat{d'})(\mathbf{x}_{j;a}) \otimes \cdots \otimes \mathfrak{f}(\mathbf{x}_{\ell;a})$$
$$\equiv \mathfrak{f}(\mathbf{x}_{1;a}) \otimes \cdots \otimes (\mathfrak{m} \circ \widehat{\mathfrak{f}})(\mathbf{x}_{j;a}) \otimes \cdots \otimes \mathfrak{f}(\mathbf{x}_{\ell;a}) \mod T^{\lambda_i},$$

if $k_{j,a} < k$ for all j.

Finally we consider the case $k_{j,a} = k$ for some j. Then $k_{j',a} = 0$ for $j' \neq j$ by (5.4.46). Namely in this case

$$\mathfrak{f}(\mathbf{x}_{1;a}) \otimes \cdots \otimes (\mathfrak{f} \circ \widehat{d'})(\mathbf{x}_{j;a}) \otimes \cdots \otimes \mathfrak{f}(\mathbf{x}_{\ell;a}) = \mathfrak{f}(1)^{\otimes(j-1)} \otimes (\mathfrak{f} \circ \widehat{d'})(\mathbf{x}) \otimes \mathfrak{f}(1)^{\otimes(\ell-j)}.$$

By assumption we find $\mathfrak{f}(1) \equiv 0 \mod T^{\lambda_1}$. Hence using $\ell \geq 2$ and induction hypothesis $(\mathfrak{f} \circ \widehat{d'})(\mathbf{x}) \equiv (\mathfrak{m} \circ \widehat{\mathfrak{f}})(\mathbf{x}) \mod T^{\lambda_{i-1}}$, we have proven that (5.4.47) holds also in this case.

Now (5.4.44), (5.4.47) and (5.4.36) imply

$$\sum_{(\ell,j)\neq(1,0)} \mathfrak{G} \circ \mathfrak{m}_{\ell,j}^\circ \circ \widehat{d} \circ \widehat{\mathfrak{f}} \equiv \left(\sum_{(\ell,j)\neq(1,0)} \mathfrak{G} \circ \mathfrak{m}_{\ell,j}^\circ \circ \widehat{\mathfrak{f}} \right) \circ \widehat{d'} \equiv (\widehat{\mathfrak{f}} - \mathfrak{f}_{\Gamma_0}) \circ \widehat{d'} \mod T^{\lambda_i}.$$

This together with (5.4.43) finishes the proof of the lemma. □

We remark that $\widehat{\mathfrak{f}}$ is injective because $\mathfrak{f}_{\Gamma_0} =$ inclusion and $\widehat{\mathfrak{f}}$ is the inclusion modulo $\Lambda_{0,nov}^+$. Therefore Lemma 5.4.38 implies that $\widehat{d'} \circ \widehat{d'} = 0$ and then intern implies that $\mathfrak{f}$ is an A_∞ homomorphism. It is easy to see from the construction that $\mathfrak{f}$ induces an isomorphism on the cohomology. Theorem 5.4.2 now follows from Theorem 4.2.45. □

PROOF OF THEOREM 5.4.2′. We finally prove the statement on unit. In case when $(C, \mathfrak{m})$ is homotopy-unital, we start the construction from $(C^+, \mathfrak{m}^+)$ as in Definition 3.3.2. So it suffices to consider the case $(C, \mathfrak{m})$ is unital. We may choose $\mathcal{H}$ so that it contains unit $\mathbf{e}$. We will prove:

(5.4.48.1) $\mathfrak{f}_\Gamma(y_1 \otimes \cdots \otimes y_\ell \otimes \mathbf{e} \otimes z_1 \otimes \cdots \otimes z_{k-\ell}) = 0, \quad k > 0$

and

(5.4.48.2) $\mathfrak{f}_\Gamma(\mathbf{e}) = 0, \quad E(\Gamma) > 0$
(5.4.48.3) $\mathfrak{f}_{\Gamma_0}(\mathbf{e}) = \mathbf{e}, \quad E(\Gamma_0) = 0$

by induction on the order $>$ on Γ defined by (5.4.33). We use the notation of (5.4.36). We consider the case $\mathbf{x} = \mathbf{y} \otimes \mathbf{e} \otimes \mathbf{z}$. Then, by induction hypothesis, $\mathfrak{f}_\Gamma(\mathbf{x}) = 0$ unless

$$(5.4.49) \qquad \mathfrak{f}_\Gamma(\mathbf{x}) = \sum_{a,b} (\mathfrak{G} \circ \mathfrak{m}_{\ell,\lambda_{\eta(v)}}) (\mathfrak{f}_{\Gamma_{1,1}}(\mathbf{y}_a^1) \otimes \cdots \otimes \mathfrak{f}_{\Gamma_{1,\alpha}}(\mathbf{y}_a^\alpha)$$

$$\otimes\, \mathbf{e} \otimes \mathfrak{f}_{\Gamma_{2,1}}(\mathbf{z}_b^1) \otimes \cdots \otimes \mathfrak{f}_{\Gamma_{2,\beta}}(\mathbf{z}_b^\beta)).$$

Since $\mathbf{e}$ is unit, (5.4.49) is zero unless $\alpha + \beta = 1$, $\lambda(v) = 0$. In that case we have

$$(5.4.50) \qquad \mathfrak{f}_\Gamma(\mathbf{x}) = \mathfrak{G}(\mathfrak{f}_{\Gamma_1}(\mathbf{y})) \quad \text{or} \quad \pm\,\mathfrak{G}(\mathfrak{f}_{\Gamma_2}(\mathbf{z})).$$

We first consider $\mathfrak{G}(\mathfrak{f}_{\Gamma_1}(\mathbf{y}))$.

Suppose $k > 1$ or $E(\Gamma_1) > 0$. Then $\mathfrak{f}_{\Gamma_1}(\mathbf{y}) \in \operatorname{Im} \mathfrak{G}$ by (5.4.40). Since $\mathfrak{G} \circ \mathfrak{G} = 0$, it follows that (5.4.50) is zero in this case.

If $k = 1$ and $E(\Gamma_1) = 0$ then $\mathfrak{G}(\mathfrak{f}_{\Gamma_1}(\mathbf{y})) = y_1$. Since $y_1 \in \mathcal{H}$, it follows that $\mathfrak{G}(y_1) = 0$. Hence $\mathfrak{f}_\Gamma(\mathbf{x}) = 0$. The case $\mathfrak{G}(\mathfrak{f}_{\Gamma_2}(\mathbf{z}))$ is similar. We thus proved (5.4.48).

Using (5.4.48) we can prove that $\mathbf{e}$ is a unit the canonical model in a similar way. Then (5.4.48) again implies that $\mathfrak{f}$ is unital.

We have finished the proof of Theorem 5.4.2′. $\square$

We next prove Theorem 5.4.18.

PROOF OF THEOREM 5.4.18. We start with the following analogue of Lemma 5.4.28. Let D be as in Theorem 5.4.18. Let $\overline{D}$ be an unfiltered A_∞ bimodule such that $D = \overline{D} \otimes \Lambda_{0,nov}$. We fix a subspace

$$\mathcal{H}^k \subset \operatorname{Ker} \overline{\mathfrak{n}}_{0,0} \cap \overline{D}^k,$$

so that restriction of the projection $\operatorname{Ker} \overline{\mathfrak{n}}_{0,0} \cap \overline{C}^k \to H^k(\overline{C}; \overline{\mathfrak{n}}_{0,0})$ to $\mathcal{H}^k$ is an isomorphism. (We recall that we assumed that $H^k(\overline{C}; \overline{\mathfrak{n}}_{0,0})$ is free.) There exists a projection $\operatorname{Ker} \overline{\mathfrak{n}}_{0,0} \cap \overline{C}^k \to \mathcal{H}^k$ whose kernel coincides with $\operatorname{Im} \overline{\mathfrak{n}}_{0,0} \cap \overline{C}^k$. We extend the projection to $\overline{C}^k \to \mathcal{H}^k$ in an arbitrary way. We write corresponding idempotent map $\overline{C}^k \to \overline{C}^k$ whose image is $\mathcal{H}^k$ by $\Pi_{H,k}$. We put $\Pi_H = \sum_k \Pi_{H,k}$.

LEMMA 5.4.51. *There exists a sequence of maps* $\mathfrak{G}_k : \overline{D}^k \to \overline{D}^{k-1}$ *such that*

$$1 - \Pi_{H,k} = -\overline{\mathfrak{n}}_{0,0} \circ \mathfrak{G}_k - \mathfrak{G}_{k+1} \circ \overline{\mathfrak{n}}_{0,0}, \quad \mathfrak{G}_{k+1} \circ \mathfrak{G}_k = 0.$$

The proof is the same as that of Lemma 5.4.28 and is omitted. We put

$$\mathfrak{n}_{k_1,k_0} = \sum_i T^{\lambda_i} \mathfrak{n}_{k_1,k_0;i}$$

where $\mathfrak{n}_{k_1,k_0,i}$ does not contain T.

We can define a structure of A_∞ bimodule $\mathfrak{n}'$ on $D' = H(\overline{D}, \overline{\mathfrak{n}}_{0,0}) \otimes \Lambda_{0,nov}$ and the A_∞ bimodule homomorphism $\varphi : D' \to D$ by using the Feynman diagram as in Figure 5.4.3 as follows.

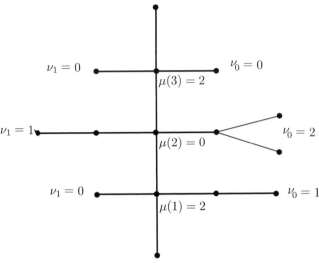

Figure 5.4.3

Let k be a nonnegative integer.

DEFINITION 5.4.52. We define $\Theta(k)$ to be the set of all triples (ν_1, μ, ν_0) such that $\nu_i : \{1, \cdots, k\} \to \mathbb{Z}_{\geq 0}$ $(i = 0, 1)$, $\mu : \{1, \cdots, k\} \to \mathbb{Z}_{\geq 0}$ such that

$$(5.4.53) \qquad \nu_1(i) + \mu(i) + \nu_0(i) > 0 \qquad \text{for any } i = 1, \cdots, k.$$

We put

$$|\nu_1| = \sum \nu_1(i), \quad |\mu| = \sum \lambda_{\mu(i)}, \quad |\nu_0| = \sum \nu_0(i).$$

We remark that Figure 5.4.3 corresponds to $\nu_1(1) = \nu_1(3) = \nu_0(3) = 0$, $\nu_1(2) = 1$, $\nu_0(1) = 1$, $\nu_0(2) = 2$, $\mu(1) = 2, \mu(2) = 0, \mu(3) = 2$.

We are going to define

$$(5.4.54) \qquad \begin{cases} \varphi_{(\nu_1,\mu,\nu_0)} : B_{|\nu_1|}C_1[1] \otimes D'[1] \otimes B_{|\nu_0|}C_0[1] \to D[1] \\ \mathfrak{n}'_{(\nu_1,\mu,\nu_0)} : B_{|\nu_1|}C_1[1] \otimes D'[1] \otimes B_{|\nu_0|}C_0[1] \to D'[1] \end{cases}$$

for each $(\nu_1, \mu, \nu_0) \in \Theta(k)$. The definition will be given inductively over k. In the case $k = 0$, there is the unique element in $\Theta(0)$ which we write $\emptyset$. For this, we just put $\varphi_\emptyset = id$, $\mathfrak{n}'_\emptyset = \mathfrak{n}_{0,0;0}$. Now suppose we have defined (5.4.54) for $k - 1$ and let $(\nu_1, \mu, \nu_0) \in \Theta(k)$. We denote by $(\nu'_1, \mu', \nu'_0) \in \Theta(k-1)$ the restriction of each component to $\{1, \cdots, k-1\}$. We define

$$(5.4.55) \qquad \begin{aligned} &\varphi_{(\nu_1,\mu,\nu_0)}(\mathbf{x} \otimes y \otimes \mathbf{z}) \\ &= \sum_{a,b} \mathfrak{G} \circ \mathfrak{n}_{\nu_1(k),\mu(k);\nu_0(k)}(\mathbf{x}_a^{(1)} \otimes \varphi_{(\nu'_1,\mu',\nu'_0)}(\mathbf{x}_a^{(2)} \otimes y \otimes \mathbf{z}_b^{(1)}) \otimes \mathbf{z}_b^{(2)}), \end{aligned}$$

$$(5.4.56) \qquad \begin{aligned} &\mathfrak{n}'_{(\nu_1,\mu,\nu_0)}(\mathbf{x} \otimes y \otimes \mathbf{z}) \\ &= \sum_{a,b} \Pi_H \circ \mathfrak{n}_{\nu_1(k),\mu(k);\nu_0(k)}(\mathbf{x}_a^{(1)} \otimes \varphi_{(\nu'_1,\mu',\nu'_0)}(\mathbf{x}_a^{(2)} \otimes y \otimes \mathbf{z}_b^{(1)}) \otimes \mathbf{z}_b^{(2)}). \end{aligned}$$

Here $\mathfrak{G}$ and Π_H are trivially extended to $\overline{C} \otimes R[e, e^{-1}]$ and $\overline{D} \otimes R[e, e^{-1}]$ respectively as in the proof of Theorem 5.4.2. For example Figure 5.4.3 corresponds to

$$\varphi_{(3,\mu,1)}(x \otimes y \otimes z_1 \otimes z_2 \otimes z_3)$$
$$= \mathfrak{G} \circ \mathfrak{n}_{0,0,2} \left(\mathfrak{G} \mathfrak{n}_{1,2;0}(x \otimes \mathfrak{n}_{0,1;1}(y \otimes z_1) \otimes z_2 \otimes z_3) \right)$$

and

$$\mathfrak{n}'_{(3,\mu,1)}(x \otimes y \otimes z_1 \otimes z_2 \otimes z_3)$$
$$= \Pi \circ \mathfrak{n}_{0,0,2} \left(\mathfrak{G} \mathfrak{n}_{1,2;0}(x \otimes \mathfrak{n}_{0,1;1}(y \otimes z_1) \otimes z_2 \otimes z_3) \right).$$

We then have

$$\mathfrak{n}'_{k_1,k_0} = \sum_{k_1 = |\nu_1|} \sum_{k_0 = |\nu_0|} T^{|\mu|} \mathfrak{n}_{(\nu_1,\mu,\nu_0)}, \quad \varphi_{k_1,k_0} = \sum_{k_1 = |\nu_1|} \sum_{k_0 = |\nu_0|} T^{|\mu|} \varphi_{(\nu_1,\mu,\nu_0)}.$$

We can check that $\mathfrak{n}'_{k_1,k_0}$ defines a structure of filtered A_∞ bimodule and φ_{k_1,k_0} defines a homotopy equivalence $D' \to D$ in the same way as in the proof of Theorem 5.4.2. Furthermore it follows that D' satisfies all the properties of the canonical model. In case when D is (homotopy) unital, we can prove that the canonical model is unital in the same way as the proof of Theorem 5.4.2'. The proof of Theorem 5.4.18 is now complete. □

5.4.5. Including the operator $\mathfrak{q}$. In this subsection we combine our discussion of the canonical model with the discussion of the bulk deformation of filtered A_∞ algebra $(H(L; \Lambda_{0,nov}), \mathfrak{m})$. For this discussion, we take the $\mathbb{Q}$ coefficients. Let $b = \operatorname{rank} H^{even}(M; \mathbb{Q})$. We choose a basis c_i of it. Let $2d_i = \deg c_i$. We put $\mathbf{c}_i = e^{d_i - 1} c_i \in H^2(M; \Lambda_{0,nov}^+)$. We choose a formal parameter $r_1, \cdots, r_b$ and put

$$\mathcal{R} = \mathbb{Q}[[r_1, \cdots, r_b]], \qquad \Lambda_{0,nov}(\mathcal{R}) = \Lambda_{0,nov} \otimes_R \mathcal{R}.$$

We are going to define a filtered A_∞ algebra $(C(L; \Lambda_{0,nov}(\mathcal{R})), \mathfrak{m}^{\mathcal{R}})$ over $\Lambda_{0,nov}(\mathcal{R})$ using the operator $\mathfrak{q}$.

Let $\mathbf{x} \in B_k C(L; \Lambda_{0,nov}(\mathcal{R}))[1]$.

DEFINITION 5.4.57.

(5.4.58)
$$\mathfrak{m}_k^{\mathcal{R}}(\mathbf{x}) = \mathfrak{q}\left(\exp\left(\sum r_i \mathbf{c}_i \right); \mathbf{x} \right).$$

The right hand side (5.4.58) can be written as

$$\sum_{k, i_1, i_2, \cdots, i_k} r_{i_1} \cdots r_{i_k} \mathfrak{q}\left(\mathbf{c}_{i_1} \cdots \mathbf{c}_{i_k}; \mathbf{x} \right) \in C(L; \Lambda_{0,nov}(\mathcal{R})).$$

We can extend $\mathfrak{m}_k^{\mathcal{R}}$ to $\mathfrak{m}_k^{\mathcal{R}} : B_k C(L; \Lambda_{0,nov}(\mathcal{R}))[1] \to C(L; \Lambda_{0,nov}(\mathcal{R}))$ in an obvious way.

LEMMA 5.4.59. $(C(L; \Lambda_{0,nov}(\mathcal{R})), \mathfrak{m}^{\mathcal{R}})$ is a filtered A_∞ algebra.

The proof is the same as the proof of Lemma 3.8.39.

PROPOSITION 5.4.60. *The filtered A_∞ algebra $(C(L;\Lambda_{0,nov}(\mathcal{R})),\mathfrak{m}^\mathcal{R})$ is independent of various choices involved up to homotopy equivalence. If $\psi : M \to M'$ is a symplectic diffeomorphism then it induces a homotopy equivalence*

$$\psi_* : (C(L;\Lambda_{0,nov}(\mathcal{R})),\mathfrak{m}^\mathcal{R}) \to (C(\psi(L);\Lambda_{0,nov}(\mathcal{R})),\mathfrak{m}^\mathcal{R}).$$

Note $\mathcal{R}$ in the domain is defined by using $H^{even}(M)$ and one in the target is defined by using $H^{even}(M')$. We identify them by ψ^{-1*}.

The proof is a minor modification of the proof of Theorem 4.6.52.

Now we consider the canonical model of $(C(L;\Lambda_{0,nov}(\mathcal{R})),\mathfrak{m}^\mathcal{R})$. We put

$$\Lambda_{0,nov}^+(\mathcal{R}) = \Lambda_{0,nov}^+ \otimes \mathcal{R}.$$

It is an ideal of $\Lambda_{0,nov}(\mathcal{R})$ (but is not a maximal ideal). We have

$$\Lambda_{0,nov}(\mathcal{R})/\Lambda_{0,nov}^+(\mathcal{R}) \cong \mathcal{R}[e,e^{-1}].$$

LEMMA 5.4.61. *Let $(C(L;\mathcal{R}),\overline{\mathfrak{m}}^\mathcal{R})$ be the A_∞ algebra over $\mathcal{R}$, which is induced from $(C(L;\Lambda_{0,nov}(\mathcal{R})),\mathfrak{m}^\mathcal{R})$. Then we have an isomorphism of A_∞ algebras*

$$(C(L;\mathcal{R}),\overline{\mathfrak{m}}^\mathcal{R}) \cong (\overline{C}(L;R),\overline{\mathfrak{m}}) \otimes_R \mathcal{R}[e,e^{-1}].$$

PROOF. This follows immediate from

$$\mathfrak{q}\left(\exp\left(\sum r_i \mathbf{c}_i\right);\mathbf{x}\right) \equiv \mathfrak{m}(\mathbf{x}) \mod \Lambda_{0,nov}^+(\mathcal{R}).$$

$\square$

COROLLARY 5.4.62. *Lemma 5.4.28 holds for $(C(L;\mathcal{R}),\overline{\mathfrak{m}}^\mathcal{R})$.*

We remark that we used the fact that R is a field in the proof of Lemma 5.4.28. Corollary 5.4.62 says that it is true in our case though $\mathcal{R}$ is not a field. As we remarked before (Remark 5.4.29) Lemma 5.4.28 is the only point where we used the assumption that R is a field in our construction of the canonical model. Hence we have

PROPOSITION 5.4.63. *There exists a unital canonical model of the filtered A_∞ algebra $(C(L;\Lambda_{0,nov}(\mathcal{R})),\mathfrak{m}^\mathcal{R})$ which is invariant of various choices up to isomorphism.*

Proposition 5.4.63 implies that there exists a super Kuranishi map

$$P_i \in \Lambda_{0,nov}[[r_1 \cdots, r_b; s_1, \cdots, s_m; h_1, \cdots, h_\ell]],$$

$(i = 1, \cdots, \ell)$, which is defined by

$$P_i = (\pi_i \circ \mathfrak{m}^\mathcal{R})\left(\exp\left(\sum s_i \mathbf{v}_i + \sum h_j \mathbf{w}_j\right)\right)$$
$$= (\pi_i \circ \mathfrak{q})\left(\exp\left(\sum r_i \mathbf{c}_i\right); \exp\left(\sum s_i \mathbf{v}_i + \sum h_j \mathbf{w}_i\right)\right),$$

where the notations are as in (5.4.9). We define

$$\mathfrak{M}_{\mathrm{def}}(C_{can}(L;\mathcal{R}),\overline{\mathfrak{m}}^\mathcal{R})^{bos} = \frac{\Lambda_{0,nov}[[r_1 \cdots, r_b; s_1, \cdots, s_m]]}{(P_1, \cdots, P_m)}.$$

It is a commutative $\mathcal{R}$ algebra. The $\mathcal{R}$ algebra isomorphism type of this algebra is an invariant of our Lagrangian submanifold.

The following can be proved by the same way as Proposition 5.4.15.

LEMMA 5.4.64.

$$Hom\left(\mathfrak{M}_{\mathrm{def}}(C_{can}(L;\mathcal{R}),\overline{\mathfrak{m}}^{\mathcal{R}})^{bos},\Lambda_{0,nov}\right) \cong \widehat{\mathcal{M}}(L)_{\mathrm{def}}.$$

The formal scheme $\mathrm{Spf}(\mathfrak{M}_{\mathrm{def}}(C_{can}(L;\mathcal{R})))$ is a formal scheme over $\mathcal{R}$. This fact is consistent with the homological mirror symmetry. We can prove 'def, weak' version in the same way.

We can also use the operator $\mathfrak{r}$ and study the case when there are two Lagrangian submanifolds. Namely we can construct a canonical model of filtered A_∞ bimodule over $\Lambda_{0,nov}^{\mathcal{R}}$. We leave the reader to work it out.

5.4.6. Wrap-up of the proofs of Theorems F,G,M,N and Corollaries O,P.

Now we bring together the results of previous sections to complete the proof of Theorems F,G,M,N. Let us consider the filtered A_∞ algebra $(C(L;\Lambda_{0,nov}),\mathfrak{m}^{\mathfrak{b}})$ constructed by Definition 3.8.38 and Lemma 3.8.39. We remark that

$$\mathfrak{m}_1^{\mathfrak{b}} \equiv \overline{\mathfrak{m}}_1 \quad \mathrm{mod}\ \Lambda_{0,nov}^+.$$

Hence the canonical model of $C(L;\Lambda_{0,nov})$ is $H(L;\Lambda_{0,nov})$ as $\Lambda_{0,nov}$ module. Namely we have $(H(L;\Lambda_{0,nov}),\mathfrak{m}_{can}^{\mathfrak{b}})$. We now apply Definition 5.4.11 to it and obtain

$$P_{m+1}^{bos},\cdots,P_{m+\ell-1}^{bos},P_{m+\ell}^{bos} \in \Lambda_{0,nov}[[s_1,\cdots,s_m]].$$

(Here we write $P_{m+\ell}^{bos}$ the component of Kuranishi map corresponding to the unit. Namely we put $\mathbf{w}_\ell = \mathbf{e}$.) By putting $\mathfrak{P}_i = P_{m+i}^{bos}$ we obtain $(\mathfrak{P}_1,\cdots,\mathfrak{P}_{\ell-1})$ as in Section 1.4. Then

$$\mathcal{M}_{\mathrm{weak}}^{\mathfrak{b}}(L) = ((\mathfrak{P}_{L,\mathrm{weak}}^{\mathfrak{b}})^{-1}(0)(\Lambda_{0,nov}^+))/\sim$$

is a consequence of the unital version of Proposition 5.4.15. Moreover the ring

$$R(\mathfrak{P}_{L,\mathrm{weak}}^{\mathfrak{b}};\Lambda_{0,nov}) = \frac{\Lambda_{0,nov}[[s_1,\cdots,s_m]]}{(\mathfrak{P}_1,\cdots,\mathfrak{P}_{\ell-1})}$$

is the ring $\mathfrak{M}_{\mathrm{weak}}(H(L;\Lambda_{0,nov}),\mathfrak{m}^{\mathfrak{b},can})^{bos}$ in Theorem 5.4.12. Hence up to continuous $\Lambda_{0,nov}$ algebra isomorphism the ring $R(\mathfrak{P}_{L,\mathrm{weak}}^{\mathfrak{b}};\Lambda_{0,nov})$ is independent of various choice involved by Theorem 4.6.52, Proposition 5.4.5 and Theorem 5.4.12.

The non-unital (non-weak) version is proved in the same way. The proof of Theorem M is complete. $\qquad\square$

We next prove Corollary 5.4.21 and Theorems F,G. We constructed in Lemma 3.8.74 the homotopy unital filtered A_∞ bimodule $(C(L^{(1)},L^{(0)};\Lambda_{0,nov}),\mathfrak{n}^{\mathfrak{b}})$ over the pair $((C(L^{(1)};\Lambda_{0,nov}),\mathfrak{m}^{\mathfrak{b}}),(C(L^{(0)};\Lambda_{0,nov}),\mathfrak{m}^{\mathfrak{b}}))$. By Proposition 5.2.43, there exists a unital filtered A_∞ bimodule $(D,\mathfrak{n})$ over the pair $H(L^{(1)};\Lambda_{0,nov}),\mathfrak{m}_{can}^{\mathfrak{b}})$ and $(H(L^{(0)};\Lambda_{0,nov}),\mathfrak{m}_{can}^{\mathfrak{b}})$ and a homotopy unital homotopy equivalence

$$(5.4.65) \qquad (D,\mathfrak{n}) \to (C(L^{(1)},L^{(0)};\Lambda_{0,nov}),\mathfrak{n}^{\mathfrak{b}})$$

over the homotopy equivalences

$$(H(L^{(i)};\Lambda_{0,nov}),\mathfrak{m}_{can}^{\mathfrak{b}}) \to (C(L^{(i)};\Lambda_{0,nov}),\mathfrak{m}^{\mathfrak{b}}).$$

Let $(C_{can}(L^{(1)}, L^{(0)}; \Lambda_{0,nov}), \mathfrak{n}_{can}^b)$ be the unital canonical model of $(D, \mathfrak{n})$ (Theorem 5.4.18). By definition

$$(C_{can}(L^{(1)}, L^{(0)}; \Lambda_{0,nov}), \mathfrak{n}_{can}^b) \cong H(D, \overline{\mathfrak{n}}_{0,0})$$

as $\Lambda_{0,nov}$ modules. Using the homotopy equivalence (5.4.65) we find that

$$C_{can}(L^{(1)}, L^{(0)}; \Lambda_{0,nov}) \cong H(C(L^{(1)}, L^{(0)}; \Lambda_{0,nov}), \overline{\mathfrak{n}}_{0,0}^b).$$

We remark that $\overline{\mathfrak{n}}_{0,0}^b = \overline{\mathfrak{n}}_{0,0} = \pm\partial$ where ∂ is the (usual) (co)boundary operator on $\cup R_h = L^{(1)} \cap L^{(0)}$ in Bott-Morse case. (In case $L^{(1)}$ is transversal to $L^{(0)}$, we have $\overline{\mathfrak{n}}_{0,0}^b = \overline{\mathfrak{n}}_{0,0} = 0$.) Therefore,

$$(5.4.66) \qquad C_{can}(L^{(1)}, L^{(0)}; \Lambda_{0,nov}) = \bigoplus_{[h,w] \in \widetilde{\pi}_0(L^{(1)} \cap L^{(0)})} H^*(R_h; \Theta_h^-) \otimes \Lambda_{0,nov}.$$

The filtered A_∞ bimodule $(C_{can}(L^{(1)}, L^{(0)}; \Lambda_{0,nov}), \mathfrak{n}_{can})$ is independent of various choice involved by Theorem 5.3.1 and Propositions 5.2.43, 5.4.20. We thus proved Corollary 5.4.21 and hence Theorem F.

We next prove Theorem G (G.2). We remark

$$HF((L^{(1)}, \mathbf{b}_1), (L^{(0)}, \mathbf{b}_0); \Lambda_{nov})$$
$$\cong H(C_{can}(L^{(1)}, L^{(0)}; \Lambda_{0,nov}); \delta_{\mathbf{b}_1, \mathbf{b}_0}) \otimes_{\Lambda_{0,nov}} \Lambda_{nov}.$$

Hence (5.4.66) implies

$$\mathrm{rank}_{\Lambda_{nov}} HF((L^{(1)}, \mathbf{b}_1), (L^{(0)}, \mathbf{b}_0); \Lambda_{nov}) \leq \sum_{h,k} \mathrm{rank}_{\mathbb{Q}} H^k(R_h; \Theta_{R_h})$$

as required.   □

We remark that, so far we completed the proof of Theorem G in the case where the pair $L^{(1)}$ and $L^{(0)}$ is of clean intersection. The general case is treated in Subsection 6.5.4.

To prove Theorem N, we consider the case where $\mathfrak{b}$ may not be zero. Then we put

$$(\mathfrak{D}(L^{(1)}, L^{(0)}; \Lambda_{0,nov}), \mathfrak{d}) = (\mathfrak{M}(C_{can}(L^{(1)}, L^{(0)}; \Lambda_{0,nov}), \mathfrak{n}_{can}^b), \mathfrak{Q}).$$

Here the right hand side is defined by Proposition 5.4.24. (N.1) is then a consequence of Lemma 5.4.25. To prove (N.2) we need the following. (In the next lemma we assume every filtered A_∞ algebras etc. are gapped.)

LEMMA 5.4.67. *Let D (resp. D') be filtered A_∞ bimodule over (C_1, C_0) (resp. (C_1', C_0')) and $\tilde{D} = D \otimes_{\Lambda_{0,nov}} \Lambda_{nov}$, $\tilde{D}' = D' \otimes_{\Lambda_{0,nov}} \Lambda_{nov}$. Let $\varphi : \tilde{D} \to \tilde{D}'$ be the weakly filtered A_∞ bimodule homomorphism. We assume that it is homotopy equivalence over $\mathfrak{f}_i : C_i \to C_i'$.*

Let $C_{i,can} \cong C_{i,can}'$ be canonical models of C_i and C_i'. Let D_{can}, D_{can}' be canonical filtered A_∞ bimodules over $(C_{1,can}, C_{0,can})$ which are homotopy equivalent over D, D'. We put $\tilde{D} = D \otimes_{\Lambda_{nov}} \Lambda_{nov}$, $\tilde{D}' = D' \otimes_{\Lambda_{nov}} \Lambda_{nov}$.

Then $\tilde{D}$ is homotopy equivalent to $\tilde{D}'$ over identity.

PROOF. Let $\mathfrak{g}_i : C_{i,can} \to C_i$, $\mathfrak{g}_i' : C_{i,can} \to C_i'$ be homotopy equivalences and $\mathfrak{g}_i^{-1}$, $\mathfrak{g}_i'^{-1}$ be their homotopy inverses. Let $\phi : D_{can} \to D$, $\phi' : D'_{can} \to D'$ be homotopy equivalence over $\mathfrak{f}_1, \mathfrak{f}_0$ and ϕ^{-1}, ϕ'^{-1} be their homotopy inverse over $\mathfrak{f}_1^{-1}, \mathfrak{f}_0^{-1}$. Then

$$(5.4.68) \qquad (\phi'^{-1} \otimes_{\Lambda_{0,nov}} \Lambda_{nov}) \circ \varphi \circ (\phi \otimes_{\Lambda_{0,nov}} \Lambda_{nov}) : \tilde{D} \to \tilde{D}'$$

is a homotopy equivalence over $\mathfrak{g}_1'^{-1} \circ \mathfrak{f}_1 \circ \mathfrak{g}_1$, $\mathfrak{g}_0'^{-1} \circ \mathfrak{f}_0 \circ \mathfrak{g}_0$. Note we may choose $\mathfrak{g}_i$, $\mathfrak{g}_i'$ such that $\mathfrak{g}_i'^{-1} \circ \mathfrak{f}_i \circ \mathfrak{g}_i$ is homotopic to identity. Hence we can deform (5.4.68) to a homotopy equivalence over identity. (Proposition 5.2.43.)   □

Now using Lemma 5.4.67, (N.2) follows from Theorem 5.3.14.   □

REMARK 5.4.69. We remark that $\tilde{D}_{can}$ is *not* isomorphic to $\tilde{D}'_{can}$ in general, in the situation of Lemma 5.4.67. In fact in the situation of Theorem F,

$$\text{rank}_{\Lambda_{0,nov}} C_{can}(L^{(1)}, L^{(0)}; \Lambda_{0,nov})$$

is the sum of Betti numbers of $L^{(1)} \cap L^{(0)}$, which is *not* an invariant when we move $L^{(0)}$, $L^{(1)}$ by two Hamiltonian diffeomorphisms.

We now turn to the proofs of Corollaries O and P. Let M be a symplectic manifold with $c_1(M) = 0$ and let L be a Lagrangian submanifold such that $\mu_L : H_2(M, L) \to \mathbb{Z}$ is zero. We assume the same condition for $L^{(1)}, L^{(0)}$.

Now we remark that the generator e in $\Lambda_{0,nov}$ appears always as the form $e^{\mu_L(\beta)/2}$ in the construction of the filtered A_∞ algebra $(C(L; \Lambda_{0,nov}), \mathfrak{m})$. Hence in our case we can define an filtered A_∞ algebra over Λ_0. (See (Conv.5) in Chapter 1.) We define Λ_+ by requiring $\lambda_i > 0$.

Moreover, it is easy to see all the algebraic argument in Chapters 3,4,5 works if we consider Λ_0 in place of $\Lambda_{0,nov}$. Therefore, if $\mathfrak{b} \in H^2(L; \Lambda_+)$, we have a canonical model $(H(L; \Lambda_0), \mathfrak{m}_{can}^{\mathfrak{b}})$.

To perform the construction of Subsection 5.4.1 and define a Kuranishi map in our situation, we proceed as follows. Let us put $m = \text{rank } H^1(L; \mathbb{Q})$. (Note in Subsection 5.4.1 we put $m = \text{rank } H^{odd}(L; \mathbb{Q})$.) We have $H^1(L; \Lambda_0) = \Lambda_0^{\oplus m}$. Let $\mathbf{v}_1, \cdots, \mathbf{v}_m$ be the basis of $H^1(L; \Lambda_0)$. Similarly we put $\ell = \text{rank } H^2(L; \mathbb{Q})$ and $\mathbf{w}_1, \cdots, \mathbf{w}_\ell$ be the basis of $H^2(L; \Lambda_0) = \Lambda_0^{\oplus \ell}$. Let π_i be the projection to the i the factor. Then we define

$$(5.4.70) \qquad \begin{aligned} P_i(s_1, \cdots, s_m) &= (\pi_i \circ \mathfrak{m}^{\mathfrak{b}})(\exp(s_1\mathbf{v}_1 + \cdots + s_m\mathbf{v}_m)) \\ &\in \Lambda_{0,nov}[[s_1, \cdots, s_m]] \end{aligned}$$

in the same way as (5.4.9). Hence we obtain

$$\mathfrak{P}_L^{\mathfrak{b}} = (P_1, \cdots, P_\ell) : H^1(L; \Lambda_+) \to H^2(L; \Lambda_+).$$

The required equality $\mathcal{M}^{\mathfrak{b}}(L; \Lambda_+) = (\mathfrak{P}_L^{\mathfrak{b}})^{-1}(0)(\Lambda_+)$ then follows in the same way as the proof of Theorem P by using the following lemma.

LEMMA 5.4.71. *Let C be a filtered A_∞ algebra over Λ_0. We assume C is unital and $C^0 = \Lambda_0 \mathbf{e}$, where $\mathbf{e}$ is a unit.*

Then the gauge equivalence relation $\sim$ on

$$\widehat{\mathcal{M}}(C) = \{b \in C^1 \mid \mathfrak{m}(e^b) = 0\}$$

is trivial.

PROOF. Let $b_1, b_0 \in \widehat{\mathcal{M}}(C)$ we assume $b_1 \sim b_0$. Then, by Proposition 4.3.9, there exists $(b_1, c, b_0) \in C^{[0,1]}$ such that $b_1 - b_0 = \mathfrak{m}(e^{b_1} c e^{b_0})$. Since $\deg b_i = 1$ it follows that $\deg c = 0$. Hence, by assumption, $c = \rho \mathbf{e}$, for $\rho \in \Lambda_0$. Therefore $\mathfrak{m}(e^{b_1} c e^{b_0}) = 0$. Namely $b_1 = b_0$. □

We next prove (O.4). We assume that $m[\omega] \in H^2(M, L; \mathbb{Z})$. We remark that in the construction of $(C(L; \Lambda_{0,nov}), \mathfrak{m})$ the parameter T appears only in the form $T^{\omega \cap \beta}$ where $\beta \in \pi_2(M, L)$. Hence the coefficient ring is reduced to $\mathbb{Q}[[T^{1/m}]]$.

Now we consider the case we have two Lagrangian submanifolds $L^{(1)}, L^{(0)}$ with vanishing Maslov index and prove (O.1), (O.2). This is the point discussed in Remark 5.1.18 Subsection 5.1.4. We prove the following lemma. (We use the notation of Subsection 2.2.1.)

LEMMA 5.4.72. *If $\mu_{L^{(i)}} : H_2(M; L^{(i)}) \to \mathbb{Z}$ is zero, then*

$$I_\mu : \pi_1(\Omega(L^{(0)}, L^{(1)}; \ell_0)) \to \mathbb{Z}$$

is also zero.

PROOF. Let $Lag(M) \to M$ be the bundle such that the fiber $Lag_p(M)$ of $p \in M$ is the Lagrangian Grassmannian $\Lambda(T_p M)$. (See Subsection 2.1.1.) By [**Sei00, Fuk02II**] we can use the condition $c_1(M) = 0$ to show that there exists a $\mathbb{Z}$ cover $\widetilde{Lag}(M) \to Lag(M)$ such that each fiber of $\widetilde{Lag}(M) \to M$ is the universal cover of $\Lambda(T_p M)$.

We have a section $s_{L^{(i)}}$ of the restriction of $Lag(M) \to M$ to $L^{(i)}$. Namely $s_{L^{(i)}}(p) = T_p(L^{(i)}) \in \Lambda(T_p M)$. The obstruction to lift $s_{L^{(i)}}$ to $\tilde{s}_{L^{(i)}} : L^{(i)} \to \widetilde{Lag}(M)$ is the image of the $\mu_{L^{(i)}} \in H_2(M, L^{(i)})$ to $H_1(L^{(i)})$. (See [**Fuk02II**].) We assumed that this is zero. Hence there exists a lift $\tilde{s}_{L^{(i)}}$.

Now let $C : S^1 \times [0,1] \to M$ a map such that $C(S^1 \times \{i\}) \subset L^{(i)}$. ($C$ represents an element of $\pi_1(\Omega(L^{(0)}, L^{(1)}; \ell_0))$.)

The pullback of $\widetilde{Lag}(M)$ by C is trivial bundle (since the fiber is connected). Hence $\tilde{s}_{L^{(i)}}$ defines maps $S^1 \times \{i\} \to \widetilde{Lag}(M)$. Since $\pi_1(\widetilde{Lag}(M)) \to \pi_1 M$ is an isomorphism, $\tilde{s}_{L^{(0)}}$ is homotopic to $\tilde{s}_{L^{(1)}}$. It implies that there exists a section $\tilde{s}$ of the pullback of $\widetilde{Lag}(M)$ by C such that $\tilde{s}$ coincides with the restriction of $\tilde{s}_{L^{(i)}}$ on $S^1 \times \{i\}$. The section $\tilde{s}$ induces a section s of the pullback of $Lag(M)$ by C which coincides with the restriction of $s_{L^{(i)}}$ on $S^1 \times \{i\}$. This implies $I_\mu(C) = 0$, by the definition of I_μ. □

Now we assume that $L^{(1)}$ intersects cleanly with $L^{(0)}$ in addition and put $L^{(0)} \cap L^{(1)} = \cup R_h$. We fix ℓ_0 a constant path to R_{h_0}. We choose such ℓ_0 to each of the component $\Omega(L^{(0)}, L^{(1)})$. Lemma 5.4.72 implies that $\mu([h, w]; \ell_0)$ is independent of w and depends only on h.

Now we put

$$\widehat{CF}_{BM}(L^{(1)}, L^{(0)}; \Lambda_0) = \left(C(R_h; \Theta_{R_h}) \otimes_{\mathbb{Q}} \Lambda_h \right) \otimes_{\mathbb{Q}} \Lambda_0.$$

(Compare a similar definition of $\widehat{CF}_{BM}(L^{(1)}, L^{(0)}; \Lambda_{0,nov})$ in Subsection 3.7.5.) We define an equivalence relation on it by modifying (3.7.19) as follows.

$$S \otimes [h, w] \otimes T^\lambda \sim S' \otimes [h', w'] \otimes T^{\lambda'}$$

if and only if

(5.4.73.1) $h = h'$,
(5.4.73.2) $S = S'$,
(5.4.73.3) $\lambda + \int_w \omega = \lambda' + \int_{w'} \omega$.

(Note the condition corresponding to (3.7.19.3) is missing here.)

We take the nonnegative energy part of $\widehat{CF}_{BM}(L^{(1)}, L^{(0)}; \Lambda_0)/\sim$ and denote it by $C(L^{(1)}, L^{(0)}; \Lambda_0)$. (See Subsections 3.7.4, 3.7.5.) Using the fact that $\mu([h, w]; \ell_0)$ is independent of w, we can show

$$C(L^{(1)}, L^{(0)}; \Lambda_0) \cong \bigoplus_h C(R_h; \Theta_{R_h}) \,\hat{\otimes}_{\mathbb{R}}\, \Lambda_0.$$

Moreover we can define a degree on it by

$$\deg(S \otimes [h, w] \otimes T^\lambda) = \deg S + \mu([h, w]; \ell_0).$$

Now we can repeat the whole construction of the filtered A_∞ bimodule in Section 3.7 over Λ_0, by just eliminating e appearing in the formulas. It implies (O.1), (O.2), (O.3) in the same way as Theorem G. The proof of Corollary R is now complete. $\square$

REMARK 5.4.74. In case when $L^{(i)}$ are rational *in the sense of* [**Fuk03I**] (see Remark 6.2.4) we can reduce the coefficient ring of $C(L^{(1)}, L^{(0)}; \Lambda_0)$ (and of Floer cohomology) to $\mathbb{Q}[[T^{1/m}]][T^{-1}]$.

The rationality does *not* imply $\omega(B) \in \mathbb{Q}$ for $B \in \pi(p, q)$ (see Definition 2.3.7 for notation). So we need some modification of boundary operator so that it is defined over $\mathbb{Q}[[T^{1/m}]][T^{-1}]$. See [**Fuk03I**] for the way to do so.

CHAPTER 6

Spectral sequences

6.1. Statement of the results in Chapter 6

The purpose of this chapter is to construct a spectral sequence from a filtered differential $\Lambda_{0,nov}$ module, Theorems D,E and G. We then prove Theorems H,I,J,K and L. A similar spectral sequence was constructed by the second named author in [**Oh96I,II**] for the case of monotone Lagrangian submanifolds. In the monotone Lagrangian cases, the spectral sequence constructed in this chapter coincides with the one constructed in [**Oh96I**]. But we like to mention that there are two differences between these two constructions: The first difference is that the Morse-Witten complex is used in [**Oh96I**] while the singular chain complex are used here. Although this is rather a technical point, because of various "higher order" terms appearing in our situation here, it seems more difficult to work with Morse-Witten complex as done in [**Oh96I**]. The other one is that the Morse index was used to define a filtration in [**Oh96I**], while we use the *energy* here. However in case of monotone Lagrangian submanifolds, the two filtrations coincide by the definition of monotonicity.

We need to study general properties of the module over our universal Novikov ring to construct our spectral sequence and study its convergence. Since the universal Novikov ring is *not* Noetherian, a careful treatment is required to perform the construction.

6.1.1. The spectral sequence.
To state our results in this chapter, let us briefly recall the basic properties on the universal Novikov ring $\Lambda_{nov}(R)$ and its subring $\Lambda_{0,nov}(R)$ where R is a commutative ring. In the case $R = \mathbb{Q}$, we will omit R in the notations, that is, $\Lambda_{nov} = \Lambda_{nov}(\mathbb{Q})$, $\Lambda_{0,nov} = \Lambda_{0,nov}(\mathbb{Q})$. By putting $\deg T^{\lambda} e^{n} = 2n$, Λ_{nov} and $\Lambda_{0,nov}$ become graded rings. Let $\Lambda_{nov}^{(k)}$ and $\Lambda_{0,nov}^{(k)}$ be the grading k part of them, respectively. We defined a filtration $F^{\lambda}\Lambda_{nov}$ of Λ_{nov} by

$$(6.1.1) \qquad F^{\lambda}\Lambda_{nov} = \left\{ \sum a_i T^{\lambda_i} e^{n_i} \mid \lambda_i \geq \lambda \right\}.$$

It induces a filtration on $\Lambda_{0,nov}$. Those filtrations define uniform structures on Λ_{nov} and $\Lambda_{0,nov}$, which are complete.

The above filtration on Λ_{nov} induces another filtrations on Λ_{nov} and $\Lambda_{0,nov}$ defined by

$$(6.1.2) \qquad \mathfrak{F}^{q}\Lambda_{nov} = F^{q\lambda_0}\Lambda_{nov}, \quad \mathfrak{F}^{q}\Lambda_{0,nov} = F^{q\lambda_0}\Lambda_{0,nov}.$$

Here λ_0 is a positive number to be determined later. ($q \in \mathbb{Z}_{\geq 0}$ for $\Lambda_{0,nov}$ and $q \in \mathbb{Z}$ for Λ_{nov}.) The number λ_0 is related to the gapped condition (Condition 6.3.16).

We then have the associated graded modules

$$(6.1.3) \qquad gr_q(\mathfrak{F}\Lambda_{nov}) = \frac{\mathfrak{F}^q \Lambda_{nov}}{\mathfrak{F}^{q+1}\Lambda_{nov}}, \quad gr_q(\mathfrak{F}\Lambda_{0,nov}) = \frac{\mathfrak{F}^q \Lambda_{0,nov}}{\mathfrak{F}^{q+1}\Lambda_{0,nov}}.$$

The main result of this chapter is Theorem D in introduction, that gives the spectral sequence which describes the relationship between (singular) cohomology and Floer cohomology. We prove it in Section 6.4.

The construction of the spectral sequence and its convergence proof are given in Section 6.3 in the purely algebraic context. The property we assume there is verified in Subsection 6.4.1 in our geometric situation. Hence the proofs (D.1),(D.2) are completed there. To prove (D.3), we will use the operators $\mathfrak{p}$ and $\mathfrak{q}$ introduced in Section 3.8. We will do it in Subsection 6.4.2. The proof of Theorem D is completed in Subsection 6.4.5, where we prove (D.4).

We remark that we cannot remove the additional assumption $\mathbf{b}_1 = \mathbf{b}_0$ from (D.3). (See Remark 6.4.12.)

For a relatively spin pair $(L^{(0)}, L^{(1)})$ of Lagrangian submanifolds of M, we can also construct the Bott-Morse version of the spectral sequence as follows. As for the notations in Theorem 6.1.4, see Lemma-Definition 3.8.75.

Let $(L^{(0)}, L^{(1)})$ be a relatively spin pair of Lagrangian submanifolds which has clean intersection. Let $L^{(1)} \cap L^{(0)} = \cup_{h \in \pi_0(L^{(1)} \cap L^{(0)})} R_h$ be the decomposition to the connected components and $\mu_L([h, w])$ be the Maslov-Morse index. (See Definition 3.7.62.) Θ_h^- is a local system induced by a representation $\pi_1(R_h) \to \{\pm 1\}$. (See Definition 8.8.2.) See (4.3.27) for Π_{amb} and Lemma 4.3.28 for $\mathfrak{PO}$. We refer Subsection 3.7.5 (Definition 3.7.52 and Proposition 3.7.59) for other notations.

THEOREM 6.1.4. *Let $(L^{(0)}, L^{(1)})$ be a relatively spin pair of Lagrangian submanifolds of M. Then for each $\mathbf{b}_i \in \mathcal{M}_{\mathrm{weak,def}}(L^{(i)})$ satisfying*

$$\mathfrak{PO}_{L^{(0)}}(\mathbf{b}_0) = \mathfrak{PO}_{L^{(1)}}(\mathbf{b}_1), \quad \pi_{\mathrm{amb}}(\mathbf{b}_0) = \pi_{\mathrm{amb}}(\mathbf{b}_1)$$

there exists a spectral sequence $\{E_r^{p,q}, \delta_r\}$ with the following properties:

$$(6.1.5.1) \qquad E_2^{p,q} = \bigoplus_{k, \, [h,w] \in \tilde{\pi}_0(L^{(1)} \cap L^{(0)})} H^{k-\mu([h,w])}(R_h; \Theta_h^-) \otimes gr_q(\mathfrak{F}\Lambda_{0,nov}^{(p-k)}).$$

$(6.1.5.2)$ *There exists a filtration $\mathfrak{F}^* HF((L^{(1)}, (\mathfrak{b}, b_1)), (L^{(0)}, (\mathfrak{b}, b_0)); \Lambda_{0,nov})$ on the Floer cohomology $HF((L^{(1)}, \mathbf{b}_1), (L^{(0)}, \mathbf{b}_0); \Lambda_{0,nov})$ such that*

$$E_\infty^{p,q} \cong \frac{\mathfrak{F}^q HF^p((L^{(1)}, \mathbf{b}_1), (L^{(0)}, \mathbf{b}_0); \Lambda_{0,nov})}{\mathfrak{F}^{q+1} HF((L^{(1)}, \mathbf{b}_1), (L^{(0)}, \mathbf{b}_0); \Lambda_{0,nov})}.$$

$(6.1.5.3)$ *The spectral sequence is compatible with the bimodule structure of the Floer cohomology $HF((L^{(1)}, \mathbf{b}_1), (L^{(0)}, \mathbf{b}_0); \Lambda_{0,nov})$ over a pair of Floer cohomologies $HF((L^{(j)}, \mathbf{b}_j), (L^{(j)}, \mathbf{b}_j); \Lambda_{0,nov})$ $(j = 0, 1)$, which are defined in Subsection 3.8.10, in the following sense: The filtration $\mathfrak{F}$ is compatible with the bimodule structure. E_r in Theorem 6.1.4 is a bimodule over E_r in Theorem D such that δ_r is a derivation. The isomorphisms in (6.1.5.1) and (6.1.5.2) are bimodule isomorphisms.*

To prove Theorems D and 6.1.4 we develop algebraic results in Section 6.3 and apply it to our complexes $(C(L; \Lambda_{0,nov}), \mathfrak{m}_1^{\mathfrak{b},b})$ or $(C(L^{(1)}, L^{(0)}; \Lambda_{0.nov}), \delta_{\mathbf{b}_0,\mathbf{b}_1})$ associated to a Lagrangian submanifold or a pair of Lagrangian submanifolds, respectively.

REMARK 6.1.6. Since the ring Λ_{nov} is a localization of $\Lambda_{0,nov}$, it is flat over $\Lambda_{0,nov}$. Furthermore, we have to note that we will use the projective limit to define E_∞-terms in the spectral sequence (Definition 6.3.23). However we will find in Theorem 6.3.28 that when the complex is a weakly finite differential graded module, there exists r_0 such that $E_{r_0}^{p,q} \cong E_{r_0+1}^{p,q} \cong \cdots \cong E_\infty^{p,q}$. Therefore the spectral sequence in Theorems D and 6.1.4 can be also constructed over Λ_{nov}, which is obtained by changing the coefficient ring to Λ_{nov}. We also recall that we proved in Section 5.3 (see Theorem 4.1.5) that

$$(6.1.7) \quad HF((L,(\mathfrak{b},b)),\psi;\Lambda_{nov}) \cong HF((L,(\mathfrak{b},b)),(L,(\mathfrak{b},b));\Lambda_{0,nov}) \otimes_{\Lambda_{0,nov}} \Lambda_{nov},$$

where ψ is a Hamiltonian diffeomorphism and

$$(6.1.8) \quad HF((L,(\mathfrak{b},b)),\psi;\Lambda_{nov}) = HF((L,(\mathfrak{b},b)),(\psi(L),(\psi_*(\mathfrak{b}),\psi_*(b)));\Lambda_{nov})$$

is the Floer cohomology with Λ_{nov} coefficient. (6.1.7) and (D.3) imply Theorem H in introduction. (See Subsection 6.5.1.)

6.1.2. Non-vanishing theorem and a Maslov class conjecture. Recall that the Poincaré dual of the fundamental cycle of L is a homotopy unit of our filtered A_∞ algebra. Using this, we can show a non-vanishing theorem of the Floer cohomology.

THEOREM 6.1.9. *Let $L \subset M$ be a relatively spin Lagrangian submanifold and $\mathbf{b} = (\mathfrak{b},b) \in \mathcal{M}_{\mathrm{def,weak}}(L)$. Then the spectral sequence in Theorem D has the following properties for $\mathbf{b} = \mathbf{b}_1 = \mathbf{b}_0$.*

Denote by $PD([L]) \in H^0(L;\mathbb{Q})$ and $PD([pt]) \in H^n(L;\mathbb{Q})$ the Poincaré duals of the fundamental cycle and the point class in L respectively. We regard them as the terms in $E_2 = H(L;\mathbb{Q}) \otimes gr_*(\mathfrak{F}\Lambda_{0,nov})$. Then we can show the following:

$(6.1.10)$ *For every r, we have*

$$(6.1.10.1) \quad \delta_r(PD([L]) - \mathfrak{h}_2^{+M}(e^{\mathfrak{b}},e^{\mathfrak{b}}\overline{\otimes}e^{\mathfrak{b}})) = 0,$$

$$(6.1.10.2) \quad PD([pt]) \notin \mathrm{Im}(\delta_r).$$

$(6.1.10)$ *holds over Λ_{nov} coefficient also.*
In addition, we make the following assumption:

ASSUMPTION 6.1.11. *The Maslov index for any pseudo-holomorphic disc with boundary in L is non-positive.*

$(6.1.12)$ *Then for every r, we have*

$$(6.1.12.1) \quad PD([L]) - \mathfrak{h}_2^{+M}(e^{\mathfrak{b}},e^{\mathfrak{b}}\overline{\otimes}e^{\mathfrak{b}}) \notin \mathrm{Im}(\delta_r),$$

$$(6.1.12.2) \quad \delta_r(PD([pt])) = 0.$$

$(6.1.12)$ *holds over Λ_{nov} coefficient also.*
Therefore under Assumption 6.1.11, $PD([pt])$ and $PD([L])$ determine elements in E_∞. They are linearly independent. In particular, we have

$$HF((L,\mathbf{b});\Lambda_{nov}) \neq \{0\}.$$

See Subsection 3.8.4 (3.8.35.4) as for the notation of $\mathfrak{h}_2^{+M}$. We remark that under Assumption 6.1.11 the weak unobstructedness after bulk deformation is equivalent to the unobstructedness after bulk deformation. We also remark that we may replace Assumption 6.1.11 by the following topological condition.

ASSUMPTION 6.1.13. If $\mu_L(\beta) > 0$ for $\beta \in \pi_2(M, L)$, then $\omega(\beta) < 0$.

We note that Theorem E in introduction is an immediate consequence of Theorem 6.1.9. In case $\mathbf{b}_1 \neq \mathbf{b}_0$ we have the following version of Theorem 6.1.9.

THEOREM 6.1.14. Let us consider $\mathbf{b}_1, \mathbf{b}_0 \in \mathcal{M}_{\text{weak,def}}(L)$ with

$$\mathfrak{PO}(\mathbf{b}_1) = \mathfrak{PO}(\mathbf{b}_0), \qquad \pi_{\text{amb}}(\mathbf{b}_1) = \pi_{\text{amb}}(\mathbf{b}_0).$$

Here $(\mathbf{b}_i = (\mathfrak{b}, b_i))$.
Then we have

$$(6.1.10.1') \qquad\qquad \delta_r(PD([L]) - \mathfrak{h}_2^{+M}(e^{\mathfrak{b}}, e^{b_1}\overline{\otimes}e^{b_0})) = 0.$$

Under the additional Assumption 6.1.11, we have

$$(6.1.12.1') \qquad\qquad PD([L]) - \mathfrak{h}_2^{+M}(e^{\mathfrak{b}}, e^{b_1}\overline{\otimes}e^{b_0}) \notin \text{Im}(\delta_r),$$

$$(6.1.12.2') \qquad\qquad \delta_r(PD([pt])) = 0.$$

$(6.1.12.1')$ holds over Λ_{nov} coefficient also.

As applications of the non-vanishing theorem, we can show the following theorems (Theorem 6.1.15 and Theorem 6.1.17) which will be proved in Subsection 6.4.4.

THEOREM 6.1.15. Let $L \subset M$ be a relatively spin Lagrangian submanifold. Assume that $H^2(M; \mathbb{Q}) \to H^2(L; \mathbb{Q})$ is surjective and the Maslov index of L is zero on $\pi_2(M, L)$. Then L is unobstructed after bulk deformation and we have

$$HF((L, \mathbf{b}), (L, \mathbf{b}); \Lambda_{nov}) \neq 0$$

for any $\mathbf{b} \in \mathcal{M}_{\text{def}}(L)$.

We remark that the assumption that the Maslov index is zero implies that $c_1(M) = 0$ on $\pi_2(M)$. For instance, the Maslov index of a special Lagrangian submanifold is zero [**Daz81**]. Combining this theorem with a result by Thomas and Yau [**ThYa02**], we can find that if L is as in Theorem 6.1.15, then there exists at most one special Lagrangian submanifold in the Hamiltonian deformation class.

Since the Floer cohomology over the coefficient Λ_{nov} is invariant under the Hamiltonian deformation, we immediately obtain the following corollary concerning so called the Maslov index conjecture.

COROLLARY 6.1.16. Let $L \subset M$ be a relatively spin Lagrangian submanifold. Assume that $H^2(M; \mathbb{Q}) \to H^2(L; \mathbb{Q})$ is surjective and there is a Hamiltonian diffeomorphism ψ such that

$$L \cap \psi(L) = \emptyset.$$

Then the Maslov index of L is not zero.

Furthermore, we can estimate the minimal Maslov index as follows. Let Σ_L be the minimal Maslov number of L, which is a non-negative integer defined by $\text{Image}(\mu_L) = \Sigma_L \mathbb{Z}$, where $\mu_L : \pi_2(M, L) \to \mathbb{Z}$ is the Maslov index homomorphism.

THEOREM 6.1.17. *Let $L \subset M$ be an n-dimensional relatively spin Lagrangian submanifold. Assume that there is a Hamiltonian diffeomorphism ψ such that $L \cap \psi(L) = \emptyset$.*

(1) *If L is weakly unobstructed after bulk deformation then $\Sigma_L \neq 0$.*
(2) *Assume that there exists $(\mathfrak{b}, b) \in \widehat{\mathcal{M}}_{\mathrm{weak,def}}(L)$ such that*

$$\mathfrak{b} \in H^2(M; \mathbb{C}) \otimes \Lambda^+_{0,nov}, \quad b \in H^1(L; \mathbb{C}) \otimes \Lambda^+_{0,nov},$$

in addition. Then we have the following inequality:

$$2 \leq \Sigma_L \leq n + 1.$$

We remark that M is not necessarily closed. The results in this book can be applied when M is tame in the sense of Gromov [**Grom85**], (for instance, $M = \mathbb{C}^n$), as far as L is compact. Corollary 6.1.16 then implies Theorem K in introduction.

We will further discuss the minimal Maslov number in [**FOOO09I**] for the case when M is spherically positive.

Some history on the various results on the Maslov class of compact Lagrangian embeddings $L \subset \mathbb{C}^n$ is now in order. We first note that in $\mathbb{C}^n$ the homomorphism $\mu_L : \pi_2(\mathbb{C}^n, L) \to \mathbb{Z}$ descends to a cohomology class $\mu_L \in H^1(L, \mathbb{Z})$, which is called the standard Maslov class of $L \subset \mathbb{C}^n$ defined in [**Arn67**].

There are two prominent conjectures concerning the structure of the Maslov class μ_L for $L \subset \mathbb{C}^n$. The first one, commonly called the *Maslov class conjecture*, states that for any compact Lagrangian embedding $L \subset \mathbb{C}^n$, the Maslov class μ_L is non-zero. The only previously known cases are the case of *tori* $L \cong T^n$ or more generally the case of $L \subset \mathbb{C}^n$ that admits a metric of non-positive curvature proved by Viterbo [**Vit90**], and the *two-dimensional* case in $\mathbb{C}^2$ [**Pol91I**]. This conjecture can be strengthened to the conjecture of the existence of $\beta \in \pi_2(M, L)$ satisfying $E(\beta) > 0$, $\mu_L(\beta) > 0$ for any *displaceable* Lagrangian submanifold $L \subset M$, i.e. for any L that allows a Hamiltonian diffeomorphism $\phi : M \to M$ such that $\phi(L) \cap L = \emptyset$. Indeed, in both [**Vit90**] and [**Pol91I**] this stronger statement was proved.

The other conjecture or question, which is commonly called *Audin's question* [**Aud88**], states that for any embedded Lagrangian tori in $\mathbb{C}^n$, we have $\Sigma_L = 2$. Again this follows from [**Vit90**, **Pol91I**] for $n = 2$. The second named author proved in [**Oh96I**] that this conjecture holds for the monotone Lagrangian tori $T^n \subset \mathbb{C}^n$ if $n \leq 24$.

After the year-2000 version of this book circulated, several other results have appeared and announced. First, we will use the compatibility (D.4) of the spectral sequence with the product structure and remove the restriction on the dimension in Theorem 6.4.35 and answer Audin's question in full generality for the monotone Lagrangian tori. This idea of using the compatibility is due to Seidel [**Sei01**]. See also [**Bi04**, **Buh06**]. We will discuss this point at the end of Section 6.4.

Using the idea from the symplectic field theory [**EGH00**], Eliashberg provided a scheme of providing the affirmative answer to Audin's question [**Eli01**] which was further detailed by Cieliebak and Mohnke [**CiMo04**]. The first named author [**Fuk05II**] outlined that, combined with the idea from string topology [**ChSu99**], Lagrangian Floer theory can also be used to provide a different scheme of proving Audin's question and other results concerning *aspherical* Lagrangian submanifolds.

6.1.3. Applications to Lagrangian intersections. In the course of the construction of the spectral sequence we will prove the following structure theorem on the Floer cohomology.

THEOREM 6.1.18. *Let L be a relatively spin Lagrangian submanifold. Then for each $(\mathfrak{b},b) \in \mathcal{M}_{\text{weak,def}}(L)$, there exist numbers ℓ_p, m_p and $\lambda_{p,i}$ such that*

$$(6.1.19.1) \quad HF^p((L,(\mathfrak{b},b));\Lambda_{0,nov}) \cong \Big(\bigoplus_{i=1}^{m_p} \big(\Lambda_{0,nov}^{(0)}/F^{\lambda_{p,i}}\Lambda_{0,nov}^{(0)} \big) \Big) \bigoplus (\Lambda_{0,nov}^{(0)})^{\oplus \ell_p}$$

as $\Lambda_{0,nov}^{(0)}$ modules.

We remark that (6.1.19.1) implies that

$$(6.1.19.2) \qquad\qquad HF^p((L,(\mathfrak{b},b));\Lambda_{nov}) \cong (\Lambda_{nov}^{(0)})^{\oplus \ell_p}$$

as $\Lambda_{nov}^{(0)}$ modules, which are $\mathbb{Z}$-graded. We recall $\Lambda_{0,nov} \cong \Lambda_{0,nov}^{(0)}[e,e^{-1}]$ and e has degree two. Therefore $HF^p((L,(\mathfrak{b},b));\Lambda_{0,nov})$ is periodic with period 2 as a $\Lambda_{0,nov}^{(0)}$ module and so is $HF^p((L,(\mathfrak{b},b));\Lambda_{nov})$ as a $\Lambda_{nov}^{(0)}$ module.

THEOREM 6.1.20. *Let $(L^{(0)}, L^{(1)})$ be a pair of relatively spin Lagrangian submanifolds of M. We assume that it is of clean intersection. Then for each $\mathbf{b}_i \in \mathcal{M}_{\text{weak,def}}(L^{(i)})$ with $\mathfrak{PD}(\mathbf{b}_0) = \mathfrak{PD}(\mathbf{b}_1)$, $\pi_{\text{amb}}(\mathbf{b}_1) = \pi_{\text{amb}}(\mathbf{b}_0)$, there exist numbers ℓ_p, m_p and $\lambda_{p,i}$ such that*

$$HF^p((L^{(1)},\mathbf{b}_1),(L^{(0)},\mathbf{b}_0);\Lambda_{0,nov}))$$
$$(6.1.21.1)$$
$$\cong \Big(\bigoplus_{i=1}^{m_p} \big(\Lambda_{0,nov}^{(0)}/F^{\lambda_{p,i}}\Lambda_{0,nov}^{(0)} \big) \Big) \bigoplus (\Lambda_{0,nov}^{(0)})^{\oplus \ell_p}$$

as $\Lambda_{0,nov}^{(0)}$ modules.

We remark (6.1.21.1) implies that

$$(6.1.21.2) \qquad HF^p((L^{(1)},\mathbf{b}_1),(L^{(0)},\mathbf{b}_0);\Lambda_{nov})) \cong (\Lambda_{nov}^{(0)})^{\oplus \ell_p}$$

as $\Lambda_{nov}^{(0)}$ modules, which are $\mathbb{Z}$-graded. We recall $\Lambda_{0,nov} \cong \Lambda_{0,nov}^{(0)}[e,e^{-1}]$ and e has degree two. Therefore $HF^p((L^{(1)},\mathbf{b}_1),(L^{(0)},\mathbf{b}_0);\Lambda_{nov}))$ is periodic with period 2 as a $\Lambda_{nov}^{(0)}$ module.

We put

$$(6.1.22) \qquad \{\lambda_i \mid i = 1,2,\cdots\} = \{\lambda_{p,i} \mid p = 0,1, \ i = 1,2,\cdots\}.$$

If we choose λ_i so that $\lambda_i \le \lambda_{i+1}$, then λ_i (with multiplicity) are uniquely determined. We say λ_i the *torsion exponents* of $HF((L^{(1)},\mathbf{b}_1),(L^{(0)},\mathbf{b}_0);\Lambda_{0,nov})$. Note we are working over rational coefficient. The torsion here means the torsion part of the $\Lambda_{0,nov}$ module. $\ell_0 + \ell_1$ is called the Betti number of the Floer cohomology.

The last section of this chapter is devoted to the study of Lagrangian intersections. One is the estimate of the number of the intersection points of L and $\psi(L)$, where ψ is a Hamiltonian diffeomorphism. We will prove Theorems H and I in Subsections 6.5.1 and 6.5.2, respectively.

We like to emphasize again that the Floer cohomology $HF((L,b);\Lambda_{0,nov})$ for a single Lagrangian submanifold is independent of the various choices we made in the course of its definition. It follows from Theorem 4.1.3 and Theorem 4.1.4 that the rank of the "free part" of the Floer cohomology is also an invariant. When we prove Theorems H and I, we will study the rank of the free part of $HF((L, b); \Lambda_{0,nov})$.

On the other hand, if we move two Lagrangian submanifolds by different symplectic or Hamiltonian diffeomorphisms, the Floer cohomology of the pair is *not* an invariant over $\Lambda_{0,nov}$, but an invariant over Λ_{nov}. More precisely the "torsion part" of the Floer cohomology over $\Lambda_{0,nov}$ is not an invariant. In this sense the torsion part can be regarded as describing the *dependence* of the Hamiltonian isotopy. Theorem J in introduction describe such a phenomenon.

Let $\psi : M \to M$ be a Hamiltonian diffeomorphism and μ its Hofer distance ([**Hof90, HoZe94**]) from identity. (See Subsection 5.3.5). We assume that $\psi(L^{(0)})$ is transversal to $L^{(1)}$. We put

$$b(\mu) = \#\{i \mid \lambda_i \geq \mu\}.$$

Here λ_i are given in (6.1.22). Then Theorem J states the inequality

$$(6.1.23) \qquad \#(\psi(L^{(0)}) \cap L^{(1)}) \geq a + 2b(\mu).$$

Theorem J is a consequence of the following Theorem 6.1.25 which shows that the torsion exponent of Floer cohomology is a Lipschitz function with Lipschitz constant one with respect to the Hofer distance. (See Subsection 6.5.3.) Let $\{\psi_\rho^{(j)}\}_\rho$ $(j = 0, 1)$ be Hamiltonian isotopies. (Here $\rho \in [0, 1]$ and $\psi_0^{(j)}$ is identity). We put $\psi^{(j)} = \psi_1^{(j)}$ and denote by

$$(6.1.24) \qquad \mu = \mathfrak{C}(\{\psi_\rho^{(0)}\}_\rho, \{\psi_\rho^{(1)}\}_\rho) = \|\{\psi_\rho^{(0)}\}_\rho\| + \|\{\psi_\rho^{(1)}\}_\rho\|$$

the constant given in (5.3.40). (Namely $\|\{\psi_\rho^{(0)}\}_\rho\|$ is the Hofer length of the Hamiltonian isotopies.) In the next theorem, we change the enumeration of the torsion exponents λ_i, λ_i' to $\lambda_{\downarrow i}$, $\lambda_{\downarrow i}'$ so that $\lambda_{\downarrow i} \geq \lambda_{\downarrow i+1}$, $\lambda_{\downarrow i}' \geq \lambda_{\downarrow i+1}'$.

THEOREM 6.1.25. *Let $\lambda_{\downarrow i}$, $i = 1, \cdots, b$ be the torsion exponents of the Floer cohomology $HF((L^{(1)}, \mathbf{b}_1), (L^{(0)}, \mathbf{b}_0); \Lambda_{0,nov})$ and let $\lambda_{\downarrow i}'$, $i = 1, \cdots, b'$ be the torsion exponents of the Floer cohomology*

$$HF((\psi^{(1)} L^{(1)}, \psi_*^{(1)} \mathbf{b}_1), (\psi^{(0)} L^{(0)}, \psi_*^{(0)} \mathbf{b}_0); \Lambda_{0,nov}).$$

We assume $\lambda_{\downarrow i} \geq \lambda_{\downarrow i+1}$, $\lambda_{\downarrow i}' \geq \lambda_{\downarrow i+1}'$. Let μ be as in (6.1.24).
If $\lambda_{\downarrow i} > \mu$ then $i \leq b'$ and

$$|\lambda_{\downarrow i} - \lambda_{\downarrow i}'| \leq \mu.$$

In particular, $\lambda_{\downarrow i}$ are continuous for each i as far as $\lambda_{\downarrow i} > 0$.

In [**Chek96**], Chekanov proved that if the Hofer norm of ψ is smaller than the area of any non trivial pseudo-holomorphic discs with boundary in L, and if $\psi(L)$ is transversal to L, then $\#(\psi(L) \cap L)$ is not smaller than the Betti number of L. His result follows from Theorem 6.5.47. In fact, our proof thereof is similar to Chekanov's. Theorems J, 6.1.25 and 6.5.47 may be regarded as an improvement of Chekanov's result by using Floer cohomology.

We will use Theorem 6.1.25 to show that Floer cohomology over $\Lambda_{0,nov}$ is defined for an arbitrary relatively spin pair $L^{(0)}, L^{(1)}$ (which is not necessary of clean intersection) such that it is independent of various choices involved such as almost complex structure or perturbation. (Definition 6.5.39).

REMARK 6.1.26. In Theorem 6.1.25, we concern with the torsion exponents of Floer cohomology and its continuity. Torsion exponent is a number which is realized as an energy of a sum of pseudo-holomorphic discs. It is independent of almost complex structures and perturbation. The number is extracted from the set

$$(6.1.27) \qquad \{E(\beta) \mid \beta \in \pi_2(M,L) \text{ is realized by a pseudo-holomorphic disc.}\}$$

in the way that is independent of various choices we made. (We remark that (6.1.27) itself depends on the choice of almost complex structures.)

It seems very likely that we can extract more numbers using the product structures $\mathfrak{m}_k$ on Floer cohomology, in such a way that they are invariant of J and perturbations, and are continuous with respect to Hofer distance.

They may be regarded as a topological and Lagrangian analogue of spectral invariant of Hamiltonian diffeomorphisms. (See [Oh04].)

After the filtered A_∞ algebra is constructed and is proven to be well defined up to homotopy equivalence, extracting such an information is rather an algebraic problem than geometric or analytic ones. We however do not yet know what is the optimal way to extract numbers from our filtered A_∞ algebra or bimodule. So we here restrict ourselves to the study of torsion exponents, which depends only on the additive structure of Floer cohomology.

REMARK 6.1.28. The discussion on the torsion of Floer cohomology may also be related to mirror symmetry in the following way: Recall that $T = q$ can be regarded as a parameter $\in D^2(\epsilon)$ which parameterizes a maximal degenerate family of complex manifolds in the mirror. (See Section 1.4.) Inverting T (that is using Λ_{nov} in place of $\Lambda_{0,nov}$) corresponds to considering the punctured disc $D^2(\epsilon) \setminus \{0\}$ instead of $D^2(\epsilon)$. (In other words, it is related to rigid analytic space as we mentioned in Remark 1.23.) Regarding Floer cohomology as a $\Lambda_{0,nov}$ module (rather than a Λ_{nov} module) corresponds to fixing an extension of the mirror object to the fiber at $0 \in D^2(\epsilon)$. The discussion of Section 6.5 shows that this extension depends on the choice of the representative in the given Hamiltonian isotopy class in a rather delicate (and interesting) way.

6.2. A toy model: rational Lagrangian submanifolds

As we mentioned in the previous section, the coefficient ring $\Lambda_{0,nov}$ is not Noetherian. Because of this, even if we define the spectral sequence, it is not obvious to prove that the $E_r^{p,q}$-term is finitely generated and (D.2) converges. The main part of the proof of Theorems D and 6.1.4 is devoted to resolve these problems. Before we construct our spectral sequence for general cases, we will demonstrate its construction and usage proving Theorem I, in certain simple situation. In this simple situation, the coefficient ring turns out to be Noetherian.

We use the energy filtration to construct our spectral sequence. We first recall some notations. Let L be a relatively spin Lagrangian submanifold in (M,ω) and ψ a Hamiltonian diffeomorphism. Suppose that L is unobstructed and transversal to $\psi(L)$. We recall $\Pi(L) = \pi_2(M,L)/\sim$ as in Definition 2.4.17. Then $\Pi(L)$ is the group of covering transformations of the covering $\widetilde{\Omega}(L,\psi(L);\ell_0) \to \Omega(L,\psi(L);\ell_0)$. (See Subsection 2.4.3.) We take $\ell_0 = \ell_{can}$ where the right hand side is defined in Subsection 2.3.2. For an element $[(\ell,w)] \in \widetilde{\Omega}(L,\psi(L);\ell_0)$, we put $\mathcal{A}([\ell,w]) = \int w^*\omega$. Then we have a group homomorphism, which is called *energy*, $E : \Pi(L) \longrightarrow$

$\mathbb{R}$ defined by

$$E(g) = \mathcal{A}(g \cdot [(\ell, w)]) - \mathcal{A}([(\ell, w)]),$$

which is independent of choice of $[(\ell, w)]$, (see Subsection 2.2.1). Note in Subsection 2.2.1 we defined $E : \Pi(L) \longrightarrow \mathbb{R}$ in the case where $L^{(0)}$ and $L^{(1)}$ intersect transversely. The definition of E for the case of clean intersection is similar.

Now in this section we put the following condition on L.

DEFINITION 6.2.1.

(6.2.2.1)   We call a Lagrangian submanifold *rational* if the subgroup

$$E(\Pi(L)) = \{E(\beta) \mid \beta \in \Pi(L)\} \subset \mathbb{R}$$

is discrete.

(6.2.2.2)   Let $L \subset M$ be a rational Lagrangian submanifold. We say that it is *rationally unobstructed* if there exists a monoid G that satisfies Condition 3.1.6 and contains the set of pairs $\{(E(\beta), \mu_L(\beta)) \mid \beta \in \Pi(L)\}$, such that

(6.2.3.1) $\pi(G) \subset \mathbb{R}$ is isomorphic to $\mathbb{Z}_{>0}$ as a monoid.
(6.2.3.2) $(C(L), \mathfrak{m})$ is unobstructed over G in the sense of Definition 3.6.16.

The weak and/or def version of rationally unobstructedness can be defined in a similar way. (For the def version we need to assume that $\mathfrak{b} \in H^2(M; \Lambda_{0,nov})$ also has the form $\sum_{(\lambda_i, \mu_i) \in G} \mathfrak{b}_i T^{\lambda_i} e^{\mu_i/2}$. ($\mathfrak{b}_i \in H^*(M; R)$.)

REMARK 6.2.4. In some of other references (for example in [**Fuk03I**]) the rationality of L is defined in a different way: We assume $[\omega] \in H^2(M; \mathbb{Z})$. Take a complex line bundle $\mathcal{L} \to M$ with $U(1)$ connection ∇ such that its first Chern form is ω. Then L was said to be rational if the holonomy group of the restriction of ∇ to L is of finite order. This definition is equivalent to Definition 6.2.1 in the case when M is simply connected but is more restrictive than Definition 6.2.1 in general.

Let G be the monoid given in Definition 6.2.1. We will fix G throughout this section. Now we introduce the following Novikov ring

$$(6.2.5.1) \qquad \widehat{\Lambda}(G) = \left\{ \sum_i a_i T^{\lambda_i} e^{n_i} \in \Lambda_{nov} \;\middle|\; \lambda_i \in E(G), \; a_i \in R \right\},$$

and its subring

$$(6.2.5.2) \qquad \widehat{\Lambda}_+(G) = \left\{ \sum_i a_i T^{\lambda_i} e^{n_i} \in \Lambda_{0,nov} \;\middle|\; \lambda_i \in E(G) \right\} = \Lambda_{0,nov} \cap \widehat{\Lambda}(G).$$

We remark that they are related to but different from the ring $\Lambda^R(L)$ defined right after Definition 2.4.17.

The degree of an element of $\widehat{\Lambda}(G)$ is the same as that in Λ_{nov}. The Novikov ring $\widehat{\Lambda}(G)$ is a localization of $\widehat{\Lambda}_+(G)$. Note that $\widehat{\Lambda}_+(G)$ is Noetherian if G satisfies (6.2.3.1). (In fact its degree 0 part $\widehat{\Lambda}_+(G)^{(0)}$ is a discrete valuation ring if R is a field.) This simplifies our study of the spectral sequence. In this section, we prove Theorem I by using our spectral sequence over $\widehat{\Lambda}(G)$ when L is rational and is rationally unobstructed. In this case the convergence of the spectral sequence follows from the standard argument. We also remark that the property (D.3) which will be used here can be proved without assuming that the coefficient ring is Noetherian. (See Subsection 6.4.2.)

By (6.2.3.1) we have $E(G) = \mathbb{Z}_{>0} \cdot \lambda_0$, $(\lambda_0 > 0)$. Then we indeed have

$$(6.2.6) \qquad \widehat{\Lambda}_+(G) \cong R[[T^{\lambda_0}]][e, e^{-1}].$$

The filtration of $\Lambda_{0,nov}$ defined by (6.1.1) induces a filtration on $\widehat{\Lambda}_+(G)$. We put

$$\mathfrak{F}^m \widehat{\Lambda}_+(G) = F^{m\lambda_0} \widehat{\Lambda}_+(G).$$

We remark that $\Lambda_{0,nov}$ is flat as a $\widehat{\Lambda}_+(G)$ module. Therefore a spectral sequence in Theorem D is induced. To prove Theorem I in our case, we will work with $\widehat{\Lambda}(G)$ instead of with $\widehat{\Lambda}_+(G)$, as we noted in the previous section. In this case, we have

$$(6.2.7) \qquad \widehat{\Lambda}(G) \cong R[[T^{\lambda_0}]][T^{-\lambda_0}][e, e^{-1}].$$

The filtration of Λ_{nov} in (6.1.2) also induces a filtration on $\widehat{\Lambda}(G)$. We put

$$\mathfrak{F}^m \widehat{\Lambda}(G) = F^{m\lambda_0} \widehat{\Lambda}(G).$$

Then it follows that we have

$$gr_q(\mathfrak{F}\widehat{\Lambda}_+(G)) \cong R[e, e^{-1}].$$

We take a countably generated submodule $C^k(L; R)$ of the free R module $S^k(L; R)$ generated by smooth singular $(n-k)$-simplices on L. We denote by $C(L; \widehat{\Lambda}(G))$ the completion of $C(L, R) \otimes_R \widehat{\Lambda}(G)$. The filtration $\mathfrak{F}^* \widehat{\Lambda}(G)$ induces a filtration on $C(L; \widehat{\Lambda}(G))$ which we denote by $\mathfrak{F}^* C(L; \widehat{\Lambda}(G))$. The degree is the sum of the degrees of $C(L; R)$ and $\widehat{\Lambda}(G)$. Since L is unobstructed over G, there exists a bounding cochain $b \in \mathcal{M}(L)$. Moreover we can choose b so that it is contained in $C(L; \widehat{\Lambda}(G))$. Then, we have the deformed A_∞ algebra $(C(L; \widehat{\Lambda}(G)), \mathfrak{m}^b)$ with $\mathfrak{m}_0^b = 0$ from Proposition 3.6.10. Thus $\mathfrak{m}_1^b$ defines the coboundary operator on $C(L; \widehat{\Lambda}(G))$ to enable us to obtain the deformed Floer cohomology $HF((L, b), (L, b); \widehat{\Lambda}(G))$ with this coefficient ring. We omit b from our notation in this section whenever no confusion can occur. The filtration on $C(L, \widehat{\Lambda}(G))$ induces the spectral sequence we are defining.

We first note that there is an isomorphism

$$(6.2.8) \qquad gr_*(\mathfrak{F}C(L; \widehat{\Lambda}(L))) \cong C(L; R) \otimes gr_*(\mathfrak{F}\widehat{\Lambda}(G))$$

as $gr_*(\mathfrak{F}^* \widehat{\Lambda}(G))$ modules. By construction of the differential (Definition 3.5.6), the differential induced on (6.2.8) is $(-1)^n \partial \otimes id$ where ∂ is the classical boundary operator on $C(L; R)$. Therefore we obtain the spectral sequence $E_r^{p,q}$ where E_2-term is given by

$$(6.2.9) \qquad E_2^{p,q} = \bigoplus_{k=0}^{n} H^k(L; R) \otimes gr_q(\mathfrak{F}\widehat{\Lambda}(G)^{(p-k)}).$$

Here $\widehat{\Lambda}(G)^{(p-k)}$ denotes the degree $p - k$ part. We can also show that there exists a filtration on $HF^p((L, L; \widehat{\Lambda}(G))$ such that

$$(6.2.10) \qquad E_\infty^{p,q} \cong \mathfrak{F}^q HF^p(L, L; \widehat{\Lambda}(G)) / \mathfrak{F}^{q+1} HF^p(L, L; \widehat{\Lambda}(G)).$$

We remark that the proof of convergence of the above spectral sequence works for an arbitrary commutative ring R.

Note that multiplications by T^{λ_0} and e give the following isomorphisms respectively:

$$T^{\lambda_0} \cdot \; : \; \mathfrak{F}^q HF^p(L, L; \widehat{\Lambda}(G)) \longrightarrow \mathfrak{F}^{q+1} HF^p(L, L; \widehat{\Lambda}(G))$$

$$e \cdot \; : \; \mathfrak{F}^q HF^p(L, L; \widehat{\Lambda}(G)) \longrightarrow \mathfrak{F}^q HF^{p+2}(L, L; \widehat{\Lambda}(G)).$$

Now consider a graded $\widehat{\Lambda}(G)$ module D that has a filtration $\mathfrak{F}^* D$ compatible with that on $\widehat{\Lambda}(G)$ in that

$$\mathfrak{F}^\ell \widehat{\Lambda}(G) \cdot \mathfrak{F}^k D \subseteq \mathfrak{F}^{k+\ell} D.$$

Let $\widehat{\Lambda}(G)^{(0)}$ be the degree 0 part of $\widehat{\Lambda}(G)$. We have

$$\widehat{\Lambda}(G)^{(0)} \cong R[[T^{\lambda_0}]][T^{-\lambda_0}]$$

which shows that, if R is a field, then $\widehat{\Lambda}(G)^{(0)}$ is a field and so the degree p part D^p of D is a vector space over $\widehat{\Lambda}(G)^{(0)}$.

DEFINITION 6.2.11. We define the t-rank (the topological rank or tentative rank) by

$$t\text{-} \operatorname{rank} D = \dim_{\widehat{\Lambda}(G)^{(0)}} D^p + \dim_{\widehat{\Lambda}(G)^{(0)}} D^{p+1}.$$

Since the multiplication by e defines an isomorphism $D^p \cong D^{p+2}$, it follows that the right hand side is independent of p.

Hereafter we put $R = \mathbb{Q}$. (The argument of the rest of this section works for arbitrary field R in case Floer cohomology is defined over $\Lambda_{0,nov}(R)$ and L is rational.)

LEMMA 6.2.12. *For any q, we have:*

$$t\text{-} \operatorname{rank} HF(L, L; \widehat{\Lambda}(G))$$
$$= \dim_{\mathbb{Q}} \mathfrak{F}^q HF^p(L, L; \widehat{\Lambda}(G))/\mathfrak{F}^{q+1} HF^p(L, L; \widehat{\Lambda}(G))$$
$$\quad + \dim_{\mathbb{Q}} \mathfrak{F}^q HF^{p+1}(L, L; \widehat{\Lambda}(G))/\mathfrak{F}^{q+1} HF^{p+1}(L, L; \widehat{\Lambda}(G))$$
$$= \dim_{\mathbb{Q}} E_\infty^{p,q} + \dim_{\mathbb{Q}} E_\infty^{p+1,q}.$$

The proof is easy and so omitted.

The following lemma easily follows from Theorem 3.7.21 and Theorem 4.1.3.

LEMMA 6.2.13. *If ψ is a Hamiltonian diffeomorphism and if L is transversal to $\psi(L)$, then*

$$\#(L \cap \psi(L)) \geq t\text{-} \operatorname{rank} HF((L, b), (L, b); \widehat{\Lambda}(G))$$

for any $b \in \mathcal{M}(L)$.

We now estimate $\dim_{\mathbb{Q}} E_\infty^{p,q} + \dim_{\mathbb{Q}} E_\infty^{p+1,q}$ from below. Let $\delta_r : E_r \to E_r$ be the coboundary operator of the spectral sequence. We have $\delta_r \delta_r = 0$ and

$$E_{r+1} = \operatorname{Ker} \delta_r / \operatorname{Im} \delta_r.$$

E_r is a $gr_*(\mathfrak{F}\widehat{\Lambda}(G))$ module and $gr_*(\mathfrak{F}\widehat{\Lambda}(G)) \cong \widehat{\Lambda}(G)$. Therefore we can define t-$\operatorname{rank} E_r$ by Definition 6.2.11.

LEMMA 6.2.14.

$$t\text{-} \operatorname{rank} E_r - 2\, t\text{-} \operatorname{rank} \operatorname{Im} \delta_r = t\text{-} \operatorname{rank} E_{r+1} \leq t\text{-} \operatorname{rank} E_r.$$

PROOF. There exist short exact sequences of $\widehat{\Lambda}(G)$ modules:

$$0 \to \operatorname{Ker} \delta_r \to E_r \to (\operatorname{Im} \delta_r)[-1] \to 0,$$
$$0 \to \operatorname{Im} \delta_r \to \operatorname{Ker} \delta_r \to E_{r+1} \to 0.$$

We obtain

$$t\text{-}\operatorname{rank} E_r = t\text{-}\operatorname{rank} \operatorname{Ker} \delta_r + t\text{-}\operatorname{rank} \operatorname{Im} \delta_r$$

from the first exact sequence. The second exact sequence then implies the lemma. $\square$

Now we give the proof of Theorem I, when L is (weakly) unobstructed (after bulk deformation) over G. From (6.2.9) and from the fact that e is of degree 2, we derive

$$t\text{-}\operatorname{rank} E_2 = \sum t\text{-}\operatorname{rank}_{\mathbb{Q}} H^*(L; \mathbb{Q}).$$

We put

$$K_2 = PD(\operatorname{Ker}(H_*(L; \mathbb{Q}) \to H_*(M; \mathbb{Q}))) \otimes_{\mathbb{Q}} gr_*(\mathfrak{F}^*\widehat{\Lambda}(G)),$$
$$K_{r+1} = \frac{K_r \cap \operatorname{Ker}(\delta_r)}{K_r \cap \operatorname{Im}(\delta_r)}$$

as in (D.3). Then as we will prove in Subsection 6.4.2, we can use the operator $\mathfrak{p}$ to show

(6.2.15) $\operatorname{Im}(\delta_r) \subset K_r.$

Therefore we have

$$t\text{-}\operatorname{rank} K_{r+1} \leq t\text{-}\operatorname{rank} K_r - t\text{-}\operatorname{rank} \operatorname{Im}(\delta_r).$$

Combining this and Lemma 6.2.14, we obtain

$$t\text{-}\operatorname{rank} E_r = t\text{-}\operatorname{rank} E_2 - 2 \sum_{2 \leq i < r} t\text{-}\operatorname{rank} \operatorname{Im}(\delta_i)$$

$$= \sum \operatorname{rank}_{\mathbb{Q}} H^*(L; \mathbb{Q}) - 2 \sum_{2 \leq i < r} t\text{-}\operatorname{rank} \operatorname{Im}(\delta_i)$$

$$\geq \sum \operatorname{rank}_{\mathbb{Q}} H^*(L; \mathbb{Q}) - 2 \left(t\text{-}\operatorname{rank} K_2 - t\text{-}\operatorname{rank} K_r \right).$$

Therefore

$$t\text{-}\operatorname{rank} HF(L, L; \widehat{\Lambda}(G)) = t\text{-}\operatorname{rank} E_\infty \geq \sum \operatorname{rank}_{\mathbb{Q}} H^*(L; \mathbb{Q}) - 2\, t\text{-}\operatorname{rank} K_2.$$

The proof of Theorem I is complete (modulo the proof of (6.2.15)) for rationally unobstructed Lagrangian submanifold. $\square$

6.3. The algebraic construction of the spectral sequence

The purpose of this section is to provide an algebraic construction of a spectral sequence from a filtered differential $\Lambda_{0,nov}$ module. We first need to prepare some algebraic material for this purpose. In this section we will write $\Lambda_{0,nov}$ in place of $\Lambda_{0,nov}(R)$. Here R is an arbitrary *field*.

6.3.1. c.f.z.. We first start from the following situation. Let $V = (\Lambda_{0,nov}^{(0)})^{\oplus I}$ be a free $\Lambda_{0,nov}^{(0)}$ module, which is not necessarily finitely generated. Here we recall that $\Lambda_{0,nov}^{(0)}$ is the degree 0 part of $\Lambda_{0,nov}$. We define a filtration on V by

$$F^\lambda V = (F^\lambda \Lambda_{0,nov}^{(0)})^{\oplus I}$$

which will induce a topology on V. Let $\widehat{V}$ be the completion of V. We call such $\widehat{V}$ a *completed free filtered $\Lambda_{0,nov}^{(0)}$ module generated by energy zero elements*, or in short *c.f.z.* If V is finitely generated (as a $\Lambda_{0,nov}^{(0)}$ module) in addition, we say that it is a *finite* c.f.z. We define a function, which we call the energy function,

$$E \; : \; \widehat{V} \setminus \{0\} \longrightarrow \mathbb{R}_{\geq 0}$$

such that

$$\mathfrak{v} \in F^{E(\mathfrak{v})}V, \qquad \mathfrak{v} \notin F^\lambda V \quad \text{if } \lambda > E(\mathfrak{v}).$$

Let $\overline{V} = V/\Lambda_{0,nov}^{+,(0)}V \cong R^I$. *We always take an embedding (splitting) $\overline{V} \subset V$ as the energy 0 part of V so that its composition with the projection $V \to \overline{V}$ is the identity map.*

Let $\mathfrak{v} \in V$. We put

$$\mathfrak{v} = \sum T^{\lambda_i} v_i,$$

where $v_i \in \overline{V}$, $\lambda_i < \lambda_{i+1}$, $\lim_{i\to\infty} \lambda_i = \infty$ and $v_i \neq 0$. We call $T^{\lambda_i} v_i$ the *components* of $\mathfrak{v}$, $T^{\lambda_1} v_1$ the *leading component* and v_1 the *leading coefficient* of $\mathfrak{v}$. We denote the leading coefficient v_1 of $\mathfrak{v}$ by $\sigma(\mathfrak{v})$. We also define the leading component and the leading coefficient of an element of $\Lambda_{0,nov}^{(0)}$ in the same way.

We remark that $\sigma(v)$ is independent of the choice of the splitting $\overline{V} \subset V$.

DEFINITION 6.3.1. A (finite) set $\{\mathfrak{v}_i\}_{1\leq i\leq m}$ of elements $\mathfrak{v}_i \in \widehat{V}$, $i = 1, \cdots, m$ which generates the subspace $W \subset \widehat{V}$ is called a *standard basis* of W if the following holds: When we put $E(\mathfrak{v}_i) = \lambda_i$ and let $\sigma(\mathfrak{v}_i)$ be the leading coefficient of $\mathfrak{v}_i$, we have

(6.3.1.1) $\lambda_i \leq \lambda_{i+1}$.
(6.3.1.2) $\sigma(\mathfrak{v}_1), \cdots, \sigma(\mathfrak{v}_m)$ are linearly independent over R.

It is easy to see that W is a free $\Lambda_{0,nov}^{(0)}$ module if it has a standard basis.

LEMMA 6.3.2. *Any finitely generated submodule W of $\widehat{V}$ has a standard basis.*

PROOF. Assume that W is generated by the set of m elements $\mathfrak{v}_i$, $i = 1, \cdots, m$. We put $E(\mathfrak{v}_i) = \lambda_i$. We may assume $\lambda_i \leq \lambda_{i+1}$ by reordering them, if necessary.

We will modify the set so that it becomes a standard basis. Let us first take k such that

$$\lambda_1 = \cdots = \lambda_k < \lambda_{k+1}.$$

If we consider the leading coefficients $\sigma(\mathfrak{v}_j)$ of $\mathfrak{v}_j$ for $j = 1, \cdots, k$, we can find an invertible matrix $(a_{i,i'})$ with entries in R such that the linear combinations

$$\sum_{i'=1}^{k} a_{i,i'}\sigma(\mathfrak{v}_{i'})$$

are linearly independent for $i = 1, \cdots, \ell \leq k$ and become zero for $i > \ell$. By changing a part of the generators $\mathfrak{v}_1, \cdots, \mathfrak{v}_k$ by the matrix $(a_{i,i'})$, we find a generating set $\{\mathfrak{v}_i\}$ of W that satisfies (6.3.3.1), where the condition (6.3.3.n) is defined as follows:

(6.3.3.n)   When we define integer k_e's by

$$\lambda_1 = \cdots = \lambda_{k_1} < \lambda_{k_1+1} = \cdots = \lambda_{k_2} < \lambda_{k_2+1} = \cdots,$$

$\sigma(\mathfrak{v}_j)$'s for $j = 1, \cdots, k_n$ are linearly independent.

Now we will modify the given elements $\mathfrak{v}_i$'s inductively on n so that (6.3.3.n) is satisfied. Let us assume (6.3.3.n). By applying a filtered automorphism of V, we may assume that

(6.3.4) $$\mathfrak{v}_j = T^{\lambda_j}\sigma(\mathfrak{v}_j)$$

for $j = 1, \cdots, \lambda_{k_n}$.

Let $X \subset \overline{V}$ be the R linear subspace generated by $\sigma(\mathfrak{v}_j)$, $j = 1, \cdots, \lambda_{k_n}$. We consider the following two cases separately:

(6.3.5.1)   There exists $i \in \{k_n + 1, \cdots, k_{n+1}\}$ such that $\sigma(\mathfrak{v}_i) \notin X$.
(6.3.5.2) $\sigma(\mathfrak{v}_i) \in X$ for all $i \in \{k_n + 1, \cdots, k_{n+1}\}$.

We first consider the case where (6.3.5.1) is satisfied. Then we have an invertible matrix $(a_{i,i'})$ $(i, i' \in \{k_n + 1, \cdots, k_{n+1}\})$, $a_{i,j} \in R$ and $b_{i,j} \in R$ $(i \in \{k_n + 1, \cdots, k_{n+1}\}, j \in \{1, \cdots, k_n\})$ satisfying the condition (6.3.6) below, if we put

$$v'_{i,1} = \sum_{j=1}^{k_n} b_{i,j}\sigma(\mathfrak{v}_j) + \sum_{i'=k_n+1}^{k_{n+1}} a_{i,i'}\sigma(\mathfrak{v}_{i'}) :$$

(6.3.6.1)   There exists $k_n < \ell \leq k_{n+1}$ such that the union

$$\{\sigma(\mathfrak{v}_j)\}_{1 \leq j \leq k_n} \cup \{v'_{i,1}\}_{k_n+1 \leq i \leq \ell}$$

is linearly independent.
(6.3.6.2) $v'_{i,1}$ are zero for $i > \ell$.

Now for $i = k_n + 1, \cdots, k_{n+1}$, we replace $\mathfrak{v}_i$ by

$$\mathfrak{v}'_i = \sum_j b_{i,j}T^{\lambda_{k_n+1}-\lambda_j}\mathfrak{v}_j + \sum_{i'} a_{i,i'}\mathfrak{v}_{i'}.$$

Note that the leading coefficient of $\mathfrak{v}'_i$ is equal to $v'_{i,1}$ for $k_n + 1 \leq i \leq \ell$. Hence, (6.3.6.2) implies $E(\mathfrak{v}'_i) > \lambda_{k_n+1}$ for $\ell < i \leq k_{n+1}$. Now (6.3.3.$n+1$) follows from (6.3.6.1). Thus the induction works for the first case.

In case (6.3.5.2) is satisfied, for all $k_n + 1 \leq i \leq k_{n+1}$ we have

$$v'_{i,1} = \sum_{j=1}^{k_n} b_{i,j}\sigma(\mathfrak{v}_j)$$

for some $b_{i,j}$. We replace $\mathfrak{v}_i$ for $i = k_n + 1, \cdots, k_{n+1}$ by

$$\mathfrak{v}'_i = \mathfrak{v}_i - \sum_{j=1}^{k_n} b_{i,j}T^{\lambda_{k_n+1}-\lambda_j}\mathfrak{v}_j.$$

It then follows from the above that the coefficient of $\mathfrak{v}'_i$ for the energy level λ_{k_n+1} becomes

$$\sigma(\mathfrak{v}_i) - \sum_{j=1}^{k_n} b_{i,j}\sigma(\mathfrak{v}_j) = \sigma(\mathfrak{v}_i) - \sigma(\mathfrak{v}_i) = 0$$

for all $k_n + 1 \le i \le k_{n+1}$. Therefore we have

$$E(\mathfrak{v}'_i) > \lambda_{k_n+1} = \lambda_{k_{n+1}}$$

for all $k_n + 1 \le i \le k_{n+1}$. We now re-number $\mathfrak{v}_i$'s for $i = k_n + 1, \cdots$ according to their energy.

We again divide the cases into (6.3.5.1) and (6.3.5.2) and repeat the same process. If we end up with the (6.3.5.1), we go to the next step of the induction. Otherwise we continue. This process will continue infinitely many times only if all the components of $\mathfrak{v}_i$, $i = k_n + 1, \cdots$ are contained in X. (We use (6.3.4) to prove it.) In this case it is easy to see that we can eliminate all $\mathfrak{v}_i$, $i = k_n + 1, \cdots$ from the given generating set without changing the module generated by them. The proof of Lemma 6.3.2 is now complete. $\square$

The following is an immediate corollary of Lemma 6.3.2 and the remark right before it.

COROLLARY 6.3.7. *Any finitely generated submodule W of $\widehat{V}$ is free and closed.*

We remark that in the course of the proof of Lemma 6.3.2 the following is also proved.

LEMMA 6.3.2BIS. *Let W be as in Lemma 6.3.2 and $v_1, \cdots, v_m$ be a generator of W such that $E(v_i) \le E(v_{i+1})$ and $\{\sigma(v_1), \cdots, \sigma(v_k)\}$ is linearly independent over R.*
Then we may choose a standard basis $v'_1, \cdots, v'_{m'}$ such that $v_i = v'_i$ for $i = 1, \cdots, k$.

6.3.2. d.g.c.f.z. (differential graded c.f.z.). Now we consider the case of graded $\Lambda_{0,nov}$ modules.

DEFINITION 6.3.8. *Let $\widehat{C}$ be a graded $\Lambda_{0,nov}$ module. We assume that $\widehat{C}^k$ is a c.f.z. for each k. A differential graded c.f.z. (abbreviated as d.g.c.f.z) is a pair $(\widehat{C}, \delta)$ with a degree 1 operator $\delta : \widehat{C} \to \widehat{C}$ such that*

$$\delta \circ \delta = 0, \qquad \delta(F^\lambda \widehat{C}) \subseteq F^\lambda \widehat{C}.$$

We call the pair a *finite* d.g.c.f.z. if each $\widehat{C}^k$ is a finite c.f.z.

We remark that $\widehat{C}^k$ is a $\Lambda_{0,nov}^{(0)}$ module.
We now prove the following proposition. This will be essential for the proof of some convergence properties of the spectral sequence to be constructed in this section.

PROPOSITION 6.3.9. *Let W be a finitely generated $\Lambda_{0,nov}^{(0)}$ submodule of $\widehat{C}^k$. Then there exists a constant c depending only on W but independent of λ such that*

$$\delta(W) \cap F^\lambda \widehat{C}^{k+1} \subset \delta(W \cap F^{\lambda-c} \widehat{C}^k).$$

PROOF. Obviously $\delta(W)$ is a finitely generated submodule of $\widehat{C}^{k+1}$ and so has a standard basis by Lemma 6.3.2. Let $\{\mathfrak{v}_i\}$ be a standard basis of $\delta(W)$ and let $\mathfrak{w}_i \in W$ satisfy $\delta\mathfrak{w}_i = \mathfrak{v}_i$. Suppose $\mathfrak{u} \in \delta(W)$ with $E(\mathfrak{u}) = \lambda$ and

$$\mathfrak{u} = \sum a_i \mathfrak{v}_i.$$

We put $\sigma(a_i) \in R$ to be the leading coefficient of $a_i \in \Lambda^{(0)}_{0,nov}$ and let $E(\mathfrak{v}_i) = \lambda_i$ and $E(a_i) = \mu_i \geq 0$. Note that $\lambda \geq \lambda_i$ for all i with $a_i \neq 0$.

LEMMA 6.3.10. *If* $\lambda > \lambda_i$ *for all* i*, then we have* $\lambda_i + \mu_i \geq \lambda$*.*

PROOF. Suppose the contrary that there exists some i with $\lambda_i + \mu_i < \lambda$. Let $\lambda - a = \inf_i\{\lambda_i + \mu_i\}$ with $a > 0$. We will then have

$$\sum_{i:\lambda-a=\lambda_i+\mu_i} \sigma(a_i)\sigma(\mathfrak{v}_i) = 0,$$

because $E(\mathfrak{u}) = \lambda > \lambda - a$. This contradicts to the fact that the leading coefficients of $\mathfrak{v}_i$'s are linearly independent. This finishes the proof of Lemma 6.3.10. $\qquad\square$

It follows from Lemma 6.3.10 that if $\lambda > \lambda_i$ for all i with $a_i \neq 0$,

$$E(a_i) = \mu_i \geq \lambda - \lambda_i.$$

Now we put $c = \max\{\lambda_i\}$. Note that c depends only on W and is independent of λ.

If $\lambda > \lambda_i$, then there exists $b_i \in \Lambda^{(0)}_{0,nov}$ such that $T^{\lambda-c}b_i = a_i$. Hence

$$\mathfrak{u} = \delta(\sum T^{\lambda-c}b_i\mathfrak{w}_i) \in \delta(W \cap F^{\lambda-c}\widehat{C}^k).$$

On the other hand, if $\lambda = \lambda_i$ for some i, we have $\lambda = c$ and hence Proposition 6.3.9 trivially holds. Proposition 6.3.9 is proved. $\qquad\square$

LEMMA 6.3.11. *Let* V *be a finite c.f.z. and* W *its submodule such that there exists* $\mathfrak{w}_0 \in W$ *satisfying* $T^\lambda\mathfrak{w}_0 = \mathfrak{w}$ *for any* $\mathfrak{w} \in W$ *with* $E(\mathfrak{w}) = \lambda$*. Then* W *is finitely generated. Moreover it has a standard basis all of whose elements have energy* 0*.*

PROOF. Let W_{00} be the set of elements of $\overline{V}$ which are leading coefficients of some elements of W. $W_{00} \cup \{0\}$ is obviously a finite dimensional R linear subspace of $\overline{V}$, which we write as W_0. Let $\{w_i\}$ be a basis of W_0. For each w_i, we choose an element $\mathfrak{w}_i \in W$ whose leading coefficient is w_i. By the hypothesis of the lemma, we may assume $E(\mathfrak{w}_i) = 0$. We will prove that $\{\mathfrak{w}_i\}$ generates W, which will in turn imply the lemma.

By applying a filtered automorphism on V, we may assume that

(6.3.12) $$\mathfrak{w}_i = w_i \in \overline{V}.$$

Now let $\mathfrak{v} \in W$ and put

$$\mathfrak{v} = \sum T^{\lambda_i}v_i.$$

We have $v_1 \in W_0$ by definition. (6.3.12) implies $v_1 \in W$ and so $\sum_{i=2} T^{\lambda_i}v_i$ is contained in W. Hence we have $v_2 \in W_0$. Repeating the same argument, we prove that $v_i \in W_0$ for all i. It is then easy to see that $\mathfrak{v}$ is contained in the $\Lambda^{(0)}_{0,nov}$ submodule generated by $\mathfrak{w}_i$'s, since each of v_i is a linear combination of w_i's. $\qquad\square$

COROLLARY 6.3.13. *Let (C, δ) be a finite d.g.c.f.z. Then $\operatorname{Ker} \delta_k = \operatorname{Ker} \delta \cap C^k$ is finitely generated for all k. Furthermore we can take their standard bases consisting of elements of energy 0.*

PROOF. It is easy to see that $\operatorname{Ker} \delta$ satisfies the assumption of Lemma 6.3.11. $\square$

Corollary 6.3.13 and Lemma 6.3.2 immediately imply the following structure theorem on the cohomology of a finite d.g.c.f.z.

PROPOSITION 6.3.14. *Let (C, δ) be a finite d.g.c.f.z. Then for each integer p, there exist a finite number of constants $\lambda_{p,i} > 0$, $i = 1, \cdots, k_p$ and ℓ_p with $\ell_p \leq \operatorname{rank} C^p - k_p$ and ℓ_p such that*

$$(6.3.15) \qquad H^p(C, \delta) \cong \Big(\bigoplus_{i=1}^{k_p} \big(\Lambda_{0,nov}^{(0)} / F^{\lambda_{p,i}} \Lambda_{0,nov}^{(0)} \big) \Big) \bigoplus (\Lambda_{0,nov}^{(0)})^{\oplus \ell_p}.$$

If we choose $\lambda_{p,i}$ so that $\lambda_{p,i+1} \geq \lambda_{p,i}$, then $\lambda_{p,i}$ are uniquely determined.

PROOF. First note that since C^p is finite, $\operatorname{Im} \delta_p$ is finitely generated and so has a standard basis, say, $\{T^{\mu_{p,1}} u_1, T^{\mu_{p,2}} u_2, \cdots, T^{\mu_{p,k_p}} u_{k_p}\}$ for $u_i \in \overline{C}^p = C^p / \Lambda_{0,nov}^{+(0)} C^p$. Since we have $\operatorname{Im} \delta_{p-1} \subset \operatorname{Ker} \delta_p$ and $\operatorname{Ker} \delta_p$ has a basis in $\overline{C}^p$ consisting of energy zero, $u_i \in \operatorname{Ker} \delta_p$. Therefore we may extend $\{u_1, \cdots, u_{k_p}\}$ to a standard basis

$$\{u_1, u_2, \cdots, u_{k_p}, u_{k_p+1}, \cdots, u_{k_p+\ell_p}\}.$$

Now (6.3.15) immediately follows from this.

To prove the uniqueness we only need to remark

$$\dim_R \frac{T^\lambda H^p(C, \delta)}{T^\lambda \Lambda_{0,nov}^{+(0)} H^p(C, \delta)} = \ell_p + \#\{i \mid \lambda_{p,i} > \lambda\}.$$

$$\square$$

The authors do not know whether Proposition 6.3.9 (and hence the convergence of the spectral sequence) holds when we replace the field R by an arbitrary Noetherian ring.

6.3.3. Construction and convergence. Now let $(\widehat{C}, \delta)$ be a d.g.c.f.z. and $\widehat{C}^k$ a completion of C^k. We assume that C^k is *free over* $\Lambda_{0,nov}^{(0)}$. We put

$$\overline{C} = C / \Lambda_{0,nov}^{+(0)} C \cong \widehat{C} / \Lambda_{0,nov}^{+(0)} \widehat{C},$$

and let $\overline{\delta}$ be the induced derivation on $\overline{C}$. We again embed $\overline{C} \subseteq C \subseteq \widehat{C}$ as the energy 0 part. In general $\overline{C}$ is *not* a differential graded subalgebra of $\widehat{C}$. Let $\{\mathfrak{e}_i\}$ be a basis of C (over $\Lambda_{0,nov}^{(0)}$) and $\overline{\mathfrak{e}}_i$ be the corresponding basis of $\overline{C}$ over $R = \Lambda_{0,nov}^{(0)} / \Lambda_{0,nov}^{+(0)}$. We put

$$\overline{\delta}(\overline{\mathfrak{e}}_i) = \sum \delta_{0,ij} \overline{\mathfrak{e}}_j,$$

and define $\delta_0 : \widehat{C} \to \widehat{C}$ by

$$\delta_0 \mathfrak{e}_i = \sum \delta_{0,ij} \mathfrak{e}_j.$$

CONDITION 6.3.16. We say that $(\widehat{C}, \delta)$ satisfies the *gapped condition* if there exists $\lambda'' > 0$ such that for any λ we have

$$\delta \mathfrak{v} - \delta_0 \mathfrak{v} \in F^{\lambda + \lambda''} \widehat{C}$$

for all $\mathfrak{v} \in F^\lambda \widehat{C}$.

REMARK 6.3.17. If a filtered A_∞ algebra $(C, \mathfrak{m})$ with $\mathfrak{m}_0 = 0$ is G-gapped in the sense of Definition 3.2.26, $(C, \mathfrak{m}_1)$ satisfies the gapped condition above.

Assuming Condition 6.3.16, we take a constant λ_0 with $0 < \lambda_0 < \lambda''$ and define a filtration by

$$(6.3.18) \qquad \mathfrak{F}^n \widehat{C} = F^{n\lambda_0} \widehat{C}.$$

We use this filtration to define our spectral sequence. Since construction of the spectral sequence from a filtered module over a *filtered* ring is not so standard, we present its construction here for reader's convenience.

We put

$$(6.3.19.1) \qquad Z_r^{p,q}(\widehat{C}) = \{ x \in \mathfrak{F}^q \widehat{C}^p \mid \delta x \in \mathfrak{F}^{q+r-1} \widehat{C}^{p+1} \} + \mathfrak{F}^{q+1} \widehat{C}^p,$$

$$(6.3.19.2) \qquad B_r^{p,q}(\widehat{C}) = (\delta(\mathfrak{F}^{q-r+2} \widehat{C}^{p-1}) \cap \mathfrak{F}^q \widehat{C}^p) + \mathfrak{F}^{q+1} \widehat{C}^p,$$

$$(6.3.19.3) \qquad E_r^{p,q}(\widehat{C}) = Z_r^{p,q}(\widehat{C}) / B_r^{p,q}(\widehat{C}).$$

We denote

$$\Lambda^{(0)}(\lambda) = \Lambda_{0,nov}^{(0)} / F^\lambda \Lambda_{0,nov}^{(0)}.$$

We define a filtration of $\Lambda_{0,nov}^{(0)}$ by $\mathfrak{F}^n \Lambda_{0,nov}^{(0)} = F^{n\lambda_0} \Lambda_{0,nov}^{(0)}$. Then its associated graded module is given by

$$gr_*(\mathfrak{F}\Lambda_{0,nov}^{(0)}) = \bigoplus_{n \in \mathbb{Z}_{\geq 0}} gr_n(\mathfrak{F}\Lambda_{0,nov}^{(0)}),$$

where each $gr_n(\mathfrak{F}\Lambda_{0,nov}^{(0)})$ is naturally isomorphic to $\Lambda^{(0)}(\lambda_0)$. We also have

$$gr_*(\mathfrak{F}\Lambda_{0,nov}) = gr_*(\mathfrak{F}\Lambda_{0,nov}^{(0)})[e, e^{-1}] = \bigoplus_{n \in \mathbb{Z}_{\geq 0}} gr_n(\mathfrak{F}\Lambda_{0,nov}^{(0)})[e, e^{-1}].$$

Recall that $E_r^{p,q}$ has a natural structure of $\Lambda^{(0)}(\lambda_0)$ module. The multiplication by $e^{\pm 1} \in \Lambda_{0,nov}$ defines a map

$$e^{\pm 1} : E_r^{p,q}(\widehat{C}) \to E_r^{p\pm2,q}(\widehat{C}),$$

which turns $E_r(\widehat{C}) := \bigoplus_{p,q} E_r^{p,q}(\widehat{C})$ into a $gr_*(\mathfrak{F}\Lambda_{0,nov})$ module and

$$\bigoplus_{p,q} \delta_r^{p,q} : \bigoplus_{p,q} E_r^{p,q}(\widehat{C}) \to \bigoplus_{p,q} E_r^{p+1,q+r-1}(\widehat{C})$$

is a $gr(\mathfrak{F}^* \Lambda_{0,nov})$ module homomorphism.

LEMMA 6.3.20. *There exists a $\Lambda^{(0)}(\lambda_0)$ module homomorphism*

$$\delta_r^{p,q} : E_r^{p,q}(\widehat{C}) \to E_r^{p+1,q+r-1}(\widehat{C})$$

such that

(6.3.21.1) $\delta_r^{p+1,q+r-1} \circ \delta_r^{p,q} = 0,$
(6.3.21.2) $\operatorname{Ker}(\delta_r^{p,q})/\operatorname{Im}(\delta_r^{p-1,q-r+1}) \cong E_{r+1}^{p,q}(\widehat{C}),$
(6.3.21.3) $e^{\pm 1} \circ \delta_r^{p,q} = \delta_r^{p\pm 2,q} \circ e^{\pm 1}.$

PROOF. We define $\delta_r^{p,q}[x] = [\delta x] \in E_r^{p+1,q+r-1}(\widehat{C})$. The proof of (6.3.21) is standard. □

Of course, the construction of $E_r^{p,q}(\widehat{C})$ is quite standard. One difference from the standard case is that our filtration is not bounded. Namely we do *not* have $\mathfrak{F}^n\widehat{C} = 0$ for large n. Hence the convergence property of our spectral sequence is far from being trivial in general. However it is stable from below in that $\mathfrak{F}^0\widehat{C} = \widehat{C}$. As a consequence we have:

LEMMA 6.3.22. *There exists an injection*

$$E_{r+1}^{p,q}(\widehat{C}) \to E_r^{p,q}(\widehat{C})$$

if $q - r + 2 \le 0$.

PROOF. The denominator $\delta(\mathfrak{F}^{q-r+2}\widehat{C}^{p-1}) \cap \mathfrak{F}^q\widehat{C}^p + \mathfrak{F}^{q+1}\widehat{C}^p$ in the definition of $E_r^{p,q}(\widehat{C})$ is independent of r if $q - r + 2 \le 0$. □

DEFINITION 6.3.23. We define

$$E_\infty^{p,q}(\widehat{C}) = \varprojlim E_r^{p,q}(\widehat{C})$$

as the projective limit which exists by Lemma 6.3.22.

LEMMA 6.3.24. *We have an isomorphism*

$$E_2^{*,*}(\widehat{C}) \cong H(\overline{C}; \overline{\delta}) \otimes_R gr_*(\mathfrak{F}\Lambda_{0,nov})$$

as $gr_*(\mathfrak{F}\Lambda_{0,nov})$ modules.

PROOF. By definition we have

$$E_1^{*,*}(\widehat{C}) \cong \overline{C} \otimes_R gr_*(\mathfrak{F}\Lambda_{0,nov}).$$

It follows from Condition 6.3.16 that $\delta_1 = \overline{\delta}$. Hence it finishes the proof. □

DEFINITION 6.3.25. We define $\mathfrak{F}^q H(\widehat{C}, \delta)$ to be the image of $H(\mathfrak{F}^q\widehat{C}, \delta)$ in $H(\widehat{C}, \delta)$.

To relate the limit $E_\infty^{p,q}$ of the spectral sequence and $\mathfrak{F}^q H(\widehat{C}, \delta)$, we need some finiteness assumption which we now describe. Let (C, δ) and (C', δ') be d.g.c.f.z's satisfying the gap condition. Let $\varphi : C \to C'$ be a map such that $\varphi\delta = \delta'\varphi$ and let $\overline{\varphi} : \overline{C} \to \overline{C}'$ be the map induced on $\overline{C} = C/\Lambda_{0,nov}^{+(0)}C$ and $\overline{C}' = C'/\Lambda_{0,nov}^{+(0)}C'$ respectively. The induced map $\overline{\varphi}$ lifts to $\varphi_0 : C \to C'$ using the basis on C and C'.

DEFINITION 6.3.26. Under the situation above, we say that $\varphi : C \to C'$ satisfies *a gapped condition*, or is *a gapped cochain map*, if there exists λ'' such that

$$(\varphi - \varphi_0)(F^\lambda \widehat{C}) \subset F^{\lambda + \lambda''} \widehat{C}.$$

As in Remark 6.3.17, we note that if a filtered A_∞ homomorphism is G-gapped in the sense of Definition 3.2.29, the induced map satisfies the gapped condition above.

DEFINITION 6.3.27. $(\widehat{C}, \delta)$ is said to be *weakly finite* if there exists a finite d.g.c.f.z. (C', δ'), and a gapped filtered cochain map $\varphi : (\widehat{C}, \delta) \to (C', \delta')$ which induces isomorphisms on cohomologies

$$\overline{\varphi}_* : H(\overline{\widehat{C}}, \overline{\delta}) \cong H(\overline{C}', \overline{\delta}').$$

Using these definitions, we prove

THEOREM 6.3.28. *If C is weakly finite, then there exists r_0 such that:*

$$E_{r_0}^{p,q}(\widehat{C}) \cong E_{r_0+1}^{p,q}(\widehat{C}) \cong \cdots \cong E_\infty^{p,q}(\widehat{C}) \cong \mathfrak{F}^q H^p(\widehat{C}, \delta)/\mathfrak{F}^{q+1} H^p(\widehat{C}, \delta)$$

as $\Lambda^{(0)}(\lambda_0) = \Lambda_{0,nov}^{(0)}/F^{\lambda_0} \Lambda_{0,nov}^{(0)}$ modules.

PROOF. We first consider the case when C^k is finite c.f.z. (In this case we have $C^k = \widehat{C}^k$.) By Proposition 6.3.9 there exists a positive constant c such that

$$\delta(C^k) \cap F^\lambda C^{k+1} \subset \delta(F^{\lambda-c} C^k)$$

for any λ. We choose r_0 so that $(r_0 - 1)\lambda_0 - c > \lambda_0$. Now let $r \geq r_0$ and $\mathfrak{x} \in Z_r^{p,q}(C)$. We have $\mathfrak{x} = \mathfrak{x}_0 + \mathfrak{x}_1$ such that

$$\delta \mathfrak{x}_0 \in \mathfrak{F}^{r+q-1} C = F^{(r+q-1)\lambda_0} C, \quad \mathfrak{x}_1 \in \mathfrak{F}^{q+1} C.$$

Therefore, by Proposition 6.3.9, we have $\mathfrak{y}$ such that

$$\delta \mathfrak{x}_0 = \delta \mathfrak{y}, \qquad \mathfrak{y} \in F^{(r+q-1)\lambda_0-c} C \subset F^{(q+1)\lambda_0} C = \mathfrak{F}^{q+1} C.$$

In follows that

$$[\mathfrak{x}] = [\mathfrak{x} - \mathfrak{y}] = [\mathfrak{x}_0 - \mathfrak{y}] \in E_r^{p,q}(C),$$

and

$$\delta_r[\mathfrak{x}] = \delta_r[\mathfrak{x}_0 - \mathfrak{y}] = 0, \quad E_{r_0}^{p,q} \cong E_{r_0+1}^{p,q} \cong \cdots \cong E_\infty^{p,q}.$$

To prove $E_\infty^{p,q} \cong \mathfrak{F}^q H^p(C, \delta)/\mathfrak{F}^{q+1} H^p(C, \delta)$, we first construct a map

$$\pi_{p,q} : \mathfrak{F}^q H^p(C, \delta) \to E_\infty^{p,q}.$$

Let $\mathfrak{x} \in \mathfrak{F}^q C^p$ with $\delta \mathfrak{x} = 0$. Then $[\mathfrak{x}] \in E_r^{p,q}(C)$ for any $r \geq r_0$. Such $[\mathfrak{x}]$ defines an element of $E_\infty^{p,q}(C)$. Suppose that $\mathfrak{x} - \mathfrak{x}' = \delta \mathfrak{y}$. If $r > q$, we have $\mathfrak{y} \in \mathfrak{F}^{q-r} V^{p-1} = V^{p-1}$. Hence $[\mathfrak{x}] = [\mathfrak{x}']$ in $E_r^{p,q}(C)$. Therefore this assignment defines a well-defined map which we denote by $\pi_{p,q}$.

We next prove that $\pi_{p,q}$ is surjective. Let $[\mathfrak{x}] \in E_{r_0}^{p,q}(C) \cong E_\infty^{p,q}(C)$. Then, as we proved before, there exists $\mathfrak{y} \in \mathfrak{F}^{q+1} C$ such that

$$[\mathfrak{x} - \mathfrak{y}] \equiv [\mathfrak{x}] \in E_r^{p,q}(C), \quad \delta(\mathfrak{x} - \mathfrak{y}) = 0.$$

Therefore $\mathfrak{x} - \mathfrak{y}$ defines a cocycle in $\mathfrak{F}^q C^p$ and so $[\mathfrak{x} - \mathfrak{y}] \in \mathfrak{F}^q H^p(C, \delta)$ with $\pi_{p,q}[\mathfrak{x} - \mathfrak{y}] = [\mathfrak{x}]$ and hence $\pi_{p,q}$ is surjective.

We next prove the equality $\operatorname{Ker} \pi_{p,q} = \mathfrak{F}^{q+1} H^p(C, \delta)$. Let $[\mathfrak{x}] \in \mathfrak{F}^q H^p(C, \delta)$ and $\pi_{p,q}([\mathfrak{x}]) = 0$. Then for $r > q + 2$ we have

$$\mathfrak{x} \in \delta(\mathfrak{F}^{q-r+2} C^{p-1}) + \mathfrak{F}^{q+1} C^p \subset \delta(C^{p-1}) + \mathfrak{F}^{q+1} C^p.$$

Hence $[\mathfrak{x}] \in \mathfrak{F}^{q+1} H^p(C, \delta)$. This proves $\operatorname{Ker} \pi_{p,q} \subset \mathfrak{F}^{q+1} H^p(C, \delta)$. On the other hand, $\mathfrak{F}^{q+1} H^p(C, \delta) \subset \operatorname{Ker} \pi_{p,q}$ is obvious.

Finally we relax the condition that $\widehat{C}$ is finitely generated. Let (C', δ') be a finite d.g.c.f.z. and $\varphi : \widehat{C} \to C'$ a gapped cochain map which induces isomorphisms on cohomologies as in Definition 6.3.27. Then φ induces a morphism of spectral sequence. It is an isomorphism in the E_2 term and hence an isomorphism at E_∞ term. On the other hand, $\overline{\varphi}$ is assumed to induce an isomorphism $H(\overline{C}, \overline{\delta}) \to H(\overline{C}', \overline{\delta}')$. We can then prove that φ induces an isomorphism on the cohomology $H(\widehat{C}, \delta) \to H(C', \delta')$, in the same way as the proof of Proposition 4.3.18. Therefore $\pi_{p,q}$ is an isomorphism for C because it is so for C'. That completes the proof of Theorem 6.3.28. $\qquad\square$

In the case of Floer homology of periodic Hamiltonian systems, we can show that the modified Floer homology in [**Ono95**] is isomorphic to the (usual) Floer homology based on an analogous statement as Proposition 6.3.9.

6.4. The spectral sequence associated to a Lagrangian submanifold

6.4.1. Construction. So far, we have constructed the spectral sequence in a purely algebraic manner. In this section we will prove Theorem D by applying the results in the previous section to our geometric situation. In this subsection we prove (D.1) and (D.2).

Let L be a relatively spin Lagrangian submanifold of a symplectic manifold M and $(C(L, \Lambda_{0,nov}), \mathfrak{m})$ the associated filtered A_∞ algebra. Let $\mathbf{b} = (\mathfrak{b}, b) \in \mathcal{M}_{\text{weak,def}}(L)$. By the construction in Section 3.5, $C(L, \Lambda_{0,nov})$ is a c.f.z. in the sense of Subsection 6.3.1.

$(C(L, \Lambda_{0,nov}), \mathfrak{m}_1^{\mathbf{b}})$ is a chain complex. Moreover we already found that the gapped condition for $(C(L, \Lambda_{0,nov}), \mathfrak{m}_1^{\mathbf{b}})$ follows from Gromov's compactness theorem. (See Theorem 3.5.11.)

Furthermore, $(C(L, \Lambda_{0,nov}), \mathfrak{m}_1^{\mathbf{b}})$ is weakly finite in the sense of Definition 6.3.27. In fact it is chain homotopy equivalent to $(H(L; \Lambda_{0,nov}), \mathfrak{m}_1^{can, \mathfrak{b}, b'})$, where $b' \in \mathcal{M}_{\text{weak}}(H(L; \Lambda), \mathfrak{m}^{can, \mathfrak{b}})$. This is a consequence of Theorem 5.4.2.

Therefore Theorem 6.3.28 implies that we have a spectral sequence as in Theorem D (D.1), (D.2). The construction of the spectral sequence as in Theorem 6.1.4 satisfying (6.1.5.1), (6.1.5.2) is similar by using Corollary 5.4.21.

6.4.2. A condition for degeneration: proof of (D.3). In this subsection, we will prove (D.3) by using the operators $\mathfrak{p}$ constructed in Subsection 3.8.9. We recall that we have the sequence of operators

$$\mathfrak{p}_{\ell,k} : E_\ell C(M; \Lambda_{0,nov})[2] \otimes B_k^{cyc} C_{1+}(L; \Lambda_{0,nov})[1] \to S^*(M; \Lambda_{0,nov})$$

defined in Subsection 3.8.9. See Proposition 3.8.78. Then for $(\mathfrak{b}, b) \in \mathcal{M}_{\text{def}}(L)$, we define

$$(6.4.1) \qquad \mathfrak{p}_1^{\mathfrak{b}, b}(x) = \mathfrak{p}_{0,1}^{\mathfrak{b}, b}(x) := \mathfrak{p}(e^{\mathfrak{b}}, e^b x e^b) = \mathfrak{p}(e^{\mathfrak{b}} \otimes e^b x e^b)$$

for $x \in C_2(L; \Lambda_{0,nov})[1]$. Note that

$$\mathfrak{p}_1^{\mathfrak{b},b}(x) = \mathfrak{p}^{\mathfrak{b}}(e^b x e^b),$$

where the operator $\mathfrak{p}^{\mathfrak{b}}$ is already defined in Subsection 3.8.9. We also recall that

$$\delta_{(\mathfrak{b},b)}(x) = \mathfrak{q}(e^{\mathfrak{b}}, e^b x e^b) = \mathfrak{q}(e^{\mathfrak{b}} \otimes e^b x e^b).$$

See Definition 3.8.58. Then we can show the following.

LEMMA 6.4.2. *Let δ_M be the coboundary operator on $S^*(M; \Lambda_{0,nov})$ in Proposition 3.8.78. Then we have*

(6.4.3.1) $\mathfrak{p}_1^{\mathfrak{b},b} \equiv i_! \quad \mod \Lambda_{0,nov}^+,$

(6.4.3.2) $\mathfrak{p}_1^{\mathfrak{b},b} \circ \delta_{(\mathfrak{b},b)} + \delta_M \circ \mathfrak{p}_1^{\mathfrak{b},b} = 0,$

where $i_! : H^*(L; \mathbb{Q}) \to H^{*+n}(M; \mathbb{Q})$ is the Gysin homomorphism.

Proof. As $\mathfrak{b} \equiv b \equiv 0 \mod \Lambda_{0,nov}^+$, we have $\mathfrak{p}_1^{\mathfrak{b},b} \equiv \mathfrak{p}_1 \mod \Lambda_{0,nov}^+$. Then (6.4.3.1) follows from (3.8.87.1). Since $\widehat{d}^{\mathfrak{b}}(e^b x e^b) = e^b \mathfrak{m}^{\mathfrak{b}}(e^b x e^b) e^b = e^b \mathfrak{q}(e^{\mathfrak{b}}, e^b x e^b) e^b$, we have by (3.8.87.2)

$$0 = \mathfrak{p}^{\mathfrak{b}} \circ \widehat{d}^{\mathfrak{b},\mathrm{cyc}}(e^b x e^b) + \delta_M \circ \mathfrak{p}^{\mathfrak{b}}(e^b x e^b) = \mathfrak{p}^{\mathfrak{b}}(e^b \mathfrak{q}(e^{\mathfrak{b}}, e^b x e^b) e^b) + \delta_M \circ \mathfrak{p}_1^{\mathfrak{b},b}(x).$$

This proves (6.4.3.2).   □

When L is weakly unobstructed after bulk deformation, we use the operation

$$\mathfrak{p}_1^{+\mathfrak{b},b} \; : \; C_{1+}(L; \Lambda_{0,nov})^+[1] \to S^*(M; \Lambda_{0,nov})$$

defined by

(6.4.4) $\mathfrak{p}_1^{+\mathfrak{b},b}(x) = \mathfrak{p}_{0,1}^{+\mathfrak{b},b}(x) := \mathfrak{p}^+(e^{\mathfrak{b}}, e^b x e^b)$

for $(\mathfrak{b}, b) \in \mathcal{M}_{\mathrm{weak,def}}(L)$. Here $\mathfrak{p}^+$ is defined in Proposition 3.8.78. Then we can show the following lemma analogous to Lemma 6.4.2. We omit the proof of the lemma.

LEMMA 6.4.5. *Under the situation above, we have*

(6.4.6.1) $\mathfrak{p}_1^{+\mathfrak{b},b} \equiv i_! \quad \mod \Lambda_{0,nov}^+,$

(6.4.6.2) $\mathfrak{p}_1^{+\mathfrak{b},b} \circ \delta_{(\mathfrak{b},b)}^+ + \delta_M \circ \mathfrak{p}_1^{+\mathfrak{b},b} = 0.$

Here $\delta_{(\mathfrak{b},b)}^+(x) = \mathfrak{q}^+(e^{\mathfrak{b}}, e^b x e^b)$. See Definition 3.8.58.

PROOF OF THEOREM D (D.3). We put $C = C(L; \Lambda_{0,nov})$, $\delta = \delta_{\mathfrak{b},b}$. Let $x \in Z_r^{p,q}(\widehat{C})$. Namely we assume $x = y + z$ such that $\delta y \in \mathfrak{F}^{q+r-1}\widehat{C}^{p+1}$, $z \in \mathfrak{F}^{q+1}\widehat{C}^p$. Note

$$\delta_r([x]) = [\delta y] \in E_r^{p+1,q+r-1}(\widehat{C}) = \frac{Z_r^{p+1,q+r-1}(\widehat{C})}{B_r^{p+1,q+r-1}(\widehat{C})}$$

(6.4.7)

$$= \frac{Z_r^{p+1,q+r-1}(\widehat{C})}{(\delta(\mathfrak{F}^{q+1}\widehat{C}^p) \cap \mathfrak{F}^{q+r-1}\widehat{C}^{p+1}) + \mathfrak{F}^{q+r}\widehat{C}^{p+1}}.$$

By (6.4.3.2) we have

$$(6.4.8) \qquad \mathfrak{p}_1^{\mathfrak{b},b}(\delta y) = -\delta_M(\mathfrak{p}_1^{\mathfrak{b},b}(y)).$$

By (6.4.3.1), we may choose λ_0 in (6.3.18) so that

$$(6.4.9) \qquad \mathfrak{p}_1^{\mathfrak{b},b} - i_! \equiv 0 \mod T^{\lambda_0}.$$

Since $\delta y \in \mathfrak{F}^{q+r-1}\widehat{C}^{p+1} = T^{(q+r-1)\lambda_0}\widehat{C}^{p+1}$, it follows from (6.4.7) and (6.4.8) that

$$(6.4.10) \qquad i_!(\delta y) + \delta_M(\mathfrak{p}_1^{\mathfrak{b},b}(y)) \in T^{(q+r)\lambda_0}C^{p+1}(M).$$

Therefore we can write $\delta y = w_1 + w_2$ such that $w_2 \in \mathfrak{F}^{q+r}\widehat{C}^{p+1}$ and

$$(6.4.11) \qquad i_!(w_1) \in \operatorname{Im}\delta_M.$$

(We use that fact that $i_!$ and δ_M do not involve T to prove this.)

We remark that the Gysin homomorphism $i_! : H^k(L;\mathbb{Q}) \to H^{n+k}(M;\mathbb{Q})$ is identified with $i_* : H_{n-k}(L;\mathbb{Q}) \to H_{n-k}(M;\mathbb{Q})$ by Poincaré duality. Hence (6.4.7), (6.4.11) and the definition of K_r imply $\delta_r([\mathfrak{y}]) \in K_{r+1}$. The property (D.3) is proved. $\qquad\square$

The proof of (6.2.15) is similar.

REMARK 6.4.12. We remark that (D.3) does not hold for the Floer cohomology $HF((L;(\mathfrak{b},b_1)),(L;(\mathfrak{b},b_0));\Lambda_{0,nov})$ in case $b_1 \neq b_0$, in general. Let us consider $L = S^1 = S^1 \times \{0\} \subset S^1 \times S^1 = M$. If $\mathfrak{b} = 0$, $b_1 = 0$, $b_0 = T\,PD([pt])$, then

$$\delta_{b_1,b_0}(PD([S^1])) = \mathfrak{m}_2(PD([S^1]),b_0) = T \cdot PD([pt]),$$

which is not contained in $\operatorname{Ker}(i_! : H^1(L;\Lambda_{0,nov}) \to H^2(M;\Lambda_{0,nov}))$.

6.4.3. Non-vanishing theorem: proof of Theorem 6.1.9. To each pair $(\mathfrak{b},b_i) \in \mathcal{M}_{\text{weak,def}}(L)$, we can associate the coboundary operator $\delta^+_{(\mathfrak{b},b_1),(\mathfrak{b},b_0)}(x) = \mathfrak{q}^+(e^{\mathfrak{b}},e^{b_1}xe^{b_0})$. (Definition 3.8.58 and Lemma 3.8.60.) Suppose $\mathfrak{PO}(b_1) = \mathfrak{PO}(b_0)$.

We start from proving (6.1.10.1). We recall that

$$C(L;\Lambda_{0,nov})^+ = C(L;\Lambda_{0,nov}) \oplus \Lambda_{0,nov}\mathbf{e}^+ \oplus \Lambda_{0,nov}\mathbf{f}$$

as in Section 3.3 and $\mathbf{e} = PD([L])$ is the homotopy unit in $(C(L;\Lambda_{0,nov}),\mathfrak{m})$. We show the following.

LEMMA 6.4.13. $\delta^+_{(\mathfrak{b},b_1),(\mathfrak{b},b_0)}(\mathbf{f}) = \mathbf{e}^+ - \mathbf{e} + \mathfrak{h}_2^{+M}(e^{\mathfrak{b}},e^{b_1}\overline{\otimes}e^{b_0})$.

PROOF. From Definition 3.8.38 we have the filtered A_∞ algebra

$$(C(L;\Lambda_{0,nov})^+,\mathfrak{m}^{+\mathfrak{b}})$$

deformed by $\mathfrak{b}$. In this case (3.8.35.4) implies

$$\mathfrak{q}^+_{*,1}(e^{\mathfrak{b}},\mathbf{f}) = \mathbf{e}^+ - \mathbf{e} + \mathfrak{h}_2^{+M}(e^{\mathfrak{b}},1\overline{\otimes}1).$$

This is a 'def' version of (3.3.5.2). Then by (3.8.35.3), we have

$$\begin{aligned}
\delta^+_{(\mathfrak{b},b_1),(\mathfrak{b},b_0)}(\mathbf{f}) &= \mathfrak{q}^+(e^{\mathfrak{b}},e^{b_1}\mathbf{f}e^{b_0}) \\
&= \mathfrak{q}^+_{*,1}(e^{\mathfrak{b}},\mathbf{f}) + \mathfrak{h}_2^{+M}(e^{\mathfrak{b}},e^{b_1}\overline{\otimes}e^{b_0}) - \mathfrak{h}_2^{+M}(e^{\mathfrak{b}},1\overline{\otimes}1) \\
&= \mathbf{e}^+ - \mathbf{e} + \mathfrak{h}_2^{+M}(e^{\mathfrak{b}},1\overline{\otimes}1) + \mathfrak{h}_2^{+M}(e^{\mathfrak{b}},e^{b_1}\overline{\otimes}e^{b_0}) - \mathfrak{h}_2^{+M}(e^{\mathfrak{b}},1\overline{\otimes}1) \\
&= \mathbf{e}^+ - \mathbf{e} + \mathfrak{h}_2^{+M}(e^{\mathfrak{b}},e^{b_1}\overline{\otimes}e^{b_0}).
\end{aligned}$$

□

Then since $\delta^+_{(\mathfrak{b},b_1),(\mathfrak{b},b_0)}(\mathbf{e}^+) = 0$, we obtain

$$\delta^+_{(\mathfrak{b},b_1),(\mathfrak{b},b_0)}(\mathbf{e} - \mathfrak{h}_2^{+M}(e^{\mathfrak{b}}, e^{b_1}\overline{\otimes}e^{b_0})) = 0.$$

This proves (6.1.10.1).

We next prove (6.1.10.2). Since the statement over Λ_{nov} coefficient is sharper than that over $\Lambda_{0,nov}$, we work over Λ_{nov} coefficient. For the proof of (6.1.10.2), we use the operator $\mathfrak{p}$. Note that we assumed $b = b_1 = b_0$ in (6.1.10.2). Suppose to the contrary that $PD([pt]) \in \mathrm{Im}(\delta_r)$. Then we can put $T^\lambda PD([pt]) = \delta^+_{(\mathfrak{b},b)}(x)$ for some $x \in C(L;\Lambda_{0,nov})$ and $\lambda \geq 0$. Lemma 6.4.5 shows that

$$T^\lambda i_!(PD[pt]) \equiv T^\lambda \mathfrak{p}_1^{+\mathfrak{b},b}(PD[pt]) \mod T^\lambda \Lambda^+_{0,nov}$$
$$= \mathfrak{p}_1^{+\mathfrak{b},b}(\delta^+_{(\mathfrak{b},b)}(x)) = -\delta_M(\mathfrak{p}_1^{+\mathfrak{b},b}(x)).$$

Hence $i_!(PD[pt]) = 0$ in $H^{2n}(M;\mathbb{Q})$. (Note δ_M is the usual boundary operator and hence does not contain T.) On the other hand $PD([pt]) \neq 0$. This contradicts the fact that the Gysin homomorphism $i_! : H^n(L;\mathbb{Q}) \to H^{2n}(M;\mathbb{Q})$ is injective. This proves (6.1.10.2).

We now turn to the proof of (6.1.12). Here we use the assumption of Maslov index. We will also use the fact that $H^\ell(L;\mathbb{Q})$ is nonzero only for $\ell \in \{0,\cdots,n\}$. Note that $C^\ell(L;\mathbb{Q}) \subset S_{n-\ell}(L;\mathbb{Q})$ may be nonzero for $\ell < 0$. In fact there exists a nonzero singular chain on L of dimension $> n = \dim L$. By this reason we work on canonical model to prove (6.1.12).

We consider

$$(6.4.14) \qquad \mathfrak{b} = \sum_{i=1}^{\infty} e^{m_i/2}T^{\lambda_i}\mathfrak{b}_i \in H^2(M;\Lambda^+_{0,nov}),$$

with $\mathfrak{b}_i \in H(M;\mathbb{Q})$. We assume that $\deg \mathfrak{b}_i \neq 0$. (We will remove this assumption later.) Then

$$(6.4.15) \qquad m_i = 2 - \deg \mathfrak{b}_i \leq 0.$$

We put $G(L) = \{(\omega(\beta),\mu(\beta)) \in \mathbb{R}\times 2\mathbb{Z} \mid \mathcal{M}_1(\beta) \neq \emptyset\}$ and $G(L,\mathfrak{b}) = \{(\omega(\beta) + \lambda_j, \mu(\beta) + m_j) \in \mathbb{R}\times 2\mathbb{Z} \mid (\omega(\beta),\mu(\beta)) \in G(L), j = 1,2,\cdots\}$, where m_j, λ_j are as in (6.4.14).

We consider the filtered A_∞ algebra $(C(L;\Lambda_{0,nov})^+, \mathfrak{m}^{+,\mathfrak{b}})$. It is unital and $G(L;\mathfrak{b})$ gapped. We take its canonical model and denote it by $(H(L;\Lambda_{0,nov}),\mathfrak{m}^{can,\mathfrak{b}})$. It is also unital and $G(L;\mathfrak{b})$ gapped. There exists a unital and $G(L;\mathfrak{b})$ gapped homotopy equivalence

$$\mathfrak{f} : (H(L;\Lambda_{0,nov}),\mathfrak{m}^{can,\mathfrak{b}}) \to (C(L;\Lambda_{0,nov})^+, \mathfrak{m}^{+,\mathfrak{b}}).$$

It induces a map

$$\mathfrak{f}_* : \widehat{\mathcal{M}}_{\mathrm{weak}}(H(L;\Lambda_{0,nov}),\mathfrak{m}^{can,\mathfrak{b}}) \to \widehat{\mathcal{M}}_{\mathrm{weak}}(C(L;\Lambda_{0,nov})^+, \mathfrak{m}^{+,\mathfrak{b}}),$$

which induces an isomorphism between gauge equivalence classes. We consider the following condition for $b \in \widehat{\mathcal{M}}_{\mathrm{weak}}(C(L;\Lambda_{0,nov})^+, \mathfrak{m}^{+,\mathfrak{b}})$.

CONDITION 6.4.16.

$$(6.4.17) \qquad b = \sum_{i=1}^{\infty} e^{k_i/2} T^{\lambda_i} b_i$$

with $b_i \in C(L; \mathbb{Q})^+$ and $k_i \in 2\mathbb{Z}_{\leq 0}$.

LEMMA 6.4.18. *We assume that $n_i \leq 0$ for any $(\lambda_i, n_i) \in G(L)$. Then any element of $\widehat{\mathcal{M}}_{\text{weak}}(C(L; \Lambda_{0,nov})^+, \mathfrak{m}^{+,\flat})$ is gauge equivalent to one satisfying Condition 6.4.16.*

PROOF. The assumption implies that $m \leq 0$ for any $(\lambda, m) \in G(L; \flat)$. (In fact $m_i \leq 0$ where m_i is as in (6.4.14).) Therefore, since $\mathfrak{f}$ is $G(L; \flat)$ gapped, it suffices to prove the same statement for $\widehat{\mathcal{M}}_{\text{weak}}(H(L; \Lambda_{0,nov}), \mathfrak{m}^{can,\flat})$.

Let

$$(6.4.19) \qquad \tilde{b} = \sum_{i=1}^{\infty} e^{k_i/2} T^{\lambda'_i} \tilde{b}_i$$

with $\tilde{b}_i \in H(L; \mathbb{Q})$. Since $\widehat{\mathcal{M}}_{\text{weak}}(H(L; \Lambda_{0,nov}), \mathfrak{m}^{can,\flat})$ is contained in the first cohomology group $H^1(L; \Lambda_{0,nov})$, it follow that $\deg b_i = 1 - k_i$. On the other hand, $H^\ell(L; \mathbb{Q})$ is nonzero only for $\ell \in \{0, \cdots, n\}$. Moreover k_i is even. Therefore $k_i \leq 0$ as required. $\qquad \square$

We take $\tilde{b} \in \widehat{\mathcal{M}}_{\text{weak}}(H(L; \Lambda_{0,nov}), \mathfrak{m}^{can,\flat})$ and put $b = \mathfrak{f}_*(\tilde{b})$. Then b satisfies Condition 6.4.16 and any weak bounding cochain is gauge equivalent to such b. We put

$$(6.4.20) \qquad b = \sum_{i=1}^{\infty} e^{n_i/2} T^{\lambda'_i} b_i$$

and define

$$(6.4.21) \qquad \begin{aligned} G(L; \flat, b) = \{ (\omega(\beta) + \lambda'_i, \mu(\beta) + n_i) \in \mathbb{R} \times 2\mathbb{Z} \\ | \ (\omega(\beta), \mu(\beta)) \in G(L, \flat), i = 1, 2, \cdots \}. \end{aligned}$$

We define $\mathfrak{m}^{can,\flat,\tilde{b}}$, $\mathfrak{m}^{+,\flat,b}$ by deforming $\mathfrak{m}^{can,\flat}$, $\mathfrak{m}^{+,\flat}$ using $\tilde{b}$, b, respectively. Then we have $G(L; \flat, b)$-gapped and unital filtered A_∞ algebras $(H(L; \Lambda_{0,nov}), \mathfrak{m}^{can,\flat,\tilde{b}})$ and $(C(L; \Lambda_{0,nov})^+, \mathfrak{m}^{+,\flat,b})$ such that $\mathfrak{m}_0^{can,\flat,\tilde{b}}(1)$, $\mathfrak{m}_0^{+,\flat,b}(1)$ are proportional to the unit. We put $\delta_{(\flat,\tilde{b})}^{can} = \mathfrak{m}_1^{can,\flat,\tilde{b}}$, $\delta_{(\flat,b)}^+ = \mathfrak{m}_1^{+,\flat,b}$. Then we have

$$\delta_{(\flat,\tilde{b})}^{can} \circ \delta_{(\flat,\tilde{b})}^{can} = 0, \qquad \delta_{(\flat,b)}^+ \circ \delta_{(\flat,b)}^+ = 0.$$

We define

$$\varphi : (H(L; \Lambda_{0,nov}), \delta_{(\flat,\tilde{b})}^{can}) \to (C(L; \Lambda_{0,nov})^+, \delta_{(\flat,\tilde{b})}^{can}),$$

by

$$\varphi(x) = \sum_{k_1,k_2} \mathfrak{f}_{k_1+k_2+1}(\tilde{b}^{\otimes k_1}, x, \tilde{b}^{\otimes k_2}).$$

Then it is easy to see that φ is a chain map which induces an isomorphism on cohomology group. It is $G(L; \mathfrak{b}, b)$-gapped in an obvious sense. We use the unitality of $\mathfrak{f}$ to show

(6.4.22) $\varphi([PD[L]]) = \mathbf{e}^+.$

(Note $[PD[L]]$ is the unit of $(H(L; \Lambda_{0,nov}), \delta^{can}_{(\mathfrak{b},\bar{b})})$.)

Now we are in the position to complete the proof of Theorem 6.1.9.

The Poincaré dual $PD([pt])$ in $C(L; \Lambda_{0,nov})^+$ gives an element of (cohomology) degree n. We remark $C^\ell(L; \Lambda_{0,nov})^+ = 0$ for $\ell > n$. we have

$$\delta^+_{(\mathfrak{b},b)} = \sum_{(\lambda_i, n_i) \in G(L; \mathfrak{b}, b)} \delta^+_{(\mathfrak{b},b),\beta} T^{\lambda_i} e^{n_i/2}$$

and $\delta^+_{(\mathfrak{b},b),\beta} : C(L; \mathbb{Q}) \to C(L; \mathbb{Q})$ is of degree $1 - n_i$. By assumption $n_i \leq 0$. Hence $\delta^+_{(\mathfrak{b},b),\beta}(PD[pt]) = 0$. This proves (6.1.12.2).

We next prove (6.1.12.1). We first prove that the unit $[PD[L]] \in H^0(L; \mathbb{Q})$ is not in the image of $\delta^{can}_{(\mathfrak{b},\bar{b})}$. We put

$$\delta^{can}_{(\mathfrak{b},\bar{b})} = \sum_{(\lambda_i, n_i) \in G(L; \mathfrak{b}, b)} \delta^{can}_{(\mathfrak{b},b),\beta} T^{\lambda_i} e^{n_i/2}.$$

Here $\delta^{can}_{(\mathfrak{b},b),\beta} : H(L; \mathbb{Q}) \to H(L; \mathbb{Q})$ is of degree $1 - n_i$. Since $n_i \leq 0$, and since $H^\ell(L; \mathbb{Q})$ is zero for $\ell < 0$, it follows that the unit $[PD[L]] \in H^0(L; \mathbb{Q})$ is not in the image of $\delta^{can}_{(\mathfrak{b},b),\beta}$.

Therefore $[PD[L]] \in H^0(L; \mathbb{Q})$ is nonzero in $\delta^{can}_{(\mathfrak{b},b),\beta}$ cohomology. Therefore by (6.4.22), $\mathbf{e}^+$ is not zero in $H(C(L, \Lambda_{0,nov})^+, \delta^+_{(\mathfrak{b},b)})$. Since

$$PD([L]) - \mathfrak{h}^{+M}_2(e^{\mathfrak{b}}, e^{b_1} \overline{\otimes} e^{b_0})$$

is cohomologous to $\mathbf{e}^+$, it follows that it is not zero in $\delta^+_{(\mathfrak{b},b)}$ cohomology. Hence the proof of (6.1.12.1).

The linear independence of these classes follows from the fact that the filtration by the degree is preserved by the coboundary operator.

We assumed $\deg \mathfrak{b}_j \neq 0$ so far. Using (3.8.36) and Proposition 3.8.54, we can remove this assumption in the following way.

During the above proof we take a linear subspace of $C^2(M; \Lambda_{0,nov})$ which represents $H^2(M; \Lambda_{0,nov})$. We can use $C^2(M; \Lambda_{0,nov})^+$ in place of $C^2(M; \Lambda_{0,nov})$. ($C^2(M; \Lambda_{0,nov})^+$ is defined in (3.8.36).) Then we may choose

$$H^2(M; \Lambda_{0,nov}) \subset C^2(M; \Lambda_{0,nov})^+$$

such that $PD[M]$ is represented by $[\tilde{\mathbf{e}}^+]$, by virtue of (3.8.36.3).

Now, let $\mathfrak{b}_j$ be as in (6.4.14). We put

$$\mathfrak{b}' = \sum_{\deg \mathfrak{b}_i \neq 0} e^{m_i/2} T^{\lambda_i} \mathfrak{b}_i \in H^2(M; \Lambda^+_{0,nov}).$$

Since $\mathfrak{b} - \mathfrak{b}' = cPD[M] = c[\tilde{\mathbf{e}}^+]$, Proposition 3.8.54 implies

(6.4.23) $\mathfrak{q}(e^{\mathfrak{b}}, \mathbf{x}) - \mathfrak{q}(e^{\mathfrak{b}'}, \mathbf{x}) = \begin{cases} 0 & \text{unless } \mathbf{x} \in B_0C(L, \Lambda_{0,nov}), \\ cc\mathbf{e}^+ & \text{if } \mathbf{x} = 1 \in B_0C(L, \Lambda_{0,nov}). \end{cases}$

We can use it to show

$$\widehat{\mathcal{M}}_{\text{weak}}(C(L;\Lambda_{0,nov})^+, \mathfrak{m}^{+,\mathfrak{b}}) = \widehat{\mathcal{M}}_{\text{weak}}(C(L;\Lambda_{0,nov})^+, \mathfrak{m}^{+,\mathfrak{b}'})$$

and $\delta^+_{(\mathfrak{b},b)} = \delta^+_{(\mathfrak{b}',b)}$ for $b \in \widehat{\mathcal{M}}_{\text{weak}}(C(L;\Lambda_{0,nov})^+, \mathfrak{m}^{+,\mathfrak{b}})$. Therefore we can always replace $\mathfrak{b}$ by $\mathfrak{b}'$.

Therefore we have finished the proof of Theorem 6.1.9. $\square$

We remark that (6.1.12.2') does not hold for the case $b_1 \neq b_0$. The example in Remark 6.4.12 will be a counter example.

PROOF OF THEOREM L. We assume $L \subset M$ is relatively spin and $H^2(L;\mathbb{Q}) = 0$, and $\mu_L = 0$. Since the obstruction for $\mathcal{M}(L;\mathbb{Q})$ lies in $H^2(L;\mathbb{Q}) = 0$ we have bounding cochain $b \in \mathcal{M}(L;\mathbb{Q})$. Then it follows from Theorem D (D.1) and (6.1.12.1) that the element $PD([L]) - \mathfrak{h}_2^{+M}(e^b, e^{b_1} \overline{\otimes} e^{b_0})$ defines a nontrivial element of the Floer cohomology $HF((L,b),(L,b);\Lambda_{nov})$. Therefore for any Hamiltonian diffeomorphism ψ we have $\psi(L) \cap L \neq \emptyset$, as required. Suppose L is transversal to $\psi(L)$. We note that since $\mu_L = 0$ we can define Floer cohomology $HF((L,b),(L,b);\Lambda^{(0)}_{nov})$ over $\Lambda^{(0)}_{nov}$. (See Subsection 5.4.6.) In other words the integer degree is well defined. Since the degree of $PD([L]) - \mathfrak{h}_2^{+M}(e^b, e^{b_1} \overline{\otimes} e^{b_0})$ is zero (before shifted), there should be an intersection point $\psi(L) \cap L$ of Maslov index 0. Theorem L is proved. $\square$

6.4.4. Application to the Maslov class conjecture: proofs of Theorems 6.1.15 and 6.1.17.

PROOF OF THEOREM 6.1.15. From Theorems 3.1.11 and 3.8.50, the obstruction classes are in $H^{2-\mu_L(\beta_k)}(L;\mathbb{Q})/\operatorname{Im} H^{2-\mu_L(\beta_k)}(M;\mathbb{Q})$. Since $\mu_L = 0$ and the map $H^2(M,\mathbb{Q}) \to H^2(L;\mathbb{Q})$ is surjective by the assumption, all the obstruction classes vanish. Therefore L is unobstructed after bulk deformation. Now Theorem 6.1.9 concludes we have $HF((L,\mathbf{b}),(L,\mathbf{b});\Lambda_{nov}) \neq 0$. $\square$

PROOF OF THEOREM 6.1.17. We first prove (1). We assume L is weakly unobstructed after bulk deformation and $\Sigma_L = 0$. Then there exists $\mathbf{b} \in \mathcal{M}_{\text{weak,def}}(L)$. Using the assumption $\Sigma_L = 0$ and Theorem 6.1.9, we have

$$HF((L;\mathbf{b}),(L;\mathbf{b});\Lambda_{nov}) \neq 0.$$

This contradicts to our assumption that L is displaceable.

We next prove (2). Let $(\mathfrak{b},b) \in \widehat{\mathcal{M}}_{\text{weak,def}}(L)$ as in the assumption of (2).

LEMMA 6.4.24. $\pi_2(G(L;\mathfrak{b},b)) = \pi_2(G(L))$, where $\pi_2 : \mathbb{R} \times 2\mathbb{Z} \to 2\mathbb{Z}$ is the projection. Here $G(L;\mathfrak{b},b)$ is defined by (6.4.21).

PROOF. If we put $\mathfrak{b} = \sum e^{m_i/2} T^{\lambda_i} \mathfrak{b}_i$, $b = \sum e^{k_i/2} T^{\lambda'_i} b_i$ then $m_i = 2 - \deg \mathfrak{b}_i = 0$, $k_i = 1 - \deg b_i = 0$. The lemma follows from definition. $\square$

We put

$$\delta^{can}_{(\mathfrak{b},b)} = \mathfrak{m}_1^{can,\mathfrak{b},b} : H(L;\Lambda_{0,nov}) \to H(L;\Lambda_{0,nov}).$$

$(H(L;\Lambda_{0,nov}), \delta^{can}_{(\mathfrak{b},b)})$ is a chain complex whose cohomology is Floer cohomology $HF((L;\mathfrak{b},b),(L;\mathfrak{b},b))$. By Lemma 6.4.24, have

$$\delta^{can}_{(\mathfrak{b},b)} = \sum_{(\mu_i,\lambda_i) \in G(L;\mathfrak{b},b)} e^{\mu_i/2} T^{\lambda_i} \delta_i,$$

where $\delta_i : H(L;\mathbb{C}) \to H(L;\mathbb{C})$.

We now assume $\Sigma_L \notin \{2, \cdots, n+1\}$ and will deduce a contradiction. By this assumption either

(6.4.25.1) $k_i = 0$, or   (6.4.25.2) $|k_i| > n + 1$.

In case (6.4.25.2), we have $\deg \delta_i = 1 - k_i \notin \{-n, \cdots, n\}$. Since δ_i is a map between ordinary cohomology group of L (which is n dimensional), it follows that $\delta_i = 0$. This contradicts to the displacability of L. Thus we may assume $k_i = 0$.

Therefore, $PD[L] \in H^0(L;\mathbb{C})$ is not in the image of $\delta^{can}_{(\mathfrak{b},b)}$. On the other hand, since $PD[L]$ is a unit, we have $\delta^{can}_{(\mathfrak{b},b)}(PD[L]) = 0$. Thus the Floer cohomology $HF((L;\mathfrak{b},b),(L;\mathfrak{b},b);\Lambda_{nov})$ is nontrivial. This contradicts to the displaceability of L. The proof of Theorem 6.1.17 is complete. $\square$

REMARK 6.4.26. In the proof of Theorem 6.1.17, we use $PD([L])$ but do not use $PD([pt])$. Therefore the proof also works over $\Lambda_{0,nov}(\mathbb{Z})$ (resp. $\Lambda_{0,nov}(\mathbb{Z}/2\mathbb{Z})$) by considering $PD([L]) - \mathfrak{h}_2(e^b \overline{\otimes} e^b)$, in the case Floer cohomology over $\mathbb{Z}$ or $\mathbb{Z}_2$ is defined. (See [**FOOO09I**].)

6.4.5. Compatibility with the product structure. We now prove Theorem D (D.4) and which will complete the proof of Theorem D. In Subsection 3.7.7, we defined the product structure

$$\mathfrak{m}_2 : HF((L,\mathbf{b}_2),(L,\mathbf{b}_1)) \otimes HF((L,\mathbf{b}_1),(L,\mathbf{b}_0)) \to HF((L,\mathbf{b}_2),(L,\mathbf{b}_0))$$

on the Floer cohomology. It is induced by the operator $\mathfrak{m}_2^{\mathbf{b}_2,\mathbf{b}_1,\mathbf{b}_0} : \hat{C}(L) \otimes \hat{C}(L) \to \hat{C}(L)$, where

(6.4.27) $\mathfrak{m}_2^{\mathbf{b}_2,\mathbf{b}_1,\mathbf{b}_0}(x,y) = \mathfrak{m}^{\mathfrak{b}}(e^{b_2}, x, e^{b_1}, y, e^{b_0})$

and $\mathbf{b}_i = (\mathfrak{b}, b_i)$. (See (3.7.90).) By (6.4.27) it is easy to see that

(6.4.28) $\mathfrak{m}_2^{\mathbf{b}_2,\mathbf{b}_1,\mathbf{b}_0}(\mathfrak{F}^{q_1}\hat{C}(L) \otimes \mathfrak{F}^{q_2}\hat{C}(L)) \subseteq \mathfrak{F}^{q_1+q_2}\hat{C}(L)$.

This implies that the filtration $\mathfrak{F}$ on $HF((L,\mathbf{b}_j),(L,\mathbf{b}_i))$ are preserved by $\mathfrak{m}_2$.

To find a product structure on E_r it suffices to show the following:

LEMMA 6.4.29.

(6.4.30.1) $\mathfrak{m}_2^{\mathbf{b}_2,\mathbf{b}_1,\mathbf{b}_0}(Z_r^{p,q} \otimes Z_r^{p',q'}) \subseteq Z_r^{p+p',q+q'}$,

(6.4.30.2) $\mathfrak{m}_2^{\mathbf{b}_2,\mathbf{b}_1,\mathbf{b}_0}(B_r^{p,q} \otimes Z_r^{p',q'}) \subseteq B_r^{p+p',q+q'}$,

(6.4.30.3) $\mathfrak{m}_2^{\mathbf{b}_2,\mathbf{b}_1,\mathbf{b}_0}(Z_r^{p,q} \otimes B_r^{p',q'}) \subseteq B_r^{p+p',q+q'}$.

Note that we use $\delta_{\mathbf{b}_2,\mathbf{b}_1}$, $\delta_{\mathbf{b}_1,\mathbf{b}_0}$, $\delta_{\mathbf{b}_2,\mathbf{b}_0}$ to define $Z_r^{p,q}$, $Z_r^{p',q'}$, $Z_r^{p+p',q+q'}$ in (6.4.30.1), respectively. (Similarly for (6.4.30.2), (6.4.30.3).)

PROOF. We prove (6.4.30.2) only. (The other formulae are proved in the same way.) We recall

(6.4.31)
$$\begin{aligned} &\delta_{\mathbf{b}_2,\mathbf{b}_0}(\mathfrak{m}_2^{\mathbf{b}_2,\mathbf{b}_1,\mathbf{b}_0}(x,y)) \\ &= -\mathfrak{m}_2^{\mathbf{b}_2,\mathbf{b}_1,\mathbf{b}_0}(\delta_{\mathbf{b}_2,\mathbf{b}_1}(x),y) + (-1)^{\deg x}\mathfrak{m}_2^{\mathbf{b}_2,\mathbf{b}_1,\mathbf{b}_0}(x,\delta_{\mathbf{b}_1,\mathbf{b}_0}(y)). \end{aligned}$$

(See (3.7.91).) Let $x \in \delta_{\mathbf{b}_2,\mathbf{b}_1} x_1 + x_2 \in B_r^{p,q}$ where $x_1 \in \mathfrak{F}^{q-r+2} \hat{C}^{p-1}$, $\delta_{\mathbf{b}_2,\mathbf{b}_1} x_1 \in \mathfrak{F}^q \hat{C}^p$, $x_2 \in \mathfrak{F}^{q+1} \hat{C}^p$. Let $y = y_1 + y_2 \in Z_r^{p',q'}$ where $\delta_{\mathbf{b}_1,\mathbf{b}_0} y_1 \in \mathfrak{F}^{q'+r-1} \hat{C}^{p'+1}$, $y_1 \in \mathfrak{F}^{q'} \hat{C}^{p'}$, $y_2 \in \mathfrak{F}^{q'+1} \hat{C}^{p'}$. (See (6.3.19).) It is easy to see that

$$\mathbf{m}_2^{\mathbf{b}_2,\mathbf{b}_1,\mathbf{b}_0}(\delta_{\mathbf{b}_2,\mathbf{b}_1} x_1, y_2) \in \mathfrak{F}^{q+q'+1} \hat{C}^{p+p'} \subseteq B_r^{p+p',q+q'}$$

$$\mathbf{m}_2^{\mathbf{b}_2,\mathbf{b}_1,\mathbf{b}_0}(x_2, y_1) \in \mathfrak{F}^{q+q'+1} \hat{C}^{p+p'} \subseteq B_r^{p+p',q+q'}$$

$$\mathbf{m}_2^{\mathbf{b}_2,\mathbf{b}_1,\mathbf{b}_0}(x_2, y_2) \in \mathfrak{F}^{q+q'+1} \hat{C}^{p+p'} \subseteq B_r^{p+p',q+q'}.$$

On the other hand, (6.4.31) implies

$$\mathbf{m}_2^{\mathbf{b}_2,\mathbf{b}_1,\mathbf{b}_0}(\delta_{\mathbf{b}_2,\mathbf{b}_1} x_1, y_1)$$
$$= -\delta_{\mathbf{b}_2,\mathbf{b}_0}(\mathbf{m}_2^{\mathbf{b}_2,\mathbf{b}_1,\mathbf{b}_0}(x_1, y_1)) + (-1)^{\deg x} \mathbf{m}_2^{\mathbf{b}_2,\mathbf{b}_1,\mathbf{b}_0}(x_1, \delta_{\mathbf{b}_1,\mathbf{b}_0}(y_1)).$$

We have

$$\mathbf{m}_2^{\mathbf{b}_2,\mathbf{b}_1,\mathbf{b}_0}(x_1, y_1) \in \mathfrak{F}^{q+q'-r+2} \hat{C}^{p+p'-1}.$$

This implies

$$\delta_{\mathbf{b}_2,\mathbf{b}_0}(\mathbf{m}_2^{\mathbf{b}_2,\mathbf{b}_1,\mathbf{b}_0}(x_1, y_1)) \in \delta_{\mathbf{b}_2,\mathbf{b}_0}(\mathfrak{F}^{q+q'-r+2} \hat{C}^{p+p'-1}) \cap \mathfrak{F}^{q+q'} \hat{C}^{p+p'} \subseteq B_r^{p+p',q+q'}.$$

Moreover

$$\mathbf{m}_2^{\mathbf{b}_2,\mathbf{b}_1,\mathbf{b}_0}(x_1, \delta_{\mathbf{b}_1,\mathbf{b}_0}(y_1)) \in \mathfrak{F}^{q+q'+1} \hat{C}^{p+p'} \subseteq B_r^{p+p',q+q'}.$$

Thus (6.4.30.2) is proved. □

Lemma 6.4.29 implies $\mathbf{m}_2^{\mathbf{b}_2,\mathbf{b}_1,\mathbf{b}_0}$ induces a product structure $\mathbf{m}_2$ on $E_r^{p,q}$. We remark that $\mathbf{m}_2^{\mathbf{b}_2,\mathbf{b}_1,\mathbf{b}_0} \equiv \overline{\mathbf{m}}_2 \mod T^{\lambda_0} \Lambda_{0,nov}$. Compatibility of $\mathbf{m}_2$ with isomorphisms in (D.1) follows. The compatibility with the isomorphism (D.2) is obvious from definition. The formula

$$(6.4.32) \qquad \delta_r(\mathbf{m}_2(x,y)) = -\mathbf{m}_2(\delta_r(x), y) + (-1)^{\deg x} \mathbf{m}_2(x, \delta_r(y))$$

is an immediate consequence of (6.4.31). The proof of Theorem D is now complete.□

REMARK 6.4.33. The fact that the spectral sequence relating ordinal cohomology and Floer cohomology preserves product was suggested by P. Biran [**Bir04**].

PROBLEM 6.4.34. In which sense our spectral sequence is compatible with (higher) Massey product $\mathbf{m}_k$, $k \geq 3$?

The above compatibility (6.4.32) of the spectral sequence with the induced $\mathbf{m}_2$ has the following improvement of the second named author's result Theorem III [**Oh96I**] concerning the Maslov class of monotone Lagrangian tori (Audin's question): he proved the same consequence under the rather peculiar dimensional restriction $\dim L \leq 24$. The idea of using the compatibility of spectral sequence in the current proof is due to P. Seidel [**Sei01**]. L. Buhovsky proved Theorem 6.4.35 independently in [**Buh06**] where he showed the compatibility of the multiplicative structures of Oh's spectral sequence for the monotone case. His proof of the compatibility is different from ours given here in which we use the filtered A_∞ formula in a crucial way.

THEOREM 6.4.35. *Suppose that $L \subset (M, \omega)$ is a monotone Lagrangian torus such that there exists a Hamiltonian diffeomorphism ϕ with $\phi(L) \cap L = \emptyset$. Then we have its minimal Maslov number Σ_L satisfies*

$$\Sigma_L = 2.$$

PROOF. We first remark that T^n is orientable and spin, and the monotonicity implies $\Sigma_L > 0$ by definition.

We will prove the theorem by contradiction. Suppose to the contrary that $\Sigma_L \geq 3$. (Since T^n is orientable, this in fact implies $\Sigma_L \geq 4$. This fact will not be used in the proof.) The monotonicity then implies that L is unobstructed by the same argument as in [Oh96I] or in Subsection 2.4.4. It is easy to check that $b = 0$ lies in $\mathcal{M}(L)$ and so the Floer's undeformed δ satisfies $\delta\delta = 0$.

Then a simple degree counting argument using the monotonicity provides the decomposition of the boundary map into

$$\delta = \delta_{(0)} + \delta_{(1)} + \cdots + \delta_{(N)} =: \delta_{(0)} + \delta'$$

where $N \leq \left[\frac{n+2}{\Sigma_L}\right]$ and $\delta_{(k)}$ has the form

$$(6.4.36) \qquad \delta_{(k)} = \overline{\delta}_{(k)} \otimes T^{k\lambda_0} e^{k\Sigma_L}.$$

Here $\overline{\delta}_{(k)} : E_k \to E_k$ has the degree $1 - k\Sigma_L$. Since $\Sigma_L \geq 3$, this degree of $\overline{\delta}_{(k)}$ is smaller than equal to -2 for $k \geq 1$.

Now we consider the action of δ on the E_2-term

$$E_2 = H^*(T^n; \mathbb{Q}) \otimes \Lambda_{0,nov}.$$

We recall that the cohomology ring $H^*(T^n; \mathbb{Q})$ is generated by the one-dimensional cohomology classes $\alpha_1, \cdots, \alpha_n \in H^1(L; \mathbb{Q})$. By a simple degree counting, we derive

$$\delta_2(\alpha_k) = \overline{\delta}_{(k)}(\alpha_k) \cdot T^{k\lambda_0} e^{k\Sigma_L} = 0 \quad \text{for } k = 1, \cdots, n.$$

From (6.4.32) we derive

$$(6.4.37) \qquad \delta_2(\mathfrak{m}_2(\alpha_i, \alpha_j)) = \mathfrak{m}_2(\delta_2(\alpha_i), \alpha_j) + \mathfrak{m}_2(\alpha_i, \delta_2(\alpha_j)) = 0.$$

On the other hand, from the energy consideration, we have

$$\mathfrak{m}_2(\alpha_i, \alpha_j) \equiv \alpha_i \cup \alpha_j.$$

Therefore $\delta_2(\alpha_i \cup \alpha_j) = 0$ for all $i, j = 1, \cdots n$. Inductively applying the above arguments to all possible products of α_i's, we derive that the spectral sequence degenerates in the E^2-term and hence we conclude

$$HF^*(L; \Lambda_{0,nov}) \cong H^*(T^n; \mathbb{Q}) \otimes \Lambda_{0,nov}$$

which is in particular a free module over $\Lambda_{0,nov}$. Therefore

$$(6.4.38) \qquad HF^*(L; \Lambda_{nov}) \cong H^*(T^n; \mathbb{Q}) \otimes \Lambda_{nov} \neq 0.$$

(So far we have not used the assumption that $L \subset M$ is displaceable, which enters in the following last stage of the proof.) On the other hand, it follows from the invariance of $HF^*(L; \Lambda_{nov})$ and the existence of a Hamiltonian diffeomorphism ϕ with $\phi(L) \cap L = \emptyset$ implies $HF^*(L; \Lambda_{nov}) = \{0\}$. This contradicts to (6.4.38) and hence the proof of $\Sigma_L \leq 2$. Now the theorem follows since T^n is orientable and so the non-zero integer Σ_L must be even. $\qquad\square$

We can prove the following in the same way.

THEOREM 6.4.35BIS. *Suppose that* $L \subset (M, \omega)$ *is a monotone Lagrangian submanifold such that there exists a Hamiltonian diffeomorphism* ϕ *with* $\phi(L) \cap L = \emptyset$. *We assume also either* (1) *or* (2) *below.*

(1) $H^*(L; \mathbb{Z}_2)$ *is generated by* $H^1(L; \mathbb{Z}_2)$ *as a ring.*

(2) L *is orientable and relatively spin. There exists a commutative ring* R *such that* $H^*(L; R)$ *is generated by* $H^1(L; R)$ *and* $H^2(L; R)$ *as a ring.*

Then we have its minimal Maslov number Σ_L *satisfies* $\Sigma_L = 2$.

PROOF. Since L is monotone we can define Floer homology of arbitrary coefficient ring R. In case (1) the proof is exactly the same as the proof of Theorem 6.4.35. In case (2) we use orientability to show that if $\Sigma_L \neq 2$ then $\Sigma_L \geq 4$. Hence the proof of Theorem 6.4.35 works under the milder assumption that $H^*(L; R)$ is generated by $H^1(L; R)$ and $H^2(L; R)$ as a ring. $\qquad\square$

PROOF OF THEOREM 6.1.4. The proof is similar to the proof of Theorem D. In fact we can construct the spectral sequence satisfying (6.1.5.1), (6.1.5.2) by the results of Subsections 3.7.5 and 6.3.3. The proof of (6.1.5.3) is similar to the proof of (D.4) above. We leave the detail for the reader. $\qquad\square$

6.5. Applications to Lagrangian intersections

In this section we give applications of Floer cohomology to the problems of Lagrangian intersections. One is the estimate of the number of the intersection points of L and $\psi(L)$, where ψ is a Hamiltonian diffeomorphism, which is given in Subsections 6.5.1, 6.5.2, and the other is related to the Hofer distance of the Hamiltonian isotopy, which is discussed in Sections 6.5.3-5.

6.5.1. Proof of Theorem H. We prove Theorem H. Assume that $i_* : H_*(L; \mathbb{Q}) \to H_*(M; \mathbb{Q})$ is injective. Then by Corollary 3.8.43, L is unobstructed after bulk deformation. Thus we can define the spectral sequence satisfying Theorem D. Moreover, from (D.3) the spectral sequence collapses at the E_2-term level. It follows that

$$\#(L \cap \psi(L)) \geq \sum \operatorname{rank} HF((L, (\mathfrak{b}, b)), \psi; \Lambda_{nov}) = \sum_k \operatorname{rank} H^k(L; \mathbb{Q}).$$

Here $HF((L, (\mathfrak{b}, b)), \psi; \Lambda_{nov})$ is as in (6.1.8). $\qquad\square$

6.5.2. Proof of Theorem I. In this subsection, we prove Theorem I. The proof uses the algebraic materials presented in Subsections 6.3.1, 6.3.2, but does not use the spectral sequence in Theorem D.

In the next proposition we consider the Novikov ring $\Lambda_{0,nov} = \Lambda_{0,nov}(R)$ for a field R.

PROPOSITION 6.5.1. *Let* (C, δ) *be a finite d.g.c.f.z. We put* $C^{\{0,1\}} = C^0 \oplus C^1$. *There exist elements* $\mathfrak{z}_i$ $(i = 1, \cdots, b)$, $\mathfrak{h}_i$ $(i = 1, \cdots, a)$, $\mathfrak{b}_i$ $(i = 1, \cdots, b)$, *of* $C^{\{0,1\}}$ *with the following properties.*

(6.5.2.1) $E(\mathfrak{z}_i) = E(\mathfrak{h}_i) = E(\mathfrak{b}_i) = 0.$

(6.5.2.2) $\{\mathfrak{z}_1, \cdots, \mathfrak{z}_b, \mathfrak{b}_1, \cdots, \mathfrak{b}_b, \mathfrak{h}_1, \cdots, \mathfrak{h}_a\}$ *is a standard basis of* $C^{\{0,1\}}$.

(6.5.2.3)   *There exists* $\lambda_i \geq 0$ *such that* $\delta\mathfrak{z}_i = T^{\lambda_i}e^{p_i}\mathfrak{b}_i$. *(Here* $p_i = \deg \mathfrak{z}_i \in \{0,1\}$.)

(6.5.2.4) $\{\mathfrak{b}_1, \cdots, \mathfrak{b}_b, \mathfrak{h}_1, \cdots, \mathfrak{h}_a\}$ *is a standard basis of* $\operatorname{Ker}\delta \cap C^{\{0,1\}}$.

(6.5.2.5) $\{T^{\lambda_1}\mathfrak{b}_1, \cdots, T^{\lambda_b}\mathfrak{b}_b\}$ *is a standard basis of* $\operatorname{Im}\delta \cap C^{\{0,1\}}$.

PROOF. Let $\mathfrak{b}'_1, \cdots, \mathfrak{b}'_b$ be a standard basis of $\operatorname{Im}\delta \cap C^{\{0,1\}}$. We put $E(\mathfrak{b}'_i) = \lambda_i$. We define

$$\mathfrak{b}_i = T^{-\lambda_i}\mathfrak{b}'_i \in C.$$

We can choose $\mathfrak{z}_i \in C^{\{0,1\}}$ such that

$$\delta\mathfrak{z}_i = e^{\deg \mathfrak{z}_i}\mathfrak{b}'_i = T^{\lambda_i}e^{\deg \mathfrak{z}_i}\mathfrak{b}_i.$$

Note $\mathfrak{b}_i \in \operatorname{Ker}\delta$ and $\{\sigma(\mathfrak{b}_i) = \sigma(\mathfrak{b}'_i) \mid i = 1, \cdots, b\}$ is linearly independent. (Here $\sigma(\mathfrak{b}_i)$ is the leading coefficient of $\mathfrak{b}_i$.)

Therefore by Corollary 6.3.13 and Lemma 6.3.2bis, we can find $\mathfrak{h}_1, \cdots, \mathfrak{h}_a$ such that $\{\mathfrak{b}_1, \cdots, \mathfrak{b}_b, \mathfrak{h}_1, \cdots, \mathfrak{h}_a\}$ is a standard basis of $\operatorname{Ker}\delta \cap C^{\{0,1\}}$.

LEMMA 6.5.3. *The set*

$$\{\mathfrak{z}_1, \cdots, \mathfrak{z}_b, \mathfrak{b}_1, \cdots, \mathfrak{b}_b, \mathfrak{h}_1, \cdots, \mathfrak{h}_a\}$$

generates C *as a* $\Lambda_{0,nov}$ *module.*

PROOF. Let $\mathfrak{x} \in C$. We have $c_i \in \Lambda_{0,nov}$ such that

$$\delta\mathfrak{x} = \sum_{i=1}^{b} c_i\mathfrak{b}'_i.$$

Therefore we obtain

$$\delta\left(\mathfrak{x} - \sum_{i=1}^{b} e^{-\deg \mathfrak{z}_i}c_i\mathfrak{z}_i\right) = 0.$$

Since $\{\mathfrak{b}_1, \cdots, \mathfrak{b}_b, \mathfrak{h}_1, \cdots, \mathfrak{h}_a\}$ is a standard basis of $\operatorname{Ker}\delta \cap C^{\{0,1\}}$, there exists $d_i, e_i \in \Lambda_{0,nov}$ such that

$$\mathfrak{x} - \sum_{i=1}^{b} e^{-\deg \mathfrak{z}_i}c_i\mathfrak{z}_i = \sum_{i=1}^{b} d_i\mathfrak{b}_i + \sum_{i=1}^{a} e_i\mathfrak{h}_i.$$

This proves that $\mathfrak{x}$ is a linear combination of the elements $\mathfrak{z}_1, \cdots \mathfrak{z}_b, \mathfrak{b}_1, \cdots, \mathfrak{b}_b, \mathfrak{h}_1, \cdots, \mathfrak{h}_a$. Hence the proof. $\square$

LEMMA 6.5.4. *The set* $\{\sigma(\mathfrak{z}_1), \cdots, \sigma(\mathfrak{z}_b), \sigma(\mathfrak{b}_1), \cdots, \sigma(\mathfrak{b}_b), \sigma(\mathfrak{h}_1), \cdots, \sigma(\mathfrak{h}_a)\}$ *is linearly independent.*

PROOF. Recall that our choices of $\mathfrak{b}_i$, $\mathfrak{h}_j$ and $\mathfrak{z}_k$ imply that

$$E(\mathfrak{b}_1) = \cdots = E(\mathfrak{b}_b) = E(\mathfrak{z}_1) = \cdots = E(\mathfrak{z}_b) = E(\mathfrak{h}_1) = \cdots = E(\mathfrak{h}_a) = 0$$

and $\{\sigma(\mathfrak{b}_1), \cdots, \sigma(\mathfrak{b}_b), \sigma(\mathfrak{h}_1), \cdots, \sigma(\mathfrak{h}_a)\}$ is linearly independent. Therefore, if the conclusion is false, we may assume without loss of any generality that $\sigma(\mathfrak{z}_1)$ can be written as a linear combination of the set

$$\{\sigma(\mathfrak{z}_2), \cdots, \sigma(\mathfrak{z}_b), \sigma(\mathfrak{b}_1), \cdots, \sigma(\mathfrak{b}_b), \sigma(\mathfrak{h}_1), \cdots, \sigma(\mathfrak{h}_a)\}.$$

Lemma 6.5.3 then implies that this set generates $\overline{C}$ as an R vector space. (Here $\overline{C}$ is the R vector space such that $\overline{C} \otimes_R \Lambda_{0,nov} = C$.)

It follows that $\{\mathfrak{z}_2, \cdots, \mathfrak{z}_b, \mathfrak{b}_1, \cdots, \mathfrak{b}_b, \mathfrak{h}_1, \cdots, \mathfrak{h}_a\}$ generates C as a $\Lambda_{0,nov}$ module. Therefore $\{e^{-\deg \mathfrak{z}_2} \delta \mathfrak{z}_2, \cdots, e^{-\deg \mathfrak{z}_b} \delta \mathfrak{z}_b\} = \{\mathfrak{b}'_2, \cdots, \mathfrak{b}'_b\}$ generates $\operatorname{Im} \delta$. This is a contradiction to the choice made so that $\{\mathfrak{b}'_1, \cdots, \mathfrak{b}'_b\}$ is a standard basis of $\operatorname{Im} \delta \cap C^{\{0,1\}}$. $\square$

Proof of Proposition 6.5.1 is complete. $\square$

REMARK 6.5.5. Using the notation of Proposition 6.5.1 we have

$$\frac{\operatorname{Ker} \delta}{\operatorname{Im} \delta} = (\Lambda_{0,nov}^{(0)})^{\oplus a} \oplus \bigoplus_{i=1}^{b} \frac{\Lambda_{0,nov}^{(0)}}{T^{\lambda_i} \Lambda_{0,nov}^{(0)}}.$$

Namely a is the Betti number and λ_i's are the torsion exponents.

Now we go back to the geometric situation and prove Theorem I. Let L be a relatively spin Lagrangian submanifold of M. Using the canonical model in the same was as Subsection 6.4.1, we have a finite d.g.c.f.z., denoted by (C, δ), that is chain homotopy equivalent to $(C(L; \Lambda_{0,nov})^+, \delta_{(\mathfrak{b},b)}^+)$. We take $R = \mathbb{Q}$. We may assume that $\delta \equiv 0 \mod \Lambda_{0,nov}^+$.

We apply Proposition 6.5.1 and obtain a standard basis

$$\{\mathfrak{z}_1, \cdots, \mathfrak{z}_b, \mathfrak{b}_1, \cdots, \mathfrak{b}_b, \mathfrak{h}_1, \cdots, \mathfrak{h}_a\}$$

of $C^{\{0,1\}}$. Here we prove the following lemma on the leading coefficients $\sigma(\mathfrak{b}_i)$.

LEMMA 6.5.6. We have $i_!(\sigma(\mathfrak{b}_i)) = 0$ for $i = 1, 2, \cdots, b$.

PROOF. Let

$$\varphi : (C, \delta) \to (C(L; \Lambda_{0,nov})^+, \delta_{(\mathfrak{b},b)}^+)$$

be a cochain map preserving the filtration and inducing the isomorphisms

$$H(C, \delta) \cong H(C(L; \Lambda_{0,nov})^+, \delta_{(\mathfrak{b},b)}^+)$$

and $\overline{C} = H(\overline{C}, \overline{\delta}) \cong H(L; \mathbb{Q})$. We recall the map

$$\mathfrak{p}_1^{+\mathfrak{b},b} : C(L; \Lambda_{0,nov})^+ \to S^*(M; \Lambda_{0,nov})$$

from Lemma 6.4.5 which satisfies

$$\delta_M \circ \mathfrak{p}_1^{+\mathfrak{b},b} = -\mathfrak{p}_1^{+\mathfrak{b},b} \circ \delta_{(\mathfrak{b},b)}^+,$$

where δ_M is the classical coboundary operator with $\Lambda_{0,nov}$ coefficient

$$\delta_M : S^*(M; \Lambda_{0,nov}) \to S^*(M; \Lambda_{0,nov}).$$

Moreover we also have

(6.5.7) $\qquad (i_! - \mathfrak{p}_1^{+\mathfrak{b},b})(F^\lambda C(L; \Lambda_{0,nov})^+) \subset F^{\lambda+\lambda_0} C(M; \Lambda_{0,nov})$

from (6.4.9), where the constant λ_0 is defined by

$$\lambda_0 = \inf\{\beta \cap [\omega] \mid \beta \in \Pi(M; L), \mathcal{M}(\beta) \neq \emptyset, \beta \neq \beta_0\}.$$

By the choice we made for $\mathfrak{z}_i$ in the beginning of the proof of Proposition 6.5.1, we have

$$\delta\mathfrak{z}_i \equiv T^{\lambda_i} e^{\deg \mathfrak{z}_i} \sigma(\mathfrak{b}_i) \quad \mod T^{\lambda_i} \Lambda^+_{0,nov}.$$

On the other hand

$$(i_! - \mathfrak{p}_1^{+\mathfrak{b},b})\varphi\delta(\mathfrak{z}_i) \in F^{\lambda+\lambda_0} C$$

by (6.5.7). Therefore we have

$$\begin{aligned}
(6.5.8) \qquad i_!\varphi\delta(\mathfrak{z}_i) &= (i_! - \mathfrak{p}_1^{+\mathfrak{b},b})\varphi\delta(\mathfrak{z}_i) + \mathfrak{p}_1^{+\mathfrak{b},b}\varphi\delta(\mathfrak{z}_i) \\
&= (i_! - \mathfrak{p}_1^{+\mathfrak{b},b})\varphi\delta(\mathfrak{z}_i) \pm \mathfrak{p}_1^{+\mathfrak{b},b}\delta^+_{(\mathfrak{b},b)}\varphi(\mathfrak{z}_i) \\
&\equiv \pm\delta_M \mathfrak{p}_1^{+\mathfrak{b},b}\varphi(\mathfrak{z}_i) \quad \mod F^{\lambda_i+\lambda_0} C(M;\Lambda_{0,nov}).
\end{aligned}$$

We also have

$$(6.5.9) \qquad\qquad \delta_0\delta(\mathfrak{z}_i) \equiv 0 \quad \mod T^{\lambda_i+\lambda'_0} C$$

for some positive λ'_0, because we have

$$0 = \delta\delta(\mathfrak{z}_i) = (\delta_0 + \delta')\delta(\mathfrak{z}_i) = \delta_0\delta(\mathfrak{z}_i) + \delta'\delta(\mathfrak{z}_i)$$

and we know that $\delta'\delta(\mathfrak{z}_i)$ lies in $F^{\lambda_i+\lambda'_0} C$. Here δ_0 is the coboundary operator induced by $\overline{\delta} : \overline{C} \to \overline{C}$ and δ' is the higher order term of δ. Since φ induces an isomorphism $H(\overline{C}, \overline{\delta}) \cong H(L; \mathbb{Q})$, (6.5.8) and (6.5.9) imply that

$$i_!(\sigma(\mathfrak{b}_i)) = e^p (i_! \circ \varphi_*)([T^{-\lambda_i}\delta(\mathfrak{z}_i)]) = 0 \in H^p(M; \mathbb{Q})$$

for some $p \in \mathbb{Z}$. The proof of Lemma 6.5.6 is complete. $\qquad\qquad\square$

Now we are ready to complete the proof of Theorem I. Lemma 6.5.6 implies

$$(6.5.10) \qquad\qquad b \leq \sum_p \text{rank}_{\mathbb{Q}} \text{Ker}(i_! : H^p(L; \mathbb{Q}) \to H^p(M; \mathbb{Q})).$$

On the other hand, Proposition 6.5.1 implies

$$(6.5.11) \quad a + 2b = \sum_p \text{rank}_{\mathbb{Q}} H^p(L; \mathbb{Q}),$$

$$(6.5.12) \quad a = \text{rank}_{\Lambda_{nov}} HF((L, (\mathfrak{b}, b)), (L, (\mathfrak{b}, b)); \Lambda_{nov}).$$

Combining (6.5.10) – (6.5.12) we have obtained

$$\text{rank}_{\Lambda_{nov}} HF((L, (\mathfrak{b}, b)), (L, (\mathfrak{b}, b)); \Lambda_{nov})$$
$$\geq \sum \text{rank}_{\mathbb{Q}} H_p(L; \mathbb{Q}) - 2\,\text{rank}_{\mathbb{Q}} \text{Ker}(i_! : H^*(L; \mathbb{Q}) \to H^*(M; \mathbb{Q})).$$

Hence the proof of Theorem I. $\qquad\qquad\square$

6.5.3. Torsion of the Floer cohomology and Hofer distance: proof of Theorem J.

PROOF OF THEOREM 6.1.25 $\Rightarrow$ THEOREM J. We use the notation of Theorem 6.1.25. Theorem 6.1.25 immediately implies $b' \geq b(\mu)$. On the other hand it is easy to see that

$$\#(\psi^{(0)}(L^{(0)}) \cap \psi^{(1)}(L^{(1)})) \geq a' + 2b'.$$

This fact and $a = a'$ imply Theorem J. $\qquad\qquad\square$

EXAMPLE 6.5.13. Let Σ be a Riemann surface and $L^{(0)}, L^{(1)}$ be two circles on it. We assume that there exists a unique disc $D^2 \subset \Sigma$ contributing a component $\langle \delta[p], [q] \rangle$ of the coboundary operator and there is no such disc for $\langle \delta[q], [p] \rangle$. Let μ be the area of D^2. It is easy to see that

$$HF((L^{(1)}, 0), (L^{(0)}, 0); \Lambda_{0,nov}) \cong \frac{\Lambda_{0,nov}}{T^\mu \Lambda_{0,nov}}.$$

It is easy to find an Hamiltonian isotopy ψ such that $\psi(L^{(0)}) \cap L^{(1)} = \emptyset$ and the Hofer distance of ψ from identity is $\mu + \epsilon$ for any $\epsilon > 0$. Theorem J is thus optimal in this case. (See Figure 6.5.1).

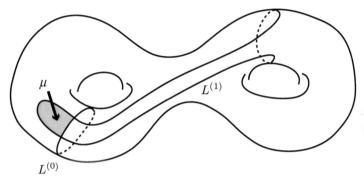

Figure 6.5.1

PROOF OF THEOREM 6.1.25. For the simplicity of the notation, we will restrict ourselves to the case of a transversal pair $(L^{(0)}, L^{(1)})$ where both $L^{(0)}$ and $L^{(1)}$ are unobstructed. The general cases of the clean intersection pair of $(L^{(0)}, L^{(1)})$ where $L^{(i)}$ are weakly unobstructed or weakly unobstructed after bulk deformations can be treated in the same way, except that we need to carefully choose the countably generated subcomplex of the singular chain complex of the intersection manifold $L^{(0)} \cap L^{(1)}$. We leave this modification to the interested readers.

Let $\{\psi_\rho^{(j)}\}_\rho$ $(j = 0, 1)$ and μ be as in (6.1.24). We put $L^{(j)\prime} = \psi^{(j)}(L^{(j)})$. We use the notation as Subsection 5.3.2. We consider the weakly filtered A_∞ bimodule homomorphism

$$(6.5.14) \qquad \varphi : (C(L^{(1)}, L^{(0)}; \Lambda_{nov}), \mathfrak{n}_{k_1, k_0}^{J_t, \mathfrak{s}}) \to (C(L^{(1)\prime}, L^{(0)\prime}; \Lambda_{nov}), \mathfrak{n}_{k_1, k_0}^{J'_t, \mathfrak{s}'})$$

over $(\mathfrak{g}^{1, \psi^{(1)}, \{J_\rho^{(1)}\}_\rho, \mathfrak{s}_1^{\text{top}(\rho)}}, \mathfrak{g}^{0, \psi^{(0)}, \{J_\rho^{(0)}\}_\rho, \mathfrak{s}_0^{\text{top}(\rho)}})$ with energy loss μ. (See Definition 5.2.1 and (5.3.15)). (Here we write $C(L^{(1)}, L^{(0)}; \Lambda_{nov})$ for $C_2(L^{(1)}, L^{(0)}; \Lambda_{nov})$ since we assumed that $L^{(0)}$ is transversal to $L^{(1)}$.) We define a bimodule homomorphism $\phi(x) = \varphi(e^{b_1} \otimes x \otimes e^{b_0})$. We have

$$(6.5.15) \qquad \phi \circ \delta_{b_1, b_0} = \delta_{\psi_*^{(1)} b_1, \psi_*^{(0)} b_0} \circ \phi.$$

Here $\psi_*^{(j)} b_j = \mathfrak{g}_*^{j, \psi^{(j)}, \{J_\rho^{(j)}\}_\rho, \mathfrak{s}_j^{\text{top}(\rho)}}(b_j) \in \mathcal{M}(\psi^{(j)}(L^{(j)}))$. Since the energy loss of φ is μ it follows that ϕ induces a bimodule homomorphism

$$(6.5.16) \qquad \phi : T^{\lambda + \mu} C((L^{(1)}, L^{(0)}); \Lambda_{0, nov}) \to T^\lambda C((L^{(1)\prime}, L^{(0)\prime}); \Lambda_{0, nov}).$$

We consider the isotopy $\{\psi^{(j)}\}_{\rho}^{-1} = \{\psi_{1-\rho}^{(j)} \circ (\psi^{(j)})^{-1}\}_{\rho}$ which is a Hamiltonian isotopy from identity to $(\psi^{(j)})^{-1}$. We remark that

$$\|\{\psi_{\rho}^{(j)}\}_{\rho}\| = \|\{\psi^{(j)}\}_{\rho}^{-1}\|.$$

Here $\|\{\psi_{\rho}\}_{\rho}\|$ is the Hofer length of the family of Hamiltonian isotopy. (See (5.3.40).)

Therefore in the same way we have the induced homomorphism:

(6.5.17) $\phi'' : T^{\mu+\lambda} C((L^{(1)}{}', L^{(0)}{}'); \Lambda_{0,nov}) \to T^{\lambda} C((L^{(1)}, L^{(0)}); \Lambda_{0,nov})$

defined by

(6.5.18) $\phi''(x) = \varphi''(e^{\psi_*^{(1)} b_1} \otimes x \otimes e^{\psi_*^{(0)} b_0}).$

Here φ'' is a weakly filtered A_∞ bimodule homomorphism associated to $\{\psi^{(j)}\}_{\rho}^{-1}$. We have the identity

(6.5.19) $\delta_{((\psi^{(1)})^{-1})_*(\psi_*^{(1)}(b_1)),((\psi^{(0)})^{-1})_*(\psi_*^{(0)}(b_0))} \circ \phi'' = \phi'' \circ \delta_{\psi_*^{(1)} b_1, \psi_*^{(0)} b_0}.$

It follows from Theorem 4.1.3, that $((\psi^{(j)})^{-1})_*(\psi_*^{(j)}(b_i))$ is gauge equivalent to b_i. Therefore Proposition 5.2.37 implies the existence of a homomorphism

$$\mathfrak{i} : C((L^{(1)}, L^{(0)}); \Lambda_{0,nov}) \to C((L^{(1)}, L^{(0)}); \Lambda_{0,nov})$$

such that

(6.5.20) $\mathfrak{i} \circ \delta_{((\psi^{(1)})^{-1})_*(\psi_*^{(1)}(b_1)),((\psi^{(0)})^{-1})_*(\psi_*^{(0)}(b_0))} = \delta_{b_1,b_0} \circ \mathfrak{i}$

and

(6.5.21) $\mathfrak{i} \equiv id \mod \Lambda_{0,nov}^+.$

If we put $\phi' = \mathfrak{i} \circ \phi''$, then (6.5.19) and (6.5.20) imply

(6.5.22) $\phi' \circ \delta_{\psi_*^{(1)} b_1, \psi_*^{(0)} b_0} = \delta_{b_1,b_0} \circ \phi'.$

LEMMA 6.5.23. *For each $\lambda \geq 0$, the composition*

$$\phi' \circ \phi : T^{2\mu+\lambda} C((L^{(1)}, L^{(0)}); \Lambda_{0,nov}) \to T^{\lambda} C((L^{(1)}, L^{(0)}); \Lambda_{0,nov})$$

is cochain homotopic to the inclusion

$$T^{2\mu+\lambda} C((L^{(1)}, L^{(0)}); \Lambda_{0,nov}) \to T^{\lambda} C((L^{(1)}, L^{(0)}); \Lambda_{0,nov}).$$

PROOF. For $s \in [0,1]$ and $T > 0$, we consider a smooth function $\chi_{s,T}$ with the following properties.

(6.5.24.1) $\chi_{s,T}$ is non decreasing on $(-\infty, 0]$ and non increasing on $[0, \infty)$.
(6.5.24.2) $\chi_{s,T}(t) \equiv s$ for $t \in [-T, T]$.
(6.5.24.3) $\chi_{s,T}(t) \equiv 0$ for $|t|$ sufficiently large.

For each s, T, we define a Hamiltonian deformation $\{\psi_{\sigma,s,T}^{(j)}\}_{\sigma}$ by

(6.5.25) $\psi_{\sigma,s,T}^{(j)} = \psi_{\chi_{s,T}(\sigma)}^{(j)}.$

We remark

(6.5.26) $\|\{\psi_{\sigma,s,T}^{(j)}\}_{\sigma}\| \leq 2\mu.$

For each s, T we use time ordered product with respect to σ of the family $\{\psi_{\sigma,s,T}^{(j)}\}_\sigma$ to obtain a weakly filtered A_∞ bimodule homomorphism. (See Subsection 5.3.2). It induces
$$\phi_{s,T} : C((L^{(1)}, L^{(0)}); \Lambda_{nov}) \to C((L^{(1)}, L^{(0)}); \Lambda_{nov}).$$
We use Proposition 5.3.45 and (6.5.26) to find that

(6.5.27) $$\phi_{s,T}(T^{\mu+\lambda}C((L^{(1)}, L^{(0)}); \Lambda_{0,nov})) \subseteq T^\lambda C((L^{(1)}, L^{(0)}); \Lambda_{0,nov}).$$

We put $s = 1$. By a well established gluing argument (see the proof of Theorem 5.3.39), we find that

(6.5.28) $$\lim_{T \to \infty} \phi_{1,T} = \phi'' \circ \phi$$

on $T^{2\mu}C((L^{(1)}, L^{(0)}); \Lambda_{0,nov})$. We consider the family $\{\psi_{\sigma,s,T}^{(j)}\}_{s,\sigma}$ for T large. We remark that $\chi_{0,T}(t) \equiv 0$.

We use the time-ordered product with respect to σ and time-wise product with respect to s to obtain a homotopy between two filtered A_∞ bimodule homomorphisms $\varphi_{1,T}$ and $\varphi_{0,T}$. (See Subsection 5.3.3.) We remark that $\phi_{0,T}$ is an identity and $\phi_{1,T}$ converges to $\varphi'' \circ \varphi$. Here φ is as in (6.5.14) and φ'' is as in (6.5.18). It is easy to see that this implies Lemma 6.5.23, using the definitions of ϕ, ϕ', (6.5.26) and Proposition 5.3.45. $\square$

REMARK 6.5.29. In fact the slight modification of the energy estimate shows that the composition $\phi' \circ \phi$ induces a homomorphism

$$\phi' \circ \phi : T^{\mu+\lambda}C((L^{(1)}, L^{(0)}); \Lambda_{0,nov}) \to T^\lambda C((L^{(1)}, L^{(0)}); \Lambda_{0,nov})$$

which is cochain homotopic to the inclusion. We will not use it however.

Let $\lambda \geq 2\mu$. We have chain maps

(6.5.30.1)
$$\phi : (T^\lambda C((L^{(1)}, L^{(0)}); \Lambda_{0,nov}), \delta_{b_1,b_0})$$
$$\longrightarrow (T^{\lambda-\mu}C((L^{(1)\prime}, L^{(0)\prime}); \Lambda_{0,nov}), \delta_{\psi_*^{(1)}b_1, \psi_*^{(0)}b_0})$$

and

(6.5.30.2)
$$\phi' : (T^{\lambda-\mu}C((L^{(1)\prime}, L^{(0)\prime}); \Lambda_{0,nov}), \delta_{\psi_*^{(1)}b_1, \psi_*^{(0)}b_0})$$
$$\longrightarrow (T^{\lambda-2\mu}C((L^{(1)}, L^{(0)}); \Lambda_{0,nov}), \delta_{b_1,b_0})$$

such that $\phi' \circ \phi$ is chain homotopy equivalent to the inclusion

$$\phi : (T^\lambda C((L^{(1)}, L^{(0)}); \Lambda_{0,nov}), \delta_{b_1,b_0}) \longrightarrow (T^{\lambda-2\mu}C((L^{(1)}, L^{(0)}); \Lambda_{0,nov}), \delta_{b_1,b_0}).$$

Here we use the following:

LEMMA 6.5.31. Let D be a finitely generated $\Lambda_{0,nov}^{(0)}$ module that is isomorphic to

$$D \cong (\Lambda_{0,nov}^{(0)})^A \oplus \bigoplus_{i=1}^{B} \frac{\Lambda_{0,nov}^{(0)}}{T^{c_i}\Lambda_{0,nov}^{(0)}}.$$

(1) For each $\lambda > 0$ the minimum number of generators of $T^\lambda D$ as $\Lambda_{0,nov}$ module is $A + \#\{i \mid c_i > \lambda\}$.

(2) Any finitely generated submodule D' of $T^\lambda D$ is generated by the less than $A + \#\{i \mid c_i > \lambda\}$ elements.

PROOF. (1) follows from $T^\lambda D/T^\lambda \Lambda_{0,nov}^{+(0)} D \cong \mathbb{Q}^{A+\#\{i|c_i>\lambda\}}$.

To prove (2), we first remark that it suffices to consider the case when $\lambda = 0$, since we can apply the same argument to $T^\lambda D$. We put $\tilde{D} = (\Lambda_{0,nov}^{(0)})^{A+B}$ and consider the natural projection $\pi : \tilde{D} \to D$. We lift the generators of D' to $\tilde{D}$ and let $\tilde{D}'$ be the submodule generated by them. Then $\tilde{D}'$ is finitely generated and $\pi(\tilde{D}') = D'$. Using standard basis (Lemma 6.3.2) we find that $\tilde{D}'$ is generated by $A + B$ elements. It follows that D' is generated by $A + B$ elements, as required. $\square$

(6.5.30) induces the homomorphisms

$$\phi_* : T^\lambda HF((L^{(1)}, L^{(0)}); \Lambda_{0,nov}) \to T^{\lambda-\mu} HF((L^{(1)\prime}, L^{(0)\prime}); \Lambda_{0,nov})$$

and

$$\phi'_* : T^{\lambda-\mu} HF((L^{(1)\prime}, L^{(0)\prime}); \Lambda_{0,nov}) \to T^{\lambda-2\mu} HF((L^{(1)}, L^{(0)}); \Lambda_{0,nov})$$

whose composition $\phi'_* \circ \phi_*$ is the same as the natural inclusion. Since the $\Lambda_{0,nov}$ module $T^{\lambda-\mu} HF((L^{(1)\prime}, L^{(0)\prime}); \Lambda_{0,nov})$ is generated by $a + b'(\lambda - \mu)$ elements, it follows from Lemma 6.5.31 (2) that the image of $T^\lambda HF((L^{(1)}, L^{(0)}); \Lambda_{0,nov})$ in $T^{\lambda-2\mu} HF((L^{(1)}, L^{(0)}); \Lambda_{0,nov})$ is generated by $a + b'(\lambda - \mu)$ elements. Therefore using Lemma 6.5.31 (1), we find

$$(6.5.32) \qquad a + b(\lambda) \le a + b'(\lambda - \mu).$$

Now we prove Theorem 6.1.25 under the additional assumption $\lambda_{\downarrow i} > 3\mu$. (Note in Theorem 6.1.25, we enumerate the torsion exponents so that $\lambda_{\downarrow i} \ge \lambda_{\downarrow i+1}$.) We remark that "$\lambda_{\downarrow i} \ge \lambda$ and $i \le b$" is equivalent to $b(\lambda) \ge i$. We use (6.5.32) for $\lambda = \lambda_{\downarrow i}$ to find that

$$b' \ge b'(\lambda_{\downarrow i} - \mu) \ge b'(\lambda_{\downarrow i}) \ge i$$

and $\lambda'_{\downarrow i} \ge \lambda_{\downarrow i} - \mu$. This proves $\lambda'_{\downarrow i} \ge \lambda_{\downarrow i} - \mu > 3\mu - \mu = 2\mu$. We obtain $\lambda_{\downarrow i} \ge \lambda'_{\downarrow i} - \mu$ by a similar argument with $L^{(j)}$ and $L^{(j)\prime}$ exchanged, using $\lambda'_{\downarrow i} > 2\mu$. That proves Theorem 6.1.25 in case $\lambda_{\downarrow i} > 3\mu$.

To prove the general case we partition the Hamiltonian isotopy into small pieces so that we can apply the above arguments to each of the pieces. The detail of this argument is in order.

We use the same notation as Theorem 6.1.25. We take a partition $\rho_0 = 0 < \rho_1 < \cdots < \rho_N = 1$ with the following properties (6.5.33).

$$(6.5.33) \qquad \lambda_{\downarrow i} - \sum_{k=1}^{j} \mu_k > 3\mu_{j+1}, \qquad j = 0, 1, 2, \cdots, N-1.$$

Here

$$\mu_i = dist(\psi_{\rho_{i-1}}^{(1)}, \psi_{\rho_i}^{(1)}) + dist(\psi_{\rho_{i-1}}^{(0)}, \psi_{\rho_i}^{(0)})$$

where $dist$ stands for Hofer distance. Since $\sum_j \mu_j = \mu < \lambda_{\downarrow i}$, we can find such ρ_i. In fact, we may take

$$\mu_{j+1} = \min\left\{\frac{1}{4}\left(\lambda_{\downarrow i} - \sum_{k=1}^{j} \mu_k\right), \mu - \sum_{k=1}^{j} \mu_k\right\},$$

inductively. By perturbing the isotopies $\psi_\rho^{(0)}$, $\psi_\rho^{(1)}$ slightly, we may assume that $\psi_{\rho_j}^{(0)}(L^{(0)})$ is transversal to $\psi_{\rho_j}^{(1)}(L^{(1)})$ for each $j = 0, \cdots, N$.

Let $\lambda_{\downarrow i}(j)$ be the i-th torsion exponent of $HF(\psi_{\rho_j}^{(0)}(L^{(0)}), \psi_{\rho_j}^{(1)}(L^{(1)}); \Lambda_{0,nov})$. (We enumerate them so that $\lambda_{\downarrow i}(j) \geq \lambda_{\downarrow i+1}(j)$.) We will then prove the following by induction on j

$$(6.5.34) \qquad \lambda_{\downarrow i}(j) \geq \lambda_{\downarrow i} - \sum_{k=1}^{j} \mu_k.$$

In fact, if we assume (6.5.34) for j then (6.5.33) implies that $\lambda_{\downarrow i}(j) \geq 3\mu_{j+1}$. Therefore we can apply Theorem 6.1.25 (since it is already established under this additional assumption) to show (6.5.34) for $j + 1$.

Since $\lambda_{\downarrow i}(N) = \lambda'_{\downarrow i}$, it follows that

$$\lambda'_{\downarrow i} \geq \lambda_{\downarrow i} - \sum \mu_k = \lambda_{\downarrow i} - \mu.$$

The proof of the inequality in the opposite direction is similar. The proof of Theorem 6.1.25 is now complete. $\qquad \square$

Partitioning Hamiltonian isotopies to control the energy loss was also used in [**Ono95**] to show that the modified Floer homology is well-defined, i.e., independent of the choice of filtrations.

6.5.4. Floer cohomologies of Lagrangian submanifolds that do not intersect cleanly. We next apply Theorem 6.1.25 to define Floer cohomology over $\Lambda_{0,nov}$ in the case when $L^{(0)}$ and $L^{(1)}$ are *not* necessarily of clean intersection.

Assume that a pair $(L^{(0)}, L^{(1)})$ is relatively spin and weakly unobstructed after bulk deformation. Let $\mathbf{b}_j \in \mathcal{M}_{\mathrm{weak,def}}(L^{(j)})$ for $j = 0, 1$ such that $\pi_{\mathrm{amb}}(\mathbf{b}_0) = \pi_{\mathrm{amb}}(\mathbf{b}_1)$ and $\mathfrak{PD}(\mathbf{b}_0) = \mathfrak{PD}(\mathbf{b}_1)$. We then can define the Floer cohomology $HF((L^{(1)}, \mathbf{b}_1), (L^{(0)}, \mathbf{b}_0); \Lambda_{nov})$ over the Λ_{nov} coefficients. This is because the Floer cohomology over Λ_{nov} is invariant of Hamiltonian isotopy and we can always perturb $L^{(i)}$ so that they intersect transversely and the resulting cohomology is canonically isomorphic.

We would like to define the Floer cohomology $HF((L^{(1)}, \mathbf{b}_1), (L^{(0)}, \mathbf{b}_0); \Lambda_{0,nov})$ over the $\Lambda_{0,nov}$-coefficients, using Theorem 6.1.25.

We consider two sequences of Hamiltonian diffeomorphisms $\psi_m^{(0)}$, $\psi_m^{(1)}$, ($m = 1, 2, 3, \cdots$) such that

(6.5.35.1) $\psi_m^{(0)}(L^{(0)})$ has clean intersection with $\psi_m^{(1)}(L^{(1)})$.

(6.5.35.2) $\lim_{m \to \infty} dist(\psi_m^{(i)}, id) = 0$ where $dist$ is the Hofer distance.

Proposition 6.5.38 below says that the Floer cohomology

$$HF((\psi_m^{(1)}(L^{(1)}), \psi_{m*}^{(1)}\mathbf{b}_1), (\psi_m^{(0)}(L^{(0)}), \psi_{m*}^{(0)}\mathbf{b}_0); \Lambda_{0,nov})$$

converges as $m \to \infty$ in the sense we define below.

DEFINITION 6.5.36. Let $\lambda_{m,\downarrow 1}, \cdots, \lambda_{m,\downarrow b_m}$ ($m = 1, 2, \cdots, \infty$) be sequences of positive numbers such that $\lambda_{m,\downarrow i} \geq \lambda_{m,\downarrow i+1}$. We assume $b_m < \infty$ for $m \neq \infty$. (But b_∞ itself could be infinity.) If $b_\infty = \infty$ we assume that $\lim_{i \to \infty} \lambda_{\infty,\downarrow i} = 0$ in addition. We say

$$\lim_{m \to \infty} (\lambda_{m,\downarrow 1}, \cdots, \lambda_{m,\downarrow b_m}) = (\lambda_{\infty,\downarrow 1}, \cdots, \lambda_{\infty,\downarrow b_\infty}),$$

if $\lim b_m = b_\infty$ and $\lim_{m \to \infty} \lambda_{m,\downarrow i} = \lambda_{\infty,\downarrow i}$ for each i.

REMARK 6.5.37. In the situation of Proposition 6.5.38 we may have infinitely many $\lambda_{\infty,\downarrow i}$ such that $\lim_{i\to\infty} \lambda_{\infty,\downarrow i} = 0$. For this case we need to enumerate $\lambda_{\infty,\downarrow i}$ so that $\lambda_{\infty,\downarrow i} \geq \lambda_{\infty,\downarrow i+1}$.

PROPOSITION 6.5.38. *Let* $\psi_m^{(0)}, \psi_m^{(1)}$ *be two sequences of Hamiltonian diffeomorphisms satisfying* (6.5.35). *We put*

$$HF((\psi_m^{(1)}(L^{(1)}), \psi_{m*}^{(1)}\mathbf{b}_1), (\psi_m^{(0)}(L^{(0)}), \psi_{m*}^{(0)}\mathbf{b}_0); \Lambda_{0,nov})$$

$$\cong (\Lambda_{0,nov})^a \oplus \bigoplus_{i=1}^{b_m} \frac{\Lambda_{0,nov}}{T^{\lambda_{m,\downarrow i}}\Lambda_{0,nov}}.$$

Then there exists $\lambda_{\infty,\downarrow 1}, \cdots, \lambda_{\infty,\downarrow b_\infty}$ *as in Definition 6.5.36, such that*

$$\lim_{m\to\infty} (\lambda_{m,\downarrow 1}, \cdots, \lambda_{m,\downarrow b_m}) = (\lambda_{\infty,\downarrow 1}, \cdots, \lambda_{\infty,\downarrow b_\infty})$$

in the sense of Definition 6.5.36.

Proposition 6.5.38 is an immediate consequence of Theorem 6.1.25.

DEFINITION 6.5.39. We put

$$HF((L^{(1)}, \mathbf{b}_1), (L^{(0)}, \mathbf{b}_0); \Lambda_{0,nov}) = (\Lambda_{0,nov})^a \oplus \bigoplus_{i=1}^{b_\infty} \frac{\Lambda_{0,nov}}{T^{\lambda_{\infty,\downarrow i}}\Lambda_{0,nov}}.$$

We remark that $\lim_{m\to\infty}(\lambda_{m,\downarrow 1}, \cdots, \lambda_{m,\downarrow b_m})$ converges *without* taking subsequence. Hence the right hand side of Definition 6.5.39 is independent of the choice of $\psi_m^{(j)}$.

We remark that we proved Theorem G in Chapter 5 in case when $L^{(1)}$ has clean intersection with $L^{(0)}$. The general case is a consequence of Proposition 6.5.38 and Definition 6.5.39. The fact that the Floer cohomology in Definition 6.5.39 satisfies (G.3),(G.4) follows from the definition. We can check (G.5) using the proof of Theorem 6.1.25. We omit the detail of the check of (G.5), since we do not use it.

EXAMPLE 6.5.40. Let

$$X = \{x + \sqrt{-1}e^{-1/|x|}\sin 1/|x| \mid |x| \leq 1\} \subset \mathbb{C}, \qquad Y = [-1,1] \times \{0\} \subset \mathbb{C}.$$

We can find Lagrangian submanifolds $L^{(1)}, L^{(0)} \subset T^2$, $p \in L^{(1)} \cap L^{(0)}$, a neighborhood U of p and a symplectic diffeomorphism $F : U \to F(U) \subset \mathbb{C}$ onto its image such that $F(p) = 0$, and $F(L^{(0)} \cap U) = X$, $F(L^{(1)} \cap U) = Y$. (See Figure 6.5.2).

It is easy to see that $HF((L^{(1)}, \mathbf{b}_1), (L^{(0)}, \mathbf{b}_0); \Lambda_{0,nov})$ is not finitely generated. (In other words $b_\infty = \infty$.)

We remark that Floer cohomology $HF((L^{(1)}, \mathbf{b}_1), (L^{(0)}, \mathbf{b}_0); \Lambda_{0,nov})$ is finitely generated if $L^{(1)}$ has clean intersection with $L^{(0)}$.

We can find a similar example in higher dimension, for example, by taking a direct product of the above example with (T^{2n}, T^n).

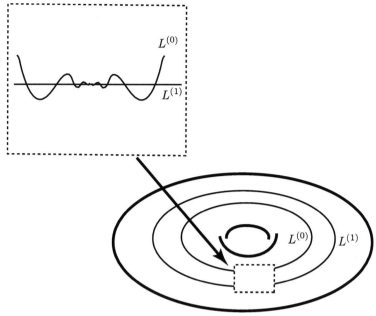

Figure 6.5.2

We remark that Theorems J and 6.1.25 both hold in the case when $L^{(1)}$ does not have clean intersection with $L^{(0)}$ using Definition 6.5.39. Combined with Example 6.5.40 it implies the following.

COROLLARY 6.5.41. *In each dimension, there exists a pair $L^{(1)}, L^{(0)}$ of Lagrangian submanifolds and $N(\epsilon)$ such that $\lim_{\epsilon \to 0} N(\epsilon) = \infty$, and if ψ is a Hamiltonian isotopy whose Hofer distance from the identity is smaller than ϵ then*

$$\#(\psi(L^{(0)}) \cap L^{(1)}) \geq N(\epsilon).$$

6.5.5. Unobstructedness modulo T^E. In Theorem J, we assumed that $L^{(0)}, L^{(1)}$ are weakly unobstructed after bulk deformations. However, it is easy to see that a similar result holds under a slightly milder assumption.

DEFINITION 6.5.42. A relatively spin Lagrangian submanifold $L \subset M$ is said to be *unobstructed modulo T^E*, if there exists a cochain $b \in C^1(L; \Lambda_{0,nov}^+)$ such that

$$(6.5.43.1) \qquad\qquad \hat{d}(e^b) \equiv 0 \mod T^E.$$

L is said to be *weakly unobstructed modulo T^E*, if there exists a cochain $b \in C^1(L; \Lambda_{0,nov}^+)^+$ such that

$$(6.5.43.2) \qquad\qquad \hat{d}(e^b) \equiv 0 \mod (T^E, \mathbf{e}^+).$$

L is said to be *unobstructed modulo T^E after bulk deformation*, if there exist $b \in C^1(L; \Lambda_{0,nov}^+)$ and $\mathfrak{b} \in H^2(L; \Lambda_{0,nov}^+)$ such that

$$(6.5.43.3) \qquad\qquad \mathfrak{q}(e^{\mathfrak{b}}, e^b) \equiv 0 \mod T^E.$$

L is said to be *weakly unobstructed modulo T^E after bulk deformation*, if there exist $b \in C^1(L; \Lambda_{0,nov}^+)^+$ and $\mathfrak{b} \in H^2(L; \Lambda_{0,nov}^+)$ such that

$$(6.5.43.4) \qquad \mathfrak{q}(e^{\mathfrak{b}}, e^b) \equiv 0 \mod (T^E, \mathbf{e}^+).$$

When (6.5.43.2) or (6.5.43.4) is satisfied, we define the potential function

$$\mathfrak{PO}(\mathfrak{b}, b) \in \Lambda_{0,nov}/T^E \Lambda_{0,nov}$$

by

$$\mathfrak{q}(e^{\mathfrak{b}}, e^b) - \mathfrak{PO}(\mathfrak{b}, b)\mathbf{e}^+ \equiv 0 \mod T^E.$$

We remark that for any L, there always exists some positive constant E such that L is unobstructed modulo T^E.

The proof of the following lemma is a straightforward modification of the proof of Proposition 3.7.17.

LEMMA-DEFINITION 6.5.44. *We assume that $L^{(0)}$ has clean intersection with $L^{(1)}$. If $b_i \in C^1(L^{(i)}; \Lambda_{0,nov}^+)$ and $\mathfrak{b} \in H^2(M; \Lambda_{0,nov}^+)$ satisfy (6.5.43.4), then we define*

$$\mathfrak{m}_1^{(\mathfrak{b}, b_1),(\mathfrak{b}, b_0)} : C^*(L^{(1)}, L^{(0)}; \Lambda_{0,nov}) \to C^{*+1}(L^{(1)}, L^{(0)}; \Lambda_{0,nov})$$

by

$$\delta_{(\mathfrak{b}, b_1),(\mathfrak{b}, b_0)}(x) = \mathfrak{r}(e^{\mathfrak{b}}, e^{b_1} x e^{b_0}).$$

If $\mathfrak{PO}(\mathfrak{b}, b_0) = \mathfrak{PO}(\mathfrak{b}, b_1)$, we have

$$\delta_{(\mathfrak{b}, b_1),(\mathfrak{b}, b_0)} \circ \delta_{(\mathfrak{b}, b_1),(\mathfrak{b}, b_0)} \equiv 0 \mod T^E.$$

DEFINITION 6.5.45. Under the same condition as Lemma-Definition 6.5.44 we define a $\Lambda_{0,nov}/T^E \Lambda_{0,nov}$ module

$$HF((L^{(1)}, (\mathfrak{b}, b_1)), (L^{(0)}, (\mathfrak{b}, b_0)); \Lambda_{0,nov}/T^E \Lambda_{0,nov})$$

by

$$\operatorname{Ker} \delta_{(\mathfrak{b}, b_1),(\mathfrak{b}, b_0)} / \operatorname{Im} \delta_{(\mathfrak{b}, b_1),(\mathfrak{b}, b_0)}.$$

In a way similar to the proof of Proposition 6.3.14 we can prove that

$$(6.5.46) \quad HF((L^{(1)}, (\mathfrak{b}, b_1)), (L^{(0)}, (\mathfrak{b}, b_0)); \Lambda_{0,nov}/T^E \Lambda_{0,nov}) \cong \bigoplus_i \frac{\Lambda_{0,nov}}{T^{\lambda_i} \Lambda_{0,nov}}$$

for some $0 < \lambda_i \leq E$. In this situation, Theorem J can be generalized as follows.

THEOREM 6.5.47. *Under the assumption of Definition 6.5.45 we define λ_i by (6.5.46). We put*

$$b(\mu) = \#\{i \mid E > \lambda_i \geq \mu\}, \qquad a(i) = \#\{i \mid E = \lambda_i\}.$$

If μ is the Hofer distance of an Hamiltonian diffeomorphism $\psi : M \to M$ from the identity, then we have

$$\#(\psi(L^{(0)}) \cap L^{(1)}) \geq a(\mu) + 2b(\mu).$$

The proof is a minor modification of the proof of Theorem J and is omitted. We can also generalize Theorem 6.1.25 in the same way.

We remark that Theorem 6.5.47 slightly generalizes Chekanov's theorem in [**Chek96,98**].